GOOD WORKS

GOOD WORKS

A Guide to Careers in Social Change

FIFTH EDITION

Edited by Donna Colvin

Preface by Ralph Nader

BARRICADE BOOKS • NEW YORK

Published by Barricade Books Inc.
61 Fourth Avenue
New York, NY 10003

Printed in the United States of America.

Library of Congress Cataloging-in-Publication Data

Good works: a guide to careers in social change / edited by Donna Colvin—5th edition
p. cm.
Includes bibliographical references and index.
ISBN 0-9623032-8-3: $24.00
1. Associations, institutions, etc.—United States—Directories. 2. Social service—United States—Directories. 3. Social services—Vocational guidance—United States.
I. Colvin, Donna
AS29.5.G66 1993; aa12 04-19-93
331.7'02'02573—dc20 93-15886
CIP

First printing

This edition of Good Works is dedicated to Philip M. Stern. Mr. Stern has funded a variety of "good works" and through his own personal commitment, has produced many "good works." His books on the poor in Washington, D.C., the legal profession, taxpayer concerns and more recently, the damaging impact of political action committees (PACs) on Congress have helped to highlight the impact one person can have in first calling attention to, and then building a momentum toward resolving problems.

Ralph Nader

Contents

Editor's Acknowledgements

Previous editors — Karen Aptakin, Kathleen Hughes, Joan Anzalone and Jessica Cowan — all determined the format and structure of the present *Good Works*. While successive editions, including this one, continue to expand in size and scope, these earlier contributors have largely shaped the direction of *Good Works*, and no new edition would be successful without their contributions.

Also deserving of thanks for their contributions to this edition are Naseem Saab, whose computer wizardry kept the project going; Melissa Klein and Eric Hadley, whose tireless efforts provided the core research for this edition; Bob Buckley and Yuri Huta for helping iron out the wrinkles; Steve Perlah and Billy Treger for their willingness to drop everything when asked and help with proofreading and research; Elizabeth Barrett and Yael Bloom for endless hours of proofreading; Jon Gilbert at Barricade Books for his editing assistance, advice on completing the book and insistence on deadlines; and Rachel Ruby, who contributed much of the early effort that made this book possible.

Katherine Isaac, Tony Mazocchi, Russell Mokhiber and Joel Rogers all generously shared their knowledge, expertise and time in developing the Resource section of the book. John Richard has been the guiding force behind *Good Works* from its first edition to this latest, and his determination has kept it alive through numerous challenges.

A special debt of gratitude is owed to Ralph Nader, who originally came up with the idea for *Good Works*, and who has been a teacher, role model and inspiration to all of those involved in producing *Good Works*, as well as many of those whose organizations grace its pages.

D.C

Preface

For years, during meetings with college students on campus, the same questions came forth: Where can I find work in consumer protection? Or in ecology? Or in neighborhood organizing? Or in women's rights, civil rights, governmental reform, corporate accountability, consumer cooperatives? And for years, the replies were a few scattered addresses jotted down on the backs of envelopes or bits of scrap paper.

I did not find, of course, this way of responding either satisfactory or systematic. So, it was with considerable pleasure that I attended a conference on Careers in Social Change at Princeton University in February 1979 to share some observations with students about the need to assemble information describing citizen career opportunities and make it readily available to students, libraries and placement offices. One of the attendees, Karen Aptakin, a Princeton senior, wrote us shortly thereafter expressing interest in working toward this objective.

Upon graduation, Karen accepted our invitation to come to Washington and begin the Center for Study of Responsive Law's first project on social change careers. After months of detailed research, we published the first edition of *Good Works: A Guide to Social Change Careers*. The directory has been widely acclaimed as a landmark resource. More importantly, it has already helped thousands of students — as well as older people changing careers — to connect their idealism with employment opportunities.

Good Works has established a permanent place for itself on the shelves of career centers and libraries in universities and colleges nationwide. It speaks to the needs both of organizations (civic, local, national) that are always looking for new and dedicated persons, and job-seekers hungry for alternatives to traditional corporate careers.

This larger *Good Works* contains current information on over 1000 social change groups around the country. In addition to the road map covering such a varied terrain, this latest edition includes profiles of dedicated individuals who are building careers around their concerns as citizens — profiles that give an idea of the excitement involved in doing this self-fulfilling work.

The commonly accepted definitions of worthy and remunerative work in any society need periodic expansion. In a nation characterized by a progression of humane values, what starts out as a sensitive effort by a few volunteers often matures into more deeply rooted structures defending and implementing these values on a daily basis. Fire fighters, libraries, soil conservation programs, legal services for the poor, feeding programs for the hungry, laws protecting the many against the few, educational institutions and services — these are a small sample of social improvements stimulated into being by people who had a broader definition of life's work than their contemporary cultures recognized.

Today, as our society comes under even greater pressures and risks, young people should have the opportunity to raise their sights and expand their horizons well beyond the vocational training that comprises so much of what is called their formal education. They should see that there are positions whose essence includes the right, if not the duty, to take their conscience to work every day. There are positions that encourage people to be primary human beings, not secondary persons who have to prostrate themselves before the imperatives of corporate or governmental managers in order to make a living.

Taking one's conscience to work opens more doors to the wedding of analytic skills developed values for a better society. More creativity, initiative and idealism result. Psychological satisfaction and other forms of job enrichment flow from such good works. Certainly the demand for such work is increasing. Citizens' groups all over the country are redoubling their efforts to defend the fundamental rights of Americans and to strive for safe products, healthy environments and workplaces, civil liberties and civil rights. New civic efforts, which are organizing people on matters as disparate as the nuclear arms race, toxic dumps and local schools, are in need of a wide spread of talent to consolidate their energies into permanent structure. Consumer buying groups — from heating fuel to insurance —

can use business administration and marketing skills along with suitable computer applications. The student public interest research groups (PIRGs), now operating in over 30 states, have full-time professional staffs carrying civic projects, defined by their student boards, into reality. They are always looking for good resumes. The expansion of telecommunications into cable, video and other outlets does not have to be restricted to Madison Avenue definitions of content. A whole new set of people, values and needs can find expression if the citizen-entrepreneurs are at work to help people know or find out more about their world.

As you leaf through the pages of the volume, consider the relative importance of the work reflected by these groups as compared with many of the corporate job interviews young people have at the college placement office. With so much of our economy afflicted by trivial jobs chasing manipulated wants, with so many of our public institutions replete with drone-like sinecures, there are serious unmet needs — shelter, food, education, health, justice, peace, safety — that go begging for enduring, imaginative and problem-solving attention. There are no opportunities in this volume for marketing underarm deodorants, promoting a chemical food dye or shuffling inconsequential papers around. There are, instead, openings for people who want to work the frontiers of a just society, who want to be such a society's pioneers in foreseeing and forestalling abuses while inventing a future in pursuit of genuine happiness.

Nourishing the taproots of an ever deeper democratic society can be considered one of life's great joys. Fulfilling one's talents and dreams in such a quest is the antithesis of jobs that, however well paid, make you feel that you are just putting your time in, that life begins after the nine-to-five drudgery is over.

Students who wish to sample work for social justice can use this volume for internship prospects. Many a student has honed his or her writing, research, editing and advocacy skills during a summer or mid-year break, or even a full semester earning course credit for clinical education. The wonderful aspect of social change work is the multiple exercise of your abilities that is involved. This work is not like the narrow-gauged responses on a multiple-choice standardized test. This work invites the application and development of multiple intelligences through the elaboration of one's mind, heart and personality. No tunnel vision here.

The flow from knowledge to action draws upon the complete person with his or her catalytic and synergistic potential. Almost every skill and academic discipline can find a ready use in the complex drive for social change and in the protection and advancement of people and environmental rights in our society. Commitment, a reasonable self-confidence, a resiliency to overcome recurring adversities, a zest for work and the ability to focus on larger goals without neglecting the daily details are some obvious traits of advantage. A sense of humor for perspective and self-control also comes in handy.

And in good stead is an appreciation that there are not that many countries in the world where civic work can be carried forward as it can be in the United States under the blessings of our Constitution and the active citizens who give its words both foundation and life.

We ask readers to provide suggestions and examples of successful uses of these listings for subsequent editions of *Good Works* improving further on its content, comprehensiveness and distribution. Also, we hope that future meetings of college and university placement administrators will take up the challenge posed here to broaden their service to students beyond customary business and governmental career offerings.

Ralph Nader
Washington, D.C.

Introduction

The serious concerns this society faces as it moves through the 1990s are etched deeply into the daily lives of Americans. The problems in energy, health care, poverty, minority opportunity, environmental pollution, taxes, corporate lawlessness and citizen powerlessness — all bear witness to the vast discrepancies between the founding pioneers' dream and today's reality.

Though complex and often frustrating, these fundamental issues are being joined by active citizens across the country who recognize that implicit in citizenship is the duty to work toward making the country's performance consonant with its promise. Even now, as the difficulties seem more intractable than ever before, Americans conscious of their responsibility are working for solutions.

Their work covers many issues and a diversity of strategies and styles. But they are all working to make a variety of institutions accountable to civic needs.

They are working for social change.

Social change work requires people of diverse talents and interests. In every location, on every issue energetic people are needed — to research, advocate, litigate and fundraise; to manage organizations efficiently; to mobilize people; and to publicize the issues by writing and speaking.

What are they doing?

- In Santa Fe the staff of the New Mexico Solar Energy Association designs and builds solar energy equipment for low-income people.
- In Washington, D.C., lobbyists at the Consumer Federation of America and other groups present Congress and federal agencies with worker and consumer perspectives.
- In six locations across Michigan the staff of Citizens for Better Care takes complaints about nursing home improprieties and files lawsuits to protect seniors rights.
- In Pennsylvania the canvassers and organizers for Pennsylvania Citizen Action go door-to-door in low-and moderate-income areas, soliciting neighbors to join together in a democratic membership organization that will take direct action on issues of concern to its members: pressuring legislators to support a national bill that would curb insurance companies ability to fix policy prices; or designing an environmental packaging and labeling act to increase recycling and limit the state's production of global warming gases.
- Scattered across 12 southern states, over 150 field staff with the Federation of Southern Cooperatives provide information, technical assistance and management advice to small minority farmers and craftspeople banding together to form producer cooperatives and credit unions.
- Across the country attorneys with the American Civil Liberties Union take individual cases involving abridgement of the freedoms guaranteed by our Constitution's Bill of Rights.
- In Herein, Illinois, the four-person staff of the Illinois Stewardship Alliance researches coal and energy issues and provides assistance to farmer groups concerned with reclaiming stripmined land.

Tactics among these groups can vary widely. But few organizations rely exclusively on any one tactic — most find that the lines blur. Still, four broad strands can be identified: educating the public, empowering citizens, changing institutional behavior and developing alternative institutions.

The belief that people must first understand a problem in order to resolve it motivates groups concerned with educating the public. Their methods include producing reports and newsletters, organizing training programs and conferences and utilizing innovative theater and film productions.

Groups working at empowering citizens seek to organize people into membership organizations around some common interest — a geographical unit such as a community or workplace or common concerns such as energy or taxes — and to teach the members how to build and maintain an organization that can take direct action. Members lobby, hold rallies, meet with officials and confront and seek to influence decisionmakers in other ways. Citizen empowerment groups also provide technical assistance to other groups working for social change — teaching and consulting on administration, public relations, fundraising and other organizational needs.

Those interested in changing institutional behavior operate in a different area. Some groups choose to work through the judicial system, using the courts to challenge government or corporate conduct. Others use the legislative system: they lobby federal, state and local lawmakers for progressive legislation. Consumer advocacy groups frequently publicize patterns of consumer complaints to force business or government to develop remedies. Other organizations provide social or legal assistance to low-income persons often cut off from these vital services.

A final approach of groups working for social change is developing alternative institutions. These include consumer cooperatives — businesses owned and democratically operated by consumers that can make the marketplace both more competitive and more responsive to people's needs.

What is the lifestyle like?

Salaries vary — not nearly enough to make you well-to-do but comfortable enough to live on.

Usually there is a high degree of cooperation and informality in the offices of organizations working for social change.

Weekly hours on the job tend to be slightly longer than the traditional 40 — but then most people who enjoy and believe in their work, whatever it is, don't stop at eight hours a day. Fresh into the job, many newcomers to citizen work will often lose track of the clock — letting a vacation or a weekend go by, a novel go unread, a friend go one more week without a letter or phone call. However, many learn to pace themselves, recognizing that their work — for all the urgency they feel — is an enduring commitment best integrated with their other interests.

Why choose social change work?

The opportunities for learning and for acquiring new skills are vast. A rule of thumb is that the smaller the staff — and many social change groups are fairly small — the less specialized job definitions will be, since each individual will need to cover a range of functions.

A fundraiser, for example, may also be expected to handle press and public relations. And many organizations, regardless of size, are very open to individuals suggestions for new projects.

If the organization decides to issue a leaflet and there isn't a graphics person on staff, someone is going to have to learn computer graphics or layout and pasteup. If the organization decides to take on a timely new issue area, someone's going to have to be well informed in that area. In fact, some people who may not be committed to social change as a vocation spend several "training" years in it to acquire skills they might wait much longer to develop in more traditional jobs.

Yet no matter what their motivations or level of commitment, those who sample social change work find — often to their surprise — that they can acquire valuable insights that continue to influence their perspectives and actions over the rest of their lives. In fact, many who plan to make a commitment of a few years like the Peace Corps before getting on with their careers never leave. They find that social change provides an opportunity, ultimately, to express one's values, help others and influence the shape of some corner of the world — rare attributes for any career.

Seeking social change work

When students, about to plunge into the job market, go to their college placement offices to gather information on social change opportunities, they are often disappointed: few placement offices have available information about career options that fit the bill. Instead, such offices inundate job-seeking students with recruitment materials from corporate and government employers.

College career offices, by definition, have a responsibility to enrich a student's sense of career alternatives. However, the near absence of information about careers in social change leaves many students in the dark about these opportunities. Some progressive career offices have sought to remedy the career information imbalance by holding Alternative Career Fairs, establishing public interest speakers' series and forums, hiring public interest career counselors, surveying area social change organizations for news of jobs and internship openings and creating public interest internships and fellowships to help students on financial aid do initial work with social change organizations.

Another way to provide balance would be for career offices to ask corporations to contribute to a placement fund to absorb the traveling expenses of public interest recruiters who could not otherwise afford to visit campuses. (When this was proposed by Ralph Nader before the Eastern College Personnel Officers convention in 1978, one corporate recruiter came up and volunteered to contribute to such a travel fund on behalf of his company.) Counselors should also make students aware of the wide variety of social change careers and the broad span of talents such work can utilize.

The problem is not only in college placement offices, however. The independent career counseling publications currently available offer little guidance to the student seeking social change work. Books depicting employment possibilities in industries such as banking or communications are expansive on traditional business opportunities. There's no mention in the banking category, however, of the alternatives open to someone interested in helping blighted urban neighborhoods overcome bank redlining, nor any discussion in the communications chapter of opportunities for someone interested in increasing the average citizen's access to the airwaves.

The career literature that lists generic jobs works similarly — it has no place for scientists who want to work for a solar future or writers who would edit newsletters for community organizations. To college students whose vocabulary of job possibilities is frequently acquired at the college placement office and through these guides, such alternatives remain, consequently, invisible.

This book helps bring those career opportunities to the fore. By interviewing activists, providing facts on over 1000 organizations now engaged in this work, and listing resources for further reference, we wish to furnish students with information they need to find social change careers on their own.

How To Use This Guide

We're not going to teach the dynamics of the successful handshake, what clothing to wear to an interview or how to write the prefect resume. You can learn all these arts elsewhere.

Nor do we tell you how to figure yourself out; how to decide what motivations are the right ones to have; or what you really want to do. That's up to you.

But if you think you might be interested in social change work, this book can be a useful resource. We provide you with profiles of people engaged in full-time citizen work, listings of organizations and a compilation of resources and networks.

Here's how to use the book:
Read the Profiles section to sense the breadth of backgrounds and motivations that characterize people who view social change as a calling, and the diversity of work awaiting you. You'll also begin to get a feel for what particular jobs are like.

The staff listings of over 1000 groups in the Directory section will help you begin your search. In response to our survey, the organizations have described in their own words their goals, projects and staff needs.

You will notice that some the groups listed have small budgets or are completely staffed by volunteers. Even though these organizations may not be sources for jobs at this time, we have included them as volunteer and internship opportunities, and because funding can change considerably from year to year — meaning that jobs might be available soon where none are now.

Note too that we do not provide listings for specific job openings; we're not a periodical and so we offer more general and long-lasting information. (For current openings, see the monthly bulletins, tabloids and placement services listed in the Resources section).

Keep in mind that the directory listings may be inconsistent from group to group — organizations provided their information in different forms. For example, many groups whose staffs share a number of duties found it difficult to categorize individual staff members functions. In most instances, task-sharing is represented by the use of fractions. Alternately, fractions may indicate that a particular function is performed by a part-time staff person.

Another variance occurs among the figures posted for salaries. In the Salary/year category we requested figures for average starting pay. Generally, figures are provided for recent college graduates or entry level positions, and for positions requiring an advanced degree or more experience. Some organizations provided only one figure or salary range. This could mean that their staff earn similar salaries; that the job description — and not specifically education or experience — determine salary; or that their staff is composed entirely of professional or support staff. In this last case, some groups may have opted to list in this category the starting salary for an attorney, others for an administrative Assistant.

The figure provided by most organizations for Staff openings/year is an average number, which may reflect normal yearly turnover, anticipated growth or a combination of both.

If an organization interests you, write to them for specifics. Tell them you saw this listing and want more information to give you a better understanding of their work.

Use the directory listings to get in touch with organizations not listed in the book. For example, if you are interested in energy groups but there aren't any listed for a particular city, call an energy group in another city and ask them for suggestions. If energy groups exist near you, chances are they'll know of them. Or find a social change group listed in your city — even one dealing with different issues — and ask them if they know of any local groups working in your area of interest. A campus PIRG, or Public Interest Research Group, is often a good place to begin. (See the PIRG directory in the Resources section).

Do not limit yourself to the Directory section in finding groups. The Bibliographies and Directories listing in the Resources section suggests many guides with specific issue concerns such as human rights, the environment, women and progressive publications.

You should also use the Directory listings to get a sense of the kinds of social change work being done in the United States today. The listings we provide here are by no means an exhaustive inventory of such groups. Some groups did not respond to our survey in time to be included in this edition. Good Luck.

Profiles

Eve Bargmann

Director, Primary Care Medicine Residency Program
George Washington University Medical School

"[Free clinics] are just stop-gaps. We really need to have access to proper health care for everybody. I don't want to be portrayed as the thousand points of light so people will say 'okay, the nonprofits are taking care of everybody so we can spend money on war.'"

Eve Bargmann saw medicine as a profession ready-made for someone who wanted to help others.

After keeping her nose to the books for four years studying chemistry at the University of Georgia in Athens, Bargmann was eager to launch a challenging, people-oriented career.

By the end of her first year at the University of North Carolina medical school, she had learned a great deal about what medicine offered people — and what it failed to offer. More often than not, she realized, poor people go without medical care until they are seriously ill. It is rare that the millions of Americans without medical insurance get the kind of early treatment for minor problems that can make a vast difference in their day-to-day lives, and stem life-threatening complications later on.

"I went into medicine genuinely wanting to be able to help out, and upon getting there I was surprised by the number of gaps, the extent to which we weren't doing as much as we could with the tremendous resources available," Bargmann recalls.

During medical school, she volunteered at a free medical clinic in Chapel Hill, and at a crisis counseling center. She specialized in internal medicine.

When she finished her residency, Bargmann decided to focus on health policy issues by working for Public Citizen's Health Research Group in Washington, D.C. There she researched issues relating to worker health and safety, prescription drug safety and access in the United States to quality medical care. She made a deal to work what was considered part-time for the busy organization — 40 hours a week — and took Thursday nights and Fridays to work at a free health clinic.

Called Zaccheus, the clinic was an offshoot of a free soup kitchen with the same name. The clinic served mostly homeless people, though homelessness is not a requirement for care. To be accessible to those in need, the clinic is located in an impoverished neighborhood near Washington's so-called red-light district on 14th Street.

When Bargmann left the clinic late at night, the area was teeming with prostitutes, pimps, drug dealers and drug abusers, some of whom occasionally sought medical help at the clinic.

But most of the patients were people with no home and no job, or whose jobs were low-paying and offered no medical coverage.

With only basic resources at the clinic, Bargmann perfected the scavenger approach to medicine. The clinic could handle basic health problems. In cases of serious injuries or illness, hospital emergency rooms wouldn't turn away medically indigent people. But many of the problems Bargmann saw at the clinic fell somewhere in between.

"If someone looked like they had a broken leg, or they were just beaten up, you could send them to the emergency room," Bargmann says. "If someone had a bleeding ulcer, or looked like they had colon cancer or needed thyroid testing, that took work." A patient would need x-rays, for example, to determine if symptoms were caused by an ulcer. The clinic had no x-ray machine, but in its early stages an ulcer typically does not qualify someone for emergency care. Yet, left untreated it can become serious. The clinic developed a network of supportive physicians, specialists and dentists who would help out. Tracking down a free x-ray or use of other costly diagnostic equipment was more difficult, however, and might take a day of calling on the phone. Sometimes it came down to shaming institutions into helping the poor, Bargmann recalls.

In 1982, Bargmann went to work full-time for the clinic, which is supported by grants and donations. She recognized the clinic was filling a need, but ever present was the gaping chasm between the poor and proper medical care. She was putting out fires, but was unable to address the simmering health problems that cause the flare-ups: untreated high blood pressure leads to heart failure; untreated diabetes leads to blindness or shuts down the kidneys; undetected cancers rage until they cannot be brought under control. The medical system, for all its miracles, was falling short; vast numbers of citizens cannot get care until fairly routine illnesses became deadly. After being part of the struggle to provide free care, the system's shortcomings are painfully clear to Bargmann and she wants the public to be aware.

"[Free clinics] are just stop-gaps," she says. "We really need to have access to proper health care for everybody.

"I don't want to be portrayed as the thousand points of light so people will say 'okay, the nonprofits are taking care of everybody so we can spend money on war.'"

In 1984, Bargmann was offered a position with George Washington University Medical School as an assistant professor and clinician. She saw the job as a sort of refresher course in modern medicine after the makeshift clinic, allowing her to work directly with new equipment and confer closely with a range of colleagues who could broaden her medical understanding. She intended to take the post for a year, then return to the Zaccheus clinic.

But that year, Bargmann launched a project that would convince her she could make more of an impact on health care at the medical school. She was successful in obtaining a grant to develop a residency rotation at the Zaccheus clinic.

It was a hit with residents.

"They really enjoy the sense of assisting people the way they couldn't elsewhere," Bargmann said. The university saw it as a good training ground in community medicine, and by 1986 a rotation at a clinic serving the poor was mandatory for the primary care residents.

But Bargmann's work didn't end there. The George Washington University campus and hospital are located in an upscale neighborhood near the Potomac River and Georgetown, home of the Kennedy Center for the Performing Arts, the Watergate Hotel and several federal agencies. While the neighborhood is removed from the seamier side of the red-light district on 14th Street, it is not immune to homelessness, and a nearby shelter for the homeless has its hands full.

Bargmann has written a grant for federal funds that would assist the medical school in "adopting" the shelter and providing staff for health care. While she awaits word on the grant, she is encouraged by crossing what was perhaps the biggest hurdle — getting the university to agree to the plan. At first, hospital officials were concerned about taking on a commitment to provide more free care.

"As any struggling urban hospital, they have to look out for their own survival," says Bargmann, who since 1987 has been director of the primary care medicine residency program. But officials came to understand that a program of ongoing, preventative medical care could save the hospital in the long run. Noting that the emergency ward is obligated to provide care to anyone in critical condition, regardless of whether they can pay, Bargmann said, "Why should [the university] wait until it has a homeless, desperately ill person if they can help earlier?" Other schools have had residency programs that place doctors in poor areas to give them that experience, but Bargmann says some of those programs gave the community "a sense people were using poor people as material." If the program she has in mind gets going, it will have residents taking on homeless and indigent citizens as patients for ongoing care, Bargmann says. That is better for the patients, and also gives doctors a better sense of the pressing need for care that Bargmann grew so familiar with at Zaccheus.

Bargmann is hopeful that the programs she is initiating will open the eyes of incoming doctors and encourage them to be advocates for better access to medical care. She says the medical community is already receptive, as the plan to adopt the Foggy Bottom shelter showed. "Residents really leaped at the idea. It struck a real chord in them," Bargmann says. "It was not so much a radical idea as something people hadn't known how to carry out."

Bargmann acknowledges that meeting the needs of the indigent won't be financially lucrative for anyone, and that is a stumbling block in a profession that has its share of people who are in it for the money. But she is convinced those who focus on money "are going to wind up groping because they know they haven't found much sense of meaning. I think we have a genuine need to have a meaning in our lives, to feel we're making a difference, to reach out to others."

Concern among doctors won't be enough to meet all the medical needs, Bargmann says, so she is among an increasing number of doctors who are pushing Congress to pass a national health care program that would ensure everyone has basic care.

"We're the only industrialized nation other than South Africa that doesn't have universal access [to health care], which I'm ashamed of," she says.

"I hope the political process, halting as it is, will be able to deal with this."

In the meantime, Bargmann still volunteers as a doctor at the Zaccheus clinic.

"I'm genuinely hopeful we'll be able to come up with a solution," Bargmann says. "In the meantime, you don't let people do without."

Susan Birmingham — Lobbyist, United States Public Interest Research Group U.S.PIRG

"Once it dawns on you that your life can be about changing destiny, it seems ludicrous to think of doing anything else."

Each day the United States produces some 160 to 230 million tons of garbage, the bulk of which is carted off to sprawling landfills located on the outskirts of cities and towns.

For Susan Birmingham, knowing the ins and outs of the nation's garbage is a must. Called the "Queen of Trash" by co-workers at U.S. Public Interest Research Group, Birmingham works to make sure that the de-cisions that are made in Congress concerning the nation's garbage policy are environmentally sound.

Being a garbage gadfly isn't the career Birmingham planned on when she was growing up, but it's one that she tackles with both enthusiasm and seriousness.

"Garbage is a resource," she says, "and it's time people started treating it as such."

Many of the landfills that the country depends on to store its trash are overflowing and few communities want to build new sites. For city and county planners it's a dire situation. Increasingly, cities and towns are looking to incinerators as a way out of the trash debacle. Unfortunately, Congress is poised to sanction the transfer from landfills to incinerators. "It once again means we don't really have to take any fundamental look at how much we're producing, why we're producing it and what we are doing with it," Birmingham says.

But Birmingham will pull out all stops to see that pro-incinerator legislation doesn't proceed. Incinerators are not a long-term solution to the country's trash problem, she says; they are fraught with unwanted side effects. "If your garbage is toxic, which our garbage is, and you burn it you are going to create toxic air emissions. There's no way around that," says Birmingham. "It's a basic law of thermodynamics — matter can't be created or destroyed." To avoid the controversy, the incinerator industry wants to rename toxic ash "special waste." It then rids the ash of the negative connotations that "hazardous" implies, she says, without getting rid of the toxics in the substance.

Added to the emissions dangers, incineration has other problems as well. Even after burning, 30 percent of the trash remains — albeit in a different form — and still must be sent to a landfill. And much like nuclear reactors, the incinerators have been plagued with cost overruns and operating records not to be envied, says Birmingham.

Although the incinerator industry is a direct opponent that Birmingham has to counter, the plastics industry is a much more well-financed and politically powerful organization. U.S.PIRG estimates that up to 80 percent of the trash in landfills could be recycled if there was an incentive to do so or a law requiring that it be done. Although the Environmental Protection Agency (EPA) figures the number is closer to 25 percent, both agree that recycling won't be done voluntarily. Needless to say, the plastics industry will fight tooth and nail to keep mandatory recycling at bay. Armed with facts on recycling, Birmingham tries to ensure that in the quest for an acceptable compromise the legislature is realistic. "I lobby members of Congress; I talk to environmental committee staff people and alert them to our position," she says. "We also do a lot of writing and research. This year we'll be looking at the incinerator record in the country. There are 167 incinerators now operating. One of our arguments against incineration is that burning precludes recycling because incinerators compete for the same resources. We're going to look at the contracts between municipalities and incinerator companies to see whether or not the contracts guarantee a certain amount of garbage. Having to feed an incinerator garbage reduces the amount of garbage available for recycling. "

Birmingham hopes that with both research and advocacy, public interest groups can begin to reshape the debate on the nation's garbage policy. "The debate around garbage, and it's hardly a debate yet, is do you on the one hand continue to mine virgin materials with no thought of sustainability and throw them away or burn them, or do you use less and reuse and recycle those virgin materials. They're fundamentally opposite approaches."

Each time the incinerator or plastics lobbyists head to Congress with their reports and their policy changes, she's there to make sure the consumer is represented. She reminds legislators and staff of the problems with incineration, the need for recycling and the rise of environmental concerns among their constituents.

"We would like to see the Congress commit the nation to a strategy of reducing the amount of garbage produced in the first place," says Birmingham. "For instance, 50 percent by volume of the materials in landfills is made up of packaging. That's outrageous. It's just an unnecessary waste of resources."

Birmingham got her start in politics in college student government. Coming from strict Catholic schools, she found the education and the participation that were available at the university level inspiring. The summer after her junior year she worked with a group outside the university to help organize welfare mothers. The work was dissatisfying, says Birmingham, because the jobs the group tried to line up for welfare recipients wouldn't have allowed a mother to pay for both child care and basic necessities.

Although the work with welfare mothers didn't continue after the summer, she decided full-time political activism was for her. She didn't go back to the university for her senior year. "It's unfortunate the educational system wasn't necessarily preparing me for what I wanted to do with my life," she says. Birmingham notes that people can contribute a great deal to society without going to graduate school.

Birmingham says commitment is the main ingredient needed to be effective in the public interest movement. "If you have the energy and enthusiasm you can do almost anything — if you set your mind to it, if you have the will," she says.

She says her decision to enter the public interest movement seemed to be inevitable once she realized how limitless the work was.

"Once it dawns on you that your life can be about changing destiny," says Birmingham, "it seems ludicrous to think of doing anything else."

She has reason for her optimism. Working in the late 1970s with MassPIRG, which was then only a rag-tag army of activists, she lobbied for changes in the Democratic and Republican Party Platforms. "We were pushing for a phaseout of nuclear power."

Then came a successful effort to enact a bottle bill in Massachusetts. After a quick but intensive lobbying campaign by PIRGers, the legislature passed a statewide law requiring that bottles be recycled. Although the industry responded with a ballot initiative to repeal the law, MassPIRG was ultimately able to turn back their drive.

While working with MassPIRG, the organization grew from a small group of committed individuals to an organization of more than 100 paid employees. And as director of the Fund For Public Interest Research she worked to see the PIRGs build momentum nationwide. The Fund allowed the PIRGs to join together to undertake efforts that would have been impossible for a PIRG to accomplish going it alone.

Although successes now aren't nearly so quick or easy in her lobbying efforts in Washington, D.C., the stakes are much higher. Millions of citizens are affected by congressional actions.

Despite the difficulty of the task, Birmingham is more than ever committed to work in the public interest movement. "What do you want to say about your life in the final analysis?" she asks. "Do you want to tell your grandchildren that you helped create the 37th new brand of dog food or shampoo or that you fought for what you believed in?"

Gale Cincotta — Director, National People's Action

"When you look around your neighborhood, you start to see what's happening — people at school boards making decisions affecting your kids' education, realtors and banks controlling the community. Instead, you *have to control your community."*

In the mid-1960s, Austin, a working-class community on Chicago's far west side, was a "changing" neighborhood with a litany of problems. Racial tensions were high, for instance, and many realtors took advantage of the tensions to make a quick profit. These "panic peddlers" created fast turnover in real estate (landing a commission every time housing changed hands) by going door-to-door telling white homeowners that black families were moving into the neighborhood, and that they should sell their homes quickly before property values plummeted.

Police protection and other city services in the neighborhood slackened, and when absentee landlords allowed housing to deteriorate, city inspectors were often lax in enforcing housing codes. Schools were overcrowded, while funding, textbooks and teachers went to wealthier districts. Bank capital was also being drained out into the suburbs, as banks and insurance companies "redlined" inner-city neighborhoods like Austin — literally drawing red lines on maps to mark the areas they considered to be bad risks, making it impossible for people within those areas to get loans or insurance policies.

Gale Cincotta lived in Austin at the time, and as she saw it she was faced with a choice: either move out or become a activist. She chose to stay.

"People tend to think that if you can't get a bank loan, there's something wrong with you; or if your kids aren't learning, there's something wrong with the kids," she says. "It's important to know it isn't you, or your kids — instead there's something wrong with the system that has to be changed. When I first realized that, I got angry. And I've stayed angry.

"The only alternative is to move — but what's the difference if you move? You have to come to a point where you stop and dig in and do something about the problems around you. When you look around your neighborhood, you start to see what's happening — people at school boards making decisions affecting your kids' education, realtors and banks controlling the community. Instead, *you* have to control your community."

For 20 years Gale has worked to make urban neighborhoods more livable for the people already there, with decent, affordable housing and services and thriving local businesses.

To accomplish her objectives, this energetic homemaker-turned-activist takes on the country's powerful, conservative institutions and puts them to use for social change. One of her most impressive victories was a commitment from large Chicago banks for over $200 million in low-interest loans to benefit the city's poor neighborhoods. In 1985 alone, the first year of the program, the First National Bank of Chicago, Harris Bank and Northern Trust issued some $20 million in loans for construction or renovation of low-income housing, and for commercial development — mostly in sections of the city where they haven't made loans in years.

Cincotta's success is due at least in part to her gutsy style of activism. "It all started with a telephone call from Gale Cincotta to my boss the chairman," said Richard Hartnack, then a senior vice president with First National. "To picture what that's like, imagine that you run a nice, quiet prison camp in Vietnam, and you get a phone call ... and it's Rambo on the line!"

As the *Wall Street Journal* put it, Cincotta is "a woman who makes bankers quake in their pinstripes." But once they stop quaking long enough to negotiate with her, they come to respect her skill, her knowledge about banking laws and community reinvestment and her perseverance. "She has a record of sticking with it." said Hartnack. "She's one person you know you can't outlast."

Cincotta first got her experience — and her

reputation — in her own working-class neighborhood in Chicago's West Side. With six sons in public schools, her initiation into activism was the PTA, where she zeroed in on the root of problems for schools in poor areas — inadequate funding that was unfairly distributed. About $250 was spent on each pupil in Austin, compared to the some $700 per pupil in the wealthier far north section of Chicago.

The resources Gale employed were drawn from the main experience she had had up to that point — managing a family. "A lot of what's called 'research' is really just common sense," she says. "If you have to run a household on very little money, you learn things.

"You look at the board of education. They have just so much money; if they put all that money in one area, they don't have it to put in another. Well, I knew if I did that with my children — if I said, 'I like you better, I'll give everything to you,' that would obviously be unfair. But that's essentially what the board of education was doing with all our kids."

Gale and her neighbors who had children in the school used the PTA's regular meetings and access to school records and the board of education to advocate for change. Gradually their active presence brought about some improvements: new audiovisual equipment was shipped in, more textbooks were provided, an addition was built onto the elementary school and eventually, a new middle school was constructed to relieve overcrowding in the other schools.

The school fight taught Gale one of the most important qualities of an organizer: patience. "With that middle school, from the time we first started fighting for it to the time the doors opened, it was five years," she says. "My son never went to that school; by the time it was finished he was too old. But you learn to interpret little things as victories, to keep you going. The first meeting with officials, where they agreed to consider the proposal, was a victory. Then there was this good decision, and that one. So the whole five years, we were celebrating each step."

Her PTA work quickly snowballed into other issues. Slumlords and housing violations were one problem Cincotta tackled next. Real estate agencies and banks were another. The realtors and banks, she learned, were contributing to the decline of her neighborhood through redlining.

Cincotta joined a new group, the Organization for a Better Austin (OBA), being formed by followers of Saul Alinsky, a community organizer whose theories and books on comunities' self-determination are the bible for many community organizers today.

With OBA Gale took her work against redlining further. "What we were told back then was that changing neighborhoods were a natural phenomenon. But we started to see that there was a lot of money being made in changing neighborhoods, and that they were being racially changed on purpose — *targeted* for change.

"First the realtors would come in, start on a block or two and pass out leaflets, telling white people they had better get out or they would lose money. Then the banks wouldn't write policies. Then police would be assigned somewhere else.

"In the meantime, people would deposit their money in the banks in these 'changing' neighborhoods, but instead of investing the money back in the neighborhood, the banks put it into suburban tract development. There were ads in the papers telling you that you were practically un-American if you didn't move out there to the suburbs. There wasn't any money for loans if you wanted to buy here in the city, or rehab here, but for a low down payment and good terms, you could move somewhere else. *That's* no natural phenomenon.

"And were the realtors making money! You can figure that they turned over a block in maybe six months. They made a commission on every house in the block, plus maybe a commission on houses where the new people coming in had lived. And the realtors scared people so badly that they would sell really low. Some of the companies bought up the property themselves, and then turned it over for huge profits."

OBA responded by going directly to the offices of the realtors to demand that they either behave professionally or leave the neighborhood. OBA asked them to sign nonsolicitation agreements, and picketed the offices of firms that refused. They also filed complaints with the Chicago Commission on Human Relations and with the Department of Registration and Education, which licenses realtors.

Cincotta's instincts about issues and tactics made her a rising star in the world of neighborhood activism in Chicago — a world largely inspired by Alinsky. Cincotta was the first woman to be elected president of an Alinsky-type group, and became a much-needed role model for women involved in community organizing, back then a field in which women were volunteer rank-and-file members while men made up the leadership and paid staff.

Despite her success, Cincotta worried that community groups were too turf-conscious and their focuses too parochial, so she started building coalitions and shaping a national, multiracial neighborhood movement in which she encouraged women to take leadership roles and run for office. In 1972 she helped create and became chairperson of the aptly named National People's Action (NPA), an umbrella organization for about 300 neighborhood groups.

Under Cincotta, NPA has worked on a wide range of issues, including housing, banking, energy costs, health care and military spending. She also directs the National Training and Information Center, which works with community groups across the country, and was appointed by Chicago Mayor Harold Washington to chair the city's Commission on Women's Affairs.

Among the staff at NPA, members of local groups active in the organization and her friends, Gale is known for her passion about issues and for her leadership qualities. She is credited with an unusual ability to "make connections" — to understand the broad cause of a local problem and assign blame to the appropriate powerful institution or institutions, while understanding the interconnectedness of the institutions themselves.

"There are other people who take things and separate them out to understand them. To me that's difficult. Some of the people I work with tell me I talk like James Joyce writes, in a stream of consciousness, weaving back and forth from one issue to another and how they're related. But that's the kind of thinking that's missing in Washington. The Department of Energy doesn't talk to Housing, so they build homes that aren't insulated, don't have solar panels and lose energy through big windows. It just isn't coordinated."

NPA has an impressive list of gains. Among others, it lobbied successfully for federal antiredlining laws and a law requiring the Department of Housing and Urban Development to reimburse individuals who were sold substandard housing under federal programs. NPA has also negotiated — with Gale doing the actual wrangling — with insurance companies and banks for hundreds of millions of dollars in grants and low-interest loans for local reinvestment programs, including several pilot low-income housing construction and rehabilitation projects around the country. Gale's tools in getting the banks to agree to the loan programs were the federal antiredlining laws she had lobbied for.

"With any issues we took on, there were people who said 'it isn't going to work,'" Cincotta says. "When we took on the Federal Housing Administration, people said, 'It's too big for you, it's a federal bureaucracy.' But we figured it out, step by step. And with our legislation, people had said, 'The banks are too big.' But we beat the bank lobby.

"People are always saying you can't do it. But maybe you can. You can do a piece of it. At least you can build a base for someone else to build on. If you say you can't do it, you won't even touch it, and then of course you can't do it.

"Doing this work is just a matter of self-confidence, and having people behind you. People call me a leader, but I say, well, if you don't have people behind you, you're not leading anything. What we have is people power." Gale still lives in Austin, in an area that is now almost entirely black. Driving west, people who live there say, you can tell when you get to Austin, because other areas that weren't organized have turned into slums. In Austin, there are still some abandoned buildings, but there's also the feeling that people have more control over their lives and neighborhood.

(*Excerpted with permission from a profile by Anne Witte Garland in* Women Activists.)

Gina Collins

Green Corps, Founder and Director

"I still believe that democracy makes sense. I enjoy working with young people because they still see the possibilities."

The founder and executive director of Green Corps exudes the idealism that she seeks to impart in her recruits. Launched in 1990, Green Corps combines environmental activism, field work and political training in a structured educational program aimed at the nation's youth. It is the nation's first true political organizing school.

Despite almost three decades of advocacy dedicated to environmental protection, few opportunities existed for transforming a passion into an effective career. Green Corps has changed that. The 1,500 applications that poured in for the 30 slots available in its first year of operation also proved that Green Corps was an idea whose time had come.

Gina Collins knew precisely what she wanted to do when she graduated from Rutgers University in the early '80's. She wanted to organize. Her classes in Women's studies, prisoner's rights and political science, along with volunteer work registering voters, inspired her; finding an outlet however, proved difficult.

After graduation, she accepted a position at New Jersey Public Interest Research Group. "I wanted to learn how to organize, " she says, and NJPIRG "was one of the only options that I had at the time." Not because she lacked talent, intelligence or determination, but because so few opportunities for organizers are available.

Collins spent seven years at NJPIRG, eventually became the Organizing Director for the group. During that time, she continued to think about her own experience after college, and the lack of options she faced. There has to be, she thought, a better way.

Green Corps first occured to her in 1988. Convinced that a structured learning environment — a school to train a cadre of political organizers — was needed, Collins spent the next two years formulating her idea and consulting her peers in the environmental and consumer movements.

In 1990 NJPIRG gave her six months paid leave to pursue her idea. Collins visited colleges, universities, career centers and environmental groups to pitch them on the utility and demand for the program. She raised about $700,000 in the first year of operations, including a three-year, $350,00 start-up grant from the Fund for Public Interest Research, a consortium of state PIRGs. She recruited prominent activists, including Lois Gibbs, Director of the Citizen's Clearinghouse for Hazardous Waste, Denis Hayes, Director of the Bullitt Foundation and Robert F. Kennedy, Jr., Director of the Environmental Litigation Clinic at Pace University to serve on the board of directors.

Finally, all that was missing was a name. Her first try, The National Environmental Organizing Project, was too dry, she discovered. Instead, she found a name "with an edge," a quality she now looks for in all her applicants. Green Corps, combines "green" (for the environmental movement and the Peace Corps). Collins says, "it paints a picture of people working as a team to protect the environment."

Green Corps resembles a boot camp for environmentalists. The 30 students accepted into the program each year get a month of intensive classroom work including political and issues training — learning the basic techniques of political organizing while also digesting treatises on the ozone layer, water pollution and endangered species. After the initial training stage, the students spend up to a year engaged in field work, a kind of high-intensity on-the-job training where both the stakes and the responsibilities are real. Each year, Green Corps chooses campaigns that adddress critical environmental problems and provide a range of experiential learning opportunities. During the 1992-1993 year, Green Corps played an important role in the following campaigns: Campaign to Save Endangered Species; Recycling Initiative's Save

America's Wilds; Clean Air Campaign; and the Rainforest Campaign. Fifty young people have graduated from Green Corps since it opened for business three years ago. Collins hopes they will go on to be "the next generation of environmental leaders, young, college-educated organizers who will be the campaign managers, field managers and executive directors of environmental organizations in the 1990s and beyond. Twenty-five of its first 40 graduates are already actively employed in environmental campaigns around the country.

Collins has three basic goals for Green Corps: bring the environmental movement back to basics by "training the next generation of leaders;" convey to the environmental community the importance of political organizers in developing a grassroots movement; and, most important, to make significant strides in environmental preservation and conservation.

Gina Collins isn't going to stop with Green Corps. She's already working on a new program: Neighborhood Greencorps, which just received a National Service grant, to teach students how to organize neighborhood initiatives. Asked where she sees herself in 10 years, she replies that " I want to organize people on their porches." She sees herself "walking up a dusty road in the south" and teaching the elderly what she is teaching the young people right now. She says that the elderly have the same hope and see the possibilities as the young people she is working with now. "Start out with hope and end with hope."

Ernesto Cortes

National Staff, Industrial Areas Foundation (IAF)
Director, Texas IAF Network

"You develop a real respect for and appreciation of the power and potential of ordinary people, who are able to do very extraordinary things."

The sun beats down on the cement block houses in San Elizario, Texas, a small town on the Mexico-U.S. border. Temperatures hover around 100 degrees for much of the summer and rainfall is scarce year round. Life is difficult in border towns — per capita incomes are low, unemployment is high and a lack of clean drinking water makes for health conditions normally found only in the Third World.

Clean water must be hauled from nearby towns or trucks, outhouses dot the landscape. The Third World conditions on the U.S. border mean that hepatitus and tuberculosis are common and infant mortality rates are far above national averages.

Many families that moved into towns like San Elizario were promised water by developers once all the houses were sold. But the developers have long since disappeared and the people who lived in the "colonias," as they are called, are still waiting for basic necessities. They have little money with which to acquire them, however, and the cities and counties where they are located are already stretching limited budgets.

Leading the fight to push the state into providing drinking water to the colonias is Ernesto Cortes, director of the Texas Industrial Areas Foundation Network — a coalition of 10 groups around the state fighting for the rights of the disadvantaged and organizing low-income and minority communities to become politically active.

In November, 1989 the coalition organized to gain support for a constitutional amendment on the ballot that would allocate $100 million for water and sewer hookups for the colonias. In an unprecedented 'get out the vote' effort, residents in the lower valley — including San Elizario — turned out in numbers 3 times their normal levels. Statewide the proposition passed by a 3-2 margin. For Cortes it was another in a long line of battles to empower low-income and minority people in his home state of Texas. Growing up Mexican in San Antonio, Cortes became involved in the fight for justice early. Attending the University of Texas in Austin when the civil rights movement was taking shape, Cortes found himself a member of the ranks battling for equal rights.

From there, he worked organizing farmworkers who were fighting for better working conditions. While working for the United Farm Workers, he organized food and support drives for striking workers and coordinated a boycott of produce harvested by nonunion workers. Then it was only a small leap to community organizing and voter registration work. Cortes says it was his Catholic upbringing that forced him into public interest work.

"I took very seriously what the church taught about justice and about equality," he says.

At first, he considered careers in fields from politics to academics, but it wasn't until he realized that people did indeed work full-time and then some at organizing that he seriously looked at the possibility of doing such work as a profession.

Today his work centers on keeping the 10 organizations that are part of the Texas IAF Network on the cutting edge of social change work. He travels the state teaching organizers the tools of the trade and helping to identify leaders that can take the organizations into new territory.

At training sessions he says people come with high expectations and often leave with the energy to accomplish seemingly insurmountable tasks. He challenges them to work hard to involve new people in their battles for better education, health care and local services. "It challenges me as well," says Cortes. "I like to read and I like to integrate my reading and my writing with my organizing."

Cortes' network was instrumental in passing a state school equalization bill, which will ensure that discrepancies between high-income areas and low-income areas do not mean discrepancies in the kinds of education the children enrolled in the school receive. The network also pushed through passage of an indigent health care bill.

By organizing in low-income and minority communities, he says, the network ensures that these areas aren't left out when the state divvies up resources and that the political leaders are responsive to the needs of the poor. "We can make a difference, we can have real impact; it's not just theoretical, it's not just abstract. It's real substantive and important," he says.

His work, he says, allows him to make a living without compromising his principles. "It enables you to integrate your values in your career," says Cortes. "I love to teach. Organizing is teaching, particularly when there are people who want to learn. It offers an opportunity to integrate an understanding of economics, an understanding of politics and an understanding of history in a very practical way." Organizing allows him to apply practically the ideas he learned while in graduate school in economics at the University of Texas-Austin.

But his work has also taught him much about the power of citizens. "We deal with people who are ordinary people, people who don't have a whole lot of say-so right now. The focus of [our work] is to draw out their potential and teach them that they can make a difference, that their values and their vision are important," says Cortes. "You develop a real respect for and appreciation of the power and potential of ordinary people, who are able to do very extraordinary things."

Meg Haenn

New England Field Director, Clean Water Action Project and Fund
Texas Field Director for ACORN

"I was raised with the idea that work was a necessary means to an end. You had to work so you could get on with the rest of your life. I never did believe that. If I feel I'm accomplishing something, then that's all that matters."

For Meg Haenn getting involved in public interest work wasn't something she planned to do. She just drifted into it and was "swept away."

In June of 1982 Haenn was taking a break from her job in food management at a hotel in Philadelphia in order to reevaluate her career goals when she heard about a nuclear freeze rally being held in New York City. She decided to go, and at the rally she met some friends who encouraged her to do some work on the freeze campaign. She decided to give it a try.

"You just get swept up in something that dynamic. Afterwards you look back and discover why you made the choice you did. Then you can make a conscious commitment and can understand exactly where you want to go from there."

Haenn was concerned about the environment, but she realized that she wanted to affect those problems by tackling the larger political structures of lawmaking and enforcement. She took a job canvassing with the League of Conservation Voters, a national nonpartisan political campaign committee that supports environmental candidates and rates Congress on environmental voting records.

As a canvasser for the League, Haenn was responsible for distributing voter information and charts on candidates, educating people on the issues, soliciting campaign contributions, and getting out the vote: registering voters, enlisting volunteers to organize precincts or work phone banks, or just convincing people to show up at the polls on election day.

"At first I was nervous. But after knocking on a few doors, you realize that two thirds of the people you talk to are going to sign your petition, two thirds of those will contribute or pledge to support the candidate, and a third of these will probably be willing to write a letter to a member of Congress or actively campaign.

"I noticed that the question people asked most often wasn't about the issues or the candidates. Instead they wanted to know why I was doing this. I realized that my reaction was the key to the interaction. By being assertive rather than aggressive, by expressing pure concern, by being honest about why I was there, I could influence the outcome of each conversation.

"And it worked. It worked because I believe very strongly that it's a big neighborhood that we live in. We've got to start taking responsibility beyond our own four walls, for the people down the road, for the people in the next state and the people across the country.

"With that belief backing you up, you have quite a lot of power when you knock on someone's door and say 'This is what you and I are responsible for, and I want you to accept that responsibility, sign this and write a check.'

"Of course, the first couple of times someone actually writes a check, you are surprised. But then you realize that people want to buy into the ownership of the issues at hand — issues that we're working on and that our government isn't doing enough about.

"Educating the public is my passion, and that's what the canvass operation is all about. It enables you to reach and to activate an incredibly broad base of people, and it gives you hard cash to fund special projects."

At the League, Haenn had several opportunities to observe and appreciate this "incredible people power" in action. "In a number of elections our candidates have won by margins equivalent to the number of votes we pulled out."

Other times, she says, going door-to-door brought her face to face with the reality behind the issue she was promoting. "I've canvassed in Manville, Pennsylvania, the asbestos capital of the United States, and have heard horror stories at those doors. I've canvassed a woman who cried because her husband had died the month before from working with formaldehyde. I've met a woman whose two children had both had bone marrow transplants because of a cancer that the doctor said had been environmentally caused. "Those people write checks and ask what else they can do. The best thing you can do for someone who has had that kind of loss is to channel them toward some constructive activity, so they can feel that they are working to take control of what has hurt them."

"Those encounters," Haenn adds, "put you in tears, and they strengthen your resolve to keep on going, because they remind you of what you are working for."

After a year with the League, Haenn decided to take a job with the Clean Water Action Project in Washington, a national group that conducts research, lobbying, and citizen organizing aimed at — as the name suggests — eliminating water pollution, safeguarding drinking water and protecting water resources and wetlands. Some recent projects and issues include a campaign for stronger laws against toxic dumping, compensation for victims and the reauthorization of the Superfund law.

As canvass director, Haenn oversaw the project's grassroots operation. "I had to target the areas to canvass, obtain permits and check for possible overlap with other canvass operations. Once the turf was 'cleared and mapped out,' I had to make sure that canvassers could get to the destinations, which meant dealing with frequent auto breakdowns. I also did the paperwork for the canvass and maintained its books: writing reports and position papers, doing payroll, balancing the budget. It's multi-faceted; you have to be very adaptable."

Chiefly responsible for hiring and training the canvassers, Haenn expected a similar range of talents and flexibility in the people she hired. "I looked for a strong commitment to the issues, good communication skills and a high energy level. Most of the folks who come on board here are pretty idealistic and driven; people with a strong sense of mission.

"I also wanted people who were able and willing to adapt quickly to new situations. If you're going to work in the public interest field, you have to be able to do your share of fundraising, writing and research." Haenn incorporated part-time internships with other facets of the organization, including lobbying, research, administrative assistance, in the training session for her canvassers, along with factual briefings on the issues and lessons in the art of persuasive communicating.

Being behind the scenes and absorbed in directing the canvass, Haenn says, at times made her feel distant from the field operation itself. "A big part of my job was building the canvass leadership and morale, but sometimes I looked at the groups of canvassers and had a hard time pinpointing what *I* did for them. Canvassers make such a team, and they do so much for each other.

"The supportive relationships you make in organizations like this help you sustain your energy, cope with rejection or exhaustion. Seeing how committed the people around you are, how much of themselves they invest in their work can really give you a needed boost."

The skills she learned as canvass director led to her current position as director of finance and administration. Haenn splits her time between managing the finances of the Clean Water Action Fund and supervising canvass operations in New England.

Haenn points out that canvassing is a multi-dimensional education which "makes you highly employable as it makes you a better person. You canvass people from low-income to the very wealthy, and you get a clear picture of what and who the public really is. You learn to be objective with people, to listen and respond to their concerns and needs and to adjust your vocabulary so that you can communicate effectively with anyone. You also learn a lot about yourself — and you become tougher, more resilient."

It's a valuable education, but also one which requires a considerable commitment of time and energy. "Canvassers work from 2 to 10 p.m., but my day is usually from 10 a.m. to midnight. I actually prefer working on Saturdays because it's quiet in the office. I don't mind the hours, because I know the value of the work, and the more I take on the more I accomplish.

"I was raised with the idea that work was a necessary means to an end — work so you could go on with the rest of your life. I never did believe that. If I feel I'm accomplishing something, then that's all that matters."

"Sure, there's a sacrifice involved. But I *do* have a personal life. The friends I choose to have right now are active in the same kind of work, so they understand. We try to be supportive. I always make sure I get home in time to feed the dog," she adds.

Haenn explains grinning that she brings her dog and cat along whenever she travels, and when she began at Clean Water, she visited offices in Florida, Virginia and Minnesota to learn the basics of directing a canvass.

"My mother always used to say, 'It's such a bohemian lifestyle. When are you going to get a real job?' Finally I told her 'I'm pretty gone on this, so you're going to have to accept it.'"

Haenn reports that her mother now accepts the fact that her daughter is a "lifer" in the public interest movement. "They don't have my birth certificate," she jokes, "but I've committed just about everything else I have to doing this."

"I've grown so much through this experience," she admits. She describes her personal growth as partly religious. "How can anyone live in this messed-up world and not believe in something? "Seriously, though, there's a quote in the Bible about how so much knowledge can bring about so much sorrow. And it's true. The more you learn about how government is run, how bureaucracies deal with crucial issues, the more you begin to despair about how we ever got ourselves into such a mess in the first place."

For Meg Haenn such reflections lead not to stagnation, but to renewed energy and action. "If you're going to complain, you've got to buy into solutions right away. The next question always has to be 'And how do we get ourselves out of this mess?' We just have to keep asking those questions and keep coming up with different solutions."

Ralph Hotchkiss

Inventor, MacArthur Fellow

"It's making a living doing my hobby. It's just as challenging, just as much fun as I ever could have dreamed."

Growing up on the outskirts of Rockford, Illinois, Ralf Hotchkiss never had any doubt about what he wanted to be. "My goal was always to be an inventor," says Hotchkiss. From farm mechanics who jimmied old vehicles together for yet another season of plowing or harvesting or built from scratch a new piece of equipment, he found his best role models.

His first inventions weren't exactly patentable. At age seven he put together a set of wings. It took only a single jump off a nearby fence and several bruises to convince Hotchkiss that it took more than wings to fly. His next inventions were much more down to earth. He created a six-seater bicycle, built sailboats out of plywood and bongo drums fashioned after organ pipes.

In ninth grade he first coupled his love of inventing with public interest work. Inspired by Helen Keller's writing, he began looking at ways to allow blind people to have the mobility that seemed reserved only for the sighted world. He created a distance sensing device, which worked in ways similar to today's autofocus cameras and a curb sensing cane, which used audio reflections to warn of an upcoming curb.

After a severe motocycle accident, Hotchkiss found new motivation to couple his inventing with helping people with disabilities. "After I became a wheelchair rider myself, I switched to mostly wheelchair design," he says. He built his first wheelchair because there was nothing on the market that provided both the versatility and flexibility he wanted. Not satisfied with wheelchairs that limited their occupants to the straight and narrow, he created a wheelchair that opened the world up to its user. His first chair climbed stairs and hills and made its way through forests by using catepillar treads.

It was a speech by Ralph Nader in 1968 at Oberlin College, where Hotchkiss was a student, that first put him into contact with the organized public interest movement. He signed up to work for Nader in Washington, D.C. that very night.

With a group of other college recruits, they stormed the city during the Christmas break. Their first investigation led them on a tour of all the popular nightclubs in the city on New Year's Eve. But instead of partaking of the revelry they were measuring the decibel levels of the music being played. What they found was noise levels far in excess of what was considered safe and often at levels that would deafen the unsuspecting crowd.

Next they studied product and automobile safety and highway design. After each investigation they would issue a report presenting the facts they had uncovered. In a month they had inundated consumers with information on behavior and products that were harmful to their health. Most of all, says Hotchkiss, it was a learning experience. They learned how to scrounge through the federal libraries and agencies for information on a myriad of consumer issues. "It was a very interesting and challenging month," says Hotchkiss.

At the end of his stay in Washington, Hotchkiss was ready for more. He signed up for the following summer. During his next stint at the Nader office he began work on *The Lemon Book*, a car owners' manual that told consumers how their cars worked and what to do if the car had problems.

While at Nader's office he also got to try his hand at both product testing and inventing. "We persuaded a mobile home manufacturer to hook up a giant tow truck and measure the force it took to rip a mobile home off its foundation," says Hotchkiss. "Our calculations had shown that none of the 'tie downs' on the market were good for much at all because they had no lateral strength to speak of."

The ad hoc testing showed that their calculations were in fact correct and in a subsequent test, using a configuration based on a new model that the Nader team recommended, the mobile home held.

"We were inventing at the same time as critiquing other people's inventions and negotiating with the National Bureau of Standards and the National Highway Traffic Safety Administration and the myriad of government and private agencies that affect what inventions will be used and which won't."

Hotchkiss made a point of seeking out inventors everywhere he went. He talked with them about their frustrations as well as their techniques. "By working with current inventors and helping them see their ideas at least tested if not used by the general public, we were directly involving ourselves in their process of invention," says Hotchkiss. "Inventing isn't just a single event; it's a whole process that goes on and on."

One of his original studies for Nader was to do a thorough search of all the auto safety inventions that had been patented by inventors over the years. One of the patents he uncovered was for a telescoping steering column which would have collapsed on impact. "It should have prevented hundreds of thousands of deaths," says Hotchkiss, since the column would no longer have impaled drivers involved in serious crashes. Despite the fact that the telescoping column had been patented in the 1920s, most automotive manufacturers refused to modify their steering wheels until the federal government stepped in and required collapsable steering columns for all new autos.

"That just made my blood boil," says Hotchkiss. "The inventor who put his lifeblood into working on patenting this very well thought-out invention had no way to see it used at all in his lifetime."

Other good inventions were changed so dramatically by the companies that introduced them that they became the exact opposite of the safety mechanisms the inventors had envisioned. "Inventors had tried to make devices they thought were wonderful," says Hotchkiss, "but they saw them turned into lethal death-dealing devices for economic reasons."

Washington was full of eye-opening realities for the young inventor. "One of the big frustrations I found as I met with inventors is that they would come up with great ideas that would make life better for all of us, that would save lives and prevent injuries, and there was no way they could sell them."

Hotchkiss says this was particularly true in the automotive industry where there was little real competition, and so even less incentive for companies to provide a safer design. "It had been monopolized to the extent that companies apparently would get together and decide not to put in certain lifesaving devices," says Hotchkiss.

Hotchkiss stayed with Nader organizations, working with the Center for Auto Safety and the Center for Concerned Engineering, full-time until the mid-1970s. His main focus remained pushing for safer designs in products ranging from automobiles to aerosol cans.

After leaving the Nader organizations, he started working on wheelchair design more seriously. His early work on high-tech wheelchair design was cut short, however. "By 1980 I began to realize there was more need at the other end of the spectrum, at the low-tech end of wheelchairs," he says.

"The vast majority of the people in the world who need wheelchairs don't have anything yet," says Hotchkiss. "They can't afford them."

There are an estimated 25 million people who need wheelchairs worldwide, says Hotchkiss, and nearly 20 million of them live in the Third World. Very few of these people will ever be able to afford wheelchairs, says Hotchkiss. For many of these people, the lack of mobility means they will have few opportunities to make a life for themselves.

Western-made wheelchairs at Western-made prices are far too costly to be imported and production in the Third World is simply not widespread.

What compounds the problem is that the limited

wheelchair manufacturing currently taking place in much of the Third World has been based on a copy of the cheapest U.S. model: the 50-pound hospital clunker. It is a wheelchair designed for the linoleum floors of hospitals. On the paved sidewalks and streets in the United States it is a struggle, but on dirt roads and footpaths it is all but impossible to maneuver. This wheelchair model is also inordinately expensive since steel is sold by the pound.

With wheelchair designers from around the world, however, Hotchkiss hopes to expand and reshape wheelchair manufacturing in the Third World. It is a mission he is driven to see fulfilled. Using his own personal experience in a wheelchair and the expertise of a network of wheelchair builders, he is working to refine a common design that can provide both affordable and versatile wheelchairs throughout the Third World.

As part of the effort, Hotchkiss teaches a course on Third World Wheelchair Building at San Francisco State University. People from Trinidad, Panama, Mexico and even Siberia descend on San Francisco to learn to construct wheelchairs. They are able to take home their prototype as well as participate in ongoing research and development. The idea is that these people return to their countries and begin manufacturing wheelchairs. Slowly, Hotchkiss hopes, such small manufacturers will begin to put a dent in the great demand for wheelchairs in the Third World.

In attempting to transform the developed world's wheelchair into a vehicle for use in the Third World, he soon found that inventors in the Third World could also improve upon the First World's design. One of the most important contributions, he says, is the discovery of a new front wheel. The choice for wheelchair riders until now has been a tire that rolls nicely but can go flat and is costly to repair, or a solid rubber tire that makes for a bumpy ride but is less destructable.

The former tire is completely out of the question for the Third World because of its price and fragility. But inventors in Zimbabwe discovered another way of making a front wheel that combines the benefits of both. The design was developed for pushcarts but can be adapted easily to wheelchairs. A group of builders in India first used the tire on a wheelchair and now another group of builders in Siberia is making molds for the tires.

"They'll take that design back from Siberia to Zimbabwe and Zimbabwe will have great front wheels for the first time ever," says Hotchkiss. To ensure that the tires are introduced quickly, Hotchkiss is hoping to send molds throughout the Third World to wheelchair manufacturers.

"Eventually that will spin back to the United States," he says. "Currently, I'm the only person in the United States who has had the luxury of riding on the new and improved tires." But he's already sure they are a winner. "They are as good as the others and they never get a flat tire," he says.

Hotchkiss says after years of refining and creating a better wheelchair there is still much to be done. But he sees the immensity of the task as just another challenge.

"It's making a living doing my hobby," he says. "It's just as challenging, just as much fun as I ever could have dreamed." By working with inventors from all across the globe, he has learned new techniques and new designs that on his own would have been nearly impossible to discover.

Most importantly, he says, "I get feedback from all these people who in some cases were stuck in the corner of a mud-floored shack." And that, he says, makes all the effort of creating a better wheelchair worthwhile.

Ann Leonard **Greenpeace International Waste Trade Project Campaigner**

"It's a clear issue. Either you think it's okay to take advantage of people's poverty by shipping them poison, or you think there is something environmentally and morally wrong with it. There is no gray area here — and there is also no time to waste being timid about stopping waste exports."

Ann Leonard's work varies daily — at different times she finds herself knee-deep in research, on the phone organizing hundreds of people for demonstrations, meeting with members of the U.S. Congress, investigating waste dumps in foreign countries, sneaking around U.S. ports or trying to get herself out of jail. Although the specifics vary day to day, the work is all toward one common goal: to prevent the United States from dumping hazardous wastes in foreign countries.

Leonard works on Greenpeace's International Waste Trade Project in Washington, D.C. With a dozen other Greenpeacers stationed around the globe, she works to prevent industrialized countries from exporting hazardous waste, incinerator ash, household garbage, sewage sludge and other wastes to developing countries.

The export of hazardous waste is a fairly recent development. It was only when the KHIAN SEA began its convoluted journey around the world in search of a dumping ground for Philadelphia's toxic incinerator ash that much of the world first learned of the existence of an international trade in toxics. The skyrocketing price of disposing of wastes in the United States and Europe had created a new breed of unscrupulous entrepreneur, one that Leonard hopes to quickly put out of business — the waste trader.

Waste traders are the brokers between the companies and municipalities that have ash, toxic waste or garbage, and any place outside the industrialized world where the waste can be dumped. For the importing countries the stakes are high. Guinea-Bissau was offered four times its gross national product to take hazardous wastes.

For Leonard, the key to stopping the waste trade is publicizing it. Once a waste-dumping scheme is exposed, it is usually shelved and the traders are forced into hiding. "The practice is so inherently reprehensible," says Leonard, "that a target government could find itself in trouble if it doesn't actively oppose it."

Leonard says it's an area where there is no room for debate. "It's a clear issue. Either you think it's okay to take advantage of people's poverty by shipping them poison, or you think there is something environmentally and morally wrong with it. There is no gray area here and there is also no time to waste being timid about stopping waste exports."

A native of Seattle, Leonard says she knew early on that she wanted to be an environmentalist. "As I grew up, my respect for the environment kept increasing," she says. "It never occurred to me that I would do anything besides work to protect it." In 1986, she moved to New York City to study environmental and political science at Barnard College of Columbia University. Internships with local environmental groups in New York and with New York's Parks Planning division intensified her resolve. After Columbia, she studied environmental politics and planning in graduate school at Cornell University.

During her years in school, Leonard often found herself frustrated with the context in which environmental projects were discussed. "Everyone seemed to know what was wrong but remained so hesitant to make changes," says Leonard. "I remember one environmental law class when we were discussing the problems with U.S. waste disposal regulations. 'Instead of focusing on who will pay for cleaning up leaking dumps,' I asked the professor, 'why not focus the law on preventing the waste in the first place?' The professor, who knew all the dangers of hazardous waste, answered that that wasn't realistic right now, that solution would have to wait."

After graduate school, Leonard moved to Washington, D.C. to work for one of the country's largest environmental groups. "I was so excited — finally I'd see some action and changes, instead of academic analyses on environmental problems." Unfortunately, what she faced was the same hesitancy to challenge the existing environmental policies, regardless of their flaws.

"People were only willing to take the smallest risks — to move the policies incrementally toward a solution," says Leonard. "Meanwhile, all reports were that the condition of the environment was worsening at a much faster pace than the snail-paced work of national environmentalists. I kept hearing that my goals and ideas were good, but not politically feasible. If politics won't allow us to do the right thing, then it's time we change what politics means."

After six months, Leonard left her job to work for Greenpeace on hazardous waste issues, and in particular the international waste trade. Waste traders thought they had found the perfect solution to rising costs and community opposition to new dumps: paying cash-starved Third World countries U.S. dollars to import First World waste. They may have been successful if Greenpeace hadn't stepped in. In short order, Greenpeace was able to mobilize opposition from around the world. Over 80 countries have already joined Greenpeace's call for an end to the international waste trade.

The environmental consequences of dangerous wastes finding their way to locations throughout the Third World mandated quick action. "It didn't matter that ending international exports of U.S. waste was not considered 'politically feasible,'" says Leonard. The first problem Greenpeace confronted, however, was the secrecy that surrounded the trade in international wastes. Leonard and her colleagues set out to change that. They talked about the implications of the trade with everyone from U.S. politicians to foreign villagers being offered waste.

With the help of 25 Greenpeace offices around the world, Leonard and her partners at Greenpeace were able to monitor the seas for ships carrying toxic waste between countries. They began an inventory of hundreds of waste trade schemes around the world. Through the *Greenpeace Waste Trade Update* they informed thousands of government officials, reporters and activist organizations on every continent about new waste trade schemes. As word of the trade spread, an ever larger network of eyes and ears was created to monitor it.

"We do lots of sleuthing — collecting information from activists, government agencies and citizens around the world," says Leonard. "In this way, we have become the international clearinghouse for information on the problem and have helped to scuttle waste shipments to Guyana, Guinea, Honduras, the Bahamas, Tonga and Guatemala, and elsewhere."

Before long, the international waste trade had become such a well-documented and well-publicized issue that Congress had to address the problem. Leonard organized a letter drive to Congressional members demanding that U.S. waste exports be stopped, and gathered signatures for a petition calling for similar action. "If something's a problem but it's not an 'issue,' nothing will get done about it on Capitol Hill," says Leonard. "We made the international waste trade an issue."

It didn't take long for Leonard to learn that in Washington, D.C. there is one group that moves slower than academics and mainstream environmentalists — politicians. The tradition in Congress is to study rather than to act. Congress discussed waste trade, held hearing after hearing on the waste trade, but in the end, failed to prohibit it.

Greenpeace, however, was undeterred. Never an organization to wait while an environmental problem festers, Greenpeace decided to act even if Congress would not.

The organization decided to confront the traders at every juncture. Leonard took information about the dangers of burning hazardous waste to the Bahamas, when the country was considering accepting 100,000 tons of hazardous waste for incineration. She took 300 people to the gates of a New Jersey company that was sending mercury waste to South Africa. She attended annual shareholder meetings to question waste trading executives in front of their shareholders. And she even spent an afternoon in jail for refusing to leave the office of a company which arranges toxic waste shipments to Africa.

"Our direct approach in confronting the problem makes people nervous and shakes them up. I see that as a benefit, not an obstacle," says Leonard. "If people are willing to dump our toxic wastes on foreign countries, they need to be shaken up."

Salim Muwakkil — Senior Editor, *In These Times*

"The choreographed discussion on race needs to be disrupted. Many are questioning rote adherence to previous strategies which portray blacks almost solely as victims. ... We have to question everything."

Salim Muwakkil, a young Air Force man stationed in Georgia, took a bullet in the gut from a white hotel clerk in 1968 after he demanded to know if he was being refused a room because he was black.

He recalls the incident with little anger. "In retrospect I can understand his problem," Muwakkil says. "I was in Georgia and acting a bit too militant," he said.

"To call yourself black in Georgia was like a declaration of revolution," he says. "I didn't recognize the panic on his face. In fact, he showed me a gun, and instead of catching the hint, I caught the bullet.

Muwakkil chose to fight back with his pen. His career in both the mainstream and progressive press, primarily covering the black community, is characterized by intellectual analysis rather than debilitating anger.

After serving four years in the Air Force, stationed mostly in Germany, Muwakkil returned to his home in New Jersey and became active in the Black Panthers. Their militant approach suited Muwakkil, who was very angry about racism. But he was also attracted to the ideals of the counter-culture — "this whole oneness and psychedelic utopianism."

"I was stuck between putting flowers in guns and putting bullets in," Muwakkil says. He began working in a factory in an effort to join the union movement, but found he was "thirsting for a college education."

He enrolled at Rutgers University in Newark and majored in political science. He also took advantage of a blossoming black studies program and was active on campus to further its development, expand the tiny minority population among students in a city that was about 70 percent black and protest the Vietnam war.

His involvement with the Black Panthers tapered off after he became discouraged when he saw members let drinking, drug use and "catting" around interfere with their commitment to the cause.

Muwakkil understood the need for role models, and he saw that in the Nation of Islam. "I saw people who seemed to be serious about rearranging their lives to make things better for black people," he says of the group. "The Nation of Islam was crafting lives out of rubble, and making something positive out of a lot of despair."

He also liked the way the group de-emphasized class, poor blacks were not denied positions of power.

Muwakkil did not interpret the Nation's "white people as devil" tenet in a strident, violent way. Instead, he understood it to mean that for blacks, accepting white, Western culture as their own "was like a cultural time bomb."

In 1972, while still in college, Muwakkil began working for Associated Press (A.P.) in New Jersey, and he also submitted articles to *Mohammed Speaks*, the national newspaper of the Nation of Islam.

He learned firsthand how differently the mainstream media approaches stories, as he recast straightforward news he wrote for A.P. in a context of outrage or celebration, depending how it affected the black community.

For example, in his story in *Mohammed Speaks* about protests at a black housing project in an Italian neighborhood, Muwakkil wrote: "As the steely voice of Kate Smith trumpeted America's promise, Newark's white racists displayed America's reality."

"A.P. wouldn't go for that, but I thought it was so clear," he recalls. Still, Muwakkil recognizes the need to have someone with his perspective covering the news for A.P. or other mainstream media. While revolutionary language won't get into the stories, it can be a revolution of sorts to cover what might otherwise be overlooked, or to quote minority and female experts whose voices are rarely heard.

In 1974 Muwakkil was asked to join the staff of *Mohammed Speaks* in Chicago, an offer he readily accepted."I mainly wanted to get the word out to black people," he said, and working for the newspaper, with nearly one million readers, was the best way. He also was aware that the paper was undoubtedly read by mainstream reporters and editors, so his work there might open their eyes to new angles on issues.

In 1976, the death of Elijah Mohammed, the leader of the Nation of Islam, left his son in charge of *Mohammed Speaks*. Its tenor changed to a more fundamentalist bent.

Muwakkil began to see limits of the movement. "There were some issues that had class dimensions, which couldn't be reduced to sheer race issues" as the Nation of Islam generally did.

The change in the paper "shook me out of an intellectual lethargy," Muwakkil said, in which he had suppressed his differing views because he had lost faith that they were valid.

He left in 1977 and began freelancing. He scraped out a living with work that ranged from writing public relations pieces and articles about successful business leaders for *Success, Inc.* magazine, to continued reporting on the black community. He also wrote book reviews for the *The New York Times* and the *The Washington Post*, which he continues to do today.

Some of his work for a well-respected local weekly paper was critical of the groups to which he had once belonged.

Predictably, the reporting was not well-received by his colleagues in the movement, but Muwakkil felt strongly then, and today, that the movement needed allies who weren't afraid to say "is this the best approach?" He knew he was in a good position for that role.

"I have credibility," he said. "I've been in the organizations but at the same time I'm critical of many of the things they talk about.

"The choreographed discussion on race needs to be disrupted," he said. "Many are questioning rote adherence to previous strategies which portray blacks almost solely as victims."

Muwakkil also challenges the "depressing residue of anti-semitism" in the black movement.

"We have to question everything. I became the mad debunker," Muwakkil recalls with a chuckle. "I relish that opportunity. It kind of energizes me."

Muwakkil's reporting isn't all critical, and he says he still sees the Nation of Islam as a positive force in the black community.

Some of his writing appeared in *In These Times*, a respected national weekly that emerged from the democratic socialist movement.

While he considered *In These Times* the best of the alternative papers, like other alternative media, it fell short in its coverage of the black community, Muwakkil says. When they offered him the job of culture editor in 1984, he "welcomed the opportunity to bring an added perspective to the paper."

He has become more of a writer than an editor for the Chicago-based paper, covering culture and politics in the black community, writing book reviews and an occasional editorial. He frequently travels to communities where trends emerge or issues are focused.

In the 1990 election, he travelled to North Carolina to cover the heated Senate race between right-wing Republican Jesse Helms and former Charlotte mayor Harvey Gantt, a liberal black.

The campaign, which Gantt lost by a narrow margin, was marked by Helm's racial divisiveness.

Helms gave his campaign a final boost with television ads designed to frighten whites about minority hiring quotas he said would result from civil rights legislation. Helms trumpeted his opposition to civil rights laws in a year that President Bush vetoed the civil rights bill and Congress could not muster enough votes to override.

That is discouraging to Muwakkil, but even more so is the soaring rate of violence and death in the black community, where fully half the men between the ages of 21 and 29 are under the control of the criminal justice system. The black community is hit hardest by the violence of the drug culture, though the majority of users are white. Unemployment rates among blacks far outpace other groups and half of all black children grow up in poverty. Dismal inner-city education extinguishes hope for many minority children, if they manage to survive an infant mortality rate three times higher than that for whites in many cities.

In many ways, times are harder for blacks today than in 1964, when the first civil rights law was passed, Muwakkil says. But his pen — or more accurately, his computer — helps him resist anger and discouragement.

As long as he sees the vital struggle for justice

continue, and as long as he can prod it further with writing that informs and insists on broader mining for solutions, Muwakkil is hopeful and energized.

Muwakkil is often asked to appear on television and radio talk shows, and he says people expect him to have the answers. They've got it wrong, he says. He's the one with the questions.

"I'm interested in exploring the contradictions, inconsistencies, paradoxes and ironies," he says. "I've become comfortable with my role as critic, as informed observer."

Helene Day O'Brien

Organizer, Association of Community Organizations for Reform Now

"Ideally, if parents had a real say they could change the course of education. The system won't pressure the schools to improve — it's got to be the parents."

When she finished college, Helene Day O'Brien was no closer to deciding what she wanted to do with her life than when she went in. At the State University of New York-Albany campus she had gone from an ardent punk rocker to an active feminist, but she still couldn't decide what she wanted to do or where.

After a stint waitressing, she decided to go to graduate school in Rochester, New York. That first summer she took a temporary position with ACORN doing research on education issues. She never went back to graduate school.

Now at 26, she works 12- to 14-hour days organizing parents in some of New York's roughest neighborhoods — Bedford-Stuyvesant, Brownsville and East New York in Brooklyn, and South Jamaica and Far Rockaway in Queens — to take a more active involvement in their children's schooling.

In the beginning she went door-to-door in the neighborhoods surrounding the schools to find parents who were interested in participating in their childrens' education but didn't know how to get involved. She talked with parents about their concerns about the school, the neighborhood and their child.

Soon a common theme emerged from parents on how the school could better meet the needs of the children in the neighborhood. She organized groups based on these issues. Fledgling school reform committees sprouted up in schools where previously there had been only minimal parent participation. At first the parents tackled basic issues: a leaky roof, a nearby lot that needed to be cleaned up, or other small but unifying issues.

"These parents know what they want; they just don't have much organizing experience," says O'Brien.

O'Brien says she developed an almost instantaneous rapport with the school activists, a bond she hadn't found in her previous endeavors at political activism. "I never felt more comfortable with people," she says. Far different from the activists she had known at school, these were "people who were struggling with day-to-day problems and still being active and politically committed."

Today, ACORN works in 20 schools in the greater New York area. Parents are pushing for a whole range of reforms, including a better student/teacher ratio, longer school days, more tutoring and more after-school programs.

"We get parents involved not only in little things like helping their kids with homework and making sure that the school is run well, but we're training them to push for their own agenda," O'Brien says.

Some of the "neighborhoods are so bad that parents don't want their kids to play outside," she says. They need after-school programs that offer activities to keep the children entertained and involved as well as to offer educational support services for children who are having a difficult time in particular areas.

Parents are also pushing for curriculum changes to make the classroom more related to the students that they are attempting to reach. Most schools teach students black history only once a year during Black

History Month even though a majority of their students are black, says O'Brien. The parents are trying to force the schools to teach students more about the history of black Americans.

In Brownsville, Brooklyn she organized parents to push for the removal of asbestos from the classrooms, and to force the cleanup of a nearby park. Parents also pushed through a school-based management program, which allows parents and teachers in a joint committee to make decisions about the school.

"Ideally, if parents had a real say they could change the course of education," she says. "The system won't pressure the schools to improve — it's got to be the parents."

Organizing parents may not seem controversial, but in New York, it invariably is. "In order to get names of parents we would often have to stand in front of a school at 8 a.m. and 3 p.m. and have parents sign a petition saying 'please call me,'" says O'Brien. "We have had the police called on us. We were physically threatened by principals and security guards. It's extremely tense."

In many situations, it's a battle for control over the schools, says O'Brien. "Many of these schools are little fifedoms. Principals and teachers don't want parents involved. They don't think parents should have a say."

Trudging the streets of New York organizing parents, O'Brien says she's finally found a career that allows her to feel like she's doing something that will have an impact on more than just her wallet. "I'm only here once. I'm not going to get a 'good' job and make a lot of money because that's the thing to do," says O'Brien. "I believe in what I'm doing. This is where I want to be. I love what I'm doing."

She says her parents and friends still aren't particularly happy with her choice of careers, but named after the famed activist Dorothy Day of the Catholic Worker Movement, she says it was almost a given that she would become involved in political battles. "I always considered myself politically oriented but I never really found a forum for it," she says.

"Out of all the jobs I've ever had I've never felt until now that every skill and talent that I have had to be used and then some," says O'Brien. "I could easily see myself doing this forever."

At times, she says, the difficulty of the task in front of her is daunting, but she says it's easy to rekindle her commitment. "Whenever you have doubts about your political commitment, what you can do is take a walk through one of the poorest neighborhoods where people are starving. If you're not doing anything, yet you believe you should be doing something, then you are going to have to answer for that to yourself."

Ed Rothschild

Director, Energy Policy and Public Affairs, Citizen Action

"I do this work because there is nothing better. I want my children to look up to me because I did something worthwhile with my life."

Edwin Rothschild knew very little about energy issues when he came to Washington, D.C. in 1971. With a degree in sociology coupled with anti-war activism at Boston University (B.U.), a year of teaching elementary school in New York City and some work toward a Ph.D., Rothschild knew he was ready to work toward social change.

His respect for Ralph Nader led him to Lowell Dodge, then-director of Nader's Center for Auto Safety, who put him to work researching energy issues.

This was an important turning point in Rothschild's life. It opened the door on a topic that would become his area of expertise. Twenty years later, Rothschild is a key spokesperson on energy issues for Citizen Action, a national consumer group with over 2.5 million members. He appears on national television shows like the MacNeil-Lehrer News Hour, is quoted in major newspapers and magazines, and has even had people ask for his autograph.

Flattery aside, Rothschild says, that kind of attention means that people are getting his message on the need to wrest control of energy policy from the big oil companies and change government policy from promoting oil consumption to conserving energy and using renewable energy like solar power.

Rothschild locates the roots of his political values in his family and upbringing. The son of Holocaust survivors, he was taught the importance of standing up for what you believe in. He credits his parents with instilling in him an appreciation of cultural diversity and liberal values and a healthy disrespect for cultural and political dogma.

When he graduated high school in 1965, Rothschild was keenly aware and supportive, as were many of his peers, of the Civil Rights Movement and the growing Anti-Vietnam War movement. As an undergraduate at Boston University during the late 1960s, he joined with other students to oppose the war. Initially he worked with Students for a Democratic Society (SDS), but he didn't like the way the group at B.U. made decisions — it was not democratic enough, he recalls.

As a student majoring in sociology, Rothschild got to know a dynamic and popular professor, Gerald Schaflander, who was teaching courses on the Sociology of Minorities and Social Theory. Studying the sociology of C. Wright Mills, Max Weber, Georg Simmel and Karl Marx, among others, Rothschild added a strong theoretical framework to his growing commitment to social change. Schaflander, who had developed a unique approach to dealing with social problems in the black ghetto of Bedford-Stuyvesant, brought his brand of participant-observer sociology to the students at B.U. On the campus, he sought to empower students through something he called the "Voice and Vote" committee. Schaflander wanted to tap students' anti-war fervor and channel it so they would gain a strong voice in university policymaking. Rothschild helped organize the Voice and Vote committee until he graduated and left for a teaching job in a New York elementary school. After a year there, and after the U.S. government ended draft deferments for teachers, he decided to enter a Ph.D. program in sociology at York University outside of Toronto, Canada.

While pursuing his coursework, Rothschild kept in touch with his old mentor, Schaflander, who had decided to establish a new type of higher learning institution to be called "Citizens College."

"It was inspired by things Ralph Nader was doing," Rothschild says. "The idea was to train social activists, linking theory with practice. They would spend a year in college and then go out and work in an institution to find out how theory they learned matched reality. Then students would return to analyze their experiences and to evaluate or redefine social and political theory."

He helped Schaflander develop the idea, but "even though it was a wonderful idea and got a lot of support, we never raised enough money to get it off the ground." Nevertheless, working on Citizens College gave Rothschild his first involvement in fundraising and expanded his organizing skills.

"Armed with a simple idea, we were able to involve dozens of people who wanted Citizens College to become a reality — writers, educators, students and political activists."

"The experience taught me a very important lesson: namely, that building new institutions requires not only good ideas and a thorough understanding of social forces, but also a willingness to commit yourself to the hard nitty-gritty work of building strong relationships based on shared values."

With his Citizens College experience, Rothschild moved to Washington, D.C. After a few months researching energy for the Center for Auto Safety, Rothschild got a job as a research assistant to David Freeman, a former energy policy advisor to Lyndon B. Johnson, who had received a grant from the Ford Foundation to do a major energy policy analysis.

"Right then and there I became much more aware of how policy worked," Rothschild recalls. He began looking into issues like natural gas pricing and was soon inspired to write a letter critical of natural gas policy to the *The Washington Post*. He didn't expect it to be published, but it was. Freeman, concerned that people would equate his assistant's more radical views with his own, told Rothschild to clear any future letters to newspapers with him.

That disturbed Rothschild, who told Freeman, "I didn't give up my Constitutional rights when I accepted the job." A few months later he wrote another letter that attacked the major oil companies and their collusive behavior. "Freeman wanted to tone it down. I quit instead," Rothschild says. "I was unhappy in this kind of role because his whole approach was trying to be all things to all people and not being very critical of the industry."

Rothschild then began volunteering for Environmentalists for McGovern to back George McGovern's bid for the presidency. Through an associate there, he learned of a job with the American Public Gas Association, a group representing municipally-owned gas companies. The association's members were small communities who approached energy policy very differently than major oil companies.

"They were ardently anti-big business" with an appealing populist approach, Rothschild said of the association. He delved into natural gas issues, writing their newsletter and doing some lobbying. That evolved into helping association members prepare Congressional testimony.

One day in late 1973, Sen. Jim Abourezk of South Dakota asked Rothschild to brief him on energy policy. A few days later the Senator offered Rothschild a job as a legislative aid on energy issues. "There aren't many people I would work for on Capitol Hill, but this was someone I very much respected," Rothschild recalls. "He didn't weasel out of issues."

The experience of working for a U.S. senator exposed Rothschild to Washington, D.C. lobbyists. He remembers going to lunch with a hired gun for Westinghouse who wanted Abourezk to support some pro-nuclear power legislation. Rothschild not only picked up the tab for his own lunch (something most legislative aides do not do), but told the lobbyist not to waste any more of his time. I t wasn't long after he took that job that energy became the focus of national concern, spawned by the oil crisis from the OPEC oil embargo.

"I learned early on how the companies can seize on a situation and use it for their advantage," Rothschild recalls. On Capitol Hill he helped draft legislation to keep the powerful oil companies in check, to prevent them from gaining a monopoly on other energy sources like coal and uranium and to extend price controls and promote renewable resources.

"That was a period for lots of activity." With evidence pointing to a critical need to develop solar power commercially, Rothschild left Capitol Hill to help his former B.U. mentor Shaflander launch the Consumers' Solar Electric Power Corporation in California, but funding for the technology was difficult to find. Rothschild returned to the American Public Gas Association as acting director in 1975 and 1976. In 1977, after consulting on energy issues for consumer groups, Rothschild became the research director for Energy Action, a group founded by Paul Newman and other progressive funders to combat oil companies' propaganda and lobbying efforts in Washington. While energy issues had become potent again with the onset of the Iranian Revolution in late 1978, their prominence subsided as Ronald Reagan came into office and gutted efforts to control oil companies and promote alternative energy and conservation.

But the Reagan years only gave energy activists more to do. Energy Action merged with Citizen/Labor Energy Coalition to become a project of Citizen Action, a national network of state and local groups, where Rothschild is director of energy policy and public affairs. Citizen Action has worked for years advocating policies to increase competition in the energy marketplace, to increase federal support for renewable energy and to set higher standards for energy efficiency for automobiles, appliances and other energy consuming equipment. Recently Citizen Action has become more active on environmental issues, including toxic waste, air pollution and global warming — issues that are now getting more attention.

With Iraqi leader Saddam Hussein's invasion of Kuwait and George Bush's decision to take the country to war, U.S. dependence on imported oil is again central to the debate over a new national energy policy. The Bush administration will emphasize efforts to increase U.S. oil production, further development of nuclear power and other policies that accomodate the energy status quo, but Rothschild is arguing for a radical shift away from the oil consumption that is ruining the nation economically and environmentally. Rothschild says he wishes the country had learned some lessons in 1974 and planned more wisely for its energy needs. But he continues to press for energy-conscious policies, animating a saying often heard among citizen activists: Don't mourn, organize. He is finding ways to make the lessons of the Persian Gulf finally hit home with legislators and policymakers.

"It becomes a launching pad for issues like the Clean Air Act, alternative fuels, energy efficiency," he says. He found the same 'silver lining' when the ExxonValdez oil tanker split open, spilling 11 million gallons of crude oil onto pristine Alaskan shores in the worst spill in U.S. history. When oil companies tried to profit from the crisis by raising gas prices at the pump almost immediately after the spill, Citizen Action called for a national boycott of Exxon. Rothschild was pictured on the front page of *USA Today* cutting his Exxon credit card, and the boycott gained national momentum.

That is a source of encouragement, and means that Citizen Action's efforts don't go unnoticed. People often approach Rothschild and say they saw him on television and are heeding his warnings about benzene hazards at the gas pump or the failure of costly premium gas to improve automobile fuel efficiency. He also measures success by how often key members of Congress follow Citizen Action's lead on investigations and legislation.

For Rothschild, working for social change has meant that there is no jarring contradiction between his personal and professional lives. Instead, he says, his activism and his home and community life reinforce one another and his convictions. Both he and his wife are deeply involved in their community — with their children's PTAs and with other community organizations.

Rothschild also believes in exposing his children to politics. In fact, during the 1988 presidential election campaign he remembers strong disagreement in the house. His wife and son supported Michael Dukakis, but Rothschild and his daughter preferred Jesse Jackson.

"I do this work because there is nothing better," says Rothschild. "I want my children to look up to me because I did something worthwhile with my life."

Peg Seminario **Director of Occupational Safety, Health and Social Security, AFL-CIO**

"The hardest thing is responding to the letters and calls of workers or the families of workers who have been diseased in the workplace and having to tell them that, right now, the legal remedies available to them are so limited. Doing something about that suffering is what my work is all about. Seeing it makes you want to work all that much harder to make sure that people are protected or are taken care of."

Many Americans earn a living by the sweat of their brows, but for a significant number of laborers, wage-getting exacts a far greater price: their health or their lives. Each year 10,000 people are killed in industrial accidents. About seven million others are injured. Over 100,000 workers die each year from exposure to deadly chemicals and occupational diseases such as brown lung and asbestosis.

The toll of dead and injured workers prompted Congress to pass the Occupational Safety and Health Act of 1970, establishing OSHA "to ensure safe and healthful working conditions for American working men and women." It has mobilized organized labor to fight for legal and technical means of combatting the hazards of the workplace.

Statistics are also part of why Peg Seminario continues to represent workers' interests in Washington, D.C. The Director of Occupational Safety, Health and Social Security for the AFL-CIO explains that she can't let up, because the problems facing workers never do.

When Seminario was graduating from Wellesley College, she decided to do her graduate work in environmental health rather than a research-oriented discipline because she didn't want to spend her time "sitting in a lab, counting things under a microscope. I wanted to apply myself to something useful."

Once in graduate school, she quickly shifted her focus to occupational issues because "that's where most of the ground-breaking applications were developing. The workplace is where most environmental problems first manifest themselves and where the greatest exposure levels occur."

Seminario, along with other students at the

Harvard School of Public Health, started the Massachusetts Coalition on Occupational Safety and Health (MassCOSH) in 1975. Modelled after similar groups in other states, the purpose of the COSH is to empower workers "from the bottom up" in creating a safe and healthy workplace. "We provided local unions with assistance and training in how to identify hazards and what to do, both legally and technically, to correct them."

Public health school was a time of intensive learning, but Seminario's real education began when she entered the workplace. "Beyond statistics," reminds AFL-CIO President Lane Kirkland, "people are people." Getting to know these people by working with them on finding solutions to their problems through MassCOSH, Seminario became sensitized to the reality of human need that words and numbers only hinted at.

"I saw that working people faced enormous problems with little power and fewer resources. I realized that in order to make any improvements at all in occupational safety and health, workers needed organization and technical assistance.

"I also found that I liked working with union people. They're real. They're people who care very much about people. That's a big part of what the labor movement has always been about: helping people to be better off by improving wages and working conditions."

Finding herself committed to the issues and the people involved in the labor movement, Seminario took her masters degree in industrial hygiene to the AFL-CIO headquarters in 1977 to do a one year internship and stayed on.

Starting out as a 23-year-old woman in a field overwhelmingly dominated by older men, Seminario encountered "a certain level of sexism. Whenever I went out in the field on a training or technical assistance call, men were initially a little skeptical about me, a 'little girl' representing their interests.

"But in every single case," she adds, "once they found that I was competent and could do the job, that was all that was important. And any trace of sexism was gone."

The "refreshing" acceptance she finds within the labor movement, she comments, contrasts drastically with the crassly chauvinistic or patronizing treatment she receives elsewhere, most notably in the political circles of Washington, D.C.

"Although people now accept me as competent, it has taken a lot of adjustment to a male kind of world. As a woman, your response is to try to be more, to be better. You have to end up being a lot more competent and a whole lot tougher."

Seminario clearly is both of these. She has to be to contend not only with sexism but also with the pervasive hostility she has encountered toward worker protection in the government regulatory agencies under the Reagan and Bush administrations.

At the AFL-CIO Seminario "does a little bit of everything to service national unions." She coordinates and represents their health and safety interests in the legislative and regulatory arenas. She also acts as a media spokesperson for the AFL-CIO and keeps member unions informed about "what's going on in Washington since they don't have the luxury and/or misfortune of being here.

"Most of my work is concerned with the regulatory agencies like OSHA and EPA. That means participating as much as we can in the nitty-gritty of what they do, providing a constructive presence in rule-making, data collection, training and enforcement. I also act as agency watchdog: beating them over the head to see that they do what they're supposed to, setting and enforcing standards to ensure that worker health and safety is protected on the job."

An uphill struggle in the best of times, Seminario's task has become nearly impossible in these worst of times ushered in under administrations hostile to the OSHA mandate that government has a responsibility to ensure worker safety and health on the job.

"Based on their deregulatory philosophy," she reports, "they have not only failed to issue new regulations but are doing everything they can to weaken the existing standards and rules that we have fought for many years to gain." These are such standards as the regulation of worker exposure to cotton dust and the rules guaranteeing access to medical records.

"They have been tearing the program apart, quietly but systematically eliminating enforcement procedures and standards ... It's tough to fight an attack that has 200 fronts at any one time, none of which is particularly focused in the public eye."

Countering this assault requires ways of "letting

them know that they aren't going to get away with rolling back important standards" by making it politically or legally unacceptable. Tactics include inducing Congress to hold oversight hearings or taking matters to court.

"We try to make the public, and particularly our membership, aware of what the administration is doing and the impact of these policies. Workers know that they [the administration] are killing the law; they're killing the program and they're killing the workers. We've tried to get our message out consistently, but also fairly, to base our criticism on well-researched and documented facts."

"Being accurate at all times," stresses Seminario, "is something you have to be very responsible about in this position. People are always trying to undermine you in some way. You have to bend over backwards to make sure that what you are stating is indeed correct. And I would not hesitate to stand by anything I put out of this office."

While Seminario finds these attacks depressing and the obstacles she encounters on a day-to-day basis trying, they reflect an underlying, generalized attitude toward workers that she identifies as "the greatest frustration in my work."

"The public at large, including the media, government, the general public, doesn't really care about the plight of workers in this country. Historically, workers' concerns have never been a primary consideration."

Seminario offers the case of the EDB regulation as an example of this attitude. "EDB is a nasty chemical that was found to be contaminating the food chain. It was brought to public attention when grain millers presented evidence of worker exposure at congressional hearings. Some industrious reporters went out and tested the grain, the bread, the meat, and, sure enough, it was in the food chain. Public outrage and a flurry of activity followed. EPA recommended some tolerance levels for consumer exposure in the range of 10 to 15 parts per billion. The occupational standard was and still is 20,000 parts per billion.

"The public is no longer concerned, but workers are still getting sick and dying from exposure to EDB. OSHA has rejected our call for a standard.

"Most people don't understand, or if they understand, they don't want to admit that a lot of people have to go to pretty stinky, lousy jobs every day to earn a living.

"It's particularly tough when you see workers maligned in the press for being overpaid. These people work hard, probably harder than anyone else. In a very basic way they are responsible for making this country what it is. And what do they get in return? Not only the criticism that they don't deserve what they make, but also the message that it doesn't matter if they're poisoned or killed on the job."

"The way to address this," says Seminario, "is to try to focus on specific issues. You let people know the facts and try to give them some kind of sensitivity to what those people are suffering.

"But what it comes down to is trying to organize working people in unions and in activities that bring real pressure to bear on policymakers. Whatever we have gotten done in the area of occupational safety and health is the result of the labor movement, working day in and day out."

"It's a long, tough fight, and I don't see it getting any easier," says Seminario.

The demands of fighting that battle are emotional as well as physical. "The work is something that I care about and am deeply committed to. It's hard not to let everything you face eat you up personally, to not get overwhelmed," she says. "Because it is overwhelming. I get a lot of letters and phone calls from workers or the families of workers who are diseased. They talk about how they've worked in a plant for 25 years, and now they're sick or their spouse has just died of a disease. They say that no one ever told them of the danger, that they never knew, and if they had, then maybe they could have done something about it. And here they are now, looking for compensation to help them with their medical bills or seeking some kind of financial assurance for their families, because they know they're going to die soon.

"The hardest thing is writing back or talking to them and having to tell them that right now the legal remedies available to them are so limited. Doing something about that suffering is what my work is really all about. Seeing it makes you want to work all that much harder to make sure these people are protected or are taken care of.

"Still, you can only do so much. There will always be a hell of a lot of problems out there. It's a matter of being disciplined about what you can and cannot do and making some very hard choices.

If you don't set goals that are realistic, you can burn out and cease to be able to work effectively."

The tangible results of her efforts are long in coming. "Working to get legislation passed or regulations set, it's not the kind of activity that immediately produces successes you can see. It takes five years just to get a regulation on the books.

"Since the day I walked in, I've been working on the Right to Know Campaign, developing and pushing the federal and state laws. Now, because of the work of lots of people, we have come a long way. The federal standard isn't good enough and there are problems with the state laws. Still this is a movement that in and of itself is going to change the behavior of chemical companies. I have no doubt that the culmination of it all will result in a major change in the kind of information and protection made available to workers."

Seminario's message is to-the-point, angering and at times grim, but it is also rousing, and moving, — never understated or over-dramatized. The inspiring thing about hearing Seminario speak is that no matter how sobering her message is her own character and unwavering commitment are evidence that the energy exists to rouse and move people and institutions in the defense of workers' rights to a safe and healthy workplace.

The situation will never let up but neither will Peg Seminario. "It has to do with basic morality, with the basic sense of what's right and what's wrong that I learned as I was growing up. It's wrong that people put in an honest day of work, and get paid back by being poisoned and losing their lives. I see myself always working in the labor movement."

Margery Tabankin **Director, Hollywwood Women's Political Committee**

"Most Americans don't understand the Third World. We are such a privileged nation. On the one hand I'm so critical of what the U.S. is doing in Central America. On the other hand I think that this country is so incredibly great that we must be generous. Rather than sending bombs and warplanes, we should offer friendship and assistance to these people who are fighting for their economic, political and social survival."

In 1966 Margery Tabankin was covering a campus demonstration for her college newspaper. Students at the University of Wisconsin were peacefully protesting Dow Chemical's recruiting on campus, when police descended on the crowd with tear gas and clubs. Tabankin, an observer and not a participant, was seriously injured and had to be hospitalized.

"That was a key event for me," explains Tabankin, I decided at that moment to be an activist, not a journalist or a reporter of other people's efforts. I had always been an involved person, in student government, housing marches and civil rights demonstrations. But now I was going to do it in a much more aggressive way."

That resolve has carried Tabankin through an impressive range of social change efforts, from protesting the Vietnam War and irresponsible foreign policy in Central America to directing the federal VISTA program, from raising millions of dollars for public interest groups to funding them as a foundation executive with the ARCA Foundation.

With the direct and no-nonsense manner of one who quickly translates conviction into action, Tabankin offers to describe her career in terms of "what I did, not what I was feeling." Her account leaves the listener (but not the speaker) breathless, awed by the sheer intensity of activity and achievement.

During her years in college academics were always a secondary consideration. "Ending the Vietnam War was my biggest personal priority in life." She helped to organize the national moratorium that closed down universities across the country for two days of protest. Tabankin was arrested then and on many other occasions on charges that were usually dropped.

She left college in 1970 to become one of the first women student trainees at organizer Saul Alinsky's training institute in Chicago. Tabankin was thrilled at the opportunity to learn the skills of community organizing from one of the most preeminent activist-theorists.

"At that time my life's dream was to be a community organizer, and it was wonderful to study with the master." After six months, though, she put that dream on hold when she learned that her mother had developed cancer. Tabankin moved back home to Newark, New Jersey, and taught black history and literature at the high school she had attended four years earlier.

After her mother passed away Tabankin moved to Washington, D.C. and took a job with the Youth Citizenship Fund in "an effort to get the 18-year-old vote ratified and to get kids registered to vote." She left that job to become the first woman president of the National Student Association, then a vital political force that coordinated student movements for civil rights and peace on college campuses across the country. Her anti-war message was so vocal that it was heard by the Vietnamese government, which invited her to visit North Vietnam in May of 1972.

"That trip changed my life in terms of my understanding and my outlook on the world. It showed me concretely what life in the Third World was like and demonstrated the devastating capability of U.S. foreign policy at its worst. At that time the U.S. government was claiming that we were hitting military targets, that we weren't damaging civilian life. I visited hospitals, schools, child care centers and laborers' homes that had been demolished by American bombs. That trip was 20 years ago, but I can describe what happened on it minute by minute as if it were yesterday."

In an effort to convey some of that vivid imagery to other Americans, Tabankin made a film of her trip and campaigned for George McGovern, screening the film on college campuses, accompanied by folk singer Phil Ochs. After the election Tabankin became director of a new Washington-based group called the Youth Project. "Like many other Vietnam protesters, I think I felt the need to shift focus from national problems to take on the more 'do-able' battles closer to where I lived. The intention of the Youth Project was to capitalize on the fever of youth activism in the country and support the efforts of young people who were interested in doing the best thing you can do in a democratic system — working for change from within.

"That's how we presented it to large funding institutions. By putting foundations in touch with the people at the grassroots level who were doing the community change work, we helped to develop a number of new projects."

As head of the Youth Project from 1972 to 1976, Tabankin learned the "first rule" of fundraising: "You don't give up. You don't walk away after the first rejection. You persist, without making a pest of yourself, and continue to provide funders with information about the project and its progress, until something clicks." And Tabankin adds that it often did.

Tabankin learned a toughness of a different order when she agreed to raise money for a campaign to replace Tony Boyle, then the president of the United Mine Workers. "He was viewed as corrupt and autocratic, and proved even worse when his opponent in the election was murdered. We removed Boyle, who was later convicted of complicity in the murder of that man and his family."

In 1977 Tabankin did something radical for campus radicals of the sixties. She went to work for the federal government. She was appointed by the Carter Administration to be director of the VISTA Program.

"VISTA is the federal volunteer agency, the domestic counterpart to the Peace Corps, which pays a stipend to individuals willing to commit themselves for two years to organizing and assisting low-income people in solving their problems. That meant everything from helping people to organize literacy programs or food banks to fighting for equitable utility rates.

"I went from being a sectarian purist on a college campus to a person who is open-minded about all arenas of change. I also went from a public interest salary of $15,000 to $47,000. I managed a corps of 5,000 volunteers, the largest ever under VISTA, a staff of 400 and a budget of more than $36 million.

"It was an incredible experience and I learned a tremendous amount. I derived enormous satisfaction from being able to direct policy from within the federal system to serve the most needy, left-out and left-behind people in this country. VISTA empowers those people by helping them to organize and to realize that they can be a potent force in changing this country."

That political appointment ended with that administration in 1981. Tabankin then became director of the ARCA foundation, an organization which funds social change groups.

As fundraiser turned funder, Tabankin says she had matured as an evaluator of social change efforts. "When I started at the Youth Project, I wanted to give money to anyone with a good idea. Pretty soon you learn that a good idea isn't enough, because you get a lot of great ideas. As a funder, you learn to look for realistic goals, sound methodology and people who have the ability to pull it off.

"Too many public interest groups assume their funds will come from the private philanthropic sector, but they need to be more self-sufficient internally. They need to target a constituency that will support them: canvassing middle-income people for funds to fight gas decontrol, giving discounts to senior citizens on generic drugs, appealing by direct mail to residential utility consumers for money to fight for equitable utility rates. Those are all effective strategies for public financing.

"I've also come to appreciate the extraordinary power of the media and how to use celebrities to promote an issue. When the Fonz registered for a library card on TV, a half-million people in this country applied for library cards in one week.

"That's a powerful force we need to use to shape national policy. When a documentary funded by the ARCA foundation called *Roses in December* about four churchwomen murdered in El Salvador was made into a TV movie called *Choices of the Heart*, it reached 25 million people in one night. That's an incredible outreach. It would take a lot of door-knocking to get the message out to that many people."

ARCA also worked to educate U.S. citizens about government policy in Central America.

"Most Americans don't understand the Third World; few have ever seen it. The Third World in itself is such an education. In Honduras the average annual income per person is $480. People there live in shacks, if they're lucky. Most have no clothes or shoes and little food to speak of.

"We are such a privileged nation. On the one hand I'm so critical of what the U.S. is doing in Central America, and on the other hand I think that this country is so incredibly great that we must be generous. Rather than sending bombs and warplanes, we should be offering friendships and economic assistance to those people who are fighting for their economic, political and social survival.

"Unfortunately, historically we have been a better country in times of economic prosperity. It's tough for people to think of generosity when they're hurting as badly as they are right now. I wish I could take every one of them to a Third World country. They would quickly realize how wonderful they have it here.

"On a recent trip to El Salvador, a woman undressed to show us that her breasts had been hacked off. She told us that she and her daughter had been raped and other family members murdered by death squads. Seeing that kind of thing really puts everything else in perspective."

Tabankin is always concerned about U.S. military intervention, "but if it comes to war people will have to protest. I'd like to think that people will always fight for what makes this country great, for what we hold dear."

Tabankin points out that the activism of the sixties was not as widespread as it appeared. "Alinsky said that if you organize five percent of the people, you can create a revolution. I believe that, because the student movement was organized by that core of really strongly committed social conscience believers. Most of the other students cared but didn't work full-time. They didn't organize the buses going to the March on Washington; they showed up and put their bodies on the bus.

"That's what the public interest movement is like. It's a small core of incredibly committed and capable people who pull others along."

Still, she admits, "The campuses are a tremendous disappointment. Students are a great potential force for positive change. They're not married; they don't have kids, responsibilities, entrapments that you have later on in life."

The high degree of selflessness required to work in the public interest, Tabankin says, is sometimes difficult. "When you serve a constituency, you must be at their beck and call at all times. You have to be prepared to make that commitment to work which doesn't leave a lot of time for family life."

In the course of her career, Tabankin has broken many barriers of gender and has often held reponsible positions higher than those of male colleagues. "In some cases there were men who resented my prominence in a campaign or organization." But, she muses, that problem was never as acute as it might have been. "I'm pretty formidable."

As a woman, Tabankin also has felt that her personal needs have been frustrated by the demands of her work. "My personal life has always suffered. I have been extremely successful politically, and I have neglected the personal side. I think it's because I haven't worked hard enough at it."

In 1987, Tabankin was forced into doing a better job balancing her personal life with her work. A debilitating exhaustion, later diagnosed as Chronic Fatigue Syndrome, put her out of commission for months and gave her time to reevaluate her years of working 16- hour days without time set aside for rest and relaxation. Although she never reconsidered her commitment to social change work, she knew she had to make some changes. When she was back on her feet, she decided to move from the corridors of power to "Tinsel Town."

Tabankin continues her work with the Barbra Streisand Foundation, funding environmental, peace and civil liberties projects, and heads up the Hollywood Women's Political Committee (HWPC). At the HWPC she educates the Hollywood elite on the issues of the day and works to use their status to gain additional publicity and dollars for progressive causes. Even the pace remains much the same. For Tabankin, 20 years at the forefront of the social change movement has been a challenge and a privilege.

"The psychic rewards are tremendous. Helping other people has been so spiritually and psychically rewarding. Forget about what I do for people. I'm talking about what it does for me. No dollar equivalent could ever put a value on the good feelings I get. I can't imagine doing anything else."

Cora Tucker

Founder and Director, Citizens for a Better America

"I think politicians have to be responsive if enough pressure can be brought to bear on them. You can complain, I can complain, but that's just two people. A politician needs to get piles of letters saying 'vote for this bill, because if you don't, you won't be in office much longer!'"

Cora Tucker is something of an institution in Halifax County, Virginia, a rural county bordering North Carolina. In more than a dozen years, she has missed only a handful of the county board of supervisors' monthly meetings. Her name appears in the letters columns of the two daily newspapers several times a week — either signed onto her own letter or, almost as often, vilified in someone else's. She seems to know and be known by every black person on the street, in the post offices, and in stores and restaurants. And she is known by white and black people alike as having taken on many of the local, white-controlled institutions. Her main concern is simply fighting for the underdog, which she does in many ways — from social work-like visits to the elderly and invalids, to legal fights against racial discrimination, registering people to vote and lobbying on issues like health care and the environment.

Cora was born in 1941 ten miles from where she lives now, near the Halifax county seat, in the small town of South Boston. Her father was a school teacher and later a railway porter. He died when Cora was three, and her mother and the nine children became sharecroppers on white men's farms.

It was as a sharecropper, Cora says, that she learned how to do community organizing. She started by trying to help other sharecroppers to get things like better heating and food stamps. "I didn't call it 'organizing' then," she says. "I just called it 'being concerned.' When you do sharecropping, you move around a lot. So I got to know everybody in the county, and to know what people's problems were."

Cora went to work very young, planting and plowing with the others in the family. "My mama worked hard," Cora says. "She would plow and do all the things the men did. She was independent; she raised her children alone for 18 years. When I was little, I felt so bad that she had to work that hard just so we could survive. There was welfare out there — all kinds of help, if only somebody had told her how to go about getting it. She had very little education, and didn't know how to go down to the welfare office for help. As I got older, I was upset by that and made up my mind, when I was about eight or nine years old, that if I ever got grown, I'd make sure that everybody knew how to get everything there was to get."

By the time Cora learned about welfare, her mother wouldn't take advantage of it. She was proud, and she told the children to have self-respect. Cora took the advice to heart.

In her high school, which was segregated at the time (Halifax County schools didn't integrate until 1969, under court order), Cora entered an essay contest on the topic of "what America means to me." She was taken by surprise when her bitter essay about growing up black in the South won a statewide award. But on awards night she was in for another surprise. The winners were to have their essays read, and then shake hands with the Virginia governor. Cora's mother was in the audience beaming, along with Cora's friends and teachers. But when her essay was read, Cora didn't recognize it — it had been rewritten, and the less critical sentiments weren't hers at all. She refused to greet the governor. "I disappointed everyone; my mother even cried."

The only person who supported her that night, she says, was a high school literature teacher, whom she credits as an important influence on her. "He spent a lot of time with me, encouraging me. Every time an issue came up that I felt strongly about, he'd have me write about it — letters to the editor that never got printed. He told me, 'Nobody can make you a second-class citizen but you. You should be involved in what's going on around you.'

At 17 she dropped out of high school to get married. As she describes it, the next several years were consumed with housekeeping and having children — six of them in rapid succession. She and her husband adopted a seventh. "But just as soon as my baby started school, I went out and got a job."

Halifax County has several textile and garment factories, and Cora went to work as a seamstress for one of the largest, a knit sportswear manufacturer. It was a fairly new operation, and the mostly women employees were expected to do everything, from lifting fabric bolts weighing 40 or 50 pounds each, to sitting at sewing machines for eight-hour stretches. There was no union; the county boasted in promotional material that less than 5 percent of the county's workforce was unionized.

"People got back injuries, two people even had heart attacks in the factory, because of the working conditions. I once got a woman to come down from Baltimore to talk about forming a union, but people got frightened because the bosses warned us that if there was any union activity, we'd lose our jobs."

Cora worked at the factory for seven years, but in 1976 hurt her back and had to leave her job. Over the next few years she had surgery several times, first for her back, then for cancer (for which she has had to have periodic treatments ever since). In the meantime she had become active in the community.

In the 1960s she had participated in organizations like the National Association for the Advancement of Colored People (NAACP), and another group called the Assemblies, but they moved too slowly for her tastes. ("They weren't really interested in taking on the power structure," she complains.)

She had also organized her own letter writing campaign in support of the federal Voting Rights Act to make it easier for blacks to vote. She had gone around to local churches, speaking to people and encouraging them to write to their representatives in Washington. She also took advantage of knowing women who ran beauty parlors — she provided the paper and pens, so that women could write letters while they sat under the hair dryers.

"People would say to me, 'What good will it do?' But I think politicians have to be responsive if enough pressure can be brought to bear on them. You can complain, I can complain, but that's just two people. A politician needs to get piles of letters saying 'vote for this bill, because if you don't, you won't be in office much longer!'" Cora was responsible for generating 500 letters supporting the voting law.

She takes voting very seriously. In 1977, she campaigned for a populist candidate for Virginia governor. She was undergoing cancer treatments at the time, but they made her tired, so she stopped the treatments in order to register people to vote. She had taught herself to drive, and personally rode around the county from house to house, filling her car with everyone there who was of voting age, driving them to the court house to register and then home again. She's credited with having registered over 1,000 people this way, and on election day, she personally drove many of them to the polling place.

Cora's house is always filled with neighborhood teenagers, white and black. Cora became a confidante for the young people, and she encouraged them to read about black history and to be concerned about the community.

One of the things that upset the teenagers was the fate of a county recreation center. Halifax had no recreation facilities, and the county had applied for money from the federal Department of Housing and Urban Development (HUD) to build a center. When HUD awarded the county $500,000, however, the county turned it down because, as Cora puts it, there were "too many strings attached" — meaning it would have to be integrated.

"When I heard about the recreation center, I went to the county board meeting and raised hell," she says. "But they went ahead and did what they wanted anyway. What I realized then was that if I had had all those kids come with me to the meeting, there would have been some changes. You need warm bodies — persons present and accounted for — if you want to get things done."

In 1975, Cora founded her own organization, Citizens for a Better America. CBA's first project was a study of black spending and employment patterns in the county. The study was based on a survey of 300 people; it took two years to complete, with Cora's teenage friends doing much of the legwork.

The findings painted a clear picture of inequality. Blacks made up nearly half the county population, and according to the survey, spent a disproportionate share of their salaries on food, cars and furniture. But, as the study pointed out, there were very few black employees at the grocery stores where their money was spent, not a single black salesperson in the furniture stores and no black salesperson at the auto dealerships. Blacks weren't represented at all on newspaper or radio station staffs.

Cora saw to it that the survey results were publishing in the local newspaper. The next step was to act on the results. The survey had uncovered problems with hiring practices and promotions of blacks in the school system, so Cora complained to the school board. After waiting in vain for the board to respond, CBA filed a complaint with what was then the federal Department of Health, Education and Welfare (HEW). An HEW investigation confirmed the problems, and the agency threatened to cut off federal education funds to the county if the discrimination wasn't corrected. The county promised that the next principals it hired would be black.

CBA then took on other aspects of the county government. The survey had found that of all the county employees, only seven percent were black — chiefly custodial workers or workers hired with federal Comprehensive Employment Training Administration (CETA) funds. Only one black person in the county government made over $20,000 a year. When the county refused to negotiate with Cora's organization about their hiring practices, CBA filed a complaint with the federal revenue sharing program. A Virginia state senator was successful in getting a federal investigation into the complaint stalled, but Cora went over his head, to the congressional Black Caucus and Maryland's black congressman, Parren Mitchell. Mitchell contacted Senator Edward Kennedy's office, which pressed to have the investigation completed. The findings confirmed CBA's and the county was told to improve its hiring practices or stand to lose federal revenues.

CBA also initiated a boycott of local businesses that didn't hire minorities — Cora avoided the term "boycott" and instead called the action the "Spend Your Money Wisely Campaign." Leaflets were distributed listing the stores that hired black employees and urging people, "Where Blacks are not HIRED, Blacks should not buy!"

Cora was developing a reputation. She started having frequent contact with the congressional Black Caucus and would be called occasionally to testify in Washington on welfare issues. "They don't usually get people like me to testify; they get all these 'experts' instead. But every once in a while, it's good for them to hear from someone who isn't a professional, whose English isn't good and who talks from a grassroots level."

It wasn't just in Washington that her reputation was growing, but back home, too. "A lot of the white power structure don't really like me. They think I'm a troublemaker, but I'm not really. I just believe what I believe in. Then there are black people too, who think that I want too much too soon. But when you think about it, black people have been in America 360-some years, so when is the time ever going to be right? The time doesn't *get* right; you make it right. So I'm not offended by what anybody says about me."

Sometimes the problem isn't just what people say; it's what they do. Cora has had many experiences with harassment. At first it was phone calls, from people threatening to burn her house down or telling her to "go back to Africa." Once she wrote a letter to the editor saying, "This is an open letter to all the people who call me and ask, 'what do you niggers want now?' and hang up before I can tell them ...

"Blacks and poor people want to share in the economic progress of Halifax County, and when we get our children educated and motivated we would like them to come back to Halifax County and do something other than push mops and brooms. And a few of us would like our grandchildren to grow up near us, and if our children decide to make their home elsewhere it will be due to choice and not an economic necessity."

The harassment has taken other forms as well. Cora was run off the highway one night, and had all four tires slashed one day when her car was parked in town. Once she was in the post office and a man recognized her, walked over, and spit on her. She came home from a meeting one night to find that someone had drenched her bed with gasoline. But Cora views the abuses with amazing equanimity: "If you stop doing things because somebody says something bad about you or does something to you," she says, "then you'll never get *anything* done."

And she wasn't making only enemies; she was also gaining a following. People credit Cora with having stamina and with inspiring others. An old friend of hers who runs a corner grocery says, "She keeps people fired up; she won't let us get lazy. It's because of her that I even watch the news!" One woman who was in school with Cora and now works for the county government says, "She was always making noise at school. We knew she'd grow up noisy. But it's good noise. When Cora talks, she knows what she's talking about."

Cora is very religious. In an essay called "Halifax County and Blacks," under a subtitle "Things Blacks Must Do To Succeed," Cora once wrote, "First, blacks must go to church. The church is the backbone of black progress." Every summer for several years Cora has organized a "Citizenship Day of Prayer" on the lawn of the county courthouse in South Boston, which attracts hundreds of people who probably wouldn't gather if the event were called a rally. At the event a list of grievances is always read off, including complaints about such things as how people are treated by the welfare system, unfair employment practices or disproportionate suspensions of black pupils in the schools.

Problems like that — and what to do about them — are raised regularly at Citizens for a Better America meetings, held the fourth Friday of each month at a local funeral home.

And Cora's work goes far beyond Halifax. CBA itself has chapters in several other places, including one started in Baltimore by one of Cora's sisters. In addition, when a new coalition group, Virginia Action, was started in the state in 1980, Cora was on the founding committee and was elected its first president. She also became active on the board of its national affiliate, Citizen Action. And in 1981, on top of everything else she was doing, this woman who as a girl had refused to shake the governor's hand was talked into running as a write-in protest candidate for governor by several black groups. She didn't get many votes, but her campaign was covered in the press, and she thinks that she raised issues about black people's concerns that otherwise would have been ignored.

Cora stays extremely busy. Several years ago, she went back and got her graduate equivalency diploma, and took some courses at the community college. She thought she might want her degree.

"I used to think I wanted to be a social worker. But I changed my mind, because you can't do as much inside the system as you can on the outside. There are so many people who become social workers and then sit there with their hands tied. What people really need is somebody on the outside who's going to go and raise hell for them about laws and regulations."

(*Excerpted with permission from a profile by Anne Witte Garland in* Women Activists.)

Directory

1000 FRIENDS OF OREGON

503 SW Third Avenue, Suite 300
Portland, OR 97204
(503) 223-4396

Director: Robert Liberty

Purpose: A public interest law firm with the purpose of ensuring the proper implementation of Oregon's statewide land use laws.

Methods of operation: Litigation (25%), community organizing (25%), training and technical assistance (25%), publications (10%), research (5%), lobbying (5%), public education (5%)

Constituency: Rural community; farmers and foresters; urban planners; all those interested in protecting Oregon's quality of life

Recent issues and projects: A national demonstration project promoting sustainable patterns of suburban development

Major publications: *Landmark* newsletter; various status reports; *Citizen's Guide to Land Use Planning*

Budget: $900,000

Funding: Individual contributions (33%), foundations (33%), gifts (33%)

Staff: 10
3 Attorneys
1 Organizer
1 Paralegal
1 Writer/Editor
1 Office Manager
1 Issue Expert
1 Typist
1 Bookkeeper/Accountant

Staff openings/year: 1

Work Week: 40-50 hours

Salary/year: $18,000 (Recent College Graduate); $26,000 (Graduate with advanced degree)

Benefits: Health insurance, family leave, paid vacation and sick leave, credit union

Part-Time Employees: 2

Summer Employees: 1

Volunteers: Yes

Interns: 1
Length: 3 months
Duties: Research; project coordinator
Remuneration: Monthly stipend

Jobs advertised: Word of mouth, placement offices, newspapers

To apply: Contact Henry R. Richmond

20/20 VISION

69 South Pleasant Street, Suite 203
Amherst, MA 01002
(413) 253-2939

Other Offices: Albany, CA; Washington, DC

Director: Lois Barber, Jeremy Sherman, Co-Directors

Purpose: To engage citizens in effective communication with policymakers to redefine American priorities and shift spending from military defense to defense of the environment and to meet human needs.

Methods of operation: Research (20%), publications (20%), public education (20%), training and technical assistance (20%), community organizing (10%), lobbying (10%)

Membership: 5,000 citizens from across the nation

Major publications: Subscribers receive 12 action postcards a year (one a month). Each features one subject on our nation's military or environmental policies and recommends one 20-minute action.

Budget: $250,000

Funding: Individual contributions (70%), foundations (20%), direct mail (10%)

Staff: 8
2 Organizers
1 Issue Expert
1 Grassroots Fundraiser
1 Writer/Editor
1 Bookkeeper/Accountant
1 Research Intern
1/2 Office Manager
1/2 Foundation Fundraiser

Staff openings/year: 2

Work Week: 40 hours

Salary/year: $20,000 (Recent College Graduate); $24,000 (Graduate with advanced degree)

Benefits: Health insurance, pregnancy leave, paid vacation

Part-Time Employees: 1

Summer Employees: 1

Volunteers: 2

Interns: 2
Length: 4 months
Duties: Research assistant; field organizer assistant
Remuneration: Negotiable

Jobs advertised: Through college internship offices; local papers

To apply: Contact Lois Barber, Director

Remarks: 20/20 works to invigorate our democracy by engaging citizens in the democratic process. We have over 100 local projects organized in 33 states. Over 5,000 citizens subscribe to our service and spend 20 minutes every month getting their opinions to the right policymakers at the right time. It works! We help change policymakers' minds - they change their votes.

70001 TRAINING & EMPLOYMENT INSTITUTE

501 School Street, SW, Suite 600
Washington, DC 20024
(202) 484-0103

President: Lawrence C. Brown, Jr.

Purpose: 70001 provides education, job skills training and motivation to economically and educationally disadvantaged youth, usually between the ages of 16 and 21 years old.

Methods of operation: Human services (40%), training and technical assistance (40%), research (5%), lobbying (5%), publications (5%), direct action (5%)

Constituency: Teachers, principals, administrators, private industry councils, community-based organizations

Recent issues and projects: The WAVE (Work, Achievement, and Values in Education) is a new dropout prevention program in 51 middle and high schools nationwide. The Public Service Academy in New York City places interns in local government jobs.

Major publications: Bimonthly newspaper: *Going Places!*; monthly newsletter: *UPDATE*; *Corporate Report*, annually; feature articles

Budget: $6,000,000

Funding: Local contracts (60%), U.S. Department of Labor (25%), foundations (10%), individual contributions (5%)

Staff: 299
200 Organizers
70 Typists
20 Bookkeeper/Accountants
2 Writers/Editors
2 Press Aides
2 Foundation Fundraisers
1 Office Manager
1 Researcher
1 Lobbyist

Work Week: 40 hours

Salary/year: $Varies (Recent College Graduate); $Varies (Graduate with advanced degree)

Benefits: Health insurance, life insurance, pregnancy leave, pension, tuition reimbursement, paid vacation

Part-Time Employees: 20

Volunteers: 500

Interns: 2 per semester in Washington, DC
Length: 1 semester
Duties: Editorial, legislative and fundraising support
Remuneration: Depends on program

Jobs advertised: Internally and through classified advertising

To apply: Contact John F. Dougherty

9TO5, NATIONAL ASSOCIATION OF WORKING WOMEN

614 Superior Avenue, NW
Cleveland, OH 44113
(216) 566-9308

Other Offices: Atlanta, GA; Milwaukee, WI; Long Island, NY; Los Angeles, CA

Director: Karen Nussbaum, Executive Director

Purpose: 9to5 is a membership organization for office workers, whose purpose is to win better pay, rights and respect on the job through organizing, advocacy, research and public education.

Methods of operation: Training and technical assistance (25%), public education (20%), community organizing (20%), research (15%), human services (10%), publications (8%), lobbying (2%)

Membership: Office workers, mainly women

Recent issues and projects: Office Survival

Hotline, a toll-free service which provides counseling and referrals on workplace problems; Job Retention Project, which works with recent graduates of clerical training programs to teach them job survival skills; research, lobbying and advocacy on computer monitoring, family medical leave and child care.

Major publications: *9to5 Newsletter* (10 times annually); *9to5: The Working Woman's Guide to Office Survival*; *Solutions for the New Work Force: Policies for a New Social Contract*; numerous reports; fact sheets

Budget: $400,000

Funding: Foundations (55%), individual contributions (20%), direct mail (10%), membership dues (10%), telephone solicitation (5%)

Staff: 12
4 Organizers
2 Typists
1 Writer/Editor
1 Researcher
1 Foundation Fundraiser
1 Hotline Counselor
1 Job Retention Project Coordinator
1 Bookkeeper/Accountant
1 Office Manager (part-time)

Staff openings/year: 2

Work Week: 40 hours

Salary/year: $Varies (Recent College Graduate); $Varies (Graduate with advanced degree)

Benefits: Health insurance, life insurance, pregnancy leave, paid vacation

Part-Time Employees: 3

Volunteers: 1

Interns: Yes; number varies
Length: Flexible
Duties: Assist with research, public information, hotline
Remuneration: Unpaid; academic credit available

Jobs advertised: Local papers; classified ads in national publications (e.g. *The Nation*); mailings to contacts in other organizations; 9to5 chapters

To apply: Contact Deborah Van Kleef, Administrative Director

A BETTER CHANCE, INC.
419 Boylston Street
Boston, MA 02116
(617) 421-0950

Other Offices: New York, NY; Los Angeles, CA; Oakland, CA; Newark, NJ

President: Judith Griffin

Purpose: A Better Chance, Inc. provides students of color with access to expanded educational opportunities for college and career preparation.

Methods of operation: Human service (100%)

Constituency: Independent schools and public schools

Recent issues and projects: For over 30 years A Better Chance, Inc. has been placing students into the nation's top independent and selected public schools. There are over 8,000 alumni from the program.

Major publications: *Students: Pathways to College*

Budget: $1,600,000

Funding: Individual contributions, foundations, corporations

Staff: 20
Including:
4 Program Officers
3 Foundation Fundraisers

Staff openings/year: 1

Work Week: 37 hours

Salary/year: $19,000 (Recent College Graduate); $21,000 (Graduate with advanced degree)

Benefits: Health insurance, pension

Part-Time Employees: 2

Interns: No, but willing to accept applications

AARP WOMEN'S INITIATIVE
601 E Street, NW
Washington, DC 20049
(202) 434-2400

Manager: Maxine Forman

Purpose: The mission of AARP's Women's Initiative is to ensure that the economic, social, health and long-term care needs of midlife and older women are met.

Methods of operation: Advocacy, public education, volunteer spokesperson program, publications

Membership: AARP's membership is open to all those 50 and above

Recent issues and projects: Forum on older battered women; forum on older women and AIDS; pensions and Social Security; national Women's History Month; research on nontraditional households; financial aid for midlife and older women returning to school; women's health issues

Major publications: *AARP WIN* (networking newsletter on issues of the Women's Initiative); *Women, Pensions, and Divorce: Small Reforms That Could Make a Big Difference*; *Abused Elders or Older Battered Women?* (report on the forum); *Hormone Replacement Therapy: Facts to Help You Decide*; *Women's Health Issues: Taking Action*; and a variety of other fact sheets on issues of concern to midlife and older women

Funding: The Women's Initiative receives its budget as a department of the AARP.

Staff: 6
1 Manager
3 Senior Program Specialists
2 Administrative Assistants

Staff openings/year: 0-2

Work Week: 35 hours

Salary/year: $Varies (Recent College Graduate); $Varies (Graduate with advanced degree)

Benefits: Health insurance, pregnancy leave, pension, tuition reimbursement, paid vacation, life insurance option, leave without pay, adoption benefits, Employee Assistance Program

Volunteers: 40-50 spokespersons

Interns: Yes
Length: 3-6 months
Duties: Worked out on individual basis with department supervisor
Remuneration: Varies, stipend may be available

Jobs advertised: All jobs are posted internally. Qualified internal applicants are given an interview. If no suitable match is found through internal applicant pool, then job is advertised externally.

To apply: Contact AARP Human Resources Department

ABALONE ALLIANCE

2940 16th Street, Room 310
San Francisco, CA 94103
(415) 861-0592

Purpose: We are an informational clearinghouse on nuclear power issues and alternative energy. We are working for the shutdown of all nuclear power (including weapons/ militarism) and the adoption of a "soft path" energy policy.

Methods of operation: Community organizing (20%), research (20%), training and technical assistance (20%), public education (15%), publications (15%), direct action (5%), human services (5%)

Constituency: Mostly white; progressive; wide age range

Recent issues and projects: We are currently setting up a national computer bulletin board system on energy issues for the North American Greens.

Major publications: *Ward Valley Alert*, Informational Updates

Budget: $12,000

Funding: Direct mail (50%), individual contributions (25%), resource sales, tabling (25%)

Staff:
All Volunteer

Volunteers: Yes

Interns: None currently, but willing to accept applications

To apply: Contact Roger Herried, Staff

ABENAKI SELF HELP

P.O. Box 279, Depot Street
Swanton, VT 05488
(802) 868-2559

Other Offices: Manchester, NH

Director: Marty Hubert

Purpose: Self determination of the Abenaki nation provides job training, cultural and social service programs, low-income housing and economic development.

Methods of operation: Human services (50%), training and technical assistance (30%), direct action (10%), community organizing (5%), research

(1%), lobbying (1%), litigation (1%), public education (1%), publications (1%)

Constituency: Abenaki Indian Community

Recent issues and projects: Recent projects include: Arts cooperative; Federal recognition

Major publications: *Abenaki Newsletter*

Budget: $150,000

Funding: Federal funding (80%), foundations (20%)

Staff: 7
1 Organizer
1 Foundation Fundraiser
1 Typist
1 Bookkeeper/Accountant
2 Caseworkers
1 Housing Manager

Staff openings/year: 0-1

Work Week: 40-50 hours

Salary/year: $20,000

Benefits: Paid vacation

Part-Time Employees: Varies

Summer Employees: None

Volunteers: None

Interns: None, but willing to accept applications

Jobs advertised: Local newspapers and newsletters

To apply: Contact Marty Herbert, Director

ACCESS: A SECURITY INFORMATION SERVICE

1511 K Street, NW, Suite 643
Washington, DC 20036
(202) 783-6050

Director: Mary E. Lord

Purpose: Founded in 1985 as a nonprofit, non-advocacy information clearinghouse on international security and peace issues. Our goal is to inform and encourage public debate on these vital issues.

Methods of operation: Data collection, maintenance (50%), publications (30%), public education (20%)

Recent issues and projects: We operate an Inquiry and Speaker Referral Service and publish topical briefing papers, directories and occasional special reports.

Major publications: *ACCESS Security Spectrum*, 2 per year; *ACCESS Resource Brief*, 8 times/year; *The ACCESS Resource Guide*; *Peace and International Security Internships in the Washington, DC Area, 1988-89*; *Information on National Security Issues*; *Search for Security: The ACCESS Guide to Foundations in Peace, Security, and International Relations*

Budget: $380,000

Funding: Earned income, subscriptions, sale of publications

Staff: 5
1 Information Specialists
1 Executive Director/Fundraiser
1 Information Systems Manager
1 Receptionist
1 Writer/Editor

Staff openings/year: 1

Work Week: 40 hours

Salary/year: $20,000 (Recent College Graduate); $25-30,000 (Graduate with advanced degree)

Benefits: Health insurance, life insurance, paid vacation, disability

Interns: Yes
Length: 8-10 weeks
Duties: Assist with (1) maintaining database, (2) writing briefing papers, and (3) outreach
Remuneration: $50/week stipend

Jobs advertised: *Washington Post*; ACCESS: Networking in the Public Interest (Cambridge, MA); small mailing to other DC nonprofits

To apply: Contact Susan Krutt

ACCESS: NETWORKING IN THE PUBLIC INTEREST

50 Beacon Street
Boston, MA 02108
(617) 720-5627

Director: Jim Clark

Purpose: ACCESS works to help people become more involved (at the career level) in addressing public challenges. Since 1985, ACCESS has served as the nation's only comprehensive clearinghouse of information regarding employment in public and community service.

Methods of operation: Publishing, information

acquisition, resource and referral

Constituency: Non-profits, professionals and job seekers

Major publications: *Community Jobs: The National Employment Newspaper for the Non-Profit Sector*; *Community Jobs/NY,NJ*; *Community Jobs/DC*; *Opportunities in Public Interest Law.* Also provide career development services, database searches (from their database of more than 4,000 organizations), and the ACCESS Resume Bank for staff/board diversity.

Budget: $600,000

Funding: Subscriptions (60%), foundations (40%)

Staff: 6
1 Writer/Editor
1 Office Manager
1 Outreach Director
1 Outreach Assistant Director
1 Art Director
1 Executive Director

Staff openings/year: 0-1

Work Week: 40-50 hours

Salary/year: $19,000 (Recent College Graduate); $Varies (Graduate with advanced degree)

Benefits: Health insurance, paid vacation, life insurance

Part-Time Employees: 10

Summer Employees: 1-2

Volunteers: 5

Interns: 1-2
Length: 4-10 weeks
Duties: Special projects
Remuneration: Stipend

Jobs advertised: Through our newspaper

To apply: Contact Jim Clark, Executive Director

ACCION INTERNATIONAL
130 Prospect Street
Cambridge, MA 02139
(617) 492-4930

Other Offices: New York, NY; Albuquerque, NM; San Antonio, TX; Washington, DC

Director: William Burrus

Purpose: Founded in 1961, ACCION International is a private, nonprofit organization which fights poverty and hunger by encouraging the economic self-reliance of impoverished working women and men in the Americas. ACCION provides credit and basic business training for the self-employed.

Methods of operation: Publications, training and technical assistance, fundraising

Recent issues and projects: Over three decades, ACCION has become an internationally recognized leader in microenterprise development and has worked in virtually every Latin American country and in several areas of the United States. In 1992 alone, ACCION provided loans to 147,000 small businesses, creating 126,000 jobs and benefitting 588,000 family members.

Major publications: *ACCION International Bulletin*; write or call for catalogue of publications

Budget: $4,000,000

Funding: Foundations (50%), corporations (25%), individual contributions (20%), direct mail (5%)

Staff: 15
1 Writer/Editor
1 Office Manager
2 Foundation Fundraisers
2 Bookkeepers/Accountants
2 Grassroots Fundraisers
7 Department Directors

Staff openings/year: Varies

Work Week: 40 hours

Salary/year: $20,000 (Recent College Graduate); $25,000 (Graduate with advanced degree)

Benefits: Health insurance, pension, paid vacation, life insurance, pregnancy leave, tuition reimbursement

Part-Time Employees: 1

Summer Employees: No

Volunteers: Occasionally

Interns: Yes
Length: Internships usually last 1 yr.
Duties: Varied
Remuneration: Depends, usually unpaid

Jobs advertised: Local newspapers, word of mouth

To apply: Contact (in writing) Cheryl Witty, Executive Assistant

ACCOUNTANTS FOR THE PUBLIC INTEREST (API)

1012 14th Street, NW, Suite 906
Washington, DC 20005
(202) 347-1668

Director: Douglas Mitchell

Purpose: To provide volunteer accounting assistance to nonprofits, small businesses and individuals who cannot afford professional services.

Methods of operation: Publications (50%), human services (50%)

Constituency: Composed of accountants who choose to volunteer their time as accountants to those in need

Recent issues and projects: Completed writing a five booklet series on nonprofit management topics such as: *Making Public Disclosure*; *Filing Nonprofit Tax Forms; Tracking Special Monies*; *Tracking Special Monies*; and *Selecting Computer Software*

Major publications: *API Account*, newsletter to members; *What a Difference Nonprofits Make: A Guide to Accounting Procedures*; *What A Difference Preparation Makes: A Guide to the Nonprofit Audit*

Funding: Individual contributions (75%), foundations (25%)

Staff: 7
2 Writers/Editors
1 Office Managers
1 Foundation Fundraiser
1 Typist
1 Bookkeeper/Accountant
1 Caseworker

Work Week: 40 hours

Salary/year: $18,000 (Recent College Graduate); $22,000 (Graduate with advanced degree)

Benefits: Health insurance, paid vacation

Jobs advertised: Through the local newspaper

ACCREDITATION COUNCIL ON SERVICES FOR PEOPLE WITH DISABILITIES

8100 Professional Place, Suite 204
Landover, MD 20785
(310) 459-3191

Other Offices: Lincoln, NB; St. Louis, MO

Director: Jim Gardner, Ph.D.

Purpose: The goal of the Accreditation Council is to increase quality in services for people with disabilities through the development of standards, dissemination of publications, provision of consultation and operation of a national accreditation program.

Methods of operation: Training and technical assistance (40%), human services (40%), publications (20%)

Recent issues and projects: Development of quality indicators that measure the outcomes of services on service recipients rather than compliance with organizational process.

Major publications: *Update on Quality*, quarterly newsletter; *Outcome Based Performance Measures*

Budget: $1,400,000

Funding: Fee for Service (95%)

Staff: 8
3 Office Managers
2 Issue Experts
3 Quality Enhancement Coordinators

Staff openings/year: 1-2

Work Week: 40 hours

Salary/year: $32,000 (Graduate with advanced degree)

Benefits: Health insurance, pension, paid vacation, life insurance, family leave, tuition reimbursement

Part-Time Employees: 30

Summer Employees: None

Volunteers: None

Interns: None, but willing to accept applications

Jobs advertised: In the newsletter

To apply: Contact Sylvia Nodler, Director of Operations

ACTION ALLIANCE OF SENIOR CITIZENS OF GREATER PHILADELPHIA

1211 Chestnut Street, #810
Philadelphia, PA 19107
(215) 564-1622

Director: Joseph Willard

Purpose: Organizing senior citizens to address issues that affect their lives. We are a coalition of 320 senior citizen groups in Philadelphia.

Methods of operation: Community organizing (25%), direct action (25%), research (20%), lobbying (20%), public education (10%)

Membership: 320 senior citizen groups and 13,500 individuals

Recent issues and projects: (1) Pressing for legislation to ban overcharges by physicians; (2) working for a city law to require grocery stores to put prices on items; (3) fighting to preserve transportation programs for seniors; (4) pressing for a consumer advocate to help hold down gas rates

Major publications: Newsletter

Budget: $200,000

Funding: Individual contributions (55%), fundraisers (25%), foundations (20%)

Staff: 4
3 1/2 Organizers
1 Office Manager

Staff openings/year: 1

Work Week: 40-45 hours

Salary/year: $16,500

Benefits: Health insurance, life insurance, pregnancy leave, paid vacation

Volunteers: 500+

Jobs advertised: Local papers; mailings to local agencies; *Community Jobs*

To apply: Contact Joe Willard

ACTION FOR CORPORATE ACCOUNTABILITY

129 Church Street
New Haven, CT 06510
(203) 787-0061

Director: Karlyn Sturmer

Purpose: Action alerts the public to corporate practices which cause infant death and disease and takes direct action to stop these practices. Action also seeks to protect a woman's right to an informed choice about infant feeding practices that affect her own and her children's health.

Methods of operation: Public education (25%), direct action (25%), organizing (25%), research (10%), training and technical assistance (10%), publications (5%)

Membership: 11,000 activists nationwide who bring their background in health, women's rights, the environment, consumer rights, peace and justice to this issue

Recent issues and projects: Action runs the boycott against Nestle and American Home Products in the United States. In 1993 Action began an international monitoring project to develop local capacity in 24 countries across the globe to document marketing abuses.

Major publications: *Action News*, newsletter

Budget: $140,000

Funding: Foundations (52%), religious organizations (24%), direct mail (20%), other (4%)

Staff: 3
1 Organizer
1 Office Manager
1 Director

Staff openings/year: 1-2

Work Week: 40 hours

Salary/year: $19,000 (Recent College Graduate); $28,000 (Graduate with advanced degree)

Benefits: Health insurance, paid vacation, family leave

Part-Time Employees: None

Summer Employees: None

Volunteers: 10

Interns: Yes
Length: 4 months
Duties: Organizing, writing, researching

Jobs advertised: Radio and statewide papers, some national jobs hotlines

To apply: Contact Karlyn Sturman

ACTION ON SMOKING AND HEALTH (ASH)

2013 H Street, NW
Washington, DC 20006
(202) 659-4310

Director: John F. Banzhaf, III

Purpose: Legal action for nonsmokers' rights for the past 25 years. ASH was responsible for removing cigarette commercials from the airwaves, establishing the legal concept of nonsmoking sections generally, and obtaining rules to ban smoking from domestic airline flights. Over the past 23 years ASH attorneys have filed hundreds of legal petitions to government agencies to limit smoking and make sure rules are enforced.

Methods of operation: Litigation (50%), public education (25%), publications (20%), research (5%)

Constituency: Individuals nationwide who are concerned about the smoking problem, and especially concerned with their right to breathe air free of tobacco smoke

Recent issues and projects: ASH is in the process of filing a petition against OSHA (Occupational Safety and Health Administration) to establish guidelines for tobacco smoke exposure in the workplace. Currently there are no safe lower limits to exposure. A new strategy is being launched to assist sensitive nonsmokers to avail themselves of the protections of the Americans with Disabilities Act through legal action.

Major publications: *Action on Smoking and Health Review*, published 8 times a year; numerous legal briefs

Budget: $1,000,000

Funding: Individual contributions (90%), foundations (10%)

Staff: 9
3 Attorneys
3 Grassroots Fundraisers
1 Office Manager
1 Administrative Assistant
1 Paralegal

Staff openings/year: 0-2

Work Week: 40 hours

Salary/year: $25,000

Benefits: Health insurance, life insurance, generous sick leave and paid vacation

Part-Time Employees: 1

Interns: 2

Jobs advertised: Legal positions in trade magazines and newspaper; fundraising positions in trade magazines; paralegal/secretarial positions at agencies and in local paper

To apply: Contact Athena Mueller, General Counsel

ACTIVISM 2000 PROJECT

P.O. Box E
Kensington, MD 20895
(301) 929-8808

Director: Wendy Schaeter Lesko

Purpose: The Activism 2000 Project seeks to inspire and encourage people of all ages, especially those not yet old enough to vote, to search for solutions to some of today's toughest problems. We teach young people from all walks of life, honor students, at-risk youth, even incarcerated juveniles, how they can voice to the powers-that-be their ideas for improving our schools, cities and the environment.

Methods of operation: Research (25%), public education (20%), training and technical assistance (20%), publications (15%), community organizing (10%), lobbying (10%)

Constituency: Individual students, teachers, school administrators, community organizations, youth groups, state, local and federal government agencies

Recent issues and projects: Recent projects include: working in coalition with organizations involved with combatting violence; state coalitions on tobacco control and legislative initiatives involving youth; integrating political advocacy in social studies curriculum and community service

Major publications: *No Kidding Around! America's Activists are Changing our World and You Can Too*; *Violence in America* info-starter; *Pointers on Producing PSA's and Video*

Staff: 1
1/2 Public Information Director
1/2 Administrative Assistant

Work Week: 40 hours

Salary/year: $Varies (Recent College Graduate); $Varies (Graduate with advanced degree)

Part-Time Employees: 2

Summer Employees: Yes

Volunteers: Yes

Interns: None

Jobs advertised: Informal; word of mouth network

To apply: Contact Wendy Schaetzer Lesko, Executive Director

Remarks: As of 1994, the Activism 2000 Project does not expect to hire any full-time staff, but part-time researchers and other positions are possible in the future. By 1996, this small national clearinghouse expects to expand its operations and staff.

ACTIVISTS CONCERNED WITH TOXICS IN OUR NEIGHBORHOODS (ACTION)

1080 US 22 West, P.O. Box 67
Circleville, OH 43113
(614) 474-1240

Director: Cynthia Giller, Advisory Council

Purpose: ACTION is a grassroots volunteer group working on threats to the environment in Ohio, such as the Bowers Landfill Superfund Site, the Barthelmas Landfill, sewage/sludge, PPG's Regional Hazardous Waste Incinerator, PPG's groundwater contamination, solid waste/recycling, and out-of-state ash/trash traffic. ACTION maintains an environmental library, speaks to area organizations and church groups, networks with other environmental groups nationwide, and provides information through newsletters, letters to the editor, radio and TV programs, and public meetings.

Methods of operation: Public education (70%), community organizing (10%), direct action (10%), research (10%)

Constituency: General public - all professions, all ages

Major publications: *ACTION Newsletter*

Budget: $2,500

Funding: Individual contributions (50%), fundraisers (50%)

Staff:
All volunteer, including:
2 Bookkeeper/Accountants
2 Grassroots Fundraisers
2 Writer/Editors
1 Attorney
1 Office Manager
1 Typist
1 Organizer

Work Week: 20 hours

Volunteers: 20

Interns: None currently, but willing to accept applications
Remuneration: Cannot provide financial assistance, but can provide housing

To apply: Contact Cynthia Giller

ADIRONDACK COUNCIL, INC.

P.O. Box D-2
Elizabethtown, NY 12932
(518) 873-2240

Director: Timothy Burke

Purpose: A nonprofit environmental advocacy organization dedicated to the protection and preservation of the Adirondack Park.

Methods of operation: Public education (30%), publications (30%), research (20%), lobbying (10%), litigation (10%)

Constituency: Primarily New York state residents

Recent issues and projects: Development threats to the Park; New York State Bond Act to acquire public lands and easements in the Park; 2020 Vision Series (a series of special reports depicting a vision for the Park in the year 2020)

Major publications: Quarterly newsletter; *State of the Park Report*; *2020 Vision Series*

Budget: $1,500,000

Funding: Direct mail (40%), foundations (30%), individual contributions (20%), telephone solicitation (10%)

Staff: 11
4 Issue Experts
3 Typists
1 Fundraiser
1 Attorney
1 Administrator
1 Writer/Editor

Staff openings/year: 1

Work Week: 40 hours

Salary/year: $22,000 (Recent College Graduate); $40,000 (Graduate with advanced degree)

Benefits: Health insurance, life insurance, pension, paid vacation, disability

Part-Time Employees: 3

Interns: Sometimes

Jobs advertised: Contacts; newspapers; *Environmental Opportunities*; *Chronicle of Philanthropy*

To apply: Contact Donna Beal, Administrator

ADVOCACY INSTITUTE

1730 Rhode Island Avenue, NW, Suite 600
Washington, DC 20036-3118
(202) 659-8475

Director: David Cohen, Michael Pertschuk, Kathleen Sheekey

Purpose: To make public interest advocates more effective by teaching advocacy skills such as lobbying, coalition building and media advocacy.

Methods of operation: Training and technical assistance (80%), research (10%), publications (5%), public education (3%), lobbying (2%)

Constituency: Public interest organizations and their supporters

Recent issues and projects: The Advocacy Institute works with public interest organizations on specific issues like arms control, smoking and public health, the environment, whistleblower protection, Central American policy, and energy efficiency.

Major publications: Books: *Giantkillers*; *The People Rising*; Reports: *Preemption and the Public Interest*; *Media Guidelines for Smoking Control Advocates*; *Change for the Better*; *Building New Dimensions in Public Interest Leadership*; *The Elements of a Successful Public Interest Advocacy Campaign*; *Why Not Work for a Change?*; Monthly newsletter: *The Advocate's Advocate*

Budget: $2,000,000

Funding: Foundations (70%), individual contributions (30%)

Staff: 35
15 Issue Experts
2 Attorneys
5 Support Staff
2 Campaign Managers
1 Office Manager
9 Researchers/Program Associates
1 Foundation Fundraiser

Staff openings/year: 2

Work Week: 40 hours

Salary/year: $22,000 (Recent College Graduate); $28,000 (Graduate with advanced degree)

Benefits: Health insurance, life insurance, pregnancy leave, child care, paid vacation, tuition reimbursement, cafeteria benefits plan

Part-Time Employees: 2

Summer Employees: 8

Volunteers: 2

Interns: 3
Length: 3 months
Duties: Participate in full range of activities
Remuneration: Stipend available

Jobs advertised: Newspapers (*Washington Post*; *Roll Call*)

To apply: Contact Frieda P. King, Operational Manager

ADVOCATES FOR CHILDREN OF NEW YORK, INC.

24-16 Bridge Plaza South
Long Island City, NY 11101
(718) 729-8866

Director: Galen D. Kirkland

Purpose: To protect educational entitlements and due process rights of disadvantaged public school children in New York City

Methods of operation: Case advocacy, public education (30%), training and technical assistance (20%), litigation (20%), research (10%), publications (10%), community organizing (10%)

Constituency: Public school students and their families

Recent issues and projects: Use of suspensions/expulsions as punishment; homeless children's education; access to schools for undocumented youths; educational funding; parent involvement in schools

Major publications: *The Advocate*, 4 per year; *Securing an Appropriate Education for Children with Handicapping Conditions in New York City: A Guide to Effective Advocacy*; *Learning in Limbo: The Educational Deprivation of Homeless Children*; *Immigrant Children Challenges and Opportunities*

for Our Schools; Segregated and Second Rate: Special Education in NY; And *Miles to go: Barriers to Academic Achievement and Innovative Strategies for the Delivery of Educational Services for Homeless Children*

Budget: $1,000,000

Funding: Foundations (40%), government (40%), legal fees (10%), individual contributions (10%)

Staff: 19
9 Paralegals
3 Attorneys
4 Support Staff
1 Intake
1 Executive Director
1 Fiscal Officer

Staff openings/year: 0-2

Work Week: 35 hours

Salary/year: $20,000 (Recent College Graduate); $24,000 (Graduate with advanced degree)

Benefits: Health insurance, life insurance, parenting leave, paid vacation, personal days, sick days

Part-Time Employees: 4

Summer Employees: 1-3

Volunteers: 0-3

Interns: 0-2
Length: 1 semester to 1 school year
Duties: Vary
Remuneration: Work-study, foundation supported

Jobs advertised: Local papers; affirmative action mailing list; word of mouth

To apply: Contact Diana Autin, Managing Attorney

ADVOCATES FOR YOUTH

1025 Vermont Ave., NW, Suite 200
Washington, DC 20005
(202) 347-5700

Other Offices: Los Angeles, CA

Director: Margaret Pruitt Clark

Purpose: Advocates for Youth (formerly the Center for Population Options) works to increase the opportunities for and abilities of youth to make health decisions about sexuality. Since 1980, Advocates for Youth has provided information, education and advocacy to youth-serving agencies and professionals, policymakers and the media.

Methods of operation: Research, lobbying, publications, public education, training and technical assistance

Recent issues and projects: Recent projects include: HIV Prevention Education Initiative; Teens for AIDS Prevention; condom availability; school-based health care; life planning education

Major publications: *When I'm Grown*; *Life Planning Education*; *Condoms Availability in Schools*; *Peer-to-Peer: Youth Preventing HIV Infection*; *Talking With TV*

Budget: $2,000,000

Funding: Foundations (95%), individual contributions (5%)

Staff: 28
5 Organizers
4 Writers/Editors
2 Office Managers
1 Researcher
2 Lobbyists
2 Press Aides
1 Foundation Fundraiser
2 Bookkeepers/Editors

Staff openings/year: 1-2

Work Week: 35-40 hours

Benefits: Health insurance, paid vacation, life insurance, family leave

Part-Time Employees: None

Volunteers: None

Interns: 4
Length: 2-3 months
Remuneration: Stipend varies

Jobs advertised: *Washington Post*, *Opportunities in Public Affairs*, *Roll Call*

To apply: Contact Sandy Villareal

AFFILIATED MEDIA FOUNDATION MOVEMENT (AMFM)

1024 Elysian Fields Avenue
New Orleans, LA 70117
(504) 943-5713

Other Offices: Dallas, TX; Little Rock, AR; Salinas/Watsonville, CA

Purpose: AMFM is a national association of community groups, labor organizations and broadcast facilities committed to developing broadcast media as a vehicle for progressive social change. AMFM assists low- and moderate-income community groups to gain access to and ownership of radio and TV stations in order to inform and encourage the participation of poor and disenfranchised people in issues which affect their lives and communities.

Methods of operation: Public education, community organizing, broadcast, training and technical assistance

Constituency: Low- to moderate-income people

Recent issues and projects: Helped construct two radio stations and one television station; constructing ten translator stations in Louisiana and Texas

Major publications: Newsletter: *Open Channels*, published irregularly

Budget: $100,000

Funding: Benefits, grassroots fundraising (40%), individual, listener and sponsor contributions (30%), canvassing (20%), foundations (10%)

Staff:
6 Organizers
3 Station Managers
3 Office Managers
2 News/Public Affairs Directors
2 Volunteer Coordinators
2 Community Outreach Directors

Work Week: 40+ hours

Salary/year: $12,000

Benefits: Health insurance, pregnancy leave, pension, paid vacation

Part-Time Employees: 10

Summer Employees: 10

Volunteers: 300

Interns: Yes
Length: Summer
Duties: Vary
Remuneration: Flexible; sometimes salaried

Jobs advertised: Local newspapers; national progressive periodicals

To apply: Contact Susan Adams, Training Coordinator

Remarks: KNON-FM in Dallas has a budget of $250,000; KABF-FM in Little Rock: $150,000; CCTN-TV in Salinas/Watsonville: $250,000.

AFL-CIO ORGANIZING INSTITUTE

1444 Eye Street, NW, Suite 216
Washington, DC 20005
(202) 408-0700 or (800) 848-3021

Other Offices: San Francisco, CA

Director: Richard Bensinger

Purpose: To promote and foster union organizing campaigns throughout the country.

Methods of operation: Training and technical assistance (70%), recruiting (25%), public education (5%)

Constituency: International unions affiliated with the AFL-CIO

Recent issues and projects: RTP Program is designed to Recruit, Train and Place as many as 200 new union organizers in jobs with international unions. Screening and training program ongoing.

Funding: AFL-CIO

Staff: 47
1 Executive Director
1 Associate Director
2 Senior Associates
35 Apprentice Organizers
1 Institute Fellow
5 Part-time Recruiters
1 Office Manager
1 Recruitment Director

Staff openings/year: 100

Work Week: 60+ hours

Salary/year: $20-30,000

Benefits: Health insurance, life insurance, pension, credit union, paid vacation, room and board while traveling

Interns: Yes
Length: 4-6 weeks
Duties: Intern and apprenticeship in preparation for permanent placement
Remuneration: $175-250/week for internship; $400-600/week for apprenticeship; transportation and housing for both

To apply: Contact Allison Porter, Director of Recruitment

Remarks: Screening process includes the following: 10 question application, interview, weekend training programs offered monthly.

AFRICA FUND

198 Broadway, Room 402
New York, NY 10038
(212) 962-1210

Director: Jennifer Davis

Purpose: To support the struggle for African freedom and independence through assistance and educational campaigns in the U.S.

Methods of operation: Research, public education, publications

Recent issues and projects: Following Mandela's call, working with state legislators and city councilors to lift sanctions and support socially responsible investment and targeted investment and at overcoming the legacy of apartheid and support for social reconstruction. The Fund has launched a campaign to help ensure the election in South Africa is free and fair, including support for voter education and an electionwatcher campaign to keep the United States informed.

Major publications: *Africa Fund News* (twice a year); *Bitter Inheritance - Overcoming the Legacy of Apartheid* by Michael Fleshman; *Voting in the Shadow of Apartheid*

Budget: $600,000

Funding: Individual contributions, foundations, direct mail

Staff: 7
4 Organizers
1 Executive Director
1 Office Manager
1 Researcher

Work Week: 60 hours

Salary/year: $20,000

Benefits: Health insurance, paid vacation

Part-Time Employees: 3

Volunteers: Yes

Interns: Yes
Length: 1-3 months
Duties: Working with staff on current projects
Remuneration: Usually none

Jobs advertised: Africa publications

To apply: Contact Adrena Ifill, Associate Director

AFRICA NEWS SERVICE, INC.

P.O. Box 3851
Durham, NC 27702
(919) 286-0747

Director: Bertie Howard, Executive Director

Purpose: Africa News Service, Inc. is a nonprofit, educational news agency dedicated to encouraging and promoting an accurate understanding of Africa and its people, through news and information. ANS produces *Africa News On-Line*, a bi-weekly newspaper distributed electronically; radio reports and features for U.S. and international broadcasters; feature and investigative reports; and maintains a major archive of Africa-related material.

Methods of operation: Publications (30%), research (20%), special projects (20%), radio production (30%)

Constituency: Individuals, organizations and institutions with an interest in Africa

Recent issues and projects: Began production of a 12-part radio series with National Public Radio, *Africa in the Post Cold War World* and an accompanying multimedia course pack.

Major publications: *Africa News*, biweekly news digest; *The Africa News Cookbook: African Cooking for Western Kitchens*

Budget: $900,000

Funding: Foundations (60%), sales of services and products (30%), individual contributions (10%)

Staff: 6
1 Editor
1 President/Managing Editor
1 Executive Director
1 Accounts Manager
1 News Assistant
1 Producer

Staff openings/year: 1

Work Week: 45 hours

Salary/year: $13-25,000

Benefits: Health insurance, life insurance, maternity/paternity leave, paid vacation and personal leave, workers compensation insurance, dental insurance, long-term disability insurance

Part-Time Employees: 3

Volunteers: Yes

Interns: 1-4

Length: 6 weeks
Duties: Generally work with news team in news gathering, research, writing, crosslisting/reference work. Possible for students to design a project.
Remuneration: Unpaid

Jobs advertised: Primarily local papers; occasionally trade journals; announcements to other Africa interest groups

To apply: Contact Bertie Howard, Executive Director

AFRICAN AMERICAN RESOURCE CENTER

500 Howard Place, NW, Founders Library, 3rd Floor
Washington, DC 20059
(202) 806-7242

Director: Mr. E. Ethelbert Miller

Purpose: To collect and distribute information about the African American experience. The Center supports the academic activities of the Department of Afro-American studies at Howard. The Center also provides material and information to the Washington, DC community.

Methods of operation: Research (90%), public education (10%)

Constituency: Academic community: teachers; scholars and students

Recent issues and projects: Collecting information about contemporary African American writers and intellectuals.

Budget: $5,000

Funding: University budget (100%)

Staff: 1

Benefits: Health insurance, pension, paid vacation, credit union

Part-Time Employees: None

Summer Employees: 2

Volunteers: 1

Interns: None

To apply: Please contact Mr. E. Ethelbert Miller

AIDS ACTION COUNCIL

1875 Connecticut Ave., NW, Suite 700
Washington, DC 20009
(202) 986-1300

Director: Daniel T. Bross

Purpose: AIDS Action is the voice of AIDS in Washington, representing AIDS communities throughout the nation. AIDS Action is two organizations. While AIDS Action Council is a 501(c)(4) entitiy that lobbies the federal government, AIDS Action Foundation, a 501(c)(3) organization, works to develop federal HIV/AIDS policies to increase AIDS research and improve treatment and prevention.

Methods of operation: Lobbying (40%), community organizing (30%), media relations (20%), publications (10%)

Membership: People with AIDS, AIDS service organizations across the country

Recent issues and projects: AIDS Action works to improve the lives of people living with HIV/AIDS by educating the nation's policy makers. Our efforts have had a direct impact on the lives of all people living with HIV by providing them with discrimination protection, access to sufficient drug treatments, the promise of additional research and the lifeline of federal funds that translate into services.

Major publications: *AIDS Action Update*, bi-monthly newsletter; *AIDS Action Briefing*, issue papers; *Health Care Reform Action News*; fact sheets; brochures; reports. Please write for a publications brochure for complete listing.

Budget: $2,000,000

Funding: Individual contributions (50%), foundations (50%)

Staff: 20
2 Organizers
1 Office Manager
4 Lobbyists
2 Press Aids
2 Foundation Fundraisers
2 Issue Experts
1 Bookkeeper/Accountant
1 Grassroots Fundraiser
1 Executive Director
4 Administrative Assistant

Staff openings/year: 3-4

Work Week: 40 hours

Salary/year: $25,000

Benefits: Health insurance, paid vacation

Part-Time Employees: 3

Summer Employees: None

Volunteers: 1-6

Interns: 2
Length: 3 months
Duties: Various duties; interns are currently working in Public Affairs and Government Affairs
Remuneration: None

Jobs advertised: *Washington Post, Roll Call,* referrals and job boards

To apply: Please contact Bellen Joyner, Administrative Coordinator

AIDS FOUNDATION OF CHICAGO

411 S. Wells
Chicago, IL 60607
(312) 642-5454

Director: Karen Fishman

Purpose: The largest local source of private philanthropic support for AIDS programs and services, the AIDS Foundation of Chicago was founded in 1985 to provide central leadership in the fight against the epidemic. Through its Service Providers Council, AFC coordinates the activities of a growing network of over 100 local agencies committed to AIDS care and prevention. The foundation is also Illinois principal advocate for people living with HIV and the organizations that serve them, working at the local, state and federal levels to build support for enlightened and compassionate AIDS policies and for increased public funding for AIDS services.

Methods of operation: Lobbying, grantmaking, community organizing, training and technical assistance

Constituency: Chicago area HIV/AIDS service providers

Recent issues and projects: Since the inception of its private grantmaking program in 1988, the foundation has given away more than $2.3 million to support AIDS care, education and prevention programs reaching thousands of men, women and children throughout the metropolitan area.

Budget: $4,000,000

Funding: Public (65%), individual contributions (25%), foundations (10%)

Staff: 16
2 Organizers
3 Office Managers
2 Lobbyists
1 Foundation Fundraiser
1 Issue Expert
2 Bookkeepers/Accountants
2 Caseworkers
3 Grassroots Fundraisers

Staff openings/year: 1

Work Week: 50 hours

Salary/year: $19,000

Benefits: Health insurance, pension, paid vacation, life insurance, family leave

Part-Time Employees: 2

Summer Employees: None

Volunteers: 4

Interns: 1
Length: 3 months
Duties: Assistance identifying available resources for clients
Remuneration: Varies

AIDS LEGAL COUNCIL OF CHICAGO

220 S. State Street, Suite 1330
Chicago, IL 60604
(312) 427-8990

Director: Susan Curry

Purpose: The Council provides a full spectrum of legal assistance to people with HIV/AIDS who cannot otherwise afford an attorney. Legal matters must be HIV related.

Methods of operation: Legal counseling, assistance and intervention (70%), litigation (10%), training and technical assistance (10%), public education (8%), publications (2%)

Recent issues and projects: Recent projects include: outreach office at Cook County Hospital focusing on government entitlements; co-drafted new Illinois standby guardianship legislation

Major publications: *AIDS: The Legal Issues - A Guide for the Public*

Budget: $300,000

Staff: 7
1 Attorney
2 Paralegal
1 Office Manager
1 Caseworker
1 Outreach Director
1 Intake Specialist

Work Week: 40 hours

Benefits: Health insurance, paid vacation, paid sick leave

Part-Time Employees: 2

Summer Employees: None

Volunteers: 70

Interns: 1-3
Length: 3 months
Duties: Legal research, client intake and counseling

Jobs advertised: Local newspaper, newsletters, national magazines

To apply: Please contact Susan J. Curry, Executive Director

AIDS NATIONAL INTERFAITH NETWORK

110 Maryland Ave., NE, Suite 504
Washington, DC 20002
(202) 546-0807

Director: Ken South

Purpose: To assist AIDS ministries by providing networking opportunities, information and resource sharing; to represent the AIDS interfaith community on Capitol Hill. Nearly 3,000 national religious denominations and groups; divisions of national religious denominations and groups; national religious denominations AIDS networks; interfaith AIDS networks; ecumenical AIDS networks; AIDS ministries; congregational AIDS ministries.

Methods of operation: Technical assistance, collaboration, public policy advocacy, information, publications, National Interfaith AIDS Ministries Database

Constituency: Nearly 3,000 national religious denominations and groups

Recent issues and projects: National Skills Building Conference; AIDS Housing; AIDS Advocacy in African American Churches Project; Council of National Religious AIDS Networks

Major publications: *The HIV/AIDS Housing Handbook: Federal Resources Available to Meet the Housing Needs of People with HIV/AIDS*; *AIDS and Your Religious Community*

Budget: $300,000

Funding: Foundations (45%), government grants (30%), religious denominations (10%), individuals (5%), memberships (10%)

Staff: 4
1 Executive Director
1 Associate Director for Resource Development
1 Director of Communications
1 Administrative Assistant

Staff openings/year: 0-1

Work Week: 40 hours

Salary/year: $Varies (Recent College Graduate); $Varies (Graduate with advanced degree)

Benefits: Health insurance, life insurance, and paid vacation

Part-Time Employees: 2

Volunteers: Yes

Interns: Yes
Length: 1 year
Duties: Projects vary
Remuneration: None at this time

Jobs advertised: Through network

AIDS PROJECT - LOS ANGELES

1313 N. Vine Street
Los Angeles, CA 90028
(213) 993-1600

Director: James Loyce, Jr.

Purpose: APLA is a nonprofit, community based organization which is a direct provider of, and resource for, HIV/AIDS services and information, and an advocate at all levels of government for people with HIV/AIDS.

Methods of operation: Lobbying, publications, human services community organizing, public education, training and technical assistance

Constituency: Over 4,000 clients

Recent issues and projects: Recent projects and accomplishments include: increasing the federal appropriations for the Ryan White Care Act by $213 million for FY94; reorganizing the Centers for Disease Control to include the first community planning process, the Prevention Working Group;

increasing the state HIV prevention and education, an anonymous testing funds for FY95 by $5 million; protecting critical Medi-Cal benefits from being cut from the state budget; enacting legislation which closes loopholes used to deny health insurance to people with HIV; defeating two bills that would have mandated HIV names reporting and eliminated anonymous testing; and protecting comprehensive care centers and county hospitals from being closed due to proposed county budget cuts

Major publications: *Positive Living* (monthly circ. 8,000); *HIV LA* (semi-annual circ. 10,000); *Optimist* (quarterly publication, circ. 50,000); *Catalyst* (policy publication, circ. 800); and an annual report

Budget: $19,000,000

Funding: Individual contributions (76%), other (18%), direct mail (6%)

Staff: 220
4 Writers/Editors
4 Attorneys
2 Paralegals
30 Office Managers
3 Researchers
10 Lobbyists
2 Press Aides
20 Foundation Fundraisers
10 Issue Experts
10 Bookkeepers/Accountants
80 Caseworkers
4 Campaign Managers
40 Support Staff

Staff openings/year: 30

Work Week: 40 hours

Salary/year: $22-25,000 (Recent College Graduate); $28 - 30,000 (Graduate with advanced degree)

Benefits: Health insurance, paid vacation, life insurance, credit union, family leave

Part-Time Employees: 20

Summer Employees: None

Volunteers: 2,500

Interns: Varies
Length: College semester - 3 months
Duties: Vary upon department. We presently have 12 interns in our Mental Health Department
Remuneration: Volunteer basis, for college credit and "on-the-job" training

Jobs advertised: Internal job board, sharing job listings with other agencies, listings in local news publications, journals of philanthropy, area colleges, law schools, specialized training institutes, JOBLINE (a telephone listing)

To apply: Please contact Bill Scott, Recruitment Specialist of Human Resources Department

---

AIDS SURVIVAL PROJECT

44 12th Street
Atlanta, GA 30309
(404) 874-7926

Director: Mark King

Purpose: As a membership organization comprised of HIV positive individuals and concerned friends, AIDS Survival Project plays an important role in the AIDS epidemic. Our purpose is to provide those of us affected by HIV disease with the information and support we need to make well informed choices about our lives. This unique focus insures a passionate and committed response to the diverse and changing needs of people with HIV/AIDS, because their voices are our voices.

Methods of operation: Human services (25%), community organizing (20%), research (20%), publications (15%), direct action (5%), training and technical assistance (5%)

Recent issues and projects: Recent projects include: advocacy; peer counseling; Operation: Survive!; support groups and volunteer opportunities

Major publications: *AIDS Survival Project News* (monthly publication)

Budget: $215,000

Funding: Individual contributions, foundations, direct mail

Staff: 5
1 Organizer
1 Writer/Editor
1/2 Office Manager
1/2 Researcher
1/2 Foundation Fundraiser
1/2 Bookkeeper/Accountant
1/2 Grassroots Fundraiser

Staff openings/year: 0-1

Work Week: 50 + hours

Salary/year: $20,000 (Recent College Graduate); $Varies (Graduate with advanced degree)

Benefits: Health insurance, paid vacation

Part-Time Employees: 1

Summer Employees: None

Volunteers: 70

Interns: None at this time

Jobs advertised: Local and national papers and AIDS related journals

To apply: Please contact Mark King, Executive Director

ALABAMA CENTER FOR HIGHER EDUCATION

2328 Second Avenue, North
Birmingham, AL 35203
(205) 324-7886

Director: Charlena H. Bray

Purpose: The Alabama Center for Higher Education (ACHE) is a consortium of the seven, four-year historically black colleges and universities in the state: Alabama A&M University, Normal; Alabama State University, Montgomery; Miles College, Birmingham; Oakwood College, Huntsville; Stillman College, Tuscaloosa; Talladega College, Talladega; and Tuskegee University, Tuskegee. Organized for the primary purpose of promoting inter-institutional cooperation among the member institutions, ACHE has since 1972 served as a sponsor for the TRIO Program serving veterans while each member sponsored various other projects.

Methods of operation: Human services (75%), training and technical assistance (20%), community organizing (5%)

Constituency: College students and potential college students age 19 years and above

Recent issues and projects: Recent projects include: Veterans and education programs - cutbacks in Federal Financial Aid and funding for TRIO Programs; and Recruitment of qualified minorities in the workforce (internships).

Major publications: Internship Student Manual; *Mentoring and Networking*; *Two of the Keys to Insuring Success for an Effective TRIO Program*

Budget: $182,000

Funding: USDOE (97%), other (3%)

Staff: 4
2 Caseworkers
1 Typist
1 Project Director

Staff openings/year: 0-1

Work Week: 40 hours

Salary/year: $21,000 (Recent College Graduate); $35,000 (Graduate with advanced degree)

Benefits: Health insurance, pension, paid vacation, life insurance, credit union, family leave

Part-Time Employees: 1

Summer Employees: None

Volunteers: None

Interns: 1
Length: 10 weeks
Duties: Assist with community services for 4-H youth/nutrition services
Remuneration: Interns receive a living allowance

Jobs advertised: Newspapers; through state, regional and national organization's job banks and word of mouth

To apply: Please contact Colette Monroe, Project Director

ALABAMA COALITION AGAINST HUNGER

P.O. Box 409
Auburn, AL 36830
(205) 821-8336

Director: Gerald Sanders

Purpose: Reduction in hunger and poverty in Alabama; expansion of and improvement in welfare benefits; and empowerment of poor

Methods of operation: Community organizing (60%), lobbying (10%), direct action (10%), public education (10%), research (5%), training and technical assistance (5%)

Constituency: Low-income

Recent issues and projects: (1) Reduction in barriers to Food Stamp participation, (2) increased Aid for Dependent Children (AFDC) benefits, (3) state tax reform, (4) protection of recipient rights on welfare reform (5) Campaign to end childhood hunger (6) School breakfast expansion

Major publications: Fact sheets on assistance programs and issues; reports on hunger/poverty in Alabama; Quarterly Newsletter; *Annual Guide to Food Assistance*

Budget: $65,000

Funding: Public funds (50%), foundations (40%), individual contributions (10%)

Staff: 3
3 Organizers

Staff openings/year: 1

Work Week: 50 hours

Salary/year: $12,000 (Recent College Graduate); $19,000 (Graduate with advanced degree)

Benefits: Health insurance, pension, credit union, paid vacation

Volunteers: Yes

Interns: 3 per year
Length: 4 months
Duties: Researching, organizing, writing
Remuneration: No assistance available

Jobs advertised: Newspaper; announcements to other organizations/agencies

To apply: Contact Carol Gundlach, State Coordinator

ALABAMA CONSERVANCY

2717 7th Avenue South, Suite 201
Birmingham, AL 35233
(205) 322-3126

Other Offices: Anniston, AL

Director: Patrick Byington

Purpose: To protect and preserve Alabama's environment through conservation and pollution prevention. Our goals are toxics use reduction, greater recycling and conservation of our state forests.

Methods of operation: Publications (20%), community organizing (20%), public education (20%), clearinghouse for all state environmental community (20%), research (10%), lobbying (10%)

Membership: 1,200 middle-class, high educational level professors; 1,000 individual members; 40 organizational and 10 chapters and affiliations

Recent issues and projects: Alabama Recycling Initiative; sustainable forestry project; Christmas tree recycling; non-game wildlife legislation

Major publications: *The Alabama Conservancy*; *State News*

Funding: Individual contributions (50%), direct mail (50%)

Staff: 2
1 Executive Director
1 Office Manager

Staff openings/year: 1

Work Week: 45 hours

Salary/year: $17,500

Benefits: Paid vacation

Part-Time Employees: 1

Volunteers: 15

Interns: 10
Length: Summer/3 months
Duties: Research, canvassing
Remuneration: Room and board

Jobs advertised: Local papers - *Birmingham News*, etc.

To apply: Contact Patrick Byington

ALABAMA COUNCIL ON HUMAN RELATIONS, INC.

P.O. Box 409, 319 West Glenn Ave.
Auburn, AL 36831
(205) 821-8336

Director: Nancy S. Spears

Purpose: ACRH is committed to equality and opportunity for all citizens of Alabama. Headquartered in Auburn, ACHR offers statewide and local programs to benefit Lee County citizens with low-incomes. ACHR's 29 programs include Head Start, WIC and energy assistance.

Methods of operation: Human services (89%), training and technical assistance (5%), research (1%), lobbying (1%), publications (1%), community organizing (1%), direct action (1%), public education

Membership: ACHR is a statewide membership organization open to all concerned citizens.

Recent issues and projects: ACHR has been awarded HOME funds for construction of reasonably priced apartments for people with low to moderate incomes. In 1995, ACHR also will extend Head Start to rural Russell County, which has never had this service before.

Major publications: Newsletter

Budget: $4,030,000

Funding: Government grants (98%), foundations

(2%)

Staff: 151
2 Organizers
2 Writers/Editors
1 Office Manager
3 Typists
6 Bookkeepers/Accountants
12 Caseworkers
73 Child Care/Education Specialists
15 Bus Drivers
13 Health/Nutrition Specialists
10 Maintenance
12 Administrative Assistants
2 Outreach Coordinators

Staff openings/year: 10

Work Week: 40 hours

Salary/year: $Varies (Recent College Graduate); $Varies (Graduate with advanced degree)

Benefits: Health insurance, pension, paid vacation, life insurance, credit union, family leave, child care and health expenses

Part-Time Employees: 6

Volunteers: 110

Interns: Flexible
Length: Six months
Duties: Social work; early childhood education; child care; speech/language
Remuneration: Unpaid

Jobs advertised: Through area media -- East Alabama and Southwest Georgia

To apply: Please send resumes to Janet Burns

Remarks: ACHR's activities do include some research and issue investigation, as well as a very small amount of lobbying. These duties are spread among several staff members rather than assigned to individuals who perform no other duties. The vast majority of ACHR's work consists of directly providing social services to persons in need.

ALASKA CENTER FOR THE ENVIRONMENT

519 W. 8th, Suite 201
Anchorage, AK 99501
(907) 274-3621

Other Offices: Wasilla, AK

Director: Kevin Harun

Purpose: Conservation of Alaska's natural resources

Methods of operation: Public education (25%), training and technical assistance (25%), community organizing (20%), research (20%), lobbying (5%), litigation (5%)

Constituency: 80% Alaskan

Recent issues and projects: State land use management; environmental education; hazardous waste and pollution; oil spill

Major publications: Newsletter: *Center News*; occasional reports

Budget: $400,000

Funding: Individual contributions, foundations, events

Staff: 8
6 Issue Experts
2 Administrative Staff

Staff openings/year: 1

Work Week: 50-60 hours

Salary/year: $23,000

Benefits: Health insurance

Interns: 3
Length: 6 months
Duties: Variable - research, organizing
Remuneration: Some stipends available

Jobs advertised: Locally and nationally in newsletters

To apply: Contact the Executive Director

ALASKA CIVIL LIBERTIES UNION

P.O. Box 201844
Anchorage, AK 99520
(907) 274-2258

Director: Randall P. Burns

Purpose: To assure that the Bill of Rights is preserved for each new generation and that Alaska's unique constitutional provisions are also defended and maintained.

Methods of operation: Lobbying (25%), litigation (25%), public education (25%), community organizing (15%), direct action (10%)

Recent issues and projects: Successfully fought against attempts to stop state funding of abortions for indigent women; have fought against death penalty in Alaska; and have cases in court on public schools and privacy of attorney contacts

Major publications: Quarterly newsletter

Budget: $85,000

Funding: Individual contributions (50%), foundations (50%)

Staff: 1
1 Director

Staff openings/year: 1

Work Week: 40 hours

Salary/year: $28,000 (Recent College Graduate); $28,000 (Graduate with advanced degree)

Benefits: Health insurance, pension, paid vacation

Part-Time Employees: Yes

Summer Employees: None

Volunteers: 2

Interns: Yes
Length: Summer
Duties: Paralegal
Remuneration: Volunteer or sometimes a small stipend or housing provided

Jobs advertised: Newspapers

To apply: Contact Randall Burns, Director

ALASKA CONSERVATION FOUNDATION

430 West Seventh Avenue, Suite 215
Anchorage, AK 99501
(907) 276-1917

Director: Mr. Jan Koniquberg

Purpose: To provide financial support and technical assistance to the greater environmental movement in Alaska.

Methods of operation: Grantmaking (90%), training and technical assistance (10%)

Constituency: People in all 50 states that love Alaska and the wildness it represents

Recent issues and projects: Established special campaigns to promote protection of Alaska's coastal rainforests, marine and arctic ecosystem. Granted $840,586 in grants to 46 organizations in fiscal year 1993.

Major publications: *Focus*; *Dispatch*; and the Annual report

Budget: $1,500,000

Funding: Foundations (49%), individual contributions, direct mail (42%), workplace/business (6%)

Staff: 3
1 Receptionist/Administrative Assistant
1 Grassroots Fundraiser
1/2 General Organizing/Administration
1/2 Foundation Fundraiser
1/2 Office Manager
1/2 Bookkeeper/Accountant

Staff openings/year: 1

Work Week: 45 hours

Salary/year: $23-45,000

Benefits: Health insurance, life insurance, pregnancy leave, paid vacation

Part-Time Employees: 1

Volunteers: 3

Jobs advertised: Through the social change/environmental network (funders and organizations) nationally. Some national philanthropy journals.

To apply: Contact Jan Koniquberg, Executive Director

ALASKA ENVIRONMENTAL LOBBY

P.O. Box 22151
Juneau, AK 99802
(907) 463-3366

Director: Russell Heath

Purpose: AEL operates as a coalition of 20 Alaskan environmental groups, with the intent of influencing legislation and administrative policy on natural resource issues.

Methods of operation: Legislator/administrator education (50%), training and technical assistance (25%), lobbying (20%), research (5%)

Membership: We represent a coalition of 20 Alaskan environmental groups, who collectively have about 7,000 members.

Recent issues and projects: Priorities for 1994 are in the areas of forestry, mining, hazardous materials and waste, oil spills, state land policy and designations, and resource agency budgets.

Major publications: Newsletters; Issue papers; and reports to our member groups

Budget: $65,000

Funding: Dues, raffle, auction and other fundraisers (77%), direct mail (20%), foundations (3%)

Staff: 2
1 Executive Director/Lobbyist
1 Executive Assistant

Work Week: 80 hours

Salary/year: $20,000 (Recent College Graduate); $Varies (Graduate with advanced degree)

Part-Time Employees: 1

Volunteers: Yes

Interns: 10 volunteer interns per session
Length: 1 month
Duties: Citizen lobbyists
Remuneration: We pay airfare within Alaska, $15/day for food, find housing with sympathetic locals

Jobs advertised: Member group newsletters; word of mouth

To apply: For the executive assistant position, contact the executive director; for the executive director position, contact executive director in the spring of even-numbered years, and get on search committee's mailing list.

Remarks: The executive director position is currently a 7 months/year position. Applicants must have close familiarity with Alaskan environmental issues, politics and society. Thus, is it almost required that they be Alaskan residents and that they have been volunteers in our program. An opening for the executive assistant job is rare. The volunteer program also requires Alaska residents due to the need for lobbyists that are credible to legislators.

ALASKA HEALTH PROJECT

1818 W. Northern Lights Blvd., Suite 103
Anchorage, AK 99517
(907) 276-2864

Director: Bill Ashton

Purpose: To provide information and advocacy on occupational and environmental health

Methods of operation: Training and technical assistance (30%), public education (25%), direct action (20%), community organizing (10%), publications (10%), research (5%)

Constituency: Union members, small businesses and native groups

Recent issues and projects: Waste reduction assistance program for small businesses; used oil management report for state of Alaska; Painter's Hazardous Materials Certification Curriculum; Statewide 800 number for occupational and environmental health issues and for indoor air quality information; working with the Alaska Native Health Board on the Community Hazardous Materials Management Program (CHAMP), designed to provide technical assistance to Native villages concerned about hazardous materials in their communities

Major publications: *Profiting From Waste Reduction in Your Small Business*; *Keep This in Your Tool Box*; waste reduction factsheets and detailed waste reduction audits

Budget: $500,000

Funding: Government grants, contracts (64%), foundations (20%), individual contributions (15%), direct mail (1%)

Staff: 7
2 Occupational Health Trainers
1 Technical Assistant
1 Office Manager
1 Executive Director/Technical Assistant
1 Bookkeeper/Accountant
1 Training Coordinator

Staff openings/year: 1

Work Week: 40 hours

Salary/year: $26,000 (Recent College Graduate); $29,120 (Graduate with advanced degree)

Benefits: Health insurance, life insurance, pregnancy leave, paid vacation, option for tax deferred annuity for retirement, staff development fund

Part-Time Employees: 1

Summer Employees: As needed

Volunteers: 2

Interns: 4 per year
Length: 1 semester
Duties: Assist with waste reduction audits. We use graduate students from the University of Alaska School of Engineering.
Remuneration: $500/audit

Jobs advertised: Word of mouth; local newspaper; professional journal

To apply: Contact Bill Ashton, Executive Director

ALASKA PUBLIC INTEREST RESEARCH GROUP (AKPIRG)

P.O. Box 101093
Anchorage, AK 99510
(907) 278-3661

Director: Steve Conn

Purpose: AKPIRG is the state's only consumer advocacy group, providing people with the information to be able to participate in, and be treated, equally by economic, political and social institutions. Goals include: acting as a government watchdog and providing consumer services.

Methods of operation: Research (55%), lobbying (10%), publications (10%), fundraising (10%), direct action (10%), community organizing (5%)

Membership: 7,000 members statewide; more that 50% in Anchorage (city of 250,000); liberal; 25-40; professional; average income is $35,000

Recent issues and projects: Enforcement of Consumer Protection Law; campaign finance reform initiative; oil watch; utility issues; water and sewer problems; Village Alaska, radioactive waste; Citizens Utility Board

Major publications: Quarterly newsletter: *On Record*; *Guide to Legal Assistance*; *Guide to Anchorage Banking Services*; *What You Can Do About Your Utility's Rates and Services*; *Alaska's Energy Future*; *Open Secrets*; *Votes on Key Issues of the '87-'88 Alaska Legislative Session*

Budget: $55,000

Funding: Individual contributions (30%), canvassing (30%), fundraising (30%), direct mail (5%), telephone solicitation (5%)

Staff: 1
30 Canvassers (summer)
1 Executive Director

Staff openings/year: 2

Work Week: 60 hours

Salary/year: $18,000 (Recent College Graduate); $22,000 (Graduate with advanced degree)

Benefits: None

Part-Time Employees: 1/2

Summer Employees: 50

Volunteers: 10

Interns: Yes
Length: 3 months
Duties: Research, clerical, fundraising, lobbying
Remuneration: Housing; monthly stipend (average $1,000); unpaid in exchange for credit and letters of recommendation

Jobs advertised: Newspaper; trade journals; word of mouth; university; flyers

To apply: Contact Steve Conn. Interested applicants should call before sending resumes.

ALASKA WILDLIFE ALLIANCE

P.O. Box 202022
Anchorage, AK 99520
(907) 277-0897

Director: Stephen Wells

Purpose: Wildlife management reform in the state of Alaska. Our primary focus has been on predator control issues.

Methods of operation: Research, lobbying, litigation, publications, community organizing, public education

Membership: People concerned about wildlife in Alaska - mostly non-consumptive user interests, although we have some hunters and trappers

Recent issues and projects: We are working to stop Land and Shoot wolf hunting, for better protection for humpback whales in Glacier Bay National Park and Preserve, for trapping reform on the Kenai National Wildlife Refuge, against logging in Prince William Sound.

Major publications: Bimonthly newsletter

Funding: Individual contributions (90%), foundations (10%)

Staff: 2
1 Executive Director
1 Associate Director

Benefits: Health insurance, life insurance, paid vacation

Part-Time Employees: 1

Summer Employees: 1

Volunteers: 4-7

Interns: Yes
Length: 3 months
Duties: Research, prepare comments, lobby, routine office work
Remuneration: Pay for or find housing

Jobs advertised: Regional environmental job papers, and by all organizations on our list

To apply: Contact Sandra Arnold, Associate Director

ALASKA WOMEN'S RESOURCE CENTER (AWRC)

111 West Ninth Avenue, Suite 4
Anchorage, AK 99501
(907) 276-0528

Director: Mary Grisco

Purpose: We are a women's resource and counseling agency providing a continuum of core services in the areas of substance abuse, domestic violence, prematernal information, parenting, employment and information and referral. We also operate the only halfway house for women recovering from substance abuse.

Methods of operation: Direct action (85%), publications (5%), public education (5%), training and technical assistance (5%)

Constituency: Low and low/moderate income women

Recent issues and projects: Including children in our 10-bed halfway house for recovering substance abusing women.

Major publications: Bi-monthly newsletter

Budget: $800,000

Funding: Grants from governmental agencies (98%), foundations (1.5%), individual contributions (1%)

Staff: 24
17 Counselors
1 Executive Director
2 Program Directors
1 Secretary
1 Fiscal Officer
1 Volunteer Coordinator
1 Development Coordinator

Staff openings/year: 2-5

Work Week: 40 hours

Salary/year: $22 - 32,000

Benefits: Health insurance (including dental), paid vacation, subsidized training

Part-Time Employees: 2

Volunteers: 50

Interns: 1-3
Length: 4-9 months
Duties: Varied, depending upon program assignment
Remuneration: Negotiable

Jobs advertised: Newspapers; inhouse; state DOL (Department of Labor); other social service organizations

To apply: Contact Executive Director

ALEXANDER GRAHAM BELL ASSOCIATION FOR THE DEAF, INC.

3417 Volta Place, NW
Washington, DC 20007-2778
(202) 337-5220 Voice/TDD

Purpose: Provides services and support for the hearing impaired. Established in 1890 to encourage the use of residual hearing and the teaching of speech and speechreading.

Recent issues and projects: Hearing Alert! public education program to encourage early identification of hearing loss, particularly in infants, and to promote the need for prompt remedial action. Children's Rights - to ensure that hearing-impaired children and adolescents get the support, encouragement and educational opportunities they need. Parent/Infant Preschool Services Financial Aid Program; Free First-Year Parent Membership Awards; Arts and Sciences Award; regional educational conferences and workshops; Biennial International Convention; research library

Major publications: *The Volta Review*, 4 issues/year; *Newsounds* reports on legislation and other news affecting the hearing impaired, 10 times/year; *Our Kids* magazine

Funding: Membership dues, corporate contributions, foundations, individuals, publication sales. Approximately 5% of the Association's income is provided by interest from trust funds set up by Professor Bell.

ALICE HAMILTON OCCUPATIONAL HEALTH CENTER (AHOHC)

408 Seventh Street, SE
Washington, DC 20003
(202) 543-0005

Other Offices: Landover, MD

Director: Brian W. Christopher

Purpose: The AHOHC provides training, technical assistance and advocacy in the fields of occupational and environmental health. Safe workplaces and communities is our organizational goal.

Methods of operation: Training and technical assistance (65%), research (10%), public education (10%), lobbying (5%), publications (5%), community organizing (5%)

Membership: Membership consists of labor union locals, individual workers from all backgrounds primarily in Maryland, Washington, D.C. and Virginia

Recent issues and projects: Provision of training to public employees involved in emergency responses to chemical accidents; Projecto Travajo Seguro serving Spanish language community in DC with information and training; played a major role in increased awareness of lead paint hazards

Major publications: *Alice Hamilton Quarterly*; *Occupational Injury in the DC Latino Community* (report); *Right-to-Know for Workers* (book); *Model Training Curriculum for Lead Paint Abatement* (book)

Budget: $750,000

Funding: Government grants (45%), contracts (40%), foundations (10%), individual contributions (5%)

Staff: 20
2 Organizers
1 Writer/Editor
2 Office Managers
8 Issue Experts
1 Administrative Assistant
1 Bookkeeper/Accountant
3 Project Directors

Staff openings/year: 2

Work Week: 40 hours

Salary/year: $25,000 (Recent College Graduate); $28,000 (Graduate with advanced degree)

Benefits: Health insurance, paid vacation, life insurance and tuition reimbursement

Part-Time Employees: 1

Summer Employees: None

Volunteers: 12

Interns: 2 per year
Length: 1 quarter or semester
Duties: Varied
Remuneration: Stipends are sometimes available

Jobs advertised: Local newspapers, universities, schools of public health and professional journals

To apply: Contact Brian Christopher, Executive Director

ALLIANCE FOR ACID RAIN MONITORING (ALLARM)

c/o C. Wilderman P.O. Box 1773,
Dickinson Col. Dept. Env. Std.
Carlisle, PA 17013
(717) 245-1573

Director: Candie Wilderman

Purpose: ALLARM, run by Dickinson College students, is a citizen monitoring organization. Volunteers monitor streams and lakes for the effect of acid precipitation. The goals of ALLARM are public education, and promotion of environmental stewardship.

Methods of operation: Community organizing (50%), public education (30%), training and technical assistance (10%), publications (10%)

Constituency: Very diverse. ALLARM volunteers range in age from 5 to 85, in occupation from blue collar to Ph.D.'s, and in education from grammar school to graduate levels.

Recent issues and projects: ALLARM holds workshops, attends conferences and publishes newsletters. Also analyzes the data annually.

Major publications: Newsletter: *Stream of Consciousness*

Staff: 1
1 Coordinator, unpaid

Work Week: 10 hours

Part-Time Employees: 8

Summer Employees: 1

Volunteers: 450

Interns: 1
Length: 6 week summer or semester long
Duties: Administration of the program
Remuneration: Negotiable

Jobs advertised: Usually through Dickinson College

To apply: Contact Dr. Candie Wilderman, Director

ALLIANCE FOR AFFORDABLE ENERGY

604 Julia Street, 3rd Floor
New Orleans, LA 70130
(504) 525-0778

Director: Gary Groesch

Purpose: The Alliance was founded in 1985 to promote safe and affordable energy services in New Orleans and Louisiana.

Methods of operation: Public education (55%), community organizing (20%), publications (10%), research (10%), direct action (5%)

Constituency: People interested in energy conservation

Recent issues and projects: Last year our major projects were to (1) fight yearly mandatory rate hikes, (2) promote municipalization of local utilities, and (3) conduct Least-cost Leadership Education Program.

Major publications: *Bright Ideas*, a newsletter about least-cost developments in Louisiana and around the nation

Budget: $82,600

Funding: Grants (50%), individual contributions (30%), direct mail (20%)

Staff: 3
2 Issue Experts
1 Foundation Fundraiser
1/2 Meetings Coordinator
1/2 Mailing List Manager

Staff openings/year: 1

Work Week: 60 hours

Salary/year: $7,000 (Recent College Graduate); $Varies (Graduate with advanced degree)

Benefits: Health insurance

Part-Time Employees: Yes

Volunteers: Yes

Interns: Yes
Length: 9 months
Duties: Special project duties
Remuneration: Where possible

To apply: Contact Douglas Nicodemus, Development Director

ALLIANCE FOR JUSTICE

1601 Connecticut Avenue, NW, Suite 600
Washington, DC 20009
(202) 332-3224

Director: Nan Aron

Purpose: The Alliance is a national association of public interest legal organizations. Since its inception in 1980, the Alliance has focused the talents and resources of its members on key issues affecting the survival of public interest law. The Alliance's work includes encouraging the continuation and expansion of public interest representation, promoting reform of the legal system, monitoring the selection of federal judges, and preserving the right of nonprofits to advocate on behalf of their constituencies.

Methods of operation: Research (40%), public education (25%), publications (20%), lobbying (15%)

Recent issues and projects: Judicial Selection Project monitors the appointments of judges to all levels of the federal bench. The Advocacy Forum guards against threats to restrict or tax advocacy on behalf of the whole community. Study on how the standing doctrine has been eroded by the Burger and Rehnquist courts. The Federal Courts Project investigates the coordinated approach developed by corporations and business groups to tilt the courts in their favor.

Major publications: Quarterly newsletter: *Pipeline*; *Liberty and Justice for All: Public Interest Law in the 1980s and Beyond* (Nov 1988); *Charting a Course for Advocacy* (Nov 1989);

Budget: $420,000

Funding: Individual contributions, foundations

Staff: 7
3 Attorneys
3 Writers/Editors
1 1/2 Lobbyist
1/2 Bookkeeper/Accountant
1/2 Office Manager

Staff openings/year: 1

Work Week: 45 hours

Salary/year: $20,000 (Recent College Graduate); $30,000 (Graduate with advanced degree)

Benefits: Health insurance, pregnancy leave, paid vacation

Part-Time Employees: 3

Interns: 4
Length: Need interns year round
Duties: Legal research, mailings to nationwide network, background for studies, statistical analysis, legal analysis
Remuneration: Unpaid; students often get school funding

Jobs advertised: *Washington Post*; *Community Jobs*; *City Paper*

To apply: Contact Carol Seifert, Deputy Director

ALLIANCE FOR THE WILD ROCKIES

P.O. Box 8731
Missoula, MT 59807
(406) 721-5420

Other Offices: Bozeman, MT

Director: Mike Bader

Purpose: To secure the integrity of the ecosystems of the Northern Rockies and the biological linkage zones between them and ensure scientifically and economically sound land management policies.

Methods of operation: Community organizing (25%), research (20%), public education (20%), lobbying (10%), litigation (15%), training and technical assistance (5%)

Membership: 5,000 individual members and more than 500 businesses/organizations

Recent issues and projects: Lawsuit to protect the bull trout; congressional introduction of our public lands proposal, the Northern Rockies Ecosystem Protection Act (HR2638); endangered species habitat project; economic studies

Major publications: *The Networker*, quarterly publication; issue alerts; research reports

Budget: $260,000

Funding: Individual contributions (40%), foundations (40%), contributions (20%)

Staff: 4
1 Office Manager
3 Campaign Managers

Staff openings/year: 0-1

Work Week: 50 hours

Salary/year: $Varies (Recent College Graduate); $Varies (Graduate with advanced degree)

Benefits: Health insurance, paid vacation, life insurance

Part-Time Employees: 1

Summer Employees: None

Volunteers: 20

Interns: 5-8
Length: 3 months
Duties: Assist with research projects on endangered species, economics and public outreach
Remuneration: Small stipends occasionally available

Jobs advertised: Through other organizations and in-house

To apply: Contact Mike Bader, Executive Director

Remarks: We stress grassroots organizing and citizen involvement as the key means for substantive change in natural resource policies. Internships involve hands-on work that is made available to the public. Our major program is our National Public Lands Campaign.

ALTERNATIVE ENERGY RESOURCES ORGANIZATION

25 S. Ewing, Rm 214
Helena, MT 59601
(406) 443-7272

Director: Pam Mavrolas

Purpose: AERO is a 20-year-old grassroots nonprofit citizen organization working for: (1) a regionally sustainable food system which supports family farmers and their communities, is ecologically-sound using less energy and building soil health, while providing consumers with nutritious, affordable, safe food; (2) a human-scale, decentralized energy system that relies on renewable resources and conservation; and (3) communities shaped by the principles of meeting local needs with local resources to the fullest extent possible.

Methods of operation: Public education (50%), research (20%), community organizing (15%), training and technical assistance (9%), lobbying (1%)

Constituency: Farmers, ranchers, townspeople

Recent issues and projects: AERO is creating innovative new programs to meet the challenges of the 1990s and beyond. We are starting a new effort to help beginning farmers in Montana get into agriculture. We recently helped organize a new coalition called the Montana Transportation Project.

We are also continuing to expand our Farm Improvement Club program.

Major publications: Guidebooks to viable farming practices; *Sun Times* magazine

Budget: $220,000

Funding: Individual contributions, membership, grants

Staff: 4
1 Director
2 Program Managers
1 Office Manager

Work Week: 40-50 hours

Salary/year: $22,000

Benefits: Health insurance, paid vacation, sick leave, IRA contribution, on-going educational training

Part-Time Employees: 2

Summer Employees: 1

Volunteers: 40

Jobs advertised: Montana newspapers, *Community Jobs*

To apply: Contact Pam Mavrolas, Director

ALTERNATIVE PRESS CENTER

P.O. Box 33109
Baltimore, MD 21218-0401
(410) 243-2471

Director: Bill Wilson

Purpose: Publishers of the *Alternative Press Index*, a quarterly subject index to over 200 alternative and radical publications. Similar in format to *Readers Guide to Periodical Literature*, Alternative Press Center exists to make accessible and increase awareness of the alternative press.

Methods of operation: Publications (80%), public education (20%)

Constituency: The majority of our subscribers are university libraries, then public libraries, then movement groups, then individuals.

Major publications: *Alternative Press Index*

Budget: $70,000

Funding: Subscriptions (100%)

Staff: 2
2 Indexers

Work Week: 30 hours

Benefits: Paid vacation

Part-Time Employees: 2

Jobs advertised: Locally

AMERICAN AGRICULTURE MOVEMENT

100 Maryland Avenue, NE, Suite 500A, Box 69
Washington, DC 20002
(202) 544-5750

Other Offices: Brownsville, TN; Des Arc, AR

Director: Charles Perry

Purpose: A loose-knit organization of state members working to gain fair prices in the marketplace for farm commodities and to save the family farm.

Methods of operation: Lobbying, publications, organizing, public education

Constituency: Producing farmers, ranchers, agribusiness

Recent issues and projects: Working to halt increases in excise taxes, as they adversely affect rural Americans; lobbying for adequate farm credit legislation; oppose price freezes; working to refinance farmers who are losing their farms; working with other groups to deliver food to America's hungry people

Major publications: Newspaper: *American Agriculture Movement Reporter*

Funding: Member dues

Staff: 3
1 Executive Director
1 Director, Federal and State Relations
1 Secretary

Work Week: 50-60 hours

Benefits: Health insurance, life insurance, pregnancy leave, pension, paid vacation

Part-Time Employees: Occasionally

Volunteers: Yes

Interns: Yes
Length: 3 months
Duties: General office work
Remuneration: Unpaid

Jobs advertised: Local newspapers; word of mouth

To apply: Contact Jennifer Moldovan, Secretary

AMERICAN ASSOCIATION OF RETIRED PERSONS (AARP)

601 E Street, NW
Washington, DC 20049
(202) 434-2811

Other Offices: Boston, MA; New York, NY; Harrisburg, PA; St. Petersburg, FL; Atlanta, GA; Alexandria, VA; Chicago, IL; Midvale, UT; Long Beach, CA; Seattle, WA; Westwood, KS; Dallas, TX; Sacramento, CA; Columbus, OH; Golden, CO

Director: Horace B. Deets, Executive Director

Purpose: AARP is a nonprofit membership organization dedicated to addressing the needs and interests of persons 50 and older. We seek through education, advocacy and service to enhance the quality of life for all by promoting independence, dignity and purpose.

Membership: Any person 50 and over

Recent issues and projects: Major initiatives: Health Care Campaign; Minority Affairs Initiative; Women's Initiative; Worker Equity Initiative. Advocacy projects include AARP/VOTE; Citizen Representation; Federal Affairs; Long-Term Care Campaign; PRONET (Medical/hospital Peer Review Organizations); State Legislation; Utility Intervention Project. Services to members include airline discount, automobile insurance, car rental discount, health insurance, homeowners insurance, hotel/motel discount, credit union, investment program, pharmacy and travel services.

Major publications: *Modern Maturity* magazine; *AARP News Bulletin*, 11 times/year; numerous other periodicals, newsletters, books, guides, reports and brochure. Contact national office for publications list.

Funding: Total operating expenses: $359,700,000

Staff:
1,800 total

Work Week: 37.5 hours

Salary/year: $Varies (Recent College Graduate); $Varies (Graduate with advanced degree)

Benefits: Health insurance, life insurance, pregnancy leave, pension, credit union, tuition reimbursement, paid vacation

Part-Time Employees: 56

Volunteers: 200,000

Interns: 15
Length: 10 weeks
Remuneration: $10.00 an hour

Jobs advertised: Newspapers

To apply: Contact Human Resources Department

AMERICAN ASSOCIATION OF UNIVERSITY WOMEN -- NEW JERSEY INC.

30 Putnam Street
Somerville, NJ 08876
(908) 685-7550

President: Jacqueline Ann D'Alessio

Purpose: AAUW promotes equity for women and girls, education and self-development over the life span and positive societal change.

Methods of operation: Research (30%), training and technical assistance (20%), lobbying (10%), publications (10%), community organizing (10%), direct action (10%), public education (10%)

Constituency: College graduates

Recent issues and projects: *Shortchanging Girls*; *Shortchanging America*; a report on the status of girls in public schools; *Hostile Hallways*, a report on sexual harassment in America's schools

Major publications: *The Garden Statement*

Budget: $31,400

Volunteers: 31

Interns: None at this time; willing to accept applications

To apply: Contact Jacqueline Ann D'Alessio, President

AMERICAN BAR ASSOCIATION, PUBLIC SERVICES DIVISION

1800 M Street, NW
Washington, DC 20036
(202) 331-2276

Director: Elissa C. Lichtenstein

Purpose: Provide leadership in identification, development and reform of law and law-related policies that promote the ideals of a just society and that ensure equal rights and protections for all, particularly vulnerable populations.

Methods of operation: Research, publications and videos, public education, training and technical assistance nationwide, symposia, workshops and conferences, model legislation, policy development for American Bar Association, speeches and professional papers

Constituency: Vulnerable populations (immigrants, homeless persons and disabled persons) and broad societal concerns (energy, environmental, bio-ethics, elections, national security, international peace)

Recent issues and projects: AIDS and developmentally disabled persons; public interest law internship; human rights essay contest; guardianship; trade and environmental regulation in the Pacific Rim region; immigrant asylum assistance project in Texas

Major publications: *Environmental Law*; *Energy Bulletin*; *Mental and Physical Disability Law Reporter*; *AIDS and Persons with Developmental Disabilities*; *Bioethics Bulletin*, research studies

Budget: $2,000,000

Funding: Foundations, government, corporations (66%), ABA dues (34%)

Staff: 30
9-11 Attorneys/Issue Experts
11 Typists
5 Law Clerks/Researchers (part-time)
2 Writer/Editors
1 Bookkeeper
1 Administrator

Staff openings/year: 2-4

Work Week: 37.5 hours

Salary/year: $30-32,000 (Graduate with advanced degree)

Benefits: Health insurance, life insurance, pregnancy/paid disability leave, pension, tuition reimbursement, paid vacation, paid administrative leave, employee counseling program, 401(k) plan, flexible benefits program

Part-Time Employees: 5

Summer Employees: 2-5 law clerks

Volunteers: 2-5 interns

Interns: ABA Division summer internship or other
Duties: ABA Division: design legal research and writing project that is published at end of summer. Other internships with projects as need arises.
Remuneration: interns paid biweekly

Jobs advertised: Newspapers; journals; law school placement offices

To apply: Contact Albin Burkman, Director, Administrative Services Department

AMERICAN CIVIL LIBERTIES UNION (ACLU), WASHINGTON OFFICE

122 Maryland Avenue, NE
Washington, DC 20002
(202) 544-1681

Other Offices: New York, NY

Director: Laura Lee

Purpose: To secure the enactment of legislation which expands the rights and liberties of Americans and to prevent the enactment of legislation that interferes with such rights

Methods of operation: Lobbying (70%), research (15%), publications (15%)

Constituency: ACLU members

Recent issues and projects: Repeal of the McCarran-Walters Immigration Act. Pro-Choice legislation. Prevent the enactment of crime or drug legislation which violates constitutional rights. Passage of the Americans with Disabilities Act and other civil rights legislation. Enactment of voter registration legislation.

Major publications: Newsletter: *Civil Liberties Alert*, reporting events in Congress related to civil liberties

Budget: $1,000,000

Funding: Direct mail (60%), foundations (40%)

Staff: 19
9 Lobbyists

5 Administrative Assistants
2 Office Managers
2 Writers/Editors
1 Organizer

Staff openings/year: 2-3

Work Week: 35 hours

Salary/year: $21,000

Benefits: Health insurance, life insurance, pregnancy leave, pension, paid vacation, law school loans

Volunteers: 3

Interns: 10-15
Length: Summer or semester
Duties: Assist with research and support. Law students do legal research.
Remuneration: No pay for undergraduates. Law students are paid modestly.

Jobs advertised: Job announcements mailed to a list of organizations and to groups specializing in affirmative action outreach. Notices are also posted on an office bulletin board, and advertisements are placed in appropriate publications.

To apply: Contact the office c/o the Administrative Director

Remarks: ACLU's national headquarters is in New York City, with ACLU affiliates in most states.

AMERICAN CIVIL LIBERTIES UNION OF KENTUCKY

425 W. Muhammad Ali, Suite 230
Louisville, KY 40202
(502) 581-1181

Director: Everett Hoffman

Purpose: To defend the constitutional rights of all citizens by fighting to protect: Freedom of Speech; Freedom of Conscience; Freedom of Religion and Separation of Church and State; The Right to Privacy; Reproductive Freedom; and Freedom from Police Misconduct

Methods of operation: Lobbying, litigation, public education

Membership: 1300 members throughout Kentucky

Major publications: *The Torch*

Funding: Individual contributions

Staff: 12
1 Organizer
2 Writers/Editors
1 Office Manager
2 Lobbyists
2 Foundation Fundraisers
2 Issue Experts
1 Administrative Assistant
1 Bookkeeper/Accountant

Staff openings/year: 0

Work Week: 40 hours

Salary/year: $Varies (Recent College Graduate); $Varies (Graduate with advanced degree)

Benefits: Health insurance, pension, paid vacation, life insurance

Part-Time Employees: No

Summer Employees: No

Volunteers: No

Interns: No

Jobs advertised: Newspapers throughout Kentucky, listing with ACLU national office

---

AMERICAN CIVIL LIBERTIES UNION OF SOUTHERN CALIFORNIA

1616 Beverly Blvd.
Los Angeles, CA 90026
(213) 977-9500

Director: Ramona Ripston

Purpose: Established in 1920, the ACLU assures that the Bill of Rights, amendments to the Constitution that guard against unwarranted governmental control, are preserved for each new generation.

Methods of operation: Litigation (50%), lobbying (15%), community organizing (15%), public education (10%), research (5%), publications (5%)

Membership: Grassroots

Recent issues and projects: The ACLU Foundation-SC has ongoing litigation in the areas of the First Amendment, rights of children, the mentally ill, the homeless, gays and lesbians, and gender discrimination. Its lobbying arm is active in protecting the rights of immigrants and played a major role in defeating school vouchers in CA.

Major publications: Our newsletter *Open Forum* is published 4 times a year. Special reports on civil liberties issues are also published. Recent reports include school safety, police use of pepper spray and civil liberties violations during the L.A. riots. We also publish brochures, including a bilingual brochure on sexual harassment.

Budget: $2,500,000

Funding: Individual contributions (78%), direct mail (10%), events (10%), foundations (2%)

Staff: 31
1 Organizer
8 Attorneys
1 Office Manager
1 Lobbyist
3 Press Aides
2 Foundation Fundraisers
4 Legal Secretaries
2 Bookkeepers/Accountants
1 Grassroots Fundraiser
4 Office Workers
2 Associate Directors
1 Administrative Assistant
1 Executive Director

Staff openings/year: 2

Work Week: 40 hours

Salary/year: $24,000 (Recent College Graduate); $30,000 (Graduate with advanced degree)

Part-Time Employees: None

Summer Employees: 20 law students

Volunteers: 5

Interns: 20 law students in the summer
Length: Full semester or full summer
Duties: Law students assist with legal work; 1-2 college students help with lobbying; 5 high school students do clerical work
Remuneration: Work study or volunteer

Jobs advertised: Newspapers, public interest publications, mailing list maintained to nonprofits, colleges, etc.

To apply: Contact Elizabeth Schroeder, Associate Director

AMERICAN CIVIL LIBERTIES UNION OF TEXAS

1004 West Avenue
Austin, TX 98701
(512) 477-5849

Director: Jay Jacobson

Purpose: Preserve and expand liberties in the Bill of Rights, fight discrimination based on racial, gender, disability and sexual orientation.

Methods of operation: Public education (50%), lobbying (20%), litigation (10%), direct action (10%), research (5%), publications (5%)

Constituency: People who are concerned about protecting individual rights

Recent issues and projects: Litigation about Dallas curfew, lobbying against Austin loitering ordinance. Organizing to fight bigotry, censorship and violations of the establishment clause.

Major publications: Send for publication list

Budget: $200,000

Funding: Individual contributions (100%)

Staff: 3
2 Regional Directors
1 Executive Director

Work Week: 45-55 hours

Benefits: Health insurance, pension, paid vacation, life insurance, family leave

Part-Time Employees: 2

Summer Employees: 2

Volunteers: Unlimited

Interns: 1
Length: Semester
Duties: Usually select a project to work on such as immigration rights, police brutality, etc.
Remuneration: None

To apply: Contact Margaret Walker

AMERICAN CIVIL LIBERTIES UNION OF VERMONT

P.O. Box 810
Montpelier, VT 05601
(802) 223-6304

Director: Leslie Williams

Purpose: ACLU of Vermont is an affiliate of the national ACLU, dedicated to preserving and defending individual civil liberties. We do this through litigation, public education and lobbying in the state of Vermont.

Methods of operation: Litigation (40%), public education (40%), lobbying (15%), research (2%), direct action (2%), publications (1%)

Membership: 1800-2000 Vermont residents

Recent issues and projects: Prison reform; reproductive rights; passage of bill outlawing discrimination on basis of sexual orientation; visits to schools, distribution of videos and educational materials on constitution and civil liberties

Major publications: Annual report; newsletter; Vermont Constitution (first 21 articles); National ACLU briefing papers and other publications

Budget: $120,000

Funding: Individual contributions (70%), direct mail (30%)

Staff: 2
1 Executive Director
1 Associate Director/Finance Officer

Staff openings/year: 0-1

Work Week: 35 hours

Salary/year: $Varies (Recent College Graduate); $Varies (Graduate with advanced degree)

Benefits: Health insurance, pension, paid vacation, pregnancy leave

Part-Time Employees: 1

Volunteers: 5-6

Interns: 3-4
Length: 2-3 months
Duties: Legal aide; office work; lobbying; public education
Remuneration: Minimal, can sometimes contribute

Jobs advertised: Local papers; through ACLU affiliate network if full-time

To apply: Contact Leslie Williams, Executive Director

AMERICAN CIVIL LIBERTIES UNION-CA

1663 Mission Street, Suite 460
San Francisco, CA 94103
(415) 621-2493

Director: Dorothy Ehrlich

Purpose: Dedicated to preserving and defending the principles embodied in the Bill of Rights.

Methods of operation: Lobbying, litigation, publications, community organizing, public education

Constituency: People concerned with civil liberties

Recent issues and projects: Howard Friedman First Amendment Project: Outreach to high school students to develop a greater understanding and appreciation for the First Amendment.

Major publications: *ACLU Newsletter*

Budget: $2,000,000

Staff: 24
18 Organizers
1 Writer/Editor
5 Attorneys
3 Paralegals/Legal Assistant
1 1/2 Office Managers
1 Executive Director
1 Lobbyist
5 1/2 Foundation Fundraisers
2 Bookkeepers/Accountants
1/2 Press Aide
1 Receptionist/Assistant/Office Manager

Staff openings/year: 2-3

Work Week: 37.50 hours

Salary/year: $Varies (Recent College Graduate); $Varies (Graduate with advanced degree)

Benefits: Health insurance, pension, child care, paid vacation, life insurance, pregnancy leave

Part-Time Employees: Yes

Summer Employees: None

Volunteers: 17

Interns: 7-8 a semester
Length: 1-2 semesters or 6-12 months
Duties: Varies according to department -- research, writing, coordinating meetings, help with events and mass mailings
Remuneration: None

Jobs advertised: Local newspapers; mailings to other organizations

To apply: Contact Mila De Guzman, Administrative Coordinator

AMERICAN COUNCIL FOR AN ENERGY-EFFICIENT ECONOMY

1001 Connecticut Ave. #801
Washington, DC 20036
(202) 429-8873

Other Offices: Berkeley, CA

Director: Howard Geller

Purpose: ACEEE is dedicated to advancing energy efficiency as a means of promoting both economic prosperity and environmental protection. They conduct projects in eight areas: national energy policy; efficiency and economic development; utility issues; transportation; buildings; appliances and equipment; industry; and international.

Methods of operation: Research (60%), publications (20%), conference organizing (10%), public education (5%), training and technical assistance (5%)

Constituency: Professional

Recent issues and projects: Many of ACEEE's proposals were incorporated into the Energy Policy Act of 1992, other legislation and President Clinton's Climate Change Action Plan.

Major publications: Write for our extensive list of books, reports and consumer guides.

Budget: $1,700,000

Funding: Foundations (35%), publications and conferences (35%), sponsored research (30%)

Staff: 13
1 Office Manager
8 Researchers
1 Administrative Assistant
3 Conference and Publication Staff

Staff openings/year: 0-2

Work Week: 40 hours

Salary/year: $Varies (Recent College Graduate); $Varies (Graduate with advanced degree)

Benefits: Health insurance, child care, paid vacation, life insurance, tuition reimbursement (benefits are offered through "cafeteria plan")

Part-Time Employees: None

Summer Employees: None

Volunteers: None

Interns: None

Jobs advertised: *Community Jobs*; trade newsletters; informal networking

To apply: Contact John Morrill, Business Manager

AMERICAN COUNCIL OF THE BLIND

1155 15th Street, NW, Suite 720
Washington, DC 20005
(202) 467-5081

Director: Oral Miller, National Representative

Purpose: The American Council of the Blind is a national membership organization established to promote the independence, dignity and well-being of blind and visually impaired people. Members are blind, visually impaired, or fully sighted people from all walks of life. People who are blind and visually impaired comprise the vast majority of members and are responsible for governing, administering and setting organizational policy. Formed in 1961, ACB is one of the largest organizations of blind people in the U.S. with over 70 state and special interest affiliated and a national network of chapters and members.

Methods of operation: Lobbying, litigation, publications, direct action, public education and community organizing, human services

Membership: Visually impaired persons, their families and person who work with visually impaired persons

Recent issues and projects: One of ACB's recent projects has been encouraging the nation's subway systems to make their platform edges be accessible as mandated by the ADA. Several blind persons around the country have died in the past year or so as a result of falling from platforms which do not have edge markings which are detectable to the visually impaired.

Major publications: *Braille Forum*, monthly magazine

Budget: $1,000,000

Funding: Individual contributions, thrift stores, legacies, bequests and dues from local member units

Staff: 12
1 Writer/Editor
2 Issue Experts
1 Accountant/Bookkeeper
1 Administrative Assistant
1 Office Manager
1 Membership/Affiliate Coordinator
5 Administrative Assistants

Staff openings/year: 1

Work Week: 40 hours

Salary/year: $18-19,000 (Recent College Graduate); $Varies (Graduate with advanced degree)

Benefits: Health insurance, pension, paid vacation, life insurance

Part-Time Employees: No

Summer Employees: No

Volunteers: No

Interns: Yes
Length: 8 weeks in the summer
Duties: Administrative, research, organizing
Remuneration: Reasonable pay and housing

Jobs advertised: *Washington Post*, local papers

To apply: Will be noted in advertisement

AMERICAN FORESTS

1516 P Street, NW
Washington, DC 20013
(202) 667-3300

Director: R. Neil Sampson

Purpose: American Forests promotes and preserves all values and benefits of trees and forests in rural and urban areas.

Methods of operation: Direct action (25%), public education (25%), research (15%), publications (15%), training and technical assistance (10%), lobbying (5%), community organizing (5%)

Constituency: Individuals who care about forests and the environment

Recent issues and projects: Recent projects include: empowering people and communities to improve the environment with better quality and more trees; Forest Health Initiative

Major publications: *American Forests* magazine; *Urban Forests* magazine; *Hotline* newsletter

Budget: $4,000,000

Funding: Government grants (50%), individual contributions (35%), foundations (5%)

Staff: 35
1 Organizer
5 Writers/Editors
4 Researchers
2 Legislative Experts
2 Press Aides
4 Foundation Fundraisers
8 Issue Experts
2 Bookkeepers/Accountants
5 Campaign Managers

Staff openings/year: 1

Work Week: 40 hours

Salary/year: $18,000 (Recent College Graduate); $20,000 (Graduate with advanced degree)

Benefits: Health insurance, pension, paid vacation, life insurance, parking

Part-Time Employees: 2

Summer Employees: None

Volunteers: 2

Interns: 8-12
Length: Semester (3-5 months)
Duties: Program specific
Remuneration: $50 a week stipend; accreditation; fellowship for those with degrees

Jobs advertised: Environmental publications; *The Washington Post*

AMERICAN FORUM

1250 National Press Building
Washington, DC 20003
(202) 638-1431

Director: Denice Zeck

Purpose: The American Forum is an idea machine for the progressive community. Distributing op-ed commentary to the media in Southern states, the American Forum can reach 5.9 million households and 10.75 million listeners/viewers through radio and TV.

Methods of operation: Public education (100%)

Recent issues and projects: Children's issues, civil rights, criminal justice, education, electoral reforms, health, labor, social justice, civil liberties, consumer issues, economic justice, elderly issues, environmental issues, housing, peace issues, women's issues

Major publications: Prepare and distribute media packets, which include an op-ed, press release, and public service announcement, on a monthly basis in southern states

Budget: $500,000

Funding: Foundations (80%), individual contributions (20%)

Staff: 5
2 Writers/Editors
1 Press Aide
1 Executive Director
1 Production Coordinator

Work Week: 40+ hours

Salary/year: $18,000

Benefits: Health insurance, paid vacation

Interns: 2
Length: As long as intern is available
Duties: Assist in production of media packets; call media and work with authors on local (state level) talk show programs
Remuneration: Unpaid

Jobs advertised: Alternative newspapers; local papers; job bulletins at public interest groups; through local university career services

To apply: Contact Tracey Bennett

AMERICAN FOUNDATION FOR THE BLIND

15 West 16th Street
New York, NY 10011
(212) 620-2000

Other Offices: Washington, DC; San Francisco, CA; Chicago, IL; Atlanta, GA; Dallas, TX

President: Carl R. Angusto

Purpose: The American Foundation for the Blind (AFB) is a leading national resource for people who are blind or visually impaired, the organizations which serve them and the general public. A nonprofit organization founded in 1921 and recognized as Helen Keller's cause in the United States, AFB has as its mission to enable persons who are blind or visually impaired to achieve equality of access and opportunity that will ensure freedom of choice in their lives. AFB is headquartered in New York City, with regional centers in Chicago, Dallas, San Francisco and Washington, DC.

Methods of operation: Research, lobbying, publications, public education, training and technical assistance

Recent issues and projects: Recent issues include: Accessibility; appropriate services for blind people; health care reform; information superhighway; ADA; public education; education of blind children; aging and blindness; literacy

Major publications: *AFB News*; *Journal of Visual Impairment and Blindness*; and an entire catalog of books, pamphlets, reports and videos

Budget: $12,000,000

Funding: Individual contributions, foundations, direct mail

Staff: 125

Staff includes:
Writers/Editors
Attorneys
Office Managers
Researchers
Lobbyists
Foundation Fundraisers
Issue Experts
Administrative Assistants
Bookkeepers/Accountants
Grassroots Fundraisers

Staff openings/year: 0-5

Work Week: 35 hours

Salary/year: $Varies (Recent College Graduate); $Varies (Graduate with advanced degree)

Benefits: Health insurance, pension, paid vacation, life insurance, family leave

Part-Time Employees: Yes

Summer Employees: None

Volunteers: Yes

Interns: Yes
Length: 2-3 months
Duties: Office work, research, writing, etc.
Remuneration: None

Jobs advertised: Newspapers, professional publications

To apply: Please contact Kelly Bleach, Director of Personnel

AMERICAN FRIENDS SERVICE COMMITTEE (AFSC)

1501 Cherry Street
Philadelphia, PA 19102
(215) 241-7000

Other Offices: Atlanta, GA; Baltimore, MD; Cambridge, MA; Chicago, IL; Dayton, OH; Des Moines, IA; New York, NY; Pasadena, CA; Oakland, CA; Seattle, WA

Director: Kara Newell

Purpose: An independent Quaker organization founded in 1917 to provide conscientious objectors with a vehicle for aiding civilian victims during World War I. Today it carries out programs of service, development, justice, and peace as an expression of belief in the dignity and worth of every person, and faith in the power of love and nonviolence to bring about social improvement. The work of the AFSC is supported by thousands of people of different persuasions who care about these goals and programs.

Methods of operation: Human services, organizing, public education, training and technical assistance

Constituency: General public

Recent issues and projects: The AFSC has three major program divisions: the Community Relations Division, which carries out programs aimed at social justice and the empowerment of racial, sexual, economic, and social minorities in the U.S.; the Peace Education Division, which carries out programs promoting disarmament and peace conversion at home, and U.S. foreign policies based on the principles of peace, justice, and self-determination for all peoples; the International Division, which carries out programs designed to help relieve suffering, promote reconciliation, and contribute to self-help projects abroad.

Major publications: Newsletter: *Quaker Service Bulletin*

Budget: $26,000,000

Funding: Contributions, bequests, investments, program service fees

Staff: 401
163 national, 31 overseas, 207 regional, including:
50 Organizers
39 Typists
20 Bookkeeper/Accountants
15 Office Managers
10 Fundraisers
5 Writer/Editors
1 Press Aide

Staff openings/year: 80 total

Work Week: 35 hours

Salary/year: $14-17,000 min.

Benefits: Health insurance, life insurance, pension, credit union, pregnancy leave

Part-Time Employees: Yes

Volunteers: Yes

Interns: Occasionally

Jobs advertised: Newspapers; publish monthly list of staff openings

To apply: Contact Rick Boardman

AMERICAN GEOGRAPHICAL SOCIETY

156 Fifth Ave., Suite 600
New York, NY 10010
(212) 242-0214

Director: Mary Lynne Bird

Purpose: Encourage geographical research and inquiry; make results available to members and to the general public

Methods of operation: Publications; public education and encourage research through awards

Membership: Half are professional geographers, the other half are non-geographers with serious interest in subject

Recent issues and projects: Business geography teaching in schools in 15 states; education travel program; materials for teachers; information for media, government and business; speakers for business audience

Major publications: *FOCUS* (magazine); *Ubique* (newsletter); *Geographical Review* (scholarly journal)

Budget: $650,000

Funding: Publications (50%), individual contributions (15%), foundations (15%), investment income (10%)

Staff: 4
1 Executive Director
2 Writers/Editors
1 Office Manager

Staff openings/year: 0-1

Work Week: 40 hours

Salary/year: $25,000 (Recent College Graduate); $30,000 (Graduate with advanced degree)

Benefits: Health insurance, pension

Part-Time Employees: 2

Summer Employees: None

Volunteers: None

Interns: 2 per year
Length: 2-3 months
Duties: Varies with qualifications
Remuneration: Completely self-funded

Jobs advertised: Professional publications, *New York Times*

To apply: Mary Lynne Bird, Executive Director

AMERICAN INDIAN HEALTH SERVICE OF CHICAGO

838 West Irving Park Road
Chicago, IL 60613
(312) 883-9100

Director: Tim Vermillion

Purpose: To increase financial and cultural accessibility to health and human services for American Indians. The Health Service operates medical and dental clinics for American Indians.

Methods of operation: Human services (91%), community development, educational advocacy (5%), research (1%), publications (1%), public education (1%), training and technical assistance (1%)

Constituency: American Indian community in Chicago

Recent issues and projects: Development of culturally appropriate approaches to prenatal education for American Indians. Development of microcomputer-based Health Information system. Development of family services, youth development program and substance abuse program.

Budget: $300,000

Funding: Indian Health Service, foundations, United Way, churches, tribes

Staff: 14
4 Community Health Workers
1 Executive Director
1 Medical Assistant
1 Office Manager
1 Director of Community Services
Contract Physicians and Nurse Practitioners
1 Nurse Manager
3 Prevention Specialists
2 Community Outreach Workers

Staff openings/year: 1

Work Week: 40 hours

Salary/year: $10-24,000

Benefits: Health insurance, pregnancy leave, life insurance, credit union, paid vacation

Part-Time Employees: 5

Volunteers: 4

Interns: Yes
Length: 3-4 months, negotiable
Duties: Program planning and development, policy research, advocacy, systems development, direct service
Remuneration: Unpaid

Jobs advertised: Local Indian newsletters and Indian organizations

To apply: Contact Paul Allen

AMERICAN JEWISH CONGRESS

2027 Massachusetts Ave., NW
Washington, DC 20036
(202) 332-4001

Director: Mark J. Pelavin

Methods of operation: Research, lobbying, litigation, publications, community organizing, direct action, public education, training and technical assistance

Membership: 50,000 American Jews

Recent issues and projects: Recent projects include: health care and health care reform; crime policy; economic issues

Major publications: *Congress Monthly*; *AJ Congress Boycott Report*

Funding: Individual contributions, direct mail

Staff: 3
1 Washington Representative
1 Administrative Assistant
1 Legal Assistant

Staff openings/year: 0-1

Work Week: 50 hours

Salary/year: $20,000

Benefits: Health insurance, paid vacation, pension, life insurance, family leave

Part-Time Employees: None

Summer Employees: None

Volunteers: Yes

Interns: 3
Length: Flexible, generally 3-6 months
Duties: Legislative research, writing, attend and report on Congressional committee hearings
Remuneration: None

To apply: Please contact David Harris

Remarks: Staff is fairly stable. What we can really

offer is internship opportunities. Internships are open to qualified undergraduate, graduate and postgraduate students who have as their major area of interest political science, international relations, public administration, Judaic studies, domestic affairs, or related areas. We will assist legislative interns in obtaining credit for their work.

AMERICAN LABOR EDUCATION CENTER

2000 P Street, NW, Suite 300
Washington, DC 20036
(202) 828-5170

Director: Karen Ohmans

Purpose: To produce educational materials and conduct training for workers on labor-related issues.

Methods of operation: Materials, training and technical assistance, public education

Constituency: Service union members, union staff and labor educators

Recent issues and projects: Occupational health and safety; internal and new organizing; international labor issues

Funding: Fees for services

Staff: 2
1 Writer/Editors
1 Graphic Designers

Work Week: 50 hours

Benefits: Health insurance, life insurance, pregnancy leave, pension, paid vacation, dental insurance

Interns: None currently, but willing to accept applications
Remuneration: Unpaid

To apply: Contact Karen Ohmans, Director

AMERICAN LUNG ASSOCIATION

1740 Broadway
New York, NY 10019-4374
(212) 315-8700

Director: John R. Garrison

Purpose: The conquest of lung disease and promotion of healthy lungs.

Methods of operation: Research, lobbying, publications, human services, community organizing, direct action, public education/management method, training and technical assistance, professional education

Constituency: Anyone interested in lung disease

Recent issues and projects: All smoking and tobacco issues, air pollution (ambient and indoor), TB and AIDS, asthma, lung disease prevention and care

Major publications: *American Journal of Respiratory and Critical Care Medicine* and *American Journal of Respiratory Cell and Molecular Biology*

Funding: Individual contributions, direct mail, special events; varies with each local association

Staff:
1500 professional staff nationwide including:
Writers/Editors
Health Education Specialists
Grassroots Fundraisers
Program Specialists
Communications Specialists
Office Managers
Bookkeepers/Accountants
Administrative Assistants

Work Week: 35-40 hours

Benefits: Health insurance, life insurance, pregnancy leave, pension

Part-Time Employees: Yes

Summer Employees: Yes

Volunteers: Yes

Interns: Yes
Length: Varies by local office

Jobs advertised: Local newspapers; colleges and university personnel offices; professional societies (for example, for health education specialists)

To apply: Contact Executive Director of the local Association

Remarks: Each Lung Association is separately incorporated and does its own recruiting and hiring. Budgets range in size from less than $200,000 to over $2 million. Personnel benefits are determined at the local level. Interested persons should contact each local Lung Association in communities where they are interested in working. There are Lung Associations in all 50 states, DC, Puerto Rico and the Virgin Islands.

AMERICAN PEACE TEST

P.O. Box 26725
Las Vegas, NV 89126
(702) 386-9834 Testing Alert (702) 731-9646

Director: Staff Collective

Purpose: APT is working toward a Comprehensive Test Ban Treaty and the worldwide cessation of nuclear weapons testing. We also consider the stopping of flight missile testing as part of our focus. We are working toward this goal by organizing demonstrations at the Nevada Test Site.

Constituency: Nationally-based grassroots constituency

Recent issues and projects: APT's last major event was Healing Global Wounds, October 2-12, 1992. Approximately 3,000 people participated in this event, with 500 committing civil resistance. Last major campaign was countdown '93 with grassroots coordination actions at Los Alamos and Livermore Nuclear Labs.

Major publications: Newspaper: *The Test Banner*

Budget: $200,000

Staff: 3
3 Organizers

Staff openings/year: 1

Work Week: 40 - 50 hours

Volunteers: 15 - 20

Interns: None currently, but willing to accept applications

Jobs advertised: Movement papers and journals

To apply: Contact one of the organizers

AMERICAN RED CROSS

17th & D Streets, NW
Washington, DC 20006
(202) 737-8300

Director: Elizabeth Dole

Purpose: The American Red Cross is a humanitarian organization, led by volunteers, that provides relief to victims of disasters and helps people prevent, prepare for, and respond to emergencies. It does this through services that are consistent with its congressional charter and the fundamental principles of the International Red Cross and Red Crescent Movement.

Methods of operation: Research, lobbying, litigation, publications, human services, community organizing, direct action, public education, training and technical assistance

Constituency: People concerned about helping people in need, through voluntary service

Recent issues and projects: Recent projects include national disaster relief for LA earthquake, Georgia floods, Bosnia and Rwanda relief

Major publications: Annual reports; first aid and water safety instructional books; HIV education materials

Funding: Annual budget: $1.3 billion

Staff:
2,300 Staff Nationwide
Staff at Main Headquarters include:
8 Attorneys
2 Paralegals
4 Lobbyists
56 Development/Marketing
50 Accountants
75 Caseworkers
20 Writers/Editors

Staff openings/year: 100

Work Week: 25-35 hours

Benefits: Health insurance, pension, paid vacation, life insurance, credit union

Part-Time Employees: 60

Summer Employees: 25-30

Volunteers: 100,000

Interns: 100
Length: 3-4 months
Duties: Cultural diversity and laboratories

Jobs advertised: Internal postings, *Washington Post*, trade journals

To apply: Contact Human Resources, attention: staffing

AMERICAN RIVERS

801 Pennsylvania Avenue, SE, Suite 400
Washington, DC 20003
(202) 547-6900

Other Offices: Phoenix, AZ; Seattle, WA

Director: Kevin J. Coyle

Purpose: The mission of American Rivers is to preserve and restore America's river systems and to foster a river stewardship ethic.

Methods of operation: Litigation (20%), lobbying (30%), direct action (15%), public education (20%), research (5%), community organizing (5%), training and technical assistance (5%)

Constituency: Local river activists, recreational river enthusiasts, conservationists

Recent issues and projects: There are 6 major program areas: (1) Nationally significant rivers; (2) Hydropower policy reform; (3) Endangered aquatic/vipanian species (4) Western instream flow; (5) Clean water protection (6) Urban rivers

Major publications: Newsletter: *American Rivers.* Books: *American Rivers Guide to Wild and Scenic Designation*; *Outstanding Rivers List*; *Rivers at Risk* (Citizen's Guide to Hydropower)

Budget: $2,400,000

Funding: Individual contributions (38%), foundations (33%), conference interest (13%), telephone solicitation (10%), direct mail (6%)

Staff: 20
5 Attorneys
3 Issue Experts
4 Foundation Fundraisers
1 Typists
2 Bookkeepers/Accountants
1 Writer/Editor
2 Lobbyist
1 Office Manager
1 Researcher

Staff openings/year: 2

Work Week: 45 hours

Salary/year: $21,000 (Recent College Graduate); $26,000 (Graduate with advanced degree)

Benefits: Health insurance, life insurance, pension, paid vacation

Summer Employees: none

Volunteers: 5-6

Interns: 8-10
Length: 6 months-1 year
Duties: Research, writing, phone calls, office work
Remuneration: none

Jobs advertised: In the newspaper; in conservation publications; through memos to other groups; by word of mouth

To apply: Contact Kirsten Bevinetto Artman, Executive Assistant to the President

AMERICAN SOCIAL HEALTH ASSOCIATION

100 Capitola Drive
Durham, NC 27713
(919) 361-8400

Other Offices: Washington, DC

Director: Peggy Clarke

Purpose: The mission of the American Social Health Association is to stop sexually transmitted disease and their harmful consequences to individuals, families and communities.

Methods of operation: Public education (60%), research (10%), lobbying (10%), publications (10%), training and technical assistance (10%)

Constituency: Anyone interested or concerned about STDs

Recent issues and projects: Formation and leadership of the National STD Coalition; formation of the Women's Health Program; expansion of the National Herpes Hotline; Finding the Words program initiative

Major publications: Three quarterly newsletters: *The Helper*; *HPV News*; *STD News*; *Managing Herpes: How to Live and Love with a Chronic STD*

Budget: $8,856,000

Funding: Government (90.92%), individual contributions (8.72%), foundations (.36%)

Staff: 100
4 Writers/Editors
2 Office Managers
1 Researcher
2 Lobbyists
2 Foundation Fundraisers
5 Issue Experts
7 Administrative Assistants
4 Bookkeepers/Accountants
9 Managers
33 Supervisors

8 Professionals
3 Technicians

Staff openings/year: 12

Work Week: 40 hours

Salary/year: $22,050 (Recent College Graduate); $31,000 (Graduate with advanced degree)

Benefits: Health insurance, pension, paid vacation, life insurance, credit union, family leave

Part-Time Employees: 206

Summer Employees: None

Volunteers: 9

Interns: None, but willing to accept applications

To apply: ASHA Job Line: 919-361-4804 or Director of Human Resources

Remarks: ASHA, founded in 1914, is the only nongovernmental organization in the U.S. dedicated solely to the prevention and control of all sexually transmitted diseases. ASHA works to achieve this goal through its programs of public education, research and advocacy.

AMERICAN SOCIETY ON AGING

833 Market Street, Suite 511
San Francisco, CA 94103
(415) 882-2910

Director: Gloria Cavanaugh

Purpose: To enhance the well-being of older persons and their families through professional education and information dissemination.

Methods of operation: Professional and public education (70%), publications (20%), minority elder initiative (10%)

Constituency: Professionals in aging and aging-related fields

Recent issues and projects: Conferences on Alzheimer's disease, long-term care, wellness, case management. Publications on retirement, counseling elders, hospital cost-containment, senior power, generational competition for resources, etc.

Major publications: Bimonthly newspaper: *The Aging Connection*; quarterly journal: *Generations*; monograph: *Long-Term Care: Who's Responsible?*

Budget: $2,000,000

Funding: Conference fees (50%), memberships, subscriptions (35%), foundations (15%)

Staff: 23
4 Typists
3 Conference Coordinators
3 Writer/Editors
2 Foundation Fundraisers
2 Bookkeeper/Accountants
2 Marketing/Membership Assistants
1 Executive Director
1 Education Director
1 Marketing Director
1 Data Processing Coordinator
1 Business Manager
1 Issue Expert
1 Receptionist

Work Week: 37.5 hours

Benefits: Health insurance, pregnancy leave, pension, paid vacation, dental insurance

Part-Time Employees: 2

Volunteers: 3-5

Interns: Yes
Length: 6 months
Duties: Publications; public policy
Remuneration: Non-paying

Jobs advertised: Newspapers; newsletters

To apply: Contact Pamela Arnold, Business Manager

AMERICAN-ARAB ANTI-DISCRIMINATION COMMITTEE (ADC)

4201 Connecticut Avenue, NW, Suite 500
Washington, DC 20008
(202) 244-2990

Other Offices: Detroit, MI; Los Angeles, CA; Chicago, IL; Amman, JORDAN

President: Albet Mokhiber

Purpose: ADC is a grassroots, civil rights service organization. Our primary goals are to combat anti-Arab stereotyping, defamation and discrimination; to promote a better understanding of the cultural heritage of Arab Americans; and to encourage a more balanced policy in the Middle East.

Methods of operation: Research, grassroots political action, community organizing, litigation, publications, direct action, coalition work

Constituency: Predominantly Arab Americans of

all national origins and concerned U.S. citizens (1/4-1/3 of ADC membership)

Recent issues and projects: ADC was actively involved in the Middle East peace talks while pushing for action on Israeli human rights violations in the occupied territories. Other projects included a special conference on the crisis in Somalia and calling for a more balanced policy toward Bosnia. Ongoing projects include combatting Arab bashing in the media; a campaign to introduce accurate information on the Arab world and Islam in the nation's schools; the internship and leadership development program for college age students; and, outreach to other civil rights and social justice organizations.

Major publications: Newsletter: *ADC Times*, 10/year; *ADC Issue Papers*, 3-4/year on topics of interest to the community; *Intern Perspectives*, newsletter produced by interns at the end of the summer; an annual Activity Report; and, an annual calendar on Middle East facts

Funding: Membership, individual contributions

Staff: 20
3 Organizers
1 Attorneys
1 Office Manager
2 Fundraisers
2 Typists
1 Press Aide
1 Executive Director
1 Receptionist
1 Outreach/Coalition Work
2 Writers/Editors/Researchers
1 Data Entry
1 Mailroom
2 Bookkeepers/Accountants

Staff openings/year: 2-3

Work Week: 40-50 hours

Salary/year: $15-18,000 (Recent College Graduate); $19-20,000 (Graduate with advanced degree)

Benefits: Health insurance, dental insurance, life insurance, pregnancy leave, 3 weeks paternity leave, paid vacation, tuition reimbursement

Part-Time Employees: 2

Volunteers: 8-10

Interns: 1-2 during academic year; 20 in summer
Length: Summer or semester
Duties: Assist with departments (e.g. Organizing, Research and Publications); 8-10 placed in Congressional offices; 2-3 placed with Coalition groups
Remuneration: Minimum wage stipend

Jobs advertised: Through other Arab-American organizations; word of mouth; our newsletter; newspaper

To apply: For staff positions, contact Lamia Doumani; for internships, contact Intern Coordinator

AMERICANS FOR DEMOCRATIC ACTION

1625 K Street, NW, Suite 210
Washington, DC 20006
(202) 785-5980

Other Offices: Winston-Salem, NC; Tempe, AZ; Chicago, IL

Director: Amy Isaacs

Purpose: To educate the American public as to the significant issues; to lobby on behalf of these issues; to work through their public action committee (PAC) in supporting candidates whose views are similar to ADA's; to produce weekly, quarterly, and yearly publications and analysis for mass distribution

Methods of operation: Lobbying (30%), publications (25-30%), community organizing (20%), public education (10-15%), direct action (10%)

Membership: Extremely dedicated, long-standing, liberal members, representing all demographics

Recent issues and projects: The publication of ADA's *1993 Voting Records*; monthly economic reports, a drug policy conference examining methods of drug prevention and treatment; an upcoming symposium about political parties, alternative voting patterns, etc.; an upcoming conference on Employment and the Economy; gays and lesbians in the military; women's rights, civil rights, military conversion

Major publications: Newsletters: *ADAction News and Notes* weekly, *ADA Today* quarterly; Annual Voting Records; *A New National Energy Strategy*; *A Liberal Economic Program for the Nineties*; *The Urban Crisis: Problems and Solutions*; *Toward New Strategies for Demand Reduction Policy: A Policy Forum*

Budget: $500,000

Funding: Individual contributions (50%), direct mail (25%), labor (25%)

Staff: 9
5 Lobbyists
4 Typists
4 Issue Experts
2-3 Writers/Editors
2-3 Press Aides
2-3 Campaign Managers
2 Bookkeepers/Accountants
2 Office Managers
2 Organizers
1 Grassroots Fundraiser

Staff openings/year: 1

Work Week: 45-50 hours

Salary/year: $18,000

Benefits: Health insurance, life insurance, pregnancy leave, paid vacation

Part-Time Employees: 2-3

Volunteers: Yes

Interns: 4-5
Length: 3-5 months
Duties: Lobby, attend meetings, write reports, write letters to Congress, some administrative, represent ADA at coalition meetings
Remuneration: Credits received, no financial compensation

Jobs advertised: Job announcements to DC offices

To apply: Contact Dianna Wentz, Assistant to the National Director

---

AMNESTY INTERNATIONAL, USA
322 Eighth Avenue
New York, NY 10001
(212) 807-8400

Other Offices: Somerville, MA; Washington, DC; Atlanta, GA; Los Angeles, CA; San Francisco, CA; Nederland, CO; Chicago, IL

Director: Curt Goering, Acting Director

Purpose: Amnesty International is a worldwide movement independent of any government, political persuasion or religious creed. It seeks the release of prisoners of conscience: people detained for their beliefs, color, sex, ethnic origin, language or religion, who have not used or advocated violence. It works for fair and prompt trials for all political prisoners. It opposes the death penalty and torture of all prisoners.

Methods of operation: Community organizing, public education, publications

Membership: 400,000 members in the USA, many organized into local and campus groups

Recent issues and projects: Campaigns on China, Peru, Colombia, Death Penalty (abolition)

Major publications: *AI Report* published by AI International Secretariat, in London; *Amnesty Action*, bimonthly newspaper of AIUSA; *SAY* monthly for high school and college students; Refugee Reports; Country Reports; *Community News*, for religious groups; newsletters for Legal Support Network and Health Professional Network

Budget: $22,000,000

Funding: Direct mail (82.8%), individual contributions (5.6%), foundations (1.5%), other (10.1%)

Staff: 83
Including:
4 Administrative Assistants
6 Office Managers
7 Bookkeepers/Accountants
3 Press Aides
4 Direct Mail Department
1 Foundation Fundraiser
1 Attorney
1 Computer Expert
2 Writers/Editors

Staff openings/year: 6-10

Work Week: 35-40 hours

Salary/year: $22,000 (Recent College Graduate); $Varies (Graduate with advanced degree)

Benefits: Health insurance, life insurance, pregnancy leave, pension, paid vacation

Part-Time Employees: 5

Volunteers: 20

Interns: 20
Length: 5 months
Duties: Work with program coordinators
Remuneration: Some receive work-study payments, some just expenses

Jobs advertised: Amnesty International publications; newspapers; word of mouth; college placement offices

To apply: Contact Diana Quick for internships; Connie Harshman for salaried positions; Betsy Ross for volunteer positions.

ANIMAL LEGAL DEFENSE FUND

1363 Lincoln Avenue, Suite 7
San Rafael, CA 94901
(415) 459-0885

Other Offices: Rockville, MD

Director: Joyce Tischler

Purpose: The Animal Legal Defense Fund is a public interest law organization that focuses on protecting animals and establishing their legal rights.

Methods of operation: Litigation (80%), public education (15%), publications (5%)

Constituency: General public interested in animals

Recent issues and projects: Recent projects include: lawsuits against U.S. Department of Agriculture for violating Animal Welfare Act (protection of animals used in research); Zero Tolerance for Cruelty Project (stronger enforcement of cruelty laws)

Major publications: Quarterly newsletter; law review devoted to animal law issues in conjunction with Lewis and Clark Law School

Budget: $500,000

Funding: Direct mail (95%), individual contributions (4%), foundations (1%)

Staff: 7
3 Attorneys
2 Typists
1 Writer/Editor
1 Issue Expert

Staff openings/year: 1-2

Work Week: 40-60 hours

Salary/year: $23,000 (Recent College Graduate); $36,000 (Graduate with advanced degree)

Benefits: Health insurance, paid vacation

Part-Time Employees: 2

Summer Employees: 2 Law Clerks

Interns: Varies
Length: School term or summer
Duties: Interns serve as law clerks; help develop legal cases
Remuneration: $3,000 for 2-month summer law internship

Jobs advertised: Mailings to animal rights groups; mailings to law schools; ad in ALDF's mailings to its attorney/law school members

To apply: Contact Joyce Tischler, Executive Director

ANIMAL RIGHTS NETWORK, INC./THE ANIMALS' AGENDA

P.O. Box 25881
Baltimore, MD 21224
(410) 675-4566

Editor: Kim W. Stallwood

Purpose: The *Animals Agenda* is a magazine dedicated to informing people about animal rights and cruelty-free living for the purpose of inspiring action for animals.

Methods of operation: Publications (100%)

Major publications: *The Animals' Agenda* magazine, 6 times a year

Budget: $250,000

Funding: Subscriptions (42%), foundations (19%), ads (18%), individual contributions (9%), bequests (2%)

Staff: 5
1 Editors
1 Advertising
1 Art Production
1 Administrative Assistant
1 Director

Staff openings/year: 1-2

Work Week: 50 hours

Salary/year: $22,000

Benefits: Health insurance, life insurance, paid vacation

Part-Time Employees: 0

Volunteers: 2

Interns: 1
Length: 2 months in summer
Duties: Various
Remuneration: Minimum wage

Jobs advertised: In magazines and trade papers

To apply: Contact Kim W. Stallwood

Remarks: Only vegetarians need apply! A meat-eater wouldn't be happy here.

ANTARCTICA PROJECT

P.O. Box 76920
Washington, DC 20076
(202) 544-0236

Director: Beth Marks

Purpose: A nonprofit organization dedicated to preserving the wilderness attributes and scientific value of the Antarctic. Secretariat of the Antarctic and Southern Ocean Coalition (ASOC), composed of 226 conservation organizations in 44 countries.

Methods of operation: Lobbying (30%), community organizing (30%), direct action (20%), publications (10%), public education (10%)

Membership: Approximately 180 private citizens in the U.S. and abroad

Recent issues and projects: The ratification and implementation of the Antarctic Environmental Protocol, the creation of a whole sanctuary around Antarctica, the adoption of sound fishing regulations

Major publications: Please write or call for recent listing of publications.

Budget: $120,000

Funding: Foundations (70%), individual contributions (20%), sales/interest (10%)

Staff: 2
1 Office Manager
1 Lobbyist

Staff openings/year: 0

Work Week: 50-60 hours

Salary/year: $20,000 (Recent College Graduate); $40,000 (Graduate with advanced degree)

Benefits: Health insurance, paid vacation

Part-Time Employees: 1

Interns: Yes
Length: Summer or semester
Duties: Work on issues involving the future of Antarctica
Remuneration: Unpaid

Jobs advertised: Schools, local newspaper

To apply: Please contact Charles Webb, Office Manager

APPALACHIA SCIENCE IN THE PUBLIC INTEREST

P.O. Box 298
Livingston, KY 40445
(606) 453-2105

Director: Al Fritsch, S.J.

Purpose: To make science and technology responsive to the needs of the poor of Central Appalachia.

Methods of operation: Research (20%), demonstration (20%), publications (20%), public education (10%), training and technical assistance (10%), direct action (10%), human services (5%), community organizing (5%)

Constituency: Appalachian, socially concerned folks

Recent issues and projects: Appalachian Forestry Project; Safe and Affordable Housing Project; Rockcastle Resource Center; Resource Auditing Service; Appropriate Technology for Appalachians; citizen monitoring of reclamation lands, hazardous waste sites and water quality systems

Major publications: Quarterly newsletter: *Appalachian Alternatives*; The Simple Lifestyle Calendar; ASPI Technical Papers

Budget: $360,000

Funding: Sales and consulting (32%), donated foods and services (32%), foundations (16%), individual contributions (10%), direct mail (10%)

Staff: 8
1 Appropriate Technologist
2 Researchers
2 Writers/Editors
1 Office Manager
2 Grounds Managers

Staff openings/year: 1-2

Work Week: 40 hours

Salary/year: $14,000 (Recent College Graduate); $Varies (Graduate with advanced degree)

Benefits: Health insurance, paid vacation, pregnancy leave

Part-Time Employees: 8

Summer Employees: 2

Volunteers: 5

Interns: 2

Length: Semester or summer

Jobs advertised: Word of mouth

To apply: Contact Al Fritsch, Director

APPALACHIAN CENTER FOR ECONOMIC NETWORKS

94 North Columbus Road
Athens, GA 45701
(614) 592-3854

President: June Holley

Purpose: ACEnet is a nonprofit community development organization implementing several projects designed to revitalize the economy of Appalachian Ohio, all involving flexible manufacturing networks (FMNs). Flexible manufacturing networks bring together groups of small firms to collaboratively manufacture items for custom or niche markets that they couldn't produce by themselves. ACEnet also convenes diverse groups within the economic development community to collaboratively design new programs to meet the needs of networked firms. Founded in 1985, ACEnet has become increasingly involved in initiatives focusing on information and communications technologies and workforce/workplace development. ACEnet also runs a small business incubator.

Methods of operation: Research (15%), publications (15%), direct action (15%), training and technical assistance (10%), public education (5%)

Recent issues and projects: Designed and implemented a targeted training program resulting in successful transition from welfare to work; facilitated formation of regional Free-Net; in the process of building a licensed kitchen incubator facility; administer a revolving loan fund which only lends to firms involved in networks or joint ventures

Major publications: Over 20 papers

Budget: $500,000

Funding: Foundations (50%), government (50%)

Staff: 13
4 Program Staff
3 Administrative Assistants
2 Writers/Editors
2 Bookkeepers/Accountants
1 Researcher
1 Office Manager

Staff openings/year: 2-5

Work Week: 50 hours

Salary/year: $22,000 (Recent College Graduate); $25,000 (Graduate with advanced degree)

Benefits: Health insurance, child care, family leave, vacation

Part-Time Employees: 2

Summer Employees: None

Volunteers: None

Interns: None currently, but willing to accept applications

Jobs advertised: Newspaper

To apply: Contact Amy Borgstrom Somers

APPALACHIAN OHIO PUBLIC INTEREST CENTER

36 South Congress Street
Athens, OH 45701
(614) 593-7490

Director: Carol Kuhre

Purpose: The Appalachian Ohio Public Interest Center promotes sustainable job creation through training and re-training of individuals and groups.

Methods of operation: Community organizing (50%), research (10%), human services (10%), direct action (10%), public education (10%), training and technical assistance

Constituency: A wide range of individuals from all economic groups

Recent issues and projects: An ABLE conference on Appalachian History and Culture, EPA Education Fund seminars on recycling, medical and housing issues, agriculture and more.

Major publications: *The AOPIC Report*, a bi-monthly newsletter

Budget: $100,000

Funding: Other organizations (72%), individual contributions (25%), foundations(3%)

Staff: 3
2 Organizers
1 Office Manager

Staff openings/year: 1

Work Week: 35 hours

Salary/year: $8,000

Benefits: Paid vacation, family leave

Part-Time Employees: None

Summer Employees: None

Volunteers: Yes

Interns: Yes
Length: 3 months
Duties: Varied, according to students area of study
Remuneration: None, these positions are volunteer only

Jobs advertised: Local newspapers and by word of mouth

To apply: Contact Carol Kuhre, Executive Director

Remarks: Only individuals with a sincere interest in grassroots social change, sustainability and the environment need inquire. Most of our positions are on a volunteer basis with little or no pay. We do not lobby.

APPLESEED FOUNDATION
1901 Pennsylvania Ave., NW, Suite 301
Washington, DC 20006
(202) 728-0725

Other Offices: Boston, MA

Director: Richard J. Medalie

Purpose: Organize statewide Centers for Law in the Public Interest across the country. These Centers are community based advocacy groups, working for systemic reform in areas of concern in their areas, ie. government.

Methods of operation: Research, lobbying, litigation, community organizing, direct action, public education

Constituency: Organized by Harvard Law School Class of 1958

Recent issues and projects: Recent issues include: accountability; human rights; consumer and environmental protection; corporate crimes; education; and criminal justice

Budget: $150,000

Funding: Individual contributions (100%)

Staff: 1
1 Attorney

Staff openings/year: 2

Work Week: 40-50 hours

Salary/year: $30,000 (Graduate with advanced degree)

Benefits: Health insurance, paid vacation, family leave

Part-Time Employees: 1

Summer Employees: 4

Volunteers: 1

Interns: 1
Length: 3-4 months
Duties: Researching and preparing potential projects for Centers; assisting in organizing and needs assessment
Remuneration: None

Jobs advertised: Listings at law schools, word of mouth

To apply: Contact Linda Singer, Deputy Director

APROVECHO INSTITUTE
80574 Hazelton Road
Cottage Grove, OR 97424
(503) 942-9434

Director: Dean Still

Purpose: The Spanish word "Aprovecho" means "I make the best use of ... ." Aprovecho is a small, nonprofit organization that helps people take charge of their own lives, using technologies which make the best use of their own skills and resources. We offer tools and methods for creatively handling the inevitable changes coming from dwindling world resources. We research and teach innovative techniques for housing, cooking, heating and small scale food production. We emphasize processes in which people and societies achieve greater self-reliance and harmony with the Earth. We encourage cross-cultural exchanges and promote successful indigenous ways of conserving energy and resources.

Methods of operation: Public education (40%), research (25%), publications (15%), human services (5%), community organizing (5%), direct action (5%), training and technical assistance (5%)

Membership: Includes all types of people: foresters, organic farmers and gardeners, teachers, writers, professionals, photographers, pragmatic idealists and tinkerers, many of whom are scattered across the world

Recent issues and projects: Aprovecho is concentrating on developing a backlog of inventions such as easily built, inexpensive wood stoves, heaters, a solar refrigerator, more efficient solar desalinator, etc. These devices are designed to be built in small cities anywhere in the world. We are publishing plans and manuals concerning these devices.

Major publications: Newsletter: *News From Aprovecho*; Periodical: *Skipping Stones*; *A Gardeners Guide to Fava Beans*

Budget: $20,000

Funding: Individual contributions (100%)

Staff:
All volunteer, including:
Office Manager
Maintenance Manager
Office Co-Manager
Land and Garden Manager
Newsletter Editor

Staff openings/year: 2-3

Work Week: 20 hours

Benefits: Room and board exchange, or room and board plus small stipend for qualified consultants

Part-Time Employees: 5 consultants

Volunteers: 10

Interns: Sometimes
Length: 1 year
Duties: Various, including garden research, office help, teaching assistance, etc.
Remuneration: Interns pay $175/month (includes room and board), or creative financing is available

Jobs advertised: Local papers; permaculture activists; Oregon Peaceworkers; *News from Aprovecho* newsletter

To apply: Contact Kristin Andersen, Office Manager

ARIZONA CENTER FOR LAW IN THE PUBLIC INTEREST

3724 N. Third Street, Suite 300
Phoenix, AZ 85012
(602) 274-6287

Other Offices: Tucson, AZ

Director: Timothy M. Hogan

Purpose: To provide an effective voice for the public at-large and for individuals and groups that otherwise would be unable to obtain effective legal representation

Methods of operation: Research, lobbying, litigation, public education, training and technical assistance

Membership: Approximately 4,000 individuals, law firms, foundations, and corporations provide financial support to the Center each year.

Recent issues and projects: The Center's work primarily focuses on six areas: environmental protection; human rights, including those of the disabled and mentally ill; health care; consumer rights; government accountability; and civil rights.

Major publications: Quarterly newsletter; 15-year report; brochure

Budget: $900,000

Funding: Government grants (72%), individual contributions (13%), foundations (11%), direct mail (4%)

Staff: 21
6 Attorneys
4 Paralegals/Advocates
3 Secretaries
2 Office Manager/Legal Secretaries
1 Development Director
2 Bookkeepers/Accountants
1 Receptionist
1 Intake Secretary
1 Intaker

Staff openings/year: 1-2

Work Week: 40-50 hours

Salary/year: $14-24,000 (Recent College Graduate); $30-50,000 (Graduate with advanced degree)

Benefits: Health insurance, life insurance, pregnancy/parental leave, credit union, board, tuition reimbursement, paid vacation, dental insurance, sabbatical (attorneys)

Part-Time Employees: 1

Volunteers: 4

Interns: 2-3
Length: Semester
Duties: Clerkships; college student research internships
Remuneration: Students have received course credit only in the past

Jobs advertised: Newspapers

To apply: Contact Katie Norton, Director of Administration and Development

---

ARIZONA CITIZEN ACTION
2039 E. Broadway #133
Tempe, AZ 85282
(602) 921-3090

Director: Jim Driscoll

Purpose: State's largest consumer/environmental organization; state affiliate of citizen action

Methods of operation: Public education (50%); community organizing (25%); lobbying (20%); publications (5%); training and technical assistance (5%)

Membership: 20,000 members from door-to-door canvass

Recent issues and projects: Single Payer National Health Care campaign

Major publications: Monthly newsletter; others by national office

Budget: $50,000

Funding: Individual contributions (100%)

Staff: 1
1 State Director

Staff openings/year: Varies

Work Week: 40 hours

Benefits: Health insurance

Part-Time Employees: Canvassers

Summer Employees: Varies

Volunteers: Yes

Interns: Yes
Duties: Researching, writing, organizing

Jobs advertised: Local newspapers

To apply: Contact Jim Driscoll, State Director

ARIZONA COALITION AGAINST DOMESTIC VIOLENCE
301 West Hatcher
Phoenix, AZ 85021
(602) 495-5429

Director: Sharon Ersch

Purpose: Advocacy on behalf of battered women by education, networking, lobbying, organizing, etc.

Methods of operation: Community organizing (20%), lobbying (20%), public education (20%), training and technical assistance (20%), litigation (5%), research (5%), publications (5%), human services (5%)

Constituency: Agencies and individuals who work with battered women

Recent issues and projects: Legislative agenda, court watch project, police training, judicial training

Budget: $100,000

Funding: State (53%), Federal (47%)

Staff: 2
1 Executive Director
1 Administrative Assistant

Work Week: 40 hours

Salary/year: $22,000 (Recent College Graduate); $30,000 (Graduate with advanced degree)

Part-Time Employees: 1

Volunteers: 3

Interns: None currently, but willing to accept applications

To apply: Contact Sharon Ersch, Executive Director

ARKANSAS COALITION AGAINST VIOLENCE TO WOMEN AND CHILDREN
7509 Cantrell Road, #213
Little Rock, AR 72207
(501) 663-4668

Manager: Schatzi Riley, Coalition Coordinator

Purpose: ACAVWC is a network of battered women and their advocates working to enable those involved in domestic violence to choose their own options and control their own lives. They strive to end the oppressions which make domestic violence possible, including sexism, racism, classism and homophobia.

Methods of operation: Training and technical assistance (40%), community organizing (35%), public education (15%), public policy development/monitoring (10%)

Constituency: Member organizations/shelter programs, battered women/formerly battered women, advocates

Recent issues and projects: Our most recent project is the passage of domestic violence legislation and organizing/providing support to incarcerated battered women.

Major publications: Quarterly newsletter: *Common Ground*

Budget: $20,000

Funding: Individual contributions, foundations

Staff: 1
1/2 Organizer
1/2 Office Manager
1/2 Issue expert

Staff openings/year: 1-2

Work Week: 40 hours

Salary/year: $18,500

Benefits: Health insurance, paid vacation

Part-Time Employees: 1

Volunteers: 10-15

Interns: None currently, but willing to accept applications

Jobs advertised: Local papers; regionally and nationally through National Coalition Against Domestic Violence

To apply: Contact Shatzi Riley, Coalition Coordinator

Remarks: It is helpful for interested applicants to have an understanding of the dynamics of battering and the connection between individual and societal violence and oppression. All decision-making is by consensus and strives to reflect the input and diversity of the battered women's movement.

ARCTIC TO AMAZONIA ALLIANCE

P.O. Box 73, 1 Main Street
Strafford, VT 05072
(802) 765-4337

Director: Erik VanLennep

Purpose: The Arctic to Amazonia Alliance is a charitable, nonprofit, educational organization devoted to constructive and nonviolent social change at the local, grassroots level, with the clear understanding that local actions greatly impact regional and global issues. Their primary purpose is to facilitate better communication and understanding between Indigenous and non-Indigenous peoples, particularly regarding the relationships among human rights, social justice, economics and the environment. They seek to develop working models for more respectful stewardship of the earth's natural ecosystems.

Methods of operation: Public education (30%), community organizing (30%), publications (15%), direct action (5-10%), research (10%)

Constituency: "Mainstream" people who wish to learn as well as network with developing countries and Indigenous people.

Recent issues and projects: Recent projects include: Save James Bay Campaign; New England Tropical Forest Project; Indigenous Art Shows; Fleece Drive in support of Navajo Weaving Project; upcoming "Reclaiming the Forests" campaign

Major publications: *The Report* (semi-annual attempts, funding permitting, to publish quarterly)

Budget: $150,000

Funding: In-kind contributions (50%), individual contributions (35%), foundations (15%)

Staff:
1 1/2 time staff person at the time
Volunteers and Staff:
3 Organizers
2 Writers/Editors
1/2 Attorney
1 Office Manager
1 Researcher
1 Foundation Fundraiser
3 Issue Experts
2 Administrative Assistants
1 1/2 Bookkeepers/Accountants
1-7 Grassroots Fundraisers
4 Campaign Managers

Staff openings/year: 3 unpaid

Work Week: 60+ hours

Part-Time Employees: No

Summer Employees: 2-3

Volunteers: 2-10

Interns: 2-3
Length: 3 months or more
Duties: Designed with intern according to needs
Remuneration: Sometimes accommodations are donated

To apply: Send letter of interest, brief resume and a writing sample to Erik VanLennep, Director

ARTISTS UNLIMITED

158 Thomas Street, Suite 14
Seattle, WA 98109
(206) 441-8480

Director: Julianne Jaz

Purpose: To provide education on professional development in the arts to adults with disabilities.

Methods of operation: Research, training and technical assistance, direct service

Constituency: Adults with disabilities, broad spectrum of people concerned with arts and disabilities issues

Recent issues and projects: Current issues include: Collaborating with Very Special Arts and WA State Arts Commission (WSAC) to get artists with disabilities through application process and ultimately to be chosen for the artists in residence roster of WSAC; creating a mentorship program for those same artists to assist them in really being able to succeed as artists-in-residence; collaborating in A Very Special Arts WA in a 2 year grant from the MEA-Arts for under served populations; and creating a Business Planning Committee to begin the process in their own agents to contract with their artists to formally represent their work commercially as a means of providing them, as well as the agency, with income.

Major publications: A statewide needs assessment concerning the current state of accessibility to the arts for people of all ages with disabilities in Washington, to be published soon.

Budget: $150,000

Funding: Individual contributions (58.74%), grants (38.76%), earned income (2.5%)

Staff:
All part-time positions:
1 Office Manager
3 Professional Artists
2 Managers
1 Studio Attendant

Staff openings/year: 1-2

Work Week: 23.5 hours

Benefits: Health Insurance, paid vacation

Part-Time Employees: 7

Summer Employees: No

Volunteers: 75

Interns: Hope to start intern program in 1995

Jobs advertised: Local newspapers, *Sound Opportunities*, word of mouth

To apply: Contact Julianne Jaz

ASIA RESOURCE CENTER

P.O. Box 15275
Washington, DC 20003
(202) 547-1114

Director: Roger Rumpf

Purpose: To work for peace, justice and human rights in Asia; to foster understanding and communication between the peoples of Asia and the U.S.; and to act as an educational resource on Asia.

Methods of operation: Public education (50%), publications (20%), research (10%), direct action (10%), human services (5%), lobbying (5%)

Constituency: Those interested in Asian affairs and peace/justice issues

Recent issues and projects: Recent issues include: human rights; social justice; development and impact of U.S. policy particularly in Indochina, Taiwan, and Thailand

Major publications: ADA distributes books, videos, slideshows, exhibits and newsletters. Publications include; *Indochina Newsletter*; *Taiwan at the Crossroads*; *Taiwan Communique* newsletter; *Senseless Casualties: The Aids Crisis in SE Asia*

Budget: $80,000

Funding: Foundations (50%), individual contributions (30%), sales (10%), churches (10%)

Staff: 2
1 Director
1 Associate Director

Work Week: 65 hours

Salary/year: $20,000

Benefits: Health insurance, life insurance

Volunteers: Yes

Interns: Yes
Length: 3-12 months
Duties: Research, office work, organization, fundraising
Remuneration: Transportation to office reimbursed

To apply: Contact Roger Rumpf, Director

Remarks: ARC encourages volunteer associates to

organize activities in their local communities.

ASIAN COUNSELING & REFERRAL SERVICE

1032 S. Jackson Street, Suite 200
Seattle, WA 98104
(206) 461-3606

Other Offices: Bellevue, WA

Director: Andres Tangalin

Purpose: ACRS is a community based, multi-cultural, multilingual, private, nonprofit organization which provides and advocates for human services to empower Asian and Pacific Islander individuals and communities to obtain social and economic well being.

Methods of operation: Human services (75%), public education (10%), community organizing (5%), direct action (5%), training and technical assistance (5%)

Recent issues and projects: Recent projects include: the Beacon House; advocating for mentally ill API; advocating for API elderly

Major publications: Quarterly newsletter

Budget: $3,100,000

Funding: Government (70%), canvassing (10%), individual contributions (10%), telephone solicitation (5%), foundations (5%)

Staff: 45
2 Organizers
1 Office Manager
1 Foundation Fundraiser
5 Issue Experts
1 Bookkeeper/Accountant
35 Caseworkers

Staff openings/year: 2

Work Week: 40 hours

Salary/year: $24,500 (Recent College Graduate); $29,000 (Graduate with advanced degree)

Benefits: Health insurance, paid vacation, pregnancy leave, tuition reimbursement

Part-Time Employees: None

Summer Employees: None

Volunteers: Yes

Interns: Yes
Length: 1 year
Duties: Learning MH case management

Jobs advertised: Local ethnic newspapers, posted in agency

To apply: Contact the Program Directors

ASIAN IMMIGRANT WOMEN ADVOCATES

310 - 8th Street, #301
Oakland, CA 94607
(510) 268-0192

Other Offices: San Jose, CA

Director: Young Shin

Purpose: The Asian Immigrant Women Advocates works to empower and to improve the living and working conditions of low-income Asian immigrant women workers.

Methods of operation: Community organizing (70%), human services (13%), public education (7%), publications (5%), research (5%)

Constituency: Low-income, limited English speaking Asian immigrant women employed in the hotel, garment, electronics and home care industries

Recent issues and projects: Recent projects include: Workplace Literacy classes which focus on workers and immigrants rights; the Leadership Development program develops leadership and advocacy skills among women workers; The Environmental Safety and Health Project educates over 5,000 electronics assembly workers in the "Silicon Valley" about occupational health and safety issues at the workplace; The Garment Workers Justice Campaign demands corporate responsibility on the part of the manufacturer for the unfair treatment of workers and unsafe working conditions in the garment industry.

Major publications: *AIWA News* newsletter in Chinese, Korean and English

Budget: $200,000

Funding: Foundations (94%), direct mail (5%), government (1%)

Staff: 4
3 Organizers/Media/Fundraisers/Researchers
1 Office Manager

Staff openings/year: 0-1

Work Week: 37.5 hours

Salary/year: $18,000 (Recent College Graduate);

$Varies (Graduate with advanced degree)

Benefits: Health insurance, paid vacation, life insurance, dental insurance

Part-Time Employees: 4

Summer Employees: None

Volunteers: 3

Interns: None at this time

Jobs advertised: Announcements are placed in the newsletter, other organizations and schools

To apply: Contact Laura K. Lee, Administrative Assistant

ASIAN LAW CAUCUS, INC.

468 Bush Street, 3rd Floor
San Francisco, CA 94108
(415) 391-1655

Director: Paul M. Igasaki

Purpose: Established in 1972, the Asian Law Caucus is committed to the pursuit of equality and justice and strives to create an educated community which may assert its rights and participate actively in American society. To serve the needs of predominantly monolingual low-income Asian Pacific Americans, we provide legal services and educational programs in the areas of civil rights, housing, employment, immigration and the rights of the elderly. Services are provided in English and seven Asian languages.

Methods of operation: Human services (75%), litigation (50%), community organizing (30%), public education (25%)

Constituency: Low-income, Asian Pacific, Americans living in the greater San Francisco Bay Area

Major publications: *Asian Law Caucus Reporter*, newsletter published twice a year

Budget: $800,000

Funding: Foundations (75%), individual contributions (18%), other (7%)

Staff: 15
5 Attorneys
3 Paralegals
1 Office Manager
1 Press Aide
1 Foundation Fundraiser
1 Bookkeeper/Accountant
1 Grassroots Fundraiser
1 Community Outreach Worker
1 Legal Secretary

Staff openings/year: 1

Work Week: 40 hours

Salary/year: $22,000 (Recent College Graduate); $32,000 (Graduate with advanced degree)

Benefits: Health insurance, paid vacation, dental insurance

Part-Time Employees: 2

Summer Employees: None

Volunteers: 1

Interns: 1-4
Length: 10 week period
Duties: Law clerks: legal research, writing and interviewing clients
Remuneration: Small grants for summer; credit during the school year

Jobs advertised: Jobs are advertised through other community agencies and through *Opportunity NOCs* and the Public Interest Clearinghouse *Job Alert!*

To apply: Please contact Paul M. Igasaki, Executive Director

ASOCIACION NACIONAL PRO PERSONAS MAYORES

3325 Wilshire Blvd., Suite 800
Los Angeles, CA 90010
(213) 487-1922

Other Offices: Tucson, AZ; Miami, FL; Tampa, FL; Philadelphia, PA; San Diego, CA; Puerto Rico; Kansas City, KS; Chicago, IL; New Orleans, IL; Detroit, MI; San Antonio, TX; Laredo, TX; El Paso, TX; Washington, DC

Director: Carmela Lacavo

Purpose: To improve the quality of life for Hispanic elderly by providing employment, housing and related social services.

Methods of operation: Human services (85%), publications (5%), public education (5%), training and technical assistance (5%)

Constituency: Elderly Hispanics

Recent issues and projects: Recent projects include: Project Esperanza, established a toll free

elderly persons in applying for SSI
ject MAS provides bilingual emergency
materials; El Pueblo CDC builds
housing for Hispanic families

Major publications: *A National Study to Assess the Needs of Hispanic Elderly*; *National Hispanic Community Based Organization Directory*

Budget: $15,000,000

Funding: Government grants (100%)

Staff: 44
1 Writer/Editor
1 Office Manager
2 Administrative Assistants
9 Bookkeepers/Accountants
2 Administrators
25 Regional Coordinators
2 Secretaries
2 Clerical

Work Week: 40 hours

Benefits: Health insurance, pension, paid vacation, life insurance, credit union, training courses

Part-Time Employees: 1

Summer Employees: 1

Volunteers: None

Interns: 6
Length: 6 months
Duties: Assigned to administrative duties with host agencies
Remuneration: Salary paid jointly by ANPPM and host agency; fringe benefits

Jobs advertised: Local newspapers

To apply: Contact Mr. Henry Rodriquez

ASPIRA ASSOCIATION, INC.

1112 16th Street, NW, Suite 340
Washington, DC 20036
(202) 835-3600

Director: Ronald Blacklaurch-Moreno

Purpose: ASPIRA's mission is to empower the Latino Community through education and leadership development of its youth.

Methods of operation: Training and technical assistance (65%), public education (20%), research (7%), publications (5%)

Constituency: Youth clubs

Recent issues and projects: One of the major programs is the ASPIRA Public Policy Leadership program. It provides students the opportunity to study public policy and work with local leaders in community services internships. A few of these go on to Washington, DC for the national internship.

Major publications: *ASPIRA News*, quarterly national newsletter; issue briefs; fact sheets

Budget: $1,156,538

Funding: Individual contributions, foundations

Staff: 13
1 Office Manager
1 Executive Director
1 Lobbyist
5 Administrative Assistants
1 Bookkeeper/Accountant
4 Program Managers

Staff openings/year: 3

Work Week: 35 hours

Salary/year: $20,000 (Recent College Graduate); $30,000 (Graduate with advanced degree)

Benefits: Health insurance, pension, paid vacation, life insurance, tuition reimbursement

Part-Time Employees: 2

Summer Employees: None

Volunteers: Varies

Interns: 2
Length: 10 weeks

Jobs advertised: Newspapers

To apply: Contact Ronald Blackburn

ASSOCIATION FOR COMMUNITY BASED EDUCATION (ACBE)

1805 Florida Ave., NW
Washington, DC 20009
(202) 462-6333

Other Offices: Salinas, CA

Director: Christofer Zachariadis

Purpose: ACBE is a national membership organization of community-based groups that provide education linked to the culture and economic development of their communities. Through special projects, training, grants, publications and information services, ACBE strives to strengthen member groups and build support for the concept of community-based education.

Methods of operation: Grant programs (25%), training and technical assistance (25%), research (20%), publications (20%), public education (10%)

Constituency: Diverse group of community-based organizations nationwide, both rural and urban, and from many cultural and racial makeups

Recent issues and projects: Research, evaluation, training and technical assistance to community-based literacy programs. Economic development, community-wide education linked to community development and organizing. Community-based college programs.

Major publications: Monthly newsletter: *CBE Report*; membership directory; fundraising source directories; reports on literacy; student outcome evaluation; literacy program evaluation tools; national directory of literacy programs

Budget: $750,000

Funding: Foundations (95%), membership (5%)

Staff: 10

Staff openings/year: 2

Work Week: 40 hours

Salary/year: $Varies

Benefits: Health insurance, life insurance, paid vacation, pension

Part-Time Employees: 2

Summer Employees: 1

Volunteers: 1

Interns: 2
Length: As long as possible
Duties: Writing, research, communication
Remuneration: Stipend is negotiable

Jobs advertised: *Washington Post*; newsletters

To apply: Contact Personnel Office

Remarks: The Salinas, CA office is the Rural Development Center.

ASSOCIATION FOR NEIGHBORHOOD AND HOUSING DEVELOPMENT

236 West 27th Street
New York, NY 10001
(212) 463-9600

Director: Jay Small

Purpose: ANHD is a federation of four dozen nonprofit community-based housing organizations serving low and mixed income communities throughout New York City. ANHD's mission is (a) to advocate for public policies which will produce and preserve affordable low and moderate income housing, and (b) to provide technical assistance to community-based organizations working to improve their housing and neighborhood conditions.

Methods of operation: Advocacy (40%), research (30%), publications (10%), public education (10%)

Constituency: Four dozen nonprofit community-based housing organizations serving low and mixed income communities throughout New York City

Recent issues and projects: Analysis, critique and organizing around New York City's Owned Housing Stock programs. Housing Budget Campaign, Organizers Working Group coordinating the Community Housing Association of Managers and Producers (CHAMP) a trade association for developers and managers of low-income property.

Major publications: *The ANHD Weekly Reader*; *Missing the Mark: Subsidized Housing for the Privileged, Displacing the Poor*, an analysis of the City's Ten-Year Housing Plan; various technical assistance publications

Budget: $304,000

Funding: Foundations and corporations (94%), membership dues (5%), government contracts (1%)

Staff: 4
1 Executive Director
1 Policy Analyst
1 Office Manager
1 CHAMP Director
1/2 Associate Director

Staff openings/year: 2

Work Week: 40-45 hours

Salary/year: $26,000 (Recent College Graduate); $32,000 (Graduate with advanced degree)

Benefits: Health insurance, life insurance, paid vacation, compensatory time

Part-Time Employees: 1

Summer Employees: 1-2

Volunteers: 1-2

Interns: 1
Length: Summer

Duties: Research assistant and organizing projects
Remuneration: Through university work-study programs

Jobs advertised: Local housing and community development publications; schools

To apply: Contact Jay Small, Executive Director

ASSOCIATION FOR UNION DEMOCRACY

500 State Street, 2nd Floor
Brooklyn, NY 11217
(718) 855-6650

Other Offices: Oakland, CA; Boston, MA

Director: Susan Jennik

Purpose: To advance the principles and practices of internal democracy in the North American labor movement as an end in and of itself, and as a means to strengthen the labor movement.

Methods of operation: Publications (25%), public education (15%), training and technical assistance (25%), research (10%), human services (10%), direct action (5%), community organizing (5%), lobbying (5%)

Constituency: Insurgent trade union activists, radicals in and out of trade unions, civil liberty lawyers, liberals, university labor relations faculty, anti-organized crime people

Recent issues and projects: Support anti-corruption pro-democracy forces within unions; Support for the right of self-expression for dissidents through litigation, public relations and counseling; Women's and Latino Workers Project

Major publications: *Union Democracy Review*; *Democratic Rights for Union Members - A Guide to Internal Union Democracy*; *How to Get An Honest Union Election*; *Union Democracy and Landrum-Griffin*;

Budget: $200,000

Funding: Foundations (60%), individual contributions (30%), literature and novelty sales (5%), fundraising affairs (5%)

Staff: 4
2 Organizers
1 Writer/Editor
1 Attorney

Staff openings/year: 0

Work Week: 40 hours

Salary/year: $22-30,000 (Graduate with advanced degree)

Benefits: Health insurance, life insurance, paid vacation

Part-Time Employees: 2

Summer Employees: 1-2

Volunteers: As many as possible

Interns: None currently, but willing to accept applications

Jobs advertised: *Community Jobs*; various left publications; word of mouth

To apply: Contact Susan Jennik, Executive Director

ASSOCIATION FOR WOMEN IN SCIENCE, INC.

1522 K Street, NW
Washington, DC 20005
(202) 408-0742

Director: Catherine Jay Didion

Purpose: AWIS encourages the participation of girls and women in science by promoting science and education in the school and communities. AWIS is a 22-year-old, nonprofit, educational organization that strives to improve educational and employment opportunities for girls and women in all science fields.

Methods of operation: Human services (50%), publications (45%), research (5%)

Membership: 60 local chapters with 4,700 AWIS members; more than 60 percent hold doctorates in their fields (lifesciences, physical sciences, mathematics, social sciences and engineers)

Recent issues and projects: AWIS and its 60 local chapters have recently completed a three-year, $400,000 mentoring program with support from the Alfred P. Sloan Foundation. This program was designed to encourage and retain undergraduate and graduate women in the Sciences.

Major publications: *A Hand Up: Women Mentoring*; *Women in Science*; *Mentoring Means Future Scientists*; *Grants at a Glance*; *AWIS* magazine

Budget: $100,000

Funding: Individual contributions, foundations

Staff: 3
1 Organizer

1 Office Manager
1 Bookkeeper/Accountant

Staff openings/year: 0

Work Week: 40 hours

Salary/year: $Varies (Recent College Graduate); $Varies (Graduate with advanced degree)

Benefits: Health insurance, paid vacation, tuition reimbursement

Part-Time Employees: 2

Summer Employees: Varies

Volunteers: 1

Interns: 5
Length: 3 months
Duties: Program development and management, legislative analysis, magazine chapters, research, special projects
Remuneration: Stipends available

To apply: Contact Catherine Jay Didion, Executive Director

ASSOCIATION OF COMMUNITY ORGANIZATIONS FOR REFORM NOW (ACORN)

845 Flatbush Avenue
Brooklyn, NY 11226
(718) 693-6700 DC: (202) 547-9292

Other Offices: Chicago, IL; Atlanta, GA; New Orleans, LA; Denver, CO; Oakland, CA; Little Rock, AR; Bridgeport, CT; Washington, DC; St. Paul, MN; Boston, MA; Philadelphia, PA; Detroit, MI; Phoenix, AZ; San Jose, CA; Des Moines, IA; Baltimore, MD; St. Louis, MO; Dallas, TX; Seattle, WA; Milwaukee, WI

Director: Wade Rathke, Madeline Talbott, Steven Kest

Purpose: ACORN's first priority is building organizations in low-income communities. Organizers are on the streets every day knocking on doors and recruiting new members. Major campaigns mobilize the unorganized majority of low-income families to win specific benefits through membership efforts.

Methods of operation: Community organizing (50%), direct action (30%), research (10%), lobbying (10%)

Membership: Low to moderate income families

Recent issues and projects: ACORN currently works on the following issues: housing, community reinvestment, financial reform, schools, jobs, voter participation, toxics, health, and neighborhood safety

Funding: Foundations (30%), membership dues and local fundraising (70%)

Staff: 175
150 + Neighborhood Organizers
25 Support Staff (lobbyists, researchers, administrative staff, etc.)

Work Week: 50-60 hours

Salary/year: $12,000 - 16,000

Benefits: Paid vacation, and sick leave

Summer Employees: Yes

Interns: Yes
Length: 2 months-1 year
Duties: Research, community organizing
Remuneration: Arrangements will be made with intern, salary paid

Jobs advertised: Local and national publications

To apply: Contact Madeline Talbott, Field Director, 117 W. Harrison St. Chicago, IL 60605

Remarks: We are a national organization with offices in 20 states, including those listed in other offices. ACORN is always looking for committed and progressive individuals to work as community organizers at our offices nationwide.

ASSOCIATION OF FOREST SERVICE EMPLOYEES FOR ENVIRONMENTAL ETHICS

P.O. Box 11615
Eugene, OR 97440
(503) 484-2692

Director: Andy Stahl

Purpose: To forge a socially responsible value system for the forest service based on a land ethic which ensures ecologically and economically sustainable resource management.

Methods of operation: Direct action (30%), research (20%), publications (20%), community organizing (14%), public education (10%), lobbying (1%)

Membership: 1000 Forest Service employees and

8,500 general public throughout the United States

Recent issues and projects: Recent issues include: Developing a Forest Service employee alternative plan for managing the forests in eastern Oregon and Washington; monitoring "lost forests"; publishing *Inner Voice*; organizing Forest Service Employees; helping develop watershed management plans in the southeast

Major publications: *Inner Voice*; *Activist*; *Tongass at the Crossroads*; *Toward Excellence in the U.S. Forest Service*; *Rocky Mountain Challenge*

Budget: $650,000

Funding: Foundations (50%), direct mail (28%), individual contributions (20%), publications (2%)

Staff: 8
1 Organizer
1 Writer/Editor
1 Office Manager
1/2 Foundation Fundraiser
1/2 Grassroots Fundraiser
2 Issue Experts
1 Administrative Assistant
1 Database Specialist/Publications Designer

Staff openings/year: 0-1

Work Week: 40 hours

Salary/year: $22,000 (Recent College Graduate); $24,000 (Graduate with advanced degree)

Benefits: Health and dental insurance, paid vacation, family leave, 403B

Part-Time Employees: 2

Summer Employees: None

Volunteers: 1-3

Interns: 1-2
Length: 6 months
Duties: Research
Remuneration: School credit, possibly a small stipend

Jobs advertised: *Community Jobs*, *Environmental Opportunities*, *High Country News*

To apply: Contact Shannon Cantrell, Director of Administration and Finance

AVIATION CONSUMER ACTION PROJECT (ACAP)

P.O. Box 19029
Washington, DC 20036
(202) 638-4000 (800) 836-0236

Director: Tom O'Mara

Purpose: ACAP works to promote airline safety and the rights of the travelling public before public agencies, the executive branch and Congress. It is the only nonprofit consumer organization working full-time on aviation matters. ACAP serves as a valuable resource of data for attorneys, journalists and researchers seeking information on air safety issues. ACAP is regularly contacted by whistleblowers wishing to share problems on safety hazards. ACAP has alerted the public to a number of air safety problems and is regularly invited to testify before Congress and appear on national television programs to discuss air safety.

Methods of operation: Direct action (35%), research (25%), media contact and public education (20%), publications (15%), lobbying (5%)

Constituency: Contributors are members of the public interested in supporting our work to improve air safety, service and passenger rights.

Recent issues and projects: Prompted the Federal Aviation Administration (FAA) in 1989 to charter the Aviation Security Advisory Committee to make sure that the public is represented effectively in discussions with the FAA about what security measures airlines should be required to implement. Helped to get established the President's Commission on Aviation Security and Terrorism in August 1989. The FAA has proposed a rule to be issued in final form in 1990 to require improved crashworthiness standards for all seats installed in scheduled passenger aircraft. ACAP petitioned FAA to provide infant seats for use on aircraft and FAA issued a proposed rule in March 1990. Also support smoking ban on domestic U.S. flights and protective breathing devices for all passengers.

Major publications: *Facts and Advice for Airline Passengers*, a consumer information booklet; membership is $35.00

Funding: Direct mail (70%), individual contributions (30%)

Staff: 4
2 Attorneys
2 Lobbyists

Staff openings/year: 0-1

Work Week: 40 hours

Benefits: Health insurance

Volunteers: 1-2

Interns: Yes
Length: Summer
Duties: Research, consumer complaint evaluation and response
Remuneration: Volunteer

Jobs advertised: Local newspapers

To apply: Contact Christopher J. Witkowski, Director

BAKERY, CONFECTIONERY AND TOBACCO WORKERS INTERNATIONAL UNION

10401 Connecticut Avenue
Kensington, MD 20895-3961
(301) 933-8600

President: Frank Hurt

Purpose: Represents 135,000 members (primarily employed in production) in baking, confectionery and tobacco industries. Primary services to membership include collective bargaining, grievance handling, legislative and political action.

Methods of operation: Staff departments include Public Relations (communications, legislative/political activities, civil rights); Research; Education; Organization

Recent issues and projects: In 1988 the organization hired an outside consulting firm to assist the executive officers with strategic planning. The process is ongoing. Three task forces were set up to study three primary issues and make recommendations concerning youth involvement, leadership involvement and technological change.

Major publications: *BC&T News*, for membership, published 9 times/year; *BC&T Report*, monthly leadership newsletter; company-focused newsletter, when necessary; pamphlets; convention materials (every 4 years)

Funding: Dues, investments

Staff: 21
11 Secretarial/Clerical
2 Education
2 Writers/Editors
2 Researchers
1 President
1 Executive Vice President
1 Secretary-Treasurer
1 Comptroller

Work Week: 32.5 hours

Benefits: Health insurance, life insurance, pregnancy leave, pension, credit union, paid vacation

Interns: 1-3
Length: Semester or summer
Duties: Work in PR Department on publications/communications/legislation, or in Research Department on various projects
Remuneration: $325 college grads; $275 undergraduates. Stipend for undergraduate receiving credit and working p-t.

Jobs advertised: When available, positions are advertised in *Community Jobs* and with college placement offices.

To apply: Contact Carolyn J. Jacobson, Director of Public Relations

Remarks: The intern would primarily be researching and writing articles for the *BC&T News* and the *BC&T Report*. He or she will also be expected to accompany department staff to various meetings in Washington, DC related to BC&T activities or to attend some of these meetings in place of the staff and report on them. He or she will also be expected to work on special projects as they arise, i.e. a legislative campaign or research project. Strong writing ability is required with course work or background in journalism preferred. Willingness to work for a labor union is essential.

BALTIMORE NEIGHBORHOODS, INC.

2217 Saint Paul Street
Baltimore, MD 21218
(410) 243-6007 (800) 487-6007

Director: George B. Laurent

Purpose: Justice in housing: tenant rights, elimination of illegal discrimination. BNI's goals are (1) to create an open housing market; (2) to maintain viable interracial communities; (3) to fight discrimination and prejudice; (4) to inform tenants of their rights and responsibilities and improve tenant-landlord relations; and (5) to help increase the supply of housing for low and moderate income people.

Methods of operation: Litigation, direct action (60%), human services (20%), community organizing (20%)

Constituency: Civil rights-minded people

Recent issues and projects: BNI monitors the practices of the housing industry for discrimination and publishes studies showing the extent of compliance and non-compliance with Federal and Maryland Fair Housing laws; encourages affirmative marketing of real estate; informs minorities of their rights under the law; works with and monitors the activities of federal and state agencies which have a responsibility to end discrimination in housing; handles complaints of discrimination; helps in cases where a neighborhood is experiencing racial tension and/or harassment of newcomers; initiates and helps coordinate support for laws improving the rights of tenants; operates statewide telephone information of counseling service for tenants and landlords

Major publications: *Guides To Tenant-Landlord Law* for State of Maryland

Budget: $300,000

Funding: Government contracts (50%), United Way (13%), other contributions (37%)

Staff: 10
1 Executive Director
1 Associate Director
1 Secretary
1 Organizer
2 Tenant Counselors
2 Testing Coordinators
1/2 Office Manager
1/2 Bookkeeper

Work Week: 35 hours

Salary/year: $16,000

Benefits: Health insurance, life insurance, pension, credit union, paid vacation

Volunteers: 100

Jobs advertised: Newspaper; Urban League; NAACP; state employment; women's groups

To apply: Contact George B. Laurent

BATTERED WOMEN'S ALTERNATIVES

P.O. Box 6406
Concord, CA 94524-1406
(415) 676-2845

Other Offices: Martinez, CA; Antioch, CA; Richmond, CA

Director: Rollie Mullen

Purpose: BWA is the authority on domestic violence in Contra Costa County and is recognized as a model program in California. Since 1977 BWA has provided counseling, shelter, legal support, job counseling and living skills planning, a men's treatment program and outreach and teen program education.

Methods of operation: Human services (60%), public education (15%), training and technical assistance (10%), community organizing (10%), publications (3%), lobbying (2%)

Constituency: Victims and perpetrators of domestic violence in Contra Costa County, California

Recent issues and projects: BWA has just begun a capital campaign to build a new emergency shelter and additional transition housing apartments. Total cost of the project is estimated to be $1.4 million

Major publications: Quarterly newsletter: *Options*, to a mailing list of 4,000; *Salad for 20*; a children's book about living in a domestic violence shelter; video: *My Girl* (on teen dating violence and abuse) and training manual *Teens Need Teens*, both of which have been distributed nationally

Budget: $1,505,725

Funding: Government grants (32%), individual contributions (51%), foundations (5%), other (12%)

Staff: 44
17 Counselors
5 Issue Experts
4 Administrative Coordinators
3 Intern Supervisors
2 Teen Services Staff Trainers
2 Paralegals
1 Development Assistant
2 Bookkeepers/Accountants
1 Education and Outreach Trainers
1 Executive Director
1 Director of Community Development
1 Teen Services Director
1 Attorney

1 Director of Volunteers
1 Director of Community Education and Personnel
1 Job Placement Counselor

Staff openings/year: 4-5

Work Week: 40 hours

Salary/year: $19,700 (Recent College Graduate); $21,800 (Graduate with advanced degree)

Benefits: Health and dental insurance, paid vacation and sick leave, family leave

Part-Time Employees: 26

Volunteers: 225

Interns: 23
Length: 18 months
Duties: Individual counseling; phone counseling; paralegal work; group counseling
Remuneration: Phone counseling is done in lieu of paid supervision

Jobs advertised: In-house posting; newspapers; extensive mailings; posting at local agencies and colleges; word of mouth

To apply: Contact Nancy Coppola, Personnel Assistant

BAY AREA INSTITUTE/PACIFIC NEWS SERVICE

450 Mission Street, Suite 506
San Francisco, CA 94105
(415) 243-4364

Director: Sandy Close

Purpose: A network of scholars, writers, journalists and community activists working together to research and report on the least known, least understood and most unsafe sides of issues and trends affecting our society.

Methods of operation: Public education (100%), including research (40%), publications (20%), community organizing (20%), training and technical assistance (20%)

Constituency: Newspaper editors, magazine editors, TV editors, policymakers, foundation representatives, media audience

Recent issues and projects: Articles published daily for newspaper subscribers; provide story consulting for TV; write special reports, magazine articles and books on areas of major concern such as youth, race relations, immigration, religion, U.S.-Third World relations, culture, human rights; and organize forums for foundations and policymakers that give them access to community voices they rarely hear

Major publications: A weekly collection of 5 to 7 stories wired during the week, sent to individual (nonmedia) subscribers. *YO!* (Youth Outlook), a bimonthly newspaper by and about teenagers, distributed nationally

Budget: $375,000

Funding: Foundations (60%), subscriptions, consulting (35%), individual contributions (5%)

Staff: 8
6 Writers/Editors
1 Office Manager
1 Editorial Assistant

Staff openings/year: 0-1

Work Week: 65 hours

Salary/year: $26,000 (Graduate with advanced degree)

Benefits: Health insurance, paid vacation

Part-Time Employees: 8

Volunteers: yes

Interns: 8
Length: 6 months
Duties: Reporting, writing, editing stories and designing graphics for *YO!*
Remuneration: Weekly stipend, paid for contract pieces

Jobs advertised: Word of mouth

To apply: Contact Sandy Close

BEGINNING FARMER SUSTAINABLE AGRICULTURE PROJECT

P.O. Box 736, 104 East Main
Hartington, NE 68739
(402) 254-6893

Other Offices: Walthill, NE

Director: Wyatt Fraas, Project Leader

Purpose: Advise agricultural and social policy agencies and decisionmakers on needs and benefits of beginning small farmers; encourage, educate and facilitate beginning farmers and local mutual, help circles; stimulate public dialogue on the sustainability of rural communities.

Methods of operation: Research (50%),

publications (15%), public education (10%), training and technical assistance (25%)

Constituency: Serve small to mid-size farmers, especially beginning and re-entering farmers

Recent issues and projects: On-farm research, farmer workshops and courses on agricultural alternatives, facilitate local mutual-help groups

Major publications: *Resourceful Farming Primer*; *Small Farm Energy Primer*; *Beneath the Wheels of Fortune*; *Fit for a Pig*; *Resource Audit and Planning Guide*

Budget: $175,000

Funding: Foundations (90%), individual contributions (10%)

Staff: 3
1 Project Leader
1 Research Assistant
1 Office Manager

Staff openings/year: 0-1

Work Week: 40 hours

Salary/year: $15,000 (Recent College Graduate); $25,000 (Graduate with advanced degree)

Benefits: Health insurance, paid vacation

Part-Time Employees: None

Summer Employees: None

Volunteers: None

Interns: None; but willing to accept applications

Jobs advertised: Environmental journals and listing services

To apply: Contact Chuck Hassebrook, Program Leader

BERKELEY COMMUNITY LAW CENTER

3130 Shattuck Avenue
Berkeley, CA 94705
(415) 548-4040

Director: Bernida Reagan

Purpose: The Center provides legal services for the poor and homeless in Berkeley, Oakland and Emeryville. The Center, opened in September 1988, was founded by law students at the University of California, Berkeley in response to federal budget cuts that reduced legal services offered to the 15 percent of Alameda County's residents who live below the official poverty line.

Methods of operation: Litigation (60%), human services (10%), public education (10%), research (5%), lobbying (5%), training and technical assistance (5%), community organizing (5%)

Constituency: Low-income residents/homeless/people with HIV infection

Recent issues and projects: Recent projects include: welfare (raising property limit to enable more people to get welfare); opposing program that would require homeless to go to welfare hotels in lieu of aid

Major publications: Newsletters

Budget: $450,000

Funding: Individual contributions, foundations, federal government

Staff: 8
6 Attorneys
2 Administrative Assistants
20 Interns/Caseworkers

Work Week: 40 hours

Benefits: Health insurance, life insurance, pregnancy leave, paid vacation, bar dues

Summer Employees: 10

Volunteers: 5

Interns: 45 per year
Length: 15 weeks
Duties: Interview clients, research, writing, oral advocacy
Remuneration: Work-study $10/hour or law school public interest grants

Jobs advertised: Through law schools and public interest publications

To apply: Contact Bernida Reagan

BET TZEDEK LEGAL SERVICES

145 South Fairfax Avenue, Suite 200
Los Angeles, CA 90036
(213) 939-0506

Other Offices: North Hollywood, CA

Director: Michael Feuer

Purpose: To provide free legal services to the poor and elderly residents of Los Angeles County.

Methods of operation: Litigation (90%), public education (5%), training and technical assistance

(5%)

Constituency: Senior citizens; private and public interest legal communities

Recent issues and projects: Nursing Home Advocacy Project; Homeless Project; Home Equity Fraud Prevention Task Force; legal outreach to seniors at multipurpose senior citizens' centers

Major publications: Annual report, newsletters, occasional op-ed articles; *Nursing Home Companion: A User Friendly Guide to Nursing Home Laws and Practices*

Budget: $2,600,000

Funding: Individual contributions (10%), foundations (10%), direct mail (5%), other (75%)

Staff: 50
Including:
18 Attorneys
8 Paralegals
4 Office Managers
10 Typists
3 Bookkeepers/Accountants
2 Foundation Fundraisers
1 Press Aide

Staff openings/year: 3

Work Week: 45 hours

Salary/year: $25,000 (Recent College Graduate); $30,000 (Graduate with advanced degree)

Benefits: Health insurance, pension, pregnancy leave

Part-Time Employees: 3

Summer Employees: 9

Volunteers: 350

Interns: 25
Length: 1 semester
Duties: Legal representation, support
Remuneration: Stipends available for law students

Jobs advertised: Mailings; paid advertisements

To apply: Contact Michael Feuer, Executive Director

BETTER GOVERNMENT ASSOCIATION

230 North Michigan Avenue, Suite 1710
Chicago, IL 60601
(312) 641-1181

Director: J. Terrence Brunner

Purpose: To combat waste, inefficiency and corruption in government. Frequently works with local and national news media on a variety of investigative projects.

Methods of operation: Investigative reporting, research, public education

Constituency: Individuals, academics and business people interested in improving governmental performance

Recent issues and projects: Casino gambling; minority contractors; police promotional exams; public health; environment; nursing homes

Major publications: Newsletter, investigative exposes on local and national news media and staff reports

Budget: $500,000

Funding: Individual contributions, foundations, direct mail

Staff: 8
3 Investigators
2 Attorneys
1 Fundraiser
1 Writer/Editor
1 Office Manager

Staff openings/year: 0-1

Work Week: 50 hours

Salary/year: $15,000 (Recent College Graduate); $20,000 (Graduate with advanced degree)

Benefits: Health insurance, life insurance

Part-Time Employees: 1

Summer Employees: 2-3

Volunteers: Yes

Interns: Yes
Length: 2-3 months

Jobs advertised: Word of mouth

To apply: Contact J. Terrence Brunner

BHOPAL ACTION RESOURCE CENTER

777 United Nations Plaza, Suite 9A
New York, NY 10017
(212) 972-9877

Director: David Dembo

Purpose: The program seeks to help the victims of Union Carbide's Bhopal disaster in their struggles for justice and accountability, and works with other victim groups to achieve greater accountability of transnational corporations and governments. The Center is a program of the Council on International and Public Affairs.

Methods of operation: Public education (45%), publications (30%), research (20%)

Constituency: We work with representatives of victim groups worldwide.

Recent issues and projects: Bhopal Action sponsored, with other groups, a tour for some Bhopal victims of communities at risk from industrial hazards in the U.S., U.K., and Ireland. Co-founded Communities Concerned About Corporations to work on Bhopal-type issues in the U.S. with community, religious, environmental and other groups.

Major publications: *Worker Empowerment in a Changing Economy (1991)*; *Abuse of Power* (1990); *Nothing to Lose But Our Lives* (1988); *The Bhopal Tragedy* (1986); *Briefing Papers on Bhopal* (#1-10); many other books on related subjects

Budget: $30,000

Funding: Book sales (80%), individual contributions (5%), foundations (10%)

Staff: 5
3 Writer/Editors
1 Attorney
1 Researcher

Benefits: Health insurance, life insurance, paid vacation

Part-Time Employees: 3

Interns: 1
Length: 1 semester
Duties: Research, bibliographies
Remuneration: None

Jobs advertised: Work-study positions are listed at Columbia University.

To apply: Contact David Dembo, Program Director

BIG MOUNTAIN LEGAL OFFICE

P.O. Box 1509
Flagstaff, AZ 86002
(602) 779-1560

Director: Lee Phillips, Attorney at Law

Purpose: We are a 501(c)(3) public interest law office. We provide quality legal representation to the individual Indian persons facing relocation from their ancestral homelands.

Methods of operation: Public education (25%), litigation (75%)

Constituency: We have supporters from all walks of life from all over the country and the world. Our clients are traditional Navajo Indians.

Recent issues and projects: First Amendment/freedom of religion lawsuit - denied at federal court level; Ninth Circuit Court of Appeals has ordered the United States, the Hopi Tribe and the Navajo Tribe to participate in federal mediation with our office as legal representative of the traditional Navajo families - mediation began in 1990 and is ongoing.

Major publications: Newsletter

Funding: Foundations (60%), individual contributions (40%)

Volunteers: 2

Interns: Yes
Length: As long as you can stay
Duties: Vary depending on need; mostly legal research
Remuneration: Must be financially independent

To apply: Contact Lee Phillips, Director

BIO-INTEGRAL RESOURCE CENTER

P.O. Box 7414
Berkeley, CA 94707
(415) 524-2567

Director: Sheila Daar

Purpose: To provide information on the least toxic ways to manage pests.

Methods of operation: Research, publications, public education, training and technical assistance

Constituency: Professionals in pest control, agriculture, landscape maintenance, building maintenance, and gardeners and members of the public

Recent issues and projects: Research and planning with various agencies on approaches to pest control which are non-toxic or least-toxic. Advising the public on same.

Major publications: *IPM Practitioner*; *Common Sense Pest Control Quarterly*; many reports, booklets and books

Budget: $400,000

Funding: Membership, sale of publications (60%), foundations and contracts (35-40%), individual contributions (0-5%)

Staff: 13
2 Writers/Editors
1 Bookkeeper/Accountant
1 Membership Manager
1 Data Base Manager
1 Office Manager
1 Organizer
1 Executive Director
5 IPM Specialists

Staff openings/year: 1-2

Work Week: 40 hours

Part-Time Employees: 3-5

Summer Employees: 1-2

Volunteers: 5

Interns: 2
Length: 6 months
Duties: Research; library management

Jobs advertised: Word of mouth; college bulletin boards; university agencies

To apply: Contact Shea Gordon, Office Manager

BODY POSITIVE

2095 Broadway, Suite 306
New York, NY 10023
(212) 721-1346

Director: Frank Carbone

Purpose: To educate, support and empower HIV positive people and their partners so they can take steps to remain healthy.

Methods of operation: Human services (25%), publications (25%), public education (25%), training and technical assistance (25%)

Recent issues and projects: We are establishing peer support groups and peer education programs in all boroughs of New York City.

Major publications: *The Body Positive* magazine, published 11 times yearly

Budget: $600,000

Funding: Public (40%), foundations (40%), individual contributions (20%)

Staff: 8
1 Executive Director
1 Outreach Coordinator
1 Education Director
1 Support Services Director
1 Writer/Editor
1 Foundation Fundraiser
1 Office Manager
1 Volunteer Coordinator

Staff openings/year: 2

Work Week: 50-60 hours

Salary/year: $24-30,000 (Recent College Graduate); $32-36,000 (Graduate with advanced degree)

Benefits: Health insurance, paid vacation

Volunteers: 145

Jobs advertised: Newspaper; via HIV organizations

To apply: Contact Frank Carbone, Executive Director

BOSTON CARES

P.O. Box 406
Boston, MA 02102
(617) 472-2272

Director: Julie Fingersh

Purpose: Boston Cares is a community outreach program geared toward young professionals who are trying to balance full time careers with their desire to help their city through projects addressing new Americans, hunger, homelessness and other civic concerns.

Methods of operation: Direct action (40%), human services (20%), community organizing (20%), research (20%)

Constituency: Young professionals between ages of 22-25

Major publications: *Boston Cares News*, monthly newsletter

Budget: $50,000

Funding: Individual contributions, foundations, direct mail, events

Staff: 1
1 Director

Staff openings/year: 1

Work Week: 40 hours

Salary/year: $20,000

Benefits: Health insurance, paid vacation

Part-Time Employees: None

Summer Employees: None

Volunteers: 70

Interns: Yes
Length: Summer or semester
Duties: Volunteer recruitment, support for Director

To apply: Contact Julie Fingersh

Remarks: We would welcome the efforts of a very bright, motivated intern who is resourceful, creative and independent thinker with an interest in community service. Proven intern will have first shot at full time position.

BOSTON HUD TENANT ALLIANCE

434 Massachusetts Avenue, Suite 203
Boston, MA 02118
(617) 267-2949

Director: Michael Kane

Purpose: Since 1983, BHTA has stopped displacement and won protections for thousands of tenants in financially distressed and "expiring use" HUD housing. Currently, the Alliance works with 12 tenant groups, assisting in basic organizing and development strategies leading to alternative ownership and management.

Methods of operation: Training and technical assistance (40%), community organizing (40%), research (5%), lobbying (5%), publications (5%), human services (5%)

Constituency: Low-income; people of color; tenants

Budget: $180,000

Funding: Foundations (100%)

Staff: 4
2 Organizers
1 Executive Director
1 Office Manager

Staff openings/year: 1

Work Week: 50 hours

Salary/year: $20,000

Benefits: Health insurance, life insurance, pregnancy leave, paid vacation, dental

Volunteers: 2

Interns: None currently, but willing to accept applications

Jobs advertised: Local newspapers; other organizations

To apply: Contact Michael Kane, Director

BOSTON WOMEN'S HEALTH BOOK COLLECTIVE

240 A Elm Street
Somerville, MA 02144-2935
(617) 625-0277

Director: Judy Norsigian

Purpose: Women's health education, advocacy and activism.

Methods of operation: Public education (65%), training and technical assistance (10%), publications (9%), research (5%), community organizing (5%), direct action (5%), litigation (1%)

Constituency: Mostly women, some men

Recent issues and projects: *Our Bodies, Ourselves* translation/adaptation projects in four developing country regions; obtaining tampon absorbency labeling requirements by the FDA; working on childbearing and midwifery concerns; contraception - serving on the National Academy of Sciences (NAS) Committee on Contraceptive Development

Major publications: *The New Our Bodies Ourselves*; *Ourselves and Our Children*; collaborated on *Ourselves Growing Older* and *Changing Bodies, Changing Lives*

Budget: $250,000

Funding: Foundations (55%), royalties income (20%), individual contributions (15%), literature sales and honorarium (10%)

Staff: 13

Staff openings/year: 1

Work Week: 35-45 hours

Salary/year: $Depends on exp. (Recent College Graduate); $Depends on exp. (Graduate with advanced degree)

Benefits: Health insurance, pregnancy leave, small pension, paid vacation

Part-Time Employees: 3

Volunteers: 5

Jobs advertised: Newspapers; mailings; word of mouth

To apply: Contact Judy Norsigian, Co-Director: (617) 625-0271 direct line

BREAD AND ROSES COMMUNITY FUND

924 Cherry Street, Second Floor
Philadelphia, PA 19107
(215) 928-1880

Director: Judy Claude

Purpose: Bread and Roses is an alternative foundation raising funds to make grants to grassroots activist groups working for social justice.

Methods of operation: Fundraising, grantmaking (90%), public education (5%), training and technical assistance (5%)

Recent issues and projects: We provide funding to groups doing activist work in areas such as: community organizing, peace, women's rights, gay liberation, international solidarity, health, labor, and culture. We provide services to grantees and donors.

Budget: $400,000

Funding: Individual contributions (70%), workplace solicitation (15%), direct mail (15%)

Staff: 3
1 Director
1 Program Coordinator
1 Administrative Coordinator

Staff openings/year: 1

Work Week: 40 hours

Salary/year: $23,000

Benefits: Health insurance, pregnancy/parental leave, child care, paid vacation

Part-Time Employees: 1

Summer Employees: 0

Volunteers: 3

Interns: Yes
Length: 6 months to one year
Duties: Special projects. We only accept interns from other programs.
Remuneration: No compensation available

Jobs advertised: Newspaper; progressive periodicals; mailings

To apply: Contact Judy Claude, Director

BREAD FOR THE CITY

1525 7th Street, NW
Washington, DC 20001
(202) 332-0440

Director: Rev. Charles Parker

Purpose: To provide emergency food, clothing and social work services to low-income residents of the District of Columbia.

Methods of operation: Human services, training and technical assistance, lobbying

Constituency: Residents of the District of Columbia who are elderly, disabled or parents with dependent children

Major publications: Monthly newsletter: *Breadcrumbs*

Budget: $850,000

Funding: Individual contributions, foundations, religious organizations, corporations and the government

Staff: 14
1 Executive Director
2 Site Coordinator
1 Clothing Coordinator
2 Drivers
2 Social Work Directors
1 Newsletter/Fundraiser
1 Assistant Director
1 Data Entry
1 Bookkeeper

Staff openings/year: 3

Work Week: 40 hours

Salary/year: $17-30,000

Benefits: Health insurance, pregnancy/parental leave, paid vacation, tuition reimbursement (limited), dental insurance

Part-Time Employees: 3

Volunteers: 70

Interns: Yes
Length: 1-2 years
Duties: Vary depending on intern's program
Remuneration: Stipends available

Jobs advertised: Newspaper; internal postings

To apply: Contact Rev. Charles Parker, Executive Director

Remarks: Our 4 full-time volunteers receive a

stipend and housing.

BREAD FOR THE WORLD

1100 Wayne Ave., Suite 1000
Silver Spring, MD 20910
(301) 608-2400

Other Offices: Minneapolis, MN; Chicago, IL; Los Angeles, CA

President: Arthur Simon

Purpose: Bread for the World is a nationwide Christian movement that seeks justice for the world's hungry people by lobbying our nation's decision-makers.

Methods of operation: Research, publications, community organizing, public education, lobbying by members

Membership: Christian citizens in the U.S.; membership of 41,000

Recent issues and projects: Child nutrition and WIC (Special Supplemental Food Program for Women, Infants and Children); minimum wage increase; child care; renewing U.S. grain reserves in 1990 farm bill; Central America; Third World debt; halting military aid to South Africa; foreign aid reform; foreign aid funding; agriculture and food policy

Major publications: Newsletter (10 times/year); annual report; Offering of Letters kit (once/year); 8-10 background papers per year. The Bread for the World Institute on Hunger and Development, a sister organization, publishing annual reports on global hunger and occasional papers

Budget: $2,600,000

Funding: Individual contributions (85%), direct mail (15%)

Staff: 42
12 Organizers
5 Issue Experts
7 Researchers
3 Writers/Editors
3 Fundraisers
2 Bookkeepers/Accountants
3 Media Staff
2 Administrators
2 Membership Records
2 Mailroom
1 Personnel Director
1 Administrative Assistant
1 Office Manager
1 Computer Systems
1 Art Director
1 Librarian

Staff openings/year: 5

Work Week: 37.5 hours

Salary/year: $21-55,000

Benefits: Health insurance, life insurance, maternity/ paternity leave, pension, paid vacation

Part-Time Employees: 5

Summer Employees: 10-15

Volunteers: 22

Interns: 8 at present
Length: 1-2 years, except for summer
Duties: Interns work in various departments (i.e. Issues, Organizing, Media, Communications, Development) with permanent staff members.
Remuneration: Stipended interns earn $12,000 per year

Jobs advertised: Newspaper ads; newsletter; announcements to other social justice organizations and church groups

To apply: Contact Personnel Director

BREAK AWAY: THE ALTERNATIVE BREAK CONNECTION

6026 Station B
Nashville, TN 37235
(615) 343-0385

Director: Michael Magevney

Purpose: To promote service through alternative break programs which immerse students in often vastly different cultures, heighten social awareness and advocate life-long social action.

Methods of operation: Training and technical assistance (65%), publications (25%), direct action (10%)

Constituency: College students, universities, community based organizations

Recent issues and projects: Last year over 5,000 students volunteered during their spring break.

Major publications: *Connections*; *Break Away: Organizing an Alternative Spring Break*

Budget: $150,000

Funding: Foundations (90%), services (10%)

Staff: 11
3 Organizers
2 Writers/Editors
1 Office Managers
1 Foundation Fundraisers
3 Issue Experts
1 Bookkeeper/Accountant

Staff openings/year: 1-2

Work Week: 50 hours

Salary/year: $18,000 (Recent College Graduate); $Varies (Graduate with advanced degree)

Benefits: Health insurance, paid vacation, pregnancy leave

Part-Time Employees: 4

Summer Employees: 4

Volunteers: 1

Interns: 4
Length: 10 weeks
Duties: Project specific
Remuneration: $200/week and housing stipend

Jobs advertised: Newsletters, mailings, conference outreach

To apply: Contact Michael Magevney

BROOKLYN LEGAL SERVICES CORPORATION

65 Court Street
Brooklyn, NY 11201
(718) 237-5500

Director: John C. Gray, Jr.

Purpose: The Brooklyn Legal Services Corporation provides free legal help in civil cases to low-income people from southern and western Brooklyn

Methods of operation: Litigation (50%), advocacy (40%), research (5%), lobbying, publications, public education and training (5%)

Recent issues and projects: Current priorities are: housing; family; government benefits; consumer rights; employment; health; education; and disability rights. We also have an HIV outreach project.

Major publications: Quarterly newsletter

Budget: $3,700,000

Funding: Government (95%), foundations (4%), individual contributions (1%)

Staff: 60
32 Attorneys
16 Paralegals
1 Office Manager
6 Administrative Assistants
2 Receptionists
2 Investigators
1 Development Administrator

Staff openings/year: 5

Work Week: 40 hours

Salary/year: $22,000 (Recent College Graduate); $30,000 (Graduate with advanced degree)

Benefits: Health insurance, pension, paid vacation, life insurance, family leave

Part-Time Employees: 3

Summer Employees: 20

Volunteers: 5

Interns: 25
Length: School term or over summer
Duties: Assist attorneys with interviews, factual and legal research and writing
Remuneration: Work study or volunteer

Jobs advertised: Circulate lists to law schools, bar associations, student and attorney groups

To apply: John C. Gray, Jr., Project Director

Remarks: We hire attorneys and recent college grads and others to be paralegals. We have summer and term internships for law students.

BURLINGTON COMMUNITY LAND TRUST

P.O. Box 523
Burlington, VT 05401
(802) 864-8204

Director: Brenda Torpy

Purpose: BCLT is the nation's leading Community Land Trust (CLT). Its mission is to take housing off of the speculative market and to provide access to land to low and moderate income individuals in the community. We do this by buying property and holding it in perpetuity. The house on the land is sold to a low or moderate income family or individual. They lease the land. There is a limited equity covenant on the land, so that when the family sells they take only 25% of the social equity with them. The remaining 75% stays with the house so the next generation of buyers can buy the house at an even more affordable rate.

Methods of operation: Direct action (75%), human services (10%), public education (10%), community organizing (5%)

Membership: All residents of housing in the trust are members. In addition, any community member who subscribes the basic principles of the organization can become members.

Recent issues and projects: As of this year, the Burlington Community Land Trust will have over 250 units of housing in trust.

Budget: $250,000

Funding: Government grants (50%), direct mail (20%), foundations (20%), individual contributions (10%)

Staff: 10
1 Organizer
1 Issue Expert
1 Fundraiser
2 Bookkeepers/Accountants
1 Administrative Assistant
1 Caseworker

Staff openings/year: 2

Work Week: 40 hours

Salary/year: $25,000 (Recent College Graduate); $Varies (Graduate with advanced degree)

Benefits: Health insurance, life insurance, family leave, vacation

Part-Time Employees: None

Summer Employees: None

Volunteers: 15

Interns: 3
Length: 6 months
Duties: Fundraising, property management
Remuneration: None

Jobs advertised: Local newspapers

To apply: Please contact Brenda Torpy, Executive Director

BUSINESS AND PROFESSIONAL PEOPLE FOR THE PUBLIC INTEREST

17 East Monroe Street, #212
Chicago, IL 60603
(312) 641-5570

Director: Alexander Polikoff

Purpose: BPI provides legal representation for under-represented groups in matters that can have a significant impact on policy areas affecting the quality of life for all.

Methods of operation: Research (50%), litigation (25%), public education (20%), publications (5%)

Recent issues and projects: BPI's multi-issue agenda focuses on open housing, defense of the environment and responsible energy policies, as well as support for Chicago school reform through a project that provides volunteer legal advice to local school councils, promotion of comprehensive children and family support services, and exploration of small schools (schools-within-schools).

Major publications: Annual report; newsletter 3 times a year

Budget: $825,000

Funding: Foundations (62%), annual fundraiser (21%), individual contributions (12%), interest, miscellaneous (5%)

Staff: 7
3 Attorneys
1 Office Manager
2 Administrative Assistants
1 Bookkeeper/Accountant

Staff openings/year: 0-1

Work Week: 35 hours

Salary/year: $Varies (Recent College Graduate); $Varies (Graduate with advanced degree)

Benefits: Health insurance, paid vacation, life insurance, family leave

Part-Time Employees: 2

Summer Employees: Varies

Volunteers: Varies

Interns: Varies
Length: Summer or semester
Duties: Research
Remuneration: Varies

To apply: Please contact Marissa Manos, Administrative Director

CALIFORNIA ATTORNEYS FOR CRIMINAL JUSTICE

10551 Jefferson Boulevard
Culver City, CA 90232
(213) 204-0502

Director: Mary Warner

Purpose: Protection of constitutional rights of criminal defendants; improvement of the criminal justice system; elimination of the death penalty; provide continuing education programs and publications for criminal defense lawyers.

Methods of operation: Training and technical assistance for lawyers (50%), publications (20%), community organizing, litigation/amicus briefs, lobbying (30%)

Membership: Criminal defense lawyers and associated professionals

Recent issues and projects: Exposure of government misconduct in the use of informants in criminal trials - sponsored legislation to restrict this.

Major publications: *Forum* magazine, 6 times/year; *1989 Complete Sentencing Handbook*; *1993 Contempt Defense Manual*

Funding: Individual contributions (100%)

Staff: 4
2 Clerical
1 Executive Director
1 Computer Operator (dBase)

Work Week: 40+ hours

Benefits: Health insurance, paid vacation

Volunteers: Yes

Jobs advertised: *Los Angeles Times* classifieds

To apply: Contact Mary Warner

Remarks: The organization's legislative advocate is 660 J Street, Suite 200, Sacramento, CA 95814.

CALIFORNIA CENTER FOR LAW AND THE DEAF

1539 Webster Street
Oakland, CA 94612
(510) 251-6420

Other Offices: San Jose, CA; Fremont, CA

Director: John F. Levesque

Purpose: Nonprofit legal services corporation. Provides legal services for deaf and hearing-impaired clients in the areas of discrimination, access and special education.

Methods of operation: Legal services to organizations and individuals, litigation, lobbying, publications, community organizing, public education, training and technical assistance

Constituency: Deaf and hard-of hearing individuals and organizations

Recent issues and projects: Access legislation for state courts; state access regulations for public facilities; special education legislation; access to TV broadcasts of emergency information; state public utilities proceedings involving telecommunications access

Major publications: Bimonthly newsletter column; brochures on deaf rights and court access

Budget: $239,390

Funding: State Bar contracts, attorneys' fees (100%)

Staff: 5
Including:
3 Attorneys
1 Paralegals
1 Legal Secretary/Assistant
1/4 Office Assistant

Staff openings/year: 1

Work Week: 35 hours

Salary/year: $20 - 25,000

Benefits: Health insurance, life insurance, pregnancy leave, paid vacation

Part-Time Employees: 11

Summer Employees: 1-2

Volunteers: 1

Interns: 1
Length: 3 months
Duties: Law clerks
Remuneration: Subsidized either through work-study or National Lawyers Guild

Jobs advertised: Various law publications nationwide; law schools; specialized mailing list; legal newspapers

To apply: Contact J. Kendrick Kresse, Supervising Attorney

CALIFORNIA CONSERVATION CORPS

1530 Capitol Avenue
Sacramento, CA 95814
(916) 445-0307

Director: Al Aramiburu

Purpose: The California Conservation Corps is a state agency that pairs up two of the state's most precious resources, youth and the environment, to benefit both. The CCC hires young men and women between the ages of 18 and 23 for a year of natural resource work throughout the state.

Methods of operation: Providing natural resource work and emergency assistance following natural disasters. Three million hours per year.

Constituency: Young men and women ages 18-23

Recent issues and projects: The CCC undertakes a wide range of urban and rural conservation projects, including what is believed to be the largest stream restoration and fish habitat improvement project in the nation. On a day-to-day basis, the Corps works with local state, and federal agencies to provide natural resource work of public benefit. The CCC also provides thousands of hours of assistance following natural disasters, most recently helping out after the Northridge earthquake and the Mailibu and Laguna Beach fires.

Budget: $50,000,000

Funding: Government (100%)

Staff: 400
75 Administrative Staff
325 Field Staff

Work Week: 40 hours

Salary/year: $Varies (Recent College Graduate); $Varies (Graduate with advanced degree)

Benefits: Health insurance, pension, paid vacation and sick leave, life insurance, credit union, family leave

Part-Time Employees: Yes

Summer Employees: No

Volunteers: Yes

Interns: None

Jobs advertised: Newspapers, 800 Number, employment office, job fairs, PSAS, word of mouth

To apply: Contact the personnel office

Remarks: The CCC has been in operation for 18 years and is the oldest and largest youth corps of its kind in the country. Nearly 60,000 young men and women have participated in the program. A model for youth employment and conservation programs worldwide, the CCC has been honored with the United Nations Environmental Program medal for leadership in involving youth in environmental projects. The CCC has both residential and nonresidential opportunities for young people, in urban as well as rural parts of CA. Corpsmembers tackle a wide range of environmental projects during their year in the CCC. There are also several special opportunities they may apply for, including the energy program, the backcountry trails program and the Australian work exchange.

CALIFORNIA HOMELESS COALITION

926 J Street, Room 422
Sacramento, CA 95814
(916) 447-0390

Other Offices: Los Angeles, CA

Director: Callie Hutchison, Executive Director

Purpose: The California Homeless Coalition is a statewide organization that seeks to eliminate homelessness and create housing opportunities for all Californians.

Methods of operation: Public education (30%), community organizing (20%), publications (15%), lobbying (14%), research (10%), training and technical assistance (10%), litigation (1%)

Constituency: Individuals and groups in California interested in ending homelessness and assisting those who are homeless

Recent issues and projects: Organized a major conference in Los Angeles called "Educating Homeless Children." Helped form the California Right to Housing Campaign, which supports the funding of housing for homeless and low-income people. With two other organizations, planned the annual conference with more than 500 attending. Publish and keep data current for *Directory of Services to Homeless People in California.* Producing a video and other materials combatting the "Not In My Backyard Syndrome."

Major publications: *Making Connections: An Election Year Guide to Housing and Homelessness in California*; two videos *Hope for the Future: Educating Homeless Children and Youth* and

Neighbors in Need which shows how people become homeless and how to help overcome neighborhood fears and opposition to the construction and placement of homeless service agencies and affordable housing developments; *California Homeless and Housing Coalition Newsletter*, which is published three times a year

Budget: $320,000

Funding: Foundations (50%), telemarketing (20%), service fees (20%), individual contributions (5%), subscriptions, publications and sale of videos (5%)

Staff: 4

Work Week: 40 hours

Salary/year: $20,000 - 35,000

Benefits: Paid vacation, sick leave, holidays, family leave, paid staff development, compensatory leave and health care funding

Part-Time Employees: 3

Volunteers: 10

Interns: 1
Length: Varies

Jobs advertised: Newspapers, newsletters, word of mouth

To apply: Callie Hutchison, Executive Director

CALIFORNIA INSTITUTE FOR RURAL STUDIES

P.O. Box 2143
Davis, CA 95617
(916) 756-6555

Other Offices: Newman, CA; Modesto, CA

Director: Don Villarejo

Purpose: We seek to build a rural society that is ecologically balanced, socially just and economically sustainable.

Methods of operation: Research (40%), community organizing (25%), training and technical assistance (25%), publications (5%), public education (5%)

Constituency: Farm workers, rural community residents

Recent issues and projects: Advocacy against toxic waste injection wells; technical assistance with transition to sustainable agriculture; exposing abuse of water subsidies; technical assistance to farm workers

Major publications: Newsletters: *Rural California Report* and *Semilla*; *Research for Action*; *Mixtec Migrants in California Agriculture*; *California's Agriculture Dilemma: Higher Production*; *Lower Wages*; *Una Guia para Trabajadores Agricolas en California*

Budget: $500,000

Funding: Health and dental insurance, paid vacation

Staff: 12
1 Executive Director/Researcher
1 Foundation Fundraiser
3 Project Directors/Organizers
1 Office Manager/Bookkeeper
2 Editors/Layout Artists
1 Librarian
2 Library Assistants
1 Student Assistant

Work Week: 40 hours

Salary/year: $20,000 (Recent College Graduate); $30,000 (Graduate with advanced degree)

Benefits: Health and dental insurance, paid vacation

Part-Time Employees: 4

Volunteers: 1

Interns: Yes
Length: 2-3 months
Duties: Research project followed by report
Remuneration: Stipend from program budget

Jobs advertised: Newspaper/academic newsletters

To apply: Contact Don Villarejo, Executive Director

CALIFORNIA LAWYERS FOR THE ARTS

Fort Mason Center, Building C, Room 255
San Francisco, CA 94123
(415) 775-7200

Other Offices: Los Angeles, CA

Director: Alma Robinson, Esq.

Purpose: To provide legal services, education, and self-help information to artists, performers, and arts organizations of all disciplines. Programs and services are designed to respond to the needs of the California arts community and help artists understand and apply legal concepts for their benefit. A collaborative mediation project provides alternative dispute resolution services throughout the country.

Methods of operation: Human services (60%), public education (19%), research (4%), publications (4%), community organizing (4%), direct action (4%), training and technical assistance (4%), lobbying (1%)

Constituency: Artists, performers, attorneys, organizations

Recent issues and projects: Earthquake relief for the arts workshops and consultations; ongoing seminars and workshops that cover a variety of practical issues and topics. Examples include: copyrights, artist/gallery agreements, tenants rights and organizational issues.

Major publications: Quarterly newsletter; approximately 10 book publications; journals

Budget: $440,000

Funding: Grants, earned income, foundations, individual contributions, contracted services

Staff: 9
1 Program Assistant
1 Bookkeeper
4 Program Coordinators
1 Grantwriting Intern
1 Publicity Intern
1 Director

Staff openings/year: 1-2

Work Week: 40 hours

Salary/year: $16-20,000 (Recent College Graduate); $20-24,000 (Graduate with advanced degree)

Benefits: Health insurance, paid vacation

Part-Time Employees: 3

Summer Employees: 1 work-study

Volunteers: 15 annually

Interns: 5
Length: 1-3 months
Duties: Legal referral, dispute resolution, grant writing, publicity, program assistant
Remuneration: Work-study; unpaid

Jobs advertised: Intern programs on campus; newsletter; word of mouth; job boards; newspaper listings

To apply: Contact Oliver Rosenthal

Remarks: We also have a program that provides information on how to find/buy live/work art studio space. This program needs interns as well. We are open to talking with anybody attracted to the arts, has an interest in art or entertainment law, or is interested in nonprofit management.

CALIFORNIA NEWSREEL

149 Ninth Street
San Francisco, CA 94103
(415) 621-6196

Director: Lawrence Daressa/Laurence Adelman

Purpose: To provide educators, business and community organizations with educational films and videos. We both produce and distribute documentaries.

Methods of operation: Public education (80%), publications (20%)

Constituency: Universities/colleges, community organizations, churches, businesses

Recent issues and projects: *African American Perspectives* is our continuing collection of films examining the African-American experience. Our library of African Cinema is the leading source of film and video from Africa in the U.S.

Major publications: Several catalogs are printed annually.

Budget: $700,000

Funding: Business income (80%), foundations (20%)

Staff: 5
4 Promotion
1 Office Manager

Work Week: 35 hours

Salary/year: $40,000

Benefits: Health insurance, paid vacation

Part-Time Employees: 2

Interns: Yes, college credit, no stipend

Jobs advertised: Generally word of mouth

To apply: Contact Lawrence Daressa

CALIFORNIA PUBLIC INTEREST RESEARCH GROUP (CALPIRG)

1147 South Robertson Boulevard, Suite 203
Los Angeles, CA 90035
(213) 278-9244

Other Offices: Berkeley, CA; San Diego, CA; Sacramento, CA; San Francisco, CA; Santa Cruz, CA; Santa Barbara, CA

Director: Deborah Bruns

Purpose: Research and advocacy on environmental and consumer issues in California. Citizenship training for students, teaching them valuable research and organizing skills.

Methods of operation: Research, lobbying, litigation, publications, community organizing, public education

Membership: 120,000 citizen members throughout California

Recent issues and projects: Toxics use reduction campaign; clean air campaign; pesticide reduction; offshore oil drilling, bottle bill. Consumer issues include car repairs, safe art supplies, fair banking services and consumer price surveys. Open government projects include initiative campaign reform, campaign finance reform, and the annual legislative votes index.

Major publications: Quarterly newsletter: *CALPIRG Citizen Agenda*; *CALPIRG Reports* (monthly consumer guide done by our San Diego office); *Toxic Hazards in L.A. County*; *Who Chooses Your Food? - A Study of the Effects of Cosmetic Standards on the Quality of Produce*; *Dumping on the Clean Water Act - A California Publicly-Owned Water Treatment Works Survey*

Budget: $750,000

Funding: Student fees (50%), canvassing, telephone solicitation (33%), foundations (5%), direct mail (3%), other (9%)

Staff: 62
30 Canvassers
10 Canvass Directors and Assistant Directors
7 Organizers
4 Telephone Outreach and Assistant Directors
3 Office Managers
2 Lobbyists
2 Researchers
1 Executive Director
1 Consumer Expert
1 Attorney
1 Administrative Director
1/4 Bookkeeper/Accountant

Work Week: 50-60 hours

Salary/year: $11,500 (Recent College Graduate); $15,000 (Graduate with advanced degree)

Benefits: Health insurance, pregnancy leave, paid vacation, student loan payment plan

Part-Time Employees: 15; phone canvassers

Summer Employees: 100's for canvassing

Volunteers: Yes

Interns: Yes
Length: 3 months
Duties: Research, organizing, and general office work
Remuneration: Stipends or academic credit

Jobs advertised: Local newspapers; college placement offices; posters

To apply: Contact Deborah Bruns, Executive Director; Kevin Brown, Administrative Director; or Julie Peters, Regional Canvass Director

CALIFORNIA RURAL LEGAL ASSISTANCE

2111 Mission Street, Suite 401
San Francisco, CA 94110
(415) 864-3405

Other Offices: Delano, CA; El Centro, CA; Gilroy, CA; Madera, CA; Marysville, CA; Modesto, CA; Oxnard, CA; Oceanside, CA; Coachella, CA; Salinas, CA; San Luis Obispo, CA; Sacramento, CA; Santa Maria, CA; Santa Rosa, CA; Fresno, CA; Stockton, CA

Director: Jose Padilla

Purpose: To provide free legal services to low-income people in rural California.

Methods of operation: Litigation, lobbying, human services, public education, training and technical assistance

Constituency: Poor people in rural California

Recent issues and projects: Extensive litigation on behalf of low-income people throughout California. Issues: educational opportunity; working conditions in agriculture; absence of stable, adequate jobs; unpaid or underpaid workers; access to government benefits; new immigrants and civil rights; environmental justice and rural health.

Major publications: Monthly newsletter: *El Noticiero*

Budget: $7,000,000

Funding: Federal and state government

Staff: 128
Including:
55 Attorneys
20 Community Workers
15 Office Managers
4 Legislative Advocates
3 Bookkeepers/Accountants

Staff openings/year: 0-5

Work Week: 37.5 hours

Salary/year: $23,000 (Graduate with advanced degree)

Benefits: Health insurance, life insurance, pregnancy leave, paid vacation, tuition reimbursement for employment-related classes

Summer Employees: Yes

Volunteers: 0-10

Interns: 0-10
Length: 3 months; summer/school term
Duties: Legal research and writing
Remuneration: Mostly volunteer. Some work-study money available.

Jobs advertised: Legal publications (e.g. *The Clearinghouse Review*)

To apply: Contact local CRLA office in which you are interested, or write to Jesus Ovosco, Human Resources Director in the San Francisco office

CALIFORNIA TAX REFORM ASSOCIATION

926 J Street, Suite 710
Sacramento, CA 95814
(916) 446-4300

Director: Lenny Goldberg

Purpose: Advocacy for progressive tax reform.

Methods of operation: Lobbying (60%), research (15%), publications (15%), public education (10%)

Constituency: Public sector labor unions, individual members, public interest groups

Recent issues and projects: Rewriting and passing change in state spending limit; research and proposals for reform of Proposition 13 (property tax law); conforming with federal tax reform

Major publications: Newsletter: *Tax Back Talk*; *Taxation with Representation: A Citizen's Guide to Reforming Proposition 13*

Budget: $50,000

Funding: Labor unions (60%), individual contributions (25%), foundations (15%)

Staff: 1
1 Lobbyist/Issue Expert
1/3 Office Manager
1/5 Writer/Editor
1/10 Bookkeeper/Accountant

Staff openings/year: 0-1

Part-Time Employees: No

Interns: Yes
Length: Varies

To apply: Contact Lenny Goldberg, Executive Director

Remarks: We're low-budget, on contract, and add staff on a project-by-project basis (e.g. research assistant). We play a unique role in countering the tax lobbyists of the business sector and the right-wing anti-tax organizations.

CALIFORNIA WOMEN'S LAW CENTER

6024 Wilshire Blvd.
Los Angeles, CA 90036
(213) 935-4101

Director: Abby J. Leibman

Purpose: CWLC is a policy and support center working to advance and protect the legal interests of women and girls in California. We provide legal advocacy, training, community education and outreach and publication in the areas of sex discrimination, family law, violence against women, reproductive rights and child care.

Methods of operation: Training and technical assistance (30%), community organizing (25%), public education (10%), publications (10%), litigation (10%), research (10%)

Constituency: Women and girls in California

Recent issues and projects: Coordinating a coalition of over 100 women's organizations to advocate for women's voices to be included in the rebuilding of Los Angeles; launching a Women's Health Initiative to create greater access to health care; examining the interactions among welfare reform, family law, domestic violence and child care.

Major publications: *The Women's Coalition, A Blueprint from the Women of Los Angeles for Rebuilding L.A.*; *Using the Law to Empower Immigrant Women: Information and Resources for Service Providers to Immigrant Women in California*; *Sexual Harassment at Work*

Budget: $392,000

Funding: Foundations (30%), State Bar (25%), individual contributions (25%), direct mail (20%)

Staff: 5
3 Attorneys
1 Office Manager
1 Administrative Assistant

Staff openings/year: 1

Work Week: 40 hours

Salary/year: $32,000 (Graduate with advanced degree)

Benefits: Health insurance, paid vacation, annuity fund, family leave

Part-Time Employees: None

Summer Employees: None

Volunteers: 1-5

Interns: 1-3
Length: 3 months
Duties: Research and writing
Remuneration: Unpaid internships

Jobs advertised: Announcements are sent to other legal services agencies, nonprofit bulletins and law schools. Newspaper ads are run for non-attorney positions.

To apply: Please contact Abby J. Leibman, Executive Director

CAMBRIDGE DOCUMENTARY FILMS, INC.

242 Lexington Ave.
Cambridge, MA 02138
(617) 354-3677

Director: Margaret Lazarus

Purpose: To produce and distribute videos and films that promote social justice

Methods of operation: Film/videos (40%), public education/distribution (40%), research (20%)

Constituency: Universities

Recent issues and projects: CDF recently completed a film on domestic violence and have successfully advocated with other groups for the commutation of women imprisoned for killing their abusers in self-defense. CDF has made films and videos on labor history, reproductive health hazards in the workplace, rape, the image of women in the media, the selling of alcohol, career education, and prejudice against lesbians and gay men.

Major publications: *Defending Our Lives*; *Still Killing Us Softly*; *Rape Culture*; *Pink Triangles*; *Not Just a Job*; *Eugene Debs and the American Movement*; *Hazardous Inheritance*; *Killing Us Softly*; *Calling the Shots*; *The Barefoot Doctors of Rural China*; *Taking Our Bodies Back*

Budget: $300,000

Funding: Rental and sale of publications (80%), foundations (20%)

Staff: 4
2 Producers
1 Office Manager
1 Distributer

Staff openings/year: 1

Work Week: 40 hours

Salary/year: $24,000 (Recent College Graduate); $25,000 (Graduate with advanced degree)

Benefits: Health insurance, pension, child care, paid vacation, family leave

Part-Time Employees: 1

Summer Employees: None

Volunteers: 1

Interns: Yes
Length: 6 month internship

Jobs advertised: Request resumes

To apply: Contact Margaret Lazarus

CAMPUS COMPACT - THE PROJECT FOR PUBLIC AND COMMUNITY SERVICE

Brown University, P.O. Box 1975
Providence, RI 02912
(401) 863-1119

Director: Nancy C. Rhodes

Purpose: Campus Compact is a national coalition of college and university presidents. It was created to expand opportunities for public and community service in higher education and to advocate the importance of civic responsibility in student learning.

Membership: University and college presidents

Recent issues and projects: Integrating service with academic study; mentoring - Campus Partners in Learning; National Community Service Trust Act; Community Service in higher education including community colleges and historically black colleges and universities

Staff: 9

Staff openings/year: 1-2

Work Week: 40 hours

Salary/year: $Varies (Recent College Graduate); $Varies (Graduate with advanced degree)

Benefits: Health insurance, retirement plan, child care, paid vacation, life insurance, pregnancy leave, tuition reimbursement, dental insurance, worker's compensation, sick leave, bereavement leave, vision and hearing care, travel/accident insurance

Part-Time Employees: None

Summer Employees: 4-6

Volunteers: None

Interns: 2-6 each year
Length: 3-12 months
Duties: Varies
Remuneration: $6/hour minimum

Jobs advertised: Journals, newsletters, newspapers

To apply: Send resume to the office

CAMPUS OUTREACH OPPORTUNITIES LEAGUE

411 Washington Ave. North, Suite 110
Minneapolis, MN 55108
(612) 333-2665

Other Offices: Boston, MA; East Lansing, MI; Washington, DC; Durham, NC

Director: Kristin Parrish

Purpose: To promote and support college student involvement in community service and social action.

Methods of operation: Training and technical assistance (70%), conferences (20%), publications (5%), mini-grants (5%)

Constituency: Students, faculty, staff and community leaders committed to student involvement in community service

Recent issues and projects: Providing consulting and training; mini-grants; technical assistance; 4-day national conference. Promoting effective and meaningful efforts to address root causes.

Major publications: *Light One Candle*, quotebook; *Hunger Action*; *Literacy Action*; *Education Action*

Budget: $1,200,000

Funding: Foundations/government (75%), fees and sales (20%), individual contributions (5%)

Staff: 27
2 Office Managers
13 Program Managers
6 Trainers/Consultants
4 Conference Organizers
2 Administrative Field Support

Staff openings/year: 6

Work Week: 60 hours

Salary/year: $18,000 (Recent College Graduate); $23,000 (Graduate with advanced degree)

Benefits: Health insurance, pension, paid vacation, life insurance, family leave

Part-Time Employees: 3

Summer Employees: 6

Volunteers: 20

Interns: 6
Length: 6 months
Duties: Varies by program

Remuneration: A limited number of stipends available

Jobs advertised: Mailings to members and affiliates, and ads in *Community Jobs*

To apply: Contact Kristin Parrish

CATALYST

250 Park Avenue South
New York, NY 10003-1459
(212) 777-8900

President: Sheila W. Wellington

Purpose: Catalyst works with business to effect change for women through research, advisory services and communication.

Methods of operation: Research (40%), advisory services to companies (40%), educating the general population and businesses in particular (20%)

Constituency: Corporations provide nearly all funding. Most are among Fortune 500 listings

Recent issues and projects: Study on flexible work arrangements; report on women in engineering; report on quality child care

Major publications: *Perspective* monthly newsletter to contributors; research reports on mentoring, flexible work arrangements, parental leave, women in engineering

Funding: Corporate funders, foundations

Staff: 38
1 President
3 Vice Presidents
1 Executive Director, Corporate Board Res.
6 Directors
1 Controller
6 Senior Associates
12 Associates
8 Assistants

Staff openings/year: 6

Work Week: 40-50 hours

Salary/year: $21,000

Benefits: Health insurance, life insurance, pregnancy leave, paid vacation

Part-Time Employees: 4

Interns: 0-10 per year
Length: 2-3 months
Duties: Varied
Remuneration: $7.50/day for travel stipend

Jobs advertised: Newspapers; some college career offices

To apply: Contact Director of Operations

CATHOLIC NETWORK OF VOLUNTEER SERVICE

4121 Harewood Road, NE
Washington, DC 20017
(202) 529-1100 (800) 543-5046

Director: Sister Ellen Cavanaugh

Purpose: A clearinghouse of information, education, recruitment, referral and support of lay people who are seeking information about full-time volunteer programs ranging from a few weeks to several years. Lay Volunteer Missioners are people who believe they can make a difference in life with their life!

Methods of operation: Research, publications, human services, public education, counseling, referral services

Membership: 160 membership organizations that support lay volunteers to serve those in need both in the U.S. and overseas in the Third World

Recent issues and projects: Annual conference; annual directory; bimonthly pamphlet; workshop for potential programs; regional member offices; international recruitment

Budget: $800,000

Funding: Membership fees, churches, foundations and grants, donations

Staff: 4
1 Executive Director
1 Executive Secretary
1 Computer Operator
1 Receptionist

Staff openings/year: 0-1

Work Week: 40-50 hours

Salary/year: $Varies (Recent College Graduate); $Varies (Graduate with advanced degree)

Part-Time Employees: Yes

Volunteers: Yes

Interns: 1

To apply: Contact Sister Ellen Cavanaugh, Executive Director

Remarks: Today lay volunteers are a growing

population. They receive a small allowance, room and board, travel money, medical expenses and the gratitude of an entire world. They are people who give a hundredfold and receive a hundredfold.

CATHOLICS FOR A FREE CHOICE (CFFC)

1436 U Street, NW, Suite 301
Washington, DC 20009-3916
(202) 986-6093

Other Offices: Monteverde, URUGUAY; Mexico City, MEXICO

Director: Frances Kissling

Purpose: CFFC is a national educational organization that supports the right to legal reproductive health care, especially to family planning and abortion. CFFC also works to reduce the incidence of abortion and to increase women's choices in childbearing and childrearing through advocacy of social and economic programs.

Methods of operation: Public education (35%), publications (25%), community organizing (25%), lobbying (10%), research (5%)

Constituency: Pro-choice Catholics and others interested in the moral and ethical issues of reproductive rights

Recent issues and projects: A national public affairs program that provides policymakers with the data to make informed public policy decisions. An active public education and media program, including publications, a speaker's bureau, seminars and conferences. Grassroots advocacy through the Key Activist program, which assists local groups with educational and legislative projects. An international network focused on education and information exchange. CFFC monitors and reports on the public policy initiatives of the U.S. Catholic Conference which affect women's reproductive health and U.S. population policy; the Latino Initiative provides information about reproductive health care and public policy to Hispanic/Latina organizations across the country.

Major publications: Bi-monthly news journal: *Conscience*; *Abortion: A Guide to Making Ethical Choices*; *I am here to say*, an abortion in good faith series; Spanish language publications including a quarterly news journal, *Conciencia*, and *Mujeres e Iglesia: Sexualidad y Aborto en America Latina*

Budget: $1,200,000

Funding: Foundations (80%), individual contributions (15%), telephone solicitation (5%)

Staff: 15
4 Issue Experts
1 Office Manager
1 President
5 Administrative Staff
2 Writers/Editors
1 Organizer
1 Development Staff

Staff openings/year: 2

Work Week: 35-40 hours

Salary/year: $20,000 (Recent College Graduate); $23,000 (Graduate with advanced degree)

Benefits: Health insurance, pregnancy leave, pension, paid vacation

Part-Time Employees: 3

Volunteers: 25 grassroots

Interns: 1-2
Length: 1 semester or summer
Duties: Research on legislation, Catholic church positions on legislation; public relations; contact with in-district supporters of legislation
Remuneration: Interns are not paid; college credit can be arranged

Jobs advertised: Through progressive organizations, newspapers, and appropriate journals

To apply: Contact Mary Jean Collins, Public Affairs Director

CENTER FOR AUTO SAFETY

2001 S Street, NW, Suite 410
Washington, DC 20009
(202) 328-7700

Director: Clarence M. Ditlow

Purpose: Research and advocacy on fuel efficiency and emissions, vehicle safety, economy and reliability. Works to reduce deaths and injuries from defective cars, and to inform consumers about consumer transportation issues.

Methods of operation: Research (50%), public education (20%), training and technical assistance (15%), publications (10%), litigation (5%)

Constituency: Growing membership of 15,000. Provides assistance to all consumers who call or write our office.

Recent issues and projects: Six-month study on child safety seats yielded major evidence of manufacturer failure to produce safe child seats and failure of federal government to enforce standards on seats. Ongoing research into GM pickup truck fires. Advocacy for better lemon laws, other warranty issues.

Major publications: *The Lemon Book*, a self-help manual to assist consumers in purchasing reliable and safe cars and handling auto problems as they arise. Quarterly newsletter: *The Lemon Times*. Bimonthly newsletter: *IMPACT*.

Budget: $750,000

Funding: Individual contributions (25%), foundations (25%), sales of publications and subscriptions (25%), direct mail (10%)

Staff: 13
7 Researchers
3 Attorneys
1 Writer/Editor
1 Office Manager
1 Bookkeeper/Accountant

Staff openings/year: 2

Work Week: 40 hours

Salary/year: $17,000 (Recent College Graduate); $23,000 (Graduate with advanced degree)

Benefits: Health insurance, life insurance, pregnancy leave, paid vacation, pension

Interns: 6
Length: 3 months
Duties: Research assistants
Remuneration: Stipend of approximately $160/week

Jobs advertised: Newspaper; bulletin boards

To apply: Contact Faith C. Little, Controller

CENTER FOR COMMUNITY CHANGE

1000 Wisconsin Avenue, NW
Washington, DC 20007
(202) 342-0519

Other Offices: San Francisco, CA

Director: Pablo Eisenberg

Purpose: Help poor Americans help themselves by building strong community organizations and to help them create jobs, build affordable housing, raise money and develop effective community programs.

Methods of operation: Training and technical assistance (75%), research and development, public policy (14%), research (5%), publications (5%), lobbying (1%)

Constituency: Low-income community-based organizations; minorities

Recent issues and projects: Assist local organizations to work on community credit issues; work to preserve and improve public housing; create more housing trust funds, which are new sources of money for low-income housing; work to change Community Development Block Grant program to better help low-income communities

Major publications: Quarterly periodical: *Community Change*; *CRA Reporter* (community reinvestment alternatives); 3 publications on housing trust funds; special reports on public housing, how to use the Community Reinvestment Act, etc.

Budget: $4,000,000

Funding: Foundations and corporations (77%), individual contributions (6%), other (17%)

Staff: 42
7 Issue Experts
6 Administrative Assistants
3 Organizational Development Specialists
6 Community Development Specialists
1 Writer/Editor
1 Director of Administrative Services
1 Director of Communications
1 Fundraiser
3 Housing Development Specialists
1 Economic Development Specialist
1 Attorney
4 Directors-Com./Training/Dev/Field/S.Proj.
3 (2)Bookkeeper/Accountant (1) Office Manager
2 Community Organization Specialists
2 Regional Directors

Staff openings/year: 2

Work Week: 40 plus hours

Salary/year: $26,000

Benefits: Health insurance, life insurance, pregnancy leave, pension, paid vacation, partial tuition reimbursement, disability insurance, sabbaticals

Part-Time Employees: 3

Summer Employees: Occasionally

Interns: Occasionally

To apply: Contact Pablo Eisenberg

CENTER FOR COMMUNITY SELF-HELP

413 East Chapel Hill Street
Durham, NC 27701
(919) 683-9686

Other Offices: Asheville, NC; Charlotte, NC

Director: Kate McKee, Associate Director

Purpose: Economic development. Self-Help provides financing and technical assistance to women, minorities and rural folk across North Carolina to promote home and business ownership and the development of cooperatives. Two affiliates are: Self-Help Credit Union and Self-Help Ventures Fund.

Methods of operation: Lending (60%), training and technical assistance (17%), community organizing (15%), research (5%), public education (2%), publications (1%)

Constituency: Low-income women, minorities and rural North Carolinians and progressive wealthy people

Recent issues and projects: Creation of $50 million statewide loan pool for low to moderate income homebuyers; "partnership lending" with local community-based revolving loan fund; child care financing program

Major publications: Newsletter: *Self-Help Update*, 3 times/year

Budget: $379,000

Funding: Foundations, earned income

Staff: 22
8 Lenders
4 Organizers
4 Issue Experts
2 Bookkeepers/Accountants
1 Paralegal
1 Office Manager
1 Typist
1/2 Writer/Editor
1/2 Press Aide

Staff openings/year: 2

Work Week: 40 hours

Salary/year: $18,000 (Recent College Graduate); $20,000 (Graduate with advanced degree)

Benefits: Health insurance, pregnancy leave, credit union, paid vacation

Part-Time Employees: Yes

Volunteers: Yes

Interns: 1
Length: Summer or longer
Duties: Research, account analysis
Remuneration: Need based

Jobs advertised: Word of mouth and local newspapers

To apply: Contact Kate McKee, Associate Director

CENTER FOR CONSTITUTIONAL RIGHTS

666 Broadway, 7th Floor
New York, NY 10012
(212) 614-6464

Other Offices: Greenville, MS

Director: Dorothy M. Zellner, Acting Executive Director

Purpose: A national public interest law firm, working for constitutional and human rights under the U.S. Constitution and international human rights laws, with offices in New York and Mississippi.

Methods of operation: Research, litigation, publications, public education

Constituency: Progressives and communities of color across the country

Recent issues and projects: Litigation on civil and human rights issues: racial justice, women's rights, anti-nuclear, anti-torture

Major publications: *Annual Docket Report*; newsletter published twice yearly; several pamphlets on the issues they research and litigate

Funding: Foundations, direct mail, individual donors

Staff: 14
7 Support Staff
7 Attorneys

Work Week: 40+ hours

Benefits: Health/dental insurance, pregnancy leave, and paid vacation

Volunteers: Yes

Interns: Yes; Ella Baker Student Program
Length: Throughout the year
Duties: Legal writing and research

Jobs advertised: Word of mouth; announcements sent to other public interest groups; advertisements in *The Nation*; and other progressive publications

To apply: Contact Director

CENTER FOR DEFENSE INFORMATION

1500 Massachusetts Avenue, NW
Washington, DC 20005
(202) 862-0700

Other Offices: New York, NY

Director: Rear Admiral Eugene J. Carroll, Jr., USN (Ret.)

Purpose: Founded in 1972 by senior, retired military officers, CDI is the foremost independent military affairs research center. It offers appraisals on weapons systems, military policy and spending. CDI is committed to further reductions in nuclear arsenals, to cutting military spending to $200 billion a year, to avoid buying weapons we do not need and to stop paying too much for those we do purchase. The Center accepts no military contracts or money for its services from government or military industries.

Methods of operation: Public education by means of research (50%); television production (25%); publications (25%)

Constituency: Private citizens, legislators, government officials, members of the media and institutions all over the U.S. and around the world

Recent issues and projects: A half-hour weekly television series produced entirely in-house for viewing on more than 1500 PBS and cable outlets. Recent programs examined civilian tasks for the military, U.S. arms sales and the hidden costs of the military.

Major publications: *Defense Monitor* (8 page monograph published 10 times/year); "America's Defense Monitor" (weekly television series); *Question of the week* radio commentary program; fact sheets, press interviews, briefings and speeches

Budget: $1,400,000

Funding: Individual contributions (33%), foundations (33%), direct mail (32%), other (1%)

Staff: 23
8 Researchers/Writers
4 Producers/Television Crew
3 Issue Experts
2 Executive Assistants
1 Information Systems Manager
1 Computer Assistant/Bookkeeper
1 Writer/Editor
1 Office Manager
1 Press Aide
1 Foundation Fundraiser

Staff openings/year: 1-5

Work Week: 40-50 hours

Salary/year: $Varies (Recent College Graduate); $Varies (Graduate with advanced degree)

Benefits: Health insurance, paid vacation

Part-Time Employees: 1-4

Volunteers: 1-3

Interns: 2-4
Length: Semester system
Duties: Research, TV production and administrative assistance
Remuneration: $700/month stipend

Jobs advertised: Directories; universities; flyers to similarly oriented nonprofit groups; newspaper advertisements

To apply: Contact Lt. Colonel Piers M. Wood, USAR, Chief of Staff

CENTER FOR DEMOCRACY AND CITIZENSHIP/PROJECT PUBLIC LIFE

301 19th Avenue, South
Minneapolis, MN 55455
(612) 625-0142

Director: Harry Boyte

Purpose: The Center for Democracy and Citizenship works to strengthen community and civic capacities for public problem-solving and to democratize patterns of professional interactions with citizens and communities.

Methods of operation: Training and technical assistance (40%), community organizing (30%), research (20%), publications (10%)

Constituency: Diverse group of CBO's, health professional organizers, educators, extension agents, government workers

Recent issues and projects: Two recent projects are: the Citizenship and Community Service Initiative and a collaboration of nongovernmental organizations for citizenship

Major publications: *Commonwealth: A Return to Citizen Politics*; *Free Spaces*; *Reinventing Citizenship*; *Doing Politics*; *Making the Rules*; *The New Citizenship*; *White Paper*

Budget: $350,000

Funding: Foundations

Staff: 3
1/2 Organizer
1/2 Office Manager
1 Researcher/Theorist
1 Foundation Fundraiser

Staff openings/year: 2

Work Week: 50 hours

Benefits: Health insurance, pension, paid vacation, credit union, family leave, tuition reimbursement

Part-Time Employees: 2

Summer Employees: Yes

Volunteers: 4

Interns: Yes
Length: Academic year or summer
Duties: Research, administrative assistance
Remuneration: Through university or scholarship programs

Jobs advertised: University

To apply: Contact Tim Sheldon, Center Administrator

CENTER FOR DEMOCRATIC RENEWAL

P.O. Box 50469
Atlanta, GA 30302
(404) 221-0025

Other Offices: Kansas City, MO

Director: Ms. Beni Ivey

Purpose: National clearinghouse of information on far right, white supremacist, neo-Nazi and other hate organizations and activities. Community development for non-violent opposition to organized hate activities and groups, movements and government practices that promote hatred and bigotry.

Methods of operation: Publications (25%), community organizing (20%), research (15%), training and technical assistance (15%), public education (10%), direct action (10%)

Constituency: Civil and human rights activists and organizations

Recent issues and projects: Georgia Project: intensive, ongoing rural grassroots community organizing against institutionalized racism. National Program: debriefing and refocusing a former major white supremacist and assisting him in becoming an effective anti-extremist advocate.

Major publications: *When Hate Groups Come to Town: A Handbook of Effective Community Responses*; *The Monitor*, periodical; *Weekly Update*, limited circulation brief; and an extensive list of books, monographs, etc,

Budget: $500,000

Funding: Foundations

Staff: 11
3 Organizers
2 Writers/Editors
2 Researchers
2 Issue Experts
1 Typist
1 Bookkeeper/Accountant

Staff openings/year: Varies

Work Week: 45 hours

Salary/year: $20,000 (Recent College Graduate); $25,000 (Graduate with advanced degree)

Benefits: Health insurance, paid vacation, life insurance, parking

Part-Time Employees: 1

Summer Employees: None

Volunteers: 3

Interns: 3
Length: 3-6 months
Duties: Varies
Remuneration: All volunteer

Jobs advertised: Local newspapers

To apply: Contact Loretta Ross, National Program Director

CENTER FOR ECOLOGICAL TECHNOLOGY, INC. (CET)

147 Tyler Street
Pittsfield, MA 01201
(413) 445-4556

Other Offices: Northampton, MA

Director: Alan Silverstein

Purpose: CET's goals are to protect the environment, increase our energy self-reliance and reduce our dependency on expensive and polluting technologies.

Methods of operation: Public education (50%), training and technical assistance (25%), publications (15%), community organizing (10%)

Recent issues and projects: Conducts Demand Side Management programs for local utility companies; operates a consumer oil heating cooperative; provides sales of weatherization materials, water conservation devices, radon test kits; conducts solid waste education programs for cities and towns including home composting, demonstration program to assist rural businesses in implementing waste reduction and recycling programs, linking farms with organic waste generators.

Major publications: Newsletter: *Energy News*; *Berkshire Energy Manual*; slide shows on "Passive Solar Retrofits" and "TAP Solar Collectors"

Budget: $1,000,000

Staff: 30
10 Issue Experts
5 Office Managers
12 Field Staff
3 Caseworkers

Staff openings/year: 2-3

Work Week: 40 hours

Salary/year: $23,000 (Recent College Graduate); $28,000 (Graduate with advanced degree)

Benefits: Health insurance, pregnancy leave, paid vacation

Volunteers: 2-4

Interns: Yes

Jobs advertised: Community-based organizations network; newsletters; classified advertisements

To apply: Contact Alan Silverstein, Director

CENTER FOR ECONOMIC CONVERSION

222C View Street
Mountain View, CA 94041
(415) 968-8798

Director: Michael Closson

Purpose: Public education and organizational assistance in economic conversion planning.

Methods of operation: Organizational administration (30%), public education (20%), training and technical assistance (20%), publications (20%), community organizing (10%)

Constituency: Concerned individuals and organizations

Recent issues and projects: California Conversion Initiative Campaign; base closing consulting; public speaking engagements

Major publications: Quarterly: *Plowshare Press*; video: *Building a Sustainable Economy*; teacher's kit

Budget: $120,000

Funding: Individual contributions (63%), foundations (15%), consulting, honoraria (10%), publications (2%)

Staff: 3
1 Executive Director
1 Program Director/Editor
1 Office Manager

Work Week: 40+ hours

Salary/year: $20,000

Benefits: Health insurance, pregnancy leave, paid vacation, sick leave

Volunteers: 6

Interns: 1
Length: 1 semester
Duties: Usually research projects
Remuneration: None

Jobs advertised: Newspaper; word of mouth

To apply: Contact Michael Closson

CENTER FOR ECONOMIC DEMOCRACY

P.O. Box 64
Olympia, WA 98507
(206) 357-4705

Director: Zachary Lyons

Purpose: To increase public awareness that every dollar is a vote, and to provide information regarding boycotts and other consumer-related issues in order that consumers will be better informed in casting their economic votes.

Methods of operation: Publications (70%), distribution (15%), public education (15%)

Constituency: Co-ops, individual consumers, religious bodies, peace and justice groups and committees, environmental, labor and animal rights groups

Major publications: *The Boycott Quarterly, The Boycott Monthly*

Budget: $10,000

Funding: Subscriptions (20%), newsstand sales (40%), loans and donations (40%)

Staff: 2
1 Part-time Writer/Researcher/Editor
1 Part-time Copy/Proof Reader

Staff openings/year: 0-1

Work Week: 30 hours

Salary/year: $Varies (Recent College Graduate); $Varies (Graduate with advanced degree)

Summer Employees: None

Volunteers: None

Interns: None at this time

To apply: Contact Zach Lyons, Director

CENTER FOR ENVIRONMENTAL CITIZENSHIP

1400 16th Street, NW, P.O. Box 24
Washington, DC 20009
(202) 939-3316

Director: Brian Trelstad

Purpose: CEC's mission is to engage a diverse group of student environmentalists in the public problem process. Through trainings, workshops and an electronic mail network CEC prepares campus environmentalist groups to develop and execute major issues campaigns.

Methods of operation: Training and technical assistance (40%), public education (10%), research (10%), lobbying (5%), publications (5%)

Constituency: Student environmentalists

Recent issues and projects: Trainings were held in the fall of 1993 in NY, DC, OH, TN and 10 sites are planned for 1994 Spring. CEC did the domestic outreach for the Campus Earth Summit at Yale University, and is currently assisting the League of Conservation Voters in the Campaign Fellowship Project.

Major publications: *Student Political Organizing Guide*; *A Map of Student Environmentalism*

Budget: $200,000

Funding: Grants (50%), foundations (40%), individual contributions (10%)

Staff: 4
1 Organizer
1/2 Writer/Editor
1/2 Office Manager
1/2 Press Aide
1/3 Foundation Fundraiser
1 Issue Expert
1/3 Bookkeeper/Accountant

Staff openings/year: 1

Work Week: 50 hours

Salary/year: $16,500 (Recent College Graduate); $Varies (Graduate with advanced degree)

Benefits: Health insurance, paid vacation, life insurance,

Part-Time Employees: 1

Summer Employees: Maybe

Volunteers: 1

Interns: Yes
Length: 4 months to 1 year
Duties: Everything!
Remuneration: None, arrangements for credit

Jobs advertised: Regional environmental publications, word of mouth, training attendees, internet

To apply: Please contact Lisa Lincoln: Media Director/Office Manager

---

CENTER FOR ENVIRONMENTAL EDUCATION

881 Alma Real Drive, Suite 300
Pacific Palisades, CA 90272
(310) 454-4585

Director: Cory Walsh

Purpose: The Center for Environmental Education is a nonprofit environmental education resource center. Collect and make available materials to teachers, students and all interested. Work within the community to promote environmental awareness.

Methods of operation: Resource Center (80%), research (10%), publications (10%)

Constituency: Teachers, students, parents, government agencies

Recent issues and projects: On-going work to promote environmental education and have it integrated into the school curricula nationwide.

Major publications: Bi-annual newsletter; *Blueprint for a Green School*, 1994 scholastic guidebook for schools to be published in September

Budget: $300,000

Funding: Individual contributions (70%), foundations (20%), corporations (10%)

Staff: 5
1 Office Manager
1 Researcher
1 Foundation Fundraiser
1 Administrative Assistant
1 Outreach Coordinator

Staff openings/year: 1

Work Week: 40 hours

Salary/year: $23,000 (Recent College Graduate); $25,000 (Graduate with advanced degree)

Benefits: Health insurance, paid vacation, life insurance, pregnancy leave

Part-Time Employees: 1

Summer Employees: 1-4

Volunteers: 1-10

Interns: 1
Length: Varies
Duties: Database, outreach, research
Remuneration: Nominal salary

Jobs advertised: Word of mouth, newspaper

To apply: Contact Cory Walsh, Executive Director

CENTER FOR HISPANIC POLICY AND ADVOCACY

421 Elmwood Avenue
Providence, RI 02907
(401) 467-0111

Director: Jose Gonzalez

Purpose: To improve the conditions of Rhode Island's Hispanic community through broad-based planning and advocacy and education efforts.

Methods of operation: Training and technical assistance (30%), public education (20%), maintaining community center housing (20%), community organizing (10%), human services (5%), publications (5%), lobbying (5%), research (5%)

Membership: Latino constituency, general membership

Recent issues and projects: Recent projects include: leadership development; voter registration; Hispanic dropout prevention

Major publications: Quarterly newsletter

Budget: $132,000

Funding: Government (69%), foundations (28%), individual contributions (3%)

Staff: 3
1 Foundation Fundraiser
1 Issue Expert
1 Secretary

Staff openings/year: 1-2

Work Week: 40 hours

Salary/year: $20,000 (Recent College Graduate); $30,000 (Graduate with advanced degree)

Benefits: Paid vacation, health insurance

Part-Time Employees: None

Summer Employees: None

Volunteers: 12

Interns: 2
Length: 3 months
Duties: Varies

Jobs advertised: In local newspapers

To apply: Please contact Christina Abuelo, Resource Development Coordinator

CENTER FOR IMMIGRANTS RIGHTS

48 Saint Marks Place, 4th Floor
New York, NY 10003
(212) 505-6890

Director: Jackson Chin

Purpose: The Center for Immigrants Rights (CIR) is a nonprofit independent organization which provides legal assistance, community outreach and education, policy advocacy and technical support. Its mission is to defend the rights of immigrant newcomers, documented and undocumented, in the areas of immigration, employment rights, access to public entitlements/health and civil rights.

Methods of operation: Public education (30%), training and technical assistance (25%), community organizing (20%), publications (5%), litigation (5%), lobbying (5%), research (5%)

Constituency: Immigrants, advocates, lawyers, low-income community-based service providers, health facilities, shelters and CBO's

Recent issues and projects: Recent projects include: Daylaborers Organizing and Leadership Training Project; Citywide Immigrant Workplace Rights Project; Immigrant Women and Childrens Rights Project; CIR immigrant rights phone-line; 45 hour immigration paralegal training course; workshops and clinics

Major publications: *CIR Report*; *Immigrant Status and Legal Access to Health Care*; *Access to New York Health Cares Services For Immigrants*; other legal education lay materials, factsheets and "know your rights" materials

Budget: $330,000

Funding: Foundations (65%), local government (25%0, individual contributions (15%)

Staff: 6
1 Organizer
2 Attorneys
1 Paralegal
1 Office Manager
1/2 Foundation Fundraiser
1 Education Director

Staff openings/year: 0-2

Work Week: 40-50 hours

Salary/year: $22,000 (Recent College Graduate); $26-35,000 (Graduate with advanced degree)

Benefits: Health insurance, paid vacation, dental

Part-Time Employees: 2

Summer Employees: Yes

Volunteers: 3-5

Interns: 3-5
Length: 10-12 weeks
Duties: Research, hotline intake, client interviews, community outreach
Remuneration: No stipends

Jobs advertised: College career centers, law schools, networking

To apply: Contact Executive Director

Remarks: Our staff is bilingual, committed to advancing the civil and human rights of America's immigrants, with special attention to the metro-New York area; CIR offers academic and other volunteer internships for college students and law students. CIR has a 13 year-old history in the immigrant rights arena and works closely with local and national networks to advance protections and to defend the rights of newcomers, asylum-seekers and refugees.

CENTER FOR INVESTIGATIVE REPORTING

530 Howard Street, 2nd Floor
San Francisco, CA 94105-3007
(415) 543-1200

Other Offices: Washington, DC

Director: Sharon Tiller, Executive Director

Purpose: To serve as a base for investigative journalists; to train novice journalists in investigative techniques; and to help educate the public about the individuals and institutions that shape our lives.

Methods of operation: Research (40%), publications (40%), training and technical assistance (15%), public education (5%)

Constituency: The concerned public, policymakers, legislators and other public officials

Recent issues and projects: Natural resources/ environment; public health; immigration; international affairs; First Amendment/Freedom of Information; the public trust

Major publications: CIR stories are published in newspapers and magazines and broadcast on television locally, nationally and internationally. In addition, CIR publishes an average of one book annually.

Budget: $1,000,000

Funding: Foundations (50%), earned (40%), individual contributions (10%)

Staff: 9
4 Writers/Editors
5 Administrative Assistants

Staff openings/year: Varies

Work Week: 40 hours

Salary/year: $25,000 (Recent College Graduate); $30,000 (Graduate with advanced degree)

Benefits: Health insurance, life insurance,

pregnancy leave, paid vacation, tuition reimbursement

Part-Time Employees: 4

Volunteers: 2

Interns: 12-15/year
Length: 3-7 months
Duties: Work individually with editorial staff on research, story preparation, writing; participate in weekly seminars; assist with administration
Remuneration: Stipend of $100/month

Jobs advertised: Newspaper classifieds and bulletin boards

To apply: Contact James Curtis, Administration

CENTER FOR LABOR RESEARCH AND EDUCATION

Inst. of Industrial Relations, University of California
Berkeley, CA 94720
(510) 642-6432

Director: Mary Ruth Gross, Chair

Purpose: Practical labor education for trade unionists; conferences and publications on issues of concern to labor.

Methods of operation: Training and technical assistance (80%), publications (20%)

Constituency: Labor unions; Labor researchers

Recent issues and projects: Labor/Management Cooperative in California public schools; changes in American work-place

Major publications: *California Workers' Rights*; *Teaching Labor Education in the Public Schools*; *What To Do When You Get Burned By The Press*

Funding: University of California (90%), charge backs (10%)

Staff: 4
2 Educators/Trainers
2 Clerical/Administrative Support

Work Week: 40 hours

Salary/year: $Varies (Recent College Graduate); $Varies (Graduate with advanced degree)

Benefits: Health insurance, pregnancy leave, pension, paid vacation, limited tuition reimbursement at UC Berkeley

Interns: Usually 1
Length: 1 year, half-time
Duties: Publication skills - must be UC Berkeley graduate student
Remuneration: Half-pay

Jobs advertised: Clerical/administrative staff: through UC internal employment listing. Teaching staff: search outside, focused on labor and labor education programs

CENTER FOR LAW AND EDUCATION

955 Massachusetts Avenue
Cambridge, MA 02139
(617) 876-6611

Other Offices: Washington, DC

Director: Kathleen Boundy and Paul Weekstein

Purpose: The Center for Law and Education provides support services on education issues to advocates working on behalf of low-income students and parents. Its mission is to take a leadership role in improving the quality of public education for low-income students throughout the nation and to enable low-income communities to address their own public education problems effectively.

Methods of operation: Research (45%), training and technical assistance (20%), publications (15%), litigation (15%), lobbying (5%)

Constituency: Indigent students and their parents

Recent issues and projects: The Center for Law and Education's 5 top priorities are: Chapter 1 and state and federal education reform; rights of students with disabilities; vocational education and school to work; violence in schools; and early intervention/early childhood education

Major publications: *NewsNotes*, CLE's quarterly newsletter; *Educational Rights of Students with Disabilities*; *Advocacy Handbook*; *The Family Is Critical to Student Achievement*

Budget: $1,200,000

Funding: Foundations (50%), Legal Services Corporations (50%)

Staff: 15
2 Writers/Editors
8 Attorneys
1 Education Advocate
1 Office Manager
2 Administrative Assistants

1 Business Manager

Staff openings/year: 0-1

Work Week: 50 hours

Salary/year: $30,000 (Graduate with advanced degree)

Benefits: Health insurance, paid vacation

Part-Time Employees: 1

Summer Employees: 1-2

Volunteers: 3

Interns: Yes-law students
Length: Summer or semester
Duties: Research and writing
Remuneration: $300 per week

Jobs advertised: *New York Times*, *Washington Post*, Bar Association, civil rights groups, etc.

To apply: Contact Kathleen Boundy

CENTER FOR LAW AND SOCIAL POLICY (CLASP)

1616 P Street, NW, Suite 350
Washington, DC 20036
(202) 328-5140

Director: Alan W. Houseman

Purpose: CLASP is a national public interest organization with expertise in both law and policy affecting the poor. Through education, policy, research and advocacy, CLASP seeks to improve the economic conditions of low-income families with children and to secure access for the poor to our civil justice system.

Methods of operation: Training and technical assistance (30%), publications (40%), research (10%), litigation (5%), public education (10%), lobbying (5%)

Constituency: Legal services and poverty advocates

Recent issues and projects: Promoting (1) streamlined child support enforcement and a national child support assurance system; (2) expanded access of teen parents and impoverished adults to education and training programs; and (3) welfare and income support policies that enhance work, reduce poverty and support family well-being. In addition, we are helping revitalize the federal legal services program.

Major publications: Newsletters: *Family Matters*; *States Update The Rush to Reform: 1992 State AFDC Legislative and Waiver Actions*; *Answers and Questions: The JOBS Program*; *Turning Promises Into Realities: A Guide to Implementing the Child Support Provisions of the Family Support Act; Needling the System: Welfare Agency Approaches to Preschool Immunization*; *The Devil is in the Details: Key Questions in the Effort to End Welfare as We Know It*

Budget: $700,000

Funding: Foundations (90%), individual contributions (10%)

Staff: 13
4 Attorneys
5 Policy Analysts
1 Administrator
2 Secretaries
1 Bookkeeper/Accountant

Staff openings/year: 1

Work Week: 40 hours

Salary/year: $25,000 (Recent College Graduate); $30,000 (Graduate with advanced degree)

Benefits: Health insurance, life insurance, pregnancy leave, paid vacation

Part-Time Employees: 1

Summer Employees: 1

Interns: Yes
Length: 2-5 months
Duties: Policy research/advocacy
Remuneration: Full time: $250/week

Jobs advertised: Law schools

To apply: Contact Alan W. Houseman

CENTER FOR LAW IN THE PUBLIC INTEREST

5750 Wilshire Blvd., Suite 561
Los Angeles, CA 90036
(310) 470-3017

Director: Jack Nicholl

Purpose: CLIPI is a private, nonprofit organization, established in 1971 to provide free legal services on a broad range of important issues: civil rights, free speech, affordable housing, the homeless, consumer fraud, fair elections, environmental protection, land use, corporate and governmental accountability.

Methods of operation: Litigation (95%), administration (3%), lobbying (1%), publications

(1%)

Constituency: Individuals interested in civil rights and environmental protection, consumer protection and housing issues

Recent issues and projects: Challenge Proposition 13; challenge EPA's performance as set out in the Clean Air Act; employment discrimination cases in the Bay area

Major publications: Biannual newsletter: *CLIPI News Briefs*

Funding: Foundations (30%), direct mail (3%), individual contributions (1%), other (66%)

Staff: 1
1 Part-time Executive Director

Work Week: 20 hours

Part-Time Employees: 1

Remarks: The Center for Law in the Public Interest recently restructured into a funding organization. We are no longer a law firm and therefore, we do not employ attorneys or law students. The private firm which handles much of our public interest environmental protection and consumer issues is Hall and Associates, 10951 West Pico Boulevard, Third Floor, Los Angeles, CA 90064.

CENTER FOR LIVING DEMOCRACY

RR Black Fox Road
Brattleboro, VT 05301
(802) 254-1234

Director: Paul Martin DuBois and Frances Moore Lappe

Purpose: To transform America's practice of democracy into a rewarding way of life that involves us daily in our schools, workplaces and communities. To spread innovations in democratic practice through our learning center, trainings and public education.

Methods of operation: Public Education (60%), publications (15%), training and technical assistance (15%), research (10%)

Constituency: Very broad, general public, active citizens, citizen organizations and public agencies

Recent issues and projects: Completion of book: *The Quickening of America: Rebuilding Our Nation, Remaking Our Lives* by F.M. Lappe and P.M. DuBois

Major publications: *The Quickening of America: Rebuilding Our Nation, Remaking Our Lives*

Budget: $180,000

Funding: Individual Contributions (70%), Foundations (10%), Direct Mail (10%), Royalties (10%)

Staff: 3
2 Co-Directors
1 Executive Coordinator

Staff openings/year: 2

Work Week: 40 hours

Salary/year: $20,000 (Recent College Graduate); $Varies (Graduate with advanced degree)

Benefits: Health insurance, paid vacation

Part-Time Employees: None

Summer Employees: None

Volunteers: 5

Interns: Not at this time

Jobs advertised: Local papers

To apply: Contact Sara Warner-Philips

CENTER FOR MARINE CONSERVATION

1725 DeSales Street, NW
Washington, DC 20036
(202) 429-5609

Other Offices: Hampton, VA; St. Petersburg, FL; San Francisco, CA

Director: Roger McManus

Purpose: Protection of the marine environment and its wildlife.

Methods of operation: Research (25%), public education (25%), training and technical assistance (20%), publications (20%), direct action (7%), lobbying (2%), litigation (1%)

Constituency: People interested in conserving the marine environment

Recent issues and projects: Marine sanctuaries, marine debris, marine mammal issues, sea turtles and Turtle Excluder Devices (TEDs), fisheries, conservatories, and marine biological diversity.

Major publications: Quarterlies: *CMC News* and *Sanctuary Currents*; various books and reports

Budget: $7,000,000

Funding: Direct mail (50%), individual contributions (25%), foundations (25%), investments and catalogue sales

Staff: 65

Staff openings/year: 10

Work Week: 40 hours

Salary/year: $20,000 (Recent College Graduate); $Varies (Graduate with advanced degree)

Benefits: Health insurance, life insurance, paid vacation, pregnancy leave, dental insurance

Part-Time Employees: Yes

Volunteers: 10

Interns: 4
Length: 2-3 months
Duties: Writing, research, lobbying, correspondence with public
Remuneration: Volunteer

Jobs advertised: Job descriptions mailed to other nonprofits; classifieds; etc.

To apply: Contact Administration Department

CENTER FOR MAXIMUM POTENTIAL BUILDING SYSTEMS

8604 F.M. 969
Austin, TX 78724
(512) 928-4786

Director: Pliny Fisk III and Gail Vittori, Co-Directors

Purpose: Establishing regional approaches to developing life support systems - shelter, energy, waste, water, food. The Center was established in 1975 as a nonprofit appropriate technology research, education and demonstration organization. Since its inception, the Center has provided technical assistance to local and national governments, community groups, private firms and individuals in their pursuit of resource efficient building and energy systems, ecological land planning, and sustainable cities and regions.

Methods of operation: Training and technical assistance (30%), research (30%), public education (20%), community organizing (10%), publications (10%)

Constituency: Diverse regional, national and international constituencies, including community organizers, architects, engineers, housing activists, economists, etc.

Recent issues and projects: (1) Blueprint Demonstration Farm, Loredo, Texas (sustainable ag/bldg, decertification, urban-rural linkage); (2) demonstration owner-builder home for Central Texas using indigenous materials; (3) sustainable cities national forum/university lectures, etc.; (4) education and demonstration center for temperate grasslands on sustainability and appropriate technology

Major publications: *The Caliche Report*; *Indigenous Building Materials Compendium*; *Appropriate Technology Working Atlas for the State of Texas*; *Bioregional Planning and Appropriate Technology for Nicaragua's Miskito Indians*; *Bioregions and Biotechnologies: A Potentially New Planning Tool for Stable State Economic Development*; *Crystal City Passive Solar Water Heater*

Budget: $300,000

Funding: Foundations and Government (80%), individual contributions (20%)

Staff: 3
2 Co-Directors
1 Project Manager

Work Week: 50 hours

Salary/year: $24,000

Benefits: Health insurance; some housing and board

Part-Time Employees: 2

Summer Employees: Yes

Volunteers: 2

Interns: Yes

Jobs advertised: Word of mouth

To apply: Contact Pliny Fisk III or Gail Vittori

CENTER FOR MEDIA AND VALUES

1962 South Shenandoah Street
Los Angeles, CA 90034
(310) 559-2944

Director: Elizabeth Thoman

Purpose: We offer programs and services to provide leadership for a media awareness/education movement in the 1990's. We have pioneered a new methodology for media awareness/analysis/reflection/action.

Methods of operation: Publications (50%), research (25%), public education (25%)

Constituency: Teachers, youth workers, church leaders, education coordinators

Recent issues and projects: Magazine issue topics have included: Media and Gender, a two part series including "Men, Myth and Media" and "Redesigning Women"; Alcohol and tobacco ads "Selling Addiction"; Media ad war "Images of Conflict"; "Living in the Image Culture"; "Citizenship in the Media Age" a multi-media educational resource package; and "Beyond Blame: Violence in the Media"

Major publications: *Media and Values* magazine

Funding: Sales/subscriptions (30%), individual contributions (17%), memberships (20%), foundations (33%)

Staff: 6
1 Executive Director
1 Writer/Editor
1 Administrator
1 Promotion/PR Coordinator
1 Assistant Editor
1 Customer Service Representative

Staff openings/year: 1-2

Work Week: 40+ hours

Salary/year: $25,000 (Recent College Graduate); $28,000 (Graduate with advanced degree)

Benefits: Health insurance, life insurance, paid vacation

Part-Time Employees: 4-6

Volunteers: 2

Jobs advertised: Locally mostly - area colleges and universities

To apply: Contact Jill Larson, Administrator

CENTER FOR MEDICAL CONSUMERS

237 Thompson Street
New York, NY 10012
(212) 674-7105

Director: Arthur Levin

Purpose: Information source for the lay public. Maintain a free medical reference library.

Methods of operation: Public education, publications (90%)

Constituency: Laypeople as well as practitioners

Recent issues and projects: Publish consumer's guides to hospitals with the lowest mortality for certain surgical procedures, and to mammography screening facilities in New York City.

Major publications: Monthly newsletter: *Health Facts*

Budget: $125,000

Funding: Newsletter subscriptions and guides (95%), individual contributions (5%)

Staff: 2
Including:
1 Office Manager
1 Associate Director/Editor

Work Week: 50 hours

Salary/year: $20,000

Benefits: Health insurance, paid vacation

Volunteers: Yes

Jobs advertised: Word of mouth; sometimes ads in local newspapers

Remarks: No paid openings will be available in the near future. We will accept volunteers in our library.

CENTER FOR NATIONAL POLICY

1 Massachusetts Avenue, NW
Washington, DC 20008
(202) 682-1800

Director: Maureen Steinbrunner

Purpose: The Center for National Policy is a nonprofit research organization dedicated to developing new approaches and creative solutions to major issues confronting the nation.

Methods of operation: Research (33%), publications (33%), public education (33%)

Recent issues and projects: Recent projects include: Study of the U.S. economy and the labor force; spearheading of a task force on community building in troubled urban neighborhoods; work on focusing attention on the issue of population; involvement with U.S. policy towards Cambodia and Vietnam

Major publications: *Democrats and the American Idea*; *Adolescence and Poverty*; *America Tomorrow: The Choices We Face*; *Exploring Cambodia: Issues and Reality in a Time of Transition*

Staff: 10
2 Organizers
1 Office Manager
1 Researcher
2 Press Aides
1 Foundation Fundraiser
2 Issue Experts
1 Administrative Assistant

Staff openings/year: 1

Work Week: 40 hours

Salary/year: $18,000

Benefits: Health insurance, paid vacation

Part-Time Employees: None

Summer Employees: 2

Volunteers: 2

Interns: 2
Length: 3 months
Duties: Administrative, research
Remuneration: $1000 for 3 months during summer

To apply: Contact Erin Boggs

CENTER FOR NATIONAL SECURITY STUDIES

122 Maryland Avenue, NE
Washington, DC 20002
(202) 675-2327

Director: Kate Martin

Purpose: To prevent claims of national security from being used to erode individual liberties or constitutional procedures. To protect the right of individuals to participate fully in the public debate about national security issues.

Methods of operation: Litigation (30%), public education (30%), research (20%), publications (10%), lobbying (10%)

Recent issues and projects: Free Trade in Ideas Project to remove the barriers erected by the American government to the flow of information and ideas into and out of the United States. War Powers and Covert Action Project to illuminate the issues involved in the decision to intervene militarily in the affairs of other nations. Works to protect privacy from illegal government surveillance.

Major publications: Newsletter: *First Principles*, which describes recent events relating to national security and civil liberties and which publishes articles on major issues; CNSS Rep. #11: *FBI Misguided Probe of CISPES* and CNSS Rep. #110: *Covert Operations and the Democratic Process: The Implications of the Iran/Contra Affairs*

Budget: $725,000

Funding: Foundations (95%), individual contributions (5%)

Staff: 8
3 Attorneys
2 Typists
1 Writer/Editor
1 Researcher
1 Office Manager

Staff openings/year: 1-2

Work Week: 40 + hours

Salary/year: $Varies

Benefits: Health insurance, life insurance, parental leave, pension, paid vacation, law school loans

Volunteers: 3

Interns: 10-15
Length: Summer or semester
Duties: Assist with research and support. Law students do legal research.
Remuneration: No pay for undergraduates. Law students paid modestly.

Jobs advertised: Job announcements are mailed to a list of organizations and to groups specializing in affirmative action outreach. Notices are also posted on an office bulletin board, and advertisements are placed in appropriate publications.

To apply: Contact the Office Administrator

CENTER FOR NEIGHBORHOOD TECHNOLOGY

2125 West North Avenue
Chicago, IL 60647
(312) 278-4800

Director: Scott Bernstein

Purpose: CNT is a non-profit research, advocacy and technical assistance agency which works to create community economic development opportunities out of environmental problems. Current work focuses on transportation and air quality, sustainable work focuses on transportation and air quality, sustainable manufacturing, community energy and materials reuse and recycling.

Methods of operation: Policy research and advocacy (60%), technical assistance (25%), publications (15%)

Constituency: Community development and community organization groups in Chicago's low and moderate income neighborhoods

Recent issues and projects: Transit-oriented community planning in context of ISTEA and Clean Air Act mandates; energy conservation in public buildings with savings targeted to community purposes; development of pollution prevention financing for small manufacturers; demonstrations of non-chlorine "drycleaning" technology; *The Neighborhood Works* news magazine.

Major publications: *The Neighborhood Works* (6 times/year); *Sustainable Manufacturing: Saving Jobs and Saving the Environment*; *Beyond Recycling*; *Sustainable Transportation*; *Working Neighborhoods*

Budget: $1,600,000

Funding: Fee for service (35%), foundations (55%), subscriptions, sales, other (5%), individual contributions (5%)

Staff: 22
8 Program Managers
2 Technical (e.g. Engineers, Energy Auditors)
2 Issue Experts
2 Editors
3 Administrative Assistants
1 Office Manager
2 Bookkeepers/Accountants
1 Fundraiser
1 Computer Manager

Staff openings/year: 3-8

Work Week: 37.5 hours

Benefits: Health insurance, paid vacation

Part-Time Employees: 2

Summer Employees: 0

Interns: 2-6; we have interns from other programs
Duties: For public issues, environmental and technical roles
Remuneration: Negotiable

Jobs advertised: Mailings to community groups in Chicago; newspaper ads

To apply: Contact Stephen A. Perkins, Associate Director

CENTER FOR ORGANIZATIONAL AND COMMUNITY DEVELOPMENT

377 Hills South, University of Massachusetts
Amherst, MA 01003
(413) 545-2038 (413) 45-2231

Director: Sally Habana-Hafner, Coordinator

Purpose: Established to help citizens and citizen groups become more effective. Offers workshops, consultation services and training materials that help citizens develop the critical skills necessary for effective citizen involvement. Provides individualized training workshops and assistance uniquely designed from a careful analysis of organizational needs.

Methods of operation: Research, lobbying, publications, organizing, public education, training and technical assistance, networking

Constituency: Focus on citizens in neighboring communities, but also do outreach statewide through agencies.

Recent issues and projects: Citizen Involvement Training Program; Participatory Research and Learning Project; National Priorities Project; Partnership and Coalition Project; Multicultural Development Project

Major publications: Citizen involvement training manuals and partnership/interorganizational collaboration materials, including: *Partnerships for Community Development: Resources for Practitioners and Trainers*; *Planning, for a Change*; *Power: A Repossessional Manual*; *Beyond Schools: Education for Economic, Social and Personal Development*; *Cross-Cultural Approaches to Community Development*

Budget: $85,000

Funding: Publication sales, Department of Public Health, contracts

Staff: 4
1 1/2 Researchers
1 Trainer
1/2 Organizer
1/2 Writer/Editor
1/2 Office Manager

Staff openings/year: 0-1

Work Week: 40 hours

Salary/year: $17,500

Benefits: Health insurance, pension, life insurance, credit union, tuition reimbursement, holidays

Part-Time Employees: Yes

Volunteers: Yes

Interns: Yes
Length: 1 semester
Duties: Training, writing, editing
Remuneration: Academic credit

Jobs advertised: Newspapers; job listings

To apply: Contact Sally Habana-Hafner, Coordinator

CENTER FOR PARTY DEVELOPMENT

Catholic University/Pol. Dept., P.O. Box 2057
Reston, VA 22090
(703) 709-9460

President: Dr. Ralph M. Goldman

Purpose: The Center for Party Development is a multipartisan, interdisciplinary and multi-university nonprofit organization dedicated to research, education and the professionalization of party politics in the United States, overseas and transnationally.

Methods of operation: Publications (60%), research (25%), public education (15%)

Constituency: Political party staffs, scholars, journalists, corporate executives, diplomats

Recent issues and projects: Recent projects include: a survey of former Members of Congress regarding their view of the role of the parties in Congress; inaugurated an Essay Series, that is, booklets dealing with subjects pertinent to political parties, party institutions and party systems; prepared articles on political parties for encyclopedias; drafted a proposal for the establishment of a commission to study the organization, management and financing of U.S. parties; and will shortly inaugurate a book series dealing with issues of party development

Major publications: *Party Development*, newsletter 5 times a year

Staff:
No full-time salaried staff at this time

Part-Time Employees: 2

Summer Employees: None

Volunteers: 5

Interns: Being developed, inquiries invited

To apply: Contact Ralph M. Goldman, President

CENTER FOR POLICY ALTERNATIVES

1875 Connecticut Avenue, NW, Suite 710
Washington, DC 20009
(202) 387-6030

Director: Linda Tarr-Whelan

Purpose: The Center is a policy resource organization specializing in innovation and reform by America's state governments. CPA bases its work on three pillars of progressive public policies: effective alternative models which support equitable economic growth and full democratic participation, educated leadership among public officials and advocates, and on-site field activities and public education which support these efforts.

Methods of operation: Research, publications, community organizing, public education, training and technical assistance

Constituency: State government officials, both elected and appointed; local advocacy groups

Recent issues and projects: Working in major areas of environmental quality, voter participation, family and work, economic development and women's economic justice. Have held conferences, round-tables, provided technical assistance and published materials in all of the above areas.

Major publications: Newsletter: *Alternatives*; *Public Capital: Revitalizing America's Communities*; *A New Housing Policy for America: Recapturing the American Dream*; *The Pesticides Crisis: A Blueprint for State Action*; *Legislative Sourcebook on Financial Deregulation*; *Women's Economic Justice Agenda: Ideas for the States.* Also *Update* and *Leadership Briefs* from the Women's Economic Justice Center

Budget: $1,200,000

Funding: Individual contributions, foundations, corporations, other

Staff: 18
8 Issue Experts
4 Foundation Fundraisers
3 Researchers
1 Attorney
1 Office Manager

1 Bookkeeper/Accountant

Staff openings/year: 0-1

Work Week: 40 hours

Salary/year: $Varies (Recent College Graduate); $Varies (Graduate with advanced degree)

Benefits: Health insurance, life insurance, pregnancy leave, pension, tuition reimbursement, paid vacation

Part-Time Employees: 3

Summer Employees: Yes

Interns: Yes
Length: School year or semester
Duties: Varies with program assignment
Remuneration: Volunteer

Jobs advertised: Local newspapers; nonprofit organizations

To apply: Contact Sara Rogge, Operations Assistant

CENTER FOR PSYCHOLOGY AND SOCIAL CHANGE

1493 Cambridge Street
Cambridge, MA 02139
(617) 497-1553

Director: Vivienne Simon

Purpose: The Center, an affiliate of the Harvard Medical School at The Cambridge Hospital, focuses on inter-disciplinary projects, research and public education programs that contribute to the development of a new psychology of a sustainable world at peace.

Methods of operation: Research (50%), publications (25%), public education and training (25%)

Recent issues and projects: The Center is contributing to the development of a new model of mental health and psychotherapy based on the theory and practice of ecopsychology, as well as, the psychology of place and bioregionalism; training for educators and parents in the political development of children in the media age; investigation into extraordinary experiences and their role in personal transformation; and psychologically sensitive interactive conflict resolution in international disputes.

Major publications: *Center Piece*, features information and reports on Center projects and research. Research papers and studies also published in journals and anthologies.

Budget: $550,000

Funding: Individual contributions (50%), foundations (50%)

Staff: 8
1 Executive Director
1 Associate Director
1 Office Manager
5 Project Staff
1/2 Bookkeeper
10 Part-time Researchers

Staff openings/year: 1-2

Work Week: 40 hours

Salary/year: $17,000 (Recent College Graduate); $21,000 (Graduate with advanced degree)

Benefits: Health insurance, life insurance, family leave, child care compensation, paid vacation

Part-Time Employees: 11

Summer Employees: 1-2

Volunteers: 3-5

Interns: 3-5
Length: 1-2 semesters
Duties: Distribution of general information from the Center to the public; special projects; development of Center bibliography
Remuneration: Small stipend or work-study

Jobs advertised: Flyers at local schools, student employment offices, nonprofit job listings

To apply: Contact Mary Ellen Hynes, Associate Director or Heather Simpson, Office Manager

Remarks: The Center is represented at the United Nations as a non-governmental organization.

CENTER FOR PUBLIC REPRESENTATION

121 South Pinckney Street
Madison, WI 53703
(608) 251-4008

Director: Michael Gregg Pritchard

Purpose: Founded in 1974, CPR is Wisconsin's first public interest law firm. Its goal is to represent under-represented groups or individuals in Wisconsin's government process. After researching current and continuing problems, CPR proposes solutions and appears before state, local and federal agencies, Wisconsin courts, and the Wisconsin Legislature.

Methods of operation: Nonprofit law firm taking on individual and multiple plaintiff cases and class action suits

Constituency: Children, women, disabled people, minorities, consumers, the elderly

Recent issues and projects: (1) Training Center: conducting workshops and seminars on public interest issues and helping citizens help themselves; (2) Ombudsman: acting as "watchdog" to assure open, responsive government and to stop consumer ripoffs in the marketplace; (3) Publishing House: publishing self-help guides for consumers and manuals for advocates and professionals. CPR's current efforts cover a wide range of interests in elderly, families, consumers, women and health.

Major publications: Quarterly newsletter: *Public Eye*; over two dozen publications on consumer affairs, open government and advocacy, and the problems facing consumers, children and the elderly

Budget: $1,300,000

Funding: Government contracts, foundation grants, contributions, sales, training fees

Staff: 12
7 Attorneys
5 Paralegals
Administration Staff
Publications Distribution Staff
Trainings Staff
Information and Referral Staff
Administration Staff

Staff openings/year: 1-2

Work Week: 37.5 hours

Benefits: Health insurance, life insurance, parental leave

Part-Time Employees: Yes

Volunteers: Yes

Interns: Yes

To apply: Contact office

CENTER FOR RESEARCH AND DEVELOPMENT IN LAW-RELATED EDUCATION

2714 Henning Drive
Winston-Salem, NC 27106-4502
(910) 721-3355

Director: Julia Hardin

Purpose: To prepare students for effective citizenship through innovative strategies created by teachers for teachers.

Methods of operation: Research (15), publication (15%), training and technical assistance (70%)

Membership: Civics teachers, K-12, nationwide

Recent issues and projects: LEGACY partnership program for teachers and attorneys in civics education; Building an LRE Bridge program for state law-related education programs; National Repository for Educational Materials on Civics

Major publications: Lesson plan manuals, *SPLICE* Newsletter (Teachers Speak Out on Law-Related Education); *LRE Bridge Newsleter*

Budget: $250,000

Funding: Individual contributions (5%), foundations (10%) and federal grants (85%)

Staff: 3
1 Writer/Editor
1 Office Manager
1 Director

Staff openings/year: 1

Work Week: 65 hours

Benefits: Paid vacation

Part-Time Employees: 2-3

Summer Employees: 1-2

Volunteers: Varies

Interns: None; but willing to accept applications

Jobs advertised: Newspapers; journals; grassroots network

To apply: Julia Hardin, Executive Director

CENTER FOR RESPONSIVE POLITICS

1320 19th Street, NW, Suite M-1
Washington, DC 20036
(202) 857-0044

Director: Ellen S. Miller

Purpose: CRP is a bipartisan, nonprofit organization that conducts research and in-depth studies on key Congressional, campaign finance and other political and public policy concerns. The

Center is a clearinghouse for information and statistics on money in politics for the public, the press and activists.

Methods of operation: Research (70%), public education, publications (30%)

Constituency: Research is directed toward Congress, "DC decision-makers," academics and media

Recent issues and projects: Recent studies by CRP include: Open Secrets; State Open Secrets; National Library on Money and Politics; Conferences for Issue Activists; Soft Money Research; FEC Watch; *Money and Politics* newsletter; Legal Challenges Project; and Media Outreach

Major publications: The Center issues periodic reports that document role of private money in politics.

Budget: $300,000

Funding: Foundations

Staff: 3
4 Researchers (1 part-time)

Staff openings/year: 1-2

Work Week: 40 hours

Salary/year: $18,000 (Recent College Graduate); $30,000 (Graduate with advanced degree)

Benefits: Health insurance, life insurance, paid vacation

Part-Time Employees: 1

Summer Employees: 1-2

Interns: 3-6 per year
Length: 4 months
Duties: Research, data entry, assist press secretary, project director
Remuneration: Stipend for summer interns

Jobs advertised: Papers; nonprofit newsletters

To apply: Contact Sheila Krumholz, Executive Assistant

CENTER FOR RURAL AFFAIRS

P.O. Box 406
Walthill, NE 68067
(402) 846-5428

Other Offices: Hartington, NE

Director: Marty Strange, Program Leader

Purpose: Build sustainable rural communities at home and abroad consistent with social and economic justice, stewardship of the natural environment, broad distribution of wealth and opportunity for all people to earn just incomes and own and control productive resources.

Methods of operation: Research (40%), public education (40%), publications (15%), lobbying (5%)

Constituency: Serve small to mid-size family farmers, rural residents, and like-minded urban citizens.

Recent issues and projects: Community-based loan programs; linking beginning farmers with landowners; beginning farmer support network, education and advocacy; on-farm research; global warming; international trade impacts; federal ag credit policy; federal farm bill and conservation legislation; state corporate farming bills; rural community education; land-grant and federal agricultural research; Nebraska tax reform, Picotte Center restoration

Major publications: Monthly newsletters; *Family Farming, The Great Trade Debate, Farm Program Options Guide, A School at the Center, Choices for the Heartland, Beneath the Wheels of Fortune, The Portable Symposium, Resourceful Farming Primer, Small Farm Energy primer, Fit for a Pig, Resource Audit and Planning Guide, Neither Here Nor There, Half a Glass of Water*

Budget: $1,000,000

Funding: Foundations (75%), individual contributions (25%)

Staff: 20
1 Program Director
1 Administrative Director
2 Program Leaders
6 Project Leaders
10 Organizers, Assistants, Specialists, and Support Staff

Staff openings/year: 1

Work Week: 40 hours

Salary/year: $18,000

Benefits: Health insurance, life insurance, pension, paid vacation

Part-Time Employees: 3

Summer Employees: 1

Interns: 3
Length: 1 year
Duties: Project-dependent

Remuneration: Average salary: $15,600 + benefits

Jobs advertised: Our newsletter; *Community Jobs*

To apply: Contact Don Ralston, Administrative Director

CENTER FOR SAFETY IN THE ARTS
5 Beekman Street, Suite 820
New York, NY 10038
(212) 227-6220

Director: Michael McCann, Ph.D., Program Manager

Purpose: To provide education and information on health and safety hazards and precautions in the visual and performing arts.

Methods of operation: Research, lobbying, publications, public education, training and technical assistance, answering written and telephone inquiries on specific problems (approx. 50/day)

Constituency: Visual and performing artists and technicians, schools, university art departments, parents, museums personnel and home hobbyists

Recent issues and projects: Current projects include: working to bring about national legislation mandating labelling of art materials; developing manual on health and safety in the motion picture and television industry.

Major publications: Produce and distribute over 90 publications, including *Art Hazards News*, *Artist Beware*, and *Health Hazards Manual for Artists*

Budget: $250,000

Funding: Individual contributions, government grants, sale of publications, lectures, consultations

Staff: 7
2 Writers/Editors
2 Issue Experts
2 Researchers
1 Executive Director
1 Secretary (part-time)
1 Foundation Fundraiser (part-time)
1 Accountant (part-time)
1 Bookkeeper (part-time)

Staff openings/year: 1

Work Week: 40 hours

Salary/year: $32,000 (Recent College Graduate); $38,000 (Graduate with advanced degree)

Benefits: Health insurance, pension, paid vacation, pregnancy leave, sick days, personal days and flexible hours

Part-Time Employees: Yes

Volunteers: 1

Interns: 1
Length: 6 months
Duties: Research, library and writing
Remuneration: Work-study

Jobs advertised: *New York Times*; posting at universities and health and safety and arts organizations

To apply: Contact Thomas E. Russock, Executive Director

CENTER FOR SCIENCE IN THE PUBLIC INTEREST (CSPI)
1875 Connecticut Avenue, NW, Suite 300
Washington, DC 20009
(202) 332-9110

Director: Michael F. Jacobson, Ph.D.

Purpose: Research, education, and advocacy on nutrition, diet, food safety, alcohol and related health issues.

Methods of operation: Public education (33%), supporting services (26%), publications (18%), research (16%), litigation (5%), lobbying (2%)

Constituency: Individuals; health professionals

Recent issues and projects: Americans for Safe Food

Major publications: *Nutrition Action Healthletter*; *Booze News*; *Marketing Disease to Hispanics*

Budget: $12,000,000

Funding: Direct mail (62%), individual contributions (17%), publication sales (11%), foundations (4%)

Staff: 35
6 Issue Experts
4 Data Entry/Customer Service
2 Researchers
3 Attorneys
2 Mail Room/Orders
2 Writers/Editors
1 Executive Director
1 Deputy Director
1 Paralegal
1 Lobbyist
1 Foundation Fundraiser

2 Bookkeepers/Accountants
1 Human Resource Manager
3 Direct Mail Specialists
5 Administrative Assistants

Staff openings/year: 5

Work Week: 40-50 hours

Salary/year: $19,000 (Recent College Graduate); $22,000 (Graduate with advanced degree)

Benefits: Health insurance, life insurance, pregnancy leave, pension, paid vacation

Part-Time Employees: 1

Summer Employees: 5

Volunteers: 1

Interns: 3; 9 Workstudy
Length: 4 months
Duties: Research, correspondence, filing
Remuneration: $700/month stipend

Jobs advertised: Local newspapers; mailing to DC public interest groups

To apply: Contact Human Resources Department

CENTER FOR SOCIAL CHANGE PRACTICE AND THEORY

Heller Graduate School, Brandeis University
Waltham, MA 02254-9110
(617) 736-3827

Director: Professor David G. Gil

Purpose: The Center's work is based on the recognition that human ills are rooted in societal structures and dynamics, and in values which often justify and maintain the prevailing social order. Accordingly the Center's work is oriented toward transforming social, economic and political institutions which result in injustice, exploitation, discrimination, conflict in human relations and ecological destruction into alternative institutions conducive to human development.

Methods of operation: Education (35%), publications (30%), research (30%), lobbying (5%)

Constituency: Students, human service workers, colleagues, community groups

Recent issues and projects: Promoting a Constitutional amendment to guarantee employment and income; organizing conferences on the Future of Work and Democratic Socialism; organizing human service workers' support groups for radical practice; promoting legislation to count unremunerated work in the Gross National Product (HR 966)

Major publications: *Toward Social and Economic Justice* (1985); *The Future of Work* (1987). The Center is co-publisher of *Changing Work Magazine, Unravelling Social policy*; and *Assessing and Promoting Compliance in the U.S. with Economic and Social Human Rights*

Funding: University salaries (100%)

Staff: 1
1 Director/Professor
1/3 Typist

Benefits: Health insurance, pension, paid vacation, life insurance

Part-Time Employees: 1/3

Volunteers: 1-2

To apply: Contact David Gil

Remarks: The Center offers courses, colloquia and workshops at the School and in the community. It works with Ph.D. students on dissertation projects within the domain and also with other students interested in its orientation. It offers consultation to individuals and organizations, and it plans to sponsor visiting scholars and activists in residence at the School. It also maintains a publications program and organizes conferences.

CENTER FOR THE STUDY OF COMMERCIALISM

1875 Connecticut Ave., NW, Suite 300
Washington, DC 20009
(202) 332-9110

Director: Michael Jacobson

Purpose: A nonprofit advocacy group that exposes and opposes excessive commercialism in America.

Methods of operation: Publications (30%), research (20%), direct action (20%), public education (20%), lobbying (5%), litigation (5%)

Membership: People concerned with excessive commercialism and communications professors

Recent issues and projects: Commercials in the classroom, telemarketing, commercialization of public broadcasting, product placement in movies

Major publications: *Advice* newsletter; *Marketing Madness* (forthcoming book); *How Advertising*

Pressure Can Corrupt a Free Press (report)

Budget: $100,000

Funding: Foundations (90%), individual contributions (10%)

Staff: 1
1 Research Assistant/Intern

Staff openings/year: 0-1

Work Week: 45 hours

Salary/year: $19,000 (Recent College Graduate); $24,000 (Graduate with advanced degree)

Benefits: Health insurance, paid vacation

Part-Time Employees: No

Summer Employees: Yes

Volunteers: No

Interns: Yes
Length: Semester
Duties: Research, writing administrative
Remuneration: None

Jobs advertised: Through nonprofits and publications

To apply: Contact Karen Brown

CENTER FOR THE STUDY OF RACE AND ETHNICITY IN AMERICA

Brown University, P.O. Box 1886
Providence, RI 02912
(401) 863-3880

Director: Dr. Rhett Jones

Purpose: The Center for the Study of Race and Ethnicity in America facilitates teaching and research on African Americans, Asian Americans, Latinos and Native Americans.

Methods of operation: Training and technical assistance (25%), public education (30%), publications (15%), community organizing (5%), research (25%)

Membership: Approximately 50 Brown faculty are the Center's affiliated members

Recent issues and projects: CSREA sponsors annual lecture series, provides research grants to faculty, graduate and undergraduate students, publishes newsletters and limited-circulation publications. It is the coordinating office of New England.

Major publications: Newsletter; limited-circulation publications, *Handbook of the Southern Consortium on Race and Ethnicity; CSREA Report*

Funding: University (100%)

Staff: 1
1 Office Manager
1 Associate Director (part-time)
1 Organizer (part-time)

Benefits: Health insurance, pension, paid vacation, life insurance, tuition reimbursement

Part-Time Employees: 2

Summer Employees: Yes

Volunteers: 20

Interns: No

CENTER FOR THE STUDY OF SERVICES

733 15th Street, NW, Suite 820
Washington, DC 20005
(202) 347-7283

Other Offices: San Francisco, CA

President: Robert Krughoff

Purpose: The Center publishes *Washington Consumers' Checkbook* and *Bay Area Consumers' Checkbook*, which provide ratings and advice regarding the quality and prices of local service providers including auto repair firms, hospitals, plumbers, banks, photo-finishing operations, etc. Our primary goal is to provide consumers with solid, research-based information about the local marketplace that enables them to make informed decisions when purchasing consumer services. As consumers act on our information incentive is created for service firms and retailers to improve quality and hold down prices, which in turn can improve the efficiency/quality of the marketplace for all consumers. We also offer a national car shopping service called CarBargains.

Methods of operation: Research, publications

Recent issues and projects: The Center is a regional "Consumer Reports" in effect, providing consumers with actual ratings from other consumers of the type and quality of service available in the local marketplace. The Center also publish two editions of *Bargains*, a guide to low-priced retailers for specific makes and models of big ticket items.

Major publications: *Washington Consumers'*

Checkbook; *Bay Area Consumers' Checkbook*; annual *Guide to Health Insurance Plans for Federal Employees*. Other special publications have included a guide to IRA's, a guide to long distance telephone service, a guide to hospitals (national), and DC and Bay Area restaurant guides based on real data from local consumers.

Funding: Individual contributions, telephone solicitation, subscriptions, publications sales

Staff: 24
9 Researchers
5 Subscription Fulfillment Department
5 Telefundraisers (part-time)
4 Researchers (part-time)
3 Administrative Department Managers
2 Publications Department Managers

Staff openings/year: 3-4

Work Week: 45 hours

Salary/year: $13-18,000

Benefits: Health insurance, paid vacation

Part-Time Employees: 5-10

Summer Employees: Varies

Volunteers: 3; not limited

Interns: Yes
Length: 4 months; minimum 20 hrs/week
Duties: Research Assistant - assigned to staff members or project team to help out as a "junior staff" member
Remuneration: $30-60/week reimbursement stipend

Jobs advertised: *Washington Post*, *City Paper*, *Washington Blade*, *Community Jobs*, and announcements to local public interest job boards like Common Cause or Sierra Club

To apply: Contact Research Manager or Intern Coordinator

CENTER FOR THIRD WORLD ORGANIZING

1218 East 21st Street
Oakland, CA 94606
(510) 533-7583

Director: Rinku Sen and Francis Calpotura, Co-Directors

Purpose: To provide training and support for organizers of color. To build a network of organizations which promote the interests of minority communities. Provide analysis of issues primarily concerning Third World communities in the U.S.

Methods of operation: Training and technical assistance (30%), publications (25%), community organizing (30%), research (15%)

Constituency: Researchers, writers, and activists of color; community members

Recent issues and projects: Organizing campaign around health care in Oakland; Minority Activist Apprenticeship Training Program (MAAP); Saturday school for community members; Community Strategic Training Initiative (CSTI); State of Our Nations, bringing together a diverse group of Native people to work on current issues in Indian communities; Women of Color Resource Center; Community Development Institute

Major publications: *The Minority Trendsletter*; *The Activists Guide to Religious Fundraising*; *Fundraising for Social Change*

Budget: $300,000

Funding: Foundations, individual contributions (50%), churches (25%), publications, consultations (20%), direct mail (5%)

Staff: 11
2 Organizers
2 Foundation Fundraisers
1 Program Director
1 Campaign Manager
1 Writer/Editor
1 Bookkeeper/Accountant
1 Office Manager
1 Researcher
1 Grassroots Fundraiser

Staff openings/year: 2-3

Work Week: 40-65 hours

Salary/year: $15-24,000

Benefits: Health and dental insurance, life insurance, paid vacation

Part-Time Employees: 3

Summer Employees: 3-5

Volunteers: 4

Interns: 30
Length: 3 months/summer; 6 during year
Duties: Vary
Remuneration: Vary

Jobs advertised: Ads in *Community Jobs*; local papers

To apply: Contact Rinku Sen, Co-Director

CENTER FOR WOMEN POLICY STUDIES

2000 P Street, NW, Suite 508
Washington, DC 20036
(202) 872-1770

Director: Leslie R. Wolfe

Purpose: CWPS, founded in 1972, was the first policy institute to focus specifically on the social, legal and economic status of women. The Center's policy, research, and advocacy programs concentrate on educational equity, work, family and workplace diversity issues, women's health, and women and AIDS - recognizing that all issues affecting women are interrelated. Underlying all of the Center's work is the premise that sex and race bias throughout society must be addressed simultaneously; policies and programs for "women in general" or "minorities in general" are not enough.

Methods of operation: Research (40%), publications (20%), public education (20%), training and technical assistance (10%), lobbying (10%)

Constituency: Policymakers, feminist organizations, education associations, other advocacy groups

Recent issues and projects: Educational Equity Policy Studies Program, National Resource Center on Women and AIDS, Reproductive Laws for the 1990s, Feminist Futures program and conference by, for and about women in their 20's

Major publications: *The SAT Gender Gap: Identifying the Causes*; *Earnings Sharing in Social Security: A Model for Reform*; *The Guide to Resources on Women and AIDS*; *Violence Against Women as Bias Motivated Hate Crime* publication catalog available

Budget: $600,000

Funding: Foundations (70%), corporations (10%), publication sales (10%), individual contributions (5%), events (5%)

Staff: 7
7 Issue Experts

Staff openings/year: 1

Work Week: 40 hours

Salary/year: $25,000 (Recent College Graduate); $28-35,000 (Graduate with advanced degree)

Benefits: Health insurance, life insurance, family leave, paid vacation, sick leave

Part-Time Employees: 2

Summer Employees: 0-2

Volunteers: 0-10

Interns: 3-5 per semester
Length: Varies; usually 1 semester
Remuneration: Work-study available; no stipends

Jobs advertised: Progressive newsletters; mailings to applicants whose resumes are on file; mailings to women's organizations

To apply: Send letter of inquiry and resume to Leslie R. Wolfe, Executive Director

CENTER FOR WOMEN'S ECONOMIC ALTERNATIVES

212 North Maple Street, P.O. Box 1033
Ahoskie, NC 27910
(919) 332-4179

Director: Carolyn Hall

Purpose: The Center is a community-based 501(c)(3) organization committed to the empowerment of low-income and poor working women through education and support of their organizing efforts. The overall goal is to create a workplace free of all oppression, where workers can earn a decent wage and have dignity and pride in their work in a healthy, safe workplace.

Methods of operation: Community organizing (65%), research (10%), lobbying (6%), litigation (5%), publications (5%), direct action (3%), public education (3%), training and technical assistance (3%)

Constituency: Majority are women, Black, working, poor, rural, undereducated

Recent issues and projects: Ninety percent of CWEA's work is with poultry workers and the poultry industry. The largest employer in this region is Perdue Farms. CWEA is the force that caused an OSHA inspection of two Perdue processing plants. Much publicity has been focused on the occupational disease and injuries caused by the industry. CWEA works to create awareness of the occupational hazards and exploitation of the workforce, which just happens to be 95% Black women. CWEA's six major projects are: Workplace Advocacy Project, National Poultry Project, Leadership Initiative, Environmental Racism Project, and Membership Development.

Budget: $210,000

Funding: Foundations (75%), individual

contributions (5%), direct mail (2%), other (18%)

Staff: 4
1 Director of Administration
2 Project Coordinators
1 Office Coordinator/Bookkeeper

Staff openings/year: 2

Work Week: 45-48 hours

Salary/year: $15,000 (Recent College Graduate); $25,000 (Graduate with advanced degree)

Benefits: Health insurance

Part-Time Employees: 3

Volunteers: 3

Interns: None currently, but willing to accept applications
Duties: Could utilize them in research, public education and leafleting
Remuneration: No funds available, but could assist in locating housing

Jobs advertised: Local and state newspapers; Employment Security; networking organizations; word of mouth

To apply: Contact Carolyn Hall, Board Chairperson

CENTER FOR WOMEN'S STUDIES AND SERVICES
2467 E Street
San Diego, CA 92102
(619) 233-8984

Director: Terry Carrilio

Purpose: Meet the unmet needs of women. Focus on assistance, advocacy and education for victims of sexual assault and family violence.

Methods of operation: Human services (82%), public education (10%), community organizing (5%), publications (3%)

Membership: $25 membership fee

Recent issues and projects: CWSS' newest project is the opening of a shelter for battered women and beginning a divorce clinic for battered women.

Major publications: *CWSS Newsletter*

Budget: $500,000

Funding: Government and United Way (88%), foundations (10%), individual contributions (2%)

Staff: 12
6 Administrators
2 Caseworkers
1 Office Manager
1 Paralegal
1 Education Specialist
1 Typist

Staff openings/year: 1

Work Week: 37 1/2 hours

Salary/year: $21,000 (Recent College Graduate); $25,000 (Graduate with advanced degree)

Benefits: Health insurance, pregnancy leave, paid vacation, credit union

Part-Time Employees: 3

Volunteers: 70

Interns: 12
Length: 6 months-2 years
Duties: Counseling internships
Remuneration: Unpaid

Jobs advertised: Local newspaper; mailing list; job postings

To apply: Contact Vera Herbst, Administrative Assistant

CENTER OF CONCERN
3700 13th Street, NW
Washington, DC 20017
(202) 635-2757

Director: James Hug, S.J.

Purpose: An independent interdisciplinary group engaged in social analysis, theological reflection and public education around changes of social justice with particular stress on the international dimension. Center of Concern holds consultant status with the United Nations.

Methods of operation: Research, lobbying, publications, organizing, public education, consulting

Constituency: Church communities and individuals interested in faith and justice issues

Recent issues and projects: The Women's Project; recently published *Transforming Feminism*, by Maria Riley; coordinated the Coalition for Peace in the Horn of Africa; work for the rights to health care for all

Major publications: Bimonthly newsletter: *Center Focus*; *Social Analysis: A Linking of Faith and*

Justice; *Opting For the Poor*, by Peter Henriot; *Social Revelations*, by Jim Hug; *Dimensions of the Healing Ministry*, edited by Jim Hug

Budget: $450,000

Funding: Contract income, grants, donations, direct mail

Staff: 11
6 Researchers
3 Support Staff
2 Administrative/Development

Staff openings/year: 1

Work Week: 40-60 hours

Salary/year: $18,000 (Recent College Graduate); $25,000 (Graduate with advanced degree)

Benefits: Health insurance, life insurance, pregnancy leave, paid vacation, dental insurance

Part-Time Employees: 1

Volunteers: 2

Interns: Yes
Length: Summer or semester
Duties: Research assistance
Remuneration: Work-study or other outside funding; help to find housing

Jobs advertised: Announcements sent to other organizations; *Washington Post*; word of mouth

To apply: Contact J.M. Deren

CENTER ON BUDGET AND POLICY PRIORITIES

777 N Capitol Street, NE, Suite 705
Washington, DC 20002
(202) 408-1080

Director: Robert Greenstein

Purpose: Provide research and analysis which focuses on the impact of changes in federal and state policies on low-income Americans.

Methods of operation: Publications (40%), training and technical assistance (30%), research (15%), public education (10%), lobbying (5%)

Recent issues and projects: Trends in poverty and income; developing policies to aid the working poor; effects of federal budget and tax policies on income distribution; state fiscal project examines state budget and tax policies towards reducing poverty; Earned Income Tax Credit campaign to aid the working poor; reduce work penalties in the welfare system; improve education and training programs for low-income people; reform the unemployment insurance system

Major publications: *Learning for Earning*; *WIC Newsletter* - updates on the Special Supplemental Food Program for Women, Infants, and Children. Major reports include: *Making Work Pay: The Unfinished Agenda; A New Direction: The Clinton Budget and Economic Plan, The States and the Poor: How Budget Decisions Affected Low-income People in 1992, A Place to Call Home: The Low-income Housing in 44 Major Metropolitan Areas* and *Where Have all the Dollars Gone? A State-by-State Analysis of Income Disparities*

Budget: $2,900,000

Funding: Foundations (90%), publications (9%), individual contributions (1%)

Staff: 36
10 Researchers
5 Issue Experts
3 Fundraisers
3 Managers
2 Lobbyists
2 Press Aides
2 Bookkeepers/Accountants
1 Office Administrator
1 Information Systems Manager
7 Administrative Aides

Staff openings/year: 0-1

Work Week: 40 hours

Salary/year: $Low 20's (Recent College Graduate); $Mid-high 20's (Graduate with advanced degree)

Benefits: Health insurance, life insurance, family leave, pension, paid vacation, medical reimbursement plan, dependent child care plan

Part-Time Employees: 7

Summer Employees: Interns only

Interns: 2-5
Length: College semester; full summer
Duties: Research, writing, administrative
Remuneration: College credit or stipend

Jobs advertised: Newspapers; nonprofits

To apply: Contact James Hawkins, Administrator

CENTER ON RACE, POVERTY, AND THE ENVIRONMENT

2111 Mission Street, Suite 401
San Francisco, CA 94110
(415) 864-3405

Director: Ralph Santiago Abascal

Purpose: To provide legal and technical assistance to grassroots groups in California and legal services attorneys nationwide who are fighting environmental hazards; to work with communities at risk to develop community-based, community-led responses to environmental dangers.

Methods of operation: Community organizing (40%), litigation (20%), administrative advocacy (20%), technical assistance (20%)

Constituency: Poor people in California who are facing environmental hazards

Major publications: Quarterly newsletter *Race, Poverty and the Environment*; bi-annual newsletter *Environmental Poverty Law Working Group News*; Training manual on environmental poverty law, *Empowerment as the Key to Environmental Protection: The Need for Environmental Poverty Law*

Budget: $200,000

Funding: Foundations (100%)

Staff: 3
2 Attorneys
1 Organizer

Staff openings/year: 0

Work Week: 50-55 hours

Salary/year: $30,000 (Graduate with advanced degree)

Benefits: Health insurance, life insurance, pregnancy leave, education allowance

Volunteers: 5

Interns: 7
Length: 3 months; summer/school term
Duties: Community organizing, research and writing, legal work
Remuneration: Bring your own funds

Jobs advertised: Law school campuses

To apply: Contact Luke Cole, Project Coordinator

Remarks: The Center on Race, Poverty and the Environment works to empower low-income communities to resist environmental dangers. Its environmental justice work focuses on working with low-income communities in California and the West, and providing technical and legal assistance to poor peoples' lawyers nationwide who are taking on environmental poverty law cases.

CENTER ON WAR & THE CHILD

35 Benton Street, P.O. Box 487
Eureka Springs, AR 72632
(501) 253-8900

Director: Richard Parker

Purpose: Seeks to "challenge those institutions and practices within societies which glorify and enhance war and violence in the mind of the child." Informs and educates members and the public; mobilizes effective public response; advocates on behalf of children. Conducts and promotes research regarding the effects of war and violence on children and the processes by which the institution of war is culturally transmitted to children.

Methods of operation: Public education (35%), publications (25%), research (25%), training and technical assistance (15%)

Constituency: Parents, educators and others with professional involvement with children

Recent issues and projects: Studies have been completed on children as victims of conflict in Afghanistan, Iran, Uganda, El Salvador, Guatemala and Mozambique; war toy audiovisual ("Disarming the Children"); education/action packets on the following topics: *Parenting for Peace*, *Teaching Peace*, *War Toys*, *Television Violence*, *Children and Nuclear War*, and *The Child Soldier*; war toy brochure: *The Arms Race in Your Neighborhood*

Major publications: Quarterly: *WarChild Monitor International*, focuses on issues pertaining to the victimization and militarization of children by war; quarterly *CWC Networker*, available to CWC Associates only

Funding: Individual contributions (60%), direct mail (20%), other (20%)

Staff:
2 Writers/Editors
2 Researchers
2 Issue Experts
1 Director
1 Foundation Fundraiser
1 Typist

Work Week: 35 hours

Part-Time Employees: 2

Volunteers: 1

Interns: Yes
Length: 2-3 months
Duties: Engage in study/research on issues directly related to children and war; may also opt to focus on the socialization of children to violence
Remuneration: Stipend

Jobs advertised: Peace publications

To apply: Contact Richard Parker, Director

CENTRAL AMERICAN REFUGEE CENTER (CARECEN)

3112 Mt. Pleasant Street, NW
Washington, DC 20010
(202) 328-9799

Director: Evelyn Garcia

Purpose: To work for the recognition of the rights of Central American refugees in the United States and to save and empower the Central American Community.

Methods of operation: Litigation, human services, community organizing, public education

Constituency: Central American refugees in the Washington, DC metropolitan area

Recent issues and projects: Participation in litigation on behalf of refugee rights. Documentation of human rights violations in El Salvador.

Budget: $800,000

Funding: Individual contributions, foundations, direct mail, contracts

Staff: 22

Staff openings/year: 5

Work Week: 35 hours

Salary/year: $Varies (Recent College Graduate); $Varies (Graduate with advanced degree)

Benefits: Health insurance, paid vacation

Part-Time Employees: Yes

Summer Employees: Yes

Volunteers: Yes

Interns: Yes

To apply: Contact Saul Solorzano, Executive Director

CENTRAL COMMITTEE FOR CONSCIENTIOUS OBJECTORS (CCCO) - WESTERN REGION

655 Sutter #514
San Francisco, CA 94102
(415) 474-3002

Other Offices: Philadelphia, PA

Director: Staff Collective

Purpose: CCCO protects and promotes conscientious objection to war. We advocate for GI rights and counter the militarization of students by military recruiters and JROTC.

Methods of operation: Public education (30%), publications (30%), training and technical assistance (25%), research (15%)

Recent issues and projects: We are researching and organizing to stop the planned increase of high school JROTC programs from 1600 to 3500 nationwide

Major publications: *The Objector*

Budget: $120,000

Funding: Individual contributions (90%), other (10%)

Staff: 2

Staff openings/year: 1/2

Work Week: 45 hours

Salary/year: $18,600

Benefits: Health insurance, paid vacation

Part-Time Employees: 1/2

Volunteers: Yes

Interns: Yes
Length: 3 months
Duties: Editorial, public relations, organizing
Remuneration: Flexible

Jobs advertised: Newspapers and progressive periodicals

To apply: Contact Judy Rohrer, Sam Diener, or Carlos Lezama

CENTRAL PENNSYLVANIA LEGAL SERVICES

Stevens House, 10 South Prince Street
Lancaster, PA 17603-3997
(717) 299-3621

Other Offices: York, PA; Harrisburg, PA; Reading, PA; Lebanon, PA

Director: Jane Ransom

Purpose: Central Pennsylvania Legal Service is a nonprofit organization that represents low-income individuals with legal problems. CPLS handles civil cases in the following areas: government benefits (SSI, welfare), family, unemployment compensation, housing and consumer law.

Methods of operation: Direct action (75%), litigation (10%), training and technical assistance (10%), human services (3%), public education (2%)

Recent issues and projects: Because of funding cutbacks, CPLS has been handling only emergency cases for a number of years. However, we recently implemented new priorities which include emergency and impact cases.

Major publications: Noteworthy cases are published in the *PLS Review*, which comes out of Harrisburg

Budget: $2,000,000

Funding: Government funds, local contracts and Bar Association support (100%)

Staff: 60
23 Attorneys
20 Secretaries/Receptionists
14 Paralegals
1 Executive Director
1 Bookkeeper/Accountant
1 Program Administrator
1 Foundation Fundraiser

Work Week: 35 hours

Salary/year: $13,000 (Recent College Graduate); $20,000 (Graduate with advanced degree)

Benefits: Health insurance, life insurance, pregnancy leave, paid vacation

Part-Time Employees: 3

Summer Employees: Not usually

Volunteers: Sometimes

Interns: No, not at this time

Jobs advertised: Local newspapers; Bar publications; *Clearinghouse Review*; law schools

To apply: Contact Samuel W. Milkes, Executive Director

CENTRAL STATES EDUCATION CENTER

809 South Fifth
Champaign, IL 61820
(217) 344-2371

Director: John W. Thompson

Purpose: Our mission is to help local citizens protect their local environment. We provide technical assistance to grassroots citizen groups on waste issues.

Methods of operation: Community organizing (76%), training and technical assistance (20%), publications (4%)

Constituency: Citizens in rural areas

Recent issues and projects: Organize citizen groups in the Midwest to stop unsafe waste disposal facilities.

Major publications: Monthly bulletin; books: *Waste Reduction and the Model Community*; *Hazardous Waste: An Introduction*

Budget: $110,000

Funding: Foundations (50%), individual contributions (35%), telephone solicitation (10%), direct mail (5%)

Staff: 5
3 Researchers
2 Organizers

Staff openings/year: 1

Work Week: 50 hours

Salary/year: $20,000 (Recent College Graduate); $22,000 (Graduate with advanced degree)

Benefits: Paid vacation

Part-Time Employees: 4

Volunteers: 10

Jobs advertised: Newspaper; notify other environmental groups

To apply: Contact John W. Thompson

Remarks: We employ several research assistants who are completing Ph.D. work in geology and civil engineering. We are always looking for experienced grassroots organizers with a technical background.

CHAMPAIGN COUNTY HEALTH CARE CONSUMERS (CCHCC)

44 Main Street, Room 208
Champaign, IL 61820
(217) 352-6533

Director: Imani Bazzell

Purpose: Obtaining and maintaining accessible and affordable health care for residents of Champaign County through public education, direct action, research and self empowerment.

Methods of operation: Community organizing, direct action (50%), research (20%), public education (15%), training and technical assistance (5%), publications (5%), human services (5%)

Recent issues and projects: Researching. The organization has task forces and committees to work on specific problems: Senior Task Force, Low-income Task Force, Women's Health Task Force, and HMO Task Force.

Major publications: Quarterly newsletter: *Health Care Consumer*; *Health Care Directory for Champaign County*

Budget: $205,000

Funding: Individual contributions (42.5%), foundations (27.8%), canvassing doors/phones (22.7%), other (7%)

Staff: 9
6 Organizers
2 Issue Experts
1 Grassroots Fundraiser
Canvassers

Work Week: 50 hours

Salary/year: $14,800 (Recent College Graduate); $15,800 (Graduate with advanced degree)

Benefits: Health insurance, family leave, paid vacation, union

Part-Time Employees: 3

Summer Employees: Yes

Volunteers: Yes

Interns: Yes
Length: Unlimited
Duties: Canvass, Research
Remuneration: Negotiable

Jobs advertised: College placements; local newspapers; internship book

To apply: Contact Imani Bazzell, Executive Director

CHESAPEAKE BAY FOUNDATION

162 Prince George Street
Annapolis, MD 21401
(301) 268-8816

Other Offices: Richmond, VA; Harrisburg, PA; Norfolk, VA

President: William C. Baker

Purpose: The Chesapeake Bay Foundation is a private, nonprofit conservation organization dedicated to the restoration and preservation of the Chesapeake Bay and its natural resources.

Methods of operation: Direct action (46%), public education (46%), lobbying (2%), litigation (2%), publications (2%), community organizing (2%)

Membership: Located in Chesapeake Bay region

Recent issues and projects: Claggett Farm Education Center, providing a practical model of how conservation practices can reduce environmental risks without jeopardizing profitability. Environmental Defense Program, with oil drilling, toxics, pesticides and pretreatment concerns and grassroots activities. Environmental Education Program, with 16 centers, mobile boat programs, a farm program, and a stream restoration program to involve students in improving water quality in their local streams. Lands Program: monitoring and supporting land use regulation and encouraging private land conservation.

Major publications: *CBF Annual Report*; *CBF News*, quarterly; *BayWatcher Bulletin*, for active members; *Simple Ways to Save the Bay*; six how-to pamphlets on the many ways you can Save the Bay.

Budget: $6,730,000

Funding: Grants and gifts (43.2%), membership contributions (35.2%), education contracts/tuition (13.3%), investment income (7.8%), merchandising sales (.4%)

Staff: 118
40 Field Educators
25 Issue Experts
14 Support Staff
11 Membership/Merchandise Staff

3 Attorneys
8 Foundation Fundraisers
4 Organizers
4 Writer/Editors
4 Office Managers
3 Bookkeeper/Accountants
2 Computer/Graphics

Staff openings/year: Varies

Work Week: 40 hours

Salary/year: $15-18,000

Benefits: Health insurance, life insurance, pregnancy leave, pension, paid vacation, tuition reimbursement, disability, sick leave, dental insurance, vision insurance

Part-Time Employees: 9

Summer Employees: 13 (varies)

Volunteers: 250

Interns: 2 (varies)
Length: 3-6 months
Duties: Too numerous to list. Basically assist program projects.
Remuneration: Varied

Jobs advertised: Newspaper; circulate to other organizations, companies, contacts; environmental publications

To apply: Contact the Personnel Director

CHESTER COMMUNITY IMPROVEMENT PROJECT

412 Avenue of the States, P.O. Box 541
Chester, PA 19016
(215) 876-8663

Director: Lisa R. Gaffney

Purpose: Improve the quality of life for the residents of the west side of Chester by rehabilitating abandoned properties and selling them to low and moderate income families.

Methods of operation: Direct action (75%), public education (20%), research (5%)

Constituency: Residents of Chester (mostly low/moderate income working people)

Recent issues and projects: Home Buying Counseling Program; Tax Abatement Program; Lead Paint Abatement

Budget: $120,000

Funding: Foundations (40%), program income (30%), government (20%),individual contributions (10%)

Staff: 4
1 Director
1 Construction Manager
1 Crew Leader
1 Carpenter

Staff openings/year: 2

Work Week: 40 hours

Salary/year: $17,000 (Recent College Graduate); $22,000 (Graduate with advanced degree)

Benefits: Health insurance, paid vacation

Part-Time Employees: Yes

Summer Employees: Yes

Volunteers: 100s

Interns: 2
Length: 3 months
Duties: Varies
Remuneration: Swarthmore College students paid $450/month by the college; others would need to arrange something

Jobs advertised: Local paper

To apply: Contact Kent James

CHICAGO LEGAL AID TO INCARCERATED MOTHERS (CLAIM)

205 West Randolph, Suite 830
Chicago, IL 60606
(312) 332-5537

Director: Gail T. Smith

Purpose: CLAIM provides legal services, client education and policy advocacy for women prisoners in Illinois and their children. We also serve fathers as appropriate upon request.

Methods of operation: Litigation (35%), advocacy (25%), training and technical assistance (10%), publications (10%), public education (5%), community organizing (15%)

Constituency: Clients are imprisoned, or recently released, parents. Volunteers are lawyers or paralegals.

Recent issues and projects: CLAIM established a pool of volunteer lawyers to represent clients on a pro bono basis. We also have a volunteer Jail

Project to provide on-site services in the Cook County Jail Women's Division. CLAIM teaches classes on family law inside correctional centers. In March, 1992, CLAIM launched the Advocacy Project to organize formerly imprisoned women in the Chicago area.

Major publications: Newsletter; *Handbook for Incarcerated Parents in Illinois*

Budget: $250,000

Funding: Foundations (80%), individual contributions (13%), corporate and law firms (5%), direct mail (2%)

Staff: 5
2 Attorneys
1 Office Manager
1 Advocacy Coordinator
1 Paralegal

Staff openings/year: 0 - 1

Work Week: 42-65 hours

Salary/year: $20,000 (Recent College Graduate); $30,000 (Graduate with advanced degree)

Benefits: Health insurance, paid vacation, life insurance, pregnancy leave (unpaid)

Summer Employees: Yes; volunteer only

Volunteers: 150

Interns: 1
Length: 1 semester or longer
Duties: Legal interns conduct client interviews and negotiation, and do legal research. Undergraduates write, assist with court clerking, etc.
Remuneration: Unable to pay

Jobs advertised: Law school placement offices; undergraduate interns by word of mouth

To apply: Contact Amy Kraus, Director of Volunteer Programs

CHICANO FEDERATION OF SAN DIEGO COUNTY, INC.

610 22nd Street
San Diego, CA 92102
(619) 236-1228

Director: Ray Uzeta

Purpose: The Chicano Federation of San Diego County, Inc.'s mission is to develop leadership in the Mexican American community, promote community development, provide quality services and to advocate on behalf of the Latino community.

Methods of operation: Human services (50%), training and technical assistance (20%), public education (15%), community organizing (10%), direct action (2%), litigation (2%), research (1%)

Constituency: Services are provided to the low-income of San Diego County including individuals, families, senior citizens, neighborhoods, agencies and communities.

Recent issues and projects: The federation has recently completed Vista Serena, 21 units of affordable housing for seniors. Works have started on our second unit, with negotiation for development of a third project in the near future. We also Co-Founded One Vote, which registered over 7,000 new Latino voters.

Major publications: Annual reports

Budget: $550,000

Funding: Government and United Way (80%), foundations (15%), individual contributions (5%)

Staff: 17
5 Caseworkers
2 Training and Education Specialists
2 Administrators
1 Receptionist
1 Bookkeeper/Accountant
1 Typist
1 Executive Secretary
1 Special Project Manager
1 Housing Specialist

Staff openings/year: 2

Work Week: 40 hours

Salary/year: $17,000 (Recent College Graduate); $18,000 (Graduate with advanced degree)

Benefits: Health insurance, paid vacation, pregnancy leave, credit union

Part-Time Employees: 0

Summer Employees: Yes

Volunteers: 10

Interns: 2-4
Length: School semester
Duties: Depend on interest and need of both intern and agency

Jobs advertised: Announcements are mailed to other social service agencies, local employment development departments and local newspapers

To apply: Contact Mary Ellen Mackin, Assistant Director

CHICANOS POR LA CAUSA, INC.

1112 East Buckeye Road
Phoenix, AZ 85034-4043
(602) 257-0700

Other Offices: Somerton, AZ; Nogales, AZ; Tucson, AZ

Director: Pete C. Garcia

Purpose: To provide greater opportunities for constituents to obtain quality and affordable housing, a good education, and meaningful employment; thereby promoting self-sufficiency and instilling dignity in the community we serve.

Methods of operation: Publications, human services, community organizing, direct action, public education, training and technical assistance

Constituency: Residents of South Phoenix

Recent issues and projects: Since 1969, CPLC has evolved into one of the largest community development corporations (CDC's) providing services/programs and economic development planning for people from all social and economic groups in Arizona. These programs and services are designed to encourage and help people improve their living circumstances. In addition to social-service programs, CPLC spearheads residential, commercial, and industrial development projects, as well as numerous small business lending programs.

Major publications: Bi-monthly newsletter

Budget: $7,000,000

Funding: Grants for service (95%), foundations (4%), individual contributions (1%)

Staff: 250
4 Office Managers
5 Foundation Fundraisers
21 Bookkeepers/Accountants
25 Caseworkers
200 Counselors

Staff openings/year: 10

Work Week: 40 hours

Salary/year: $16,000 (Recent College Graduate); $18,000 (Graduate with advanced degree)

Benefits: Health insurance, pension, paid vacation, life insurance, credit union, tuition reimbursement

Part-Time Employees: 30

Summer Employees: 140

Volunteers: 5,000 (50 regulars)

Interns: Yes
Length: 2 semesters
Duties: Depending on major and agreement with school
Remuneration: No paid internships

Jobs advertised: Internal posting, contact local University, newspaper ads

To apply: Contact Lupe Chaves, Personnel Manager

CHILD CARE ACTION CAMPAIGN

330 Seventh Avenue, 17th Floor
New York, NY 10001
(212) 239-0138

Director: Barbara Reisman

Purpose: The Child Care Action Campaign is a national nonprofit coalition of individuals and organizations whose goal is to improve the lives of children and their families by expanding the supply of quality, affordable child care. Since its founding in 1983, CCAC has been a convener, catalyst, creator of media messages, and resource for parents, policymakers and child care providers. CCAC has taken the lead in making quality child care both a bottom line economic issue and a fundamental component of education reform.

Methods of operation: Public education (35%), research (25%), training and technical assistance (20%), lobbying (10%), publications (10%)

Constituency: Parents, child care providers, corporations, women's organizations, academia, media

Recent issues and projects: "Child Care and Education: The Critical Connection" is a multi-year project to educate policymakers and the public about the relationship between child care and education and to develop models of comprehensive care and education for children from birth to age 13. Other ongoing projects include work on child care and welfare reform, financing alternatives, and parent education.

Major publications: Bimonthly newsletter: *Child Care ActioNews*; *Not Too Small to Care: Small Businesses and Child Care*; *Investing in the Future: Child Care Financing Options for the Public and Private Sectors*; *Where They Stand: A Digest of Organizational Policies on Child Care and Education*; plus 29 information guides on a wide range of child care topics.

Budget: $1,000,000

Funding: Corporate contributions (30%), annual benefit (30%), foundations (20%), individual contributions (20%)

Staff: 13
1 Executive Director
1 Program Director
1 Development Director
1 Office Manager
3 Program Associates
1 Public Relations Director
5 Support Staff

Staff openings/year: 1-2

Work Week: 45-50 hours

Salary/year: $21,000 (Recent College Graduate); $30,000 (Graduate with advanced degree)

Benefits: Health insurance, life insurance, parental leave, child care (DCAP), paid vacation

Part-Time Employees: Yes

Volunteers: Yes

Interns: 2-6
Length: 10-12 wks; summers; semesters
Duties: Specific project responsibilities; research
Remuneration: Unpaid; housing may be available on a limited basis; help with receiving academic credit

Jobs advertised: College, graduate school listings; newspapers; public interest publications and organizations

To apply: Contact Diane Foy, Program Associate

CHILD CARE LAW CENTER

22 Second Street, 5th Floor
San Francisco, CA 94105
(415) 495-5498

Director: Carol Stevenson

Purpose: The Child Care Law Center is the only organization in the country working exclusively on the legal issues concerning the establishment and provision of child care. The Center's major objective is to use legal tools to foster the development of quality, affordable child care programs.

Methods of operation: Research, litigation, publications, public education, training and technical assistance

Constituency: Child care providers, low-income families, policy-makers, administrators, etc.

Recent issues and projects: Recent projects include: working on the child care aspect of federal welfare reform; improving utilization of child care entitlements and subsidies by low-income families; and providing training to the child care field on the impact of the Americans with Disabilities Act

Major publications: *Legal Update*, quarterly newsletter; send for publications list

Staff: 8
4 Attorneys
1 Paralegal
1 Office Manager
1 Researcher
2 Administrative Assistants

Work Week: 35 hours

Benefits: Health insurance, child care, paid vacation, life insurance, family leave

Part-Time Employees: 3

Summer Employees: Yes

Volunteers: Yes

Interns: Yes
Length: Semester
Remuneration: Work-study/volunteer

Jobs advertised: Law placement offices, public interest clearinghouse, directories

To apply: Contact Abby Cohen for legal positions and Carol Stevenson, Executive Director for other jobs

CHILD WELFARE LEAGUE OF AMERICA

440 First Street, NW, Suite 310
Washington, DC 20001-2085
(202) 638-2952

Other Offices: San Dimas, CA; Ohawa, ON

Director: David S. Liederman

Purpose: CWLA has over 700 members - both government and voluntary child welfare agencies in the U.S. and Canada. CWLA sets standards for practice, provides training, consultation, conferences, publications and public policy work on behalf of abused, neglected, abandoned and otherwise troubled children and their families.

Methods of operation: Lobbying (10%), publications (20%), training and technical assistance (70%)

Membership: 200 child welfare agencies in the U.S. and Canada

Recent issues and projects: A national commission on Family Foster Care; responding to AIDS affected children and their families; North American Chemical Dependency Steering Committee; promoting culturally responsive child welfare practice; Children's Campaign

Major publications: Bimonthly: *Child Welfare Journal*; newsletters: *Children's Monitor*; *Washington Social Legislation Bulletin*; numerous books for professional staff of agencies; quarterly magazine *Children's Voice*

Budget: $7,500,000

Funding: Membership dues (86%), publication sales (15.3%), foundations (8.8%), individual contributions (11%)

Staff: 60
25 Issue Experts
8 Typists
7 Writers/Editors/Publications Department
6 Lobbyists
3 Office Managers
3 Bookkeepers/Accountants
2 Press Aides/Public Relations
1 Executive Director
2 Grassroots Fundraisers
3 Foundation Fundraisers
3/5 Researcher

Staff openings/year: 2-3

Work Week: 40-50 hours

Benefits: Health insurance, life insurance, pregnancy leave, pension, paid vacation

Part-Time Employees: Yes

Summer Employees: Yes

Volunteers: Yes

Interns: Yes
Length: 1 semester/school year
Duties: Variety of assignments depending on need

Jobs advertised: Newspaper; agency

To apply: Contact Lisa Merkel, Program Manager

CHILDHOOD LEAD ACTION PROJECT
421 Elmwood Avenue
Providence, RI 02907
(401) 785-1310

Director: Eleanor Freda

Purpose: The Childhood Lead Action Project works to prevent childhood lead poisoning in Rhode Island through education, advocacy and parent support. Currently, we are the only organization in Rhode Island dedicated to preventing childhood lead poisoning.

Methods of operation: Community organizing (40%), public education (25%), fundraising (15%), lobbying (5%), direct action (5%), training and technical assistance (5%), publications (3%), research (2%)

Constituency: Minority, low-income families, many in poor housing conditions, parents of lead-poisoned children

Recent issues and projects: Get the Lead Out Coalition worked successfully for the passage of comprehensive legislation; parent groups (English and Spanish) offer support and assistance to the parents of lead poisoned children, education in Southeast Asian community and town of East Providence.

Major publications: We do many small/short publications about lead poisoning for parents and others, re: legal, nutritional, tenant rights, educational pieces about lead poisoning prevention.

Budget: $110,000

Funding: Foundations

Staff: 3
1 Organizer
1 Office Manager
1 Educator

Staff openings/year: 1

Work Week: 35 hours

Salary/year: $20,000

Benefits: Health insurance, paid vacation

Part-Time Employees: 3

Summer Employees: Yes

Volunteers: Fluctuates

Interns: 1

Length: 1 year
Duties: Educating parents to prevent lead poisoning

Jobs advertised: *Community Jobs*, local papers, universities, other nonprofits

To apply: Please contact Eleanor Freda, Executive Director

Remarks: Flexible work arrangements and volunteer opportunities are available.

CHILDREN NOW

1212 Broadway, Suite 530
Oakland, CA 94612
(510) 763-2444

Other Offices: Los Angeles, CA; Sacramento, CA; New York, NY

Director: Lois Salisbury

Purpose: Children Now is a nonpartisan policy and advocacy organization for children, with a particular focus on children and families who are poor or at-risk.

Methods of operation: Public education (45%), publications (30%), research (16%), training and technical assistance (5%), lobbying (4%)

Constituency: A broad cross-section of parents, concerned citizens, children's advocates and community and business leaders

Recent issues and projects: Recent projects include: health care for every child and family; early childhood education and quality child care for every child in need; economic security for every child's family; quality education for every child; a safe and nurturing environment for every child

Major publications: *The County Data Book*, annual; *The State Report Card*, annual; *Unlocking Our Children's Future, An Educational Challenge*; *The Legislative Scorecard*, annual; *Children Now*, semi-annual newsletter

Budget: $2,000,000

Funding: Foundations (65%), individual contributions (20%), direct mail (15%)

Staff: 26
12 Organizers
3 Writers/Editors
2 Attorneys
3 Office Managers
1 Lobbyist
3 Press Aides
2 Administrative Assistants
2 Bookkeepers/Accountants

Staff openings/year: 0-2

Work Week: 40-50 hours

Salary/year: $21-23,000 (Recent College Graduate); $30-34,000 (Graduate with advanced degree)

Benefits: Health insurance, paid vacation, life insurance, family leave

Part-Time Employees: 4

Summer Employees: 4

Volunteers: 1-2

Interns: 4
Length: Summer or semester
Duties: Specific assignments in policy, communications and development
Remuneration: Unpaid

Jobs advertised: Local newspapers, college placement offices

To apply: Contact Susan Rothstein, Vice President

CHILDREN OF THE NIGHT

1800 North Highland Avenue, Suite 128
Hollywood, CA 90028-4520
(818) 908-0850

Other Offices: Van Nuys, CA

Director: Dr. Lois Lee

Purpose: Social services to child prostitutes ages 11-17 years old; education of the public regarding prostitution and pornography.

Methods of operation: Human services (90%), public education (10%)

Constituency: Foundations, corporations, individuals

Recent issues and projects: Acquired building to provide shelter; change in sentencing of pimps (in California)

Major publications: Newsletter

Budget: $1,500,000

Funding: Foundations (68%), individual contributions (22%), direct mail (10%)

Staff: 27
20 Caseworkers
1 Program Director

1 Administrative Director
1 Executive Assistant
1 Computer Operator
1 Administrative Assistant
1 Teacher
1 Teaching Assistant

Staff openings/year: 3-5

Work Week: 40 hours

Salary/year: $25,000 (Recent College Graduate); $30,000 (Graduate with advanced degree)

Benefits: Health insurance, life insurance, paid vacation, some school reimbursement

Part-Time Employees: 6

Volunteers: 100

Jobs advertised: *Los Angeles Times*

To apply: Contact Dr. Lois Lee

CHILDREN'S ART FOUNDATION

765 Cedar Street, Suite 201
Santa Cruz, CA 95060
(408) 426-5557

Director: William Rubel

Purpose: The purpose of the Children's Art Foundation is to encourage children's creativity.

Methods of operation: Art School (20%), publications (80%)

Constituency: Schools, libraries, individuals

Recent issues and projects: We have three major projects: (1) *Stone Soup Magazine*, writing and art by children through age 13; (2) Museum of Children's Art, international collection; (3) Art School, classes for children

Major publications: *Stone Soup Magazine*

Budget: $350,000

Funding: Membership (70%), class fees (20%), miscellaneous (10%)

Staff: 3
2 Organizers
1 Administrative Assistant
1 Typist (part-time)
1 Bookkeeper/Accountant (part-time)

Staff openings/year: 0-1

Work Week: 15-40 hours

Benefits: Health insurance, dental insurance, paid vacation

Part-Time Employees: 6

Volunteers: 3-4

Interns: None currently, but we'd like to

Jobs advertised: Newspaper

To apply: Contact Ms. Gerry Mandel, Associate Director

CHILDREN'S DEFENSE FUND

25 E Street, NW
Washington, DC 20001
(202) 628-8787

Other Offices: Columbus, OH; St. Paul, MN; Austin, TX; Bennettsville, SC; New York, NY; Cleveland, OH; Cincinnati, OH; Marlboro County, SC

President: Marian Wright Edelman

Purpose: Research and advocacy on behalf of poor children, especially minority and disabled children.

Methods of operation: Research, lobbying, publications, community organizing, direct action, public education, training and technical assistance

Recent issues and projects: Child welfare, child care, health care access, federal budget advocacy, major research on the status of children

Major publications: *CDF Reports*; *The State of America's Children*

Budget: $12,000,000

Funding: Individual contributions, foundations, corporate donations

Staff: 100
Includes:
Organizers
Writers/Editors
Attorneys
Office Managers
Researchers
Lobbyists
Press Aides
Foundation Fundraisers
Grassroots Fundraisers
Issue Experts
Typists
Bookkeeper/Accountants

Staff openings/year: 2

Work Week: 50 hours

Salary/year: $19,500 (Recent College Graduate); $30,000 (Graduate with advanced degree)

Benefits: Health insurance, life insurance, pregnancy leave, paid vacation, tuition reimbursement, cafeteria

Part-Time Employees: Yes; very few

Summer Employees: Yes

Volunteers: Occasionally

Interns: Yes
Length: 10-12 weeks
Duties: Apprenticed to one of the issue divisions
Remuneration: $200/week; also take unpaid

Jobs advertised: Newspaper; mailed announcements; internal postings

To apply: Contact Carol Caulk, Director, Administration

CHILDREN'S EXPRESS

30 Cooper Square, 4th Floor
New York, NY 10003
(212) 505-7777

Other Offices: Boston, MA; Indianapolis, IN; New York, NY; Oakland, CA; Melbourne, AUSTRALIA; Wellington, NEW ZEALAND; Washington, DC

Director: Robert Clampitt

Purpose: A nonprofit news service reported by children (ages 8 to 13) and edited by teenagers (ages 14 to 18). Children's Express is a way to involve young people in journalism. Its purpose is to change the way children and teens see and value themselves and are seen and valued by others; to encourage reading, writing, and understanding; and to stimulate the child's interest in the world. The syndicated newspaper column runs in feature or op-ed sections of newspapers, and the 1988-89 Peabody and Emmy Award-winning news magazine series can be seen on PBS television stations in reruns.

Methods of operation: Children's issues, reporting

Major publications: Quarterly newsletter; *When I Was Young I Loved School: Dropping Out and Hanging In*; Drug Conference - Harlem Bureau; *How to Plan and Print Your Own Newspaper*; *The Media and Children's Issues*; *Children's Express: How to Do It*; *Listen To Us!*; *How to Be Heard*; *Voices from the Future*

Budget: $400,000

Funding: Foundations (50%), individual contributions (25%), direct mail (25%)

Staff: 4
1 Bureau Director
1 Adult Editor
1 Administrative Assistant
1 Bureau Assistant

Staff openings/year: 2

Work Week: 40 hours

Salary/year: $17,000 (Recent College Graduate); $30,000 (Graduate with advanced degree)

Benefits: Health insurance, life insurance, paid vacation

Part-Time Employees: 2

Summer Employees: 1

Volunteers: 5

Interns: 2
Length: 3 months
Duties: Editing

Jobs advertised: Newspapers

To apply: Contact Cliff Hahn, NY Bureau Director

CHILDREN'S FOUNDATION

725 15th Street, NW, Suite 505
Washington, DC 20005
(202) 347-3300

Director: Kay Hollestelle

Purpose: The Children's Foundation works to improve the lives of children and those who care for them. Our main program areas are child care and child support enforcement.

Methods of operation: Publications (30%), training and technical assistance (30%), research (15%), community organizing (15%), public education (10%)

Constituency: Parents and child care providers

Recent issues and projects: Recent projects include: translation of our child care materials into Spanish for parents and child care providers; updating the two licensing studies (one on child care center regulations and the other on family day care regulations)

Major publications: Directory of child care associations and support groups; *Better Baby Care; Helping Children Love Themselves and Others; Family Day Care Bulletin; Child Support Bulletin*

Budget: $300,000

Funding: Foundations (60%), publications (30%), individual contributions (10%)

Staff: 3
1 Writer/Editor
1 Administrative Assistant
1 Executive Director

Work Week: 40 hours

Salary/year: $22,000 (Recent College Graduate); $26,000 (Graduate with advanced degree)

Benefits: Health insurance, paid vacation, life insurance, sick leave, family leave

Part-Time Employees: 3

Summer Employees: None

Volunteers: None

Interns: 1
Length: Generally 8 weeks
Duties: Research
Remuneration: None

Jobs advertised: Newspapers and announcements to other nonprofits

To apply: Contact Kay Hollestelle

CHILDREN'S LAW CENTER OF MASSACHUSETTS, INC.

P.o. Box 710, 37 Friend Street
Lynn, MA 01903
(617) 581-1977

Director: Anthony DeMarco

Purpose: The Children's Law Center is a nonprofit agency which represents children and youth in a wide variety of legal and administrative proceedings, including: child abuse and neglect matters; special education; school discipline and other school matters; homelessness; mental health issues; and delinquencies. The Law Center provides direct representation and seeks to ensure systemic change to improve the quality of lives of young people.

Budget: $250,000

Funding: Interest on Lawyers Trust Accounts (30%), foundations (19%), United Way (17%), individual contributions (2%)

Staff: 8
3 Attorneys
1 Office Managers
3 Researchers
1 Foundation Fundraisers

Benefits: Health insurance, paid vacation, life insurance, family leave

Part-Time Employees: 1

Summer Employees: 2

Volunteers: Varies

Interns: Varies
Length: 3 months
Duties: Advocacy work
Remuneration: $250 per week or work-study

Jobs advertised: Law schools, legal periodicals

To apply: Contact Anthony J. DeMarco for permanent positions and Rebekah Tosado for summer positions

CHILDREN'S RIGHTS COUNCIL

220 I Street, NW
Washington, DC 20002
(202) 547-6227 Memory device: (202) 547-NCCR

President: David L. Levy, Esq.

Purpose: To strengthen families, to reduce the adversarial battling over children during divorce, to assure that children have the right to two parents (and grandparents), regardless of the parents' marital situation. To work for access (visitation) enforcement mediation, fair child support and school-based programs for children at risk.

Methods of operation: Research (25%), publications (20%), public education (20%), lobbying (15%), litigation (10%), direct action (10%)

Constituency: Mental health professionals, pre-trial court services, judges, researchers, parents

Recent issues and projects: Seventh annual conference held April 1994 (with the eighth to be held in April 1995) to bring together outstanding researchers, writers and educators on children and divorce. Also educated Congress on the need to provide funds for visitation, which it did, as part of the Family Support Act of 1988 and the Appropriations Bill of 1989.

Major publications: Distribute more than 100 educational materials, including a quarterly newsletter, 25 books and 25 written reports, 50 audio-video cassettes on sole and joint custody, an anti-parental kidnapping report, crisis in family law, and "Banana Splits," a school-based program.

Budget: $120,000

Funding: Individual contributions (95%), foundations (5%)

Staff:
All part-time volunteer, including:
2 Attorneys
2 Organizers
2 Typists
2 Bookkeeper/Accountants
2 Researchers
2 Canvassers
1 Writers/Editor
1 Issue Expert

Work Week: 40 hours

Volunteers: Yes

Interns: Yes
Length: 2-6 months
Duties: Research, advocacy, writing, liaison to Congressional offices
Remuneration: None

To apply: Contact David Levy, Esq., President

Remarks: CCR has branches in New Jersey, Vermont, Pennsylvania, Florida and Ohio and 20 other States.

CITIZEN ACTION

1120 19th Street, NW, Suite 630
Washington, DC 20036
(202) 775-1580

Director: Ira Arlook

Purpose: Citizen Action is a national citizens political organization, with 3 million members in 33 states, dedicated to increasing citizen participation in economic and political decision-making. Citizen Action's national program aims to offer clear policy alternatives in health care issues, insurance reform, global warming, toxics and many other environmental, social and economic issues. Citizen Action organizes the unorganized and wins meaningful improvements in the quality of people's lives.

Methods of operation: Research, community organizing, public education, lobbying, training and technical assistance, direct action

Membership: 3 million members in 33 states

Recent issues and projects: Current campaigns include: Canadian style, single payer, national health insurance; toxic pollution prevention including both industrial toxic use reduction and pesticides; campaign finance reform and reversing global warming

Major publications: *Citizen Action News*

Staff: 20

Staff openings/year: 1-3

Work Week: 40-60 hours

Salary/year: $25,000

Benefits: Health insurance, life insurance, parental leave, vacation, dental insurance

Volunteers: Yes

Interns: 4-6 per year
Length: 3-6 months
Duties: Research, congressional advocacy, tracking, organizing
Remuneration: None

Jobs advertised: Local newspapers; organizations; *Community Jobs*; ACCESS: Networking in the Public Interest

To apply: Contact Allan St. John, Administrative Assistant

Remarks: Citizen Action has 2 national offices, in Washington and Cleveland, and has membership in 33 states.

CITIZEN ACTION OF LOUISIANA

7434 Picardy Avenue, Suite D
Baton Rouge, LA 70809
(504) 769-8896

Director: Paula Henderson

Purpose: To gain community empowerment through the passage of progressive consumer legislation

Methods of operation: Research, lobbying, community organizing, public education

Membership: We have a grassroots membership of about 75,000 across South Louisiana

Recent issues and projects: American Health

Security Act (Wellstone/Conyers), NAFTA (fair trade, not just free trade), pollution prevention and pesticide reforms

Major publications: *Poisons in our Neighborhoods*; membership newsletter; *Premiums Without Benefits* (reports)

Budget: $400,000

Funding: Canvassing (90%), Foundations (8%), Individual contributions (2%)

Staff: 14
1 Office Manager
1 Lobbyist
11 Canvassers
1 Canvass Staff Director

Staff openings/year: 20

Work Week: 60 hours

Salary/year: $15-18,000 (Recent College Graduate); $15-18,000 (Graduate with advanced degree)

Benefits: Health insurance, paid vacation, life insurance

Part-Time Employees: 4

Summer Employees: 15

Volunteers: 1

Interns: none at this time

Jobs advertised: *Baton Rouge Morning Advocate* and *The Daily Reveille*

To apply: Contact Kendall E. Jackson, Canvass Staff Director

CITIZEN ACTION OF NEBRASKA

941 O Street, Suite 600
Lincoln, NE 68508
(402) 477-8889

Director: Walt Bleich

Purpose: The purpose of the Citizen Action of Nebraska is to: win real improvements in people's lives; give people sense of their own power; and alter the relations of power.

Methods of operation: Public education (50%), lobbying (20%), direct action (15%), research (5%), publications (5%), community organizing (5%)

Constituency: Non-partisan, many independents leaning towards liberal side

Recent issues and projects: Recent projects include: sustainable energy and economic development; SEED campaign; three state legislature bills dealing with renewable energy; working for pilot project wind farm and bio-mass plant

Major publications: *SEED Campaign Reporter*

Funding: Canvassing (50%), telephone solicitation (40%), foundations (10%)

Staff: 2
1 Organizer
1 Campaign Manager

Work Week: 45 hours

Salary/year: $Varies (Recent College Graduate); $Varies (Graduate with advanced degree)

Benefits: Health insurance, paid vacation

Part-Time Employees: 9

Summer Employees: 4-5

Interns: No, but willing to accept interns

Jobs advertised: Through the network

To apply: Contact Mike Boeslager

CITIZEN ACTION OF NEW YORK

314 Central Avenue, Suite 202
Albany, NY 12206
(518) 465-4600

Other Offices: Amityville, NY; New York, NY; Binghamton, NY; Buffalo, NY

Director: Karen Scharff and Richard Kirsch

Purpose: The purpose of the Citizen Action of New York is to organize New Yorkers for progressive political change.

Methods of operation: Community organizing (25%), public education (25%), training and technical assistance (25%), research (10%), lobbying (10%), direct action (5%)

Membership: 60,000 New York families; coalition of labor, seniors, students, women, activists

Recent issues and projects: Health care for all; fair taxes; intensive recycling; occupational safety and health

Budget: $800,000

Funding: Canvassing (40%), telephone solicitation (20%), government (20%), individual contributions

(10%), foundations (10%)

Staff:
20 Canvassers
10 Organizers
2 Bookkeepers/Accountants
1 Fuel Group Manager
1 Office Manager
1 Grassroots Fundraiser

Staff openings/year: 3

Work Week: 40 hours

Salary/year: $20,000

Benefits: Health insurance, paid vacation

Part-Time Employees: 15

Summer Employees: 30

Interns: 10
Length: 3 months
Duties: Research, organizing, training
Remuneration: No pay; opportunity to raise salary

Jobs advertised: Newspaper

To apply: Contact Karen Scharff, Executive Director

CITIZEN ALERT

P.O. Box 5391
Reno, NV 89513
(702) 827-4200

Other Offices: Las Vegas, NV

Director: Bob Fulkerson

Purpose: Citizen Alert is a statewide multi-issue organization working for public participation and government accountability in issues of concern to Nevadans.

Methods of operation: Research, lobbying, publications, community organizing, direct action, public education, training and technical assistance

Recent issues and projects: Public education and action on primary energy resource development, nuclear waste, the Valmy power plant and the MX missile. Other issues include nuclear and toxic waste transportation and disposal, military air and land withdrawals from the state and the effects of nuclear testing on our state's health and world peace.

Major publications: Newsletters: *Citizen Alert*, *SkyGuard*

Staff: 2
2 full-time, 2 half-time:
2 Issue Experts
1 Organizer
1 Native American Representative
1 Writer/Editor

Work Week: 40-60 hours

Salary/year: $18,000

Benefits: Health insurance, paid vacation

Part-Time Employees: 2

Volunteers: 50-100

Interns: None currently, but willing to accept applications
Remuneration: Work-study students or volunteer

Jobs advertised: Word of mouth, environmental publications

To apply: Contact Bob Fulkerson, Executive Director

Remarks: Other office address: P.O. Box 1681, Las Vegas, NV 89125

CITIZENS ACTION COALITION OF INDIANA

3951 N. Meridian St. #300
Indianapolis, IN 46208
(317) 921-1120

Other Offices: South Bend, IN; Ft. Wayne, IN; Evansville, IN

Director: Chris Williams

Purpose: CAC is a twenty-year-old public interest advocacy organization involved in energy policy, utility policy, health care policy, environmental policy and issues concerning small farmers

Methods of operation: Research (20%), lobbying (20%), community organizing (20%), public education (20%), litigation (10%), publications (5%)

Membership: 300,000 households statewide

Recent issues and projects: Won a $150 million rebate for PSI Energy customers. Won full funding/expenditure for the state home care program. Passed an Organic Certification law for agricultural producers

Major publications: *Citizens Power* - newsletter

Budget: $2,500,000

Funding: Canvassing (60%), telephone solicitation (30%), foundations (5%), individual contributions (5%)

Staff: 85
3 Organizers
1 Writer/Editor
1 Office Manager
4 Lobbyists
1 Bookkeeper/Accountant
5 Campaign Managers
70 Canvassers

Staff openings/year: 5-10

Work Week: 40 hours

Salary/year: $18,500 (Recent College Graduate); $18,500 (Graduate with advanced degree)

Benefits: Health insurance, paid vacation, life insurance

Part-Time Employees: 30

Summer Employees: 40

Volunteers: 30

Interns: None; but willing to accept applications

Jobs advertised: Newspaper ads

To apply: Contact Christopher Williams, Executive Director

CITIZENS ADVICE BUREAU, INC.

2054 Morris Avenue
Bronx, NY 10453
(212) 365-0910

Other Offices: New York, NY

Director: Carolyn McLaughlin

Purpose: To assist low-income families and senior citizens to meet survival needs and to support policy efforts aimed at the eradication of poverty.

Methods of operation: Human services (70%), training and technical assistance (20%), community organizing (10%)

Recent issues and projects: Creation of a citywide welfare advocacy network of service providers and advocates; eviction prevention project; immigration and homeless family rights projects; mentoring "Neighbors" project for relocated homeless families; seniors program; nutrition education and outreach

Major publications: *Network Notes*, a bimonthly newsletter

Budget: $1,300,000

Funding: City and state government contracts (80%), foundations (20%)

Staff: 200

Staff openings/year: 10-15

Work Week: 35 hours

Salary/year: $22,000 (Recent College Graduate); $Varies (Graduate with advanced degree)

Benefits: Health care, vacation, sick, holiday, life insurance

Summer Employees: 1

Volunteers: 6

Interns: 8

To apply: Contact Carolyn McLaughlin, Executive Director

CITIZENS CLEARINGHOUSE FOR HAZARDOUS WASTES (CCHW)

119 Rowell Court, P.O. Box 6806
Falls Church, VA 22040
(703) 237-2249 Memory device: (703) 237-CCHW

Other Offices: Ft. Bragg, CA; Atlanta, GA; Floyd, VA; Indianapolis, IN

Director: Lois Gibbs

Purpose: To help local groups form, strengthen and beat toxic polluters and to advance the grassroots movement for environmental justice.

Methods of operation: Community organizing, training and technical assistance (75%), public education, publications, research (20%), direct action (5%)

Constituency: Working class, low-income, rural communities of color and majority women in the movement to win environmental justice

Recent issues and projects: McToxics Campaign (styrofoam bans); pesticides issues; economic development. Generally we work with local groups and organize around their issues such as dumps, incinerators, toxic discharges, medical and military waste, etc.

Major publications: Bimonthly: *Everyone's Backyard*; *Environmental Health Monthly*; plus about 60 community action guidebooks we have written

Budget: $900,000

Funding: Individual contributions (50%), foundations (40%), churches (10%)

Staff: 13
7 Organizers
2 Office Managers
2 Issue Experts
1 Writer/Editor
1 Foundation Fundraiser

Staff openings/year: 2

Work Week: 50 hours

Salary/year: $18,000 (Recent College Graduate); $Varies (Graduate with advanced degree)

Benefits: Health insurance, life insurance, pension, paid vacation

Part-Time Employees: 2

Volunteers: Yes

Interns: Yes
Length: Flexible
Duties: Depends on intern's skills
Remuneration: $200 a week

Jobs advertised: *Community Jobs*; local newspaper

To apply: Contact Administrator

CITIZENS FOR A BETTER ENVIRONMENT

501 Second Street, Suite 303
San Francisco, CA 94107
(415) 243-8373

Other Offices: Los Angeles, CA

Director: Michael Belliveau

Purpose: Grassroots organization dedicated to the immediate reduction of toxic pollution and achievement of measurable public health benefits for residents of the major urban areas in California.

Methods of operation: Research (50%), litigation (35%), public education (10%), publications (5%)

Constituency: Low/moderate-income, Californian, urban

Recent issues and projects: Published one of the most comprehensive analyses of chemical hazards in a single geographic area, *Richmond at Risk*, that documents high levels of toxic air and water pollution, hazardous waste generation and chemical accident potential in close proximity to low-income, minority neighborhoods. Won a citizens' suit in federal court that will force regulatory agencies in the San Francisco Bay Area to comply finally with the Clean Air Act.

Major publications: Extensive publications list available upon request

Funding: Canvassing (40%), direct mail (30%), foundations (20%)

Staff:
Canvassers
4 Researchers
2 Organizers
3 Attorneys
2 Office Managers
1 Writer/Editor
1 Member Services Coordinator
1 Grants Administrator
1 Bookkeeper/Accountant
1 Managing Director
1 Southern CA Regional Director
1 Finance Director

Staff openings/year: 1-2

Work Week: 40 hours

Salary/year: $Varies (Recent College Graduate); $Varies (Graduate with advanced degree)

Benefits: Health insurance, paid vacation, dental

Part-Time Employees: 3

Summer Employees: Yes

Volunteers: 5

Jobs advertised: Local papers

To apply: Contact Margaret Williams, Office Manager

CITIZENS FOR A BETTER ENVIRONMENT

407 S. Dearborn, Suite 1775
Chicago, IL 60605
(312) 939-1530

Other Offices: Milwaukee, WI; Madison, WI; Green Bay, WI; Minneapolis, MN

Director: Bill Davis

Purpose: CBE works to prevent and fight environmental health threats through research, advocacy, public education and citizen empowerment.

Methods of operation: Research, publications, public education, training and technical assistance, limited lobbying and litigation

Recent issues and projects: Developing a "model" air toxics regulatory program in Wisconsin; passage of the Illinois Groundwater Protection Act, which was named one of the "Best Bets for 1987" by the National Center for Policy Alternatives. Major projects include Chicago area Toxics Assistance Project and other work aimed at toxics use reduction and solving the solid waste problem.

Major publications: Quarterly journal: *The Environmental Review*; fact sheets - single or two-page information hand-outs on specific topics

Funding: Individual contributions, foundations, canvassing

Staff:
60 Canvassers
6 Researchers/Issue Experts
3 Canvass Directors
3 Office Managers
1 Writer/Editor
1 Foundation Fundraiser
1 Bookkeeper/Accountant
1 Regional Director
1 Vice President

Work Week: 40 hours

Benefits: Health insurance, life insurance, paid vacation

Volunteers: Yes

Interns: Yes
Length: 1 semester
Duties: Various; usually assists research personnel
Remuneration: None

Jobs advertised: Local newspapers

To apply: Contact the state office

CITIZENS FOR A BETTER ENVIRONMENT

3255 Hennepin Ave. South, Suite 150
Minneapolis, MN 55408
(612) 824-8537

Other Offices: Milwaukee, WI; Chicago, IL

Director: Lisa Doerr

Purpose: To protect human and environmental health through research, public education, public policy development, litigation and community organizing

Methods of operation: Public education (44%), community organizing (43%), research (5%), lobbying (5%), litigation (1%), publications (1%), training and technical assistance (1%)

Constituency: General public

Recent issues and projects: Reducing toxic chemical pollution through promoting pollution prevention; addressing solid waste issues

Major publications: *Environmental Review* quarterly journal

Budget: $1,000,000

Funding: Canvassing (80%), foundations (20%)

Staff: 91
60 Canvassers
5 Organizers
1 Writer/Editor
2 Attorneys
4 Office Managers
4 Researchers
4 Lobbyists
3 Foundation Fundraisers
4 Issue Experts
4 Bookkeepers/Accountants

Staff openings/year: Varies

Work Week: 30-40 hours

Salary/year: $20,000 (Recent College Graduate); $25,000 (Graduate with advanced degree)

Benefits: Health insurance, paid vacation

Part-Time Employees: Varies

Summer Employees: Yes

Volunteers: Yes

Interns: Yes
Length: Varies
Duties: Varies
Remuneration: None

Jobs advertised: Local newspapers, word of mouth

To apply: Jo Haberman, Community Organizer

CITIZENS FOR ACTION IN NEW BRITAIN (CANB)

19 Chestnut Street
New Britain, CT 06051
(203) 225-7683

Director: Jennifer Van Campen

Purpose: To build a powerful coalition of neighborhood, tenant, senior and church groups in New Britain so that residents will have a vehicle to democratically solve problems which adversely affect their lives.

Methods of operation: Community organizing (100%)

Constituency: Multi-racial (black, hispanic, white), intergenerational and predominantly low-income

Recent issues and projects: Neighborhood revitalization; affordable homeownership; organizing for community reinvestment; passed law mandating community rating for senior citizens; code enforcement; parent youth organizing

Budget: $90,000

Funding: Private foundations, government grants, United Way, individual contributions

Staff: 2
2 Organizers

Staff openings/year: 1

Work Week: 40 hours

Salary/year: $21,000

Benefits: Health insurance, paid vacation

Part-Time Employees: 1

Jobs advertised: In local newspapers; *Community Jobs*; mailings

To apply: Contact CANB Director

CITIZENS FOR ALTERNATIVES TO CHEMICAL CONTAMINATION (CACC)

8735 Maple Grove Road
Lake, MI 48632
(517) 544-3318 Fax: 517-544-2828

Other Offices: Saginaw, MI; Alpena, MI; Cadillac, MI; Madison Heights, MI

Director: Ann Hunt

Purpose: Functions as a clearinghouse for information on potentially hazardous uses of substances or chemicals, providing information on alternative options. Heavy focus on education through traditional and non-traditional channels.

Methods of operation: Public education (50%), publications (15%), research (10%), community organizing (10%), litigation (5%), direct action (5%), training and technical assistance (5%)

Constituency: Environmentally concerned citizens, mainly in the Great Lakes Basin

Recent issues and projects: Annual Environmental Conference in May; member, Michigan Environmental Conference. Issues include "low level" radioactive waste, solid waste management, pesticides regulation, toxics use reduction, water quality, oil and gas wastes and environmental education.

Major publications: Monthly newsletter, factsheets, information flyers

Budget: $25,000

Funding: Individual contributions (25%), foundations (50%), fundraising events (25%)

Staff: 1
1 Director

Work Week: 40+ hours

Salary/year: $Varies (Recent College Graduate); $Varies (Graduate with advanced degree)

Part-Time Employees: 1

Volunteers: Many

Interns: Yes

Jobs advertised: Advertised through newsletter; word of mouth; regional agencies

To apply: Contact Ann Hunt, Director

CITIZENS FOR BETTER CARE

2111 Woodward Avenue, Suite 610
Detroit, MI 48226
(313) 962-5968

Other Offices: Lansing, MI; Grand Rapids, MI; Saginaw, MI; Traverse City, MI; Iron Mountain, MI

Director: Susan Titus

Purpose: Help people who have problems in nursing homes, homes for the aged, adult board and care or other long-term care health services; help selection of those services and monitor providers of care as well as state regulators.

Methods of operation: Handling consumer complaints and requests for information (54%), developing issue papers, monitoring state and federal action (25%), public education (10%), training and technical assistance (5.5%), publications (5%), lobbying (0.5%)

Constituency: Senior citizens, health professionals, social workers, family members of those receiving long-term care

Recent issues and projects: Monitoring state enforcement of nursing home rules in relation to closing nursing homes; monitoring state implementation of new Medicaid rules for nursing home residents with spouses and development of a consumer publication on the issue; monitoring legislation to fight Medicaid discrimination

Major publications: *How to Choose a Nursing Home*; *How to Choose Long-term Care Insurance*; *Your Rights in a Nursing Home*; *Medicare Benefits for Nursing Home Care: What They Are and How to Get Them*; *Facts About Medicaid Nursing Home Eligibility*

Budget: $1,200,000

Funding: Grants (90%), United Way (30%), individual contributions (9%), foundations (1%)

Staff: 30
12 Caseworkers/Paralegals
9 Issue Experts/Supervisors
6 Secretaries
1 Executive Director
1/2 Writer/Editor
1 Office Manager
1 Accountant
1/2 Grassroots Fundraiser

Staff openings/year: 4-6

Work Week: 35-37 hours

Salary/year: $16,000 (Recent College Graduate); $19-28,000 (Graduate with advanced degree)

Benefits: Health insurance, life insurance, pregnancy leave, pension, credit union, paid vacation, disability, business expenses paid, sick time, personal leave, dental

Part-Time Employees: 5

Volunteers: 50

Interns: 3 currently
Length: No less than 6 months
Duties: Handling complaints, giving information, specific projects as negotiated (research, development of materials, etc.)
Remuneration: Pay business expenses; may pay health insurance and/or small stipend

Jobs advertised: Local newspapers; information sent to local colleges; word of mouth

To apply: Materials should be sent to Susan Titus, Executive Director

---

CITIZENS FOR PARTICIPATION IN POLITICAL ACTION (CPPAX)

25 West Street, 5th Floor
Boston, MA 02111-1213
(617) 426-3040

Director: Stephen Stephano

Purpose: Multi-issue, multi-tactical grassroots organization committed to organizing our members and the public for peace and social justice

Methods of operation: Research (20%), lobbying (20%), publications (20%), member organizing (20%), public education (20%)

Constituency: Individual progressives

Recent issues and projects: Leading the fight for single payer health care in Massachusetts. Working to cut military budget and convert economy from military to civilian. Working to elect progressives throughout the state at congressional, gubernatorial and state levels.

Major publications: *CPPAX Newsletter*; key votes of the State Legislature and Congress

Budget: $190,000

Funding: Individual contributions, telephone solicitation

Staff: 4
1 1/2 Grassroots Fundraiser
1/2 Organizer
1/2 Lobbyist
1/2 Office Manager
1/2 Writer/Editor
1/2 Issue Expert

Staff openings/year: 1

Work Week: 40 hours

Salary/year: $18,000 (Recent College Graduate); $Varies (Graduate with advanced degree)

Benefits: Health insurance, paid vacation, maternity/paternity leave

Part-Time Employees: 5 phone fundraisers

Volunteers: Yes

Interns: Yes
Length: 3 months

Duties: Support and research in any of our issue areas
Remuneration: No financial compensation available

Jobs advertised: Local papers; job descriptions sent to other progressive organizations; etc.

To apply: Contact Stephen Stephano, Executive Director

CITIZENS FOR TAX JUSTICE

1311 L Street, NW, Suite 400
Washington, DC 20005
(202) 626-3780

Other Offices: St. Paul, MN

Director: Robert S. McIntyre

Purpose: CTJ was formed in 1979 to give ordinary people a greater voice in the development of the tax laws at the national, state and local levels. CTJ fights for a fair shake for middle- and low-income families, based on the idea that people should pay taxes based upon their ability to pay them.

Methods of operation: Research, lobbying, publications, public education, training and technical assistance

Constituency: Labor, community, religious and public interest organizations

Recent issues and projects: CTJ conceived and implemented the "Crumb Campaign," a coalition effort in opposition to a capital gains tax cut. The coalition consists of more than 60 organizations representing over 20 million people. The campaign will attempt to persuade Congress to defeat the proposed tax cut for the rich through a mail campaign that is projected to bring more than 2.5 million letters to Capitol Hill.

Major publications: *The Resurgence of Business Investment and Corporate Income Taxes* (October 1989); *No Sale: Lessons for America from Sales Taxes in Europe* (1988); *Inequality and the Federal Budget Deficit* (1988); *The Corporate Tax Comeback* (1988); *Nickels and Dimes: How Sales and Excise Taxes Add Up in the 50 States* (1988)

Budget: $300,000

Funding: Individual contributions, foundations

Staff: 7
5 Researchers
3 Writers/Editors
2 Press Aides
2 Issue Experts
1 Lobbyist
1 Office Manager
1 Foundation Fundraiser

Work Week: 50 hours

Salary/year: $Varies (Recent College Graduate); $Varies (Graduate with advanced degree)

Benefits: Health insurance, pension, pregnancy leave, paid vacation

Summer Employees: 1-2

Interns: 1-2
Length: 3-6 months
Duties: Research; preparation/distribution of media advisories, press releases, publications; conference/seminar planning and management; writing
Remuneration: Negotiable; salary payable every 2 weeks

Jobs advertised: Local classifieds; various colleges and universities offering intern placement services

To apply: Contact Douglas P. Kelly, Intern Coordinator

CITIZENS UTILITY BOARD (CUB)

208 South LaSalle, Suite 584
Chicago, IL 60604
(312) 263-4282

Other Offices: Springfield, IL

Director: Martin R. Cohen

Purpose: CUB represents the interests of residential and small business utility ratepayers in matters before regulatory agencies, the Illinois General Assembly and other jurisdictions.

Methods of operation: Litigation (25%), community organizing (25%), public education (20%), lobbying (15%), publications (8%), research (5%), human services (2%)

Constituency: Cross section of Illinois residents

Recent issues and projects: Citizens Utility Board has successfully intervened in several important cases recently, including an ongoing battle with Commonwealth Edison Company over its efforts to charge ratepayers for unneeded power plant construction; three times CUB and other consumer groups have convinced the courts to overrule regulatory actions taken by the Illinois Commerce Commission. CUB was instrumental in negotiating a settlement with Commonwealth Edison that will refund $1.34 billion to Illinois consumers. CUB also had a significant impact on cases involving other electric utilities in IL as well as numerous telephone and gas utilities. CUB also has a comprehensive legislative program involving consumer protection, conservation and energy efficiency.

Major publications: Quarterly newsletter: *CUBNews*

Budget: $1,800,000

Funding: Individual contributions (100%)

Staff: 11
3 Issue Experts
2 Organizers
1 Writer/Editor
1 Attorney
1 Office Manager
1 Lobbyist
1 Typist

Staff openings/year: 1-2

Work Week: 50 hours

Salary/year: $25,000 (Recent College Graduate); $Varies (Graduate with advanced degree)

Benefits: Health insurance, pregnancy leave, pension, paid vacation

Part-Time Employees: 5

Summer Employees: 3

Volunteers: 1

Interns: 3
Length: 3 months
Remuneration: small stipend

Jobs advertised: Newspaper

To apply: Contact Martin Cohen, Associate Director

CITY LIMITS MAGAZINE
40 Prince Street
New York, NY 10012
(212) 925-9820

Director: Andrew White

Purpose: We are a monthly magazine devoted to disseminating information concerning neighborhood revitalization.

Membership: Approximately 2,000 subscribers

Recent issues and projects: Special issues on community organizing in New York; coverage of housing; economic development; public health; the urban environment; and the nonprofit sector

Major publications: *City Limits*

Budget: $200,000

Funding: Individual contributions, foundations, direct mail, sponsor payment, subscribers, advertisers

Staff: 3
3 Writers/Editors

Staff openings/year: 0-1

Work Week: 45 hours

Salary/year: $24,000

Benefits: Health insurance, paid vacation

Part-Time Employees: 3

Volunteers: 1

Interns: Yes
Length: 3 months
Duties: Up to intern to help shape; could be writing, reporting, research, office duties, etc.
Remuneration: No pay

Jobs advertised: In *City Limits*

To apply: Contact Andrew White, Editor

CITY VOLUNTEER CORPS
838 Broadway
New York, NY 10003
(212) 475-6444

Director: Toni Schmiegezow

Purpose: The City Volunteer Corps enrolls young people, ages 16-25, to complete volunteer service projects in the areas of environment, education, human service and public safety. In exchange for their year of service, volunteers receive a $5,000 scholarship, a weekly stipend, and up to nine college credits.

Methods of operation: Human service (100%)

Recent issues and projects: The City Volunteer Corps was selected by the Corporation for National Service to operate the Community Leadership Program, one of 15 demonstration models across the country.

Budget: $6,800,000

Funding: City (83%), federal (16%), foundations (1%)

Staff: 67

1 Office Manager
6 Issue Experts
5 Administrative Assistants
3 Bookkeepers/Accountants
30 Field Supervisors
2 Personnel Administrators
4 MIS and Administrative Services
10 Field Staff Support Services
4 Volunteer Recruitment
2 Volunteer Trainers

Staff openings/year: 15

Work Week: 35 hours

Salary/year: $20-25,000 (Recent College Graduate); $25-35,000 (Graduate with advanced degree)

Benefits: Health insurance, paid vacation, life insurance, family leave, tuition reimbursement

Part-Time Employees: Yes

Summer Employees: None

Volunteers: None

Interns: Yes
Length: 3-6 months
Duties: Varies according to department
Remuneration: Varies

Jobs advertised: Newspapers, postings in other organizations, college recruitment

To apply: Contact the Personnel Department

CITY YEAR, INC.

11 Stillings Street
Boston, MA 02210
(617) 350-0700

Other Offices: Providence, RI; Columbus, OH; Columbia, SC; Chicago, IL; San Jose, CA

Director: Michael Brown and Alan Khazel Co-Directors

Purpose: City Year is a National Service Program that unites young adults from diverse backgrounds for an academic year of service.

Methods of operation: Direct action (80%), human services (10%), community organizing (10%)

Constituency: 17-23 year-olds from all backgrounds

Recent issues and projects: Expansion to six cities in Fall of 1994

Major publications: *City Year and Voluntary National Service*; *Recruiting a Diverse Corps*

Budget: $10,000,000

Funding: Federal (50%), private (50%)

Staff: 175

Staff openings/year: Varies

Work Week: 60 hours

Salary/year: $18,000 (Recent College Graduate); $32,000 (Graduate with advanced degree)

Benefits: Health insurance, paid vacation

Part-Time Employees: None

Summer Employees: None

Volunteers: Varies

Interns: 4
Length: Varies - semester/summer
Duties: Varies by department
Remuneration: Will match work-study money

To apply: Please contact Liz Herdade, Human Resource Specialist

CLEAN AIR COUNCIL

1909 Chestnut Street, 2nd Floor
Philadelphia, PA 19103
(215) 567-4004 Fax: (215) 567-5791

Director: Joseph Otis Minott, Esq.

Purpose: To protect and improve environmental quality in the Delaware Valley of Pennsylvania, Southern New Jersey, and Delaware through education, advocacy, government oversight and legal action.

Methods of operation: Public education (30%), community organizing (20%), litigation (20%), training and technical assistance (10%), research (10%), publications (10%)

Constituency: All those who live in, work in or visit the Delaware Valley (includes the city of Philadelphia and metropolitan area)

Recent issues and projects: Environmentally sound solid waste management, including recycling and waste reduction; daily air quality report; indoor air pollution information center; household hazardous waste management; community right-to-know; environmental litigation; environmental equity

Major publications: Newsletters: *Fresh Air* and *Recycling Roll Call*; *There's More Than One Way to Recycling* report; *Household Hazardous Waste Safety* booklet; *Indoor Air Pollution?* booklet; *Household Hazardous Waste Collection Programs* booklet

Budget: $200,000

Funding: Foundations (40%), sponsoring associations (25%), government contract (20%), individual contributions (10%), direct mail (5%)

Staff: 5
1 Organizer
1 Campaign Manager
1 Attorney
1 Policy Analyst
1 Administrator/Fundraiser

Staff openings/year: 0-1

Work Week: 40 hours

Salary/year: $19,000 (Recent College Graduate); $22,000 (Graduate with advanced degree)

Benefits: Health insurance, life insurance, pregnancy leave, paid vacation, dental, disability

Part-Time Employees: 3

Summer Employees: 0-1

Volunteers: 10-15

Interns: 3-6
Length: 3 months
Duties: Research, develop resource files, write briefing papers for staff and/or articles for newsletters and publications and community outreach
Remuneration: Occasional stipend; otherwise work-study to qualified students

Jobs advertised: Local newspapers; colleges and universities; other environmental organizations

To apply: Contact Joseph Otis Minott, Esq., Executive Director

---

CLEAN OCEAN ACTION
P.O. Box 505, Sandy Hook
Highlands, NJ 07732
(908) 872-0111

Other Offices: Cape May, NJ

Director: Cindy Zapf

Purpose: To clean up and protect the waters of the New York Bright which is the area of water from Montaule Point, NY to Cape May, NY.

Methods of operation: Public education (35%), research (20%), litigation (20%), publications (10%), community organizing (10%), direct action (10%)

Recent issues and projects: COA is currently working to stop ocean dumping of contaminated sediments at a site six miles off the N.J. coast and is also fighting to control non-point source pollution.

Major publications: *The Clean Ocean Advocate*, monthly newsletter

Budget: $249,000

Funding: Foundations (60%), individual contributions (40%)

Staff: 6
2 Organizers
1 Writer/Editor
1 Attorney
1 Foundation Fundraiser
1 Issue Expert

Staff openings/year: 1-2

Work Week: 40-60 hours

Salary/year: $20-25,000 (Recent College Graduate); $25,000 (Graduate with advanced degree)

Benefits: Health insurance, paid vacation

Part-Time Employees: 1

Summer Employees: None

Volunteers: 20-30

Interns: 3
Length: Summer or semester
Duties: Issues research, organizing campaigns, media relations, etc.
Remuneration: Stipend available

Jobs advertised: Newspapers, position announcements circulated among environmental groups

To apply: Please contact Cindy Zapf, Executive Director

Remarks: Clean Ocean Action's offices are located on the water at beautiful Sandy Hook and Cape May Harbor. Work atmosphere is casual and fun.

CLEAN WATER ACTION

1320 18th Street, NW, Suite 300
Washington, DC 20036
(202) 457-1286 Fax: (202) 457-0287

Other Offices: Annapolis, MD; Baltimore, MD; Allentown, PA; Philadelphia, PA; New Brunswick, NJ; Belmar, NJ; Montclair, NJ; Trenton, NJ; Boston, MA; Amherst, MA; Portsmouth, NH; Providence, RI; Austin, TX; Denver, CO; Minneapolis, MN; Rochester, MN; Duluth, MN; Fargo, ND; Lansing, MI; San Francisco, CA; Miami, FL

Director: David Zwick

Purpose: National citizens' organization working for clean and safe water at an affordable cost, control of toxic chemicals, the protection of natural resources and environmental job creation strategies.

Methods of operation: Public education (25%), community organizing (25%), training and technical assistance (10%), research (10%), lobbying (10%), election (10%), publications (5%), direct action (5%)

Recent issues and projects: Recent projects include: Solid Waste Management; toxic hazards; Clean Water Act reauthorization; community and workplace safety; trade and environment; marketplace recycling; Everglades protection; energy efficiency and alternative technologies; incinerator moratorium

Major publications: *Clean Water Action News*

Budget: $11,000,000

Funding: Individual contributions through canvassing and telephone follow-up (90%), foundations (8%), workplace giving campaigns (1%), federal, state and local government grants (1%)

Staff:
400 Canvassers
20 Organizers
5 Office Managers
5 Bookkeepers/Accountants
5 Campaign Managers
3 Lobbyists
1 Researcher
2 Grassroots Fundraisers
2 Writers/Editors
2 Foundation Fundraisers

Staff openings/year: 10-200

Work Week: 45 hours

Salary/year: $16,000-50,000

Benefits: Health insurance, pregnancy leave, paid vacation

Part-Time Employees: 100

Summer Employees: 150

Volunteers: Yes

Interns: 3-10
Length: 3-6 months
Duties: Issue and electoral campaigns, researching, lobbying, canvassing, development and general office work
Remuneration: Both paid and unpaid; please inquire

Jobs advertised: National and local publications; colleges and universities, other environmental and social and economic justice groups

To apply: Contact Paul Schwartz, Assistant to Executive Director

CLEAN WATER FUND OF NORTH CAROLINA, INC.

P.O. Box 1008
Raleigh, NC 27602
(919) 832-7491

Other Offices: Asheville, NC

Director: Ted Outwater

Purpose: Clean Water Fund of North Carolina is committed to fostering citizen involvement by researching environmental problems, analyzing public policy, and educating and empowering citizens.

Methods of operation: Community organizing (40%), research (20%), publications (20%), public education (10%), training and technical assistance (10%)

Constituency: Communities/citizens with environmental problems

Recent issues and projects: Provision of lead testing for home water supplies; research and publication of groundwater report and surface water report; work with citizens concerned about proposed radioactive and hazardous waste facilities

Major publications: Newsletter: *Clean Water Update*, semi-annual; *Danger Down Under: Citizen's Guide to Groundwater Protection in NC*;

Surface Water Citizen's Guide

Budget: $100,000

Funding: Foundations (75%), individual contributions (25%)

Staff: 5
2 Directors/Jacks of all trades

Staff openings/year: 1

Work Week: 45-50 hours

Salary/year: $18,000

Benefits: Health insurance, pregnancy leave, paid vacation

Part-Time Employees: 2

Volunteers: Yes

Interns: None currently, but willing to accept applications

Jobs advertised: Area newspapers; organization newsletters; word of mouth

To apply: Contact Ted Outwater, Executive Director

CLOSE UP FOUNDATION

44 Canal Center Plaza
Alexandria, VA 22314
(703) 706-3300

Purpose: Citizenship education programs primarily for high school students.

Methods of operation: Educational (100%)

Constituency: High school teachers and full time students

Recent issues and projects: Recent projects include: Washington, DC Study Visits; The National Citizen Bee; and numerous other study visits

Major publications: *Current Issues*; *Perspectives*, *Washington Notebook*

Budget: $34,000,000

Funding: Individual tuition (70%), government (14%), foundations (8%)

Staff: 180
180-250 staff includes:
35 Organizers
5 Writers/Editors
1 Attorney
5 Office Managers
5 Researchers
1 Press Aide
5 Foundation Fundraisers
20 Typists
20 Bookkeepers/Accountan
4 Campaign Managers
100 Educators

Staff openings/year: 50-75

Work Week: 40-60 hours

Salary/year: $18,000 (Recent College Graduate); $18,000 (Graduate with advanced degree)

Benefits: Health insurance, pension, paid vacation, life insurance, family leave

Part-Time Employees: 4

Summer Employees: None

Volunteers: None

Interns: None, but willing to accept applications

Jobs advertised: D.C. area newspapers; college placement offices; regional newspapers

To apply: Contact Diann James, Human Resource Director

CO-OP AMERICA

1850 M Street, NW, Suite 700
Washington, DC 20036
(202) 872-5307

Director: Alisa Gravitz

Purpose: Co-op America's mission is to create a just and sustainable society by working in four program areas: encouraging corporate responsibility; helping socially responsible businesses emerge and thrive; educating consumers about creating social change; and creating sustainable communities.

Methods of operation: Research, public education, publications, networking/creating an "alternative marketplace"

Membership: 45,000 individual members all over the U.S. and 380 organizational members (small businesses and nonprofit organizations)

Recent issues and projects: Syndicated boycott radio show. Issues of the quarterly magazine: *What in the World Are We Working For?*, a look at socially responsible workplaces; Environmental Racism; Creating a Sustainable Society.

Major publications: *Socially Responsible Financial Planning Handbook*; *The National Green Pages*, a directory of socially and environmentally onsible ("green") businesses across the country; *he Co-op America Quarterly*; *The Co-op America Catalog*, products from green businesses; *Boycott Action News*, a nationwide coverage of boycott information

Budget: $2,500,000

Funding: Individual contributions, direct mail

Staff: 24
6 Member Services
6 Operations
4 Marketing
4 Writer/Editors
1 Executive Director
1 Director
1 Publisher
1 Art Director

Staff openings/year: 0-2

Work Week: 40 hours

Salary/year: $16-18,000

Benefits: Paid vacation, pregnancy leave, IRA, maternity/paternity leave (including for adoption), health, life, vision and dental insurance, cooperative workplace, flextime.

Part-Time Employees: 4

Interns: 25 per year
Length: 3-4 months
Duties: Writing, research, special projects, maintaining files, answering phones,etc.
Remuneration: Travel allowance

Jobs advertised: *Washington Post*; Common Cause bulletin board; career centers of area colleges; *Community Jobs*; the National Association of Student Cooperative Organizations (NASCO) newsletter in Ann Arbor, Michigan, *Washington City Paper*

To apply: Call first to find out whether we have openings. Interns often needed.

COALITION FOR BASIC HUMAN NEEDS

54 Essex Street
Cambridge, MA 02139
(617) 497-0126

Director: Mary Quinn

Purpose: The organization's purpose is to effect changes in the welfare system and society through attaining a decent standard of living for all people, gaining control and a voice within the welfare system for recipients, educating the general public about life for low-income women, countering the widely-held stereotypes that degrade them, and making the public recognize that childrearing is work.

Methods of operation: Community organizing (60%), public education (20%), direct action (10%), publications (5%), human services (3%), research (1%), lobbying (1%)

Constituency: Welfare recipients

Recent issues and projects: (1) Trying to get a bill called "Up and Out of Poverty" passed through the Legislature. The bill would raise welfare grants above the federal poverty level. Over the last 4 years, through CBHN's efforts, they have increased welfare grants by more than 40%. (2) Designed and won a $150 winter clothing allowance for each child in an AFDC unit. (3) Fought to expand the Emergency Assistance Program. (4) Won a $40 rental supplement for individuals living in private housing. (5) They are also currently fighting punitive welfare reform proposals.

Major publications: Pamphlets explaining the purpose and goals of the coalition and its gains and losses through various programs; booklet describing the components of the "Up and Out of Poverty" bill; booklet on how to plan and run a meeting with welfare officials

Budget: $200,000

Funding: Foundations (60%), fundraising (15%), direct mail (15%), individual contributions (5%), payroll through Community Works (5%)

Staff: 5
1 Director
3 Organizers
1 Statewide Campaign Coordinator

Staff openings/year: 1

Work Week: 40 hours

Salary/year: $20,000

Benefits: Health insurance, paid vacation

Part-Time Employees: 1

Volunteers: Varies

Interns: Varies
Length: Intern's school requirements
Duties: Filing regulations, doing mailings, answering the phone, attending board meetings, organizing at the Cambridge welfare office
Remuneration: With the limited amount of funds

the agency has, the internship will be unpaid.

Jobs advertised: Newspapers; colleges; flyers to organizations

To apply: Contact Tracy Lopes

COALITION FOR CRIMINAL JUSTICE REFORM FOR BATTERED WOMEN

799 Broadway, Suite 402
New York, NY 10003
(212) 673-7754

Director: Mary Haviland

Purpose: Coalition of domestic violence programs with the aim of improving the criminal justice response to battered women and their children.

Methods of operation: Community organizing (20%), training and technical assistance (20%), advocating with institutions for change (20%), research (15%), direct action (15%), public education (10%)

Constituency: Domestic violence service providers and battered women

Recent issues and projects: 1) Researching of criminal justice intervention models in other jurisdictions; 2) making recommendations for changes in current system; 3) working towards implementation of changes; 4) public education on issues; 5) creating model pilot project that helps women with prosecution process

Major publications: Working on a report on criminal justice and domestic violence

Budget: $60,000

Funding: Foundations (98%), individual contributions (2%)

Staff: 1

Staff openings/year: 1

Work Week: 40 hours

Salary/year: $25,000 (Recent College Graduate); $32,000 (Graduate with advanced degree)

Benefits: Health insurance, life insurance, pregnancy leave, pension

Part-Time Employees: 1-2 Consultants

Volunteers: 20

Interns: 3 per year
Length: 1 semester
Duties: Legal research
Remuneration: Paid by public interest grants through law schools

To apply: Contact Mary Haviland; Monday-Thursday, 9-5 pm, (212) 674-8200

COALITION FOR JUSTICE IN THE MAQUILADORAS

3120 West Ashby
San Antonio, TX 78228
(210) 732-8957

Director: Susan Mika

Purpose: The Coalition for Justice in the Maquiladoras works to press transnational corporations to adopt socially responsible business practices in the Maquiladora industry, foreign-owned factories operating in Mexico.

Methods of operation: Research, publications, community organizing

Constituency: Various religious, environmental and labor groups

Recent issues and projects: Recent issues include: Sony's violation of workers' rights and fixing of labor union elections; rise in trade defects along U.S.-Mexico border; safety, health and environmental concerns regarding Stepan Chemical Inc.

Major publications: 3 Annual Reports; 2 newsletters per year; report on health issues; report on labor issues; and a video on Stepan Chemical's Maquilador

Part-Time Employees: Yes

Interns: None, but willing to accept applications

To apply: Contact Susan Mika, President of the Board

COALITION FOR THE ENVIRONMENT

6267 Delmar Boulevard
St. Louis, MO 63130
(314) 727-0600

Director: R. Roger Pryor, Executive Director

Purpose: Full service, citizen action, environmental group focusing on state legislation and local issues.

Methods of operation: Community organizing

(40%), public education (20%), research (10%), lobbying (10%), publications (10%), direct action (5%), litigation (5%)

Membership: 25,000 members in Missouri

Recent issues and projects: Solid waste legislation; public land preservation; natural streams initiative; clean water and air; park funding; radioactive waste; forestry

Major publications: Quarterly newsletter: *ALERT*; *Legislative Network Update* (10 times during legislative session); *Citizen Action*; occasional reports and papers

Budget: $250,000

Funding: Canvassing (30%), direct mail (40%), individual contributions (20%), foundations (10%)

Staff: 20
15+ Canvassers
1 Organizer
1 Office Manager
1 Canvass Director
1 Lobbyist
1/2 Outreach/Volunteer Coordinator
1/2 Bookkeeper/Accountant

Staff openings/year: 0-3

Work Week: 40+ hours

Salary/year: $Varies (Recent College Graduate); $Varies (Graduate with advanced degree)

Benefits: Health insurance, life insurance (limited), paid vacation

Part-Time Employees: 2

Summer Employees: 20-40 canvassers

Volunteers: 6-10

Interns: Yes
Length: 1 semester (3-6 months)
Duties: Vary; usually research or community organizing
Remuneration: Small stipend available

Jobs advertised: Newspapers in St. Louis

To apply: Contact R. Roger Pryor, Executive Director

COALITION FOR THE HOMELESS

1234 Massachusetts Ave., Suite C 1015
Washington, DC 20005
(202) 374-8870

Director: Jack M. White

Purpose: To help homeless men, women and children regain self-sufficiency and return to independent living.

Methods of operation: Human services (100%)

Constituency: Members of the Greater Washington Area community

Recent issues and projects: Operate four transitional homes for homeless men, eight transitional apartments for homeless families, and three emergency shelters for homeless men

Budget: $2,500,000

Funding: Government (80%), foundations (10%), individual contributions (10%)

Staff: 53
25 Shelter Staff
13 Transitional House Staff
10 Caseworkers
2 Bookkeepers/Accountants
1 Office Manager
1 Fundraiser
1 Volunteer Coordinator

Staff openings/year: 5-10

Work Week: 40 hours

Salary/year: $18,000 (Recent College Graduate); $22,000 (Graduate with advanced degree)

Benefits: Health insurance, paid vacation

Part-Time Employees: 15

Volunteers: 200

Interns: 10
Length: Semester
Duties: Depends on internship; usually social services
Remuneration: Unpaid

Jobs advertised: *Washington Post*

To apply: Contact Monica Sanning, Director of Personnel

COALITION FOR WOMEN'S ECONOMIC DEVELOPMENT

315 West Ninth Street, Suite 408
Los Angeles, CA 90015
(213) 489-4995

Director: Forescee Hogan-Rowles

Purpose: CWED is a project which lowers the

barriers to self-employment and micro-entrepreneurship and increases opportunities for self-sufficiency among low-income men and women. The Coalition's objectives include: (1) establish a peer group training and technical assistance program to help men and women create or expand ventures that will provide an income equal to at least the annual average for women; (2) create partnerships with community organizations to offer our program in local neighborhoods; (3) provide access to start-up capital for program participants through a revolving loan fund; and (4) participate in local and statewide policy initiatives to reduce the barriers to self-employment which presently exist.

Methods of operation: Training and technical assistance (85%), community organizing (15%)

Constituency: Low-income women in Los Angeles County

Recent issues and projects: CWED started its first workshop in spring 1989.

Major publications: Newsletter: *CWED Update*

Budget: $200,000

Funding: Foundations (90%), individual contributions (10%)

Staff: 6
4 Training Facilitators
1 Director - Financial
1 Loan Fund Officer

Staff openings/year: 1-2

Work Week: 35-40 hours

Salary/year: $Varies (Recent College Graduate); $Varies (Graduate with advanced degree)

Benefits: Health insurance, paid vacation

Part-Time Employees: Yes

Volunteers: Yes

Interns: 1 student
Length: 1 college quarter
Duties: Research
Remuneration: Either course credit or work-study

Jobs advertised: Through the nonprofit network

To apply: Contact Forescee Hogan Rowles, Executive Director

COALITION OF ADVOCATES FOR THE RIGHTS OF THE INFIRM ELDERLY (CARIE)

1315 Walnut Street, Suite 900
Philadelphia, PA 19107
(215) 545-5728

Director: Bernice Soffer

Purpose: CARIE's mission is to advocate for the improvement of the quality of life for the infirm elderly by: (1) working to ensure that their rights are protected and secure; (2) promoting interaction and understanding between them and the community; (3) assuring that they receive the care they need in the most appropriate setting; and (4) accomplishing these tasks while recognizing and respecting the individual's autonomy.

Methods of operation: Community organizing (35%), direct action (30%), training and technical assistance (15%), public education (15%), publications (2.5%), research (2.5%)

Constituency: Frail elderly; their caregivers; professionals and others who are concerned with issues affecting the frail elderly

Recent issues and projects: CARIE's Elder Abuse Task Force was instrumental in advocating for adult protective services legislation and is currently advocating for much needed reforms in the state's guardianship laws. CARIE is involved in a broad range of long-term care issues and recently advocated on a local level to improve care and prevent the closing of a county-run nursing home, as well as on a state level for nursing home access. CARIE's legislative committee is active in advocating on a broad range of issues affecting the elderly, including catastrophic health care and family and medical leave.

Major publications: *CARIE Newsletter*; Final Report/AOA-funded Pennsylvania Elder Abuse Prevention Project; *Guide to the Nursing Home Application Process*; *Nursing Homes in Philadelphia: A Directory and Consumer Guide*; Caregiver Advocacy Network Newsletter; *The Fairmount Study: Effects of Involuntary Transfer on Nursing Home Residents*

Budget: $500,000

Funding: Foundations (44%), contracts (43%), United Way (7%), individual contributions (4%), miscellaneous (2%)

Staff: 14

5 Caseworkers
2 Typists
2 Organizers
2 Issue Experts
1 Writer/Editor
1 Foundation Fundraiser
1 Bookkeeper

Staff openings/year: 2-3

Work Week: 40 hours

Salary/year: $20,000

Benefits: Health insurance, pregnancy/family leave, board, paid vacation

Part-Time Employees: 1

Summer Employees: 1-2

Volunteers: 100's

Interns: 2-6
Length: 1-2 semesters
Duties: Community organizing, direct service, volunteer outreach, advocacy and grant-writing
Remuneration: Usually unpaid

Jobs advertised: Word of mouth; Coalition mailings; newsletters; university placement offices; newspaper ads

To apply: Contact Diane A. Menio, Operations Manager

COALITION OF LABOR UNION WOMEN

1126 16th Street, NW
Washington, DC 20036
(202) 466-4610

Director: Chryslt L. Bridgeforth

Purpose: Promote working women's issues in the U.S.; promote women's issues in labor movement; network on legislation and issues affecting working women; promote women in union leadership

Methods of operation: Community organizing through unions and our chapters (50%), direct action (20%), training and technical assistance (20%), publications (5%), public education (5%)

Constituency: Union members, 90% women, more than 50% minority

Recent issues and projects: American Family Day - May 1988 (parental leave, child care awareness); Bargaining for Families Conferences (skills and issues training); reproductive rights as a union issue; pay equity conference; 1993 Covergence on women's health and national health care; sexual harassment training with the Labor Institute

Major publications: Bimonthly: *CLUW News*; *Bargaining for Family Issues*; *9 to 5 Guide to Combatting Sexual Harassment*; *Is Your Job Making You Sick?*

Budget: $180,000

Funding: Individual contributions, membership dues (95%), foundations (5%)

Staff: 4
2 Organizers
1 Executive Director
1 Office Manager

Staff openings/year: 1

Work Week: 40 hours

Salary/year: $20,000 (Recent College Graduate); $25,000 (Graduate with advanced degree)

Benefits: Health insurance, life insurance, pregnancy leave, credit union, tuition reimbursement (job related), paid vacation

Volunteers: 2

Interns: Yes
Length: Summer
Duties: Assist executive director with projects
Remuneration: Stipend possible

Jobs advertised: Within labor and women's groups primarily

To apply: Contact Chrystl Bridgeforth, Executive Director

COALITION TO STOP GUN VIOLENCE

100 Maryland Avenue, NE, Suite 402
Washington, DC 20002
(202) 544-7190

Director: Michael K. Beard

Purpose: A collection of religious, professional and lay organizations working together to educate the public about abuse and petition the government to take action. The Coalition seeks to ban handguns and assault weapons from importation, manufacture, sale and transfer to private citizens. The military, police, national guard and security forces would be exempt from this ban. The Coalition's emphasis is on taking handguns and assault weapons out of private possession where they do the most harm.

Methods of operation: Research, lobbying, litigation, publications, public education

Membership: 38 national organizations

Recent issues and projects: Protecting the machine gun ban; working on federal and state assault weapons ban (California was the first state in 1988 to ban assault weapons); passage of the plastic handgun ban in 1988 and the armor-piercing bullets ban bill; working on federal waiting period and Saturday Night Special ban

Major publications: Quarterly newsletter: *The Banner*; analysis of FBI Uniform Crime Reports statistics (annually); various research projects concerning suicide, murder rates; *Kids and Guns*; *Women and Guns*; Comparison of gun control issues

Budget: $1,500,000

Funding: Direct mail, private donations, fundraising events

Staff: 5
1 Executive Director
1 Public Affairs Director
1 Issue Expert

Staff openings/year: 1

Work Week: 40 hours

Salary/year: $19,000 (Recent College Graduate); $20,500 (Graduate with advanced degree)

Benefits: Health insurance, pregnancy leave, dental insurance, paid vacation

Part-Time Employees: 1

Summer Employees: Occasionally

Volunteers: Yes

Interns: 10
Length: Semester/3 months
Duties: Research, report writing, statistical analysis
Remuneration: Unpaid

Jobs advertised: Through Coalition members, colleges and newspapers

To apply: Contact Michael Beard

Remarks: The Educational Fund to End Handgun Violence is our affiliated nonprofit, tax deductible arm, and also offers internship opportunities.

COLD MOUNTAIN, COLD RIVERS

P.O. Box 7941
Missoula, MT 59807
(406) 728-0867

Purpose: The Cold Mountain, Cold Rivers is a nonprofit organization which works with grassroots groups to develop effective media campaigns focusing on human rights and environmental issues.

Methods of operation: Public education (50%), advocacy (20%), research (15%), lobbying (5%)

Constituency: Forest activists, indigenous people, grassroots environmental/human rights groups

Recent issues and projects: Produced and distributed two video documentaries worldwide on activist campaigns to protect forests, watersheds and bio-diversity in the Greater Salmon/Selway ecosystem.

Budget: $10,000

Funding: Group donations (50%), individual contributions (30%), foundations (10%), direct mail (10%)

Staff: 2
Unpaid Staff
1 Production/Editor
1 Office Manager/Researcher/Writer/Fundraiser

Work Week: 40-50 hours

Volunteers: 3-4

Interns: None, but willing to accept applications

To apply: Contact Darrell Geist, President

Remarks: CMCR has worked for the past 4 years to highlight campaigns that defend native forests and wildlife, protect ecosystems and bio-diversity, give voice to forest activists and indigenous people's and work for ecologically-based solutions that sustain forest communities. CMCR develops low-cost, high impact media productions for distribution regionally, nationally and worldwide. Media includes videos, print media. We also hope to develop an electronic newsletter and develop strategy for using radio to get our message out. CMCR's staff are rarely paid for work performed; however, expenses are generally covered. If interested folks want to help, they must first demonstrate a conviction to environmental/human rights issues.

COLORADO CHAPTER OF PHYSICIANS FOR SOCIAL RESPONSIBILITY

1738 Wynkoop Street, Suite 1
Denver, CO 80202
(303) 298-8001

Director: Sam Cole

Purpose: To seek to expose and help lessen the dangers of Rocky Flats, curb worldwide nuclear proliferation and advocate for violence prevention measures in Colorado.

Methods of operation: Research (30%), lobbying (5%), publications (15%), community organizing (15%), direct action (5%), public education (30%)

Membership: Mostly professionals in the health care field

Recent issues and projects: Hosted national conference on disarmament and weapons production dangers; current project involves the health dangers Rocky Flats pose to workers and the community

Major publications: Newsletter - quarterly

Budget: $16,000

Funding: Individual contributions (70%), national office (30%)

Staff: 1
1 Director

Staff openings/year: 0-1

Work Week: 20 hours

Salary/year: $12,000 (Recent College Graduate); $12,000 (Graduate with advanced degree)

Benefits: None at present time

Part-Time Employees: None

Summer Employees: None

Volunteers: 3

Interns: No, but willing to accept applications

Jobs advertised: Local paper, word of mouth

To apply: Contact Sam Cole, Director.

COLORADO PUBLIC INTEREST RESEARCH GROUP (COPIRG)

1724 Gilpin Street
Denver, CO 80218
(303) 355-1861

Other Offices: Boulder, CO; Fort Collins, CO; Greeley, CO; Gunnison, CO; Pueblo, CO; Gunnison, CO

Director: Richard McClintock

Purpose: CoPIRG conducts research and advocacy on environmental, consumer and democracy issues to further the public interest in Colorado. CoPIRG is the state's largest public interest lobby group.

Methods of operation: Lobbying (25%), community organizing (25%), public education (20%), training and technical assistance (10%), research (10%), publications (10%)

Membership: 20,000 community members and 30,000 student members

Recent issues and projects: Passed Colorado Clean Air Act and Safe Drinking Water legislation. Set up pollution prevention campaign to reduce toxics use. Working now for increased recycling, clean air/transportation and campaign finance reform.

Major publications: Citizen newsletter: *CoPIRG Outlook*; student newsletter: *CoPIRG Reports*; consumer reports and guides on small claims and insurance; recycling guide

Budget: $250,000

Funding: Student contributions (60%), citizen outreach (30%), grants (10%)

Staff: 18
6 Organizers
4 Canvass Directors
2 Lobbyists/Advocates
2 Grassroots Organizers
2 Telephone Outreach Directors
1 Office Manager/Administrative Director
1 Executive Director

Staff openings/year: 4

Work Week: 50-60 hours

Salary/year: $15,000 (Recent College Graduate); $18,000 (Graduate with advanced degree)

Benefits: Health insurance, paid vacation

Part-Time Employees: 4-5

Summer Employees: 45

Volunteers: 10

Interns: 5
Length: Semester long
Duties: Research, lobbying, campaign organizing
Remuneration: Stipends available for law interns

Jobs advertised: Newspaper; postings

To apply: Contact Richard McClintock, Executive Director

COMMITTEE IN SOLIDARITY WITH THE PEOPLE OF EL SALVADOR (CISPES)

P.O. Box 12156
Washington, DC 20005
(202) 265-0890

Other Offices: New York, NY; Boston, MA; Chicago, IL; Los Angeles, CA; San Francisco, CA

Director: Angela Sanbrano

Purpose: To end all U.S. intervention in El Salvador and Central America and to support the popular movement and revolutionary struggle (specifically the FMLN/FDR) in El Salvador.

Methods of operation: Information collection and distribution, media work, training in organizing, direct action, public education, publications, community organizing

Constituency: CISPES is a grassroots organization: "members" are their "Chapters" (about 70) and "Friends" (about 50), and local El Salvador or Central America committees all over the U.S.

Recent issues and projects: October, 1989 "Steps to Freedom" walkathons to raise money for various projects in El Salvador and to protest U.S. policy; March 24th, 1990 Romero Commemoration in Washington, DC, San Francisco, Los Angeles and Austin

Major publications: Monthly newspaper: *Alert!*; flyers, educational pamphlets, posters, bumper stickers, etc.

Budget: $1,200,000

Funding: Direct mail (32%), individual contributions (28%), telephone solicitation (12%), foundations (9%), other (19%)

Staff: 21
4 Campaign Managers/Organizers
3 Grassroots Fundraisers
1 1/2 Writer/Editors
1 Executive Director
1 Political Director
1 Program Director
1 Organizational Director
1 Development Director
1 Major Donor Fundraiser
1 Information/Media Coordinator
1 Office Manager
1 Administrator
1/2 Artist

Staff openings/year: 5

Work Week: 40-80 hours

Salary/year: $13,200

Benefits: Health insurance (fully paid), pregnancy leave (3 months), 4 weeks paid vacation

Part-Time Employees: 2

Volunteers: Yes

Interns: 1-2
Length: Usually summer interns
Duties: Negotiable
Remuneration: Minimal stipend only (negotiable)

Jobs advertised: Local and progressive newspapers

To apply: Contact Julie Meyer, Administrator

Remarks: Each regional office has 2-8 paid staff each.

COMMITTEE ON US-LATIN AMERICAN RELATIONS (CUSLAR)

G-29 Anabel Taylor Hall
Ithaca, NY 14853
(607) 255-7293 Fax: (607) 255-7793

Director: Daniel Fireside

Purpose: CUSLAR is a nonprofit organization that works to promote social justice, human rights and the rights of indigenous people, women and workers in Latin America. CU.S.LAR works through education, activism and cultural exchanges between the people of the United States and Latin America.

Methods of operation: Public education (60%), maintaining resource center (20%), publications (10%), direct action (10%)

Constituency: Equally divided between Cornell undergraduates, graduate students and Ithaca community members

Recent issues and projects: Reading by Nicaraguan poet, Fr. Ernesto Cardenal; presentation by Guatemalan human rights and labor leaders; lobbying campaign to free HIV-positive Haitian political refugees from U.S. detention center; fifteenth annual Latin American Film Series at Cornell.

Major publications: *CUSLAR Newsletter*, 6 times/year

Budget: $17,000

Funding: Individuals, institutions, fundraising events and sales

Staff: 2
1 Director
1 Cornell work/study student

Staff openings/year: 0-1

Work Week: 35 hours

Salary/year: $6,000

Benefits: Health insurance, family leave, 2 weeks paid vacation

Part-Time Employees: 2

Volunteers: 10-25

Interns: 1-2
Remuneration: None. CUSLAR will provide assistance in finding low cost housing and in seeking outside funding.

Jobs advertised: Local papers; national alternative press; other solidarity groups

To apply: Contact Daniel Fireside, Director

COMMITTEE TO ABOLISH SPORT HUNTING (CASH)

P.O. Box 44
Tomkins Cove, NY 10986
(914) 429-8733

Director: Anne Muller

Purpose: To expose wildlife management practices to the public and legislators and their link to the gun manufacturers and their vested interest in perpetuating hunting at the expense of wildlife and the public.

Methods of operation: Research (30%), publications (20%), lobbying (10%), litigation (10%), community organizing (10%), direct action (10%), human services (5%), public education (5%)

Constituency: Animal rights activists

Recent issues and projects: In-depth study of Canada goose hunting and the North American Waterfowl Management Plan

Major publications: *CASH* quarterly magazine

Budget: $50,000

Funding: Individual contributions (100%)

Remarks: CASH is not in the position to hire at this moment, but are looking for volunteers.

COMMITTEE TO PROTECT JOURNALISTS

330 7th Ave., 12th Floor
New York, NY 10001
(212) 465-1004

Director: Bill Orme

Purpose: The Committee to Protect Journalists is a nonprofit, nonpartisan organization with the goal of promoting press freedoms around the world. Our six-person staff includes specialists in Latin America, Asia, Africa and Eastern Europe. The Committee monitors events through a network of journalists and human rights activists around the world, confirms the facts, protests where appropriate, shares the information with other professional groups and human rights groups, publicizes cases and publishes reports and periodicals.

Methods of operation: Publications (30%), research (45%), direct action (25%)

Constituency: Journalists, human rights advocates

Recent issues and projects: Last year, CPJ documented 1,625 individual attacks against more than 1,300 journalists and news organizations. CPJ took action on behalf of more than 500 of those journalists and news organizations; lobbying in order to get them released from prison, or in protest of their mistreatment or deaths. Other special projects include CPJ publications; one of the most recent was on journalists killed in the United States, another looked at the crackdown on the Haitian media. CPJ has responded to dangerous developments in the Balkans, Somalia and Haiti in the recent year in a number of ways; through protest letters, press releases and through a special initiative to improve transportation and safety in UN theatres.

Major publications: Quarterly newsletter: *CPJ*

Update; *Backgrounder*, bi-monthly; *Attacks on the Press*, annual; *Journalism Under Occupation* examines the status of the Palestinian press in the Israeli-occupied territories; *Attacks and Restrictions on the Press in South Africa*; *Journalists in Prison*; *Dangerous Assignments Quarterly*; *Silenced By Death*

Budget: $430,000

Funding: Individual contributions, foundations, media

Staff: 11
5 Caseworkers
1 Director
1 Development Director
1 Office Coordinator
1 Administrative Assistant
1 Publications Director
1 Business Manager

Staff openings/year: 0-1

Work Week: 45 hours

Salary/year: $18,000 (Recent College Graduate); $20,000 (Graduate with advanced degree)

Benefits: Health insurance, pension, paid vacation

Part-Time Employees: 1

Volunteers: Yes

Interns: Yes
Length: 1 semester or summer
Remuneration: Summer interns receive a stipend

Jobs advertised: Schools; human rights organizations

To apply: Contact Nicole Cordrey, Administrative Assistant

COMMON CAUSE
2030 M Street, NW
Washington, DC 20036
(202) 833-1200

Director: Fred Wertheimer

Purpose: National nonpartisan citizens' lobby group that works to improve the way government operates.

Methods of operation: Lobbying (100%), supported by research, litigation, publications and citizen organizing

Constituency: Citizens who believe in good government and citizen action

Recent issues and projects: 1994 issue priorities include: comprehensive reform of congressional campaigns; upholding standards of ethics; ensuring basic civil and equal rights

Major publications: *Common Cause Magazine*; various studies on campaign finance, ethics and the effectiveness of government agencies

Budget: $11,600,000

Funding: Individual member dues and contributions

Staff: 60
Including:
Researchers
Writers
Lobbyists
Organizers
Administrative Personnel

Staff openings/year: 20-25

Work Week: 37.5 hours

Salary/year: $19,000 (Recent College Graduate); $Varies (Graduate with advanced degree)

Benefits: Health insurance, life insurance, parental leave, pension, paid vacation, paid holidays, paid sick leave

Volunteers: 75

Interns: 10-25
Length: Semester or summer
Duties: Vary with department assignment
Remuneration: Unpaid; course credit may be arranged by students

Jobs advertised: Circulation to other public interest groups; some are also advertised in the *Washington Post* and/or publications such as *Community Jobs* and *Roll Call*; may also be listed with ACCESS: Networking in the Public Interest

To apply: Contact Dibby Johnson, Director of Personnel

Remarks: Common Cause also has offices in 47 states and the District of Columbia.

COMMUNITY ACTION TEAM, INC.
310 Columbia Boulevard
St. Helens, OR 97051
(503) 397-3511

Director: Rocky Johnson, Executive Director

Purpose: CAT, Inc. of Columbia County is a locally controlled, private, nonprofit corporation.

The mission of CAT is to combat the causes and conditions of poverty.

Recent issues and projects: (1) Children's Programs - Head Start, Latchkey, Child Care Resource and Referral, USDA Child Care Food Program; (2) Housing and Community Development - housing rehabilitation, weatherization, emergency utility assistance, homeless assistance, community development; (3) Emergency Services; (4) Senior Services; and (5) Human Resource Development Program. CAT assisted over 15,000 economically disadvantaged families and individuals, and contributed over $8,000,000 to local economy in 1989.

Funding: Government, local resources

COMMUNITY ALLIANCE WITH FAMILY FARMERS

P.O. Box 363
Davis, CA 95616
(916) 756-8518

Other Offices: San Francisco, CA

Director: Tom Haller

Purpose: The Community Alliance with Family Farmers, along with, the Community Alliance with Family Farmers Foundation work together to promote sustainable agriculture and provide support to small scale farmers. CAFF Foundation provides information and technical support to farmers making the transition to ecologically balanced farming while CAFF, the membership arm, applies grassroots pressure to reorient research priorities.

Methods of operation: Publications, community organizing, public education, training and technical assistance

Membership: Our members consist of farmers, consumers, environmentalists and rural activists

Recent issues and projects: A new project has been developed for Merced County almond growers who wish to reduce the use of pesticides and/or fertilizers. This project gives growers the opportunity to learn how to manage their orchards using cover crops, beneficial insects and other biological practices.

Major publications: *National Organic Directory*, annual; *Farmer to Farmer*, bimonthly

Budget: $630,000

Funding: Foundations (78%), publications/events (17%), direct mail (3%), individual contributions (2%)

Staff: 21
8 Writers/Editors
3 Organizers
2 Office Managers
3 Foundation Fundraisers
2 Issue Experts
1 Bookkeeper/Accountant
1 Grassroots Fundraiser
1 Campaign Manager

Staff openings/year: 1-2

Work Week: 40 hours

Salary/year: $18,000 (Recent College Graduate); $22,000 (Graduate with advanced degree)

Benefits: Health benefits, paid vacation

Part-Time Employees: 8

Summer Employees: None

Volunteers: 1

Interns: Yes
Length: Semester or quarter
Duties: Database work, research, lobby, routine office work

Jobs advertised: Trade journals, word of mouth, local newspapers

To apply: Contact Angelique Schuster, Administrative Assistant

Remarks: Our lighthouse staff is also coordinating an exciting new pilot project extending biological farming practices in almonds. Through a package of technical assistance and financial incentives, 28 almond farmers and twelve pest control advisors are learning the techniques of farming without toxic chemicals, while maintaining yield and quality. In addition to in-person activities of the Lighthouse Farm Network, we reach new farmers throughout the Central Valley with our bimonthly magazine, *Farmer to Farmer.*

COMMUNITY ECONOMIC DEVELOPMENT LAW PROJECT

220 South State Street, Suite 322
Chicago, IL 60604
(312) 939-3638

Director: Susan Kaplan, Esq.

Purpose: To provide quality, pro bono representation to Community Development

Corporations (CDCs) in low-income communities and nonprofit organizations involved in business development and the creation of affordable housing.

Methods of operation: Training and technical assistance/ broker of volunteer attorneys from private law firms (100%)

Constituency: Law firms, lawyers and community-based organizations

Recent issues and projects: Provided a team of volunteer attorneys Schiff, Hardin and Waite, who worked with Lakefront SRO Corporation on the successful development of the Harold Washington SRO apartments in the Uptown neighborhood

Budget: $100,000

Funding: Foundations (100%)

Staff: 3
2 1/2 Attorneys
1 Office Manager

Work Week: 40 hours

Salary/year: $30,000 (Graduate with advanced degree)

Benefits: Health insurance, life insurance, pregnancy leave, pension, paid vacation

Part-Time Employees: 3

Interns: Periodically, willing to accept applications

Jobs advertised: Legal channels mainly

To apply: Contact Susan Kaplan or Terri Stahulak

COMMUNITY ENVIRONMENTAL COUNCIL

930 Miramonte Drive
Santa Barbara, CA 93109
(805) 963-0583

Director: Jan Clark

Purpose: Environmental research and education

Methods of operation: Recycling and other operations (50%), public education (20%), research (20%), publications (10%)

Recent issues and projects: Hold seminars and publish on a wide variety of topics; recently, compost in California and Environmental Design Review Process. CEC runs local recycling programs and hazardous waste collection days.

Major publications: *Beyond the Crisis: Integrated Waste Management*; *The Next Frontier: Solid Waste Source Reduction*; *Bottom Line for Growth: Restructuring for Sustainability*; *A Question of Responsibility: Recycling Market Development*; *Many Factors with Recyclables: Overcoming the Barriers*

Budget: $4,000,000

Funding: Research, operations, contracts (80%), foundations (15%), individual contributions (5%)

Staff: 40
20 Recycling Operators
6 Program Coordinators
3 Bookkeepers/Accountants
5 Researchers
2 Administrative
1 Office Manager
1 Writer/Editor
2 Development

Staff openings/year: 1-2

Work Week: 40 hours

Salary/year: $Varies (Recent College Graduate); $Varies (Graduate with advanced degree)

Benefits: Health, life and disability insurance, pregnancy leave, paid vacation

Part-Time Employees: Yes

Volunteers: 10

Interns: Varies
Length: 6 months
Duties: Varies
Remuneration: $400/month plus housing and transportation

Jobs advertised: A variety of ways: papers, journals, word of mouth

To apply: Contact Jon Clark, Director

COMMUNITY FOOD RESOURCE CENTER

90 Washington Street
New York, NY 10006
(212) 349-8155 Fax: (212) 344-1422

Director: Kathy Goldman

Purpose: CFRC, founded in 1980, is a nonprofit organization that focuses on food, hunger, nutrition and income issues in New York City. Its primary goal is to increase access to nutritious food at reasonable cost for all New Yorkers, especially the hundreds of thousands of families and individuals living in poverty.

Methods of operation: Public education (50%), human services (10%), community organizing (10%), publications (10%), direct action (10%), training and technical assistance (10%)

Constituency: Low-income New York City population

Recent issues and projects: Media campaigns on federal food programs (WIC, food stamps, school meals); monitoring access problems in federal food programs; operate dinner program for senior citizens in 2 school facilities; dinner program at Community Kitchen of West Harlem

Major publications: Newsletter: *Community Food News*; reports on access to federal food programs

Budget: $1,800,000

Funding: Foundations, government grants for our direct service programs

Staff: 46
3 Direct Service Project Managers
2 Advocates
1 Executive Director
1 Administrative Assistant
1 Organizer
1 Bookkeeper/Accountant
Direct Service Staff

Staff openings/year: 0-5

Work Week: 40 hours

Salary/year: $22,000 (Recent College Graduate); $Varies (Graduate with advanced degree)

Benefits: Health insurance, life insurance, paid vacation

Part-Time Employees: Yes

Interns: None currently, but willing to accept applications

Jobs advertised: Newspapers

To apply: Contact Kathy Goldman, Executive Director

COMMUNITY FOR CREATIVE NON-VIOLENCE

425 Mitch Snyder Place, NW
Washington, DC 20001
(202) 393-1909

Purpose: CCNV is an activist community that views the breaking of bread with the victims of injustice as a responsibility born of faith. CCNV sees an equivalent need to resist the forces of injustice which victimize everyone and to demand responsibility and accountability.

Methods of operation: Human services (30%), community organizing (20%), direct action (20%), public education (20%), lobbying (10%)

Constituency: Homeless and formerly homeless activists, advocates and providers

Recent issues and projects: Recent projects include: Family Shelter Campaign; Federal Voting Rights for Homeless citizens (HR1457); computerized case management; computerized college correspondence courses; hypo/hyper-thermia centers; HUD DC Initiative for the homeless; NEA writers workshop site

Major publications: *Housing and Homelessness: A Teaching Guide*; *An Activist Guide to Managing the Media*

Budget: $800,000

Funding: Individual contributions (60%), foundations (40%)

Staff:
All are full-time resident volunteers

Staff openings/year: Varies

Work Week: 30-50 hours

Benefits: Housing, board

Part-Time Employees: None

Summer Employees: None

Volunteers: Yes

Interns: 12
Length: Semester or summer program
Duties: General building maintenance, campaign work, research, special projects
Remuneration: Room and board

Jobs advertised: Directories, bulletins, networking

To apply: Contact Karyn A. Cassella, Volunteer/Intern Coordinator

---

COMMUNITY INFORMATION EXCHANGE

1029 Vermont Avenue, NW, Suite 710
Washington, DC 20005
(202) 628-2981

Director: Kathy Desmond

Purpose: National nonprofit information service

that meets the need of urban and rural community-based groups for reliable, in-depth information on strategies and resources for community development.

Methods of operation: Information provision and technical assistance (60%), research (25%), publications (15%)

Constituency: 50% are grassroots community development organizations; the other half a mix of public and private sector agencies and organizations, such as universities, church programs, foundations, libraries, etc.

Recent issues and projects: We focus on innovations and trends in physical and economic renewal of disadvantaged communities. We continue to expand our databases, provide the latest news in community development, and help communities to "network."

Major publications: The Exchange publishes a quarterly report focusing each issue on a different community development strategy. We also produce monthly newsletters. We now also offer subscriptions to our databases.

Budget: $400,000

Funding: Government (100%)

Staff: 6
4 Researchers/Technical Assistance Experts
1 President
1 Administrator

Staff openings/year: 1

Work Week: 35 hours

Salary/year: $27,500 (Recent College Graduate); $35,000 (Graduate with advanced degree)

Benefits: Health insurance, life insurance, paid vacation, family leave, pension

Summer Employees: No

Interns: 1
Length: 1 year or less
Duties: Research, writing
Remuneration: None

Jobs advertised: Direct mail announcements to college placement offices, and to newsletters in our field

To apply: Contact Kathy Desmond, Director

COMMUNITY INFORMATION RESOURCE CENTER

P.O. Box 42663
Tucson, AZ 85733
(602) 577-2187

Director: Thomas H. Greco, Jr.

Purpose: The Community Information Resource Center (CIRC) is a networking hub, information source and gateway to resources, bringing people together and fostering the development of healthy communities. Our goal is to empower people through networking, mutual support, information access, training and organizing.

Methods of operation: Training and technical assistance (35%), public education (20%), research (20%), community organizing (15%), publications (10%)

Constituency: Self-help, mutual aid, social action, organizations, groups

Recent issues and projects: Workshops in on-line communication. Establishing a computer bulletin board for community use. Helped organize the Tucson Community Land Trust.

Major publications: *The Straw Bale Test Summary Report*

Budget: $20,000

Funding: Individual contributions (40%), fees (40%), foundations (20%)

Staff:
Volunteer Staff

Volunteers: Several

Interns: None at this time, willing to accept applications

To apply: Contact Thomas Greco, Director if you are willing to volunteer. There are no paid positions at this time.

Remarks: CIRC is a project of NEST, Inc. which serves as a tax exempt umbrella for a variety of community improvement projects. CIRC and NEST are relatively new and developing along non-traditional lines. We are not following the pattern of client/service provider; we are all peers.

UNITY JOBS: THE EMPLOYMENT NEWSPAPER FOR THE NON-PROFIT SECTOR

50 Beacon Street, 4th Floor
Boston, MA 02108
(617) 720-5627

Director: Jim Clark, Executive Director

Purpose: *COMMUNITY JOBS* is published 12 times a year by ACCESS: Networking in the Public Interest. The paper prints job and internship listings for nonprofit organizations throughout the country. In addition, it provides information of interest to people who have or wish to have a career in nonprofit work, such as stories on people who have created their own innovative nonprofit, resource lists, reviews of books and other news. ACCESS' mission is to make possible greater participation, innovation, collaboration and diversity in public and community service.

Methods of operation: Publications (50%), outreach to nonprofits (20%), other (30%)

Constituency: Job-seekers, nonprofit organizations looking for staff and students seeking internships

Recent issues and projects: ACCESS provides a number of other services helpful to job-seekers, including the *Non-Profit Organization Search* and the *Public Service Minority Resume Bank.*

Major publications: *COMMUNITY JOBS*; *Opportunities in Public Interest Law*; *Opportunities in State Government*

Budget: $800,000

Funding: Grants, subscriptions

Staff: 11
1 Executive Director
1 Director of Operations
1 National Outreach Director
1 Marketing and Advertising Director
1 Managing Editor
1 Art Director
1 Office Manager, National Office
1 Southern Regional Director
1 Midwestern Regional Director
1 Western Regional Director
1 DC Regional Director

Staff openings/year: 2

Work Week: 40 hours

Salary/year: $20-25,000 (Recent College Graduate); $25-50,000 (Graduate with advanced degree)

Benefits: Health insurance, paid vacation (2 weeks)

Part-Time Employees: 12

Volunteers: 1

Interns: 5
Length: 3 months or more
Duties: Varies; assist different staff in their work

Jobs advertised: In *COMMUNITY JOBS*

To apply: Contact Susan Bumagin, Director of Operations

COMMUNITY LEGAL AID SOCIETY, INC.

913 Washington Street
Wilmington, DE 19801
(302) 575-0660

Director: Judith A. Schuememeyer

Purpose: To provide high quality legal services in civil (non-criminal) matters to people who have low-incomes (up to 125% of poverty level) or are age 60 and over who have no other means of assistance.

Methods of operation: Legal services (80%), public education (10%), training and technical assistance (10%)

Constituency: Members of the Delaware legal community and others interested in equal access to justice

Recent issues and projects: Recent projects include: prison conditions suit; lead paint in public housing suit; community development, assistive technology for people with disabilities

Budget: $2,232,240

Funding: Federal funds (62%), foundations (21%), individual contributions (10%), direct mail (7%)

Staff: 56
19 Attorneys
16 Paralegals
3 Office Managers
13 Administrative Assistants
2 Bookkeepers/Accountants
1 Director of Finance
1 Computer Coordinator and Support Services
1 Development and Public Relations Coordinator

Staff openings/year: 4-6

Work Week: 35 hours

Salary/year: $24,000 (Recent College Graduate); $Varies (Graduate with advanced degree)

Benefits: Health insurance, pension, paid vacation, life insurance, dental insurance, family leave

Part-Time Employees: 6

Summer Employees: 3 law clerks

Volunteers: 5

Interns: 3
Length: Semester
Duties: Research, screening clients, investigations
Remuneration: Stipend or work study

Jobs advertised: Law schools, newspapers, local bar associations, law libraries, legal clearinghouse

To apply: Please contact Claire Clark

COMMUNITY NUTRITION INSTITUTE

2001 S Street, NW, Suite 530
Washington, DC 20009
(202) 462-4700

Director: Rodney Leonard

Purpose: CNI is a nonprofit consumer interest group that functions as a public advocate for safe food and health policies. Our weekly newsletter, *Nutrition Week*, reports on research and policy developments in food and nutrition, hunger and homelessness, agriculture, and other issues that affect consumers and society.

Methods of operation: Publications (80%), direct action (15%), lobbying (5%)

Constituency: Health professionals, food and nutrition providers and policymakers

Recent issues and projects: *Nutrition Week* has followed closely the debate on cholesterol. Other issues: aspartame, BST, revision of beef and poultry inspection, aflatoxin, alar.

Major publications: Newsletter: *Nutrition Week*; Nutrition Service Providers Guides; *Programs To Help Older People Eat Better*; Food Service Management Brochures; *Commonsense Organizing for the Long Haul*; *Creative Recreation and Socialization for Senior Citizen Centers*

Funding: Subscriptions (97%), foundations (3%)

Staff: 6
1 Writer/Editor
1 Editorial Assistant
1 Circulation Director
1 Executive Director
1 Administrative Director
1 Project Manager

Staff openings/year: 0-1

Work Week: 40 hours

Salary/year: $Varies (Recent College Graduate); $Varies (Graduate with advanced degree)

Benefits: Health insurance, life insurance, pregnancy leave, paid vacation

Part-Time Employees: 1

Interns: 3-4/year
Length: Flexible
Duties: Editing, writing, researching stories, clerical duties
Remuneration: Small stipend available

Jobs advertised: Mainly in *Nutrition Week* and other nutrition journals

To apply: Contact Sheila Foley, Administrative Director

COMMUNITY ORGANIZING AND TRAINING DEPARTMENT OF THE C.Y.O.

Catholic Youth Organization, 305 Michigan Avenue
Detroit, MI 48226
(313) 963-7174

Director: Suzanne Heath

Purpose: To work with disadvantaged and struggling Detroit neighborhoods to revitalize and enhance people's ability to solve problems, develop their own leadership, and build strong, representative organizations.

Methods of operation: Community organizing (60%), training and technical assistance (35%), research (5%)

Constituency: Primarily low to moderate income; city of Detroit residents; volunteers interested in revitalizing their own communities through group action

Recent issues and projects: Target Area Grassroots Organizing Project develops new groups and strengthens existing organizations to revitalize the community through effective volunteer involvement and group action. Customized training is offered to groups in the Tri-County area to meet their specific organizing or development needs. Demonstration Projects: organized two alternative dispute resolution centers. Implemented a youth volunteer project to develop skills to avoid drug abuse; assisted a group in developing economic survival plans.

Budget: $370,000

Funding: Foundations (99%), fees (1%)

Staff: 7
5 Organizers
1 Administrative Assistant
1 Department Director

Staff openings/year: 1

Work Week: 40 hours

Salary/year: $14,000 (Recent College Graduate); $17,000 (Graduate with advanced degree)

Benefits: Health insurance, life insurance, pregnancy leave (unpaid), pension, credit union, paid vacation, tax deferred savings, adjustable work schedule, time off for overtime worked, professional union

Part-Time Employees: 1

Summer Employees: Yes, as needed

Volunteers: Yes

Interns: Yes
Length: 3 months
Duties: Regular staff organizing responsibilities
Remuneration: Reimbursement for job-related expenses; other arrangements/stipends can be negotiated

Jobs advertised: Announcements at colleges; *Community Jobs*; newspapers; word of mouth

To apply: Contact Suzanne Heath, Department Director

COMMUNITY TRAINING AND RESOURCE CENTER

47 Ann Street, 6th Floor
New York, NY 10038-2515
(212) 964-7200

Director: Anne Pasmanick

Purpose: Train tenant organizers; research housing and tenant rights issues; serve as a clearinghouse for tenant, housing and community organizations

Methods of operation: Training and technical assistance (35%), research (35%), publications (15%), public education (15%)

Constituency: Tenants and tenant rights advocates; neighborhood and community activists

Recent issues and projects: Run school for housing organizers; publish tenant rights fact sheets; analysis of loss of housing in New York City affordable to low-income persons and families; analysis of effects of co-op/condo conversions

Major publications: *Worlds Apart: Housing, Race/Ethnicity and Income in New York City, 1978-1987* (1989); *The New Redlining: A Study of Bank Branch Closings in New York City 1977-1984* (1986); numerous fact sheets

Budget: $225,000

Funding: Foundations (85%), government (15%)

Staff: 5
1 Executive Director
1 Director of Training
1 Issue Expert
1 Office Manager
1 Researcher

Staff openings/year: 1

Work Week: 50 hours

Salary/year: $20,000 (Recent College Graduate); $22,500 (Graduate with advanced degree)

Benefits: Health insurance, life insurance, paid vacation; we are exploring establishing a retirement plan

Part-Time Employees: 1

Volunteers: 3-5

Interns: 2-3
Length: Varies: usually 2-3 months
Duties: Research
Remuneration: Varies

Jobs advertised: Different sources depending on type of skills being sought

To apply: Contact Anne Pasmanick, Executive Director

COMMUNITY TRANSPORTATION ASSOCIATION OF AMERICA

1440 New York Ave, NW, Suite 440
Washington, DC 20005
(202) 628-1480

Director: David Raphael

Purpose: CTAA is a national, professional membership association of organizations and individuals committed to removing barriers to isolation and to improving mobility for all people. CTAA conducts research, provides technical assistance, offers educational programs, and serves as an advocate in order to make coordinated community transportation services available, affordable, and accessible. CTA members see mobility as a basic human right. Public transportation can equalize opportunity for people to go to work, seek training and education, obtain necessary medical care, shop and remain independent. Mobility is critical to full participation in a democratic society.

Methods of operation: Training and technical assistance (63%), publications (25%), research (12%)

Constituency: Transit operators, human service agencies, consultants, industry supplies, state transportation offices

Recent issues and projects: Helps operate the National Rural Transit Assistance Program; Sponsors the annual Community Transportation Expo; provides financing and technical assistance to rural transportation providers through its Rural Transit Investment Program

Major publications: Monthly magazine: *Community Transportation Reporter*; monthly membership newsletter: *CTAA Express*

Staff: 23
9 Project Managers
2 Writers/Editors
1 Executive Director
1 Deputy Director
2 Bookkeepers/Accountants
2 Information Specialists
6 Support Staff

Staff openings/year: 3

Work Week: 37.5 hours

Salary/year: $19,000

Benefits: Health insurance, life insurance, pension, paid vacation, sick leave

Jobs advertised: Local newspaper; professional journals

To apply: Contact David Raphael, Executive Director

CONCERN, INC.

1794 Columbia Road, NW
Washington, DC 20009
(202) 328-8160 fax (202)387-3378

Director: Susan Boyd

Purpose: Concern, Inc. is a nonprofit, tax-exempt organization. It provides environmental information to community groups, public officials, educational institutions, private individuals, and many others involved in public education and policy development. Its goal is to help communities find solutions to environmental problems that threaten public health and the quality of life.

Methods of operation: Research (60%), publications (40%)

Membership: Have contributing members

Recent issues and projects: Environmental research and publication of community action guides on drinking water, farmland waste, household waste, pesticides and global warming.

Major publications: *Drinking Water: A Community Action Guide*; *Farmland: A Community Issue*; *Waste: Choices for Communities*; *Household Waste: Issues and Opportunities*; *Global Warming and Energy Choices*; *Pesticide in our Communities*; *Choices For Change*

Budget: $100,000

Funding: Foundations (80%), individual contributions (20%)

Staff: 5
5 full-time, 2 volunteer:
3 Researchers
2 Writers/Editors
1 Office Manager
1 Foundation Fundraiser

Work Week: 20 hours

Benefits: Paid vacation

Part-Time Employees: 7

Summer Employees: 1-2

Volunteers: 2

Interns: 1-2
Length: Varies
Duties: Research and office duties
Remuneration: $75 per week

Jobs advertised: Only internships advertised in university career offices and bulletin boards

To apply: Contact Darragh Lewis

CONCORD FEMINIST HEALTH CENTER

38 South Main Street
Concord, NH 03307
(603) 225-2739

Purpose: To provide health care to women in a feminist model.

Methods of operation: Human services (90%), publications (5%), public education (2%), direct action (1%), lobbying (1%), community organizing (1%)

Constituency: Varied; women mostly 18-25 years in age; all economic and racial backgrounds

Major publications: *Womenwise Quarterly*

Budget: $750,000

Funding: Direct services

Staff: 16
13 Health Workers
  GYN Healthworkers
  Abortion Healthworkers
2 Outreach Healthworkers
1 Writer/Editor

Staff openings/year: 1-2

Work Week: 30-40 hours

Salary/year: $Varies (Recent College Graduate); $Varies (Graduate with advanced degree)

Benefits: Health insurance, pregnancy leave, child care, paid vacation

Interns: Yes
Length: Irregular
Remuneration: None

Jobs advertised: Local newspapers

To apply: Contact the Health Center

CONGRESS WATCH

215 Pennsylvania Avenue, SE
Washington, DC 20003
(202) 546-4996

Director: Pam Gilbert

Purpose: The legislative advocacy arm of Public Citizen, a consumer and environmental organization founded by Ralph Nader. Congress Watch represents the public through lobbying, organizing, research and publications.

Methods of operation: Research (30%), lobbying (30%), community organizing (20%), public education (20%)

Constituency: Consumers, taxpayers across the country

Recent issues and projects: Mounted national drive for campaign finance reform and for congressional accountability. Fought to establish a national health insurance program, and to oppose efforts to weaken product liability laws. Launched a national campaign to warn of the detrimental impact on environmental, health and safety regulations posed by the NAFTA and GATT trade agreements. Opposed a new wave of bank deregulation.

Major publications: *Government Service for Sale: How the Revolving Door Has Been Spinning*; *Voodoo Accounting: The Toll of President Bush's Regulatory Moratorium*; *On the Road Again: An Analysis of Privately Funded Travel by Members of the U.S. Senate During the 102nd Congress*

Budget: $1,000,000

Funding: Foundations (30%), direct mail (50%), publication sales (10%), individual contributions (10%)

Staff: 18
5 Organizers
6 Lobbyists
4 Researchers
1 Director
1 Office Manager
1 Receptionist

Staff openings/year: 1-5

Work Week: 55 hours

Salary/year: $16,000 (Recent College Graduate); $21,000 (Graduate with advanced degree)

Benefits: Health insurance, pension, paid vacation, credit union

Part-Time Employees: 1

Volunteers: Yes

Interns: 3-6
Length: 10 weeks
Duties: Research, writing, monitoring legislation, office work
Remuneration: Unpaid

Jobs advertised: Postings with other organizations and at schools; advertisements

To apply: Send resume and writing sample to Director, Public Citizen's Congress Watch.

CONNECTICUT CITIZEN ACTION GROUP
45 South Main
West Hartford, CT 06107
(203) 561-6006

Other Offices: Storrs, CT

Director: Tom Swan

Purpose: CCAG, the state's largest citizen organization, brings people together to work on the community and statewide issues that concern them, developing their skills and knowledge, doing the research and lobbying that it takes to win. CCAG works to inform the public, train grassroots leaders, win on issues, build coalitions, elect citizen leaders, forge a national citizens' movement and expand grassroots financing.

Methods of operation: Public education (25%), lobbying (25%), community organizing (15%), electoral (10%), research (10%), training and technical assistance (10%), direct action (5%)

Membership: We have over 100,000 members which consists of families in Connecticut.

Recent issues and projects: Passage of auto insurance reform; establishing comprehensive, universal health insurance for Connecticut residents; lead paint poisoning prevention; campaign finance reform.

Major publications: Newsletters; *Annual Legislative Voting Index*; *Recycling Handbook*

Budget: $1,100,000

Funding: Canvassing (37%), telephone solicitation (41%), foundations (13%), individual contributions (7%), other (2%)

Staff: 15
2 Field Canvass Directors
5 Organizers
1 Co-Director
1 1/2 Telephone Canvass Directors
1 Computer Operators
1 Associate Director
1 Bookkeeper/Accountant
1 Financial Manager
1 Lobbyist
1 Master Donor Solicitor
15-80 Canvassers
10-20 Telephone Canvassers

Staff openings/year: 5

Work Week: 40 hours

Salary/year: $16,000

Benefits: Health insurance, pregnancy leave, credit union, paid vacation, $1500 salary increase for dependent children

Part-Time Employees: 20

Summer Employees: 80

Volunteers: Yes

Interns: 6
Length: 3 months
Duties: Organizing, research, political campaigns, grassroots fundraising
Remuneration: Paid interns canvass their salaries

Jobs advertised: Local newspapers

To apply: Contact Phil Young for canvass; Rosie Stanko for telephone canvass; Lynne Ide for organizing; and Judy Maslen for other positions

Remarks: Field canvassing and telephone canvassing are the entry level jobs at CCAG. Most other positions are filled internally. Canvassers can become interns or canvass directors, and then can move into other positions in the organization from there. Canvassers earn $1000/month.

CONNECTICUT FUND FOR THE ENVIRONMENT
1032 Chapel Street
New Haven, CT 06510
(203) 787-0646

Other Offices: Hartford, CT

Director: Donald S. Strait, Esq.

Purpose: CFE takes legal action for enforcement of environmental law, helps develop environmental policy for Connecticut and provides free legal and scientific advice to citizens about environmental issues.

Methods of operation: Litigation (40%), research (15%), lobbying (15%), public education (15%), publications (10%), community organizing (5%)

Constituency: Environmentally concerned citizens of Connecticut

Recent issues and projects: Helped citizens address a hazardous waste site in Norwalk; saved 16 acres of intertidal flats in Clinton Harbor from destruction by a developer; submitted comments to the state on the site selection plan for low-level radioactive waste disposal facility

Major publications: Quarterly newsletter; various educational materials on household hazardous chemicals and alternatives; *How to Make Compost* and other waste reduction brochures; *Gardening Without Pesticides*

Budget: $370,000

Funding: Individual contributions (59%), foundations (32%), special events, attorney fees (9%)

Staff: 7
2 Attorneys
1 Policy Analyst
1 Administrative Assistant
1 Executive Director
1 Office Manager
1 Membership Assistant

Staff openings/year: 0

Work Week: 40 hours

Salary/year: $16,000 (Recent College Graduate); $18,000 (Graduate with advanced degree)

Benefits: Health insurance, pregnancy leave, paid vacation

Volunteers: Yes

Interns: Yes
Length: Summer
Duties: Law interns
Remuneration: Yes

Jobs advertised: Newspaper and colleges

To apply: Contact Michael Stein, Staff Attorney

CONNECTICUT PUBLIC INTEREST RESEARCH GROUP (CONNPIRG)

300 Summit Street, Box 6000
Hartford, CT 06106
(203) 233-7554

Other Offices: Norwalk, CT; New Haven, CT; Storrs, CT; West Hartford, CT

Director: Kirsten Dunton

Purpose: Statewide nonprofit, nonpartisan environmental and consumer advocacy group.

Methods of operation: Lobbying (40%), public education (25%), research (20%), community organizing (10%), publications (5%)

Membership: 44,000 citizen members; 14,000 student members

Recent issues and projects: Hazardous waste cleanup; Campaign to Save Long Island Sound; clean air; toxics use reduction; pesticides; product safety; recycling

Major publications: Quarterly newsletter: *Citizen Agenda*; *Commitment to Cleanup* (February 1988); *Permit to Pollute* (October 1989); *Still More Permits to Pollute* (November 1989); *Exhausting Our Future* (March 1989); *Toxics Use Reduction: From Pollution Control to Pollution Prevention* (February 1989, with National Toxics Campaign); *ATVs and Children: Still at Risk* (October 1989); *The Treacherous Ten: Unsafe Toys* (November 1989)

Budget: $175,000

Funding: Canvassing (50%), telephone solicitation (25%), campus (25%)

Staff: 10
4-10 Canvass Directors
3 Organizers
1 Lobbyist
1 Office Manager
50-100 Canvassers
1 Campaign Director

Staff openings/year: 3-5

Work Week: 55-65 hours

Salary/year: $14,500-17,000

Benefits: Health insurance, paid vacation, college loan assistance

Part-Time Employees: Yes

Summer Employees: Yes

Volunteers: Yes

Interns: Yes
Length: Semester, summer
Duties: Research, organizing
Remuneration: For-credit internships

Jobs advertised: Newspapers; job postings; on-campus interviews

To apply: Contact Kirsten Dunton

CONNECTICUT WOMEN'S EDUCATION & LEGAL FUND

135 Broad Street
Hartford, CT 06105
(203) 247-6090

Director: Leslie Brett

Purpose: To work through legal and public policy strategies and community education to end sex discrimination and empower all women to be full and equal participants in society.

Methods of operation: Public education (35%), training and technical assistance (30%), publications (10%), human services (10%), research (7%), community organizing (5%), lobbying (3%)

Recent issues and projects: The Fund works with state officials, legal practitioners, scholars and activists to address public policy issues that affect women and their families. We conduct research, file amicus curiae (friend of the court) briefs, testify in legislative hearings and provide consulting and technical assistance.

Major publications: *Divorce in Connecticut*; *Do Your Divorce in Connecticut*; *Child Support in Connecticut: How to Secure What Your Child Needs*; *Sexual Harassment in the Workplace*; *Pregnancy, Family and Medical Leave in Connecticut*

Budget: $400,000

Funding: Contracts (30%), foundations (30%), individual contributions (25%), corporations (15%)

Staff: 6
1 Office Manager
1 Researcher
1 Fundraiser
1 Issue Expert
1 Administrative Assistant
1 Caseworker

Work Week: 35 hours

Benefits: Health insurance, paid vacation

Part-Time Employees: 4

Summer Employees: None

Volunteers: 2

Interns: 3
Length: 1 Semester
Duties: Implementing projects, assisting people seeking legal information

Jobs advertised: Newspapers, community organizations

To apply: Contact Tracey McDougall, Administrative Director

CONSCIENCE AND MILITARY TAX CAMPAIGN

4534 1/2 University Way, NE, Suite 204
Seattle, WA 98105
(206) 547-0952

Director: Gen Parrish and Vivien Sharples, Co-Coordinators

Purpose: We are a war tax resistance organization. We currently administer the largest escrow account of refused military and war taxes in the world. We organize public events concerning war tax, and offer tax counseling and workshops. We also lobby for passage of the Peace Tax Fund Bill.

Methods of operation: Administering escrow account (50%), publications (30%), public education (20%)

Constituency: Primarily war tax resisters and peace movement

Recent issues and projects: Direct Aid Project - redirects refused war taxes to humanitarian projects in Central America. Escrow Account for a Peace Tax Fund - an insured Savings and Loan account to allow resisters a supportive and politically powerful vehicle in which to place the war tax dollars.

Major publications: Quarterly: *Conscience*

Budget: $30,000

Funding: Interest of escrow account (60%), individual contributions (30%), direct mail (10%)

Staff: 2
Part-time staff includes:
2 Editors

Staff openings/year: 1

Work Week: 30 hours

Salary/year: $9,600

Benefits: Pregnancy leave, paid vacation

Part-Time Employees: Yes

Volunteers: 5

Interns: Yes

Jobs advertised: Through our own publication, plus local and national alternative press

To apply: Contact Gen Parrish or Vivien Sharples

CONSERVATION INTERNATIONAL

1015 18th Street, NW, Suite 1000
Washington, DC 20036
(202) 429-5660

President: Russell Mittermeier

Purpose: Conservation International is dedicated to the protection of natural ecosystems and the species that rely on these habitats for survival.

Methods of operation: Research, publications, public education, training and technical assistance

Recent issues and projects: Recent projects include: Non-timber rainforest products; ecotourism; sustainable timber harvesting; bio-diversity prospecting; conservation priority workshops; geographic information system; and debt swaps

Major publications: *Members Report*; *Debt for Nature Monograph*

Funding: Membership

Staff: 100
Including:
2 Attorneys
2 Office Managers
8 Researchers
8 Foundation Fundraisers
3 Administrative Assistants
3 Bookkeepers/Accountants
20 Scientists/Biologists
8 Public Affairs/Education
2 Writers/Editors

Staff openings/year: 3-6

Work Week: 40 hours

Salary/year: $22,000

Benefits: Health insurance, paid vacation, life insurance, credit union, family leave, board, tuition reimbursement

Part-Time Employees: 2

Summer Employees: 5-10

Volunteers: 3-5

Interns: 10-20
Length: 1 - 12 months
Duties: Depends on department
Remuneration: Varies

Jobs advertised: *Washington Post*

To apply: Contact Don Wynne

CONSERVATION LAW FOUNDATION, INC. (CLF)

62 Summer Street
Boston, MA 02110-1008
(617) 350-0990 (Fax) 617-350-4030

Other Offices: Rockland, ME; Montpelier, VT

Director: Douglas I. Foy, Executive Director

Purpose: CLF is a nonprofit, public interest environmental law organization founded in 1966. Our staff of attorneys, scientists, and policy specialists use law to improve resource management, environmental protection, and public health throughout New England. From courtrooms to town halls, CLF confronts the critical environmental issues facing the region, which include conserving natural habitats, open space, and agricultural lands; improving urban environments; protecting marine resources; reducing environmental threats to human health; preventing water and air pollution; and developing environmentally sound and economically efficient energy, water use, and transportation policies.

Membership: 5,000 members

Recent issues and projects: Settled Central Artery case in Boston, MA, a landmark case which provides a model for the future of multimodal transportation policies which will reduce automobile travel, promote mass transit and contribute to cleaner air; signed agreements with New England utilities to invest in energy conservation; awarded, with New England Electric System (NEES) the President's Environmental and Conservation Challenge Award, the nation's highest environmental honor. Currently working with New England's fishing community to address the environmental need for, and the economic implications of, restoring New England's disappearing groundfish stock; also intervening in the relicensing of hydroelectric dams on major rivers in NE.

Major publications: Quarterly newsletter. Send for publication listing of reports and articles on water, land, energy, transportation and public health work.

Budget: $2,700,000

Funding: Foundations, membership, individual contributions

Staff: 29
12 Attorneys
11 Administrative Staff
3 Scientists
3 Membership/Public Education

Staff openings/year: 2

Work Week: 40 + hours

Salary/year: $Varies (Recent College Graduate); $Varies (Graduate with advanced degree)

Benefits: Full-time: life, LTD and health insurance, paid vacation, family leave. Part-time: negotiated based on % of hours worked. Volunteers/Interns: small transportation and meal stipend. Internships are for academic credit.

Part-Time Employees: 8

Volunteers: 9

Interns: Law and graduate science students
Length: 1 semester
Duties: Vary
Remuneration: Graduate students unpaid; course credit or work-study available

Jobs advertised: Newspapers, trade papers and on-campus

To apply: Send resume with cover letter to Lois Conley, Volunteer Coordinator or Bridget Chase, Director of Individual Giving.

CONSORTIUM ON PEACE RESEARCH, EDUCATION, AND DEVELOPMENT (COPRED)

George Mason University, 4400 University Drive
Fairfax, VA 22030
(703) 323-2806

Director: Barbara J. Wien

Purpose: COPRED is a nonprofit, membership organization which fosters research and education in the areas of peace and conflict resolution.

Constituency: Peace educators, activists, researchers, advocates

Recent issues and projects: 1993 Conference "Nonviolence In a Violent World"; *Conflict Resolution Resource Directory*; *Peace Studies Directory*; *Peace Education Packet* for K-12 teachers

Major publications: *Peace Chronicle* newsletter; *Peace and Change* journal

Budget: $80,000

Funding: Individual contributions (95%), other (5%)

Staff: 3
1 Director
2 Interns

Work Week: 40 hours

Salary/year: $Varies (Recent College Graduate); $Varies (Graduate with advanced degree)

Part-Time Employees: 2

Summer Employees: Yes

Volunteers: Yes

Interns: None

To apply: Contact Barbara Wien, Director

CONSTITUTIONAL RIGHTS FOUNDATION

601 South Kingsley Drive
Los Angeles, CA 90005
(213) 487-5590

Director: Todd Clark

Purpose: The Constitutional Rights Foundation seeks to instill in our nation's youth a deeper understanding of citizenship through values expressed in our Constitution and its Bill of Rights, and educate them to become active and responsible participants in our society. CRF is dedicated to insuring our country's future by investing in our youth today.

Methods of operation: Training and technical assistance (70%), publications (20%), research (5%), public education (5%)

Constituency: Educators, lawyers, business organizations

Recent issues and projects: Recent projects include: Youth Summit/Violence Reduction; CityYouth/Police and Community Relations; Active Citizenship Today Summer Training Institutes on Service Learning; law-related education

Major publications: *Criminal Justice in America*; *Reviewing the Verdict*; *The Drug Question*; *Police Patrol*; *We the Jury*; *Letters of Liberty*; *Foundations of Freedom*; *Of Codes and Crowns*; *School Youth Service Network*, newsletter; *Bill of Rights in Action*, newsletter

Budget: $4,000,000

Funding: Government/materials sales (49%), foundations (36%), individual contributions (15%)

Staff: 37
5 Writers/Editors
5 Administrative Assistants
1 Office Manager
1 Press Aides
3 Foundation Fundraisers
2 Bookkeepers/Accountants
15-20 Trainers/Educators

Staff openings/year: 3-4

Work Week: 40-50 hours

Salary/year: $20,000 (Recent College Graduate); $30,000 (Graduate with advanced degree)

Benefits: Health insurance, pension, paid vacation, life insurance, family leave

Part-Time Employees: 2

Summer Employees: None

Volunteers: Yes

Interns: None, but willing to accept applications

Jobs advertised: Newspapers, networking with other nonprofits

To apply: Contact Helen Kwon, Personnel Manager

CONSTITUTIONAL RIGHTS FOUNDATION
601 South Kingsley Drive
Los Angeles, CA 90005
(213) 487-5590

Director: Todd Clark

Purpose: Constitutional Rights Foundation seeks to instill in our nation's youth a deeper understanding of citizenship through values expressed in our Constitution and its Bill of Rights, and educate them to become active and responsible participants in our society. CRF is dedicated to assuring our country's future by investing in our youth today.

Methods of operation: Training and technical assistance (70%), publications (20%), public education (5%)

Constituency: Educators, lawyers, business organizations

Recent issues and projects: Recent issues include: Youth Summit/Violence Reduction; City Youth/Police and Community Relations; Active Citizenship Today Summer Training Institutes on Service Learning; and law related education

Major publications: *Criminal Justice in America*; *Reviewing the Verdict*; *The Drug Question*; *Police Patrol*; *We the Jury*; *Letters of Liberty*; *Foundations of Freedom*; *Of Codes and Crowns*; *School Youth Service Network*; *Bill of Rights In Action*

Budget: $4,000,000

Funding: Government/materials sales (49%), foundations (36%), individual contributions (15%)

Staff: 40
5 Writers/Editors
1 Office Managers
1 Press Aides
3 Foundations Fundraisers
5 Clerical Support Staff
2 Bookkeepers/Accountants
15-20 Trainers/Educators

Staff openings/year: 3-4

Work Week: 40-50 hours

Salary/year: $20,000 (Recent College Graduate); $30,000 (Graduate with advanced degree)

Benefits: Health insurance, pension, paid vacation, family leave

Part-Time Employees: 2

Summer Employees: None

Volunteers: None

Interns: None, but willing to accept applications

Jobs advertised: Newspapers; networking with other non-profits

To apply: Please contact Helen Kwon, Office/Personnel Manager

CONSUMER ACTION
116 New Montgomery Street, Suite 223
San Francisco, CA 94105
(415) 777-9648

Director: Ken McEldowney

Purpose: To educate and advise the public about consumers' rights through a telephone consumer line, publications and advocacy for consumer rights in public hearings.

Methods of operation: Publications (40%), research (23%), public education (20%), direct action (5%), training and technical assistance (5%), human services (5%), lobbying (2%)

Recent issues and projects: Major emphasis currently on the banking and telephone industries with outreach efforts targeted to the immigrant and low-income populations throughout California.

Major publications: *The CA Newsletter*, which conducts and publishes surveys on banking and telephone issues; *The Consumer Services Guide*; miscellaneous pamphlets on banking and telephone issues; fact sheets on telephone issues published in 3 languages

Funding: Individual contributions, grants

Staff: 13
3 Organizers
3 Researchers
2 Writers/Editors
2 Staff Support
1 Office Manager
2 Issue Experts

Staff openings/year: 1

Work Week: 40 hours

Salary/year: $22,000-25,000 (Recent College Graduate); $23,000-28,000 (Graduate with advanced degree)

Benefits: Health insurance, life insurance, pregnancy leave, paid vacation

Volunteers: Yes

Interns: 1
Length: 1 semester-1 year
Duties: Public relations, survey assistant
Remuneration: None

Jobs advertised: Community groups

To apply: Contact Ilene Shaw, Administrator

CONSUMER EDUCATION & PROTECTIVE ASSOCIATION INTERNATIONAL, INC. (CEPA)

6048 Ogontz Avenue
Philadelphia, PA 19141
(215) 424-1441

Director: Lance Haver

Purpose: Education in regard to economic problems faced by consumers, protection of consumers against fraud, combatting rising cost of living, etc. Redress of consumer grievances by three-step process: investigate, negotiate, demonstrate.

Methods of operation: Public education (50%), direct action (50%)

Constituency: All consumers

Recent issues and projects: Auto insurance; subway and bus increases; increasing utility rates

Major publications: *Consumers Voice*

Budget: $25,000

Funding: Members and other individual contributions (100%)

Staff:
All volunteer

Volunteers: 7 full-time

Interns: None currently, but willing to accept applications
Remuneration: No financial commitment

Jobs advertised: Contact Lance Haver

CONSUMER ENERGY COUNCIL OF AMERICA RESEARCH FOUNDATION

2000 L Street, NW, Suite 802
Washington, DC 20036
(202) 659-0404 (fax) 202-659-0407

Director: Ellen Berman

Purpose: CECA/RF, the senior public interest energy policy organization in the United States, has served as a leading national resource for information, analysis and technical expertise on the social and economic impacts of a wide variety of energy and environmental policies. Additionally, CECA/RF has a unique and highly respected expertise in forging successful partnerships among public and private sector organizations, industry, state and local organizations, businesses, utilities, consumers, environmentalists and government agencies.

Methods of operation: Research (40%), publications and public education (60%)

Constituency: Public and private sector organizations, industry, state and local organizations, businesses, utilities, consumers, environmentalists and government agencies.

Recent issues and projects: CECA/RF is currently conducting a project integrating transportation policies to energy and the environment. Recent past projects include studies of environmental externalities issues and of air pollution emissions trading under the Clean Air Act Amendments of 1990. CECA recently performed studies on transmission siting and certification issues, including electromagnetic field effects and are conducting ongoing studies on the economics of conversion from oil to gas for home heating. In 1992, CECA launched a monthly newsletter, *The Quad Report*, which focusses on the linkage between demand-side management, energy efficiency and energy policy on the environment. CECA/RF publishes quarterly *The Quad Special Report* with unique studies.

Major publications: *Incorporating Environmental Externalities Into Utility Planning: Seeking A Cost-Effective Means of Assuring Environmental Quality*; *Oil, Gas, or...?*; *A Compendium of Utility Sponsored Energy Efficiency Rebate Programs*; *Bidding for Power: Competition, the Commission and the Consumer*; *Heat Pump Versus Alternative Space Conditioning Systems*

Budget: $500,000

Funding: Organizational contributions, contracts

Staff: 8
2 Researchers
1 Issue Expert
2 Writers/Editors
1 Office Manager
1 Foundation Fundraiser
1 Typist

Staff openings/year: 2-3

Work Week: 40 hours

Salary/year: $Varies (Recent College Graduate); $Varies (Graduate with advanced degree)

Benefits: Health insurance, pension, paid vacation

Part-Time Employees: 2

Interns: 2-4
Length: 10 weeks
Duties: Assist in research projects, publications, database management, writing, editing and general office duties.
Remuneration: Unpaid, some stipends available. Travel reimbursement possible.

Jobs advertised: Newspapers, periodicals, university listings

To apply: Send resume with grade point average, 2 writing samples, and three references with phone numbers to Intern Coordinator.

CONSUMER FEDERATION OF AMERICA

1424 16th Street, NW, Suite 604
Washington, DC 20036
(202) 387-6121

Director: Stephen Brobeck

Purpose: CFA is an advocacy, education and membership organization which works to advance pro-consumer policy on a variety of issues before Congress, regulatory agencies and the courts.

Methods of operation: Advocacy (50%), education (25%), member services (25%)

Membership: Member organizations include grassroots consumer groups, senior citizen organizations, labor unions, cooperatives, and other national, state and local public interest organizations.

Recent issues and projects: CFA works in the areas of telecommunications, financial services, health and safety, energy, indoor air quality and product liability.

Major publications: *CFAnews*; *Indoor Air News*; *Consumer Product Safety Newsletter*; *Annual Congressional Voting Record*; *Directory of State and Local Consumer Organizations*; and a variety of studies and testimony in our issue areas

Budget: $1,200,000

Funding: Members (30%), sale of services (30%), other (40%)

Staff: 14
6 Advocates
4 Educators
4 Administrators

Staff openings/year: 2

Work Week: 40 hours

Salary/year: $High teens (Recent College Graduate); $Mid twenties (Graduate with advanced degree)

Benefits: Health insurance, paid vacation, severance pay

Part-Time Employees: 4

Interns: 3
Length: 1 semester
Duties: Legislative/research aide; assistant to conference manager
Remuneration: Unpaid

Jobs advertised: *Washington Post* and public interest network

To apply: For positions contact Ann Lower, Assistant Director; for internships contact Mary Ponder

CONSUMER INFORMATION CENTER

P.O. Box 1449, 718 State Street (walk-ins)
Springfield, MA 01101
(413) 737-4376

Director: Jean Courtney

Purpose: The Consumer Information Center is funded by the Attorney General's Office to assist the consumers from Hampden and Hampshire County community in the area of consumer affairs. This agency handles consumer/business negotiations in the areas of automobile purchases and repairs, retail advertisement, purchases and returns, consumer credit and landlord/ tenant.

Methods of operation: Human services (80%), public education (10%), direct action (8%), research (2%)

Constituency: Includes the Massachusetts Attorney General's Office, local legislators and nonprofit community service agencies

Recent issues and projects: Elder education program: brings consumer information pertaining to elders to the elder community; Used Vehicle Express Warranty Law Seminar - program to educate used car dealers on the provisions of the recently passed M.G.L.C. 90 7N 1/4; Massachusetts Housing Investigation - utilizing caseworkers to investigate discrimination against families with children in the Hampden County Area

Major publications: Informational bulletins on recently passed legislation which affects consumers

Funding: Massachusetts Attorney General's Office (100%)

Staff: 1
1 Director

Staff openings/year: 2

Work Week: 40 hours

Benefits: Health insurance, paid vacation, pregnancy leave

Part-Time Employees: 3

Summer Employees: 1

Volunteers: 4

Interns: 6
Length: 1 semester or full school year
Duties: Caseworker, responsible for case intake and management, consumer/business mediation and consumer advice
Remuneration: Work-study

Jobs advertised: College and law school placement offices

To apply: Contact Jean Courtney, Director

Remarks: This agency is primarily staffed by trained volunteers and student interns. The degree of dedication of the staff is high and consistent. New volunteers who have these qualities are always welcome.

CONSUMER MEDIATION CLINIC OF GEORGE WASHINGTON UNIVERSITY

720 20th Street, NW, Suite SL101
Washington, DC 20052
(202) 775-8567

Director: Carol Izumi, Esq.

Purpose: CMC of George Washington University provides a free dispute resolution service for residents of the greater Washington, DC metropolitan area, including suburban Virginia and Maryland, who are having a dispute with a local business. Mediators help the parties negotiate a mutually agreeable solution.

Methods of operation: Direct action (100%). Also provide referrals if it is not possible to help.

Constituency: Consumers in DC metropolitan area

Recent issues and projects: All kinds of consumer cases: auto sales and service, defective products, mail order problems, credit reporting and billing errors, debt collection harassment, home improvement contractors, etc.

Funding: George Washington University (100%)

Staff: 4
1 Attorney
3 Student Directors

Work Week: 40 hours

Salary/year: $27,000 (Graduate with advanced degree)

Benefits: Health insurance, pension, tuition benefits, paid vacation

Volunteers: 15-20 caseworkers

Interns: 5-7
Length: 8-12 weeks during the summer
Duties: Intake, referrals, mediation of assigned cases, attend seminar
Remuneration: No compensation

Jobs advertised: In education and legal publications

To apply: Contact Carol Izumi, Supervising Attorney

CONSUMERS UNION

256 Washington Street
Mount Vernon, NY 10553
(914) 378-2000

Other Offices: Washington, DC; San Francisco, CA; Austin, TX

Director: Rhoda H. Kerpatkin

Purpose: Consumers Union, publisher of *Consumer Reports*, is a nonprofit organization established in 1936 to provide consumers with information and advice on goods, services, health and personal finance and to initiate and cooperate with individual and group efforts to maintain and enhance the quality of life for consumers.

Methods of operation: Research, lobbying, litigation, publications, community organizing, direct action, public education, training and technical assistance

Constituency: Consumers nationwide

Recent issues and projects: Three public interest law offices represent the consumer interest by initiating lawsuits; commenting on proposed government actions; testifying at legislative and regulatory proceedings; and petitioning government agencies to initiate certain actions.

Major publications: Magazines: *Consumer Reports*; *Penny Power*, a consumer magazine for children. Newsletters: *Consumer Reports Travel Letter*; *Consumer Reports Health Letter*; *Consumer Reports New Digest.* Books: publish approximately 30 books each year. Send for a complete list of publications.

Budget: $76,000,000

Funding: Publication sales (90%), individual contributions and foundations (10%)

Staff: 348
Including:
Writers/Editors
Attorneys
Office Managers
Researchers
Administrative Assistants
Bookkeepers/Accountants
Engineers
Managers

Staff openings/year: 10

Work Week: 35 hours

Benefits: Health insurance, life insurance, pregnancy leave, pension, credit union, paid vacation, tuition reimbursement, sick leave, dental insurance, optical care plans

Part-Time Employees: Yes; few

Summer Employees: Yes; few

Volunteers: Yes; few

Interns: Yes; few
Length: 1 semester
Duties: Vary according to need

Jobs advertised: *New York Times*; Gannett newspaper; *Consumer Reports*

To apply: Contact Josephine Lerro in the Mount Vernon, NY Office

COOPERATIVE RESOURCES AND SERVICES PROJECT (CRSP)

3551 White House Place
Los Angeles, CA 90004
(213) 738-1254

Director: Lois Arkin

Purpose: We are an education, training and development center for small ecological cooperatives and communities. Our major focus is the Los Angeles Eco-Village Demonstration.

Methods of operation: Training and technical assistance (5%), program development (75%), publications (5%), public education (5%), community organizing (10%)

Constituency: Income, age and ethnically diverse. All have an interest in some aspect of cooperatives, ecology and communities.

Recent issues and projects: Local Exchange Trading System (LETS): 3rd party computerized barter system of 150 members. Ecological Revolving Loan Fund (ELF): seed capital fund for ecological co-ops. Ecological Urban Village: retrofit of inner city neighborhood for sustainability.

Major publications: Newsletter: *L.A. Eco-Village and Co-Op Networker*

Budget: $25,000

Funding: Memberships (25%), individual contributions (25%), special events, forums (25%), publications (25%)

Staff:
All volunteer, including:
Architects
Farmers
Graphic Designers
Urban Planners
Organizers
Researchers
Administrators
Computer Exports
Anthropologists
Youth Workers
Teachers

Benefits: Possible board and housing

Volunteers: Yes

Interns: Yes
Length: Varies
Duties: Diverse; matched to person
Remuneration: Volunteer

Jobs advertised: Our newsletter

To apply: Contact Lois Arkin, Executive Director

COOPERATIVE URBAN MINISTRY CENTER, INC. (CUMC)

1418 Ninth Street, NW
Washington, DC 20001
(202) 232-4928

Director: Patricia Makin, Executive Director

Purpose: The purpose of CUMC is to help the poor and homeless of D.C. in providing for their basic needs, while at the same time incorporating the principle of self-help into its work and, wherever possible, helping clients to work toward independence and self-sufficiency.

Methods of operation: Human services (100%); operates as a day drop-in center

Membership: 19 area churches (interdenominational)

Recent issues and projects: We provide emergency food, clothing, shower and laundry facilities, counseling, self-help groups, mail and message services, information and referral, and a Saturday morning breakfast.

Budget: $246,800

Funding: Foundations; member churches, individual contributions, United Way, business, civic and other organizations

Staff: 3
1 Support Staff
1 Executive Director
1 Executive Assistant

Staff openings/year: 1

Work Week: 40 hours

Salary/year: $Varies (Recent College Graduate); $Varies (Graduate with advanced degree)

Benefits: Health insurance, paid vacation

Volunteers: Yes; 4-6 w/ stipend

Interns: None currently, but willing to accept applications
Remuneration: Stipend

Jobs advertised: Newspaper; word of mouth

To apply: Contact Patricia Makin, Executive Director

CORELLA AND BERTRAM F. BONNER FOUNDATION

P.O. Box 712
Princeton, NJ 08542
(609) 924-6663

Director: Wayne Meisel

Purpose: The Foundation was created to help the person who is hurting. Current programs include the Bonner Scholars Program and Crisis Ministry, a food bank and soup kitchen and an outreach program which provides matching grants.

Methods of operation: Direct action (30%), training and technical assistance (20%), grant administration (50%)

Constituency: Students attending college with high financial need.

Recent issues and projects: The Bonner Scholars Program offers financial support to students from low-income backgrounds who want to attend college and provides them with an opportunity to engage in community service activists while in school. This program is available at 22 participating colleges.

Budget: $8,000,000

Funding: Foundations (100%)

Staff: 8
1 Office Manager
2 Program Director
1 Executive Director
2 Program Associates
2 Staff Assistants

Staff openings/year: 1

Work Week: 40 hours

Salary/year: $20,000 (Recent College Graduate); $21,000 (Graduate with advanced degree)

Benefits: Health insurance, pension, paid vacation, life insurance

Part-Time Employees: None

Summer Employees: None

Volunteers: None

Interns: None

Jobs advertised: Local newspaper, career services offices

To apply: Please contact Elaine Wheeler, Office Manager

COUNCIL FOR A LIVABLE WORLD/EDUCATION FUND/PEACE PAC

110 Maryland Avenue, NE, Suite 409
Washington, DC 20002
(202) 543-6297 (Fax) 202-543-6297

Director: John Isaacs

Purpose: Council for a Livable World and Peace PAC are political action committees and lobbying organizations that raise funds for Senatorial and Congressional candidates, respectively, who have shown leadership in the campaign for nuclear arms control. The Council is dedicated to nuclear arms control, reducing the military budget and educating both the public and Congress about the threat of nuclear war. The Council lobbies vigorously to influence Congress to support its cause. CLW Education Fund seeks to educate the public on the effects of nuclear weapons/war and analyze the military budget.

Constituency: Supporters tend to be well-educated liberals

Recent issues and projects: Public education on the START Treaty; the Education Fund has a media project to introduce to the national news media peace viewpoints; working to get an international chemical weapons treaty signed and ratified; working for 50 percent cuts in the military budget over the next 5 years; handle support mailings for candidates

Major publications: Bimonthly newsletters; article reprints; candidate profiles; fact sheets; congressional voting records; briefing books

Budget: $1,500,000

Funding: Individual contributions, foundations

Staff: 12
3 Lobbyists
3 Researchers
1 Development Director
1 Assistant Development Director
1 Technical Director
1 Bookkeeper
1 Arms Trade Analyst
1 Office Manager

Staff openings/year: 2

Work Week: 40 hours

Salary/year: $15,000 (Recent College Graduate); $Varies (Graduate with advanced degree)

Benefits: Health insurance, child care, paid vacation

Part-Time Employees: 1-2

Summer Employees: 1

Volunteers: 2

Interns: Yes
Length: 3 months
Duties: Writing and research
Remuneration: Usually unpaid; small stipends for those with financial need

Jobs advertised: Among peace groups; local colleges

To apply: In the Boston office, contact Rosalie Anders; in the DC office, contact John Isaacs

Remarks: The Boston office generally handles the administrative work needed to comply with federal election, IRS, and lobbying laws. Our DC office tends to provide a more challenging internship experience; 110 Maryland Avenue, NE, Suite 211, Washington, DC 20002; (202) 543-4100.

COUNCIL FOR CONCERNED CITIZENS

1601 2nd Avenue North, 2nd Floor
Great Falls, MT 59403
(406) 727-9136

Other Offices: Billings, MT

Director: Toni Austad

Purpose: Eliminate poverty and discrimination through education and the protection and defense of civil and human rights as guaranteed by law. Our focus is on housing discrimination, particularly as it impacts Native Americans.

Methods of operation: Direct Action (30%), Human Services (40%), Community Organizing (5%), Research (5%), Training and Technical Assistance (20%)

Recent issues and projects: 1) Model education and outreach project to Native Americans for fair housing; 2) Fair Housing - Fair Lending education and enforcement; 3) Safe, affordable housing and renter advocacy; 4) Gender equity to eliminate sexism.

Major publications: Quarterly Newsletter, Annual Report

Budget: $150,000

Funding: Federal/State/Local contracts and grants (80%), memberships (5%), settlements (15%)

Staff: 4
1 Director
2 Local Fair Housing Coordinators
1 Education and Outreach Coordinator

Work Week: 20-60 hours

Salary/year: $Varies (Recent College Graduate); $Varies (Graduate with advanced degree)

Benefits: Paid vacation, sick leave, health insurance

Part-Time Employees: 3

Volunteers: 2

Interns: Yes
Duties: Projects vary
Remuneration: Financial assistance to interns is limited

Jobs advertised: Native American organizations, Colleges, Statewide media, Job Service and others.

To apply: Contact Toni Austad

COUNCIL FOR RESPONSIBLE GENETICS

5 Upland Road, Suite 3
Cambridge, MA 02140
(617) 868-0878

Director: Nachama L. Wilker

Purpose: The Council for Responsible Genetics (CRG) is a national organization of scientists and others dedicated to ensuring that biotechnology is developed safely and in the public interest. The Council believes that an informed public can and should play a leadership role in setting the direction of emerging technologies.

Methods of operation: Public education (40%), training and technical assistance (40%), publications (15%), research (5%)

Constituency: Scientists, public health advocates, trade unionists, women's health activists, environmentalists, others

Recent issues and projects: The Council's work is concentrated in three major areas: preventing the militarization of biological research; countering discrimination based on information generated by predictive genetic tests; and expanded public participation in decisions about the release of genetically altered organisms into the environment

Major publications: The CRG publishes *GENEWATCH*, the only bulletin that covers social and ethical issues in biotechnology. We have also recently completed a biotech reader for college courses.

Budget: $150,000

Funding: Foundations (80%), individual contributions (20%)

Staff: 1
1 Managing Editor (part-time)

Staff openings/year: 1

Work Week: 45-50 hours

Salary/year: $18,000

Benefits: Health insurance, pregnancy leave, paid vacation

Part-Time Employees: 2

Volunteers: 10

Interns: Yes
Length: 2 months
Duties: Varied depending on individual and needs

of organization
Remuneration: Unpaid

Jobs advertised: Local papers; nonprofit job boards in Boston; policy positions also listed in *Community Jobs* and *The Nation*

To apply: Contact Nachama L. Wilker, Executive Director

COUNCIL OF NEW YORK LAW ASSOCIATES (CNYLA)

99 Hudson Street
New York, NY 10013
(212) 219-1800

Director: Allen Bromberger

Purpose: Low-income housing development, neighborhood preservation; legal services to nonprofit organizations. CNYLA is the only source of corporate, tax and real estate legal services available on a pro bono basis to community development organizations in New York City. CNYLA provides these services through an in-house staff of 9 attorneys and a roster of over 400 volunteers from 117 law firms in the city.

Methods of operation: Training and technical assistance, publications, direct action, fundraising, volunteer placement

Constituency: Attorneys; nonprofit organizations

Major publications: *Advising Nonprofits*; *Getting Organized*

Budget: $700,000

Funding: Individual contributions, foundations

Staff: 16
8 Attorneys
2 Typists
1 Paralegal
1 Office Manager
1 Foundation Fundraiser
1 Bookkeeper/Accountant
1 Pro Bono Clearinghouse Coordinator
1 Receptionist

Staff openings/year: 4-5

Work Week: 40-50 hours

Salary/year: $25,000

Benefits: Health insurance, life insurance, pregnancy leave, pension, paid vacation, dental insurance

Part-Time Employees: 3

Summer Employees: 3-4

Volunteers: 1

Interns: 3-4
Length: 3-4 months (summer)
Duties: Law student interns assist attorneys on research and writing projects
Remuneration: Stipends

Jobs advertised: Organizational newsletter; newspapers; nonprofit listings

To apply: Contact Allen Bromberger, Executive Director

COUNCIL ON ECONOMIC PRIORITIES

30 Irving Place
New York, NY 10003
(212) 420-1133

Director: Alice Tepper Marlin

Purpose: To monitor corporate behavior as it relates to social issues and to study conversion from a military to a civilian-based economy. To enhance the incentives for better corporate performance in the areas of energy, conservation, the environment, workplace conditions and fair employment practices.

Methods of operation: Research (50%), publications (25%), public education (25%)

Membership: 5,500 members nationally

Major publications: *Shopping for A Better World*, the pocket guide to socially responsible supermarket shopping; *Conversion Information Center*; *Ethical Investing*, book; *Students Shopping For A Better World*

Budget: $1,400,000

Funding: Foundations (40%), earned income (30%), individual contributions (25%), direct mail (5%)

Staff: 17
2 Researchers
4 Secretaries/Assistants
2 Marketing/Membership
1 Executive Director/Issue Expert
5 Project Directors
1 Office Administrator
1 Accountant
1 Foundation Fundraiser

Staff openings/year: 1-2

Work Week: 40+ hours

Salary/year: $17,000 (Recent College Graduate); $20,000-40,000 (Graduate with advanced degree)

Benefits: Health insurance, life insurance, family leave, pension (after 3 years), paid vacation, tuition reimbursement

Part-Time Employees: 4

Volunteers: Yes

Interns: Yes; up to 12
Length: 3 months
Duties: Research, fact checking, etc.
Remuneration: $100/week undergraduates; $125/week graduates; $150/week Everett Public Service Program

Jobs advertised: Career guidance offices; nonprofit network; *New York Times* ads. We receive many unsolicited resumes and often hire from them.

To apply: Contact Sheila Ratner, Administrative Director

COUNCIL ON HEMISPHERIC AFFAIRS

724 9th Street, NW, Suite 401
Washington, DC 20001
(202) 393-3322

Director: Larry Birns

Purpose: COHA is a nonprofit, tax-exempt independent research and information organization, founded in 1975 to promote the common interests of the hemisphere, raise the visibility and increase the importance of the inter-American relationship, and encourage the formulation of rational and constructive U.S. policies toward Latin America and Canada. COHA subscribes to no specific political credo nor does it maintain political allegiances. It supports open and democratic political processes, just as it condemns authoritarian regimes that fail to provide their populations with even the minimal standards of political freedoms, social justice and civic guarantees.

Methods of operation: Research (50-60%), publications (40-50%)

Constituency: Our subscribers are varied - embassies, university libraries, academicians, other Latin American organizations, journalists, writers, socialist minded activists

Major publications: Biweekly *Washington Report on the Hemisphere*; *News and Analysis*, 2-3 times/week

Funding: Individual contributions, foundations

Staff: 5
2-3 Writers/Editors
1 Office Manager
30 Interns

Staff openings/year: 3-4

Work Week: 40-50 hours

Salary/year: $10,500

Part-Time Employees: 1-2

Summer Employees: Yes

Interns: Up to 30
Length: 4 months
Duties: Research, monitoring conferences, writing for our publications, covering specific issues in Congress, general office work
Remuneration: No monetary compensation is available

Jobs advertised: At schools; other publications, such as *Good Works*; word of mouth

To apply: Contact Intern Coordinator

Remarks: Interns at COHA participate in all aspects of the research, writing, and publication of our materials. Part-time internships can be arranged so interns can have a second job. Paid staff positions generally are offered only to those who have interned at COHA.

COUNCIL ON THE ENVIRONMENT OF NEW YORK CITY (CENYC)

51 Chambers Street, Room 228
New York, NY 10007
(212) 788-7900

Director: Lys McLaughlin

Purpose: CENYC, a privately funded citizens' organization in the Office of the Mayor, was formed in 1970 to promote environmental awareness among New Yorkers and develop solutions to environmental problems.

Recent issues and projects: (1) Open Space Greening Program helps community gardeners plant and care for trees, flowers and bushes, and create and maintain gardens and other green spaces; (2) Training Student Organizers Program - high school students in the five boroughs worked with TSO staff to protect wetlands, analyze New York City's waste stream, abate noise pollution, clean up our coasts and conserve energy and other environmental projects; (3) Greenmarket brings fresh and varied farm produce to New Yorkers and preserve regional farmland

Budget: $2,269,499

Funding: Foundations, individuals/corporations, government, fees and other revenues

Staff openings/year: 3-4

Work Week: 40 hours

Salary/year: $Varies (Recent College Graduate); $Varies (Graduate with advanced degree)

Volunteers: Yes

Interns: 3-5 per year
Length: Primarily in summer
Duties: Urban horticulture, waste reduction, sustainable agriculture, publicity assistant, etc.
Remuneration: Unpaid, academic credit possible

To apply: For internships and volunteer positions, contact Jennifer Hansell, Assistant Director.

COVERT ACTION INFORMATION BULLETIN

1500 Massachusetts Ave., Suite 732
Washington, DC 20005
(202) 331-9763

Other Offices: New York, NY

Purpose: *Covert Action* is a quarterly publication devoted to exposing the illegal intelligence activities of the U.S. government.

Methods of operation: Publications (70%), research (20%), public education (10%)

Constituency: Primarily progressives who are politically active, with interests in U.S. foreign policy

Recent issues and projects: Special issues of the magazine expose George Bush's connection to the CIA, domestic surveillance and the religious right.

Major publications: *Covert Action Information Bulletin*

Budget: $70,000

Funding: Subscriptions, store sales

Staff: 6
4 Writer/Editors (2 paid/2 volunteer)
1 Office Manager
1 Researcher (volunteer)

Staff openings/year: 0-1

Work Week: 40 hours

Salary/year: $17,000 (Recent College Graduate); $Varies (Graduate with advanced degree)

Benefits: Health insurance, paid vacation, transportation

Volunteers: Yes

Interns: None currently, but willing to accept applications

Jobs advertised: Word of mouth

Remarks: The address of the New York, NY office is: 145 West 4th Street, New York, NY 10012.

CRITICAL MASS ENERGY PROJECT OF PUBLIC CITIZEN

215 Pennsylvania Avenue, SE
Washington, DC 20003
(202) 546-4996

Director: Bill Magavern

Purpose: Critical Mass works to oppose nuclear power and to promote safer energy alternatives, particularly energy efficiency and renewable energy technologies. Work includes the publication of numerous studies, working with the media and citizen groups nationwide, lobbying and litigation.

Methods of operation: Research (25%), publications (25%), administrative (20%), public education (10%), lobbying (5%), litigation (5%), community organizing (5%), training and technical assistance (5%)

Constituency: Work closely with safe energy citizen groups nationwide, national and local media, members of Congress and other elected and appointed government officials.

Recent issues and projects: Stopping the Nuclear Regulatory Commission from deregulating radioactive waste; lobbying Congress to kill the Advanced Liquid Metal Reactor; researching the environmental impacts of motor vehicles and campaigning for increased fuel efficiency standards; supporting a shift in energy funding from nuclear and fossil to renewables and efficiency; investigating safety and economic problems at atomic reactors and promoting public participation in nuclear regulation.

Major publications: Quarterly newsletter, *Critical Mass*; *Nuclear Lemons: An Assessment of America's Worst Commercial Nuclear Power Plants*; *The Dark at the End of the Tunnel: Federal Clean-up Standards for Nuclear Power Plants*; *Energy Audit II: A State-by-State Profile of Energy Consumption and Conservation*

Budget: $200,000

Funding: Direct mail (60%), foundations (30%), publications (5%), individual contributions (5%)

Staff: 5
1 Director
3 Policy Analysts
1 Researcher/Administrative Assistant

Staff openings/year: 1

Work Week: 55 hours

Salary/year: $15,000 (Recent College Graduate); $18,000+ (Graduate with advanced degree)

Benefits: Health insurance, 2 weeks paid vacation, pregnancy leave (after 1 year), pension (after 3 years)

Interns: 2
Length: 2 months minimum
Duties: Researching, writing, general office assistance
Remuneration: Travel reimbursed; stipend sometimes offered

Jobs advertised: Notices sent to most national and local safe energy groups and to major public interest publications which advertise job opportunities (e.g. *Community Jobs*)

To apply: Send resume to Director

CULTURAL FORECAST

1818 Brickyard Hollow Road
Montague Center, MA 01351
(413) 367-9526 Fax: (413) 367-2671

Director: Rob A. Okun

Purpose: To produce journals, events, educational programs and exhibits examining social issues primarily through the visual arts

Methods of operation: Public education (60%), publications (20%), research (20%)

Constituency: Artists, students, activists, general public, educators

Recent issues and projects: Producing journals for the Web DuBois Foundation, North Star Fund, Rosenberg Fund For Children as well as producing special events (benefits, concerts, etc.)

Major publications: Book: *The Rosenbergs: Collected Visions of Artists and Writers*, by Rob Okun (Universe Books/St. Martin's Press, 2nd edition); Film: *Unknown Secrets*

Budget: $75,000

Funding: Direct mail (50%), book sales, speaking engagements (40%), foundations (10%)

Staff: 2
1 Writer/Editor
1 Office Manager

Work Week: 35 hours

Salary/year: $Varies (Recent College Graduate); $18,000 (Graduate with advanced degree)

Summer Employees: 1

Interns: 1
Length: 6 months-1 year
Duties: Varied

Jobs advertised: Job placement councils

To apply: Contact the office for openings.

CULTURAL SURVIVAL, INC.

215 First Street
Cambridge, MA 02142
(617) 621-3818

Director: Alexander H. See

Purpose: Advocates for the rights of indigenous peoples and ethnic minorities. Supports programs on five continents, as well as direct assistance projects designed and run by indigenous peoples; conducts research and produces publications dealing with the vital issues confronting these populations.

Methods of operation: Direct action (30%), training and technical assistance (20%), publications (20%), community organizing (20%), research (5%), public education (5%)

Recent issues and projects: We are currently working on two projects: multi-media data base documenting diversity of world's peoples; and Indigenous Peoples Tour - October 1993. CS's field programs help endangered peoples develop their organizations and secure land rights, manage natural resources and participate in the market economy.

Major publications: *Cultural Survival Quarterly*

(quarterly magazine); *State of the Peoples*, report on the present situation of indigenous peoples world wide

Budget: $1,500,000

Staff: 16
4 Writers/Editors
2 Attorneys
3 Office Managers
2 Researchers
2 Foundation Fundraisers
3 Bookkeepers/Accountants

Staff openings/year: 1

Work Week: 40 hours

Salary/year: $17,000 (Recent College Graduate); $Varies (Graduate with advanced degree)

Benefits: Health insurance, paid vacation

Part-Time Employees: No

Summer Employees: No

Volunteers: 5

Interns: 10
Length: 1 month to a semester
Duties: Besides general support in the office, interns participate in public relations, fundraising, membership, recordkeeping and pub. distribution
Remuneration: None

Jobs advertised: Newspapers, other organizations

To apply: Contact Janet McGowan, Personnel Coordinator or Pia Maybury-Lewis, Internship Coordinator

DAKOTA RESOURCE COUNCIL AND DRC EDUCATION PROJECT

P.O. Box 1095
Dickinson, ND 58602
(701) 227-1851

Other Offices: Jamestown, ND

Director: Julie Ruplinger

Purpose: The Dakota Resource Council is concerned with protecting the food producing resources of North Dakota from unsound energy and agricultural policies. The Council is dedicated to the preservation of the rural community and its economy. DRC seeks to empower North Dakotans to take an active role in the decision-making processes which affect their lives by participating at public meetings, by research and investigation, and by public education.

Methods of operation: Community organizing (50%), research (25%), direct action (10%), public education (10%), lobbying (5%)

Constituency: Farmers, ranchers, and other concerned individuals

Recent issues and projects: Input on the 1990 Farm Bill before Congress; education of the public on the monopoly power involved in the meat packing industry; groundwater protection and education; Clean Air Act reauthorization; local area's permit fight against a coal mine on their land; education and legislation for proper surface land reclamation; research and education on horizontal drilling problems and correlative rights of owners

Major publications: Newsletter: *Dakota Counsel*; *Groundwater* booklet; *Eroding the Family Farm: Agricultural Policy and Stewardship of the Land*; *Are We Polluting the Well? Effect of Ag Chemical Use on Groundwater.* Joint effort with Western Organization of Resource Councils on the following: *Who Owns the West*; *Keeping the Home on the Range*; *For Current and Future Generations: A Comparison of Non-Renewable Natural Resource Taxation*

Funding: Individual contributions, foundations, direct mail

Staff: 5
4 Organizer/Researchers
1 Staff Director (organizer, fundraiser, leadership development, etc.)

Staff openings/year: 1

Work Week: 50 hours

Salary/year: $9,800-13,000 (Recent College Graduate); $13,000 (Graduate with advanced degree)

Benefits: Health insurance, life insurance, paid vacation, professional development/training

Part-Time Employees: 2 administrative

Summer Employees: Yes

Volunteers: 3-5

Interns: None currently, but willing to accept applications

Jobs advertised: Through the North Dakota Job Service, a wide variety of colleges and universities throughout the United States, and in a few national job magazines

DAKOTA RURAL ACTION

Box 549
Brookings, SD 57006
(605) 697-5204

Director: Theresa M. Keaveny

Purpose: (1) Empower low and moderate income people to hold elected officials accountable and change institutions. (2) Preserve family farms and ranches, mainstreet businesses and natural resources. (3) Change state economic development policy.

Methods of operation: Community organizing (50%), public education, publications (15%), direct action (15%), training and technical assistance, research, lobbying (20%)

Constituency: 75% farmers and ranchers; 25% small business, clergy

Recent issues and projects: (1) Groundwater Protection Project; (2) Livestock Concentration Campaign; (3) Economic Development Project; (4) Fair Credit Campaign

Major publications: Monthly newsletter; *Legislative Alert*; fact sheets on projects; *A Balanced Approach to Prosperity in South Dakota for the '90s*

Budget: $160,000

Funding: Foundations (75%), individual contributions, direct mail, canvassing, telephone solicitation, membership (25%)

Staff: 2
1 Staff Director
3 Organizers
1 Intern, full-time

Staff openings/year: 1

Work Week: 40-60 hours

Salary/year: $14,000

Benefits: Health insurance, family leave, pension, paid vacation, disability, paid sick leave, 2 days personal leave annually

Part-Time Employees: 2

Interns: Yes
Length: 1 year
Duties: Work on the Groundwater Protection Project, either tracking bills in the legislature or as project coordinator
Remuneration: Paid $650-1,000/month with insurance, 2 weeks paid vacation, and holidays

Jobs advertised: Area colleges and universities (5 state region); national publications; letters to other public interest organizations

To apply: Contact Theresa M. Keaveny, Staff Director

DANE COUNTY SAVE OUR SECURITY SENIOR COUNCIL

122 State Street, Room 401
Madison, WI 53703
(608) 256-7626

Director: Elizabeth Schuck

Purpose: A grassroots organization which aims to involve senior citizens in the economic and political decision-making processes that affect their lives. We work primarily on issues concerning health care, housing, transportation, social security and utility rates.

Methods of operation: Community organizing (30%), public education (25%), lobbying (15%), human services (10%), publications (10%), direct action (5%), research (5%)

Membership: Our membership is 99% senior citizens who are predominantly low-income.

Recent issues and projects: In the past year we have organized campaigns against doctors overcharging above Medicare's "reasonable rates" and we administered a health care plan for low-income seniors. We also worked for ambulance fee repeal, an increase in Homestead credit funding, an increase in funds for Community Options Program and changes in subsidized housing eligibility.

Major publications: Publish a monthly newsletter for our membership, a brochure about the organization, a brochure about our health care plan and a fact sheet on low-income housing.

Budget: $7,000

Funding: Dues (90%), contributions (10%)

Staff: 1
1 President

Volunteers: 30

Interns: Willing to accept applications

To apply: Contact Elizabeth Schuck

DATACENTER

464 19th Street
Oakland, CA 94612
(510) 835-4692

Director: Fred Goff

Purpose: Public interest organization providing research and information collection on corporations, Third World issues and human rights

Methods of operation: Information search and clipping services (50%), publications (50%)

Constituency: Varied

Recent issues and projects: The DataCenter library includes extensive, specialized archives with over 400 file drawers of well organized documents and articles, more than 3,500 carefully selected books and directories and 500 shelved serial publications. This collection is supplemented by electronic resources to cover all the essential topics of the U.S. and international political economy.

Major publications: *Information Services Latin America (ISLA)*, monthly; *The Plant Shutdowns Directory*, monthly; *The Right to Know*; *Third World Resources Directories*, quarterly journal; and *CultureWatch*, monthly

Budget: $570,000

Funding: Services and publications (50%), foundations (33%), individual contributions (12%), other (5%)

Staff: 12
4 Writer/Editors
3 Researchers
2 Librarians
1 Director
1 Bookkeeper/Accountant
1 Foundation Fundraiser

Staff openings/year: 2

Work Week: 40 hours

Salary/year: $24,000 (Recent College Graduate); $Varies (Graduate with advanced degree)

Benefits: Health insurance, paid vacation, some professional education funding

Part-Time Employees: 4

Volunteers: 20/year

Interns: 1-2
Length: 1 semester
Duties: Information processing and computer work
Remuneration: Work-study; other

Jobs advertised: UC Berkeley Library School; *Community Jobs*; local sources

To apply: Contact Dan Hodge

DC CENTER FOR INDEPENDENT LIVING

1400 Florida Avenue, NE, Suite 3
Washington, DC 20002
(202) 388-0033

Director: Roger Ford

Purpose: To promote the independence of disabled DC residents. We achieve this goal by offering a broad range of independent living services to our participants.

Methods of operation: Human services, training and technical assistance

Constituency: Disabled persons within the District of Columbia proper

Recent issues and projects: Advocating for major legislation concerning persons with disabling conditions: the Americans with Disabilities Act and the Family and Medical Leave Act as well as legislation for long-term health care coverage. Demonstrations for access to public transportation services.

Major publications: *Disabled Washingtonian*; Quarterly newsletter

Budget: $540,036

Funding: Government contract (97.94%), foundations (2%), direct mail (.06%)

Staff: 13
4 Caseworkers
1 Director
1 Program Manager
1 Receptionist
2 Drivers
1 Secretary
1 Executive Secretary
1 Office Manager
1 Bookkeeper/Accountant

Staff openings/year: 1

Work Week: 40 hours

Salary/year: $16,000 (Recent College Graduate); $20,000 (Graduate with advanced degree)

Benefits: Health insurance, pregnancy leave, paid

vacation

Volunteers: Yes

Interns: None currently, but willing to accept applications

Jobs advertised: *Washington Post*; *Washington Times*; throughout the disability community by way of employment agencies, alternative publications

To apply: Contact Roger Ford, Executive Director

Remarks: We are willing to grant any qualified applicant an interview. However, there are some positions that would not be appropriate for an able-bodied person to hold. We strongly promote employment for persons with disabling conditions.

DC RAPE CRISIS CENTER

P.O. Box 21409
Washington, DC 20009
(202) 232-0789 Crisis Hotline (202) 333-7273

Director: Denise Snyder

Purpose: To provide comprehensive services to sexual assault survivors and community education on related issues.

Methods of operation: Human services (45%), public education (45%), training and technical assistance (10%)

Constituency: Anyone living in the Washington, DC metro area; we prioritize low-income and women of color

Major publications: *How to Start a Rape Crisis Center*; quarterly newsletters; publication for young children concerning sexual abuse

Budget: $450,000

Funding: Individual contributions (45%), government contracts (40%) foundations (15%)

Staff: 9
3 Counselors
3 Community Educators
3 Administrative Assistants

Staff openings/year: 1

Work Week: 40 hours

Salary/year: $22,000 (Recent College Graduate); $32,000 (Graduate with advanced degree)

Benefits: Health insurance, pregnancy leave, paid vacation

Volunteers: 120

Interns: 3-4
Length: Usually 2-4 months
Duties: Varied: counseling, education, project organizing
Remuneration: Unpaid

Jobs advertised: Local newspapers; announcements sent to local social justice organizations

To apply: Contact Denise Snyder, Executive Director

DC SERVICE CORPS

1511 K Street, NW Suite 949
Washington, DC 20005
(202) 347-4136

Director: Keith Canty

Purpose: The DC Service Corps is a full-time urban Peace Corps for young people 17-23 years old. DCSC Corpsmembers dedicate a year to furthering their education, developing leadership skills, and making a difference in their community through serving others.

Methods of operation: Human services (50%), direct action (25%), training and technical assistance (25%)

Membership: 100 young people, between the ages of 17 and 23

Recent issues and projects: Training of Corpsmembers to screen elementary school children for reading/sight disorders; and over 5,000 children were screened.

Budget: $1,000,000

Funding: Foundations (30%), National Peace Corps (70%)

Staff: 18
3 Organizers
1 Attorney
1 Office manager
2 Foundation fundraisers
8 Team leaders
1 Deputy director
1 Public information specialist

Staff openings/year: 2 or 3

Work Week: 40 hours

Salary/year: $20,000

Benefits: Health insurance, paid vacation

Summer Employees: Varies

Volunteers: 3

Interns: Varies, up to 100
Length: 3 to 9 months
Duties: Assist in completing the various projects embarked upon
Remuneration: Stipend

Jobs advertised: Newspaper, bulletins, word of mouth

DEFENDERS OF WILDLIFE

1101 14th Street, N.W.
Washington, DC 20005
(202) 659-9510

Other Offices: Sacramento, CA; Missoula, MT; Portland, OR

President: Rodger Schlickeisen

Purpose: Preserve, enhance, and protect the natural abundance and diversity of wildlife, including the integrity of natural wildlife ecosystems.

Methods of operation: Research, lobbying, litigation, publications, community organizing, direct action, public education, training and technical assistance

Recent issues and projects: Endangered species advocacy; litigation and oversight; wildlife refuge protection; marine entanglement; wild bird trade.

Major publications: *Defenders* bimonthly magazine; other reports and publications

Budget: $4,500,000

Funding: Individual contributions, foundations, direct mail, telephone solicitation

Staff: 40

Staff openings/year: 5

Work Week: 40 hours

Benefits: Health insurance, life insurance, pension, tuition reimbursement, paid vacation

Volunteers: Yes; number varies

Interns: Yes; number varies
Length: 3 months
Duties: Assist lobby/issue staff
Remuneration: None

Jobs advertised: Newspapers; word of mouth

To apply: Contact Office Manager

DEFENSE BUDGET PROJECT

777 North Capitol Street, NE, Suite 710
Washington, DC 20002
(202) 408-1517

Director: Andrew Krepinevich

Purpose: To examine (1) the defense budget, especially from a policy perspective; (2) the impact of defense spending on the economy; and (3) the conventional military situation in Europe, and provide these analyses for government, media and others.

Methods of operation: Research (35%), publications (30%), public education (20%), direct action (15%)

Constituency: We mail to a large number of media outlets, fellow researchers, Congressional offices and organizations.

Recent issues and projects: Interalia, major reports on the conventional balance in Europe, the outlook for strategic nuclear forces funding in the 1990s, and the impact of defense spending on the American economy

Major publications: Occasional major reports and more frequent short analyses on timely subjects

Budget: $400,000

Funding: Foundations (100%)

Staff: 6
3 Researchers/Issue Experts/Editors
1 Organizer
1 Foundation Fundraiser
1 Office Manager

Staff openings/year: 1

Work Week: 40+ hours

Salary/year: $Varies (Recent College Graduate); $Varies (Graduate with advanced degree)

Benefits: Health insurance, life insurance, pregnancy leave, pension, paid vacation

Part-Time Employees: 1

Interns: 1-2
Length: Jan-May, June-Aug, Sept-Dec
Duties: Some administrative/clerical; majority of time spent on research, production
Remuneration: $250/week if full-time

Jobs advertised: Notices to comparable organizations; perhaps newspaper ad

To apply: For internships, contact Michael Bryant

DEFENSE FOR CHILDREN INTERNATIONAL-USA

30 Irving Place, 9th Floor
New York, NY 10003
(212) 228-4773

Director: Dorianne Beyer, Esq.

Purpose: DCI-USA works to promote the fundamental human rights of children in the u.S. and in countries where U.S. foreign policy affects the lives of children.

Methods of operation: Research, publications, public education, training and technical assistance

Membership: National membership of child advocates, educators, individuals interested in children's rights

Recent issues and projects: On-going issues include: working for U.S. ratification of the U.N. Convention on the Rights of the child along with implementation of the Conventions standards on state and local levels. Recent study of child welfare/children's rights implications of North American economic integration.

Major publications: *Out of the Equation: Children's Rights and North American Economic Integration*

Budget: $100,000

Funding: Individual contributions (60%), foundations (40%)

Staff: 2
1 Executive Director
1 Executive Assistant

Staff openings/year: 1

Work Week: 40 hours

Salary/year: $20-24,000 (Recent College Graduate); $Varies (Graduate with advanced degree)

Benefits: Health insurance, paid vacation, family leave

Volunteers: 2-4

Interns: 2-4
Length: Varies
Duties: Research, editing, office support
Remuneration: Negotiable

Jobs advertised: Networking, newsletters

To apply: Contact Dorianne Beyer, Executive Director

DEMOCRATIC SOCIALISTS OF AMERICA

180 Varick Street, 12th Floor
New York, NY 10014
(212) 962-0390

Director: Alan Charney

Purpose: A humane social order based on popular control of resources and production, economic planning, equitable distribution, feminism, racial equality and non-oppressive relationships.

Methods of operation: Community organizing (30%), publications (25%), public education (20%), research (10%), direct action (10%)

Membership: 10,000 members in over 40 local chapters across the country

Recent issues and projects: Organizing for single-payer health care system; international solidarity through pre-NAFTA and post-NAFTA organizing; fighting racism through establishing public spaces of dialogue

Major publications: *Democratic Left*, bimonthly newsletter; *Socialist Forum*, a biannual discussion bulletin

Budget: $500,000

Funding: Individual contributions (80%), telephone solicitation (10%), foundations (5%), direct mail (5%)

Staff: 5
1 Organizer
1 Writer/Editor
1 Office Manager
1 Administrative Assistant
1 National Director

Staff openings/year: 50

Work Week: 50 hours

Salary/year: $18,000

Benefits: Health insurance, paid vacation, family leave

Part-Time Employees: None

Interns: 3
Length: 2 months
Duties: Research
Remuneration: Possibly housing and modest stipend

Jobs advertised: *Community Jobs*, local newspapers

To apply: Contact David Glenn

DES ACTION USA

1615 Broadway, Suite 510
Oakland, CA 94612
(510) 465-4011

Director: Nora Cody

Purpose: DES Action represents those exposed to the drug diethylstilbestrol (DES): women given this synthetic estrogen to prevent miscarriage, and the daughters and sons they had. Exposure to DES has created serious health problems for many of these people. DES Action works to identify those exposed, provide medical information and referrals, monitor research and advocate for the DES-exposed.

Methods of operation: Publications (30%), public education (20%), direct action (17%), human services (10%), community organizing (10%), training and technical assistance (10%), lobbying (3%)

Constituency: DES-exposed mothers, daughters and sons in all 50 states

Recent issues and projects: Health provider education: design and distribution of curriculum units about DES to medical and nursing schools. Campaign to restore government funding for the only major scientific research program on effects of DES.

Major publications: Quarterly newsletter: *DES Action VOICE*. Special booklets: *Questions and Answers about DES Exposure*; *Fertility and Pregnancy Guide*; *Reproductive Outcomes for DES Daughters*

Budget: $100,000

Funding: Individual contributions (50.5%), other (22.7%), direct mail (16.4%), foundations (10.4%)

Staff: 3

Work Week: 40 hours

Salary/year: $Varies (Recent College Graduate); $33,000 (Graduate with advanced degree)

Benefits: Health insurance, paid vacation

Part-Time Employees: 2

Volunteers: 100

Interns: None currently, but willing to accept applications

Jobs advertised: Local nonprofit biweekly; *Community Jobs*

To apply: Contact Pat Cody, Program Director

DIRECT ACTION AND RESEARCH TRAINING CENTER, INC. (DART)

137 NE 19th Street
Miami, FL 33132
(305) 576-8020 or (305) 576-8022

Director: John Calkins

Purpose: DART is a private, nonprofit organization established to provide training programs and community organizing services. DART services include: (1) Direct staffing assistance to low and moderate income communities in developing their own powerful community organizations (e.g. PULSE, PACT, JAB); (2) Consulting and training to existing community organizations; (3) Long-term relationship programs to train people to become professional community organizers; (4) Workshops on community organizing skills for community groups, religious institutions, and other agencies.

Methods of operation: Community organizing (50%), training and technical assistance (50%)

Constituency: Organize minority and/or low-income people; 22 member board

Recent issues and projects: (1) The New Organization Development Program - direct staffing to assist in developing local sponsoring committees and initial seed money, securing competent organizing staff, developing effective leadership and identifying community issues. (2) The Consulting Program - establishes ongoing consulting relationships with both new and well-established community organizations. (3) The Internship Program trains people, especially minorities and women, to become professional community organizers. Also workshops and other programs.

Budget: $180,000

Funding: Consulting fees (85%), foundations (15%)

Staff: 3
3 Trainers/Consultants

Staff openings/year: 0-1

Work Week: 60 hours

Salary/year: $Varies (Recent College Graduate);

$Varies (Graduate with advanced degree)

Benefits: Health insurance, pension, paid vacation, workers compensation, unemployment compensation

Part-Time Employees: 1

Interns: 5
Length: 3 months
Duties: On-the-job/classroom training in building powerful community organizations.
Remuneration: DART pays $1,075/month for 3 months.

Jobs advertised: Local groups; colleges; employment agencies; newspaper

To apply: Contact John Calkins, Director

Remarks: If interns are successful, they become organizers for their placement organization at the end of the internship.

DISABILITIES RIGHTS CENTER, INC.

P.O. Box 19
Concord, NH 03302-0019
(603) 228-0432

Director: Donna D. Woodfin

Purpose: To protect and advocate the rights of persons with disabilities through legal representation and systemic advocacy.

Methods of operation: Litigation (60%), training and technical assistance (20%), public education (10%), liaison with other advocacy organizations, legislative advocacy (8%), lobbying (2%)

Constituency: Individuals with developmental disabilities, mental illness and other severe disabilities

Budget: $400,000

Funding: Federal (90%)

Staff: 8
4 Attorneys
2 Paralegals
1 Executive Director
1 Office Manager

Staff openings/year: 1-2

Work Week: 37.5 hours

Salary/year: $18,000 (Recent College Graduate); $23,000 (Graduate with advanced degree)

Benefits: Health insurance, pregnancy leave, paid vacation

Part-Time Employees: 1

Summer Employees: 1

Interns: 1-2
Length: 1 school year
Duties: Research, casework (intake, meetings) as appropriate
Remuneration: Approximately $7.00/hour

Jobs advertised: Weekly bar journal; placement offices; national publications; local newspaper for non-legal positions

To apply: Contact Donna Woodfin, Executive Director, or Ron Lospennato, Legal Director

DISABILITY RIGHTS EDUCATION AND DEFENSE FUND (DREDF)

2212 6th Street
Berkeley, CA 94710
(510) 644-2555

Other Offices: Washington, DC

Purpose: Provide legal advice and representation for people with disabilities and parents of children with disabilities, especially civil rights in regards to school, employment, housing, and educating local, state and national representatives regarding disability

Methods of operation: Training and technical assistance (50%), national policy monitoring (15%), litigation (10%), community organizing (5%)

Constituency: People with disabilities or parents of children with disabilities; others who are interested in disability rights

Major publications: *Disability Rights Newsletter*

Budget: $500,000

Funding: Foundations (25%), Legal Services Trust Fund (4%), individual contributions (23%), attorneys' fees (3%), federal grants (45%)

Staff: 19
6 Attorneys
5 Issue Experts
2 Administrative Assistants
2 Legal Secretaries
1 Lobbyist
1 Receptionist
1 Bookkeeper/Accountant
1 Development Associate

Staff openings/year: 0-2

Work Week: 50 hours

Salary/year: $Varies (Recent College Graduate); $Varies (Graduate with advanced degree)

Benefits: Health insurance, pregnancy leave, paid vacation

Part-Time Employees: None

Summer Employees: 2

Volunteers: Occasional

Interns: 5-10 per semester
Length: Semester
Duties: Law student clerical tasks

Jobs advertised: Through schools

To apply: Contact the office.

DNA-PEOPLE'S LEGAL SERVICES, INC.

P.O. Box 306
Window Rock, AZ 86515
(602) 871-4151

Director: Randolph Barnhouse

Purpose: DNA is an independent nonprofit legal service organization which provides legal representation for low-income members of the Navajo Nation, Hopi Tribe and the San Juan Southern Paiute Tribe. Our goal is to help provide access to justice for members of some of the most impoverished communities in America.

Methods of operation: Litigation (95%), public education (2%), publications (1%), direct action (1%), training and technical assistance (1%)

Constituency: Low-income members of the Navajo Nation, Hopi Tribe and San Juan Southern Paiute Tribe

Recent issues and projects: Recent projects include: Domestic violence initiatives; home ownership initiative; establishment of a protection and advocacy project for Native Americans with disabilities; consumer law initiatives; class actions on jail conditions and reservation landfills

Major publications: *DNA Newsletter*

Budget: $3,500,000

Funding: Government grants (96%), foundations (2%), individual contributions (2%)

Staff: 90
29 Attorneys
1 Paralegal
3 Office Managers
26 Administrative Assistants
3 Bookkeepers/Accountants
18 Tribal Court Advocates

Work Week: 40 hours

Salary/year: $20,000 (Recent College Graduate); $23,000 (Graduate with advanced degree)

Benefits: Health insurance, pension, paid vacation, life insurance, credit union, family leave, tuition reimbursement

Part-Time Employees: 1

Summer Employees: 10

Volunteers: 5

Interns: 5
Length: 1 year
Duties: Tribal court advocate trainees
Remuneration: Minimum wage plus training

Jobs advertised: Newspapers, *Clearinghouse Review*, local bar publications

To apply: Send resume and letter of interest to Randolph Barnhouse, Executive Director

DOCUMENTATION EXCHANGE

P.O. Box 2327
Austin, TX 78768
(512) 476-9841

Director: Jill McRae

Purpose: To provide human rights documentation for refugees seeking political asylum; to contribute to the development of U.S. policies to respect the history and culture of each country and its people; to help North Americans understand the economic, political and social contexts of global events

Methods of operation: Research (40%), publications (25%), training and technical assistance (15%), public education (20%)

Constituency: Primarily pro bono attorneys representing refugees seeking political asylum. Documentation Exchange is a non-membership organization.

Recent issues and projects: Created a National Documentation Project, connecting direct service groups around the U.S. to the Center's human rights database via computer modem, to allow them direct access

Major publications: *The Central America NewsPak* and *Mexico NewsPak*, biweekly publications composed of news articles from major U.S. and Mexican press; A biannual publications catalog and distribution of books on human rights and global political issues

Budget: $250,000

Funding: Individual contributions, foundations, direct mail, fees for service

Staff: 6
1 Executive Director
1 Librarian
1 Documentation Specialist
1 Indexer/Publication Assistant
1 Program Assistant
1/2 Bookkeeper/Accountant
1/2 Editor

Staff openings/year: 1

Work Week: 35 hours

Benefits: Health insurance, pregnancy leave, paid vacation

Part-Time Employees: 3

Volunteers: 4-5

Interns: None currently, but willing to accept applications

Jobs advertised: Posted at the University of Texas, the Institute for Latin American Studies; advertisements in appropriate publications

To apply: Contact Jill McRae, Executive Director

DODGE NATURE CENTER

1795 Charlton Street
West S. Paul, MN 55118
(612) 455-4531

Director: Gregory J. Lee

Purpose: Our primary mission is to provide environmental education for children in grades K-6. To facilitate this mission, we operate a 300 acre nature preserve. We also offer additional nature oriented programs for adults and children.

Methods of operation: Public education (100%)

Membership: Local families and individuals who support our mission and use our center

Major publications: Newsletter 3 times per year; annual report

Budget: $620,000

Funding: Individual contributions (70%), facilities (12%), foundations (5%)

Staff: 11
1 Writer/Editor
1 Office Manager
1 Foundation Fundraiser
4 Interpretive Naturalists
3 Grounds Crew
1 Executive Director

Staff openings/year: 1

Work Week: 40 hours

Salary/year: $17-19,000 (Recent College Graduate); $n/a (Graduate with advanced degree)

Benefits: Health insurance, paid vacation

Part-Time Employees: Varies

Summer Employees: Varies

Volunteers: Varies

Interns: Varies
Length: 3 months
Duties: Assist with teaching and delivery of programs. Other duties as assigned.
Remuneration: Small stipend

Jobs advertised: Major positions advertised in national environmental publications. Other positions advertised locally in papers and with other nature centers.

To apply: For seasonal naturalists contact Dennis Hahn; for internships contact Eloise Dietz

DOLLARS & SENSE MAGAZINE

1 Summer Street
Somerville, MA 02143
(617) 628-8411

Director: Patricia Horn, Jim Goodno

Purpose: *Dollars & Sense* magazine is published six times a year by a collective of economists and journalists. We offer interpretations of current economic events from socialist perspectives.

Methods of operation: Publications (100%)

Constituency: Teachers, community activists, union members, people interested in left economics

Major publications: In addition to the magazine, we publish three annual classroom readers, *Real World Macro* (10th edition) and *Real World*

Banking (2nd edition)

Budget: $210,000

Funding: Subscriptions (40%), individual contributions (35%), book publishing (25%)

Staff: 4
2 Staff Editors/Managers
1 Business Manager
1 Circulation Manager

Staff openings/year: 1

Work Week: 40 hours

Salary/year: $23,000 (Recent College Graduate); $Varies (Graduate with advanced degree)

Benefits: Health insurance, paid vacation

Part-Time Employees: 2

Volunteers: Yes; D&S collective

Interns: 4 per year
Length: 3 months
Duties: Editorial and Business
Remuneration: Work-study accepted

Jobs advertised: Classified ads in *The Nation*, *In These Times*, *Dollars & Sense*, and others; mailings to organizations and individuals

To apply: Contact Betsy Reed

DOME PROJECT, INC.
486 Amsterdam Ave.
New York, NY 10024
(212) 724-1780

Director: Joel Flax

Purpose: To provide educational alternatives and enrichment to youngsters in greatest need: truants, low achievers and court-involved youth.

Methods of operation: Human services (50%), public education (30%), training and technical assistance (20%)

Recent issues and projects: For 20 years, the DOME has operated an alternative junior high school program for at-risk youngsters. Other programs include afterschool and evening activities, such as dance classes, sports, and special trips and events; the Gallery Program, to help students improve their attendance and performance at the intermediate and junior high school level; and the Juvenile Justice Program, designed to make the youth services located throughout the community available as an alternative to incarceration for young people involved in court proceedings.

Budget: $750,000

Funding: Municipal contracts and private fund-raising

Staff: 19
11 Caseworkers/Counselors
5 Teachers
1 Office Manager
1 Foundation Fundraiser
1 Executive Director

Staff openings/year: 2-3

Work Week: 40 hours

Salary/year: $20-22,000 (Recent College Graduate); $26-27,000 (Graduate with advanced degree)

Benefits: Health insurance, paid vacation

Part-Time Employees: 10

Summer Employees: 6

Volunteers: 12

Jobs advertised: We advertise full-time positions in *New York Times* and *Amsterdam News*. Others are advertised in college placement offices and through mailings to other community agencies.

To apply: Contact Jeff Paquette, Acting Executive Director

DORIS DAY ANIMAL LEAGUE
227 Massachusetts Ave., NE, Suite 100
Washington, DC 20002
(202) 546-1761

Director: Holly Hazard

Purpose: The Doris Day Animal League's overriding mission is to reduce the pain and suffering of non-human animals, to encourage the spaying and neutering of companion animals and to increase the public's awareness of its responsibility toward non-human animals through legislative initiatives, public and membership education and programs to require the enforcement of statutes and regulations which have already been enacted protecting animals.

Methods of operation: Lobbying, public education

Recent issues and projects: Since DDAL was founded in 1987, it has worked exclusively to reach these goals by utilizing sources of information, public awareness and educational materials and petitions from the general public to their elected officials. These activities can be summarized in four specific action programs: 1) Development of national, state and local legislation that will minimize the inhumane treatment of animals; 2) Petitions to the President asking for his/her support of protective legislation; 3) Identification and support of innovative state initiatives that will reduce animal suffering; and 4) Networking with other animal protection groups to promote common goals.

Major publications: *Animal Guardian*, newsletter

Budget: $1,500,000

Funding: Individual contributions (100%)

Staff: 5
2 Lobbyists
1 Foundation Fundraiser
1 Administrative Assistant
1 Bookkeeper/Accountant

Staff openings/year: 1

Work Week: 40 hours

Salary/year: $22,000

Benefits: Health insurance, pension, paid vacation, life insurance

Part-Time Employees: None

Summer Employees: None

Volunteers: None

Interns: None, but willing to accept applications

Jobs advertised: Local newspapers

To apply: Contact Holly Hazard, Executive Director

DOWNWINDERS

966 East Wilson Avenue
Salt Lake City, UT 84105
(801) 467-3238

Director: Preston J. Truman, Jr.

Purpose: To act as a watchdog on nuclear and other military-related activities, and to monitor their public health, safety and environmental impacts. Downwinders continues to spearhead the opposition to nuclear testing among downwind residents.

Methods of operation: Research (40%), public education (20%), community organizing (20%), publications (20%)

Constituency: Broad spectrum, from grassroots to scientists and policymakers

Recent issues and projects: Exposing accidental and deliberate releases of radiation from the Nevada Test Site. Defeat of the new biological warfare lab planned for Dugway, Utah. Exposing numerous safety violations at the chemical weapons plant at Dugway, Utah. Currently opposing the Airforce's planned land grab for the Electronic Combat Range.

Major publications: *Testing News*

Budget: $125,000

Funding: Individual contributions (50%), foundations (50%)

Staff: 4
2 Writers/Editors/Researchers
1 Organizer
1 Foundation Fundraiser

Staff openings/year: 1

Work Week: 40 hours

Salary/year: $10,000 (Recent College Graduate); $18,000 (Graduate with advanced degree)

Benefits: Health insurance, tuition reimbursement

Part-Time Employees: 1

Volunteers: 3

Interns: 1
Length: 3 months
Duties: Specific research projects
Remuneration: College/University sponsored

Jobs advertised: Outreach of job selection committee

To apply: Contact Preston Truman, by mail only

DULUTH CITIZENS UTILITY BOARD

1804 E. First Street
Duluth, MN 55812
(218) 724-7712715-392-4955

Director: Peter J. Nickitas

Purpose: Educate and empower Duluth citizen ratepayers to secure efficient utility service at affordable costs.

Methods of operation: Research (25%), public education (25%), community organizing (15%), direct action (15%), lobbying (10%), litigation (5%), publications (5%)

Recent issues and projects: Garbage rate

computation, making city-owned water and gas more user-friendly to low-income citizen ratepayers

Major publications: Quarterly newsletter

Remarks: This organization is very new. We have no employees yet, and our 501(c) application is in the works. We can reach out for new members via 3 monthly inserts in the Duluth Water and Gas bills each year.

EARTH DAY 2000

116 New Montgomery Street, Suite 330
San Francisco, CA 94105
(415) 495-5987

Director: Caroline Harwood

Purpose: Earth Day 2000 is an environmental consumer clearinghouse which informs the public on which products are environmentally safe. Over 5,000 members receive regular tips and ideas.

Methods of operation: Research (25%), lobbying (25%), publications (25%), public education (25%)

Recent issues and projects: Big Oil in our Classroom campaign, highlighting biased environmental curriculum from oil companies; Don't Be Fooled Awards

Major publications: *Earth Day 2000* bulletin; *Don't Be Fooled Report*

Budget: $20,000

Funding: Telephone solicitation (75%), individual contribution (25%)

Staff: 1

Staff openings/year: 1

Work Week: 40 hours

Salary/year: $14,500 (Recent College Graduate); $18,500 (Graduate with advanced degree)

Benefits: Health insurance, paid vacation,

Part-Time Employees: Yes

Summer Employees: None at this time

Volunteers: Yes

Interns: 2
Length: 3-6 months
Duties: Writing, researching, lobbying
Remuneration: None

Jobs advertised: Environmental newsletters, local and national press, nonprofit recruitment agencies

To apply: Contact Caroline Harwood

EARTH DAY NEW YORK

10 East 39th Street, Suite 601A
New York, NY 10016
(212) 686-4905

Director: Pamela Lippe

Purpose: Provides environmental education to K-12 students, business and the general public.

Methods of operation: Public education (100%)

Recent issues and projects: Provided environmental curricula to 15,000 schools in several states. Organized a series of presentations educating hundreds of business owners and property managers about new commercial recycling laws. Organize annual environmental festival attracting tens to hundreds of thousands of attendees and one hundred environmental and other nonprofit grassroots organizations.

Staff: 1

Part-Time Employees: Up to 10

Summer Employees: No

Volunteers: Up to 100

Interns: None, willing to accept applications

To apply: Contact Pamela Lippe

EARTH DAY RESOURCES

116 New Montgomery Street, Suite 530
San Francisco, CA 94105
(415) 495-5987

Director: Caroline Harwood

Purpose: Earth Day Resources keeps the grassroots spirit of Earth Day alive. We help teachers, Earth Day organizers and student activists with materials, advice and help to organize events around Earth Day and through the year.

Methods of operation: Community organizing (30%), publications (30%), public education (30%),research (10%)

Constituency: Teachers, Earth Day organizers, students, children, environmentalists, and businesses

Recent issues and projects: The Earth Day Spring Clean took place in 21 cities in April 1993, raising money for the environment and educating thousands. Working on 1994's Earth Day

Major publications: *The Earth Day Curriculum*, an interactive lesson plan in K-6 and &-12 formats; 16 environmental factsheets; campus and workplace audits, carpool and recycling workplace kits

Budget: $20,000

Funding: Fundraising events (75%), materials (25%)

Staff: 1
1 Director

Staff openings/year: 1

Work Week: 40 hours

Salary/year: $14,500 (Recent College Graduate); $18,500 (Graduate with advanced degree)

Benefits: Health insurance, paid vacation, pregnancy leave

Part-Time Employees: 1

Summer Employees: none

Volunteers: 3

Interns: 3
Length: 3-6 months
Duties: Research, press, organizing, fundraising and writing
Remuneration: none

Jobs advertised: In environmental newsletters

To apply: Contact Caroline Harwood

EARTH ISLAND INSTITUTE
300 Broadway, Suite 28
San Francisco, CA 94133
(415) 788-3666

Director: John A. Knox and David Phillips, Co-Executive Directors

Purpose: Founded by David Brower as an umbrella organization for innovative projects for the conservation, preservation and restoration of the global environment.

Methods of operation: Public education (40%), publications (30%), research (20%), community organizing (5%), direct action (5%)

Membership: National; some international members

Recent issues and projects: The International Marine Mammal Project, Sea Turtle Restoration Project, Urban Habitat Program and numerous others.

Major publications: *EI Journal*, a quarterly international news magazine on environmental issues

Budget: $1,700,000

Funding: Individual contributions (40%), foundations (25%), direct mail (20%), merchandise (10%)

Staff: 21
10 Organizers
1 Office Manager
2 1/2 Writers/Editors
2 Executive Directors
1 Bookkeeper/Accountant
5 Researchers

Staff openings/year: 0-1

Work Week: 40-70 hours

Salary/year: $15,000 (Recent College Graduate); $18-27,000 (Graduate with advanced degree)

Benefits: Health and dental insurance, paid vacation

Part-Time Employees: 1

Volunteers: 5-10

Interns: 0-2
Length: 3-4 months
Duties: Clerical, research, community outreach
Remuneration: No stipend

Jobs advertised: *San Francisco Chronicle*; *Opportunity NOCs*

To apply: Contact Donna Lee Roy, Office Assistant

EARTHRIGHT INSTITUTE
322 Gates-Briggs Building
White River Junction, VT 05001
(802) 295-7734 (800) 639-1552

Director: Martha S. Solow

Purpose: Networking, education and advocacy center for environmental concerns, focusing on solid waste and energy issues.

Methods of operation: Public education (25%), community organizing (20%), publications (20%), research and policy development (30%), lobbying (5%)

Constituency: Middle-class working people; many

connected in some way with higher education

Recent issues and projects: The Earthright Institute is currently working on the following projects: (1) Publication of energy planning guide for Vermont municipalities; (2) organizing and assisting town energy committees in conservation planning and energy program development; (3) regional and reuse programs; (4) workshops in waste reduction and energy-efficient homebuilding for businesses; (5) maintaining environmental information network and referral center

Major publications: Quarterly newsletter: *Guide to Town Energy Planning in Vermont* (1992); *Guide to Town Energy Planning in New Hampshire* (in progress); consumer guides on recycling, composting, energy efficiency, demand side management

Budget: $60,000

Funding: Membership and community contributions (49%), corporate and business sponsorships (30%), foundation grants (20%); sales (1%)

Staff: 2
1 Executive Director
1 Program Director

Staff openings/year: Varies

Work Week: 25 hours

Salary/year: $Varies (Recent College Graduate); $Varies (Graduate with advanced degree)

Benefits: Paid vacation, sick leave and personal days; training opportunities

Part-Time Employees: 2

Summer Employees: Yes; interns

Volunteers: Yes

Interns: Yes
Length: 3 months
Duties: Depends on skills; may involve research or education
Remuneration: Stipend or work/study

Jobs advertised: Local newspaper; newsletter; word of mouth

To apply: Contact Martha Solow, Executive Director

EARTHWATCH

P.O. Box 403, 680 Mount Auburn Street
Watertown, MA 02272
(617) 926-8200

Other Offices: Los Angeles, CA; Melbourne, AUSTRALIA; Oxford, ENGLAND; Moscow, RUSSIA; Tokyo, JAPAN

President: Brian Rosborough

Purpose: Earthwatch is a nonprofit institution which supports scientific field research worldwide through its EarthCorps of citizens and scholars working together to improve our understanding of the planet.

Constituency: Volunteers range in age from 16 to 83.

Recent issues and projects: Earthwatch sponsors 160 projects a year in 46 countries studying in disciplines as diverse as rain forest ecology, endangered species, public health care, archaeology, marine studies, and agriculture. We send 4,000 volunteers a year to assist scientists for 2 to 3 week periods.

Major publications: *Earthwatch*, 6 times a year; catalog in January with full listing of projects

Funding: Individual contributions (90%), foundations (8%), corporations (2%)

Staff: 50
Including:
10 Field Operations
6 Writers/Editors
4 Foundation Fundraisers
3 Public Affairs

Staff openings/year: 10

Work Week: 40 hours

Salary/year: $16,000 (Recent College Graduate); $25-30,000 (Graduate with advanced degree)

Benefits: Health insurance, pregnancy leave, pension, tuition reimbursement, paid vacation

Part-Time Employees: 2

Volunteers: Yes

Interns: Yes
Length: 1 week-1 year
Duties: Varies depending upon the department
Remuneration: Varies

Jobs advertised: Newspaper; word of mouth; company newsletter

To apply: Contact Jessica Smith, Personnel

Remarks: Volunteers need no prior experience, just willingness to learn and work. Field expeditions volunteers pay a share of costs which covers research, lodging and accommodations while in the field.

EAST BAY CONSERVATION CORPS (EBCC)

1021 Third Street
Oakland, CA 94607
(510) 891-3900

Director: Joanna Lennon

Purpose: The EBCC promotes youth development through community service and service-learning and is a catalyst for social change. By actively engaging young people in their education while addressing environmental and social issues, EBCC enhances participants academic, leadership and life skills, self-esteem, civic responsibility and environmental awareness.

Methods of operation: Environmental Stewardship/community service (65%), human service (15%), public education (10%), human services (15%), community organizing (5%), training and technical assistance (5%)

Constituency: EBCC participants range in age from 5 to 50 (most in the 12 to 25 range), are ethnically diverse, reside in the East San Francisco Bay area and, for the most part, live below standard poverty levels

Recent issues and projects: Participants work on projects that define the environment in a social and community context as well as in the performance of conservation work in both urban and wildland areas. Community service projects have included President Clinton's Summer of Service and Summer of Safety Programs.

Major publications: *East Bay Beat*, bi-annual newsletter

Budget: $5,748,588

Funding: Government (56%), fee-for-service (35%), foundations (8%), individual contributions (1%)

Staff: 64
1 Office Manager
1 Researcher
1 Foundation Fundraiser
4 Bookkeepers/Accountants
1 Caseworker
18 Corpsmember Supervisors
12 Teachers/Teacher Aids
16 Program/Direct Service Staff
10 Management/Administrative Staff

Staff openings/year: 15

Work Week: 40 hours

Salary/year: $25,000 (Recent College Graduate); $30,000 (Graduate with advanced degree)

Benefits: Health insurance, pension, paid vacation, life insurance, credit union, family leave, tuition reimbursement

Part-Time Employees: 6

Summer Employees: 22

Volunteers: 1,500

Interns: 30
Length: 1 year
Duties: Public works, recycling, administration
Remuneration: Paid by sponsor agencies and grants

Jobs advertised: Word-of-mouth, direct mail, newspapers

To apply: Contact Carlene Henderson, Recruiter

EAST COAST MIGRANT HEALTH PROJECT

1234 Massachusetts Avenue, NW, Suite 623
Washington, DC 20005
(202) 347-7377

Director: Sister Cecilia Abhold, SP

Purpose: A "people-to-people" organization providing health and allied-health professionals to supplement already existing staff at community health centers on the East Coast and to assist in the delivery of health and social services to migrant/seasonal farmworkers and their families. Staff move twice a year to serve during the harvest seasons in states between New York and Florida.

Methods of operation: Human services, public education, training and technical assistance

Constituency: Migrant and seasonal workers

Recent issues and projects: Providing employment for some migrant workers unemployed because of the Florida freeze; issues: housing

Budget: $695,000

Funding: Government

Staff:
18 in winter, 35 in summer, including:
10-25 Community Service Workers
3 Administrators
3 Registered Nurses
3 Social Workers
1 Health Educator

Staff openings/year: 10-20

Work Week: 40 hours

Salary/year: $14,400-24,000

Benefits: Health insurance, life insurance, pregnancy leave, pension, paid vacation

Summer Employees: 10-15

Volunteers: 2-5

Interns: 1
Length: 1 season
Duties: To fill position assigned, with supervision
Remuneration: With East Coast Migrant Health Project

Jobs advertised: Colleges; schools of nursing; medical schools; volunteer agencies

To apply: Contact Judith Ann Dohner, HM, Assistant Administrator

EAST NEW YORK URBAN YOUTH CORPS HOUSING DEVELOPMENT FUND COMPANY, INC.

116 Williams Avenue
Brooklyn, NY 11207
(718) 385-6700

Director: Ms. Carey Shea

Purpose: To develop and rehabilitate housing for homeless, low-income and moderate income people; to organize the community to improve the quality of life by providing youth services. The Fund is a small, grassroots organization promoting the redevelopment of a large section of Brooklyn, New York. The Organization sponsors the following activities: housing rehabilitation, recycling, food cooperative, after-school tutoring and recreation, art classes for youth, and loan packaging.

Methods of operation: Housing development (50%), community organizing (50%)

Constituency: Serves one of New York City's poorest neighborhoods. Poor, homeless, low and moderate income.

Recent issues and projects: Rehabilitate 15-unit building for use as a homeless and moderate income cooperative. Started a recycling business operated by young teens.

Budget: $190,000

Funding: Foundations (50%), government contracts (50%)

Staff: 4
1 Organizer
1 Typist
1 Issue Expert
1 Office Manager

Staff openings/year: 1

Work Week: 50 hours

Salary/year: $22,000 (Recent College Graduate); $26,000 (Graduate with advanced degree)

Benefits: Health insurance, life insurance, pregnancy leave, paid vacation

Summer Employees: 2

Volunteers: 40

Interns: 1
Length: 8 months or 6 weeks
Duties: Prepare/execute special organizing projects
Remuneration: Stipend

Jobs advertised: Mailings; postering

To apply: Contact Carey Shea, Director

ECO-CYCLE, INC.

P.O. Box 19006
Boulder, CO 80306
(303) 444-6634

Other Offices: Longmont, CO

Director: Eric Lombardi

Purpose: To collect and process a significant portion of Boulder's solid waste for the purpose of recycling; to become financially self-sufficient through earned income from the sale of recyclables; to demonstrate the potential for community development through recycling; to actively support recycling throughout Colorado; to encourage an environmental ethic through educational outreach.

Methods of operation: Material collection and

processing, public education, training and technical assistance, recycling services

Constituency: 225,000 Boulder County residents; statewide educational consulting services

Recent issues and projects: Recycling 25,000 tons of solid waste per year; attained position of financial self-sufficiency; provides comprehensive recycling service to population of 225,000; has begun an aggressive commercial recovery program; established hands-on recycling in all public schools in Boulder County; spoke to 37,000 students in the 1992-93 academic year as part of our education program; services 2 curbside recycling programs, 8 drop-off centers and commercial programs for glass, cardboard and office paper.

Major publications: *Eco-Cycle Times*; *Boulder County Recycling Guide*; residential recycling brochure; *Eco-Cycle Block Leader Newsletter*; *Eco-Cycle DEJA News* to our membership

Budget: $1,600,000

Funding: Earned income, sale of recyclables, local government, foundations, corporations, private donors

Staff: 45
Includes:
Education Coordinators
Volunteer Coordinators
Typists
Bookkeeper/Accountant
Drivers
Supervisors
Equipment Operators
Computer Operators

Staff openings/year: 4-6

Work Week: 40 hours

Salary/year: $10-25,000

Benefits: Health insurance, paid vacation, paid sick leave, health day

Part-Time Employees: 15

Volunteers: 1,000 Block Leaders

Interns: None currently, but willing to accept applications

Jobs advertised: Local newspapers

To apply: Contact Eric Lombardi, Executive Director

ECOLOGY CENTER
2530 San Pablo Avenue
Berkeley, CA 94702
(415) 548-2220

Director: Kathy Evans

Purpose: To be a source of information on recycling, ecology, nature, environment, gardening and farming.

Methods of operation: Curbside recycling (50%), public education (40%), publications (5%), community market (5%)

Constituency: Individuals interested in ecology and recycling mainly in the Bay area

Recent issues and projects: The Ecology Center runs a citywide curbside recycling service, a weekly Farmers Market, a bookstore, library, newsletter and gardening classes

Major publications: Monthly newsletter to 6,000 readers; *Vegetables Gardening*, *Raising Rabbits and Chickens*, *Backyard Composting*, *First Steps in Ecology* and other pamphlets and flyers

Budget: $350,000

Funding: Sales (50%), individual contributions (25%), government grants (25%)

Staff: 12
6 Recycling Workers
2 Issue Experts
1 Writer/Editor
1 Office Manager
1 Researcher
1 Bookkeeper/Accountant

Staff openings/year: 1

Work Week: 40 hours

Salary/year: $15,000

Benefits: Health insurance, paid vacation

Part-Time Employees: 2

Volunteers: 15

Interns: 2
Length: 6 months
Duties: Research, writing
Remuneration: Matching grants

Jobs advertised: Local and regional periodicals

To apply: Contact Karen Pickett, Information Coordinator

ECOLOGY CENTER OF ANN ARBOR

417 Detroit Street
Ann Arbor, MI 48104
(313) 761-3186

Director: Mike Garfield

Purpose: The mission of the Ecology Center is to effectively channel community resources into meaningful involvement on environmental issues. Programs include: environmental education, advocacy, recycling, environmental labor coalitions, and environmental justice programs.

Methods of operation: Service (42%), public education (25%), community organizing (15%), training and technical assistance (10%), publications (5%), lobbying (2%), direct action (1%)

Constituency: Ann Arbor and State of Michigan

Recent issues and projects: Recycle Ann Arbor does curbside recycling for the city and processes materials; public library and community resource; Michigan anti-incineration campaign; Auto Industry Project.

Major publications: Newsletters: *Ecology Reports* and *Michigan Toxics Watch*; *Consumers' Guide to Lawn and Tree Care*; *Footloose in Washtenaw: A Walker's Guide to Washtenaw County*; video tape: *Making the Connection - A Teacher's Guide to Household Hazardous Substances* (13 1/2 min.)

Budget: $1,700,000

Funding: City recycling contract (40%), foundations (35%), materials (15%), individual contributions (6%), direct mail (4%)

Staff: 40
32 Staff in Recycle Ann Arbor
2 Administrative Assistants
3 Educators
2 Community Organizers
1 Fundraiser

Work Week: 45 hours

Salary/year: $15-19,000

Benefits: Health insurance, paid vacation

Part-Time Employees: Yes

Volunteers: Yes

Interns: Yes
Length: 2-3 months
Duties: Specific to intern

Jobs advertised: Ads in local papers

To apply: For recycling positions contact Arlin Wasserman; for other positions contact Rebecca Kanner.

Remarks: The recycling program and energy programs are in the process of becoming a subsidiary and a separate organization, respectively. Without the above two programs, the annual budget is approximately $300,000 with a staff of 12.

ECONOMIC POLICY INSTITUTE

1730 Rhode Island Ave., NW
Washington, DC 20036
(202) 775-8810

Director: Jeff Faux

Purpose: The goal of the Institute is to encourage scholarship on a variety of economic issues in order to broaden the public debate about strategies to achieve a prosperous and fair economy.

Methods of operation: Research (95%), publications (5%)

Constituency: Academia and unions

Recent issues and projects: Current projects include: NAFTA, tax reforms and health care reform.

Major publications: *State of Working America*

Staff: 45
10 Writers/Editors
3 Office Managers
12 Researchers
1 Foundation Fundraiser
12 Issue Experts
5 Administrative Assistants
1 Bookkeeper/Accountant
1 Grassroots Fundraiser

Staff openings/year: 1

Work Week: 40 hours

Salary/year: $Varies (Recent College Graduate); $Varies (Graduate with advanced degree)

Benefits: Health insurance, paid vacation, life insurance, credit union

Part-Time Employees: 1

Summer Employees: 1

Volunteers: None

Interns: 1
Length: Varies
Duties: Depends on interests of the intern and needs

of EPI

Jobs advertised: Bulletins and word of mouth

To apply: Please contact Terrel Hale

EDUCATION LAW CENTER
801 Arch Street, Suite 610
Philadelphia, PA 19107
(215) 238-6970

Other Offices: Pittsburgh, PA

Director: Janet Stotland and Len Rieser, Co-Directors

Purpose: To provide quality public education for Pennsylvania students. Focus is pre-school, elementary and secondary, not higher education.

Methods of operation: Litigation (50%), case advocacy (25%), public education (10%), training and technical assistance (10%), community organizing (5%)

Constituency: Students in Pennsylvania

Recent issues and projects: Various litigation and administrative advocacy; target populations are disabled students, poor, minority and language minority families and children in substitute care

Major publications: Newsletter: *News from ELC*; *The Right to Special Education in Pennsylvania - A Guide for Parents*

Budget: $700,000

Funding: Governmental (84%), foundations (10%), individual contributions (3%), direct mail (3%)

Staff: 9
5 1/2 Attorneys
2 Paralegals
2 Typists

Staff openings/year: 0-1

Work Week: 45-50 hours

Salary/year: $18,000 (Recent College Graduate); $28,000 (Graduate with advanced degree)

Benefits: Health insurance, paid vacation, life insurance

Jobs advertised: In newspapers; circulate job announcements

To apply: Contact Janet Stotland or Len Rieser

EDUCATIONAL COMMUNICATIONS, INC.
P.O. Box 351419
Los Angeles, CA 90035
(310) 559-9160

Other Offices: Orange, CA; Riverside, CA

Director: Nancy Pearlman

Purpose: Educational Communications, Inc., a nonprofit tax-deductible organization founded in 1958, is dedicated to improving the quality of life on this planet. The group works on all environmental issues from the local to international level. Services provided include a speakers bureau, award-winning public service announcements, radio and television documentaries and weekly series and input into the decision-making process. The key purpose is to educate the public about both the problems and the solutions.

Methods of operation: Radio and TV production (50%), public education (30%), publications (5%), community organizing (5%), direct action (5%), training and technical assistance (1%), human services (1%), research (1%), lobbying (1%), litigation (1%)

Recent issues and projects: Environmental projects include: *The Compendium Newsletter*; *Econews* television series; *Environmental Directions* and *Environmental Viewpoints* radio series; the Ecology Center of Southern California, a regional conservation organization; *Ecoview* newspaper articles; *Directory of Environmental Organizations*; and *Earth Alert.* The group is also active in peace and social change causes.

Funding: Individual contributions (75%), foundations (25%)

Staff:
5 Producers/Directors/Writers

Staff openings/year: 2

Part-Time Employees: Yes

Summer Employees: Yes

Volunteers: 100

Interns: 10
Length: Up to intern
Duties: All
Remuneration: None

Jobs advertised: Listings in newsletters

To apply: Contact Leslie Lewis

EDUCATIONAL FUND TO END HANDGUN VIOLENCE

110 Maryland Avenue, NE, Box 72
Washington, DC 20002
(202) 544-7227

Director: Joshua Horwitz

Purpose: To reduce handgun violence through educational programs, youth projects and research. Also runs a Firearms Liability Clearinghouse to help attorneys litigating gun cases against manufacturers and dealers.

Methods of operation: Public education (25%), research (25%), litigation (50%)

Constituency: Attorneys who use the Firearms Liability Clearinghouse; general interest donors who feel strongly about handgun violence

Recent issues and projects: Recent projects include: Firearms Liability Clearinghouse; *Kids and Guns: A National Disgrace*; Hands without guns, a public health initiative

Major publications: Quarterly newsletter: *Firearms Litigation Reporter*; *Kids and Guns, Third Edition* (Fall, 1993; with the American Youth Work Center)

Budget: $100,000

Funding: Foundations (60%), individual contributions (40%)

Staff: 3
1 Director
1 Attorney
1 Database Librarian/Researcher

Work Week: 40 hours

Salary/year: $Varies (Recent College Graduate); $Varies (Graduate with advanced degree)

Benefits: Health insurance, pregnancy leave, paid vacation

Summer Employees: Yes

Volunteers: Yes

Interns: Yes
Length: Flexible
Duties: We create internships around a person's specific interest. Research, writing, legal assistance.
Remuneration: Negotiable; generally unpaid

Jobs advertised: Newspaper, notices at universities, other public interest groups

To apply: Contact Joshua Horwitz, Director

EDUCATORS FOR SOCIAL RESPONSIBILITY

23 Garden Street
Cambridge, MA 02138
(617) 370-2515

Other Offices: New York, NY; Madison, WI; Concord, NH; Carroboro, NC

Director: Larry Dieringer

Purpose: Educators for Social Responsibility (ESR) is a national nonprofit organization dedicated to children's ethical and social development. Our primary mission is to help young people develop a commitment to the well-being of others and to making a positive difference in the world.

Methods of operation: Training and technical assistance (50%), publications (40%), public education (10%)

Constituency: Educators, parents and students

Recent issues and projects: ESR is recognized nationally for its leadership in the fields of conflict resolution, violence prevention and diversity education. We work with educators and parents, providing professional development, resources and support. ESR has produced over 30 curricula, videotapes and other resources. Each year, ESR's national center and 25 chapters reach over 10,000 educators through workshops, institutes and conference presentations. ESR coordinates the largest school-based conflict resolution program of its kind in the country, the Resolving Conflict Creatively Program, currently serving 120,000 children from 300 schools nationwide, including New York City.

Major publications: ESR has published a number of books. Some of the most popular include: *Elementary Perspectives*; *Teaching Concepts of Peace and Conflict*; *Teaching Young Children in Volent Times*; *Conflict Resolution in the Middle School*

Budget: $1,200,000

Funding: Foundations (30%), workshop fees (30%), publication sales (20%), individual contributions (15%), membership (5%)

Staff: 7
1 1/2 Writer/Editor
2 Office Managers

1/2 Foundation Fundraiser
1/2 Bookkeeper/Accountant
1 Director
2 Trainers
1 Program Director
2 Program Assistants

Staff openings/year: 1

Work Week: 40 hours

Salary/year: $25,000

Benefits: Health insurance, pension, retirement, paid vacation, family leave

Part-Time Employees: 7

Summer Employees: None

Volunteers: Yes

Interns: Yes
Length: 4 months
Duties: Varies
Remuneration: Unpaid

To apply: Please contact Martha Plotkin, Director of Finance and Administration

EFFECTIVE ALTERNATIVE IN RECONCILIATION SERVICES (E.A.R.S.)

3319 Rochambeau Avenue
Bronx, NY 10467
(718) 654-4931

Director: Marcy May

Purpose: To empower youth in conciliation, communication and listening skills to peacefully resolve conflicts in schools, youth and community-based organizations.

Methods of operation: Training and technical assistance (100%)

Constituency: Teenagers in NYC schools (public junior and senior high schools and parochial high schools); teen trainers in summer internship program

Recent issues and projects: Train teenagers as teen trainers for school-based Conflict Resolution Programs and community-based programs; assist schools in implementing Conflict Resolution Programs, providing training for adults and young people

Budget: $600,000

Funding: Foundations (60%), government, school districts (40%)

Staff: 10
Including:
1 Foundation Fundraiser
2 Trainers/Program Coordinators

Staff openings/year: 1

Work Week: 40 hours

Salary/year: $20,000 (Recent College Graduate); $25,000 (Graduate with advanced degree)

Benefits: Benefits on case-by-case basis

Summer Employees: 10-12

Volunteers: 5

Interns: 10-12
Length: 6 summer weeks-1 year
Duties: Learn to be a trainer in conflict resolution skills
Remuneration: Teen summer interns paid; college student interns during the school year receive credit

Jobs advertised: Local organizations; word of mouth

To apply: Contact Marcy May, Director

EMPOWERMENT PROJECT

3403 Highway 54 West
Chapel Hill, NC 27516
(919) 967-1963

Other Offices: Santa Monica, CA

Director: Barbara Trent and David Kasper

Purpose: The Empowerment Project was established to provide facilities, training and other support for independent producers, artists, activists and organizations. Its purpose is to work towards democratizing access to the media and to provide the resources necessary to put the power of media in the hands of individuals and organizations working to further important human purposes.

Methods of operation: Community organizing (35%), training and technical assistance (35%), direct action (30%), research (5%)

Constituency: Low-income minority communities, artists, independent videographers and filmmakers

Recent issues and projects: Recent projects include: Hosted a conference called Media Impact: Using Film and Video for Community Empowerment; ongoing campaign to encourage North Carolina grassroots organizations to use video as part of organizing campaigns

Major publications: Documentary films produced: *Panama Deception*; *Coverup: Behind the Iran-Contra Affair*; *Taking It To the Theaters*; *Destination Nicaragua*

Budget: $355,000

Funding: Publications (46%), foundations (45%), individual contributions (9%)

Staff: 3
Plus 8 Full-time Interns
3-4 Organizers
1 Writer/Editor
1 Office Manager
1 Foundation Fundraiser
2 Issue Experts
1 Bookkeeper/Accountant
1 Grassroots Fundraisers

Staff openings/year: 1

Work Week: 40 hours

Salary/year: $24,000 (Graduate with advanced degree)

Benefits: Housing

Part-Time Employees: 1

Volunteers: 30

Interns: 9
Length: 3 months, 6 months or 1 year
Duties: Public relations, outreach, community video projects
Remuneration: Housing and small stipend

Jobs advertised: Through college co-op education programs, word-of-mouth, local newspapers

To apply: Contact Lisa Boothe, Internship Coordinator

ENERGY COORDINATING AGENCY OF PHILADELPHIA

1501 Cherry Street
Philadelphia, PA 19102
(215) 854-8030

Director: Liz Robinson

Purpose: To effectively address the energy poverty problem in Philadelphia through the coordination of all resources, improvement of programs, development of community-based organizations, research and planning.

Methods of operation: Human services (65%), training and technical assistance (5%), research (5%), lobbying (5%), publications (5%), public education (10%), community organizing (5%)

Constituency: Members include all those interested in residential energy conservation and low-income energy issues

Recent issues and projects: Administration of gas, water and electric utilities' conservation programs; citywide energy education; advocacy on state and national levels

Major publications: *Economic Impact of Low-income Conservation*; energy education literature and video training tapes; evaluations in energy education and water conservation

Budget: $2,700,000

Funding: Utility and government (80%), foundations (20%)

Staff: 15
1 Organizer/Trainer
4 Inspectors
1 Executive Director
1 Researcher
5 Administrative Assistants
1 Program Manager
1 Weatherization Manager
1 1/2 Bookkeeper/Accountant

Staff openings/year: 2

Work Week: 45 hours

Salary/year: $Varies (Recent College Graduate); $25-35,000 (Graduate with advanced degree)

Benefits: Health insurance, life insurance, pension, paid vacation

Part-Time Employees: 3

Volunteers: 2

Interns: 2-3 per year

Jobs advertised: Local paper and occasionally national search; networking

To apply: Contact Liz Robinson, Executive Director

ENVIRONMENTAL ACTION COALITION

625 Broadway
New York, NY 10012
(212) 677-1601

Director: Stephen Richardson

Purpose: Environmental education from formal school programs and teacher training to citizens' participation in active projects.

Methods of operation: Community organizing (40%), public education (40%), research (10%), lobbying (5%), publications (5%), plus general information and library maintained

Constituency: Largely New York City region individuals, with others scattered across the country

Recent issues and projects: Urban Woodlands School Planting Project; recycling in schools; apartment building recycling organizing; East Harlem Outreach Project

Major publications: Quarterly newsletter: *Cycle*; *Collision Course: Plastic Packaging vs. Solid Waste Solutions* (research report, 1989); interdisciplinary curriculum guides; *Eco-News*, an informative, cartoon-illustrated newsletter about the environment for children grades 4-6; video on school waste reduction

Budget: $300,000

Funding: Government grants (50%), individual contributions (30%), foundations (20%)

Staff: 5
1 Project Director
1 Executive Director
1 Program Associate
1 Researcher
1 Environmental Educator

Work Week: 40 hours

Salary/year: $24,000 (Recent College Graduate); $30,000 (Graduate with advanced degree)

Benefits: Health insurance, life insurance, paid vacation

Part-Time Employees: 2

Volunteers: Yes

Interns: 1-2 per year
Length: 9 months
Duties: Assistance on any mutually accepted project
Remuneration: Unpaid

Jobs advertised: Daily newspapers; colleagues' newsletters; word of mouth

To apply: Contact Stephen Richardson, Executive Director

ENVIRONMENTAL ACTION FOUNDATION

6930 Carroll Avenue, Suite 600
Takoma Park, MD 20912
(301) 891-1100 Fax: (301) 891-2218

Director: Margaret Morgan-Hubbard

Purpose: EAF promotes a healthy and sustainable environment through research, public education, organizing, advocacy and legal action.

Recent issues and projects: Work is currently focused in four major areas: toxics, utility reform, solid waste and energy conservation

Major publications: *Environmental Action*, quarterly magazine; *Wasteline* quarterly; *The Dynamic Duo: RCRA and SARA Title III*; *Making Polluters Pay: A Citizen's Guide to Legal Actions and Organizing*; *Wrapped in Plastics*; *Positive Steps Toward Waste Reduction*; *Acid Rain and Electricity Conservation*; fact packets; legislative summaries

Budget: $1,100,000

Funding: Individual contributions, foundations

Staff: 14
5 Issue Experts/Organizers
2 Magazine Editors
1 Attorney
1 Foundation Fundraiser
1 Researcher
1 Deputy Director
1 Office Manager
1 Executive Director
1 Marketing Director

Staff openings/year: 0-2

Work Week: 40 hours

Salary/year: $18,000-45,000 (Recent College Graduate); $Varies (Graduate with advanced degree)

Benefits: Health insurance, pregnancy leave, paid vacation

Volunteers: Yes

Interns: 2-5
Length: 3 months
Duties: Assist professional staff in day to day project area functions
Remuneration: None

Jobs advertised: EAF job announcements appear in local newspapers as well as other groups'/agencies' personnel areas. Also recruit personnel through university placement offices.

To apply: Contact Sheryl Harrison, Administrative Coordinator

ENVIRONMENTAL AND ENERGY STUDY INSTITUTE

122 C Street, NW, Suite 700
Washington, DC 20001
(202) 628-1400

Director: Ken Murphy

Purpose: The Environmental and Energy Study Institute (EESI) is a nonprofit organization dedicated to promoting environmentally sustainable societies. EESI believes meeting this goal requires transitions to social and economic patterns that sustain people, the environment and the natural resources upon which present and future generations depend.

Methods of operation: Research (40%), public education (30%), publications (20%), lobbying (10%)

Constituency: EESI's audience is Congress and other national policymakers -- and the people who influence them.

Recent issues and projects: EESI produces credible, timely information and innovative public policy initiatives that lead to these transitions. These products are developed and promoted through action-oriented briefings, workshops, analysis, publications, task forces and working groups.

Major publications: *Weekly Bulletin*

Budget: $1,900,000

Funding: Foundations (50%), publication sales (47%), individual contributions (3%)

Staff: 19
1 Attorney
1 Office Manager
3 Foundation Fundraisers
1 Administrative Assistant
1 Bookkeeper/Accountant
3 Program Directors
4 Program Associates

Staff openings/year: 2

Work Week: 37.5 hours

Salary/year: $20,000 (Recent College Graduate); $Varies (Graduate with advanced degree)

Benefits: Health insurance, pension, paid vacation, life insurance

Part-Time Employees: None

Summer Employees: None

Volunteers: None

Interns: Yes
Length: 3-4 months
Duties: Assist professional staff

Jobs advertised: Newspapers and our internal data base

To apply: Contact John N. Babbitt

ENVIRONMENTAL CAREERS ORGANIZATION

286 Congress Street, 3rd Floor
Boston, MA 02210
(617) 426-4375

Other Offices: Boston, MA; Cleveland, OH; Tampa, FL; San Francisco, CA; Seattle, WA

President: John R. Cook, Jr.

Purpose: ECO is a national nonprofit career organization dedicated to protecting and enhancing the environment through the development of professionals, the promotion of careers, and the inspiration of the individual action.

Major publications: *The New Complete Guide to Environmental Careers*; *Beyond the Green: Redefining and Diversifying the Environmental Movement*; *Connections*

Staff: 33
1 Office Manager
2 Researchers
4 Foundation Fundraisers
3 Issue Experts
2 Bookkeepers/Accountants
5 Regional Directors
4 Program Coordinators
5 Administrative Assistants
3 MIS Dept.

Staff openings/year: 2

Work Week: 40 hours

Salary/year: $25,000 (Recent College Graduate); $30,000 (Graduate with advanced degree)

Benefits: Health insurance, paid vacation, life insurance, family leave, dental, vision care

Part-Time Employees: 3

Summer Employees: No

Volunteers: 2

Interns: Yes
Length: Varies
Duties: Varies
Remuneration: Varies

ENVIRONMENTAL DEFENSE FUND

257 Park Avenue South
New York, NY 10010
(212) 505-2100

Other Offices: Boulder, CO; Oakland, CA; Washington, DC; Raleigh, NC; Austin, TX

Director: Frederic D. Krupp

Purpose: The Environmental Defense Fund, a leading national, New York-based nonprofit organization with 200,000 members, links science, economics, and law to create innovative, economically viable solutions to today's environmental problems.

Recent issues and projects: EDF pursues responsible reform of public policy in the fields of energy and resource conservation, toxic chemical control, water resources preservation, air quality, land use and wildlife, working through research and public education, and judicial, administrative and legislative action.

Major publications: *EDF Letter*; *Dead Heat: The Race Against the Greenhouse Effect*; *Polluted Coastal Waters: The Role of Acid Rain*; *Developing Policies for Responding to Climatic Change*; *Coming Full Circle: Successful Recycling Today*; *Ominous Future Under the Ozone Hole: Assessing Biological Impacts in Antarctica*

Budget: $18,000,000

Funding: Membership and contributions (57%), foundations (27%), bequests and endowment (7%), miscellaneous and investment income (5%), other grants (3%), attorneys' fees (1%)

Staff: 140

Staff openings/year: 10-20

Work Week: 40 hours

Salary/year: $16-22,000 (Recent College Graduate); $27-36,000 (Graduate with advanced degree)

Benefits: Health insurance, life insurance, pregnancy leave, pension, paid vacation

Part-Time Employees: 10

Summer Employees: 15-20 interns

Interns: 15-20
Length: 3-4 months

Jobs advertised: Newspapers; career placement offices; professional journals; etc.

To apply: Contact Human Resources Department

Remarks: Volunteers are welcome!

ENVIRONMENTAL FEDERATION OF CALIFORNIA/EARTH SHARE OF CALIFORNIA

116 New Montgomery, Suite 800
San Francisco, CA 94105
(415) 882-9330

Other Offices: Los Angeles, CA

Director: Nancy Snow

Purpose: The EFC was established to represent a coalition of California environmental organizations in the workplace. Our primary function is to raise funds for member groups through workplace payroll deduction giving campaigns and to educate the general public about the problems which threaten our environment and the efforts our member groups are making to find and promote solutions to those problems.

Methods of operation: Conducting workplace giving campaigns (90%), public education (10%)

Membership: 82 member environmental organizations

Recent issues and projects: We recently completed our 1993 campaign season. Our projected earnings for the 1994 campaign are $1,900,000.

Budget: $950,000

Funding: Workplace giving (95-99%), foundations (1-5%)

Staff: 8
1 Campaign Manager
1 Executive Director
1 Office Manager
1 Associate Director
1 Program Director
1 Controller
1 Admin. Assistant to Exec. Director
1 Administrative Assistant to Controller

Staff openings/year: 0-1

Work Week: 40 hours

Salary/year: $16,000

Benefits: Paid vacation, monthly health benefit/allotments

Volunteers: Approximately 75

Interns: Yes
Length: Negotiable
Duties: Research, writing, database
Remuneration: Negotiable

Jobs advertised: Opportunity NOCs; announcements mailed to member and other environmental organizations; local newspapers

To apply: Contact Jennifer Hesser, Office Manager; Nancy Snow, Executive Director; or Amy Norquist, Associate Director

ENVIRONMENTAL FORUM OF MARIN

P.O. Box 74
Larkspur, CA 94977
(415) 479-7814

Purpose: Nonprofit organization dedicated to preserving the quality of the environment through education.

Methods of operation: Public education (80%), research (5%), community organizing (5%), direct action (5%), training and technical assistance (5%)

Constituency: Citizens who have completed the Forum's annual five-month training program

Recent issues and projects: Yearly training program focusing on ecology, human impact on the environment, resource management, and citizen and community action. Active in local habitat preservation, land use planning and community education.

Major publications: Monthly newsletter

Budget: $8,000

Funding: Individual contributions (100%)

Volunteers: 200

To apply: Contact President, Board of Directors

Remarks: Staffing of the Environmental Forum of Marin is entirely volunteers who have completed the Forum training program. All public education programs and environmental activities are coordinated by the Board and members of the Forum.

ENVIRONMENTAL HEALTH COALITION

1717 Kettner Blvd. #100
San Diego, CA 92101
(619) 235-0281

Director: Diane Takvorian

Purpose: The purpose of the Environmental Health Coalition is to prevent illness and environmental degradation resulting from exposure to toxics in the home, workplace and community.

Methods of operation: Public education (50%), training and technical assistance (20%), research (15%), community organizing (10%), direct action (5%)

Recent issues and projects: Community Right to Know/Right to Act Project compiles information on over 8,000 businesses in San Diego regarding the toxic chemicals they use and waste generated; Clean Bay Campaign seeks to clean up, restore and protect San Diego Bay; Toxic-Free Neighborhoods Campaign works with low-income communities to fight toxic pollution and employs land use and planning mechanisms; Household Toxics Project educates the public about the hazards associated with common household products; Ecological Safe Substitutes Project provides shelf labeling and posters to retailers

Major publications: Bimonthly newsletter: *Toxinformer*; various fact sheets on pesticides

Budget: $300,000

Funding: Government grants (50%), foundations (40%), individual contributions (10%)

Staff: 9
6 Program Directors
1 Office Manager
1 Director
1 Organizer

Staff openings/year: 1

Work Week: 40 hours

Salary/year: $20-22,000 (Recent College Graduate); $25,000 (Graduate with advanced degree)

Benefits: Health insurance, paid vacation

Part-Time Employees: 3

Volunteers: 5-10

Interns: Yes

Length: 3-6 months
Duties: Various

To apply: Contact Diane Takvorian

ENVIRONMENTAL HEALTH WATCH
4115 Bridge Avenue, Suite 104
Cleveland, OH 44113
(216) 961-4646

Director: Stuart Greenberg, Education Director

Purpose: Nonprofit information center on hazardous materials in the home and community, established to increase public understanding of the health effects and dangers of toxic chemicals and other hazardous materials.

Methods of operation: Public education (50%), publications (25%), training and technical assistance (15%), research (10%)

Constituency: General public

Recent issues and projects: Childhood lead poisoning; right-to-know; household hazardous waste; indoor pollution.

Major publications: *Healthy House Catalog*, a national directory of products and services for indoor pollution control

Budget: $120,000

Funding: Foundations (90%), individual contributions (2.5%), direct mail (2.5%), Greater Cleveland Community Shares (5%)

Staff: 3
1 Education Director
1 Research Director
1 Program Director

Staff openings/year: 1

Work Week: 50 hours

Salary/year: $20,000 (Recent College Graduate); $30,000 (Graduate with advanced degree)

Benefits: Health insurance, life insurance, paid vacation

Part-Time Employees: 1

Summer Employees: Yes

Volunteers: 5

Interns: Yes
Length: 2-8 months
Duties: Vary
Remuneration: Sometimes able to pay small stipend

Jobs advertised: Local newspaper; *Cleveland Plain Dealer*; direct mail

To apply: Contact Stuart Greenberg, Executive Director

ENVIRONMENTAL INFORMATION ASSOCIATION
3805 Presidential Parkway, Suite 106
Atlanta, GA 30340
(404) 986-2760

Purpose: The Environmental Information Association's multidisciplinary membership collects, generates and disseminates information concerning environmental health hazards to occupants of building, industrial sites and other facility operations.

Methods of operation: Publications (20%), public education (20%), training and technical assistance (20%)

Constituency: Contractors, consultants, building owners, attorneys, architects, universities and training organizations

Recent issues and projects: Recent projects include: the Fall Regional Conference; environmental fact sheets; annual conferences; training grants

Major publications: *Environmental Choices*; *Technical Journal*

Budget: $900,000

Funding: Individual contributions, direct mail, membership

Staff: 3
1 Organizers
1 Writer/Editor
1 Office Manager

Staff openings/year: 0-1

Work Week: 40 hours

Part-Time Employees: 4

Volunteers: 100

Interns: None

ENVIRONMENTAL LAW INSTITUTE

1616 P Street, NW, Suite 200
Washington, DC 20036
(202) 328-5150

President: William Futrell

Purpose: ELI is a national nonprofit research and education institution with an interdisciplinary staff of lawyers, economists, scientists and journalists. The Institute searches for pragmatic solutions to the most pressing environmental problems and devises creative responses to help achieve national environmental goals. EIL transforms laws into action, protecting water, air quality, wildlife, and wetlands and reducing public health threats through training, research, and education for communities, governments and businesses.

Methods of operation: Public education, training and technical assistance, publications, community organizing, research

Recent issues and projects: ELI conducts activities in three broad, interrelated program areas: education and training, publications, and policy research and technical assistance. The Institute's continuing education program is the largest and most comprehensive in the field, instructing more than 30,000 attorneys, managers, students and other professionals in course topics such as Environmental Law (annual update); Hazardous Wastes, Superfund and Toxic Substances; Negotiation Skills Development; Air and Water Pollution Law; and Wetlands Law.

Major publications: *Environmental Law Reporter*; *Environmental Forum*; the *Deskbook* series (Superfund, NEPA, Environmental Law, Community Right-to-Know, Clean Water); bimonthly *National Wetlands Newsletter*; *A Practical Guide to Environmental Management*; *Our National Wetlands Heritage*

Budget: $3,000,000

Funding: Federal and state grants/contracts (26%), publications (26%), foundations (18%), research contracts (14%), individual and corporate contributions (12%), interest and royalties (3%), conferences (1%)

Staff: 60
20 Attorneys
10 Writers/Editors
10 Researchers
4 Typists
4 Bookkeepers/Accountants
1 Officer Manager
1 Director of Communications

Staff openings/year: 10

Work Week: 37.5 hours

Salary/year: $18,000 (Recent College Graduate); $30,000 (Graduate with advanced degree)

Benefits: Health insurance, life insurance, pregnancy leave, paid vacation, educational benefits

Part-Time Employees: 5

Volunteers: 2

Interns: Yes
Length: 2-3 months
Duties: Research assistant; editorial assistant
Remuneration: Minimum wage and upward

To apply: Contact Elissa Parker, Director of Research, or Barry Breen, Editor-in-chief, *Environmental Law Reporter*

ENVIRONMENTAL PLANNING LOBBY

353 Hamilton Street
Albany, NY 12210
(518) 462-5526

Director: Lee Wasserman

Purpose: Lobby New York State to pass environmentally sound legislation

Methods of operation: Lobbying (50%), research (10%), publications (10%), public education (10%), community organizing (10%)

Membership: 100 member organizations; 30,000 individuals

Major publications: *Albany Report*, magazine published 5 times/year; *Voters Guide*, annual publication listing voting records of state decision-makers

Funding: Individual contributions

Staff: 20
10 Canvassers
3 Lobbyists
2 Organizers
1 Researcher
1 Grassroots Fundraiser
1 Administrator
1 Publication Specialist
1 Support Staff

Staff openings/year: 1

Work Week: 40 hours

Salary/year: $Varies (Recent College Graduate); $Varies (Graduate with advanced degree)

Benefits: Health insurance, paid vacation, parental leave, IRA Contributions

Part-Time Employees: 2

Summer Employees: Yes; canvassers

Volunteers: 1-2

Interns: 2-6
Length: Semester
Duties: Research, office work, lobby

Jobs advertised: Local paper; *Community Jobs*; sometimes *New York Times*

To apply: Contact Amy Klein, Associate Director

ENVIRONMENTAL PROJECT ON CENTRAL AMERICA (EPOCA)

300 Broadway, Suite 28
San Francisco, CA 94133
(415) 788-3666

Director: Jane McAlevey and Dave Henson, Co-Directors

Purpose: Grassroots education and movement building around encouraging people to make the links between environmental degradation and social injustice, vis-a-vis publications and campaigns. Serves as a national resource center on this issue. They participate in grassroots fundraising to provide material aid for environmentally sustainable agricultural and energy projects.

Methods of operation: Publications (40%), speaking tours, delegations of U.S. environmentalists to the region, material aid work in the region (25%), public education (20%), research (10%), direct action (5%)

Constituency: Environmentalists, Central American solidarity activists

Recent issues and projects: 1) Grassroots El Salvador Campaign: national campaign seeking to mobilize environmentalists to call for an end to U.S. military aid to El Salvador; 2) Circulation of Grassroots Organizers Kit, which presents some methods and resources to help build a movement which will work for peace, justice and sound ecology in Central America; 3) Toxics and Guatemala Green Papers both being written.

Major publications: Series of Green Papers on various countries and environmental problems, i.e. militarization, *Nicaragua: An Environmental Perspective*, Central America; *EPOCA Updates*, which updates and informs our membership of our current programs, and provides analysis of changing events in Central America and how they relate to U.S. policy

Budget: $185,000

Funding: Foundations (65%), individual contributions (20%), merchandise (15%)

Staff: 4
1 Organizer
1 Writer/Editor
1 Office Manager
1 Researcher

Staff openings/year: 0-1

Work Week: 65 hours

Salary/year: $17,000

Benefits: Health insurance, paid vacation

Volunteers: 35

Interns: 7
Length: 6 months
Duties: Assistance on various aspects of our programmatic work and some task oriented/administrative work (75% project; 25% administrative)
Remuneration: Unpaid

Jobs advertised: *Community Jobs*; national alternative press

To apply: Contact Lisa Tweten, National Staff

ENVIRONMENTAL PROTECTION INFORMATION CENTER

P.O. Box 397
Garberville, CA 95542
(707) 923-2931

Director: Cecelia Lanman

Purpose: Preservation of old-growth forests and their biological diversity; sustainable forestry; educating the public on forest environment issues. EPIC is on the frontlines of the battle to save California's last remaining unprotected ancient forests. A grassroots group of forest activists fighting to save our forests for the future. On a small budget they have become a major "thorn-in-the-side" to the timber industry, which has been systematically destroying virgin forests at a dramatically increasing rate over the past 10 years.

Methods of operation: Litigation (50%), research (25%), lobbying (5%), public education (45%)

Constituency: Environmental activists, forest experts

Recent issues and projects: Lawsuits challenging illegal Timber Harvesting Plans; research on forest issues to provide information needed to draft Headwaters Forest Act, HR2866; clearinghouse for information on deforestation in California; support center for grassroots activists

Major publications: Newsletter

Budget: $120,000

Funding: Individual contributions (25%), foundations (25%), direct mail (25%), court awards and raffles (25%)

Staff:
All Part-time and sporadically funded
1 Administrator
3 Paralegals
1 Volunteer Coordinator
2 Bookkeepers
4 Public Education Coordinators
5 Newsletter Editors

Staff openings/year: 2

Work Week: 45 hours

Salary/year: $2,000 - 12,000 (Recent College Graduate); $Varies (Graduate with advanced degree)

Part-Time Employees: 5

Volunteers: 100

Interns: Occasional
Length: Varies
Duties: Various
Remuneration: $250/month stipend sometimes available

Jobs advertised: Locally and in direct mailings

To apply: Write for more information

ENVIRONMENTAL VOLUNTEERS

3921 E. Bayshore Road
Palo Alto, CA 94303
(415) 961-0545

Director: Debra Ting

Purpose: Environmental Volunteers is a nonprofit educational group which teaches natural science to local grade school children. They have 150 volunteer docents who are professionally trained to do this.

Methods of operation: Public education (100%)

Constituency: Active volunteer docents and community membership

Recent issues and projects: 1993-94 is the last year for the *SHARE in Nature* pilot program; volunteers work in one school the entire year, thereby making contact with the same children over and over again. Specialized training allows volunteers who ordinarily might be unable to attend the annual 14 week long training to train in one specific environmental topic in only one month (during weekend and evening hours). A strategic plan has been developed for future growth of organization.

Major publications: Community newsletter three times per year

Budget: $240,000

Funding: Grants (35%), special events (32%), individual contributions (13%), program services, (11%) investment interest (5%), product sales and annual dues (2%)

Staff: 3
1 Executive Director
1 Volunteer and Service Coordinator
1 Program Director
1/2 Administrative Assistant
1/2 Development Consultant

Staff openings/year: 0-1

Work Week: 40 hours

Salary/year: $24,000 (Recent College Graduate); $Varies (Graduate with advanced degree)

Benefits: Health insurance, paid vacation, dental insurance

Part-Time Employees: 2

Volunteers: 150+

Interns: None currently, but willing to accept applications

Jobs advertised: Newspapers; job boards

To apply: Contact Debra Ting

EQUAL RIGHTS ADVOCATES

1663 Mission Street, Suite 550
San Francisco, CA 94103
(510) 621-0672

Director: Nancy L. Davis, Executive Director

Purpose: Equal Rights Advocates is one of the oldest public interest law firms specializing in sex and race-based discrimination. ERA has evolved into a legal organization with a multi-faceted approach to addressing women's legal issues, including legal representation, public education, advice and counseling, coalition building, media relations and public policy advocacy.

Methods of operation: Litigation (40%), public education (20%), advice and counseling (10%), publications (5%), community organizing (5%), training and technical assistance (5%), public policy advocacy, grassroots lobbying (15%)

Constituency: Working women and women students

Recent issues and projects: Over the past 11 years, ERA has committed itself to becoming a multiracial, multi-ethnic organization in terms of staff and program priorities. ERA's program emphasis is on women of color and low-income women and on the interrelationship between sex and race-based discrimination.

Major publications: Quarterly newsletter: *Equal Rights Advocate*; *Pay Equity Sourcebook* (Dec. 1987); *Affirmative Action Handbook: How to Start and Defend Affirmative Action Programs*; *Know Your Rights Brochures: Sex Discrimination, Pregnancy Discrimination; Domestic Workers Rights* (in Spanish and English)

Budget: $1,000,000

Funding: Foundations (43%), individual contributions (30%), other (27%)

Staff: 12
4 Attorneys
1 Legal Secretary
1 Finance Director
1 Associate Director
1 Administrative Assistant
1 Development Assistant
1 Receptionist
1 Director of Foundation/Relations/ Special Events
1 Law Fellow

Staff openings/year: 0-2

Work Week: 37.5 hours

Salary/year: $Varies (Recent College Graduate); $Varies (Graduate with advanced degree)

Benefits: Health insurance, life insurance, parenting leave, credit union, paid vacation, dental insurance and disability leave

Part-Time Employees: 3

Volunteers: Yes

Interns: Yes
Length: 1 semester
Duties: Research, media and public relations, legal services
Remuneration: Depends; sometimes work-study

Jobs advertised: Local papers; Public Interest Clearinghouse; postings at Bay Area nonprofits and schools; Management Center newsletter

To apply: Contact Gail Kaufman, Associate Director

ESSENTIAL INFORMATION

P.O. Box 19405
Washington, DC 20036
(202) 387-8030

Director: John Richard

Purpose: EI's goals are to provide information to the public on important topics neglected by the mass media, policymakers and academics, and to provide an opportunity for beginning journalists to gain valuable experience. EI reaches these goals by publishing a monthly magazine, *Multinational Monitor*, sponsoring an investigative journalism conference, regularly giving grants to writers to pursue investigations, and conducting a periodic voter education program during election years.

Methods of operation: Publications (60%), public education (20%), research (20%)

Major publications: *Multinational Monitor*; *Poletown: Community Betrayed*; *Women Activists: Challenging the Abuse of Power*; *The Haiti Files; Silent Violence, Silent Death*

Budget: $350,000

Funding: Individual contributions (30%), foundations (30%), subscriptions (30%)

Staff:
4 Writers/Editors
1 Attorney
1 Office Manager

1 Researcher
1 Bookkeeper/Accountant
1 Issue Expert

Staff openings/year: 2

Work Week: 50 hours

Salary/year: $12,000 (Recent College Graduate); $15,000 (Graduate with advanced degree)

Benefits: Health insurance, paid vacation

Part-Time Employees: 3

Summer Employees: 3

Volunteers: 2

Interns: 6
Length: Semester
Duties: Research
Remuneration: Stipends based on experience

Jobs advertised: *The Nation*, *Community Jobs*, *The Progressive*, *In These Times*

To apply: Contact John Richard

ETHICS RESOURCE CENTER, INC.

1120 G Street, NW, Suite 200
Washington, DC 20005
(202) 737-2258

President: Gary Edwards

Purpose: The Ethics Resource Center is a nonprofit, nonpartisan and nonsectarian organization dedicated to promoting acceptance of and adherence to the highest standards of ethical conduct. Through our long-term work in business, government and character education, we are striving to restore ethics to their rightful place in everyday lives of all Americans.

Methods of operation: Public education (30%); training and technical assistance (30%); publications (20%), research (20%)

Constituency: Now initiating a grassroots constituency building effort for community-based character education programs

Recent issues and projects: Due for release this fall, the Center is currently compiling and analyzing data for its new survey report, Employee Survey on Ethics in American Business: Policies, Programs and Perceptions.

Major publications: *Ethics Journal*, published quarterly; *Creating a Workable Company Code of Ethics*; *Ethics Policies and Programs in American Business*; *Ethics Education in American Business Schools; Implementation and Enforcement of Codes of Ethics in Corporations and Associations*; *Self-Regulation Conference Proceedings*; *Common Sense and Everyday Ethics*; *The Ethical Basis of Economic Freedom*

Budget: $2,000,000

Funding: Corporations (70%), foundations (20%), individual contributions (10%)

Staff: 18
1 Writer/Editor
1 Office Manager
1 Foundation Fundraiser
3 Issue Experts
1 Bookkeeper/Accountant
1 Campaign Manager
7 Trainers
3 Administrative Assistants

Work Week: 37.5 hours

Benefits: Health insurance, paid vacation, life insurance

Part-Time Employees: Yes

Summer Employees: Yes

Volunteers: Yes

Interns: Yes
Length: One year
Duties: Work in Development, Communications and Character Education

Jobs advertised: Employment agencies, word-of-mouth and newspapers

To apply: Contact Ruth E. Sellers, Manager, Accounting and Administration

FAIR (FAIRNESS & ACCURACY IN REPORTING)

130 West 25th Street
New York, NY 10001
(212) 633-6700

Director: Jeff Cohen

Purpose: FAIR is the national media watch group offering well-documented criticism in an effort to correct bias and imbalance. FAIR focuses public awareness on the narrow corporate ownership of the press, the media's allegiance to official agendas and their insensitivity to women, labor, minorities and other public interest constituencies. FAIR seeks to invigorate the First Amendment by advocating for greater media pluralism and the inclusion of public interest voices in national debate.

Methods of operation: Research, publications, public education and activism

Constituency: Rank and file citizens and activists concerned about bias and censorship and allied groups

Recent issues and projects: Include broadening PBS' conservative, corporate talkshow lineup to include progressive and public interest programs, and diversifying the list of experts appearing throughout network TV news

Major publications: *Extra!*, FAIR's award-winning journal, 6 times a year; recent reports include: *Focus on Racism in the Media* (July/Aug. 1992); *Missing Voices: Women and the U.S. News Media* (summer 1992); *Radio Tilting Right: From NPR News to Commercial Talkshows* (April/May 1993); *Confronting Homophobia: Gays and Lesbians and the Media* (June 1993); *The Broken Promise of Public Television* (Sept./Oct. 1993)

Budget: $700,000

Funding: Foundations (50%), individual members (50%)

Staff: 9
1 Executive Director
1 Associate Director
1 Editor
1 Administrative/Activist Director
1 Research Director
1 Senior Analyst
1 Publisher
1 Organizer Director
1 Women's Desk Coordinator

Staff openings/year: 1

Work Week: 40-45 hours

Salary/year: $24,000

Benefits: Medical and dental insurance, paid vacation and camaraderie

Volunteers: Yes

Interns: Yes
Length: 1 semester
Duties: Research primarily; also office work and organizing
Remuneration: FAIR will pay travel, if necessary

Jobs advertised: Classified ads in progressive and minority-oriented publications; job notices are posted at public interest offices

To apply: Contact Steve Rendall, Senior Analyst

FAMILY & CHILD SERVICES OF DC

929 L Street, NW
Washington, DC 20001
(202) 289-1510

Other Offices: Landover Hills, MD; Alexandria, VA

Director: Rhoda L. Veney

Purpose: Since 1882 this private, nonprofit family service agency has provided professional services for children, families and seniors in the following areas: adoption; day care; foster care; camping; counseling; case management; and assessment

Methods of operation: Human services (95%), public education (5%)

Constituency: Citizens in the community who want to improve conditions for low-income children and families

Recent issues and projects: Recent projects include: finding permanent, adoptive families for black children; securing pro-bono legal services for families wanting to adopt but face financial barriers; forming guardianship review panel for consideration of senior citizens in need of protection

Major publications: Annual report

Budget: $7,000,000

Funding: Contracts (50%), United Way (20%), individual contributions (20%), foundations (10%)

Staff: 138
1 Paralegals
1 Office Managers
1/2 Foundation Fundraiser
2 Issue Experts
17 Administrative Assistants
6 Bookkeepers/Accountants
51 Social Workers
26 Foster Group Home Staff
20 Senior Center Staff
2 Retired Senior Volunteer Program
16 Other

Staff openings/year: Varies

Work Week: 37.5 hours

Salary/year: $Varies (Recent College Graduate); $28,000 (Graduate with advanced degree)

Benefits: Health insurance, pension, paid vacation, life insurance, credit union, family leave

Part-Time Employees: 10

Summer Employees: 40 + camp staff

Volunteers: 500

Interns: 1-2
Length: 8-10 weeks
Duties: Changes every summer
Remuneration: No financial support

Jobs advertised: *Washington Post* and professional journals

To apply: Executive Director (we are about to hire a half-time personnel director, until that occurs, applicants should send resumes to the Executive Director.

FARM AID, INC.
334 Broadway Suite 5
Cambridge, MA 02139
(617) 354-2922

Director: Carolyn Mugar

Purpose: To support family farmers and raise awareness of the importance of family farm agriculture

Methods of operation: Research; publications; human services; community organizing; public education; training and technical assistance; making grants to family farm support organizations

Constituency: General public

Recent issues and projects: The flood of 1993; sustainable agriculture; block land loss

Major publications: *Farm Aid News Weekly* newsletter to organizations; *Farm Aid Update* quarterly newsletter to supporters

Budget: $1,000,000

Funding: Individual contributions (90%), direct mail (10%)

Staff: 5
1 Office Manager
1 Executive Director
1 Associate Director
1 Program Director
1 Fundraising Associate

Staff openings/year: 0-1

Work Week: 40 + hours

Salary/year: $Varies (Recent College Graduate); $Varies (Graduate with advanced degree)

Benefits: Health insurance, paid vacation, pregnancy leave

Part-Time Employees: 1

Summer Employees: Varies

Volunteers: Varies

Interns: 1
Length: No average length
Duties: Research, support services
Remuneration: Stipend

Jobs advertised: *Boston Globe*; Flyers

To apply: Contact Glenda Yoder, Associate Director

FARM ANIMAL REFORM MOVEMENT
P.O. Box 30654
Bethesda, MD 20824
(301) 530-1737

Director: Alex Hershaft

Purpose: To alleviate and eliminate the abuse of animals and other destructive impacts of animal agriculture on consumer health, food resources and environmental quality.

Methods of operation: Research, lobbying, publications, organizing, public education, training, demonstrations

Recent issues and projects: Great American Meatout: promotion of meatless diet on March 20th; World Farm Animals Day: promotion of public awareness of animal abuse on October 2nd (Gandhi's birthday); National Veal Ban Action on Mother's Day.

Major publications: Quarterly *FARM Report*

Funding: Membership contributions

Staff: 6

Staff openings/year: 5

Work Week: 40-50 hours

Part-Time Employees: Yes

Volunteers: Yes

Interns: Yes
Length: Flexible
Duties: Varies with intern's interests
Remuneration: Small stipend covers living expenses

To apply: Contact Alex Hershaft

Remarks: Employees are paid $6-8/hour.

FARM LABOR ORGANIZING COMMITTEE

507 South Saint Clair Street
Toledo, OH 43602
(419) 243-3456

Other Offices: Winter Garden, FL; Plant City, FL

President: Baldemar Velasquez

Purpose: To organize farmworkers through the collective bargaining process to win basic justice and dignity for themselves and their families.

Methods of operation: Community organizing (50%), public education (20%), training and technical assistance (10%), direct action (10%), research (10%)

Constituency: Hispanic migrant farmworkers

Recent issues and projects: FLOC won a 7-year strike and boycott against Campbells, resulting in contracts that improve health, wage and labor conditions. FLOC is extending this process throughout the Midwest to end sharecropping.

Major publications: Newsletter to supporters; *Nuestra Lucha* newsletter to members

Budget: $200,000

Funding: Individual contributions, foundations

Staff: 14
8 Organizers
1 Writer/Editor
1 Office Manager
1 Researcher
1 Issue Expert
1 Bookkeeper/Accountant
1 Grassroots Fundraiser

Work Week: 40+ hours

Salary/year: $13,000-30,000

Benefits: Health insurance, pregnancy leave, paid vacation

Part-Time Employees: 2

Summer Employees: 3

Volunteers: 10

Interns: 4
Length: 3 months-1 year
Duties: Organizing, research, writing, public education
Remuneration: Varies

Jobs advertised: Word of mouth; progressive social justice and labor networks

To apply: Contact Baldemar Velasquez, President, FLOC

FARM SANCTUARY

P.O. Box 150
Watkins Glen, NY 14891
(607) 583-2225

Purpose: Farm Sanctuary is a national nonprofit organization dedicated to ending farm animal abuse.

Methods of operation: Research, lobbying, litigation, publications, community organizing, direct action, public education

Membership: Current membership of approximately 26,000 people nationwide

Recent issues and projects: Recent projects include: The Federal Downed Animal Protection Act; farm animal shelters; and the visitor center

Major publications: *Sanctuary News*, quarterly; fact sheets and other literature available

Budget: $850,000

Funding: Individual contributions, foundations, direct mail

Staff: 5
1 Office Manager
1 Grassroots Fundraiser
1 Legislative and Investigative Campaign Coord.
1 Education Coordinator
1 Farm Manager

Staff openings/year: Varies

Work Week: 40 hours

Benefits: Housing

Part-Time Employees: 2

Summer Employees: None

Volunteers: Varies

Interns: 7-11
Length: 1-3 months
Duties: Cleaning, farm maintenance, office work, educational tours
Remuneration: Room and food allowance

To apply: Contact Internship coordinator for internships and the Administrative Manager for employment

FARMWORKERS ASSOCIATION OF FLORIDA

815 S. Park Avenue
Apopka, FL 32703
(407) 886-5151

Director: Tirso Moreno

Purpose: To build a strong, multi-racial, economically, viable organization of farmworkers in Florida. Empowering farmworkers to respond to and gain control over the social, political, economic and workplace issues affecting their lives.

Methods of operation: Community organizing/advocacy (50%), direct action (20%), public education (20%), research (8%), training and technical assistance (2%)

Constituency: African-American, Hispanic (Mexican, Guatamalan, Salvadoran, Chicano) and Haitian

Recent issues and projects: Education and training of farmworkers on pesticides and other health and safety issues; organizing farmworkers on workplace and community issues; networking with other organizations on economic justice and environmental issues; providing programs for AIDS education and prevention; developing economic development projects, such as a food store, restaurant, and Workers Cooperative Harvesting Company

Major publications: *El Jale*, newsletter

Budget: $537,360

Funding: Foundations/government grants (80%), service (13%), local fundraising (4%), individual contributions (3%)

Staff: 19
14 Organizers
4 Office Managers
1 Foundation Fundraiser
1 Bookkeeper/Accountant

Staff openings/year: 1-2

Work Week: 40 hours

Salary/year: $Varies (Recent College Graduate); $Varies (Graduate with advanced degree)

Benefits: Health insurance, paid vacation, life insurance, credit union

Part-Time Employees: 11

Summer Employees: None

Volunteers: 140

Interns: None, but willing to accept applications

Jobs advertised: By word-of-mouth, within the community and in local newspapers

FEDERATION OF CHILD CARE CENTERS OF ALABAMA (FOCAL)

3703 Rosa L. Parks Avenue, P.O. Box 214
Montgomery, AL 36101
(205) 262-3456

Director: Sophia Bracy Harris

Purpose: FOCAL has the largest constituency of any child advocacy group in the state and presents the perspective of poor and minority families and providers to the decision-making process for child day care in Alabama.

Methods of operation: Research, lobbying, publications, human services, community organizing, public education, training and technical assistance

Constituency: Minority women

Recent issues and projects: Organizational development; peer education project; black women's economic development; child day care; community development; internalized oppression (youth project); leadership development

Major publications: Newsletter: *FOCAL Point*; annual report

Budget: $354,700

Funding: Individual contributions, foundations

Staff: 9
1 Publicist
2 Program Coordinators
1 Director
1 Deputy Director
1 Administrative Assistant
1 Office Manager
1 Early Childhood Education
1 Day Care Organizer

Staff openings/year: 0-2

Work Week: 35-40 hours

Salary/year: $26,500 (Recent College Graduate); $Varies (Graduate with advanced degree)

Benefits: Health insurance, pregnancy leave, pension, child care, paid vacation

Part-Time Employees: 5

Volunteers: 2-4

Interns: 1-2
Length: 2-3 months

Jobs advertised: Local and state newspapers

To apply: Contact Sophia Bracy Harris, Executive Director, or A. Jack Guillebeaux, Deputy Director

FEDERATION OF EGALITARIAN COMMUNITIES

Box GWI
Tecumseh, MO 65760
(417) 679-4682

Other Offices: Mineral, VA; Louisa, VA; Check, VA; Rutledge, MO; Scottown, OH

Director: Brenda Faye Stout

Purpose: The purpose of the Federation is to facilitate inter-community cooperation and assistance, to support other cooperative structures and to educate ourselves and the general public about the social and economic advantages of egalitarian communities.

Methods of operation: Program development and outreach (100%)

Constituency: Folks interested in exploring and promoting communal living

Recent issues and projects: Networking efforts to overcome racism and other forms of oppression; facilitation skills; participation in the Fellowship for Intentional Communities; helped to support the production of the *Directory of Intentional Communities* for *Communities Magazine*, 1993.

Major publications: Newsletters: *Leaves of Twin Oaks*, twice a year; *Windfall*, every other month; *Community Soundings*, twice a year; *Living the Dream*, book; *Sharing the Dream*, brochure

Budget: $16,000

Funding: Community contributions (90%), individual contributions (10%)

Staff: 180
180 Residents

Benefits: Housing, board, all human needs and small allowance, health care

Volunteers: Yes

Interns: Yes
Length: 4 weeks
Duties: Work with community members
Remuneration: Room and board

To apply: Contact Brenda Faye, Director

Remarks: There are currently six communities, with three communities in dialogue. Each community has a program to allow people to live and work within the community for a short visit.

FEDERATION OF OHIO RIVER COOPERATIVES

320 Outerbelt Street, Suite E
Columbus, OH 43213
(614) 861-2446

Manager: Robert J. Pickford

Purpose: Direct delivery of wholesome foods at wholesale prices to hundreds of consumer-owned retails and buying groups throughout 11 states. They offer an aggressive volume discount that applies to all purchases; full line distributor offers over 5,000 products.

Methods of operation: Direct action (70%), public education (15%), publications (15%)

Constituency: Consumers interested in controlling reasonably-priced access to natural and organic foods, and supporting organic farming.

Recent issues and projects: Organic produce and meat distribution; working with suppliers on ecologically appropriate packaging. Recently opened the first company-owned retail store in Cincinnati.

Major publications: Monthly price list and promotional information

Budget: $1,000,000

Funding: Sales (100%)

Staff:
10 salaried staff, 33 hourly wage

Staff openings/year: 4

Work Week: 40+ hours

Salary/year: $Varies (Recent College Graduate); $Varies (Graduate with advanced degree)

Benefits: Health insurance, credit union, paid vacation, 401-K plan, sick leave

Part-Time Employees: 3

Volunteers: Yes

Interns: None currently, but willing to accept applications

Jobs advertised: Local newspaper

To apply: Contact Robert J. Pickford, General Manager

FEDERATION OF SOUTHERN COOPERATIVES

P.O. Box 95
Epes, AL 35460
(205) 652-9676

Other Offices: Atlanta, GA; Albany, GA; Jackson, MS

Director: Ralph Paige

Purpose: The Federation is a service, resource and advocacy organization involving 30,000 families in over 100 cooperatives and credit unions across the rural South. Its primary focus is on the economic development needs of low-income people.

Methods of operation: Research, lobbying, publications, human services, organizing, training and technical assistance

Membership: Cooperatives and credit unions located in the South are eligible for membership.

Recent issues and projects: Primary sponsors of "Minority Farmers Rights Bill" legislation to provide affirmative action for Black and other minority farmers. Sponsors training in cooperative principles and philosophy as well as training in any skill areas necessary to operate cooperatives. The Federation also gives individualized attention to each member cooperative in trouble shooting, business planning, and resource development.

Major publications: *FSC Quarterly Newsletter*; *Some Marketing Ideas for Managers of Limited Resource Agricultural Marketing and Purchasing Cooperatives*; *Working with Black Small Farmers in the Rural South*; others

Budget: $800,000

Funding: State and federal government contracts, churches, foundations, individual contributions

Staff: 19
6 Bookkeepers/Accountants
2 Fundraisers
2 Typists
2 Office Managers
2 Agricultural Field Staff
2 Maintenance
1 Writer/Editor
1 Credit Union Specialist
1 Housing Specialist

Staff openings/year: 3

Work Week: 40 hours

Salary/year: $15-20,000

Benefits: Health insurance, life insurance, credit union, pregnancy leave, paid vacation

Part-Time Employees: Yes

Interns: Yes
Length: 6 weeks-1 year
Duties: Varied
Remuneration: Room in the Federation Dormitory plus $50/week

Jobs advertised: Community organization newsletters; letters to social change organizations

To apply: Contact John Zippert, Director of Program Operations

FELLOWSHIP OF RECONCILIATION

P.O. Box 271
Nyack, NY 10977
(914) 358-4601

Other Offices: Louisville, KY; Santa Cruz, CA

Director: Jo Becker

Purpose: The Fellowship of Reconciliation (FOR) is an international, spiritually-based movement of people who are committed to active nonviolence as a means of personal, social and political change. Current goals: 1) to reduce community violence and build racial and economic justice; 2) to demilitarize U.S. policy, promote broad disarmament and build peace; 3) to build the movement of faith-based nonviolent activists.

Methods of operation: Public education (50%), publications (25%), community organizing (15%), lobbying (5%), direct action (5%)

Recent issues and projects: Launched "Stop the Killing, Start the Healing" campaign against gun violence; cooperated with Muslim organizations to bring Bosnian refugee students to the U.S.; offer resources and workshops on nonviolence, peace, disarmament and racial justice.

Major publications: *Fellowship* bi-monthly magazine; *For Witness* semi-monthly; as well as a complete booklist. Please write or call to order.

Budget: $1,000,000

Funding: Individual contributions (60%), other (40%)

Staff: 18
2 Organizers
3 Writer/Editors
1 Office Manager
2 Fundraisers
2 Issue Experts
1 Administrative Assistant
1 Bookkeeper/Accountant
2 Mailroom/Bookstore Assistants
1 Database Administrator
1 Intern Coordinator
1 Caretaker
1 Membership Assistant

Staff openings/year: 1-2

Work Week: 35 hours

Salary/year: $20,000 (Recent College Graduate); $Varies (Graduate with advanced degree)

Benefits: Health insurance, pension, paid vacation, life insurance, credit union, pregnancy leave

Part-Time Employees: 6

Summer Employees: None

Volunteers: 2-5

Interns: 6
Length: 9 months
Duties: Work 21 hours/week, participate in seminars, field trips, community service
Remuneration: Tuition of $2,000/year; room and board provided

Jobs advertised: Mailings, magazine/newspaper ads

To apply: Contact Jo Becker, Executive Director

FEMINIST HEALTH CENTER OF PORTSMOUTH

559 Portsmouth Avenue, P.O. Box 456
Greenland, NH 03840
(603) 436-7588

Director: Internal Board of Directors

Purpose: To provide low-cost quality health care to women; to act as an advocate for women on a state and local level; to provide education and testing for women and men for sexually transmitted diseases and HIV; to act as a model for social change.

Methods of operation: Direct health care (85%), lobbying (5%), publications (5%), public education (5%)

Constituency: Politically aware and non-traditional

Recent issues and projects: Outreach and education around "safer sex" and HIV testing. Expanding services to offer Norplant, Depo Provera, IUD, Abortions (5-14 weeks).

Major publications: Newsletter: *Health News*; *Womenwise*, put out in conjunction with the Concord Feminist Health Center

Funding: Individual contributions, direct mail, other

Staff: 7
1 Physician
4 Nurse Practitioners
2 Male Peer Counselors

Staff openings/year: 2

Work Week: 32 hours

Salary/year: $Varies (Recent College Graduate); $Varies (Graduate with advanced degree)

Benefits: Health insurance, child care, pregnancy leave, paid vacation

Part-Time Employees: 4-8

Interns: None currently, but willing to accept applications

Jobs advertised: Newspapers; word of mouth

To apply: Contact Catherine Barden

Remarks: Ours is primarily a direct health care for women organizations. However we do see men at our STD (Sexually Transmitted Diseases) and HIV services. We are women-owned and women-run.

FILM NEWS NOW FOUNDATION

100 Bleecker Street, Suite 12D
New York, NY 10012
(212) 998-1577

Director: Chris Choy

Purpose: The Foundation is committed to the advancement of the presence and involvement of people of color and women in the media field. The Foundation assists, encourages, and provides services and consultations to producers of color as well as women producers.

Methods of operation: Research, publications, public education, training and technical assistance, lobbying, community organizing

Constituency: Established and emerging women and minority artists

Recent issues and projects: We've started conducting screenwriting workshops specially designed for people of color and women, continued our literature series which is aimed at promoting works by women and people of color, provided free consultations to over 100 producers of color and women, and finished a documentary on the myth of the model Asian minority.

Major publications: To be published soon is a compilation of data documenting the status of minority producers in New York state. Also soon to be published is a proceedings book of "Show the Right Thing," a national conference on multicultural film and video exhibition in New York City.

Budget: $900,000

Funding: Foundations (90%), individual contributions (10%)

Staff: 3

Work Week: 40 hours

Salary/year: $15,000

Benefits: Health insurance, paid vacation

Part-Time Employees: 2

Volunteers: 2

Interns: 2
Length: School semester
Duties: General help with mailings, office duties, research
Remuneration: Some monetary compensation

Jobs advertised: Trade magazines and newsletters; word of mouth

To apply: Contact Marina Feleo Gonzalez, Administrative Director

FLORENCE IMMIGRANT AND REFUGEE RIGHTS PROJECT, INC.

300 S. Main Suite B, PO Box 654
Florence, AZ 85232
(602) 868-0191

Director: Matthew Wilch

Purpose: The Florence Immigrant and Refugee Rights Project provides legal services to noncitizens who are detained by INS, and are facing possible deportation from the U.S.

Methods of operation: Litigation (88%), public education (12%)

Budget: $100,000

Funding: Individual contributions (5%), foundations (90%), direct mail (5%)

Staff: 8
2 Attorneys
1 Bookkeeper/accountant
4 Paralegals
1 Secretary

Work Week: 50 hours

Salary/year: $20,000 (Recent College Graduate); $25,000 (Graduate with advanced degree)

Benefits: Health insurance, paid vacation

Part-Time Employees: 1

Summer Employees: 2

Volunteers: 20

Interns: 2
Length: 1 semester
Duties: Interview clients, prepare applications, research legal issues
Remuneration: Internships for law school credit, and paid for by the law school public interest program or NLG

Jobs advertised: Law school placement programs or by word of mouth

To apply: Contact Matthew Wilch

FLORIDA JUSTICE INSTITUTE

200 South Biscayne Blvd., Suite 720
Miami, FL 33131-2310
(305) 358-2081

Director: Randall C. Berg, Jr.

Purpose: The Florida Justice Institute seeks to: improve the administration of justice to all Floridians; encourage better representation of citizens interests; and increase the ability of citizens to resolve disputes quickly and inexpensively.

Methods of operation: Litigation (95%), human services (5%)

Recent issues and projects: Recent projects include: federal pro bono project; corrections improvement project; and a housing discrimination project

Major publications: *Older Floridians Handbook*

Budget: $300,000

Funding: Foundations (66%), attorney's fees (33%)

Staff: 5

2 Attorneys
2 Legal Secretaries
1 Pro-bono Coordinator

Work Week: 40 hours

Benefits: Health insurance, pension, paid vacation, credit union

Part-Time Employees: None

Summer Employees: 2

Volunteers: None

Interns: Not at this time, willing to accept applications

Jobs advertised: Through legal publications

To apply: Contact Randall Berg, Executive Director

FLORIDA PUBLIC INTEREST RESEARCH GROUP (FPIRG)

420 East Call Street
Tallahassee, FL 32301
(904) 224-5304

Other Offices: Tampa, FL; Miami, FL

Director: Ann Whitfield

Purpose: Research, educate and advocate on environmental and consumer protection issues.

Methods of operation: Lobbying and organizing (50%), public education (30%), research (20%)

Constituency: Florida university students, general Florida citizens

Recent issues and projects: Stopping offshore oil drilling (have won series of temporary bans to protect Florida's coast, now working on permanent protection); pollution prevention; Everglades; recycling; consumer rights programs

Major publications: Quarterly newsletter: *Citizen Agenda*

Budget: $200,000

Funding: Individual contributions, foundations

Staff: 9
1 Executive Director/Lobbyist
1 Lobbyist/Issue Expert
5 Organizers
1 Administrative Director
1/2 Office Assistant

Staff openings/year: 4

Work Week: 50-60 hours

Salary/year: $14,000 (Recent College Graduate); $18,000 (Graduate with advanced degree)

Benefits: Health insurance, paid vacation

Part-Time Employees: Yes; number varies

Summer Employees: Yes

Volunteers: Yes

Interns: Yes
Length: 1 semester
Duties: Depends; can be organizing, research or lobbying

Jobs advertised: Newspapers; magazines; mailings

To apply: Contact Rick Trilsch

FOOD & WATER, INC.

P.O. Box 114
Marshfield, VT 05658
(802) 426-3700

Director: Michael Colby

Purpose: Food and Water is a national nonprofit organization coordinating educational activities and consumer involvement with regard to food irradiation, pesticides and other ecological issues.

Methods of operation: Public education (40%), direct action (30%), research (15%), lobbying (5%), community organizing (5%), training and technical assistance (5%)

Recent issues and projects: Food irradiation; low level radioactive waste; activist training

Major publications: *Safe Food News*; *Food Irradiation Action Alerts*

Budget: $350,000

Funding: Foundations (85%), individual contributions (35%)

Staff: 6
1 Foundation Fundraiser
1 Administrator
2 Organizers
1 Office Manager
1 Issue Expert/Editor

Staff openings/year: 2-3

Work Week: 40 hours

Salary/year: $16,000 (Recent College Graduate); $20,000 (Graduate with advanced degree)

Benefits: Health insurance, life insurance, family leave, paid vacation

Part-Time Employees: 3

Summer Employees: Yes

Volunteers: 5

Interns: Yes
Length: 3 months
Duties: Based on skills and experience
Remuneration: Based on skills and experience

Jobs advertised: Word of mouth; community posting; newspaper

To apply: Contact Michael Colby, Executive Director

FOOD AND HUNGER HOTLINE

252 Seventh Avenue, 15th Floor
New York, NY 10001
(212) 366-5400

Director: Ellyn Rosenthal

Purpose: (1) Hotline for people with no money and no food. Refers them to an emergency 3-day supply. (2) Technical assistance, helping community groups set up soup kitchens and food pantries. (3) Research and advocacy to change policies and end hunger. (4)Vanguard Cafe, NYC's first nonprofit restaurant

Methods of operation: Human services (50%), training and technical assistance (20%), public education (20%), research (10%)

Constituency: People with no money and no food

Major publications: *A Million Meals a Month*, a report on hunger in New York City and the emergency food network

Budget: $685,000

Funding: Individual contributions, foundations, direct mail, corporations, special events

Staff: 13
5 Hotline Operators
1 Executive Director
1 Office Manager
1 Technical Assistance Coordinator
1 Associate Director
1 Director of Programs
1 Program Development and Project Coordinator
2 Assistants

Staff openings/year: 1

Work Week: 35+ hours

Salary/year: $22,000

Benefits: Health insurance, pregnancy leave (unpaid), paid vacation

Part-Time Employees: 1-5

Volunteers: Yes, up to 10

Interns: 2
Length: No limit; summer/semester/year
Duties: Open
Remuneration: Minimal reimbursement of expenses

Jobs advertised: Newsletters in hunger network

To apply: Contact Joy Bower, Office Manager

FOOD RESEARCH AND ACTION CENTER (FRAC)

1875 Connecticut Ave., NW, Suite 540
Washington, DC 20009
(202) 986-2200

Director: Robert J. Fersh

Purpose: A nonprofit legal, research and advocacy center working at the national level to end hunger and malnutrition in the United States.

Methods of operation: Research, lobbying, litigation, publications, organizing, public education, training and technical assistance

Recent issues and projects: Food stamps; school lunch and breakfast; summer food program for children; WIC Program, the special supplemental food program for women, infants and children. FRAC helps community groups and coalitions work to improve food programs, develops written materials to help people understand national and state legislative issues, trains community advocates, provides technical assistance to the legal services community, and conducts public education campaigns.

Major publications: Bimonthly: *Foodlines*; *FRAC's Guide to the Food Stamp Program*; *Fuel for Excellence: FRAC's Guide to School Breakfast Expansion*; *Feeding the Other Half: Women and Children Left Out of WIC*; *The Relationship Between Nutrition and Learning*; *School Breakfast Scorecard*; *WIC Works*; *Summer Food Scorecard*

Budget: $1,200,000

Funding: Foundations, corporations, religious groups, individual contributions

Staff: 18
2 Staff Attorneys
3 Senior Field Organizers
2 Wordprocessing Secretaries
1 Executive Director
1 Deputy Director
1 Legal Director
1 Community Childhood Hunger Identification Project (CCHIP) Director
1 CCHIP Research Assistant
1 Director, Nutrition Policy and Research
1 Development Director
1 Associate Development Director
1 Finance and Administration Director
1 Communications Director
1 Receptionist
1 Office Manager/Executive Assistant

Staff openings/year: 2-3

Work Week: 40 hours

Salary/year: $17-23,000 (Recent College Graduate); $23-45,000 (Graduate with advanced degree)

Benefits: Health insurance, life insurance, dental insurance, pregnancy leave, paid vacation, child care tax benefits, retirement/IRA plan, union, union's credit union

Part-Time Employees: Yes

Interns: 1-5
Length: 3 months, approximately
Duties: Community and field relations, policy, research development, law clerking

Jobs advertised: Newspapers; notices sent to other groups in our network; bulletin board postings

To apply: For internships, contact Ellen Teller; for other positions, contact Rita Doherty

FOR LOVE OF CHILDREN (FLOC)

1711 14th Street, NW
Washington, DC 20009
(202) 462-8686 Fax: (202) 797-2198

Director: Fred Taylor

Purpose: Our purpose is to enable at risk children and families in the District of Columbia to engage in the development necessary for them to become self-determining, contributing citizens.

Methods of operation: Human services, organizing, training and technical assistance, transition housing and outdoor education

Constituency: A diverse range of children and families ranging from inner-city poor to suburban church groups

Recent issues and projects: The foster parent recruitment and training program; a group home for adolescent males; an outdoor education program; Hope and a Home Program for large low-income families; transitional housing; and a therapeutic day school for adolescents.

Major publications: Quarterly: *FLOC Newsletter*; annual report

Budget: $4,200,000

Funding: Local government/fees for service contracts, foundations, individuals, religious groups and corporations

Staff: 64
Includes:
Social Workers
Special Education Teachers
Program Directors
Counselors
Clerical Staff

Staff openings/year: 5

Work Week: 38 hours

Salary/year: $18,000 (Recent College Graduate); $23,000 - 45,000 (Graduate with advanced degree)

Benefits: Health insurance, life insurance, sick leave, pension plan, paid vacation, long-term disability, sabbatical after 10 years employment

Part-Time Employees: 2

Volunteers: 100+

Jobs advertised: Newspapers; other nonprofits; colleges

To apply: Contact Dorothy Dixon

Remarks: We are always in need of MSW's (Masters in Social Work) and M.Ed.'s (Masters in Education). These positions are salaried at $25-32,000, depending on experience. Counseling and teaching positions are more readily filled. We are always in need of foster parents who are willing to work with abandoned youth.

FORESIGHT INSTITUTE

10108 Hemlock Drive, P.O. Box 13267
Overland Park, KS 66212
(913) 383-3359

President: Twyla Dell

Purpose: To educate business and community leaders in environmental issues.

Methods of operation: Publications (30%), research (30%), public education (30%), training and technical assistance (10%)

Recent issues and projects: Award winning environmental leadership program.

Major publications: Newsletter: *Foresight*; Books: *Call of the Rainbow Warrior* and *Earthcare*

Budget: $150,000

Funding: Tuition (100%)

Staff: 3
1 Writer/Editor
1 Trainer
1 Director of Marketing

Staff openings/year: 3

Work Week: 40-60 hours

Salary/year: $20,000 (Recent College Graduate); $20,000 + bonus (Graduate with advanced degree)

Benefits: Health insurance

Part-Time Employees: 2

Volunteers: 8

Interns: 1
Length: 3-9 months
Duties: Research, writing, editing on environmental subjects
Remuneration: Negotiable

Jobs advertised: Word of mouth

To apply: Contact Twyla Dell, President

Remarks: It is the goal of this organization to create an environmental leadership program in every major city and on college campuses, working toward Cleanup 2000.

FOUNDATION CENTER

79 Fifth Ave.
New York, NY 10003
(212) 620-4230

Other Offices: Washington, DC; San Francisco, CA; Cleveland, OH

President: Sara Engelhardt

Purpose: The Foundation Center is a national service organization which provides factual information on foundation and corporate philanthropic giving. The Center makes this information available through its publications and libraries. The Center also maintains an employment board at its NY library listing opportunities in nonprofits.

Methods of operation: Research, publications, library services, proposal writing workshops

Recent issues and projects: Publication of proposal writing guide; opening of new reference collection in Atlanta, GA; meet the grantmakers/proposal writing workshops

Major publications: *The Foundation Directory*; *The Foundation Center's Guide to Proposal Writing*; *Foundation 1000*; *Foundation Fundamentals*; *The Foundation Grants Index*; quarterly catalog; annual report

Funding: Foundations, revenue from publications, services

Staff: 80

Work Week: 40 hours

To apply: Contact Juan Brito, Personnel Manager

FOUNDATION ON ECONOMIC TRENDS

1130 17th Street, NW, Suite 630
Washington, DC 20036
(202) 466-2823

Director: Jeremy Rifkin

Purpose: The activities of the Foundation on Economic Trends are centered around the environmental, ethical and economic concerns raised by the development of emerging technologies.

Methods of operation: Research, lobbying, public education, community organizing, litigation, publications

Recent issues and projects: Biotechnological issues, including biological warfare research, agricultural biotechnologies, and medical biotechnology

Major publications: Books: *Entropy: Into the Greenhouse World*; *Algeny*; *Time Wars*; and *Green Lifestyle Handbook*

Budget: $450,000

Funding: Foundations (80%), individual contributions (20%)

Staff: 5
1 Writer/Editor
1 Attorney
1 Office Manager
1 Researcher
1 Foundation Fundraiser

Staff openings/year: 1-2

Work Week: 40 hours

Salary/year: $15,000

Benefits: Paid vacation

Part-Time Employees: 2-3

Summer Employees: 2-3

Volunteers: 4-5

Interns: Yes
Length: Flexible
Duties: Research, writing
Remuneration: None

To apply: Contact the Director

FREESTORE/FOODBANK

Administrative Offices, 40 East McMicken
Cincinnati, OH 45210
(513) 241-1064

Other Offices: Bethel, OH

Director: Stephen Gibbs

Purpose: The agency is made up of four divisions: 1) Direct Services Division provides basic survival assistance to hungry and homeless people; 2) Foodbank Division provides a channel through which donated surplus and salvage products can move at the lowest possible cost from industrial donors to member nonprofit agencies serving the needy, the ill and infants; 3) Processing division reclaims store damaged food and non-food products for redistribution at the lowest possible cost to nonprofit organizations served by the Foodbank Division; 4) Prepared and Perishable Foods Division makes it possible to accept donations of perishable goods such as produce, meat and dairy products. Frozen prepared foods from local restaurants are donated to nonprofits.

Methods of operation: Human services (95%), training and technical assistance (5%)

Constituency: Low-income families and nonprofit organizations with a feeding program

Recent issues and projects: Repacking bulk products to help expand inventory.

Major publications: Quarterly newsletters to the public and to member agencies

Funding: Individual contributions, foundations, direct mail, other

Staff: 100
Including:
Caseworkers
Case Managers
Representative Payee Case Managers
Bookkeepers/Accountants
Receptionists
Development Assistants
Agency Relations Staff
Volunteer Coordinator
Warehouse/Stocking/Inventory Staff
Food Processing Staff
Administrative and Supervisory Staff

Staff openings/year: 2-5

Work Week: 40 hours

Salary/year: $Varies (Recent College Graduate); $Varies (Graduate with advanced degree)

Benefits: Health insurance, vision, dental and life insurance, credit union, paid vacation and sick leave, flexible benefits plan, 403 (b) plan.

Volunteers: 100

Interns: Will consider case by case

Jobs advertised: Posted within the agency and in local newspapers

To apply: Contact Amy Hunt, Human Services Manager, or Stephen Gibbs, Executive Director

Remarks: We are an innovative social services organization. Staff need to be dedicated to the missions of the agency and creative problem solvers.

FRESH AIR FOR NONSMOKERS (FANS)

P.O. Box 24052
Seattle, WA 98124
(206) 932-7011

Other Offices: Richland, WA; Yakima, WA; Spokane, WA; Vancouver, WA; Shelton, WA

Director: Robert A. Fox

Purpose: To educate the public about the health

hazard and costs of smoking or being exposed to tobacco smoke. To pass laws to prevent kids from starting to use tobacco products.

Methods of operation: Direct action (50%), human services (30%), public education (15%), lobbying (5%)

Membership: People from all walks of life from students to retired persons

Recent issues and projects: After years of work, Sea-Tac Airport is smokefree, including the restaurants and lounges. The Marlboro sign has been removed from the Kingdome. A guidebook was published with over 1000 smokefree restaurants, 17 taverns, 2 motels and 14 smokefree shopping malls.

Major publications: Quarterly newsletter

Budget: $8,000

Funding: Individual contributions (75%), foundations (25%)

Staff:
Volunteer positions only
1 President
11 Board Members

Work Week: 30 hours

Part-Time Employees: No

Summer Employees: No

Volunteers: Many

Interns: No, but willing to accept applications

Remarks: FANS is an all volunteer group registered with the Sec. of State and the IRS as an educational nonprofit organization. We authored the Seattle Clean Air Ordinance and lobbied to get it passed in 1983. We are co-authors of the Washington Clean Indoor Air Act and lobbied hard to get it passed into law in 1985. This law makes public places smokefree, but does allow for smoke areas in some places. We lobbied hard to get a bill passed into law that made schools K through 12 tobacco free.

FRIENDLY HOUSE INC.

P.O. Box 8695, 802 S. 1st Ave.
Phoenix, AZ 85030
(602) 257-1870

Director: Eugene Brassaro

Purpose: Assisting those seeking to enter the mainstream of American life by providing quality education, integration, support services and maintaining cultural values and traditions. To cooperate with other organizations providing complimentary and similar services.

Methods of operation: Human services (85%), public education (10%), research (5%)

Recent issues and projects: Recent projects include: adult education; drop-out prevention for at-risk youth; youth alternatives to risk; early child development; Even Start; high school for pregnant and parenting teens; midnight basketball for gang prevention; in home support and parent skills training for at risk abuse/neglect; family crisis counselling; drug/alcohol abuse prevention for youth and adults; anti-discrimination for employees and employers of immigrants; legal residents; cultural programs; home care; long term care for the elderly; job development and placement; neighborhood development and social work

Major publications: Qualitative and quantitative analysis to funding sources and a quarterly newsletter

Budget: $2,800,000

Funding: Government (90%), individual contributions (8%), foundations (2%)

Staff: 55
1 Attorney
3 Paralegals
1 Office Manager
1 Issue Expert
4 Typists
4 Bookkeepers/Accountants
21 Caseworkers
2 Grassroots Fundraisers
12 Teachers/Tutors
6 Administrative/Computer/Custodial

Staff openings/year: 4

Work Week: 40 hours

Salary/year: $20,000 (Recent College Graduate); $25,000 (Graduate with advanced degree)

Benefits: Health insurance, pension, paid vacation, life insurance, family leave

Part-Time Employees: 60

Summer Employees: 20

Volunteers: 15

Interns: None, but willing to accept applications

Jobs advertised: Posted internally, advertised in local newspapers, other nonprofit organizations, local universities

To apply: Contact Jan Rollo, Senior Vice President of Finance and Administrative Services

FRIENDS COMMITTEE ON LEGISLATION OF CALIFORNIA

926 J Street, Room 707
Sacramento, CA 95814
(916) 443-3734

Other Offices: Whittier, CA

Director: Emma Childers, Director of Legislation

Purpose: FCL carries out lobbying in the California Legislature for criminal justice reform, adequate human services funding, and peace. It was established by Quakers.

Methods of operation: Public education (25%), lobbying (25%), publications (20%), research (15%), fundraising (15%)

Constituency: People interested in legislative action to affect social change

Recent issues and projects: Death penalty abolition campaign; legislative workshops

Major publications: *FCL Newsletter*, published 10 times/year ($18.00); FCL Education Fund booklets, such as legislative roster, *This Life We Take* (on capital punishment), and *Lobbying State Government*

Budget: $160,000

Funding: Individual contributions (80%), direct mail (10%), events (10%)

Staff: 3
1 Lobbyist
1 Office Manager
1 Fundraiser

Staff openings/year: 0-1

Work Week: 40 hours

Salary/year: $25,000

Benefits: Health insurance, pension, paid vacation

Part-Time Employees: 1

Volunteers: 2-6

Interns: Yes
Length: 9 months (2 semesters)
Duties: Assisting the lobbyist
Remuneration: None currently

Jobs advertised: Newspaper; publications; announcements to organizations

To apply: Contact Vickie Valines, Office Manager

FRIENDS COMMITTEE ON NATIONAL LEGISLATION

245 Second Street, NE
Washington, DC 20002
(202) 547-6000 Fax: (202) 547-6019

Director: Joe Volk

Purpose: To bring Quaker values to bear on public policy. FCNL's goals are world peace, equity and justice for all, civil rights, environmental quality, and economic justice.

Methods of operation: Lobbying (66%), research and education (19%), publications (15%)

Constituency: More than 75% are members of the Society of Friends (Quakers) with strongest concentration in the Northeast, Midwest and West Coast

Recent issues and projects: Follow a vast amount of legislation and try to influence same.

Major publications: *FCNL Washington Newsletter*; *Indian Report*

Budget: $1,000,000

Funding: Individual contributions (85%), literature sales (14%), foundations (1%)

Staff: 22
8 Legislative Staff
4 Staff Assistants
1 Capital Campaign Coordinator
1 Office Manager
1 Accountant
4 Interns
1 Legislative Action Coordinator
1 Field Program Coordinator
1 Field Secretary

Staff openings/year: 0-2

Work Week: 37.5 hours

Salary/year: $12,500-18,000 (Recent College Graduate); $20,000 - 50,000 (Graduate with advanced degree)

Benefits: Health insurance, retirement, paid vacation, workers' compensation

Part-Time Employees: Occasional

Volunteers: Many

Interns: 4
Length: 11 months

Duties: Assist lobbyists, extensive program/lobby responsibility
Remuneration: Stipend adequate for basic expenses

Jobs advertised: Various publications and word of mouth

To apply: Contact the Administrative Manager

FRIENDS OF THE EARTH

218 D Street, SE
Washington, DC 20003
(202) 783-7400

Other Offices: Seattle, WA; Manila, PHILLIPINES

Director: Jane Perkins

Purpose: We are a global environmental advocacy organization. We have strong ties to hundreds of grassroots organizations working on issues ranging from groundwater protection and agricultural biotechnology to the prevention of toxic chemical accidents.

Methods of operation: Lobbying (30%), publications (25%), research (10%), human services (10%), public education (10%), litigation (5%), direct action (5%), community organizing (5%)

Constituency: Individuals (children to senior citizens), environmental activists

Recent issues and projects: (1) Concert tour with Paul McCartney; (2) activist coalition to strengthen oil spill legislation; (3) "Take Back the Coast!" against ocean polluters

Major publications: Monthly newsletter: *Friends of the Earth*; studies, reports and booklets on environmental issues

Budget: $3,200,000

Funding: Foundations (60%), individual contributions (30%), direct mail (10%)

Staff: 35
16 Lobbyist/Issue Experts
4 Researchers
3 Writer/Editors
3 Campaign Managers
2 Typists
2 Bookkeeper/Accountants
2 Foundation Fundraisers
2 Office Managers
1 Press Aide

Staff openings/year: 5

Work Week: 50 hours

Salary/year: $20,000 (Recent College Graduate); $28,000 (Graduate with advanced degree)

Benefits: Health insurance, pregnancy leave, pension, paid vacation

Part-Time Employees: 2

Summer Employees: 3

Volunteers: 3

Jobs advertised: Newspapers; community bulletin boards

To apply: Contact Ralph Bohrson, Executive Vice President

FRIENDS OF THE EVERGLADES, INC.

101 Westward Drive, #2
Miami Springs, FL 33166
(305) 888-1230

Other Offices: Miami Springs, FL

Director: Joe Podgor

Purpose: To foster an awareness and understanding of the Everglades and the human environments of South Florida in order to achieve a balanced, sustainable coexistence between each.

Methods of operation: Research, public education (30%), publications (20%), lobbying (10%), community organizing (10%), direct action (10%), training and technical assistance (10%), human services (8%), litigation (2%)

Constituency: Mostly from South Florida, but with representatives from 30 states and several foreign countries. Membership of 5,000.

Recent issues and projects: Drinking water/groundwater protection efforts lead to land use regulations; current activities have succeeded in Everglades restoration; public information center; public education programs; clearinghouse and hotline

Major publications: *Who Knows the Rain?*; *Lake Okeechobee: A Lake in Peril*; *The Dade County Environmental Story*; *Dade Toxic Substances Reports*; *The Nature of Dade County*; *Poisons in Paradise* slide show

Budget: $23,000

Funding: Individual contributions (95%), foundations (5%)

Staff:
5 Volunteer Staff

Work Week: 50 hours

Benefits: Satisfaction and results, experience and training in cutting-edge eco-work.

Volunteers: 150

Interns: 2
Length: 12 weeks in summer
Duties: Office staff, library research and maintenance, special projects, outreach
Remuneration: Interns are unpaid at present. All staff is volunteer.

Jobs advertised: We are registered with local Volunteer Clearinghouse. Our efforts earn publicity which attracts volunteers.

To apply: Contact Joe Podgor, Director of Information Service

---

FRIENDS OF THE RIVER

Fort Mason Center, Building C
San Francisco, CA 94123
(415) 771-0400

Other Offices: Sacramento, CA

Director: David Bolling

Purpose: FOR is a grassroots membership organization dedicated to the preservation of free-flowing rivers and streams and the conservation of water and energy resources.

Methods of operation: Public education (45%), community organizing (20%), white water rafting trips (10%), research (10%), publications (10%), lobbying (5%)

Constituency: The environmentally concerned; river recreationists

Recent issues and projects: The 100 Rivers Campaign is a project to obtain permanent protection for over 100 rivers and streams in national forests in California. The American River Recreation Area project would preserve this popular wilderness area and prevent construction of an expensive and dangerous Auburn Dam.

Major publications: Bimonthly newsmagazine: *Headwaters*; several river-related books

Budget: $650,000

Funding: Individual contributions (60%), special events, river trips (15%), direct mail (15%), foundations (10%)

Staff: 13
3 Issue Experts
1 1/2 Office Managers
1 1/4 River Trips Organizers
1 Administration
1 Publication Manager
1 Typist
1 Grassroots Fundraiser
1 Foundation Fundraiser
1 Organizer
1 Writer/Editor
1/2 Bookkeeper/Accountant

Staff openings/year: 1-2

Work Week: 40 hours

Salary/year: $20,000 (Recent College Graduate); $23,000 (Graduate with advanced degree)

Benefits: Partial health insurance, paid vacation

Part-Time Employees: 3

Summer Employees: 1-2

Volunteers: 1-50

Interns: Yes
Length: 3 months
Duties: Research; grassroots organizing
Remuneration: Usually work-study interns for university credit

Jobs advertised: Nonprofit classifieds; community organization bulletin boards and listings

To apply: Contact David Rouslin, Associate Director

FRIENDS OF THE THIRD WORLD, INC.

611 West Wayne Street
Fort Wayne, IN 46802-2125
(219) 422-1650

Other Offices: El Paso, TX; Sierra Vista, AZ; Orange, CA; Bloomington, IL; Albuquerque, NM

Director: James F. Goetsch

Purpose: To alleviate hunger/poverty by promoting cooperative partnerships between grassroots groups in Africa, Asia and Latin America and the United States.

Methods of operation: Alternative trading, publications, community organizing, public education, training and technical assistance

Membership: 800 co-ops; solidarity groups; nonprofits in 50 states; 10,000 individuals

Recent issues and projects: Annual Alternative Trading Conference; marketing crafts, books and food from 40 countries with educational information; organizing a woodworking co-op in Nicaragua, etc.

Major publications: Catalogs of books, crafts, food; *How to Organize a Third World Shop*; newsletter: *Alternative Trading News*

Budget: $600,000

Funding: Individual contributions (60%), sales (40%)

Staff: 5
2 Organizers
1 Writer/Editor
1 Office Manager
1 Bookkeeper/Accountant

Staff openings/year: 1

Work Week: 30-60 hours

Salary/year: $3-10,000

Volunteers: 200

Interns: 4-5
Length: 2 months-1 year
Duties: Same as paid staff
Remuneration: Room, board, $20 week stipend

Jobs advertised: Please write to us.

To apply: Contact James F. Goetsch

Remarks: We are primarily a volunteer organization, but we do encourage people to organize "Third World Shoppes" or Alternative Trading Projects in their local areas.

FUND FOR A FREE SOUTH AFRICA (FREESA)

729 Boylston Street, 5th floor
Boston, MA 02116
(617) 267-8333

Director: Mr. Themba G. Vilakazi

Purpose: FreeSA's purpose is to provide financial assistance to South African community organizations that work to address the economic and social disparities fostered by the lingering effects of apartheid.

Methods of operation: Human services (80%), direct action (15%), publications (5%)

Constituency: Individuals who have been politically active in civil rights and social justice issues

Recent issues and projects: Recent projects include: Deuhula/Leboa Library Project grant which allowed books to be shipped from U.S. to SA to serve youth in remote villages; Fence-making Project for the Blind Project supports self-employment for the sight impaired residents

Major publications: *Mamelani*, newsletter 3 times a year; Annual Report featuring descriptions of programs currently funded by FreeSA

Budget: $200,000

Funding: Individual contributions (60%), foundations (30%), direct mail (10%)

Staff: 3
3 Writers/Editors
1 Office Manager
2 Foundation Fundraiser
1 Issue Expert
1 Bookkeeper/Accountant
3 Grassroots Fundraisers
1 Campaign Manager
1 Volunteer Researcher

Staff openings/year: 0-1

Work Week: 40 hours

Benefits: Health insurance, paid vacation

Part-Time Employees: None

Summer Employees: None

Volunteers: 1

Interns: 1 -2
Length: 6 months
Duties: Assist Administrator, maintain library mailings, etc.
Remuneration: Hourly rate above minimum wage

To apply: Please contact Bobbie Patrick

FUND FOR COMMUNITY PROGRESS

1246 Chalkstone Ave
Providence, RI 02908
(401) 331-3863

Director: Nonads Hurst Voll

Purpose: Rhode Island's oldest and largest independent fundraising federation comprised of grassroots social service and advocacy agencies. The Fund raises money through work place fund-raising campaigns; giving through payroll deduction is particularly encouraged. The Fund experienced a 5% increase in donations during its 1992 campaign. Since 1982 when it began, the Fund has raised over $2 million. The Fund for Community Progress and its member agencies are strong advocates for social change and justice in Rhode Island.

Methods of operation: Fundraising for grassroots social service and advocacy agencies, organizing, training and technical assistance

Recent issues and projects: Launched Rhode Island's first *Work-A-Thon* public service project in September 1993; continues to focus on expanding workplace charitable campaigns to include nontraditional fundraising federations; promote public awareness of The Fund for Community Progress. Our goal is to build a financially stable network of social change organizations in Rhode Island.

Major publications: Newsletter

Budget: $90,000

Funding: Dues, Administrative fees and grants

Staff: 2
1 Executive Director
1 Assistant Director

Staff openings/year: 1

Work Week: 40 hours

Salary/year: $Varies (Recent College Graduate); $53,000 (Graduate with advanced degree)

Benefits: Health insurance, travel, paid vacation

Part-Time Employees: None

Summer Employees: None

Volunteers: Yes

Interns: Yes
Length: By semester(s), summer vacation
Duties: Varied - office work, communicating with board members, special projects
Remuneration: Work study program or state governmental offices' employment initiatives

Jobs advertised: *Providence Journal*, word of mouth, colleges

To apply: Contact Nondas Hurst Voll

FUND FOR INVESTIGATIVE JOURNALISM

1755 Massachusetts Avenue, NW, 419
Washington, DC 20036
(202) 462-1844

Director: Anne Grant

Purpose: Award grants to freelance journalists, with goal of improving investigative reporting and bringing to light issues, problems, answers that might otherwise go unreported.

Methods of operation: Grant-giving (100%)

Constituency: Journalists (primarily freelancers)

Recent issues and projects: Funded major recent projects relating to environment, civil liberties, computer vote fraud, HUD

Budget: $85,000

Funding: Foundations (70%), individual contributions (30%)

Staff: 1
1 Executive Director (part-time)

Work Week: 30 hours

Salary/year: $Varies (Recent College Graduate); $Varies (Graduate with advanced degree)

Part-Time Employees: 1

Volunteers: On rare occasions

Interns: None currently, but willing to accept applications

To apply: Contact Anne Grant Executive Director

FUND FOR THE FEMINIST MAJORITY

1600 Wilson Boulevard, Suite 704
Arlington, VA 22209
(703) 522-2214

Other Offices: Los Angeles, CA

President: Eleanor Smeal

Purpose: A nonprofit organization with supporters nationwide dedicated to eliminating sex discrimination and to the promotion of equality, women's rights and a feminist agenda, including safe and accessible abortion and birth control.

Methods of operation: Research, lobbying,

litigation, direct action, public education, training and technical assistance

Constituency: People who self-identify as feminists

Recent issues and projects: (1) Feminization of Power Campaign to inspire feminists to seek positions of power and leadership; (2) Gender Balance Campaign to promote bills requiring equal appointments of women and men; (3) development of videotapes to present and promote a feminist agenda; most recent tape: *Abortion: for Survival*; (4) various projects exploring the use of initiatives and referenda for women's rights; (5) various projects on contraceptive research and development, including campaigns to bring RU486 into the U.S.; (6) development of policy-oriented women's studies curriculum; (7) research project on violence against women; (8) Clinic Defense Project

Major publications: Bimonthly newsletter: *Feminist Majority Report*; *Abortion for Survival*; *Feminization of Power* organizing kits for women in law, politics, education (campus) and business; issue-oriented fact sheets

Budget: $1,000,000

Funding: Individual contributions, foundations, direct mail, telephone solicitation

Staff: 20
3 Organizers
3 Researchers
3 Issue Experts
3 Support Staff
2 Press Aides
3 Administrators
1 Bookkeeper/Accountant
2 Fundraisers

Work Week: 40-50 hours

Salary/year: $18-22,000 (Recent College Graduate); $25-30,000+ (Graduate with advanced degree)

Benefits: Health insurance, life insurance, dental insurance, pregnancy leave, paid vacation

Part-Time Employees: 1

Volunteers: Yes

Interns: Yes
Length: 3 months or more
Duties: Internships available with research, organizing and/or media responsibilities.
Remuneration: Travel stipend

Jobs advertised: Newspapers; colleges; alternative newspapers; notices to other feminist and progressive organizations

FUNDAMENTAL ACTION TO CONSERVE ENERGY (FACE)

75 Day Street
Fitchburg, MA 01420
(508) 345-5385

Director: William Stanwood

Purpose: FACE has been dedicated to preserving the environment through energy conservation, water conservation and recycling. This has been accomplished through education, a co-op store and direct service programs.

Methods of operation: Direct action (40%), community organizing (30%), human services (10%), public education (10%), training and technical assistance (10%)

Recent issues and projects: FACE has organized, and serves as the hub of the "Coalition of North Central Waste Management." Performs residential energy surveys; administered Home Energy Assistance Team Zero Interest Energy Loan Program.

Major publications: Quarterly newsletter

Budget: $120,000

Funding: Program delivery (90%), sales (10%)

Staff: 3
3 Program Managers/Educators

Staff openings/year: 0-1

Work Week: 35 hours

Salary/year: $24,000 (Recent College Graduate); $30,000 (Graduate with advanced degree)

Benefits: Health insurance, paid vacation

Part-Time Employees: 1-2

Volunteers: 1-2

Jobs advertised: Boston/local classifieds; opening notices posted throughout network

To apply: Contact William Stanwood, Executive Director

FUNDING EXCHANGE

666 Broadway, Suite 500
New York, NY 10012
(212) 529-5300

Director: Cecilia Rodriguez

Purpose: The Funding Exchange is a national network of 14 alternative regional foundations and four national grantmaking programs committed to funding progressive grassroots organizing locally and nationally. Community activists have a central role in grantmaking at the regional foundations and nationally through the Saguaro Fund, The Paul Robeson Fund for Independent Media and the OUT Fund For Lesbian And Gay Liberation. Support of the Funding Exchange comes from a variety of donors, including individuals with inherited wealth.

Methods of operation: Grantmaking and related activities (70%), local membership services (30%)

Constituency: Network of alternative foundations. Also represent 150+ individual donors who make grants through our organization.

Recent issues and projects: Distributed $5.5 million in 1989; made 500+ grants across the country; distributed $30 million in 10 years. Funds many progressive issues.

Major publications: Newsletter: *Network News*; grants listings, brochures, *We Gave Away A Fortune*, a book about individuals with inherited wealth.

Budget: $1,100,000

Funding: Individual contributions (97%), miscellaneous (3%)

Staff: 14
2 Program Officers, grantmaking
1 Executive Director
1 Director of Network Resources
1 Director of Grantmaking
1 Director of Administration
1 Development Coordinator
1 Donor Program Officer
1 Membership Associate
1 Development Associate
1 Grants Administrator
1 Bookkeeper
1 Office Manager
1 Receptionist

Staff openings/year: 1-2

Work Week: 40 hours

Salary/year: $23,000 (Recent College Graduate); $30,000 (Graduate with advanced degree)

Benefits: Health insurance, pregnancy leave, pension, paid vacation, dental, transitCheks

Jobs advertised: Local daily newspapers; trade publications; alternative press; ethnic publications; *Community Jobs*

To apply: Apply in writing only for current openings

GAY COMMUNITY NEWS
25 West Street
Boston, MA 02111
(617) 426-4469

Purpose: Established in 1973, *Gay Community News* is the oldest national lesbian and gay weekly in the United States. *GCN* is committed to a vision of lesbian and gay liberation that encompasses feminism, anti-racism, and an awareness of class issues. Each week it covers developments of local and national significance to the lesbian and gay community, oriented particularly toward grassroots activist struggles and successes. *GNC*'s organizational structure is collective and community-based. The paper is produced by a paid staff of women and men.

Methods of operation: Publications (65%), public education (25%), community organizing (10%)

Constituency: The gay and lesbian communities nationwide; mixed class, race and ethnic backgrounds

Major publications: *Gay Community News*

Budget: $325,000

Funding: Individual contributions (75%), foundations (15%), direct mail (10%)

Staff: 10
4 Writers/Editors
1 Office Manager
1 Campaign Manager
1 Typist
1 Promotions
1 Art Director
1 Advertising

Staff openings/year: 3-5

Work Week: 40 hours

Salary/year: $10,400

Benefits: Health insurance, life insurance, paid vacation

Part-Time Employees: 2

Volunteers: 50-100

Interns: 5-10

Length: 6 months
Duties: Varies with interest and skills
Remuneration: Volunteer or work-study

Jobs advertised: In *GCN*; other gay publications; to a list of 500 organizations involved in anti-racist organizing

To apply: Contact the Coordinating Editor

GIRAFFE PROJECT

P.O. Box 759, 197 Second Street
Langley, WA 98260
(206) 221-7989

President: Ann Medlock

Purpose: The Giraffe Project is a national nonprofit organization inspiring people to stick their necks out for the common good. Founded in 1982, the Project's basic mission is to find people courageously tackling problems in their communities or farther afield, then get their stories told in local and national media. These "Giraffes" inspire others to take up the challenges they see.

Methods of operation: Public education (60%), publications (20%), training and technical assistance (10%), research (5%) and human services (5%)

Constituency: Individuals from all walks of life who believe in the Giraffe Project's mission; many teachers, retired folks, volunteer and community grassroots organizations

Recent issues and projects: Recent projects include: the creation and national distribution of *Standing Tall*, a series of curriculum guides for grades K-2, 3-5, 6-9, 10-12, that teaches kids the 3 C's: courage, caring and community, then shows them how to put those qualities to work implementing their own service projects; Giraffe lectures and workshops that offer both inspiration and practical strategies to universities, companies, unions, service organizations, government agencies and national conventions; and ongoing placement of Giraffe stories in local and national media.

Major publications: *The Giraffe Project Handbook*, a guide to effective community action; *Every Day Heroes*, a story-a-weekday about Giraffes; *The Giraffe Annual* and *Giraffe News*

Budget: $350,000

Funding: Foundations (55%), individual contributions (33%), other (12%)

Staff: 4
1 Researcher
1 Press Fundraiser
1 Press Aide
1 Foundation Fundraiser

Staff openings/year: 1

Work Week: 40 hours

Salary/year: $Varies (Recent College Graduate); $Varies (Graduate with advanced degree)

Benefits: Health insurance, paid vacation

Part-Time Employees: 3

Summer Employees: None

Volunteers: 4

Interns: None at the present

Jobs advertised: In local paper and word-of-mouth

To apply: Please contact Karen Watkins, Managing Editor and Administrative Assistant.

Remarks: The Giraffe Project moves people into caring, courageous action through a simple strategy: if you want someone to take a risk for others' well being, show them someone else going first. The Giraffe Project has honored over 700 of these role models as Giraffes, individuals and groups from all over the world, for their courageous work on every issue, from cleaning up wetlands to organizing local programs for the homeless. Using their stories and the basic qualities of being a Giraffe as the basis for its unique curriculum, *Standing Tall*, the Giraffe Project is now able to reach and teach young people to become powerful positive role models themselves, showing them how real heroes stand tall for the well-being of others.

GIRLS INCORPORATED

30 East 33rd Street
New York, NY 10016
(212) 689-3700

Other Offices: Atlanta, GA; Boston, MA; Washington, DC; Indianapolis, IN; Santa Barbara, CA

Director: Isabel Stewart

Purpose: Girls Incorporated is a non-profit youth service advocacy and research organization. They serve nearly 350,000 youth in almost 750 program sites across the country.

Constituency: Girls ages 6-18

Recent issues and projects: Recent projects include: girls and substance abuse; adolescent pregnancy prevention stress; science and math instruction

Major publications: Annual report; quarterly newsletter

Budget: $4,700,000

Funding: Individual contributions, foundations

Staff: 37
3 Writers/Editors
1 Office Manager
2 Researchers
2 Foundation Fundraisers
4 Issue Experts
6 Administrative Assistants
2 Bookkeepers/Accountants
2 Grassroots Fundraisers
1 Executive Director
2 Associate Editors
1 Director of Finance
4 Program Directors
6 Service Directors
1 Communications Directors

Staff openings/year: 3

Work Week: 35 hours

Salary/year: $21,000 (Recent College Graduate); $35,000 (Graduate with advanced degree)

Benefits: Health insurance, pension, paid vacation, life insurance, family leave

Part-Time Employees: 6

Summer Employees: 1-4

Volunteers: None

Jobs advertised: Posted internally, *Youth Today, Nonprofit Times*

To apply: Personnel Department

GLOBAL EXCHANGE

2017 Mission Street, Suite 303
San Francisco, CA 94110
(415) 255-7296

Director: Medea Benjamin and Kirsten Moller, Co-Directors

Purpose: To foster close people-to-people ties between citizens of the 1st and 3rd worlds.

Methods of operation: Community organizing (30%), public education (20%) research (10%), publications (10%), human services (10%), direct action (10%) training and technical assistance (10%), lobbying

Constituency: Students; professionals; religious; concerned with social justice issues on a global level

Recent issues and projects: Monthly "reality tours" to the Third World; bring Third World speakers to the U.S.; "fair trade" (i.e. buying and selling goods at fair prices produced by Third World cooperatives); material aid; campaigns to end travel restrictions to Cuba and to fight IMF Structural adjustment; research and writing on Third World issues and U.S. foreign policy

Major publications: *Bridging the Global Gap: A Handbook to Linking Citizens of the First and Third Worlds*; *Global Exchanges* quarterly newsletter; guides to working overseas, traveling overseas, fair trade; *The Peace Corps: 120 ways to work, travel and study in developing countries*

Budget: $500,000

Funding: Individual contributions (60%), foundations (15%), sales of publications and crafts (15%), direct mail (10%)

Staff: 14
5 Organizers
2 Writer/Editors
1 Office Manager
2 Fundraisers
2 Store Managers
2 Assistant Store Managers

Staff openings/year: 1

Work Week: 50 hours

Salary/year: $18,000 (Recent College Graduate); $20,000 (Graduate with advanced degree)

Benefits: Health insurance, pregnancy leave, tuition reimbursement, paid vacation, occasional trips overseas

Volunteers: 20

Interns: 6
Length: 3-4 months
Duties: Varied, depending on project (research, organizing events, helping out in trade store, etc.)
Remuneration: No money available, but can get college credit

To apply: Contact Kirsten Moller, Administrator

Remarks: Great collective spirit within the group. New and dynamic (started October 1988), so lots of room for taking initiative. We promise you will learn a lot from any internship with us.

GLOBAL TOMORROW COALITION

1325 G Street, NW, Suite 1010
Washington, DC 20005-3104
(202) 628-4016

President: Donald R. Lesh

Purpose: GTC is a national nonprofit alliance of organizations, institutions, corporations and individuals working toward a more sustainable, equitable tomorrow. Works to build U.S. leadership on long-term, inter-related trends in environment, population, and resource use.

Methods of operation: Community organizing (30%), publications (30%), public education (25%), research (15%)

Constituency: GTC unites private citizens and more than 120 U.S. organizations representing over 10,000,000 Americans.

Recent issues and projects: The Coalition's unique non-partisan, nonconfrontational process engages leaders of key sectors of society in the application of the concept of sustainable development. GTC conducts Globescope assemblies, community forums, congressional briefings, global town meetings, and teacher-training workshops, publishes educational materials, and serves as a clearinghouse on public policy goals.

Major publications: *Citizen's Guide to Sustainable Development/Global Ecology Handbook*; *Sustainable Development: New Path of Progress*; *Sustainable Development: A Guide to Our Common Future*; *Interaction Newsletter*

Budget: $500,000

Funding: Foundations (50%), government (14%), corporate (10%), organizational members (10%), sales (10%), direct mail (1%)

Staff: 5
2 Organizers
1 Office Manager
1 Foundation Fundraiser
1 Management Services

Staff openings/year: 1/2

Work Week: 37.5 hours

Salary/year: $17,000 (Recent College Graduate); $24,000 (Graduate with advanced degree)

Benefits: Health insurance, life insurance, paid vacation

Part-Time Employees: 1

Volunteers: 2-3

Interns: Yes
Length: 3 months
Duties: Office administration, information requests, research, special projects
Remuneration: $100 a month maximum

Jobs advertised: Various networks

To apply: Contact Terry D'Addio, Director of Management Services

GOOD MONEY PUBLICATIONS, INC.

Box 363
Worcester, VT 05682
(802) 223-3911

Other Offices: Chestnut Hill, MA

President: Richie P. Lowry

Purpose: Publish newsletters, handbooks, guides and other materials for ethically and socially concerned investors. Provide social screening services for individual and institutional investors.

Methods of operation: Research (35%), publications (35%), business operations (20%), public education (10%)

Constituency: Wealthy individual investors, brokers and money managers, institutions (universities and churches), foundations

Recent issues and projects: Provided social screening services for Vermont National Bank's new "Socially Responsible Banking Fund." Preparing an Issue Paper on the banking and financial industries. Revised a guide to the socially screened mutual funds.

Major publications: Newsletters: *GOOD MONEY*, *NETBACK*; *Where Is Your Money Going?* guide to the socially screened mutual funds; Issue Papers on women's issues, the environment, animal rights, defense contractors, minorities and other issues (these describe how investors can screen their investments for these concerns)

Budget: $100,000

Funding: Direct mail (90%), social screening (10%)

Staff: 6
Staff functions include:

Writing/Editing
Researching
Typing
Bookkeeping/Accounting
Office Managing

Work Week: 30-40 hours

Benefits: Health insurance, life insurance, pregnancy leave, child care, paid vacation

Part-Time Employees: 1-2

Summer Employees: Yes; number varies

Volunteers: Yes

Interns: Yes
Length: 3-6 months
Duties: Usually research and writing
Remuneration: Negotiable

Jobs advertised: Local newspaper ad

To apply: Contact Steven Heim, Director of Research

GOOD SHEPHERD HOUSING AND FAMILY SERVICES, INC.

6301 Richmond Highway
Alexandria, VA 22306
(703) 765-9407

Director: Gene Betit

Purpose: To help low-income families and individuals and those in crisis obtain and keep decent, affordable housing.

Methods of operation: Human services and direct action (70%), community organizing (10%), research (5%), lobbying (5%), public education (5%), publications (5%)

Recent issues and projects: Recent projects include: rental/sublet program; emergency assistance; Tenants Association; Family-to-family mentoring; and furniture recycling

Major publications: Newsletter 4 times a year, annual report

Budget: $800,000

Funding: Government (44%), tenant rents (39.4%), individual contributions (6.6%), foundations (5.4%)

Staff: 6
1 Outreach Coordinator
1 Caseworker
1 Volunteer Coordinator
1 Fundraising Coordinator
1 Executive Director
1 Rental Manager
1 Emergency Coordinator

Work Week: 40 hours

Salary/year: $21,000

Benefits: Health insurance, paid vacation, family leave

Part-Time Employees: 2

Summer Employees: 2

Volunteers: 50

Interns: 1
Length: 6 months
Duties: Counseling
Remuneration: Unpaid

Jobs advertised: Local newspapers

To apply: Please contact Gene Betit, Executive Director

GOVERNMENT ACCOUNTABILITY PROJECT (GAP)

810 1st Street, NE
Washington, DC 20002
(202) 408-0034

Director: Louis A. Clark

Purpose: Provides legal assistance to "whistleblowers" - federal and corporate employees who report on the illegal, corrupt or wasteful practices where they work.

Methods of operation: Direct action (60%), litigation (15%), public education (10%), community organizing (10%), publications (5%)

Constituency: Citizens who believe in honest, accountable government and industry

Recent issues and projects: GAP assists employees from a number of nuclear weapon plants (including Fernald and Hanford) in reporting safety hazards. Helps concerned meat inspectors publicize the health menace posed by new meat inspecting methods.

Major publications: Quarterly newsletter: *Bridging the GAP*; occasional articles on whistleblowers; recent handbook: *Courage Without Martydom: A Survival Guide for Whistleblowers*

Budget: $800,000

Funding: Foundations (80%), individual

contributions (15%), direct mail (5%)

Staff: 20
12 Attorneys
3 Support Staff
1 Intake Coordinator
1 Office Manager
2 Foundation Fundraisers

Staff openings/year: Varies

Work Week: 45 hours

Salary/year: $17,000 (Recent College Graduate); $24,000 (Graduate with advanced degree)

Benefits: Health insurance, pregnancy leave, paid vacation

Part-Time Employees: 2

Interns: 45 per year
Length: 10 weeks
Remuneration: Some paid, some academic credit

Jobs advertised: Numerous special interest publications as well as major national newspapers

To apply: Contact Sarah Levitt, Assistant Clinical Director

GRANTSMANSHIP CENTER

1125 W. Sixth Street, Fifth Floor
Los Angeles, CA 90017
(213) 482-9860

President: Norton J. Kiritz

Purpose: Offers training programs and publications about grantsmanship, program management, and fundraising to staff members of public and private nonprofit organizations.

Methods of operation: Publications (50%), training and technical assistance (50%)

Constituency: Staff and managers of nonprofit organizations

Major publications: *The Grantsmanship Center Whole Nonprofit Catalog*, a compendium of sources and resources for managers and staff of nonprofit organizations, will be sent free of charge to those who request it. *The Catalog* describes our other publications and training programs.

Staff: 10
3 Writers/Editors
2 Typists
1-2 Registrars
1-2 Trainers
1 Bookkeeper/Accountant
1 Office Manager
1 Mail Room

Work Week: 37.5 hours

Benefits: Health insurance, life insurance, pension, paid vacation

Part-Time Employees: Yes

Summer Employees: Yes

Jobs advertised: *Los Angeles Times*

To apply: Contact Norton J. Kiritz, President

GRASSROOTS INTERNATIONAL

48 Grove Street, #103
Somerville, MA 02144
(617) 628-1664

Director: Tim Wise

Purpose: Grassroots International is an independent development and information agency. Channels humanitarian aid to democratic social change movements in the Third World. The partnerships is built at the grassroots level and provides a unique basis to inform the media and the public about Third World conflicts and crises and the U.S. role in them. Focus on strategically important areas where national movements are challenging economic and social inequalities and repressive political systems. Grassroots currently funds relief and development projects in Africa, the Middle East and the Phillipines. To safeguard Grassroots independence they do not accept funds from any government agency, the programs are wholly supported by private donations.

Methods of operation: Fund-generating in support of Third World development (65%), public education (30%), publications (5%)

Constituency: Indigenous organizations that do a variety of development projects

Recent issues and projects: Eritrea: Eritrean Relief Association; Southern Africa: anti-apartheid groups; Occupied Territories: Palestinian organizations supporting self-sufficiency; the Phillipines: grassroots organizations to promote land reform and prevention of environmental destruction; cleaning up former U.S. bases; and a Mexican program combatting the effects of free trade and promoting human rights and election monitoring

Major publications: Newsletter: *Insights*

Budget: $1,836,000

Funding: Foundations (14%), individual contributions (12%), in-kind (68%), churches (6%)

Staff: 6
1 Administrative Coordinator
1 Administrative Assistant
2 Program Coordinators
1 Staff Writer/Grant Writer
1 Fundraising Coordinator

Staff openings/year: 2

Work Week: 40 hours

Salary/year: $18,000 (Recent College Graduate); $25-29,000 (Graduate with advanced degree)

Benefits: Health insurance, parental leave, paid vacation, dental insurance

Part-Time Employees: Yes

Volunteers: 1

Interns: 2
Length: 1 semester
Duties: Assist one to two staff members with regular work

Jobs advertised: Local papers; mailing blitz; word of mouth

To apply: Contact Chuck Wyatt

GRASSROOTS LEADERSHIP

P.O. Box 36006
Charlotte, NC 28236
(704) 332-3090

Other Offices: Durham, NC; Orangeburg, SC

Director: Si Kahn

Purpose: Grassroots Leadership is an organizing center that provides strategic assistance to Southern communities working for social and economic justice.

Methods of operation: Community organizing (40%), training and technical assistance (40%), direct action (10%), public education (10%)

Constituency: Grassroots Leadership has a national network of participants and contributors.

Recent issues and projects: Confronting police brutality in rural South Carolina, helping organizations learn to deal with issues of race, gender and class.

Major publications: Newsletter: *Grassroots*, twice annually. We also distribute books, record albums and songbooks.

Budget: $470,000

Funding: Foundations (30%), contracts (30%), individual contributions (20%), direct mail (20%)

Staff: 6
4 Organizers
1 Office Manager
1 Grassroots Fundraiser

Staff openings/year: 1

Work Week: 50 hours

Salary/year: $Varies (Recent College Graduate); $Varies (Graduate with advanced degree)

Benefits: Health insurance, life insurance, pension, pregnancy leave, paid vacation, tuition reimbursement, sabbaticals

Part-Time Employees: 1

Summer Employees: 1

Volunteers: Occasionally

Interns: 1
Length: Varies
Duties: Interns can arrange different lengths of work and types of programs.
Remuneration: Some stipends, and expenses are reimbursed

Jobs advertised: Job descriptions are circulated to community organizations and listed in *Community Jobs*

To apply: Contact the Charlotte office

Remarks: Preference for women and men of color, women, lesbian and gay, differently abled, working class and/or Southern interns.

GRASSROOTS POLICY PROJECT

2040 S Street, N.W.
Washington, DC 20009
(202) 387-2934

Director: Richard Healey

Purpose: Promote public debate on limits of market-centered approaches to economic development and environmental problems as well as alternative policies centered on demonstrating the U.S. economy as a strategic response to growing economic, unemployment and environmental problems.

Methods of operation: Research, publications, public education, training and technical assistance

Recent issues and projects: Recent projects include: outreach and education; regional workshops on the economy and the environment; consultations with progressive local and state legislators and electoral candidates; research; and network building

Major publications: *Resource Guide to Innovative Plant Closing and Development Subsidy Legislation*, quarterly newsletter; educational materials on regional economic, environmental and democratic problems

Budget: $200,000

Funding: Foundations (95%), publications (5%)

Staff: 4
1 Organizer
1 Office Manager
1 Researcher
1 Director

Staff openings/year: 2

Work Week: 40-50 hours

Salary/year: $18,000 (Recent College Graduate); $24,000 (Graduate with advanced degree)

Part-Time Employees: 1

Summer Employees: None

Volunteers: Varies

Interns: Yes
Length: 4-6 months
Duties: Research, editing, clerical
Remuneration: Monthly stipend based on need, between $200 and $500 a month

Jobs advertised: Universities, DC job banks, networks

To apply: Contact Richard Healey or Personnel Manager

GRAY PANTHERS PROJECT FUND

2025 Pennsylvania Ave., NW, Suite 821
Washington, DC 20006
(202) 466-3132

Director: Dixie Horning

Purpose: Intergenerational organization working to fight for social and economic justice for people of all ages. Focuses on health care, economic conversion, peace, discrimination, environmental preservation, affordable housing, education and ageism.

Membership: Has 35,000 members and supporters. Active grassroots membership.

Recent issues and projects: Currently focusing on the implementation of a national health system. Holds biannual conventions.

Major publications: Bi-annual newspaper: *NETWORK*; 8 newsletters; brochures, fundraising manual, almanac

Budget: $260,000

Funding: Direct mail (100%)

Staff: 5
1 grassroots fundraiser
2 office managers
1 writer/editor
1 executive director

Staff openings/year: 2

Work Week: 40-50 hours

Salary/year: $20,000

Benefits: Health insurance, life insurance, paid vacation

Volunteers: 10

Interns: 3 per year
Length: 3 months
Duties: Research, writing, help with program development, clerical duties
Remuneration: Varies

Jobs advertised: College job boards; newspaper; word of mouth

To apply: Contact Dixie Horning, Executive Director

GREAT LAKES UNITED

SUNY College, Cassety Hall, 1300 Elmwood Avenue
Buffalo, NY 14222
(716) 886-0142

Director: Terry L. Yonker

Purpose: To protect and conserve the Great Lakes-St. Lawrence River ecosystem.

Methods of operation: Research, publications, community organizing, public education, training and technical assistance

Membership: Over 180 organizational members in 8 Great Lakes states and the provinces of Ontario and Quebec; union, sportsmen groups, governments and environmental, conservation, academic, business organizations

Recent issues and projects: Air quality, water quality, water quantity, water diversion, human health, fish and wildlife (and habitat) protection, land use, energy conservation, toxic contamination, recycling.

Major publications: Quarterly newsletter: *The Great Lakes United*; annual reports; citizens' guides to Lake Superior, Lake Michigan, Lake Ontario, Great Lakes Water Quality Agreement, etc.

Budget: $300,000

Funding: Foundations (80%), individual contributions (10%), direct mail (5%), organizational members (5%)

Staff: 7
4 Issue Experts
2 Typists
1 Office Manager

Staff openings/year: 1

Work Week: 40 hours

Salary/year: $15,000 (Recent College Graduate); $20,000 (Graduate with advanced degree)

Benefits: Health insurance, life insurance, pregnancy leave, paid vacation

Part-Time Employees: 2

Volunteers: 50+

Interns: Yes
Length: Summer, Fall
Duties: Varied, as assistant to one of our issues experts
Remuneration: Contract; no fringe benefits

Jobs advertised: Newspaper; announcement to member organizations and colleague groups and on electronic network

To apply: Contact Terry L. Yonker, Executive Director

GREATER ERIE COMMUNITY ACTION COMMITTEE

18 West 9th Street
Erie, PA 16501
(814) 459-4581

Director: R. Benjamin Wiley

Purpose: GECAC was formed for the purpose of providing a local organization for the establishment and operation of facilities and services directed toward the elimination of poverty or causes of poverty in the greater Erie area. It is dedicated to the advancement of opportunity for education and training, the opportunity to work and the opportunity to live in decency and dignity.

Methods of operation: Human services (100%)

Constituency: Erie County community

Recent issues and projects: GECAC is Erie County's Community Action Agency. Major program areas include: Aging Services; Child Development including Head Start programming; Weatherization, Housing and Energy Assistance Programs; Food and Transportation for the elderly and disadvantaged; Employment and Training Programs as well as Drug and Alcohol Services. GECAC is also a leader in Economic Development, Small and Minority Business Development and Technical Assistance.

Budget: $15,400,000

Funding: Federal, state and local human service funding (100%)

Staff: 258
65 Administration, Cooks, Drivers, Weatherization Workers
58 Caseworkers/Counselors
40 Teachers
40 Typists
27 Teacher Aides/Assistants
17 Program Directors
10 Bookkeepers/Accountants
1 Office Manager

Staff openings/year: 60-70

Work Week: 37.5 hours

Salary/year: $Varies (Recent College Graduate); $Varies (Graduate with advanced degree)

Benefits: Health insurance, life insurance, annuity, credit union, paid vacation, dental insurance

Part-Time Employees: 18

Summer Employees: 25-30

Volunteers: Yes

Interns: Yes
Length: 6 weeks
Duties: Varies per assignment, clerical, casework, etc.
Remuneration: None

Jobs advertised: Local newspapers; in-house postings; mailing list which includes 40 area businesses; government agencies; neighborhoods centers; universities; etc.

To apply: Contact Mrs. Bettie Vincent, Personnel Director

GREATER LOS ANGELES COUNCIL ON DEAFNESS, INC. (GLAD)

2222 Laverna Ave.
Los Angeles, CA 90041
(213) 478-8000

Director: Marcella M. Meyer, CEO

Purpose: The Greater Los Angeles Council on Deafness, Inc. is a nonprofit organization dedicated to the social, education, economic and cultural welfare of the deaf and hard of hearing communities. Better known as "GLAD Info, may I help you? GLAD houses one of the most comprehensive and up-to-date resource banks in the United States. Available to the general public by telephone, walk-in service or TDD, information on any aspect of deafness can be found at GLAD. GLAD advocates for deaf and hard of hearing persons experiencing discrimination in employment, education and communication access.

Methods of operation: Advocacy, lobbying, information/referral service, interpreting, community education

Membership: Approximately 2000 council organizations and approximately 50 organizations

Recent issues and projects: Recent projects include: relocation to new location; planning major renovation with expansion of current programs and additional new programs to be added for family planning

Major publications: *GLAD News*; *GLAD Council Newsletter*; *GLAD Directory of Resources*

Staff: 58
3 Office Managers
23 Issue Experts
4 Bookkeepers/Accountants
8 Caseworkers
11 Interpreters
9 Administrative

Work Week: 40 hours

Salary/year: $Varies (Recent College Graduate); $Varies (Graduate with advanced degree)

Benefits: Health insurance, pension, paid vacation, credit union, family leave

Part-Time Employees: None

Summer Employees: Yes

Volunteers: Varies

Interns: None, but willing to accept applications

To apply: Contact Marcella M. Meyer, CEO or Linda Noblegas, Executive Administrative Assistant

GREATER MIAMI SERVICE CORPS

810 N.W. 28th Street
Miami, FL 33127
(305) 638-4672

Other Offices: Florida City, FL

Director: Barbara Jordan

Purpose: To enhance the employability of young adults ages 18-23, through work assignments that provide tangible community improvements reinforce productive habits and strengthen useful skills.

Methods of operation: Training and technical assistance (75%), human services (15%), direct action (10%)

Constituency: Out-of-school; unemployed young people; residents of Dade County Florida (18-23) can apply to be program participants.

Major publications: Disaster relief, defense conversion and community restoration

Budget: $2,000,000

Funding: Government Agencies (98%), foundations (2%)

Staff: 22
2 Office Managers
3 Administrative Assistants
2 Bookkeepers/Accountants
8 Educators/Trainers
7 Project Supervisors/Managers

Staff openings/year: 4

Work Week: 40 hours

Salary/year: $Varies (Recent College Graduate); $Varies (Graduate with advanced degree)

Benefits: Health insurance, pension, child care, paid vacation, life insurance, credit union, tuition reimbursement

Part-Time Employees: None

Summer Employees: 6

Volunteers: 21

Interns: 20
Length: 2 months
Duties: Program participants assigned according to their career goals
Remuneration: Same stipend as other program participants

Jobs advertised: Metro-Dade County advertisers vacancies in local publications

To apply: Contact Vincent McRae

Remarks: Program participants receive stipend work experience educational opportunities, placement assistance and can qualify for post-service awards.

GREATER NEW HAVEN COALITION FOR PEOPLE

323 Temple Street
New Haven, CT 06511
(203) 773-9149

Director: Kathleen Hagearty

Purpose: To empower low and moderate income people through training them to effectively organize around issues of concern they raise, and to win.

Methods of operation: Research, community organizing, direct action, training and technical assistance

Constituency: Low-income public housing tenants (90% Black women); Black, White and Hispanic churches

Recent issues and projects: Public housing maintenance; homeownership; neighborhood issues--youth activity and transportation

Major publications: Quarterly newsletter; issue reports

Budget: $150,000

Funding: Foundations (50%), federal government (45%), individual contributions (5%)

Staff: 4
3 Organizers
1 Administrative Assistant

Staff openings/year: 1

Work Week: 50 hours

Salary/year: $23,000

Benefits: Health insurance, paid vacation

Part-Time Employees: 1

Interns: None currently, but willing to accept applications

Jobs advertised: *Community Jobs*; local press

To apply: Contact Minnie Anderson, Co-Director

GREEN CENTURY CAPITAL MANAGEMENT, INC.

29 Temple Place
Boston, MA 02111
(617) 482-0800

Director: Mindy Lubber

Purpose: Green Century launched the Green Century Funds, a family of environmentally responsible mutual funds, with the following goals: 1) Provide an investment opportunity that is competitive and environmentally responsible; 2) To become an active player as a shareholder of corporations and by filing corporate resolutions concerning corporate behavior on the environment; 3) To generate a new revenue stream to support environmental advocacy. GCCM is a project of the Public Interest Research Group (PIRGs).

Methods of operation: Research (100%)

Constituency: Our constituency are investors and potential (small and large) investors interested in investing in environmentally responsible companies

Recent issues and projects: GCCM is in the process of filing a number of shareholder resolutions requiring corporations to support comprehensive recycling programs and state and national bottle bill legislation.

Major publications: *Green Century Funds Investor News*

Budget: $400,000

Staff: 5

Staff openings/year: 1

Work Week: 50 hours

Salary/year: $15,000 (Recent College Graduate); $22,000 (Graduate with advanced degree)

Benefits: Health insurance, paid vacation, family leave

Part-Time Employees: No

Summer Employees: No

Volunteers: 2

Interns: 2-4 per semester

Length: Summer or semester
Duties: Research environmental record of companies, write newsletter, etc.
Remuneration: Varies

Jobs advertised: College campuses, newspapers, progressive organizations and word of mouth

To apply: Contact Adam Frank, Office Administrator

GREEN CORPS

1109 Walnut Street, 4th Floor
Philadelphia, PA 19107
(215) 829-1760

Other Offices: Boston, MA; Washington, DC; Burlington, VT; New York, NY; New Haven, CT; Princeton, NJ; Chicago, IL; Minneapolis, MN; San Francisco, CA; Sacramento, CA; Los Angeles, CA; Seattle, WA; Boulder, CO

Director: Gina C. Collins

Purpose: Green Corps has two missions: to train the next generation of environmental leaders; and to provide needed field resources to environmental campaigns at critical junctures.

Methods of operation: Training and technical assistance (50%), public education (40%), direct action (5%), publications (5%)

Constituency: Organizers work with high school and college students, as well as other interested members of the community

Recent issues and projects: Green Corps works on a series of campaigns each year. During the past year we worked on a Student Vote Campaign, Recycling Initiative with MASSPIRG, the Clean Air Campaign with Natural Resources Defense Fund, Save America's Wilds with the Sierra Club, Campaign to Save Endangered Species with the National Audubon Society and the Mitsubishi Boycott with the Rainforest Action Network

Major publications: Newsletter

Budget: $350,000

Funding: Foundations (65%), canvassing (15%), events (15%), individual contributions (5%)

Staff: 24
20 Organizers
2 Grassroots Fundraisers
1 Campaign Manager
1 Bookkeeper/Accountant

Staff openings/year: 20

Work Week: 55 hours

Salary/year: $14,500 (Recent College Graduate); $16,000 (Graduate with advanced degree)

Benefits: Health Insurance, Paid Vacation, Student Loan Repayment Program

Part-Time Employees: None

Summer Employees: Varies

Volunteers: 100

Interns: 20
Length: 4 - 6 months
Duties: Varies, frequently include recruiting and training, public speaking, writing for publication, working with media and fundraising
Remuneration: Course credit can be arranged

Jobs advertised: Through national publications and college career offices

To apply: Leslie Samuelrich, Recruitment Director, different address, please note: 37 Temple Place, Boston, MA 02111; 617-426-8506

Remarks: Green Corps is a one-year training program for recent college graduates who are interested in learning the skills and gaining the experience they need to be a leader in the environmental field. We are most interested in hiring individuals who want to work on grassroots campaigns and have some previous experience with environmental issues or on a campaign. We interview candidates each January - February. Second interviews are conducted at limited number of sites in March. We encourage candidates to contact us with questions or to request an application. Please contact our Recruitment Director at the address above.

GREENPEACE

1436 U Street, NW
Washington, DC 20009
(202) 462-1177

Other Offices: New York, NY; San Francisco, CA; Seattle, WA; Chicago, IL

Director: Barbara Dudley

Purpose: Campaigns in the areas of toxic waste elimination, nuclear disarmament, protection of marine mammals and the oceans, and alternatives to environmentally destructive energy consumption, prevention of further destruction of the ozone layer.

Methods of operation: Public education (25%), direct action (20%), community organizing (15%), research (15%), lobbying (10%), publications (10%), litigation (3%), training and technical assistance (2%)

Membership: Over 1.6 million donors/supporters

Recent issues and projects: Elimination of nuclear weapons at sea; preservation of Antarctica as a world park; moratorium on commercial whaling; put an end to 37 years of radioactive waste dumping in the ocean; work to prevent the international trade of toxic waste

Major publications: *Greenpeace Quarterly*; *The Neptune Papers*; *We All Live Downstream: The Mississippi River and the National Toxics Crisis*; *The Politics of Penta*; *Zero Discharge: A Citizen's Toxic Waste Audit Manual*; *The Greenpeace Story*; *The Greenpeace Guide to Paper*

Budget: $42,800,000

Funding: Direct mail (44%), canvassing (31%), high donors, merchandise, miscellaneous (14%), telephone solicitation (11%)

Staff: 175
40 Campaigners
13 Campaign Managers
20 Administrative Staff
15 Grassroots Fundraisers
12 Bookkeeper/Accountants
6 Press Aides
4 Researchers
7 Direct Action Support Staff
7 Office Managers
1 Writer/Editor
3 Telecommunications/Computers
4 Office Directors
4 Lobbyists
1 Executive Director
1 Attorney
100 Canvassers

Staff openings/year: 15

Work Week: 40 hours

Salary/year: $18-20,000 (Recent College Graduate); $25,000 (Graduate with advanced degree)

Benefits: Health insurance, life insurance, pregnancy leave, paid vacation

Part-Time Employees: 10

Summer Employees: 500 Canvassers

Volunteers: 50

Interns: 25
Length: 3-6 months
Duties: Research, correspondence, administration, and various other work
Remuneration: Up to $250/week

Jobs advertised: Newspapers; mailings to other organizations; campus postings; telecommunications

To apply: Call the Job Line at (202) 319-2500

Remarks: Greenpeace has 25 canvass offices nationwide.

HABITAT FOR HUMANITY INTERNATIONAL
121 Habitat Street
Americus, GA 31709-3498
(912) 924-6935

Director: Millard Fuller

Purpose: Habitat for Humanity International is a non-profit, ecumenical Christian organization dedicated to eliminating poverty from the world and to making decent housing a matter of conscience and action.

Methods of operation: Direct action (72%), human services (20%), public education (5%), publications (3%)

Constituency: Low-middle to low-upper class, predominately white

Recent issues and projects: Habitat for Humanity is now working in partnership with people in need in more than 1,000 cities in 40 countries. New projects are organized each month. Since it was founded in 1976, Habitat has constructed more than 20,000 homes.

Major publications: *Habitat World*, a bimonthly newspaper circulation over 720,000; *Bokotola*; *No More Shacks*; *The Excitement is Building* and books by Millard Fuller

Budget: $21,000,000

Funding: Individuals; churches; corporations; foundations

Staff: 70
25 Administrative
12 Organizers
12 Coordinators
10 International
3 Campaign Managers

3 Writer/Editors
2 Office Managers
2 Bookkeeper/Accountants
1 Attorney

Staff openings/year: 10-15

Work Week: 40 hours

Salary/year: $Varies (Recent College Graduate); $Varies (Graduate with advanced degree)

Benefits: Health insurance, child care, paid vacation, life insurance, pregnancy leave, disability, pension plan

Part-Time Employees: Yes

Volunteers: 100

Interns: Yes
Length: Varies
Duties: Varies

Jobs advertised: Bimonthly magazine, *Habitat World*; *Intercristo* and other magazines

To apply: Contact the Director of Human Resources

Remarks: Those who work for Habitat fall into 5 groups: 1) Volunteers - receive no assistance; 2) Volunteers - $25.00 per week stipend plus lodging; 3) Volunteers - $300.00 a month plus lodging; 4) Hourly - paid competitive to Americus workforce; and 5) Staff - salaried, based on need.

HALT - AN ORGANIZATION OF AMERICANS FOR LEGAL REFORM
1319 F Street, NW, Suite 300
Washington, DC 20004
(202) 347-9600

Director: Bill Fry

Purpose: HALT is a nonpartisan public interest group dedicated to reducing the cost and improving the quality of legal services in America. Because justice under the law should and must be equally accessible to all citizens, HALT supports legislative reforms that simplify the legal system and produces educational materials that make clients more self-reliant in handling their legal affairs.

Methods of operation: Research (30%), lobbying (30%), publications (40%)

Constituency: The general public, some lawyers and a few businesses

Recent issues and projects: An ongoing project is publishing a series of "Citizens Legal Manuals" which provide information on a variety of legal issues. HALT also works to improve existing attorney discipline systems and to repeal "unauthorized practice of law" rules which prevent non-lawyers from providing routine legal services.

Major publications: *Citizens Legal Manuals*; *How to Use Trusts to Avoid Probate Taxes*; *Fee Arbitration - Model Rules and Commentary*; *The Legal Reformer* (HALT's quarterly newsletter); and numerous research reports and position papers

Budget: $2,000,000

Funding: Direct mail (95%), foundations (5%)

Staff: 8
2 Researchers
1 Fundraiser
1 Bookkeeper/Accountant
1 Attorneys
1 Lobbyists
1 Writer/Editor
1 Office Manager

Staff openings/year: Varies

Work Week: 40-45 hours

Salary/year: $15-20,000 (Recent College Graduate); $20-30,000 (Graduate with advanced degree)

Benefits: Health insurance, life insurance, paid vacation, pregnancy leave

Part-Time Employees: 1

Volunteers: 1-2

Interns: 3-5
Length: Semester or summer
Duties: Research, writing, lobbying, phone work, conference organizing help
Remuneration: Small stipend or college credit

Jobs advertised: Newspapers; word of mouth; career placement centers

To apply: Contact Theresa Meehan Rudy

HANDGUN CONTROL, INC./CENTER TO PREVENT HANDGUN VIOLENCE
1225 I Street, NW, Suite 1100
Washington, DC 20005
(202) 898-0792

Other Offices: Los Angeles, CA; San Francisco, CA

Director: Richard Aborn

Purpose: Handgun Control, Inc. is the nation's leading lobbying organization working to reduce gun violence. Since 1974, we have helped enact stronger gun laws at the federal, state and local levels.

Methods of operation: Lobbying (50%), public education (25%), research (15%), community organizing (10%)

Recent issues and projects: The fight against gun violence requires a comprehensive, national gun policy. Handgun Control, Inc. is leading the national campaign to pass the Handgun Violence Prevention Act of 1994, (S.1882/H.R.3932), know as "Brady II."

Major publications: Fact sheets

Budget: $5,000,000

Funding: Member dues, individual contributions, foundations

Staff: 50
3 Attorneys
1 Office Manager
3 Lobbyists
3 Press Aides
4 Foundation Fundraisers
15 Administrative Assistants
4 Bookkeepers/Accountants
2 Grassroots Fundraisers
2 Law Enforcement Officers
3 Education Specialists
1 Membership Coordinator

Staff openings/year: 2-3

Work Week: 37 1/2 hours

Salary/year: $21,000 (Recent College Graduate); $30,000 (Graduate with advanced degree)

Benefits: Health insurance, pension, paid vacation, life insurance, family leave

Part-Time Employees: 3

Summer Employees: 2-3

Volunteers: 8

Interns: 6
Length: 2 - 2 1/2 months in summer
Duties: Varied, depends on department need
Remuneration: Most are nonpaid internships

Jobs advertised: Local newsletters and college bulletin boards

To apply: Please contact Tanya Bumberay, Director of Administration

HARTFORD AREAS RALLY TOGETHER

660 Park Street
Hartford, CT 06106
(203) 525-3449

Director: James M. Boucher

Purpose: Organize residents from a variety of socio-economic backgrounds to impact public-private decisions that affect their lives. Community self-determination and empowerment are primary organizational goals.

Methods of operation: Community organizing (60%), training and technical assistance (20%), direct action (10%), public education (10%), research (10%)

Membership: 55,000 people in Hartford. 30% hispanic; 15% black; 55% white

Recent issues and projects: Creation of affordable housing; affordable senior health care; anti-drug efforts; better education policies and better city services to low-moderate income neighborhoods

Major publications: Quarterly newsletter

Budget: $450,000

Funding: Foundations

Staff: 7
5 Organizers
1 Executive Director
1/2 Typist
1/2 Bookkeeper/Accountant
1/2 Office Manager

Staff openings/year: 1

Work Week: 50 hours

Salary/year: $19,500 (Recent College Graduate); $24,000 (Graduate with advanced degree)

Benefits: Health insurance, life insurance, pregnancy leave, paid vacation

Part-Time Employees: 1

Volunteers: 250

Interns: 2
Length: 8 months
Duties: Flexible, depending on what intern desires regarding various organizational projects
Remuneration: Stipend for travel

Jobs advertised: College career counseling centers; local newspapers; *Community Jobs*; trade magazines

To apply: Contact James M. Boucher

HARTFORD FOOD SYSTEM

509 Wethersfield Avenue
Hartford, CT 06114
(203) 296-9325

Director: Mark Winne

Purpose: The mission of HFS is to increase the access of low-income people to high quality, affordable food by developing sustainable food production and distribution projects.

Methods of operation: Community economic development (30%), training and technical assistance (30%), human services (20%), public education (5%), research (5%), lobbying (5%), publications (5%)

Constituency: Lower income Hartford residents; people of color; elderly

Recent issues and projects: Farm-to-Family: develops new markets for farmers in urban areas while increasing the purchasing power of low-income city residents

Major publications: Reports on several activities of Farm-to-Family are available as well as general information about HFS.

Budget: $175,000

Funding: Foundations (30%), government (30%), corporations (25%), churches (10%), individual contributions (5%)

Staff: 3
2 Project Managers
1 Issue Expert

Staff openings/year: 1

Work Week: 45 hours

Salary/year: $15-20,000 (Recent College Graduate); $25-30,000 (Graduate with advanced degree)

Benefits: Health insurance, pregnancy leave, paid vacation, certain training expenses

Part-Time Employees: 4

Summer Employees: 2

Volunteers: 2

Interns: 1-2
Length: 3-4 months
Duties: Project development and operation
Remuneration: Stipend

Jobs advertised: Through local media and at regional campuses

To apply: Contact Mark Winne, Executive Director

HAWA'IKI PERMACULTURE SERVICES

75-5260 Mamalahoa Hwy.
Holualoa, HI 96725
(808) 326-4670

Director: Craig Elevitch

Purpose: To restore abundance, diversity and self-sufficiency to the land and people of the Hawaiian Islands.

Methods of operation: Training and technical assistance 40%, direct action 40%, publications 10%, research 10%

Recent issues and projects: Numerous farm forestry designs, permaculture workshops, permaculture publications, and LISA research

Major publications: Regular contributions to local and international permaculture journals

Budget: $50,000

Funding: Business activities 100%

Staff: 3
1 Director
2 Apprentices/trainees

Staff openings/year: 2

Work Week: 60 hours

Interns: 1
Length: 6 months
Duties: All phases of permaculture design/implementation/management
Remuneration: $1,000/6 months, scholarships available

Jobs advertised: International permaculture journals

To apply: Contact Craig Elevitch, Director

HEAL THE BAY

1640 Fifth Street, Suite 112
Santa Monica, CA 90401
(310) 394-4552

President: Michael Caggiano

Purpose: Protect and restore Santa Monica Bay for people and marine life.

Methods of operation: Research, community organizing, publications, public education, litigation, training and technical assistance, habitat restoration

Constituency: West Los Angeles County

Recent issues and projects: Required city of Los Angeles to clean up sewage discharge. Currently launching Gutter Patrol Program, an action/education program for all of LA County to reduce storm drain/urban runoff; lawsuit against County sewage treatment; coastal restoration; industrial permit violator litigation.

Major publications: *Heal the Bay Newsletter*

Budget: $500,000

Funding: Individual contributions, corporate, foundation and government grants

Staff: 10
1 Executive Director
1 Staff Scientist
1 Research Scientist
2 Community Outreach Coordinators
1 Development Director
1 Administrative Assistant
1 Program Manager
1 Coastal Restoration Manager
1 Office Manager
1/2 Volunteer Coordinator

Staff openings/year: 1

Work Week: 45 hours

Salary/year: $20-25,000 (Recent College Graduate); $25,000 (Graduate with advanced degree)

Benefits: Health insurance, paid vacation

Part-Time Employees: Yes

Summer Employees: Yes

Volunteers: 100's

Interns: 1-3
Length: As long as they can stay
Duties: Depends on background of applicant
Remuneration: Volunteer

Jobs advertised: Word of mouth; classified ads; via existing networks of groups

To apply: Contact Adi Liberman, Executive Director

HEALTH ACCESS FOUNDATION & HEALTH ACCESS OF CALIFORNIA

1535 Mission Street
San Francisco, CA 94103
(415) 431-7430 Fax: (415) 431-1048

Other Offices: Los Angeles, CA

Director: Maria Y. Ferrer

Purpose: Statewide consumer health coalition of over 200 member organizations working to achieve affordable health care for all. Health Access coordinates the activities of its member organizations, policy advisors, and individual activists to educate the public, organize, develop policy and advocate in the legislature. Their campaign for health care regardless of ability to pay is in response to an environment where 1 out of 5 non-elderly Californians lacks any health care coverage, and where skyrocketing costs leave millions more underinsured.

Methods of operation: Public education (50%), public outreach and community organizing (30%), research (10%), publications (5%), lobbying (5%)

Constituency: Consumer advocacy organizations, senior groups, religious agencies, local grassroots coalitions, labor unions, and organizations representing communities of color, people w/AIDS, women and children

Recent issues and projects: Analysis of national health care plans and legislative implementation of the national plan in California

Major publications: *The California Dream, the California Nightmare: 5.2 Million People With No Health Insurance*; *The Right Way to Spend California's $70 Billion Health Care Dollars*; *How California Wastes at Least $10 in Health Care Dollars Each Year*; *In Our Best Interest*; *Preliminary Guide to the National Health Care Debate*

Budget: $350,000

Funding: Foundations (75%), individual contributions (25%)

Staff: 6
1 Organizer
1 Executive Director
1 Project Coordinator
1 Development Director
1/2 Bookkeeper
3/4 Administrative Assistant

Staff openings/year: 0-1

Work Week: 40-50 hours

Salary/year: $Varies (Recent College Graduate); $Varies (Graduate with advanced degree)

Benefits: Health insurance, pregnancy leave, pension, child care, paid vacation

Volunteers: 1-5

Interns: 1-5
Length: 3-6 months
Duties: Research, community organizing, legislative analysis, writing
Remuneration: Work-study or negotiable

Jobs advertised: Local newspapers; through member organizations

To apply: Contact Maryann O'Sullivan, Executive Director

HEALTH CARE FOR ALL

30 Winter Street, Suite 1007
Boston, MA 02108
(617) 350-7279

Director: Robert Restuccia

Purpose: Health Care For All is dedicated to the principle that health care is the right of every man, woman and child. We promote reform of the health care system on both state and national levels. We also have a health care helpline where we give out information on access to health care for people who need help.

Methods of operation: Community organizing (42%), public education (20%), human services (13%), research (12%), publications (5%), lobbying (4%), direct action (3%), litigation (1%)

Recent issues and projects: Recent projects include: Boston Health Access Project which is a community empowerment project to change the way health resources are allocated in Boston; Health Helpline which takes calls from people who don't have health care and provides information referrals.

Major publications: *Health Care For All News*, a quarterly newsletter

Budget: $400,000

Funding: Foundations (70%), individual contributions (10%), honoraria and contracts (10%), special events (10%)

Staff: 8
3 Organizers
1 Writer/Editor
1 Office Manager
1 Lobbyist/Policy Director
1 Foundation/Grassroots Fundraiser
1 Case Worker

Staff openings/year: 2

Work Week: 40 hours

Salary/year: $20,000 (Recent College Graduate); $25,000 (Graduate with advanced degree)

Benefits: Health insurance, paid vacation, parental leave

Part-Time Employees: 2

Summer Employees: 1

Volunteers: 10

Interns: 6
Length: 3 months
Duties: Community organizing, policy research, advocacy, direct service administration
Remuneration: Depends on year

Jobs advertised: *Community Jobs* newspaper, local papers, through mailing list

To apply: Contact Robert Restuccia, Executive Director

HEALTH CRISIS NETWORK

5050 Biscayne Blvd.
Miami, FL 33134
(305) 751-7775

Director: Catherine Lynch

Purpose: Health Crisis Network (HCN) is a nonprofit, community-based organization founded in 1983. HCN provides counseling and support services, public information and education in response to HIV spectrum illness for the greater Miami area.

Methods of operation: Human services (60%), public education (35%), training and technical assistance (5%)

Constituency: People affected by and concerned about HIV/AIDS

Recent issues and projects: Recent projects include: The Women's Project; Professional Training Services; The AIDS Hotline, *The Buzz*; AIDS Workplace Programs; and AIDS Awareness Program to name just a few ongoing projects.

Major publications: *Health Sources: Community Guide to HIV/AIDS Resources*; and a quarterly newsletter

Budget: $3,100,000

Funding: Government (60%), events (20%), individual contributions (5%), foundations (3%), program fees (3%), direct mail (1%), other (8%)

Staff: 54
19 Counselors
10 Educators
8 Administrative Support
2 Development
5 Caseworkers
4 Bookkeepers
5 Typists
1/2 Foundation Fundraiser
1/2 Grassroots Fundraiser

Staff openings/year: 5

Work Week: 40-45 hours

Salary/year: $19,000 (Recent College Graduate); $24,000 (Graduate with advanced degree)

Benefits: Health insurance, pension, paid vacation, credit union, family leave, tuition reimbursement

Part-Time Employees: 20

Summer Employees: None

Volunteers: 500

Interns: 2-5
Length: 3-6 months
Duties: Assist with counseling, education and fundraising
Remuneration: None

Jobs advertised: Local newspapers and postings in-house

HEALTH POLICY ADVISORY CENTER (HEALTH/PAC)

833 Broadway, Suite 1607
New York, NY 10003
(212) 267-8890

Director: Nancy McKenzie

Purpose: A health policy magazine/journal which critiques and reports on domestic and international health policy issues

Methods of operation: Publications (75%), research (20%), public education (5%)

Constituency: Health activists, academics, social workers, physicians, administrators, nurses

Recent issues and projects: The crisis in New York City's hospital system; medical rights abuses in the West Bank and Gaza Strip; policy issues surrounding women and AIDS; Analysis of health reform

Major publications: *Health/PAC Bulletin*

Budget: $100,000

Funding: Direct mail (90%), foundations (5%), individual contributions (5%)

Staff: 2
2 Writer/Editors
1 Staff Editor (part-time)
1 Office Assistant (part-time)
1 Bookkeeper (part-time)

Staff openings/year: 1

Work Week: 40 hours

Salary/year: $16,000

Benefits: Health insurance, paid vacation

Part-Time Employees: 3

Summer Employees: 1

Volunteers: 1-2

Interns: Yes, as needed
Length: Semester
Duties: Research, write, help edit, office assistance
Remuneration: None

Jobs advertised: Publications; word of mouth; posting

To apply: Contact Nancy McKenzie

HERBERT SCOVILLE JR. PEACE FELLOWSHIP

110 Maryland Ave., NE, Suite 211
Washington, DC 20002
(202) 546-0795

Director: Paul D. Revsine

Purpose: The program was established to provide college graduates with the opportunity to gain a Washington, DC perspective on arms control, peace and disarmament issues. The Fellows spend four to six months working as special project assistants on the staff of one of the participating organizations, where they conduct research and write papers. The goal is to provide a unique educational experience for people with a demonstrated commitment to arms control.

Methods of operation: Research, publication and public education

Constituency: The Fellows are all college graduates with excellent academic and extracurricular accomplishments who have a strong interest in nuclear and conventional arms control and peace issues.

Recent issues and projects: The Fellows projects focus on national security, arms transfers, the scientific and environmental aspects of nuclear weapons, international arms treaties, the military budget, and other related topics. Recent Fellows have worked on export controls and non-proliferation issues in the former Soviet Union, U.N. peacekeeping, and nuclear power in Eastern Europe.

Major publications: Fellows often write for publications of the organizations where they serve their Fellowship on the issues they research. One recent Fellow wrote a monthly article in Arms Control Today and another produced an issue paper on the B-2 bomber.

To apply: People interested in applying for the Scoville Fellowship should contact the office for application information. Application deadlines are October 15 for spring semester and March 15 for all semester. Travel expenses are paid for finalists.

HETRICK - MARTIN INSTITUTE

2 Astor Place
New York, NY 10003
(212) 674-2400

Director: Frances Kunrenther

Purpose: The Hetrick-Martin Institute concentrates on social services, advocacy, and education for lesbian, gay and bisexual youth (12-21) and their families. HMI provides counseling, a drop-in center, street outreach, training for youth and youth-serving professionals.

Methods of operation: Human services (60%), public education (20%), training and technical assistance (20%)

Constituency: Gay and lesbian youth and their supporters

Recent issues and projects: Recent projects include: peer education on gay and AIDS issues; advocacy for gay inclusion in multicultural education; advocacy for AIDS education and condoms in schools; training foster care workers in gay youth issues; and theatre program for gay youth

Major publications: *You Are Not Alone*, a directory of 170 groups nationwide serving gay youth; *FACTFILE*, on gay youth and on gay adults working with youth; *HMI Report Card*, newsletter

Budget: $2,500,000

Funding: Government (60%), individual contributions (20%), foundations (10%), direct mail (10%)

Staff: 47
1 Organizer
1 Writer/Editor
1/2 Attorney
1 Office Manager
1/2 Press Aide
1 Foundation Fundraiser
1 Issue Expert
4 Administrative Assistants
4 Bookkeepers/Accountants
30 Caseworkers
3 Grassroots Fundraisers

Work Week: 35 hours

Salary/year: $22,000 (Recent College Graduate); $25,000 (Graduate with advanced degree)

Benefits: Health insurance, paid vacation, life insurance, disability

Part-Time Employees: Yes

Summer Employees: None

Volunteers: 60

Interns: 20
Length: 6 months
Duties: Social work, clerical help, research
Remuneration: Youth interns are paid $5.00 an hour

Jobs advertised: Newspapers, mailings

To apply: Please contact Tia Nicole Leak, Youth Advocate

HIGHLANDER RESEARCH AND EDUCATION CENTER

Route 3, Box 370
New Market, TN 37820
(615) 933-3443

Director: John Gaventa

Purpose: Highlander is a research and popular education institution established in 1932 to help communities deal with the structural causes of economic, environmental and social problems in a democratic, practical and effective manner.

Methods of operation: Training and technical assistance, research, public education, publications, cultural documentation

Constituency: Members of grassroots community groups dealing with economic, environmental, social problems

Recent issues and projects: STP Schools (Stop the Poisoning; environmental education); South and Appalachia Leadership Training Program; Youth Empowerment Program

Major publications: *Deindustrialization in Tennessee*; *Power and Powerlessness*; *No Promise for Tomorrow* (videotape); *Highlander Reports* quarterly newsletter; *Communities in Economic Crisis: Appalachia and the South*

Budget: $500,000

Funding: Individual contributions, foundations

Staff: 15
9 Popular Education Program Associates
2 Facilities Managers
2 Administrators
1 Office Manager
1 Bookkeeper/Accountant

Staff openings/year: 2

Work Week: 40+ hours

Salary/year: $16,000 (Recent College Graduate); $Varies (Graduate with advanced degree)

Benefits: Health insurance, life insurance, paid vacation

Part-Time Employees: 2

Volunteers: 2-3 per year

Interns: Yes
Length: Varies
Duties: Both length and duties as agreed upon with program associates
Remuneration: No paid interns; housing sometimes available

Jobs advertised: Through networks of sister organizations

To apply: Contact Mark Harris, Administrator

HITCHCOCK CENTER FOR THE ENVIRONMENT

525 South Pleasant Street
Amherst, MA 01002
(413) 256-6006

Purpose: To foster a greater awareness and understanding of our environment and to develop environmentally literate citizens. Teach stewardship of our environment and care for the resources of our planet.

Methods of operation: Public education (50%), training and technical assistance (20%), publications (10%), human services (10%), community organizing (10%)

Constituency: Residents of the greater Pioneer Valley, Western Massachusetts, Connecticut, New York, Vermont. Serving people of all ages and backgrounds.

Recent issues and projects: Concentrating on natural history, environmental and education issues. Monitoring world's first salamander tunnels to assist mole salamanders during spring migration.

Major publications: Seasonal program catalogue of native and environmental programs

Funding: Individual contributions, foundations

Staff: 7
4 Teacher/Naturalists
1 Resource Center Coordinator
1 Center Manager
1 Executive Director
1 Bookkeeper/Accountant

Staff openings/year: 2

Work Week: 35 hours

Salary/year: $19,000 (Recent College Graduate); $25,000 (Graduate with advanced degree)

Benefits: Health insurance, pregnancy leave, paid vacation

Part-Time Employees: 3

Summer Employees: 2

Volunteers: 20

Interns: 4
Length: 5-6 months
Duties: Assist teaching staff
Remuneration: Stipend or work-study

Jobs advertised: Newspapers; flyers; newsletters

To apply: Contact Ted Watt, Center Manager

HIV LAW PROJECT

841 Broadway, Suite 608
New York, NY 10003
(212) 674-7590

Director: Terry McGovern, Esg.

Purpose: To provide legal services regarding public benefits, family issues, housing, healthcare, legal documents and immigration to low-income HIV positive individuals.

Methods of operation: Litigation (60%), community organizing (20%), public education

Recent issues and projects: S.P. V. Sullivan (1993): succeeded in changing Social Security's disability determination process to recognize more of the HIV related illnesses suffered by people of color, women, IV drug users and low-income people generally; National Task Force on AIDS Drug Development Proposal/Citizens Petition: working to change FDA regulations that exclude women from clinical drug trials.

Budget: $700,000

Funding: Foundations (60%), Government Funding (40%)

Staff: 11
3 Attorneys
2 Paralegals
1 Office Manager
1 Director of Development
1 Intake Officer
1 Receptionist
1 Deputy Director
1 Executive Director/Head Attorney

Staff openings/year: 1-2

Work Week: 40 hours

Salary/year: $20,000 (Recent College Graduate); $30,000 (Graduate with advanced degree)

Benefits: Health insurance, paid vacation, life insurance, family leave

Part-Time Employees: 1-2

Summer Employees: None

Volunteers: 15

Interns: 1-3
Length: 8 weeks (summer)
Duties: Assist attorneys, paralegals and deputy director
Remuneration: Interns must bring their own funding

Jobs advertised: *New York Times* and community posting and outreach

To apply: Please contact Terry McGovern, Executive Director

Remarks: The HIV Law Project also sponsors the Katrina Haslip Law Technical Assistance Program, a series of seminars designed to help low-income HIV positive women become advocates and spokespeople for their communities.

HOMELESS ADVOCACY PROJECT

1324 Loost Street
Philadelphia, PA 19107
(215) 893-5362

Director: Sandy Ballard

Purpose: The Homeless Advocacy Project provides free legal services and advocacy for homeless people and nonprofit community groups developing affordable housing or other services for the homeless.

Methods of operation: Legal services (77%), training and technical assistance (15%), public education (5%), lobbying (3%)

Constituency: Attorneys, paralegals and law students

Recent issues and projects: Recent projects include: opposition to welfare cuts; pending City ordinance to exempt community groups from City transfer tax; and outreach program to homeless children

Major publications: Newsletter

Budget: $140,000

Funding: Foundations (65%), individual contributions (35%)

Staff: 3
2 Attorneys
1 Paralegal

Staff openings/year: 0-1

Work Week: 40 hours

Salary/year: $20,000 (Recent College Graduate); $30,000 (Graduate with advanced degree)

Benefits: Health insurance, paid vacation, life insurance

Part-Time Employees: 1

Summer Employees: 5

Volunteers: 2

Interns: 4
Length: 1 semester
Remuneration: Work study

Jobs advertised: Locally

To apply: Please contact Sandy Ballard

HOMELESSNESS INFORMATION EXCHANGE

1612 K Street, NW, Suite 1004
Washington, DC 20006
(202) 775-1322

Director: Dana H. Harris-Trovato

Purpose: The exchange gathers and distributes information about model homeless programs and policies, funding sources, and experienced practitioners. Clients include direct service providers, governments, researchers, media and advocates.

Methods of operation: Research (45%), publications (25%), training and technical assistance (25%), public education (5%)

Constituency: Direct service providers; state, local and federal government

Recent issues and projects: We are currently working on a statistical handbook on homelessness for public libraries and reports that promote empowerment in programs and advocacy efforts.

Major publications: Quarterly newsletter: *Homewords*

Budget: $100,000

Funding: Foundations (55%), corporations (25%), publications (20%)

Staff: 3
1 Research Assistant
1 Director
1 Office Assistant

Staff openings/year: 1

Work Week: 37.5 hours

Salary/year: $24,000 (Recent College Graduate); $Varies (Graduate with advanced degree)

Benefits: Health insurance, life insurance, paid vacation, disability insurance

Part-Time Employees: 1

Volunteers: Yes; ad hoc

Interns: 3-5
Length: 3 months
Duties: Data collection, writing for national database, newsletter and maintain national library
Remuneration: None

Jobs advertised: Selected community action newsletters

To apply: Contact Dana Harris-Trovato, Director

HORIZON COMMUNICATIONS

52 Cream Hill
West Cornwall, CT 06796
(203) 672-0169

Other Offices: Cambridge, MA

Director: Janine M.H. Selendy

Purpose: To foster initiatives; to help protect and improve life on earth in the areas of health, environment, energy and technology by finding and sharing knowledge of what can be and is being done to help.

Methods of operation: Research, public education, lectures, training and technical assistance in an advisory capacity, publications

Constituency: Worldwide; diverse backgrounds

Recent issues and projects: International series of television specials featuring initiatives, with host and narrator, Lynn Redgrave. Co-productions with others, including Swedish TV, Heitong Jizng TV of Peoples Republic of China, and West German TV.

Major publications: *Bulletin*; transcripts; books to come

Funding: Individual contributions, foundations

Part-Time Employees: Yes

Summer Employees: Yes

Volunteers: Yes

Interns: Yes

To apply: Contact Janine M.H. Selendy, Executive Producer, or Dan Rosenberg, Senior Researcher

Remarks: We are just now undergoing reorganization, as we begin our U.S. nationwide broadcast on PBS.

HOUSEHOLD HAZARDOUS WASTE PROJECT

1031 E. Battlefield, Suite 214
Springfield, MO 65807
(417) 889-5000

Director: Marie Steinwachs

Purpose: The Household Hazardous Waste Project is devoted to protecting the quality of our health and the environment through increasing people's knowledge and ability to make informed decisions about hazardous products and unregulated hazardous wastes.

Methods of operation: Research (20%), publications (20%), community organizing (20%), public education (20%), training and technical assistance (20%)

Constituency: Household managers; city, county and state government; solid waste districts; youth and adult educators; environmental activists; youth; waste management industry; and product manufacturers

Recent issues and projects: Missouri waste districts are required to address household hazardous waste in a comprehensive management plan. HHWP provides training to the waste districts on household hazardous waste issues and management. HHWP is assisting with the development of a model education and technical assistance program to address the needs of unregulated small quantity generators of hazardous wastes. HHWP involves volunteers in a community education program to protect water quality by stenciling storm drains.

Major publications: *Guide to Hazardous Products Around the Home*; Guide Sheet Series; educational activities; and *Lessons in Household Hazardous Waste Management*, for teachers of grades K-3 and 4-8

Budget: $180,000

Funding: Government grants (83%), material sales (17%)

Staff: 4
2 Writers/Editors/Researchers/Educators
1 Director/Educator/Researcher/Writer/Editor
1 Office Manager/Bookkeeper/Researcher

Staff openings/year: 0.5

Work Week: 40 hours

Salary/year: $20,000 (Recent College Graduate); $23,000 (Graduate with advanced degree)

Benefits: Health insurance, pension, paid vacation, life insurance, credit union, family leave, tuition reimbursement

Part-Time Employees: Yes

Summer Employees: None

Volunteers: None

Interns: No, but willing to accept applications

Jobs advertised: Local newspapers, local college and university employment offices and Missouri Job Service

To apply: Please contact Nelda Zehner, Administrative Assistant

Remarks: The Household Hazardous Waste Project (HHWP) is a community education program of University of Missouri Extension, in cooperation with the Environmental Improvement and Energy Resources Authority. HHWP develops and promotes education and action concerning household hazardous product identification, safe use, storage, proper disposal and the selection of safer alternatives. HHWP works with a broad range of communities to establish local programs. The key to HHWP's success is in fostering cooperation among groups addressing health, waste disposal, water protection, air protection, fire safety, recycling, and poison prevention.

HOUSING & CREDIT COUNSELING, INC.

1195 SW Buchanan, Suite 203
Topeka, KS 66604-1183
(913) 234-0217

Other Offices: Lawrence, KS; Manhattan, KS

Director: Karen A. Hiller

Purpose: Facilitate safe, adequate, affordable and equitable housing situations for all people, particularly those of low and moderate income; assist with budgeting and debt repayment alternatives so that people can handle their finances on their own, with dignity and without going bankrupt.

Methods of operation: Human services (88%), public education (5%), training and technical assistance (4%), community organizing (3%)

Constituency: Low and moderate income people

Recent issues and projects: Tenant-landlord assistance (3-4,000/year); consumer credit counseling (2,000/year); fair housing; affordable housing; alternatives to bankruptcy

Major publications: *Kansas Tenants Handbook*; *Kansas Landlords Handbook*; model lease; model application form; fair housing booklet

Budget: $500,000

Funding: United Way, government, program income (97%), individual contributions (3%)

Staff: 21
13 Caseworkers
1 Executive Director
4 Receptionists/Data Entry
1 Bookkeeper/Accountant
1 Office Manager
1 Administrative Assistant

Staff openings/year: 1-2

Work Week: 40 hours

Salary/year: $16,000 (Recent College Graduate); $Varies (Graduate with advanced degree)

Benefits: Vacation and sick leave, life and disability insurance

Part-Time Employees: 1

Volunteers: Yes

Interns: 1-2
Length: 1 semester minimum
Duties: Tenant-landlord and consumer credit. Interns can be helpful in organizing and special projects.
Remuneration: Unpaid

Jobs advertised: Local newspaper

To apply: Contact Karen Hiller, Executive Director

HOUSING ASSISTANCE COUNCIL (HAC)

1025 Vermont Avenue, NW, Suite 606
Washington, DC 20005
(202) 842-8600

Other Offices: Atlanta, GA; Mill Valley, CA; Albuquerque, NM

Director: Moises Loza

Purpose: To assist in the provision of decent, sanitary, affordable housing for the rural poor.

Methods of operation: Training and technical assistance (50%), direct action (30%), research (10%), publications (10%)

Constituency: Anyone interested in rural housing for the poor

Recent issues and projects: Operate 4 loan funds, publish manuals and newsletters, monitor rural housing legislation, provide technical assistance - all ongoing

Major publications: *HAC News* (free); *State Action Memorandum*; *Rural Housing and Community Development Guide*; etc.

Budget: $2,000,000

Funding: Foundations (50%), HUD contracts (50%)

Staff: 25
8 1/2 Housing Program/TA/Loans
7 Administrative Assistants
2 Issue Experts
2 Office Managers
1 Executive Director
1 Pressroom Person
1 Bookkeeper/Accountant
1 Writer/Editor
1 Paralegal
1 Researcher
1/2 Foundation Fundraiser

Staff openings/year: 1-2

Work Week: 37.5 hours

Salary/year: $28,000

Benefits: Health insurance, life insurance, pregnancy leave, pension, credit union, paid vacation

Interns: 2
Length: Summer
Duties: Research, writing
Remuneration: Volunteer

Jobs advertised: Through the rural housing network; occasionally in the newspaper

To apply: Contact Joe Belden, Deputy Director

HOUSING ASSOCIATION OF DELAWARE VALLEY

1314 Chestnut Street, Suite 900
Philadelphia, PA 19107
(215) 545-6010

Director: Anthony Lewis

Purpose: To end racism and exploitation in the

field of housing and to ensure decent housing for all residents of the Delaware Valley regardless of race or income.

Methods of operation: Research (10%), publications (10%), public education (10%), training and technical assistance (30%), housing counseling (20%), housing development (20%)

Constituency: Residents of the Delaware Valley who are seeking solutions to housing problems

Recent issues and projects: Leadership Training and Tenant Management of public housing developments in Philadelphia. Sweat Equity rehabilitation and new construction of 28 low-income houses.

Major publications: *Community Alerting Service* - a weekly reporting service that details the activities of Philadelphia's municipal agencies; *Beyond Reach: Housing and the American Dream in Philadelphia*; *Housing Association Resource Guide* which lists funding sources in the Delaware Valley.

Budget: $2,790,000

Funding: Government (80%), foundations (10%), United Way (8%), self-generated (2%)

Staff: 12
3 Caseworkers
1 Researcher
2 Accountants
1 Office Manager
2 Administrative Assistants
1 Director of Development
1 Director of Housing Development
1 Director of Tenant Management/Training

Staff openings/year: 2

Work Week: 35 hours

Salary/year: $18,000 (Recent College Graduate); $21,000 (Graduate with advanced degree)

Benefits: Health insurance, life insurance, pension, paid vacation

Interns: Yes
Length: 3 months-1 year
Duties: Research
Remuneration: Internships are unpaid

Jobs advertised: Local newspapers

To apply: Contact Anthony Lewis, Managing Director

HOUSING COALITION OF CENTRAL NEW JERSEY

9 Elm Row
New Brunswick, NJ 08901
(908) 249-9700 Fax: (908) 249-4121

Director: Jewel Daney

Purpose: The Coalition is a private nonprofit organization which offers tenant/landlord counseling, opportunities for homesharing, guidance in filing housing discrimination complaints, assistance in obtaining affordable housing under Mt. Laurel obligations and information and referral.

Methods of operation: Human services (80%), public education (13%), research (6%), training and technical assistance (1%)

Constituency: Residents of Middlesex County and some surrounding areas seeking to maintain or improve their housing opportunities

Recent issues and projects: Plaintiff in fair housing cases. Successful in settlement of first familial status case filed with HUD under 1988 Fair Housing Amendments.

Major publications: *Desperately Seeking Housing* pamphlet

Budget: $300,000

Funding: County and municipalities, state (60%), private (29%), individual contributions (11%)

Staff: 7
1 Executive Director
1 Housing Coordinator
1 Fair Housing Coordinator
2 Counselors
1 Typist
1 Case Manager

Staff openings/year: 1

Work Week: 35 hours

Salary/year: $19,000 (Recent College Graduate); $27,000 (Graduate with advanced degree)

Benefits: Health insurance, paid vacation

Volunteers: Varies

Interns: None currently, but willing to accept applications

Jobs advertised: Flyers sent to County agencies; newspaper ads

To apply: Contact Jewel Daney, Executive Director

HOUSING COUNSELING SERVICES, INC.

2430 Ontario Road, NW
Washington, DC 20009
(202) 667-7007 Fax: (202) 462-5305

Director: Carmelita Edwards

Purpose: HCS provides comprehensive housing counseling training and advocacy to low and moderate income families to assist them in gaining control over their own lives and environments.

Methods of operation: Human services (70%), community organizing (10%), public education (10%), training and technical assistance (10%)

Constituency: Low and moderate income families in Metro Washington

Recent issues and projects: Recently completed the co-development of two tenant-sponsored limited equity co-ops

Budget: $500,000

Funding: DC and federal contracts (60%), United Way (24%), foundations (5%), individual contributions (1%)

Staff: 14
10 Caseworkers
2 Administration
2 Information Specialists

Staff openings/year: 1

Work Week: 40 hours

Salary/year: $18,000 (Recent College Graduate); $21,000 (Graduate with advanced degree)

Benefits: Health insurance, life insurance, pension, paid vacation

Volunteers: Yes

Interns: Yes
Length: 2 months-1 year
Duties: Depends on intern skills
Remuneration: None

Jobs advertised: Mailings to community groups; community newsletters

To apply: Contact Marian Siegel, Deputy Director

HOUSING LAW REFORM PROJECT OF STUDENT LEGAL SERVICES

3409 Michigan Union
Ann Arbor, MI 48109
(313) 936-0836

Director: Larry Fox, Michael Appel

Purpose: HLRP works on housing issues through organizing, research, education and law reform. HLRP focuses on student and low-income housing issues.

Methods of operation: Community organizing (30%), public education (20%), research (20%), publications (10%), litigation (10%), direct action (10%)

Constituency: University of Michigan students; tenants; low-income tenants

Recent issues and projects: Drafting tenant protection laws (rent, eviction, privacy); research on housing costs, displacement, etc; statewide tenants network; work with domestic violence network; public housing.

Funding: University of Michigan student fees (99%), foundations (1%)

Staff: 2
2 Organizers

Work Week: 40+ hours

Salary/year: $Varies (Recent College Graduate); $Varies (Graduate with advanced degree)

Benefits: Health insurance, life insurance, paid vacation

Volunteers: Yes

Interns: None currently, but willing to accept applications

Jobs advertised: Local and regional networks

To apply: Contact Larry Fox or Michael Appel, HLRP staff

HOUSING MATTERS/MASSACHUSETTS LAW REFORM INSTITUTE

69 Canal Street
Boston, MA 02114
(617) 742-9250

Director: Allan Rodgers

Purpose: *HOUSING MATTERS* is a newsletter published four times a year which covers the strategies and work being developed by housing advocates and people in need of housing. It features interviews, articles by activists, and practical information (e.g. residential technical assistance).

Methods of operation: Research, publications, lay-out

Constituency: Subscribers include a broad range across the country, including tenants, lawyers, government agencies, nonprofits, churches and housing advocates.

Recent issues and projects: Last two issues involved the following: fighting racism in our backyards; and the war on drugs target tenants

Funding: Subscriptions, grants

Staff: 2
1 Editor (part-time)
1 Assistant (part-time)

Work Week: 10 hours

Volunteers: Yes

Interns: Yes
Length: 3-4 months
Duties: Research, writing

To apply: Contact Annette R. Duke

HOUSING RESOURCE CENTER

300 North Washington Square, Suite 103
Lansing, MI 48933
(517) 487-6051

Other Offices: East Lansing, MI

Director: Rose Norwood

Purpose: Provide comprehensive housing counseling services, landlord/tenant, mortgage default, eviction prevention, security deposit assistance, and lists of low-income available housing.

Methods of operation: Human services (68%), public education (25%), publications (5%), research (1%), community organizing (1%)

Constituency: Low-income clients

Recent issues and projects: Increasingly, the number one issue is a lack of affordable housing. Also lack of ongoing funding puts strain on ability to deliver services.

Major publications: Quarterly newsletter. Four booklets on landlord/tenants law: *Leasing: The Ins and Outs*; *Eviction: Defending Your Home*; *Security Deposits: How to Get Your's Back*; *Maintenance: The Nuts and Bolts Story*; various leaflets on landlord/tenant topics

Budget: $200,000

Funding: Local government (84%), foundations (15%), individual contributions (1%)

Staff: 4
3 Caseworkers
1 Office Manager

Staff openings/year: 1

Work Week: 40 hours

Salary/year: $13-16,000 (Recent College Graduate); $16,000 (Graduate with advanced degree)

Benefits: Health insurance, paid vacation

Part-Time Employees: 6-8

Volunteers: Up to 50

Interns: 2-4
Length: 1 school term
Duties: Various landlord/tenant material production, counseling
Remuneration: None

Jobs advertised: Newspaper; student job posted at university

To apply: Contact Rose Norwood, Director

HOUSING RIGHTS, INC.

3354 Adeline Street
Berkeley, CA 94609
(510) 658-8766

Director: Marianne Lawless

Purpose: To provide full fair housing services (counseling and investigations) to residents of Berkeley and families with children in Oakland. To eliminate housing discrimination through education, mediation and litigation. Also acts as advocates for families in public housing and families who are homeless or at risk of becoming homeless.

Methods of operation: Human services (100%), including public education, lobbying, training and technical assistance, litigation, community organizing, and research

Constituency: Clients are: 87% female heads-of-households; 65% AFDC recipients (Aid to

Families with Dependent Children); almost exclusively families with children

Recent issues and projects: Work with local attorneys to handle source-of-income discrimination cases (a major barrier for homeless families); worked with local tenants' rights people for "just cause for eviction" ordinance in Oakland

Major publications: *Where Have All the Children Gone?* (1984), a manual to help combat child discrimination

Budget: $45,000

Funding: Community Development Block Grant (CDBG), Community Services Block Grant (CSBG), individual contributions (100%)

Staff: 1
1 Executive Director

Work Week: 37 hours

Salary/year: $10,500 part-time

Benefits: Health insurance, life insurance, pregnancy leave, pension, paid vacation

Part-Time Employees: 1

Volunteers: Yes

Jobs advertised: Through local housing and social services agencies

To apply: Contact Marianne Lawless, Executive Director

Remarks: A part-time Housing Counselor earns $13,500 a year.

HUDSON VALLEY GRASS ROOTS ENERGY AND ENVIRONMENTAL NETWORK

Box 208
Red Hook, NY 12571
(914) 758-4484

Director: Ruth Oja

Purpose: Hudson Valley GREEN is a membership organization of folks interested in the cause of safe energy practices and environmentalism. Our purpose is to help inform the public and participate in the general debate on matters of policy and practice concerning energy and the environment.

Methods of operation: Publications (80%), public education (10%), community organizing (5%), direct action (2%), training and technical assistance (2%), research (1%)

Constituency: Hudson Valley residents concerned with energy and the environment

Recent issues and projects: Solid waste, sustainable agriculture, development. Energy slide show. The main focus is the production of the award-winning bimonthly newspaper, *The Hudson Valley GREEN Times*.

Major publications: Quarterly paper: *The Hudson Valley GREEN Times*

Budget: $10,000

Funding: Individual contributions (95%)

Staff:
12 member volunteer Board of Directors
1 Part-time Staff

Part-Time Employees: 1

Volunteers: 12-15

Interns: 1
Length: Few months
Duties: Independent projects

Jobs advertised: Through *GREEN Times*

To apply: Contact Brian Reid, Treasurer

HUMAN ACTION COMMUNITY ORGANIZATION (H.A.C.O.)

16028 South Halsted, P.O. Box 1703
Harvey, IL 60426
(708) 339-7902

Director: Eraina B. Dunn

Purpose: To assist the community in organizing itself to constructively resolve community problems, to manage rather than suppress conflict and to encourage diverse peoples to live and grow harmoniously together. Environmental justice issues; sponsoring environmental lead abatement training; and addressing housing issues.

Methods of operation: Community organizing (20%), training and technical assistance (20%), public education (15%), direct action (15%), human services (10%), research (10%)

Constituency: Primarily low to middle income; multi-ethnic board

Recent issues and projects: Operation Safe Streets, a crime prevention program approved through the Enterprise Zone Program to organize citizens, agencies and coalitions to fight crime through neighborhood watch and citizen patrol. Also have an umbrella group organized to fight incinerator proposals called COBRA (Community Based Revitalization Alliance). As well as a lead abatement program funded by EPA including community awareness classes.

Budget: $150,000

Funding: Corporate (30%), individual contributions (50%), foundations (20%)

Staff:
Volunteer including:
5 Organizers
1 Typist
2 Grassroots Fundraisers
2 Attorneys
1 Bookkeeper/Accountant
1 Writer/Editor/Executive Director

Work Week: 40 hours

Benefits: Health insurance and life insurance for full-time volunteers

Part-Time Employees: Yes; 3-20 hours/week

Volunteers: 18

Interns: 2, from local colleges
Length: 1 semester
Duties: Varies - grassroots organizing, presentations, attending meetings, making reports to board
Remuneration: Travel allowance; possibly more

Jobs advertised: Newspaper; word of mouth; schools and other organizations

To apply: Contact Eraina Dunn, Executive Director

HUMAN ENVIRONMENT CENTER
1930 18th Street, NW #24
Washington, DC 20009
(202) 331-8387

Director: Margaret Rosenberry, Executive Director

Purpose: Nonprofit organization providing education, information, and services to encourage integration of environmental organizations, and promotion of joint activities among environmental and social equity groups. Serves as a clearinghouse and technical assistance center for youth conservation and service corps programs and operates a recruitment and placement service for minority environmental interns and professionals. Other concerns include urban parks and recreation, minority environmental issues and multi-interest coalition development.

Recent issues and projects: Minority Environmental Science Internship (high school); Minority Environmental Internship Program (college)

Major publications: *Human Environment Center News*

Funding: Foundations (90%), other (10%)

Staff: 4
1 Office Manager
1 Foundation Fundraiser
1 Issue Expert
1 Typist

Work Week: 40 hours

Benefits: Health insurance, life insurance, pregnancy leave, paid vacation

Interns: Yes
Duties: Placing interns in environmental/natural resource agencies in DC

Jobs advertised: Environmental newsletters and publications

To apply: Contact Personnel Director

HUMAN RIGHTS CAMPAIGN FUND
1012 14th Street, NW, Suite 607
Washington, DC 20005
(202) 628-4160

Other Offices: Atlanta, GA; Chicago, IL

Director: Tim McFeeley

Purpose: HRCF is the largest national lesbian and gay political organization. We are committed to securing full civil rights for lesbians and gay men and responsible federal policies on AIDS. HRCF mobilizes grassroots support and lobbies, educates and helps elect legislators who support the goals of equality for community.

Methods of operation: Research, lobbying, publications, community organizing, public education

Membership: The majority of our members and supporters are lesbians and gay Americans across the country.

Recent issues and projects: (1) All federal AIDS-related issues; (2) the federal Hate-Crimes Statistics Act; (3) the Americans with Disabilities Act; (4) the Gay and Lesbian Civil Rights Bill. Also, legislative protection of lesbians and gay men from discrimination in employment, housing and public accommodations; recognition of the legitimacy of gay and lesbian families in such matters as custody, parenting and domestic partnership; reform of immigration laws that now prohibit gay people from entering the country; an end to exclusion of gay people from military service; support of the Constitutional right of privacy, including repeal of laws criminalizing gay and lesbian relationships.

Major publications: Newsletter: *Momentum*; *Capitol Hill Updates*

Budget: $3,500,000

Funding: Foundations, events (45%), individual contributions (30%), direct mail (15%), canvassing (10%)

Staff: 26
4 Canvassers
4 Foundation Fundraisers
4 Grassroots Fundraisers
3 Lobbyists
3 Operations
3 Issue Experts
1 Secretary
1 Receptionist
1 Bookkeeper/Accountant
1 Writer/Editor
1 Office Manager

Staff openings/year: 1-2

Work Week: 40 hours

Salary/year: $16,500 (Recent College Graduate); $22,000 (Graduate with advanced degree)

Benefits: Health insurance, pregnancy leave, pension, paid vacation

Volunteers: 10

Interns: 5
Length: 3-6 months
Duties: Assistance in Political, Field, Legislative, Lesbian issues and Communications departments
Remuneration: 20 hours/week, $100 stipend

Jobs advertised: Through press releases to the gay papers

To apply: For internships, contact Eric Rosenthal

HUMAN RIGHTS INTERNET

University of Ottawa, 57 Louis Pasteur
Ottawa, ONTARIO K1N 6N5
(613) 564-3492 fax: (613) 564-4054

Director: Laurie S. Wiseberg

Purpose: The Human Rights Internet is an international communications network and clearinghouse on human rights with universal coverage. Over 2,000 organizations and individuals contribute to the network. Since accurate information is a precondition to effective action, the HRI furthers the defense of human rights through the dissemination of information. HRI also engages in extensive networking and actively promotes teaching and research on human rights.

Methods of operation: Publications (50%), research (30%), training and technical assistance (20%)

Constituency: Human rights organizations, advocates, scholars, policymakers

Recent issues and projects: Recently completed *Human Rights Directory: Latin America and the Caribbean*; now working on Asia and Middle East directories and on new issues of the directories for North America and Western Europe

Major publications: *Human Rights Internet Tribune*, a quarterly journal; *Human Rights Directories*, describing organizations in North America, Western Europe, Eastern Europe, Latin America, Africa and Asia; *Teaching Human Rights*, with syllabi for 27 human rights courses; *Access to Justice: The Struggle for Human Rights in Southeast Asia*; computerized databases; annual microfiche collection of the publications of non-governmental human rights organizations.

Budget: $500,000

Funding: Foundations

Staff: 9
5 Researchers
3 Librarians/Researchers
1 Office Manager

Staff openings/year: 0-1

Work Week: 45 hours

Salary/year: $22,000

Benefits: Health insurance, paid vacation, family leave

Part-Time Employees: 2

Summer Employees: Yes

Volunteers: Yes

Interns: Yes
Length: 2-3 months
Duties: Assisting with *Reporter*, projects, library,

information requests
Remuneration: Interns must have their own funds

Jobs advertised: Local newspapers, word of mouth, university

To apply: Contact Michael Gort

HUMAN RIGHTS WATCH

485 Fifth Avenue
New York, NY 10017
(212) 972-8400

Other Offices: Washington, DC; Los Angeles, CA; San Salvador, EL SALVADOR; London, ENGLAND

Director: Ken Roth

Purpose: Monitor the human rights practices of governments; publicize violations of human rights; launch international protests against governments that commit abuses; generate pressure on United States and other governments and international bodies to respond to abuses. Human Rights Watch is an organization that links the five Watch committees - Africa Watch, Americas Watch, Asia Watch, Helsinki Watch and Middle East Watch - and coordinates and supports their efforts.

Methods of operation: Research (40%), publications (40%), lobbying (20%)

Major publications: Newsletters: *Human Rights Watch Newsletter, News From Africa Watch, News From Americas Watch, News From Asia Watch, News From Helsinki Watch*; *Persecuting Human Rights Monitors: The CERJ In Guatemala*; *USSR: Human Rights Under Glasnost*

Funding: Foundations (90%), individual contributions (10%)

Staff: 40
15 Organizers
11 Writers/Editors/Issue Experts
5 Researchers
3 Foundation Fundraisers
1 Office Manager
1 Bookkeeper/Accountant

Staff openings/year: 3-4

Work Week: 45 hours

Salary/year: $18,000

Benefits: Health insurance, life insurance, pregnancy leave, pension, paid vacation

Part-Time Employees: 1

Volunteers: Yes

Interns: Yes
Length: Usually by semester
Duties: Administrative/clerical for undergraduates; research for law students or students getting advanced degrees
Remuneration: Unpaid

Jobs advertised: *Washington Post*; review of resumes received

To apply: Contact Catherine Schmidt

Remarks: The Washington, DC office is located at 1522 K Street, NW, Suite 910, Washington, DC, 20005. Director: Holly Burkhalter. 13 full-time salaried staff: 5 Writer/ Editor/Issue Experts, 3 Organizers, 3 Researchers, 1 Officer Manager, 1 Lobbyist.

HUMAN SERVE

622 West 113th Street, Room 410
New York, NY 10025
(212) 854-4053

Director: Richard A. Cloward

Purpose: Human Serve is a national voter registration reform organization which has pioneered and is promoting the idea that citizens should be registered to vote automatically when applying for government services. Currently working to implement the National Voter registration Act of 1993.

Methods of operation: Coalition building (35%), training and technical assistance (35%), publications (10%), research (20%)

Constituency: 70,000,000 unregistered Americans

Recent issues and projects: (1) National Voter Registration Act - drafted original language and worked to pass legislation; worked to organize broad coalition of national voting rights and civil rights groups; (2) State Motor Vehicle, Welfare and Disability Agency Voter Registration- we work with secretaries of state, governors, state legislative officials, and citizen coalitions seeking registration reform throughout the country, and we've had enormous success assisting with integration of voter registration into the delivery of government services; (3) School Program - implementation of system to register parents when they enroll their children in school.

Major publications: *Why Americans Don't Vote*, by Richard A. Cloward and Frances Fox Piven, *National Voter Registration Act Implementation Manual*

Budget: $250,000

Funding: Foundations (90%), individual contributions (7%), direct mail (3%)

Staff: 5
4 Organizers
2 Student Interns
1 Executive Director
1 Office Manager (1/2 time)

Work Week: 40-50 hours

Benefits: Health insurance, life insurance, paid vacation

Part-Time Employees: 1

Volunteers: Occasionally

Interns: Yes
Remuneration: Columbia University and Barnard College work-study programs support interns

To apply: Contact David Plotkin, Program Associate

HUNGER ACTION OF NEW YORK STATE

Central Warehouse, Room 201, Colonie & Montgomery Streets
Albany, NY 12207
(518) 434-7371

Other Offices: New York, NY

Director: Mark Dunlea

Purpose: HANNYS is a statewide membership organization of direct food providers, advocates and other individuals whose goal is to end hunger in New York state.

Methods of operation: Research (20%), community organizing (20%), lobbying (15%), public education (15%), human services (15%), direct action (10%), publications (5%)

Constituency: Emergency food programs, low-income individuals, church organizations

Recent issues and projects: Up and Out of Poverty campaign works to increase public assistance benefits and the minimum wage. The Department of Social Services Monitoring Project works to ensure that local counties provide assistance to individuals in emergency situations. Help people enroll in federal nutrition programs.

Major publications: Bimonthly newsletter: *Hunger Action*; reports on food pantries and the Department of Social Services

Budget: $300,000

Funding: Foundations (80%), individual contributions (20%)

Staff: 10
8 Organizers
1 Lobbyist
1 Fundraiser

Staff openings/year: 2

Work Week: 40 hours

Salary/year: $16,000 (Recent College Graduate); $Varies (Graduate with advanced degree)

Benefits: Health insurance, pregnancy leave, paid vacation

Part-Time Employees: 0

Volunteers: 1

Interns: 2
Length: 6 months
Duties: Negotiable
Remuneration: Unpaid

Jobs advertised: Newspaper; mailings to human service organizations

To apply: Contact Mark Dunlea, Executive Director

HUNTINGTON HUMAN RELATIONS COMMISSION

824 5th Ave., Suite 200, P.O. Box 1659
Huntington, WV 25717
(304) 696-5592

Director: Sally M. Lind

Purpose: Enforcing the Human Relations Ordinance by receiving, investigating and ruling on complaints of employment, housing and public accommodation discrimination.

Methods of operation: Case investigations, litigation, public education, training and technical assistance

Constituency: Eleven community people serve as Commissioners of diverse backgrounds.

Recent issues and projects: Commissioners began

a study regarding the possibility of including sexual orientation as a potential class; but, it has basically been dropped.

Major publications: Annual Report

Budget: $125,500

Funding: Federal Grants (100%)

Staff: 3
1 Administrative Assistant
1 Caseworker/Investigator
1 Director

Staff openings/year: 0-1

Work Week: 40 hours

Salary/year: $18,075 (Recent College Graduate); $Same (Graduate with advanced degree)

Benefits: Health insurance, pension, paid vacation, life insurance, credit union, eye care, family leave

Part-Time Employees: None

Summer Employees: None

Volunteers: None

Interns: No, but willing to accept applications

Jobs advertised: Newspapers and minority associations and groups

To apply: Contact Sally Lind, Executive Director

Remarks: The HHRC investigates complaints within the city limits of Huntington. The ordinance covers the protected classes of race, religion, color, national origin, ancestry, sex, age (40 and up) blindness, handicap and familial status (housing). The Fair Housing Act portion of the Ordinance has been ruled substantially equivalent to the Federal Fair Housing Act and the Commission is working on making its procedures equivalent. The Commission is also considered a 706 agency which means the Ordinance and procedures are equivalent to the procedures and federal laws that the Equal Employment Opportunity Commission regulates.

IDAHO CITIZEN'S NETWORK/ICN RESEARCH AND EDUCATION

P.O. Box 1927
Boise, ID 83701
(208) 385-9146

Other Offices: Burley, ID; Coeur d'Alene, ID; Kellogg, ID; Pocatello, ID

Director: Gary Sandusky

Purpose: Public interest organizing; empowerment; leadership development; policy change on health care; disability rights; toxics; utilities; local issues

Methods of operation: Research, lobbying, community organizing, direct action, public education

Constituency: Disabled; low and moderate income working people; churches; seniors; middle-income contributors

Recent issues and projects: Stopped storage of toxic chemicals in a neighborhood in Twin Falls. Registered nearly 10,000 new voters in the last 4 years. Successfully cut power rate hikes proposed by Washington Water Power and Idaho Power. Fought for and won continuing services for low-income children at the North Idaho Well Child Clinic. Lobbied successfully for the "spousal impoverishment" legislation (protects an elderly couple's income in instances of catastrophic illness, keeping their family intact) in the Idaho State Legislature. Won legislation for more accessible polling places. Convinced Idaho's legislators to establish a committee to study long-term care costs and personal care services.

Major publications: Quarterly newsletter: *Citizen Networker*; *A Crisis in Health Care*; *The Problem of the Uninsured*

Budget: $416,000

Funding: Individual contributions, canvassing (60%), foundations (30%), other (10%)

Staff: 19
9 Canvassers
6 Organizers
2 Typists
1 Director/Fundraiser/Policy Analyst
1 Bookkeeper/Accountant

Staff openings/year: 1-2

Work Week: 50 hours

Salary/year: $12-16,000

Benefits: Health insurance, child care, paid vacation

Part-Time Employees: 1

Volunteers: 60-70

Interns: Yes
Length: Based on arrangement
Duties: Vary
Remuneration: None to date

Jobs advertised: Through lists of organizations; local papers; *Community Jobs*

To apply: Contact Gary Sandusky, Director

IDAHO HUNGER ACTION COUNCIL

496 Overland, Suite 536
Boise, ID 83705
(208) 336-7010

Other Offices: Lewiston, ID

Director: Leanna Lasuen

Purpose: A "hand-up," not a "hand-out," Idaho Hunger Action Council is people working together against hunger and poverty through a Child Care Feeding Program, local chapters, networking, education and research.

Constituency: Low-income members and other concerned supporters

Recent issues and projects: Current: community health care clinics; low-income housing. Recent: Save Winter Moratorium on heat shut-offs; benefits for people during major computer glitch; low-income family training and support programs

Major publications: Monthly newsletter; *Directory of Emergency Assistance Programs in Idaho*; study on homeless children; *Under the Bridge: A Study of Hunger and Homelessness in Idaho*

Budget: $200,000

Funding: Child Care Food Program (CCFP) contract, individual contributions, foundations

Staff: 6
2 Caseworkers
1 1/2 Typist
1 Organizer
1/2 Bookkeeper/Accountant
1/2 Foundation Fundraiser
1/6 Campaign Manager
1/6 Writer/Editor
1/6 Issue Expert

Work Week: 40-50 hours

Salary/year: $9-12,000

Benefits: Health insurance and paid vacation

Volunteers: Yes

Jobs advertised: Locally; through regional progressive network

To apply: Contact Leanna Lasuen, Executive Director

IDAHO LEGAL AID SERVICES, INC.

P.O. Box 913
Boise, ID 83701-0913
(208) 336-8980

Other Offices: Coeur d'Alene, ID; Lewiston, ID; Caldwell, ID; Twin Falls, ID; Pocatello, ID; Idaho Falls, ID

Director: Ernesto G. Sanchez

Purpose: Provide legal services and community legal education to low-income residents on certain civil matters

Methods of operation: Litigation (80%), training and technical assistance (8%), public education (7%), direct action (5%)

Constituency: All Idaho residents at 125% of poverty level or below

Recent issues and projects: In 1992 closed over 7,000 cases statewide

Budget: $1,500,000

Funding: Government grants (85%), foundations (10%), other (5%)

Staff: 54
31 Attorneys
8 Office Managers
9 Typists
5 Paralegals
1 Bookkeeper/Accountant

Staff openings/year: 2

Work Week: 37.5 hours

Salary/year: $22,000

Benefits: Health and dental insurance, life insurance, parental leave, pension, credit union, paid vacation, disability insurance, sick leave, death leave, 12 paid holidays, bar dues, training, relocation travel expenses, malpractice insurance

Part-Time Employees: 4

Volunteers: 2

Interns: 7
Length: 10 weeks
Duties: Legal research, investigations, client intake
Remuneration: $1500 stipend for 10 weeks

Jobs advertised: Northwest law schools; bar journals; legal services programs nationwide

To apply: Contact Ernesto G. Sanchez, Executive

Director

IDAHO RURAL COUNCIL
P.O. Box 236
Boise, ID 83701
(208) 344-6184

Director: Becky Ihli

Purpose: A chapter-based rural citizen's organization dedicated to progressive policy changes in farming and the environment at the local and national level.

Methods of operation: Community organizing (30%), public education (30%), human services (20%), direct action (20%)

Constituency: Farmers, rural business people, concerned consumers

Recent issues and projects: Idaho Rural Council is deeply engaged now in work on the new agriculture trade rules and on the 1990 Farm Bill from the perspective of farmers and consumers. In addition to these, the IRC is currently working on waste, dairy and sustainable agriculture

Major publications: Bimonthly newsletter

Budget: $150,000

Funding: Foundations (60%), individual contributions (30%), direct mail (10%)

Staff: 3
1 Executive Director
1 Organizer
1 Administrative Assistant/Bookkeeper

Staff openings/year: 1-2

Work Week: 55-60 hours

Salary/year: $15,000

Benefits: Health insurance; you get to live in Idaho

Volunteers: 20

Interns: None currently, but willing to accept applications

Jobs advertised: *Community Jobs*; postings at other organizations

To apply: Contact Phil Lansing, Director

ILLINOIS HOMECARE ORGANIZING PROJECT
117 West Harrison Street, 2nd Floor
Chicago, IL 60605
(312) 939-7490

Director: Keith Kelleher

Purpose: The Illinois Homecare Organizing Project works to organize low-income workers for economic justice.

Methods of operation: Community organizing (90%), research (5%), training and technical assistance (5%)

Membership: Primarily African American and Latino women

Recent issues and projects: Organized several thousand minimum wage home healthcare workers in a campaign that won pay raises and benefits.

Budget: $110,000

Funding: Membership dues (80%), foundations (20%)

Staff: 11
8 Organizers
3 Office Managers

Staff openings/year: 5

Salary/year: $12 - 14,000

Benefits: Paid vacation, family leave, health insurance, travel reimbursement, holiday pay

Part-Time Employees: None

Summer Employees: 2

Volunteers: None

Interns: 3
Length: 3 months
Duties: Same as organizers

Jobs advertised: Newspapers, nonprofit publications, college recruitment

To apply: Contact Myra Obessaian, Field Director

Remarks: Request minimum of one-year commitment for organizers, car helpful. Ability to work well with people from various backgrounds, bilingual individuals encouraged to apply.

ILLINOIS PUBLIC ACTION

1 Quincy Court, Suite 714
Chicago, IL 60604
(312) 431-1600

Other Offices: Rock Island, IL; Edwardsville, IL; Champaign, IL; St. Louis, MO; Rockford, IL

Director: Robert Creamer

Purpose: IPA is Illinois' largest public interest organization. Through community outreach and the media, IPA promotes progressive positions on utility rates, toxic waste, health care costs, insurance rates and the economy.

Methods of operation: Research, lobbying, community organizing

Membership: More than 180,000 members across Illinois

Recent issues and projects: Insurance Reform Campaign in Illinois state legislature; campaign at the state level to label pesticides used on food that are known to cause cancer and birth defects.

Major publications: Monthly briefing paper

Budget: $2,000,000

Funding: Canvassing, telephone solicitation

Staff: 89
75+ Canvassers
5 Office Managers
3 Bookkeepers/Accountants
2+ Issue Experts
2 Typists
1+ Lobbyists
1 Researcher

Staff openings/year: 5

Work Week: 40+ hours

Salary/year: $14,000 (Recent College Graduate); $Varies (Graduate with advanced degree)

Benefits: Health insurance, life insurance, pregnancy leave, paid vacation

Part-Time Employees: 20+

Summer Employees: 50+

Interns: Yes
Length: 3 months
Duties: Assist research director
Remuneration: Course credit only

Jobs advertised: Newspapers

To apply: Contact Lynda DeLaforgue

ILLINOIS PUBLIC INTEREST RESEARCH GROUP (ILLINOIS PIRG)

202 South State Street, Suite 1400
Chicago, IL 60604
(312) 341-0814

Other Offices: Evanston, IL; Wheaton, IL; Champaign, IL

Director: Diane E. Brown

Purpose: Advocate for the public interest in areas of environmental and consumer protection.

Methods of operation: Research, lobbying, litigation, public education, fundraising/canvassing

Constituency: 25,000 citizen members

Recent issues and projects: Clean air; clean water; toxics use reduction

Major publications: Quarterly newsletter: *The PIRG Citizen Advocate*

Funding: Canvassing, telephone solicitation

Staff: 4
3 Canvass Directors
1 Executive Director
8-12 Canvassers year-round
50-75 Canvassers in summer

Work Week: 60 hours

Salary/year: $14,500

Benefits: Health insurance, paid vacation, college loan assistance program

Part-Time Employees: Yes

Summer Employees: Yes

Volunteers: Yes

Interns: Yes
Length: Semester
Remuneration: Course credit

Jobs advertised: Newspapers; career placement offices; college campuses

To apply: Contact Diane E. Brown, Executive Director

ILLINOIS STEWARDSHIP ALLIANCE

P.O. Box 648
Rochester, IL 62563
(217) 498-9707

Director: Renee Robinson, Acting Director

Purpose: A statewide citizens organization working to promote responsible stewardship and development of the state's natural resources in a manner that enhances local control of the economy. Goals are to promote socially, economically, and environmentally responsible natural resource development, sustainable agriculture, a strong family farm economy, and preservation of Illinois agricultural land base and rural communities.

Methods of operation: Research, lobbying, litigation, publications, organizing, public education, training and technical assistance

Constituency: Farmers, local governments, rural residents, environmentalists

Recent issues and projects: Stewardship and Family Farm Program; Citizens Coal Program

Major publications: Quarterly newsletter: *Notes*; *Your Rights in the Coalfields: Enforcement and Inspection*; *Holding Our Ground*; *Coal Mine Subsidence: Proceedings from a Citizens Conference*

Budget: $150,000

Funding: Churches, private foundations, individual contributions, fees

Staff: 4
3 Organizers
1 Director

Staff openings/year: 1-2

Work Week: 50 hours

Salary/year: $16,000 (Recent College Graduate); $Varies (Graduate with advanced degree)

Benefits: Health insurance, life insurance, family leave, 4 weeks paid vacation

Part-Time Employees: 1

Volunteers: Yes

Interns: Yes
Length: 6 months
Duties: Specific project and introduction to all aspects of public interest work
Remuneration: $500/month; assist interns in finding affordable housing

Jobs advertised: *Community Jobs*; newsletter; networks

To apply: Contact Steve Pittman

Remarks: The Illinois Stewardship Alliance is a democratically-managed organization.

ILLINOIS TENANTS UNION

4616 North Drake
Chicago, IL 60625
(312) 478-1133

Director: Michael Pensack

Purpose: ITU is a nonprofit corporation that has been providing advice and legal representation to tenants since November, 1976. Counsels tenants on their rights and how to exercise them.

Methods of operation: Public education (75%), litigation (25%)

Constituency: Tenants in the Chicago metropolitan area with problems with their landlords that permit a legal solution by advice or representation

Recent issues and projects: Enforcement of Chicago Residential Landlord and Tenant Ordinance; legal defenses and counterclaims in eviction lawsuits brought by landlords

Budget: $200,000

Funding: Individual contributions (100%)

Staff: 8
2 Paralegals
1 Attorney
1 Housing Tester
1 Organizer
2 Telemarketers
1 Administrator

Staff openings/year: 2

Work Week: 50+ hours

Salary/year: $20,000

Benefits: Car allowance

Part-Time Employees: 8 Contract Attorneys

Volunteers: Yes

Interns: None currently, but willing to accept applications

Jobs advertised: Word of mouth among tenants who have been involved as volunteers or as clients

To apply: Contact Michael Pensack, Director

IMMIGRANT LEGAL RESOURCE CENTER

1663 Mission Street, Suite 602
San Francisco, CA 94103
(415) 255-9499

Other Offices: East Palo Alto, CA

Director: Bill Ong Hing, Esq.

Purpose: A resource center which provides legal support through seminars, trainings, consultations and publications to community organizations and those in the legal professions that assist immigrants and refugees.

Methods of operation: Training and technical assistance (45%), publications (30%), community organizing (10%), research (5%), litigation (5%), public education (5%)

Recent issues and projects: Some of the top goals for this year are putting out accurate information and messages about the impact of immigrants on our society; providing training, technical assistance and new models of service delivery to assist immigrants to become naturalized citizens; advocacy in creating and maintaining a fair and effective system of political asylum; and teaching leadership skills to immigrants. Continue to coordinate a National Immigration Paralegal Training Program, through which they have trained over 800 staff of nonprofit agencies to do immigration counselling and representation. In addition, they will be do 6 trainings in 1994 and in 1995 on naturalization and continue to do advocacy and assistance on juvenile immigration issues.

Major publications: *Winning Asylum Cases (1993); California Criminal Law and Immigration* (updated 1993); *Guide for Immigration Advocates* (updated 1992); *Winning Suspension of Deportation Cases* (1992); *Winning 212(c) Cases* (updated 1993); *Family Unity Manual* (updated 1993); (partial list) and numerous packets on all aspects of immigration law and policy

Budget: $500,000

Funding: Foundations (80%), individual contributions (10%), publications and trainings (10%)

Staff: 14
2 Attorneys
2 Fellowship Attorneys
1 Assistant Director/Attorney
1 Volunteer Executive Director
1 Office Manager
1 Foundation Fundraiser
1 Program Assistant
1 Receptionist/Typist
1 Project Organizer (part-time)
1 Computer Consultant
2 1993 Summer Law Clerks
Numerous volunteers

Staff openings/year: 1

Work Week: 37.5 hours

Salary/year: $24,000 (Recent College Graduate); $27,000 (Graduate with advanced degree)

Benefits: Health insurance, pregnancy leave, paid vacation

Part-Time Employees: 5

Summer Employees: 1

Volunteers: Yes

Interns: Varies
Length: Varies
Duties: Varies

Jobs advertised: Through Opportunity NOCs, community college career centers, Public Interest Clearinghouse, *Bay Guardian, San Francisco Examiner, San Francisco Chronicle*

To apply: Contact Ingrid Faulhaber, Program Administrator

IN DEFENSE OF ANIMALS

816 W. Francisco Blvd.
San Rafael, CA 94901
(415) 453-9984

Other Offices: San Jose, CA; Richmond, VA; Shepherdstown, WV; Greneda, MS

Director: Elliot Katz

Purpose: To protect the rights, welfare and habitat of animals by ending the institutionalized exploitation and cruelty to animals

Methods of operation: Research (20%), community organizing (20%), direct action (20%), public education (20%), lobbying (10%), litigation (10%)

Membership: National membership; people concerned with justice and compassion towards other species

Recent issues and projects: Recent projects include: working to end radiation experiments on animals; boycotting Proctor and Gamble to end their animal testing; working to stop psychological and addiction experiments on animals; working to stop slaughter of wolves in Alaska; and stopping pet theft

Budget: $1,000,000

Funding: Direct mail (80%), individual contributions

Staff: 13
2 Organizers
2 Writers/Editors
1 Office Manager
1 Researcher
1 Lobbyist
2 Issue Experts
4 Campaign Managers

Staff openings/year: 2

Work Week: 40 hours

Salary/year: $18,000 (Recent College Graduate); $24,000 (Graduate with advanced degree)

Benefits: Health insurance, paid vacation, pregnancy leave

Part-Time Employees: 5

Summer Employees: None

Volunteers: Varies

Interns: None

Jobs advertised: Newsletters, animal advocacy magazines, local newspapers

To apply: Contact Elliot Katz, President

IN THESE TIMES

2040 North Milwaukee Avenue
Chicago, IL 60647
(312) 772-0100

Editor: James Weinstein

Purpose: *In These Times* is an alternative bi-weekly magazine.

Methods of operation: Public education, writing, editing (90%), research (10%)

Constituency: 35,000 subscribers, mostly active in various social or political movements

Major publications: *In These Times*

Budget: $1,100,000

Funding: Subscriptions (60%), individual contributions (25%), direct mail subscriptions (15%)

Staff: 19
14 Writers/Editors
1 Bookkeeper/Accountant
1 Circulation Promotion
1 Advertising
1 Fundraiser
1 Office Manager

Staff openings/year: 1-2

Work Week: 40 hours

Salary/year: $17,000 (Recent College Graduate); $Varies (Graduate with advanced degree)

Benefits: Health insurance, pregnancy leave, 4 weeks paid vacation

Part-Time Employees: 4-5

Volunteers: 3-4

Interns: 3-4
Length: 6 months minimum
Duties: Varies
Remuneration: Unpaid

Jobs advertised: Classified ads

To apply: Contact Miles Harvey

INDEPENDENT SECTOR (IS)

1828 L Street, NW, 12th Floor
Washington, DC 20036
(202) 223-8100

Director: Brian O'Connell

Purpose: An organization created to preserve and enhance the national tradition of giving, volunteering, and not-for-profit initiative. It is designed to serve the sector through: public education to improve the public's understanding of the voluntary sector; communication within the sector to identify shared problems and opportunities; research on the nonprofit sector; government relations to coordinate interconnections between the sector and government; and encouragement of effective nonprofit operation and management, to maximize service to individuals and society.

Constituency: Voluntary organizations, corporations, and foundations with national interests and impact in philanthropy and voluntary action; nationwide

Recent issues and projects: Advertising Council Give-Five Campaign on giving and volunteering; active on lobbying regulations, UBIT and disclosure issues for nonprofits; research and nonprofit management programs.

Major publications: Newsletters; reports

Budget: $4,700,000

Funding: Membership dues, grants

Staff: 35

Staff openings/year: 1-4

Work Week: 40-50 hours

Salary/year: $Varies (Recent College Graduate); $Varies (Graduate with advanced degree)

Benefits: Health insurance, pension, life insurance

Part-Time Employees: Yes

Volunteers: Yes

Interns: Yes
Length: 6 months-1 year
Duties: Government relations
Remuneration: Stipend available

Jobs advertised: Through affirmative action opportunity offices; notices sent to nonprofits; classified ads

To apply: Contact Brian Foss

INDIAN LAW RESOURCE CENTER
601 E Street, SE
Washington, DC 20003
(202) 547-2800

Director: Robert T. Coulter

Purpose: The Indian Law Resource Center is a nonprofit law office and advocacy organization established and directed by Indians. It provides legal help without charge to Indian nations and tribes in major cases of important Indian rights. Founded in 1978, the Center gives special attention to combating racism in the law and to the development of human rights for Indian and native peoples throughout the Americas.

Methods of operation: Research (30%), litigation (30%), training and technical assistance (20%), publications (10%), public education (10%)

Constituency: Indians of the Americas

Recent issues and projects: (1) Impending settlement of the Sioux trust funds accounting claim; (2) Final settlement of the Tonawanda Seneca Railroad claim; (3) Assisted in the return of many ancient wampum belts to the Six Nations Confederacy; (4) Assist Indians in Brazil, Central America and Alaska; (5) Pending lawsuit to recover Mohawk land; (6) Provided legal assistance to the Traditional Seminole Nation of Florida in their efforts to reclaim land and establish a land base for their people; (7) The Center represents and provides legal assistance for the Western Shoshone National Council; (8) Negotiation of return of Miskito leaders to Nicaragua; (9) Development of proposed United Nations declaration of Indian rights.

Major publications: *Indian Rights-Human Rights: Handbook for Indians on International Human Rights Complaints Procedures*; *Present and Future Status of American Indian Nations and Tribes* (1988); *The Decline of American Indian Sovereignty* (1988); numerous articles

Budget: $400,000

Funding: Foundations (80%), individual contributions (20%)

Staff: 8
5 Attorneys
1 Issue Expert
1 Typist
1 Bookkeeper/Accountant

Staff openings/year: 1

Work Week: 40 hours

Salary/year: $Varies (Recent College Graduate); $Varies (Graduate with advanced degree)

Benefits: Health insurance, life insurance, paid vacation

Summer Employees: 1

Volunteers: 0

Interns: 1
Length: 2 months-1 year; summer
Duties: Research, attend meetings, writing, reading, assistance with special projects
Remuneration: Volunteer, or paid by other organizations

INDIGENOUS PEOPLES MEDIA CENTER
77 Main Street
Tappan, NY 10983
(914) 365-0414

Director: Norman Shaifer

Purpose: Working with indigenous leaders organizing their press conferences. Developing contacts between Indigenous leaders and media contacts.

Methods of operation: Public education (70%), research (20%), community organizing (10%)

Recent issues and projects: Ran 12 press conferences at Earth's Summit. First press conference in UN press facilities in NY in 1993 and 1994. First coverage for Chapis Rebellion on PBS January 2, 1994.

Budget: $10,000

Funding: Individual contributions (80%), foundations (20%)

Part-Time Employees: 5

Summer Employees: 2

Volunteers: 4

Interns: Yes
Length: 90 days
Duties: Varies

Remarks: We seek people interested in Indigenous causes who have journalists skills to work with us on a need basis.

INFACT

Campaign Headquarters, 256 Hanover Street
Boston, MA 02113
(617) 742-4583 Fax: (617) 367-0191

Director: Elaine Lamy

Purpose: INFACT is a peoples' organization building international campaigns to stop abuses of transnational corporations and increase their accountability to people around the world.

Methods of operation: Community organizing, public education, research

Constituency: Supporters of INFACT come from all types of socio-economic, religious and racial backgrounds

Recent issues and projects: Infact is currently organizing grassroots pressure to stop the tobacco industry's marketing and promotion of tobacco to children and young people around the world.

Major publications: *INFACT Campaign Update*

Budget: $650,000

Funding: Individual contributions (65%), direct mail (20%), foundations (8%), telephone solicitation (5%), religious (2%)

Staff: 15
7 Organizers
4 Grassroots Fundraisers
1 Office Manager
1 Bookkeeper/Accountant
1 Researcher
1 Executive Director

Staff openings/year: 0-2

Work Week: 50-60 hours

Salary/year: $18,000 (Recent College Graduate); $Varies (Graduate with advanced degree)

Benefits: Health insurance, child care, paid vacation

Part-Time Employees: No

Interns: Yes

Jobs advertised: *Community Jobs* and other progressive publications; university recruitment offices; flyers posted; word of mouth

To apply: Contact varies according to position open.

INFORM, INC.

381 Park Avenue South
New York, NY 10016
(212) 689-4040

President: Joanna D. Underwood

Purpose: INFORM is a nonprofit environmental research and education organization that identifies and reports on practical actions for the preservation and conservation of natural resources and public health. Its current research focuses on such critical environmental issues as hazardous waste reduction, garbage management and urban air pollution.

Methods of operation: Research (40%), public education (40%), publications (15%), training and technical assistance (5%)

Constituency: INFORM's membership is made up of foundations, corporations and individuals.

Recent issues and projects: *Paving the Way to Natural Gas Vehicles*, an analysis of programs working to maximize the use of natural gas vehicles in the U.S.; *Making Less Garbage*, a guide to reducing waste for communities and solid waste planners; *Preventing Industrial Toxic Hazards*, a manual for citizens' groups to use in spurring reduction of toxic pollution at local manufacturing plants.

Major publications: Books mentioned below, plus *Business Recycling Manual*; *Tackling Toxics in Everyday Products*; *Burning Garbage in the U.S.*; and quarterly newsletter *INFORM Reports*

Budget: $1,654,800

Funding: Private foundations (55%), corporations (20%), individual contributions (9%), government (5%), earned income (4%), other (7%)

Staff: 27
7 Researchers
5 Communications Department
3 Administrative Assistants/Support Staff
3 Foundation Fundraisers
2 Bookkeeper/Accountants
1 Office Manager
2 Program Managers
2 Writers/Editors
1 Individual Donor Fundraiser
1 Production Manager

Staff openings/year: 3-4

Work Week: 35 hours

Salary/year: $23,000 (Recent College Graduate); $Varies (Graduate with advanced degree)

Benefits: Health insurance, life insurance, paid vacation

Summer Employees: 1

Volunteers: 1

Interns: 1-2 by project
Length: 6 months-1 year
Duties: Research

Jobs advertised: *New York Times*; other newspapers; word of mouth

To apply: Contact Denise Jaworski

INNOVATIVE COMMUNITY ENTERPRISES

209 East 10th Street, Suite 10
New York, NY 10003
(212) 529-8200

Director: Michael B. Gordon

Purpose: Innovative Community Enterprises (ICE) is set up to prove through project work that there are imaginative solutions to our most difficult social and economic problems. ICE is an educational organization that teaches an Oral History/Anti-Prejudice Program in the New York City Public School System.

Methods of operation: Public education (60%), community organizing (20%), research (10%), publications (8%), training and technical assistance (2%)

Recent issues and projects: Earth Day 1990 Children's Symposium; children's interviews of environmentalists, refugees, Native Americans, homeless people, Holocaust survivors; various environmentally-oriented, community and student projects; environmental curriculum; nation's first and only prescription drug cooperative for people with AIDS - it saves each member $3-4,000 per year; heating oil cooperative; concerts and events for which admission is a can of food; taking some ICE students to Eastern Europe in the summer of 1990.

Major publications: Oral History Newsletter: *We the People: Global Life Stories*

Budget: $200,000

Funding: Consulting contract work and government grants (90%), individual contributions (10%)

Staff: 7
3 Organizers
2 Teachers
1 Writer/Editor
1 Foundation Fundraiser

Staff openings/year: 3-6

Work Week: 55 hours

Salary/year: $18,000 (Recent College Graduate); $22,000 (Graduate with advanced degree)

Benefits: Health insurance contribution, pregnancy leave/guaranteed reemployment, paid vacation

Part-Time Employees: 8

Summer Employees: 2

Volunteers: 2

Interns: 8
Length: 3-6 months
Duties: Teaching, consumer advocacy
Remuneration: Negotiable

Jobs advertised: *Good Works*, *Village Voice*, college fairs

To apply: Contact Michael B. Gordan

INSTITUTE FOR SCIENCE AND INTERNATIONAL SECURITY

236 Massachusetts Ave., NE, Suite 500
Washington, DC 20002
(202) 547-3633

Director: David Albright

Purpose: To inform the public, press and policy makers about science and policy issues affecting national and international security especially those related to nuclear arms control and nonproliferation.

Methods of operation: Research (50%), publications (50%)

Recent issues and projects: Recent projects include: Nuclear Nonproliferation Project; Nuclear Weapons Project (U.S. Nuclear Weapons Program and Nuclear Testing)

Major publications: *ISIS Reports*; various fact sheets; numerous articles published in *Arms Control Today*; and *Bulletin of the Atomic Scientist*

Funding: Foundations (100%)

Staff: 3
Duties are shared among the 3:
Organizer
Writer/Editor
Office Manager
Researcher
Press Aide
Foundation Fundraiser
Issue Expert

Work Week: 40 hours

Salary/year: $20,000

Benefits: Health insurance, pension, paid vacation, life insurance, family leave

Part-Time Employees: 1

Summer Employees: 1

Volunteers: None

Interns: None at the time, willing to accept applications

Jobs advertised: Posted job notices

To apply: Please contact Kevin O'Neill, Administrative Assistant

INSTITUTE FOR ALTERNATIVE FUTURES

108 North Alfred Street, 2nd Floor
Alexandria, VA 22314
(703) 684-5880 Fax: (703) 684-0640

Director: Clement Bezold, Ph.D.

Purpose: IAF is a nonprofit research and educational organization and is a leading developer of techniques for aiding communities and organizations to more wisely choose their futures. IAF also works with state and local governments and the U.S. Congress to develop their foresight capabilities.

Methods of operation: Training and technical assistance (40%), direct action (40%), research (20%)

Recent issues and projects: Current projects include: 1) The Belmont Vision, a project to encourage discussion and agreement the best that health care could be in the 21st century; 2) Health futures and its use for member states for the World Health Organization and the Pan American Health Organization; 3) A video and guidebook on the future of the courts; 4) Seminar on environmentally advanced technologies; 5) Various reports and articles on hospitals, health care and the drug industry.

Major publications: *Healthy People in a Healthy World: The Belmont Vision for Health Care in America*, a report produced in 1992; *2020 Visions: Health Care Information Standards and Technologies*; *Envisioning Justice: Reinventing Courts for the 21st Century*, video and guidebook, 1993; *21st Century Learning and Health Care in the Home: Creating a National Telecommunications Network*, a report developed with the Consumer Information Research Institute in 1992; *The Future of Work and Health*

Budget: $385,000

Funding: Corporate contributions (40%), speaking and training (30%), government contracts (20%), foundations (10%)

Staff: 9
3 Consultants/Speakers
2 Researchers
2 Secretaries
1 Office Manager
1 Marketing Coordinator

Staff openings/year: 1

Work Week: 40 hours

Salary/year: $25,000 (Recent College Graduate); $30,000 (Graduate with advanced degree)

Benefits: Health insurance, paid vacation, tuition reimbursement

Part-Time Employees: 1

Summer Employees: 1

Interns: 1
Length: 4-6 months
Duties: Scanning, research, mailings, assorted duties

Jobs advertised: Word of mouth; newspaper

To apply: Contact Pat Heggy, Office Manager

INSTITUTE FOR COMMUNITY ECONOMICS

57 School Street
Springfield, MA 01105
(413) 746-8660

Director: Greg Ramm, Executive Director

Purpose: ICE is a national nonprofit organization, founded in 1967, whose purpose is to provide technical assistance and financing to community-based groups working to increase democratic local control of land and capital resources, in order to preserve perpetually affordable access to land and housing for people with low and moderate incomes.

Methods of operation: Community development finance (40%), training and technical assistance (25%), public education (10%), publications (10%), research (5%), community organizing (5%), human services (3%), lobbying (2%)

Constituency: Community land trusts, limited-equity housing cooperatives, mobile home cooperatives and other nonprofit affordable housing development organizations serving people with low and moderate incomes

Recent issues and projects: ICE operates an $11 million nationwide Revolving Loan Fund, which accepts loans from socially-motivated investors and makes low-cost financing available to innovative community groups, primarily for affordable housing development. Over $20 million placed with groups in 29 states since 1979, with no losses to investors. ICE also offers technical assistance and financing to over 100 community land trusts preserving affordable housing in 27 states. Conducts national conferences and regional seminars on community land trust development and community investment.

Major publications: Quarterly newsletter: *Community Economics*; *Community Land Trust Handbook* (228 pages, $10); *Community Loan Fund Manual* (375 pages, $45)

Budget: $400,000

Funding: Fees for services (60-70%), individual contributions (20%), foundations (10-20%)

Staff: 16
3 Technical Assistance Providers
3 Loan Officers
2 Typists
1 Office Manager
1 Writer/Editor
1 Caseworker
1 Press Aide
1 Revolving Loan Fund Manager
1 Publications Manager
1 Conference Organizer
1 Bookkeeper/Accountant

Staff openings/year: 3

Work Week: 40 hours

Salary/year: $6-15,000

Benefits: Health insurance, life insurance, pregnancy leave, board, child care, housing, tuition reimbursement, paid vacation, community membership, transportation

Part-Time Employees: 5

Volunteers: Occasionally

Interns: 3
Length: 1 year
Duties: Clerical assistance, special project assignments, community economic development training
Remuneration: Similar to full-time employees

Jobs advertised: National progressive publications and community development newsletters; college newspapers; graduate community development programs; ICE newsletter; etc.

To apply: Contact Carol Lewis, Director of Administration and Personnel

INSTITUTE FOR COMMUNITY EMPOWERMENT

4959 W. Belmont
Chicago, IL 60641
(312) 545-7288

Director: Mike Smith

Purpose: The Institute for Community Empowerment works to strengthen the democratic institutions of society by fostering community organizations and training leadership and staff in majority-based, democratically determined approaches to neighborhood concerns.

Methods of operation: Community organizing (50%), training and technical assistance (50%)

Constituency: Working class; moderate income

Recent issues and projects: ICE works with local community organizations which affiliated with or have been initiated by ICE.

Funding: Foundations, direct mail

Staff: 3

Staff openings/year: Varies

Work Week: 50 hours

Salary/year: $20,000

Benefits: Health insurance, paid vacation

Part-Time Employees: Yes

Summer Employees: None

Volunteers: Yes

Interns: Yes
Length: 3 months
Duties: Varies

To apply: Please contact Mike Smith

Remarks: ICE's actual paid staff is small. It screens applicants for its affiliated organizations.

INSTITUTE FOR CONSUMER RESPONSIBILITY (ICR)

6506 28th Avenue, NE
Seattle, WA 98115
(206) 523-0421

Director: Todd Putnam

Purpose: ICR believes that most of our current social and environmental problems are the consequence of consumer purchasing decisions -- choices which tend to: concentrate economic and political power into ever fewer hands; remove economic power and social values from communities; and reward and reinforce irresponsible corporate behavior. ICR uses boycotts and other consumer actions to educate consumers about the roles corporations and individual consumers play in society, and to increase awareness among citizens of their collective power and individual responsibilities as consumers. We believe that we cannot really compete with corporations for control of our government, but as consumers can exercise effective control over practices of corporations.

Methods of operation: Publications (45%), correspondence, filling phoned-in orders, distribution, planning, managing (30%), research (15%), public education (10%)

Constituency: Individual consumers, religious bodies, co-ops, peace and justice groups and committees, environmental and animal rights groups

Recent issues and projects: Book laying out principles of economic democracy movement and suggested path for social change; national coalition for creation of interdisciplinary, multi-organizational corporate report card project; boycott manuals; alternative phonebook listing responsible small, local businesses and educational/lifestyle/recreational resources; grant writing; boycott press packets; economic democracy coalition building; international economic democracy conference; establishing boycott information on computer bulletin boards; seeking regular boycott columns in alternative press; networking boycott information within the alternative press community

Major publications: *National Boycott News*

Budget: $400

Funding: Individual contributions (100%)

Staff: 2
All volunteer, including:
1 Bookkeeper/Accountant
1/2 Writer/Editor
1/4 Office Manager
1/16 Issue Expert
1/16 Typist
1/16 Press Aide
1/16 Public Speaker

Work Week: 40 hours

Volunteers: 2 -- staff

Interns: Please!
Length: Negotiable
Duties: Research, writing, correspondence, filling information requests, heading and planning projects
Remuneration: Free room depending upon availability, possibly one meal/day, depending on finances

Jobs advertised: Volunteers are solicited by volunteer forms included in *National Boycott News*

To apply: Contact Todd Putnam, Director

INSTITUTE FOR DEFENSE AND DISARMAMENT STUDIES

675 Massachusetts Ave., 8th Floor
Cambridge, MA 02139
(617) 354-4337

Director: Randall Forsberg, Executive Director

Purpose: Founded in 1979 by Randall Forsberg, IDDS conducts research and education on policies to minimize the risk of nuclear and conventional war, reduce military spending, and promote the growth of democratic institutions. In working for a stable, democratic peace, the Institute supports alternative defense policies that would lead to four intermediate goals: minimum deterrent nuclear arsenals; small, defense-oriented conventional forces; military nonintervention; and reduced spending.

Methods of operation: Research (60%), publications (20%), public education (20%)

Recent issues and projects: Since 1986, the Institute has focused on the Alternative Defense Project. This concerns ways to end the East-West military confrontation, which accounts for 75 percent of world military spending and most of the world's nuclear arms and advanced conventional weaponry. The Institute also compiles data on worldwide military forces, arms control talks, and peace efforts.

Major publications: Monthly bulletin: *Defense and Disarmament Alternatives*; *Arms Control Reporter*; *Cutting Conventional Forces 1: An Analysis of the Official Mandate, Statistics, and Proposals in the NATO-WTO Talks on Reducing Conventional Forces in Europe*; *Peace Resource Book 1988-1989*; Alternative Defense Working Papers and Reading Packets

Budget: $660,000

Funding: Foundations (70%), individual contributions (15%), subscriptions and other publications (15%)

Staff: 17
8 1/2 Researchers
2 1/2 Writer/Editors
1 1/2 Public Education/Outreach
1 Typist
1/2 Office Manager
1/2 Bookkeeper/Accountant
1/2 Librarian
1/2 Fundraiser

Staff openings/year: 1

Work Week: 40-45 hours

Salary/year: $Varies (Recent College Graduate); $Varies (Graduate with advanced degree)

Benefits: Health insurance, paid vacation

Part-Time Employees: 2

Summer Employees: 2

Volunteers: 2

Interns: Yes
Length: Varies; summer or semester
Duties: Vary - research, resource development
Remuneration: Stipends available

Jobs advertised: Notices at universities and research centers; major peace group newsletters/bulletins

To apply: For jobs, contact Taylor Seybolt, Administrative Director; for internships, contact Kenneth Grant, Associate

INSTITUTE FOR FOOD AND DEVELOPMENT POLICY/FOOD FIRST

398 60th Street
Oakland, CA 94618
(510) 654-4400

Director: Peter Rosset

Purpose: To explode popular myths about the root causes of hunger, poverty, and environmental decline and empower citizens to be part of the solution - locally, nationally, globally

Constituency: Activist, 20% teachers

Recent issues and projects: Major programs include the role of non-governmental organizations in strengthening the democratic process in Chile, Brazil and the Philippines. A second program examines the social and environmental impact of high speed industrialization as experienced in Thailand, South Korea, Taiwan and Singapore and increasingly emulated by other Asian countries. The effects of free trade, GATT, and structural adjustment are explored. All programs reveal the continuing heavy influence of multinational corporations in the deepening hunger and poverty experienced both in the U.S. and in the Third World.

Major publications: Quarterly *Food First News* and *Action Alerts*. Recent reports on Karela India, prospects for Third World Development, population, *Action Alerts* on the Brazil rainforest, El Salvador, the Philippines, American democracy. Recent books: *Rediscovering America's Values* and *The Philippines: Fire on the Rim*

Budget: $630,000

Funding: Individual contributions (70%), book sales and public speaking (15%), foundations (10%), direct mail (5%)

Staff: 7
3 Researchers
1 Issue Expert
1 Office Manager
1 Marketing and Sales Director
1 Writer/Editor
1 Grassroots Fundraiser

Staff openings/year: 6

Work Week: 40 hours

Salary/year: $22-26,000 (Recent College Graduate); $24,000 (Graduate with advanced degree)

Benefits: Health insurance, pregnancy leave, paid vacation

Part-Time Employees: 1

Volunteers: 5-10

Interns: 5-10
Length: 3 months-1 year
Duties: Range from research associate, grant associate, publicity assistant, database coordinator, writer
Remuneration: None except for minority students with financial need

Jobs advertised: Local colleges; affirmative action list; newspaper ads; networking with colleagues

To apply: Contact Marilyn Burchardt

Remarks: Interns and volunteers are an essential part of our work. Each year more than 100 interns and volunteers contribute more than 50,000 hours of work time while gaining valuable work experience.

INSTITUTE FOR GLOBAL COMMUNICATIONS/PEACENET/ECO NET/LABORNET

18 De Boom Street
San Francisco, CA 94107
(415) 923-0900 Fax: (415) 546-1794

Director: Geoff Sears

Purpose: To provide computer networking tools to individuals and organizations around the world working for peace, environmental sustainability, and economic justice. IGC manages the PeaceNet, EcoNet, ConflictNet and LaborNet computer networks.

Methods of operation: Online computer network service, communications, training, technical assistance.

Constituency: Individuals and organizations working for social change, peace and the environment

Recent issues and projects: Establishing new electronic networks pertaining to children's rights issues, population issues, immigration issues, and issues concerning people of color; expansion of the environmental education networks AEE, GREEN, EARN and TERC Global Lab; upgrading internet services to include Gopher, WAIS, telnet, ftp; with international partners in the Association for Progressive Communications (APC) brought new nodes on-line in Argentina and South Africa; with APC, provided telecommunications for the United Nations World Conference on Human Rights, Vienna; global networking with women's groups in preparation for the 1995 UN World Conference on Women.

Major publications: *PeaceNet World News*, an electronic digest of alternative news and information covering specific world regions; *NetNews* a bi-monthly newsletter; IGC training/User's Manual (English or Spanish).

Budget: $1,200,000

Funding: Fees for Services (85%), Foundations (15%)

Staff: 17
5 Technical Support
5 Account Services/Administration
6 Network Programs/Outreach
1 Foundation Fundraiser

Staff openings/year: 1

Work Week: 50 hours

Salary/year: $25,000 (Recent College Graduate); $Varies (Graduate with advanced degree)

Benefits: Health insurance, pregnancy leave, pension, paid vacation

Part-Time Employees: 7

Volunteers: Yes

Interns: Yes
Length: Relative to project
Duties: Relative to project

Jobs advertised: Online and word of mouth

To apply: Contact Geoff Sears

INSTITUTE FOR LOCAL SELF-RELIANCE

2425 18th Street, NW
Washington, DC 20009
(202) 232-4108

President: Neil Seldman

Purpose: To encourage the nation's cities to pursue local self-reliance as a development strategy; to combine local political authority and modern technology to generate a significant portion of their wealth internally.

Methods of operation: Research, publications, public education, training and technical assistance

Constituency: City and local officials, policymakers and community-based organizations

Recent issues and projects: Linked community youth groups with environmental agencies, state funding and private investor to start a processing plant for recycled glass, cardboard and plastics. Developing a materials policy at state levels to implement optimal use of resources for sustainable industrial and agricultural technologies.

Major publications: In-depth studies of recycling and composting programs; *The Carbohydrate Economy: Making Chemical and Industrial Materials from Plant Matter*; *Beyond 40 Percent: Record-Setting Recycling and Composting Programs*; *The New City-States*

Budget: $500,000

Funding: Foundations, contracts, publication sales

Staff: 14
4 Researchers
2 Urban Planners
3 Administrative Assistants
3 Engineers
1 Development Director
1 Business Manager

Staff openings/year: 1-2

Work Week: 40-60 hours

Salary/year: $Varies (Recent College Graduate); $Varies (Graduate with advanced degree)

Benefits: Medical/dental/life insurance, annual leave, sick leave, holiday leave

Part-Time Employees: Yes

Interns: Yes
Length: Varies
Duties: Research, writing, some administrative

Jobs advertised: Newspapers; *Community Jobs*; *Job Seeker*

To apply: Contact Jan Simpson, Business Manager

INSTITUTE FOR PEACE AND INTERNATIONAL SECURITY (IPIS)

237 Brattle Street
Cambridge, MA 02138-4645
(617) 547-3338

Director: Paul F. Walker

Purpose: IPIS is an independent nonprofit organization that sponsors both research and action projects. IPIS emphasizes timely research and action and sponsors collaborative work between academics and activists aimed at evolving policy ideas to shift the national debate away from old assumptions toward alternative strategies.

Methods of operation: Research (25%), publications (25%), community organizing (25%), public education (25%)

Constituency: Academic and grassroots elites and citizen groups

Recent issues and projects: Two of the Institute's major projects are the Committee on Common Security (CCS), a grassroots campaign to end the Cold War, and the East-West Workshop on Common Security, an annual international gathering of arms control scholars to discuss common security issues.

Major publications: *New Directions for NATO* (pamphlet published 1/89); *A Call to Action: Common Security and our Common Future*; *Peace Papers* and *Common Security Papers*, a series of academic papers; *Strategy Workbook* for local organizing

Budget: $100,000

Funding: Foundations (85%), individual contributions (15%)

Staff:
Part-time volunteers and consultants

Work Week: 40 hours

Benefits: None at this time

Interns: 1+
Length: Semester or year long
Duties: Depends on specific project
Remuneration: None

Jobs advertised: Word of mouth; college career boards

To apply: Send resume and cover letter to Paul F. Walker, Director.

INSTITUTE FOR POLICY STUDIES

1601 Connecticut Avenue, NW, Suite 500
Washington, DC 20009
(202) 234-9382

Director: Michael Shuman

Purpose: Research and public education on economics, politics, culture and social issues of democracy.

Methods of operation: Research (70%), public education (25%), publications (5%)

Constituency: General public, policymakers, community organizations

Recent issues and projects: Three working groups on Foreign Policy, World Economy, and the State of Democracy.

Major publications: *A Fate Worse Than Debt: The World Financial Crisis and the Poor*; *Quiet Riots: Race and Poverty in the United States*; *The Right to Housing: A Blueprint for Housing the Nation*; *The Success and Failure of Picasso*; *The Rockets' Red Glare: When America Goes to War - The President and the People*; *Fear of Falling: The Inner Life of the Middle Class*; etc.

Budget: $1,500,000

Funding: Foundations (60%), individual contributions (35%), publications (5%)

Staff: 28
13 Researchers
6 Issue Experts
1 Events Coordinator
1 Office Manager
1 Fundraiser
2 Office Assistants
1 Executive Director
1 Press Director
1 Finance Director
1 School Coordinator

Staff openings/year: 2-3

Work Week: 45-55 hours

Salary/year: $22,000 (Recent College Graduate); $30,000 (Graduate with advanced degree)

Benefits: Health insurance, life insurance, pregnancy leave, pension, paid vacation, sick leave, holidays, publications at cost

Volunteers: 2

Interns: 15+
Length: 3-6 months
Duties: Research, writing, organizing
Remuneration: Unpaid

Jobs advertised: Newspapers; mailings; word of mouth; job banks; bulletin boards

To apply: Contact the administrator

Remarks: The Institute for Policy Studies is the leading progressive research organization in the United States.

INSTITUTE FOR RESOURCE AND SECURITY STUDIES

27 Ellsworth Avenue
Cambridge, MA 02139
(617) 419-5177

Director: Gordon Thompson

Purpose: The IRSS was established in 1984 to conduct research and public education on the efficient use of natural resources, protection of the environment, and the furtherance of international peace and security. The Institute's work involves both in-depth studies and the preparation of public education materials accessible to a wide range of audiences.

Methods of operation: Research (60%), publications (20%), public education (15%), litigation (5%); also work with other peace groups

Constituency: Government officials, independent

analysts, students, interested lay people

Recent issues and projects: Research projects involve both technical and policy analysis in a variety of areas. All projects share, however, a focus on developing practical solutions to resource, environment or security problems. Special attention is devoted to the development and articulation of appropriate policy options. Current projects are concerned with a global approach to controlling weapons. Sustainable development, climate change, information systems and conflict resolution.

Major publications: *Working Paper* services; reports

Budget: $150,000

Funding: Foundations (50%), other (50%)

Staff: 3
2 Issue Expert
1 Office Manager
1/4 Bookkeeper/Accountant

Work Week: 40 hours

Salary/year: $20,000 (Recent College Graduate); $30,000 (Graduate with advanced degree)

Benefits: Health insurance, paid vacation

Part-Time Employees: 1

Volunteers: 1

Interns: 1
Length: 3 months
Duties: Primarily research
Remuneration: Volunteer or stipend

Jobs advertised: Contacts; newspaper

To apply: Contact Gordon Thompson, Executive Director

INSTITUTE FOR SOCIAL JUSTICE

523 West 15th Street
Little Rock, AR 72202
(501) 376-2528

Other Offices: New Orleans, LA; Washington, DC; Chicago, IL; New York, NY

Director: Elena Hanggi

Purpose: National research and training center for low and moderate income community organizations.

Methods of operation: Training and technical assistance (30%), public education (30%), research (20%), community organizing (20%)

Constituency: Low and moderate income community organizations

Recent issues and projects: Worked with ACORN to organize national citizens campaign to promote the voices and concerns of low-income communities in the debate over the Savings and Loan bailout; technical assistance to community organizations in Community Reinvestment Act challenges to bank redlining

Major publications: Handbooks and guides to organizing

Budget: $500,000

Funding: Foundations (50%), other (50%)

Staff: 10
6 Trainers
2 Issue Experts
2 Researchers

Staff openings/year: 2

Work Week: 50-60 hours

Salary/year: $12,000

Benefits: Health insurance, pregnancy leave, pension, paid vacation

Part-Time Employees: 2

Summer Employees: 2+

Volunteers: 3+

Interns: 10
Length: 1-3 months
Duties: Learn community organization skills
Remuneration: Paid

Jobs advertised: *Community Jobs*; announcements

To apply: Contact Elena Hanggi, Director

INSTITUTE FOR SOUTHERN STUDIES

P.O. Box 531
Durham, NC 27702
(919) 419-8311

Director: Isaiah Madison

Purpose: To develop research and publication projects to support grassroots organizing in the South. The Institute focuses on issues of economics, labor, political power, civil rights and the environment.

Methods of operation: Publications (50%), research (40%), training and technical assistance (10%)

Recent issues and projects: Work on the poultry industry and its impact on workers, consumers and farmers, environmental justice, community economic development.

Major publications: *Southern Exposure* magazine; *Environmental Politics: Lessons from the Grassroots*

Budget: $250,000

Funding: Foundations (50%), publication sales (35%), individual contributions (15%)

Staff: 6
2 Researchers
1 Writer/Editor
1 Executive Director
1 Circulation Director
1 Administrative Assistant

Staff openings/year: 1-2

Work Week: 40 hours

Salary/year: $20,000 (Recent College Graduate); $Varies (Graduate with advanced degree)

Benefits: Health insurance, paid vacation, life insurance, pregnancy leave

Part-Time Employees: 1

Summer Employees: Yes

Volunteers: 4-6

Interns: None currently, but willing to accept applications

Jobs advertised: *Community Jobs* and other publications

To apply: Contact the Executive Director

INSTITUTE FOR WOMEN'S POLICY RESEARCH

1400 20th Street, NW, Suite 104
Washington, DC 20036
(202) 785-5100

Director: Heidi Hartmann

Purpose: To conduct feminist-oriented research of value to policymakers, legislators and women's advocacy organizations

Methods of operation: Research (80%), publications (20%)

Recent issues and projects: Study of impact of the Pregnancy Discrimination Act of 1979; *Unnecessary Losses* study of Family and Medical Leave; research on the salaries of child care workers; study of low-income workers and low wage work; *Combining Work and Welfare: An Alternative Anti-Poverty Strategy*; Study of part-time and contingent work

Major publications: *Research News Reporter*; frequent reports

Budget: $325,000

Funding: Individual contributions, foundations, government

Staff: 8
3 Researchers
1 Director
1 Office Manager
2 Administrative Staff
1 Program Associate

Staff openings/year: 1-2

Work Week: 40 hours

Salary/year: $20,000 (Recent College Graduate); $Varies (Graduate with advanced degree)

Benefits: Health insurance, life insurance, pregnancy leave, pension, paid vacation

Part-Time Employees: 4

Volunteers: Yes

Interns: 3
Length: Semester
Duties: Varies
Remuneration: Varies

Jobs advertised: Word of mouth; newsletters

To apply: Send resume to Melinda Gish. No phone calls please.

INSTITUTE OF CULTURAL AFFAIRS

4750 N. Sheridan Road
Chicago, IL 60640
(312) 769-6363

Other Offices: Phoenix, AZ; Seattle, WA; Troy, NJ

Purpose: We help people reach consensus through use of planning methods built on our Technologies of Participation.

Methods of operation: Research, publications, human services, public education, training and technical assistance

Constituency: People in education, public service, churches, some private sector

Recent issues and projects: Leadership Options a 16 day course twice a year developing new ways to express leadership; learning labs for teachers; school reform planning in Chicago

Major publications: *Winning Through Participation*; *Participation Works*

Budget: $500,000

Funding: Individual contributions, foundations, direct mail, canvassing

Staff: 24
2 Writers/Editors
2 Office Managers
6 Researchers
2 Foundation Fundraisers
3 Bookkeepers/Accountants
1 Grassroots Fundraiser
1 Campaign Manager
5 Trainers
2 Archives

Work Week: 50 hours

Benefits: Health insurance, paid vacation, housing, pregnancy leave

Part-Time Employees: Yes

Summer Employees: None

Volunteers: Yes

Interns: Yes
Length: 6 months to 1 year
Duties: As assigned

Jobs advertised: Word of mouth

To apply: Contact George Packard

INTER-HEMISPHERIC EDUCATION RESOURCE CENTER

P.O. Box 4506
Albuquerque, NM 87196
(505) 842-8288

Director: Debra Preusch

Purpose: The goal of the Resource Center is to use information as a catalyst for social change. This is done through the publication of books, reports and policy papers.

Methods of operation: Research (60%), publications (30%), information requests (10%)

Recent issues and projects: Published a series of books on each of the Central American countries and have recently added a book on Mexico to the series. U.S.-Mexico relations are a current focus of the resource center and we have just published *Runaway America*, a book that documented the transfer of jobs from the U.S. to Mexico. We publish 2 quarterly newsletters, the *Resource Center Bulletin* and *Borderlines*.

Major publications: Quarterly publications include the *Bulletin*, which highlights our current projects, *Borderlines*, a journal of U.S.-Mexico border issues, and the *NED Backgrounder*, designed to inform interested parties about the activities of the National Endowment for Democracy. Books include: *Mexico: A Country Guide*; *Cross-Border Links: A Directory of Organizations in Canada, Mexico and the United States*; *Runaway America: U.S. Jobs and Factories on the Move*

Budget: $250,000

Funding: Foundations (50%), sales and royalties (43%), individual contributions (7%)

Staff: 6
1 Researcher
3 Writer/Editors
1 Office Manager
1 Production Manager

Work Week: 45 hours

Salary/year: $18,000 (Recent College Graduate); $23,000 (Graduate with advanced degree)

Benefits: Health insurance, paid vacation, pregnancy leave, pension, life insurance

Part-Time Employees: 6

Volunteers: 3

Interns: Yes
Length: 3-4 months
Duties: Research
Remuneration: School credit

Jobs advertised: We rarely have job openings; when we do they are usually for part-time positions. These are advertised through the college work-study program or through progressive periodicals.

To apply: Contact Debra Preusch, Director

INTERACTION: AMERICAN COUNCIL FOR VOLUNTARY INTERNATIONAL ACTION

1717 Massachusetts Ave., NW, Suite 801
Washington, DC 20036
(202) 667-8227

President: Julia V. Taft

Purpose: Interaction is a coalition of over 150 U.S.-based nonprofits working to promote human dignity and development in 165 countries around the world. Member agencies work in the fields of sustainable development, refugee assistance and protection, disaster relief and preparedness, public policy advocacy, and in educating Americans about the developing world.

Methods of operation: Coordination and promotion of member activities (55%), lobbying (15%), publications (15%), public education (8%), training and technical assistance (5%), research (2%)

Major publications: *Monday Developments*, bi-weekly newsletter; *Member Profiles*, bi-annual directory of member organizations

Budget: $3,000,000

Funding: Foundations (66%), member dues (33%)

Staff: 24
2 Organizers
2 Writers/Editors
1 Office Manager
2 Lobbyists
2 Press Aides
5 Issue Experts
2 Bookkeepers
4 Receptionists/Administrative Assistants
3 Senior Management Specialists
1 Membership Coordinator

Staff openings/year: 4

Work Week: 35 hours

Salary/year: $24,000 (Recent College Graduate); $30,000 (Graduate with advanced degree)

Benefits: Health insurance, pension, paid vacation, life insurance, family leave

Part-Time Employees: None

Summer Employees: None

Volunteers: None

Interns: 3-5
Length: Three months
Duties: Vary widely depending on skills and interests of intern
Remuneration: Usually unpaid

Jobs advertised: *Monday Developments* newsletter

To apply: Please send resumes to Julia Taft (no phone calls).

Remarks: Interaction's newsletter, *Monday Developments*, contains an extensive listing of employment opportunities, both in the U.S. and abroad, with international humanitarian organizations. Sample copies are available for $4.00. Yearly subscriptions for individuals cost $65.00, for organizations $275.00.

INTERCOMMUNITY CENTER FOR JUSTICE AND PEACE

20 Washington Square North
New York, NY 10011
(212) 475-6677

Director: Sister Marie Danaher, OP

Purpose: The Intercommunity Center for Justice and Peace works toward structural and systemic change with regard to the issues and situations that keep people poor and powerless and that militate against life on our planet.

Methods of operation: Community organizing (40%), research (20%), direct action (10%), publications (5%), lobbying (10%), education (15%)

Membership: Religious congregations of Catholic women and men form the core membership, and other interested people are "Friends of the Center"

Recent issues and projects: ICJP is involved in peace and disarmament, human rights issues, education for peace and justice and responsible investment policies. They conduct structural analysis workshops on current issues and do community organizing in Manhattan.

Major publications: *Universe Updated*, bi-monthly newsletter; *FOCUS*, monthly newsletter

Budget: $163,000

Funding: Individual contributions, foundations, membership dues

Staff: 4
1 Office Manager
1 Executive Director
1 Organizer
1 Foundation Fundraiser

Work Week: 40 hours

Salary/year: $Varies (Recent College Graduate); $Varies (Graduate with advanced degree)

Benefits: Health insurance, paid vacation, pregnancy leave

Part-Time Employees: 2

Volunteers: 4

Interns: Yes
Duties: Internship programs are arranged according to interest of intern and focus of Center at a given time
Remuneration: No financial remuneration is given

Jobs advertised: Usually through religious congregations and New York University

To apply: Contact S. Marie Danaher, Executive Director

INTERFAITH CENTER ON CORPORATE RESPONSIBILITY (ICCR)

475 Riverside Drive, Room 566
New York, NY 10115-0050
(212) 870-2293

Director: Timothy H. Smith

Purpose: As institutional investors, to hold corporations socially accountable.

Methods of operation: Shareholder campaigns (65%), publications (15%), research (10%), training and technical assistance (7%), direct action (3%)

Constituency: Protestant and Roman Catholic institutional investors

Recent issues and projects: South Africa; maquiladoras; nuclear arms production; economic conversion

Major publications: Newsletter: *The Corporate Examiner*; *Directory of Alternative Investments*; *Corporate Responsibility Challenges, Spring 1989*; *Church Proxy Resolutions 1989*

Budget: $630,000

Funding: Church members (60%), foundations (10%), direct mail (5%), individual contributions (3%)

Staff: 9
4 Program Directors
2 Secretaries
1 Executive Director
1 Writer/Editor
1 Bookkeeper/Accountant

Staff openings/year: 0-1

Work Week: 35 hours

Salary/year: $22,000 (Recent College Graduate); $32,000 (Graduate with advanced degree)

Benefits: Health insurance, life insurance, pregnancy leave, pension, credit union, paid vacation, union

Part-Time Employees: 1

Volunteers: Yes

Interns: Yes
Length: 1 year
Duties: Assist program directors: some program development, some clerical
Remuneration: The college/university has paid them

Jobs advertised: Internal posting; issue specific organizations/press (e.g. if energy staff, then environmental press and organizations)

To apply: Contact Timothy H. Smith, Executive Director

INTERNATIONAL ACADEMY AT SANTA BARBARA

800 Garden Street, Suite D
Santa Barbara, CA 93101
(805) 965-5010 Fax: (805) 965-6071

Director: Susan Shaffer

Purpose: The mission of the International Academy at Santa Barbara is to provide accessible information on global issues.

Methods of operation: Publications (95%), research (3%), public education (2%)

Recent issues and projects: In support of their goals, the International Academy will undertake such educational efforts as may be desirable and necessary, including seminars, conferences, publications, lectures, and other written and electronic dissemination of material relating to research and applications in its areas of interest.

Major publications: *Environmental Periodicals Bibliography* (in hardcopy, CD-ROM and online); *Energy Review*; *Energy Books Quarterly*; *Alternative Energy Digests*; *Waste Information Digests*; Current world leaders *Almanac and International Issues*

Budget: $325,000

Funding: Subscriptions (95%), direct mail (2%), individual contributions (2%), foundations (1%)

Staff: 10
3 Writer/Editors
1 Office Manager
1 Managing Editor
1 Proofreader
3 Indexers
1 Administrative Assistant

Staff openings/year: 1

Work Week: 40 hours

Salary/year: $22-25,000 (Recent College Graduate); $25,000 (Graduate with advanced degree)

Benefits: Health insurance, paid vacation, life insurance, credit union, pregnancy leave, dental and long-term disability insurance

Part-Time Employees: 6

Volunteers: 1

Interns:
Length: 3-6 months
Duties: Assisting the editors: indexing articles for bibliography; writing, proofreading, or desktop publishing; general editorial assignments

Jobs advertised: Through Intern programs at UCSB and SB City Colleges

To apply: Contact Susan Shaffer, Office Manager

INTERNATIONAL ALLIANCE FOR SUSTAINABLE AGRICULTURE

1701 University Avenue, SE
Minneapolis, MN 55414
(612) 331-1099 Fax: (612)379-1527

Director: Terry Gips

Purpose: An international networking organization promoting sustainable food and agriculture systems which are ecologically sound, economically viable, socially just and humane. Work in three areas at the local, national and international levels: (1) Networking and Collaboration; (2) Education; and (3) Policy Development.

Methods of operation: Public education (40%), publications (15%), research (15%), lobbying (15%), training and technical assistance (5%), community organizing (5%), direct action (5%)

Constituency: Farmers, consumers, researchers, businesses, nonprofit organizations and other concerned groups worldwide

Recent issues and projects: Sustainable agriculture and pesticide reform legislation; slide shows; 1990 Farm Bill; humane animal care; CERES Principles for corporate environmental responsibility; widespread institutional acceptance of sustainable agriculture

Major publications: Newsletter: *Manna*; *Planting the Future: A Resource Guide to Sustainable Agriculture in the Third World*; *Breaking the Pesticide Habit: Alternatives to 12 Hazardous Pesticides*; *Minnesota Green Pages*, a directory of sustainable agriculture, food and environment; *The Humane Consumer and Producer Guide* (with the Humane Society of the U.S.)

Budget: $150,000

Funding: Individual contributions (45%), Skiers Ending Hunger (10%), foundations (30%), membership (10%)

Staff: 4
1 President
1 Office Manager
1 Project Director
1 Intern
1/4 Bookkeeper

Staff openings/year: 1-3

Work Week: 40-45 hours

Salary/year: $12-15,000 (Recent College Graduate); $15-24,000 (Graduate with advanced degree)

Benefits: Health insurance, life insurance, paid vacation, free parking, great work atmosphere and location, flexible hours/vacation

Part-Time Employees: 1

Summer Employees: 3-5

Volunteers: 10-20

Interns: 1-3
Length: 2 months-1 year
Duties: Based on abilities
Remuneration: Based on need and funding

Jobs advertised: In our newsletter and various newspapers

To apply: Contact Terry Gips

INTERNATIONAL COMMITTEE OF LAWYERS FOR TIBET

347 Dolores Street, Suite 206
San Francisco, CA 94110
(415) 252-5967

Director: Beth Winters

Purpose: The International Committee of Lawyers for Tibet (ICLT) advocates self-determination for the Tibetan people through legal action and education. ICLT promotes human rights, environmental protection and peaceful resolution of the situation in Tibet.

Methods of operation: Research (30%), lobbying (20%), publications (20%), public education (20%), community organizing (5%), litigation (5%)

Membership: Attorneys and non-attorneys in 10 countries and 31 states

Recent issues and projects: Recent projects include: Article 191 Prisoners of Conscience; environment and development; economics and trade; women's issues; publications; and legal education

Major publications: *Tibet Brief*, quarterly newsletter

Budget: $90,000

Funding: Individual contributions (40%), foundations (30%), events (30%)

Staff: 1

Staff openings/year: 1

Work Week: 40 hours

Salary/year: $20,000 (Recent College Graduate); $22,000 (Graduate with advanced degree)

Benefits: Health insurance, paid vacation

Part-Time Employees: None

Summer Employees: None

Volunteers: 40

Interns: 2-4
Length: 3 months
Duties: Research; basic administrative work; writing
Remuneration: Small stipend

To apply: Contact Beth Winters

Remarks: Only 2 positions have ever been filled and both were filled from our active volunteer pool.

INTERNATIONAL HUMAN RIGHTS LAW GROUP

1601 Connecticut Avenue, NW, Suite 700
Washington, DC 20009
(202) 232-8500

Director: Gay McDougall

Purpose: The Law Group is a nonpartisan, public interest organization founded in 1978 which works to promote and protect human rights around the world through the application of international human rights law. The Law Group files cases before U.S. courts and such international forums as the Inter-American Commission on Human Rights, the United Nations Human Rights Commission and Human Rights Committee, and UNESCO. Also send on-site fact-finding missions to investigate human rights abuses in many countries around the world.

Methods of operation: Fact-finding and election observer missions (30%), international and domestic litigation (30%), publications (20%), training and technical assistance (15%), public education (5%)

Constituency: Lawyers, NGO's (non-governmental organizations), intergovernmental organizations

Recent issues and projects: Election observer projects in Kenya, Chile, Nicaragua, and Paraguay; study of independence of the judiciary in Guatemala and Ethiopia; lobbying United Nations for increased protection of women's rights

Major publications: *The Law Group Docket*; handbooks on human rights law practice, election observing; compilation of U.S. legislation relating human rights to U.S. foreign policy; reports containing findings and recommendations from its investigations

Budget: $1,000,000

Funding: Foundations (65%), individual contributions (35%)

Staff: 20
13 Attorneys
1 Office Manager
2 Foundation Fundraisers
3 Administrative Assistants
1 Receptionist

Staff openings/year: 1-2

Work Week: 40-45 hours

Salary/year: $18,000 (Recent College Graduate); $30,000 (lawyer) (Graduate with advanced degree)

Benefits: Health insurance, life insurance, paid vacation

Volunteers: 4

Interns: 4-7
Length: 1 semester
Remuneration: Unpaid

Jobs advertised: *Washington Post*; law school bulletin boards; job books and other nonprofit organization job books

To apply: Contact Intern Coordinator

INTERNATIONAL INSTITUTE FOR ENERGY CONSERVATION

750 First Street, NE, Suite 940
Washington, DC 20002
(202) 842-3388 Fax: (202) 842-1565

Other Offices: Bangkok, THAILAND; Santiago, CHILE

Director: Deborah Bleviss

Purpose: IIEC is a nonprofit organization founded in 1984 to accelerate the global adoption of energy-efficiency policies, technologies and practices to enable economic and ecologically sustainable development. IIEC's focus is on industrializing countries, including those in Central and Eastern Europe.

Methods of operation: Research (30%), public education (30%), training and technical assistance (20%), identifying developing and developed country partners and coordinating LDC activities (20%)

Recent issues and projects: (1) Electricity conservation projects in Thailand; (2) electricity conservation projects in Chile; (3) projects to spur development of a market-based infrastructure within the economies of developing and industrializing countries to deliver energy-efficiency products and services; (4) transportation projects that respond to the increasing challenge for cities to meet transportation demand while minimizing energy growth, environmental problems, and traffic growth; (5) projects to advise multilateral development banks, like the World Bank, on the incorporation of energy-efficiency policies into the overall lending practices of the banks.

Major publications: *E-Notes*; *BANKNOTE*; the annual report, the *Technical Information Directory*; and project reports such as: *Moving Toward Integrated Transport Planning*; *Energy Environment*; *Mobility in Four Asian Cities*; *Seizing the Moment*; *Global Opportunities for the Energy Efficiency Industry*; *The Least Cost Energy Path for Developing Countries*; *Energy Efficiency Investments for the Multilateral Development Banks*

Budget: $2,000,000

Funding: Foundations, government grants

Staff: 17
1 Executive Director
1 Vice President
1 Financial Administrator
1 Office Manager
2 Transportation Experts
2 Financial Analysts
1 Bank Analyst
2 Energy Planning Experts
1 Engineer
5 Research Assistants

Staff openings/year: 2-3

Work Week: 40 hours

Salary/year: $20-25,000 (Recent College Graduate); $25-35,000 (Graduate with advanced degree)

Benefits: Health insurance, life insurance, disability insurance, paid vacation, pension, dental benefits, educational benefits

Volunteers: 1-2

Interns: 1-2
Length: 3-12 months
Duties: Provide research assistance to staff; minimal staff and office support such as answering phones and information requests
Remuneration: Prefer work-study; otherwise minimum wage or higher

Jobs advertised: Local universities; announcements sent to related organizations and government departments

To apply: Contact Pat Keegan, Vice President

Remarks: We are always looking for experienced energy conservation analysts with policy implementation expertise. We would also like to hear from recent college graduates (undergraduate and graduate) who have an interest in this issue, and who have some relevant energy/environment coursework and experience.

IOWA CITIZEN ACTION NETWORK
415 10th Street
Des Moines, IA 50309
(515) 244-9311

Other Offices: Iowa City, IA

Director: Brad Lint

Purpose: Citizen lobbying group that is working to raise living standards and improve the quality of life for every Iowan. ICAN works to involve citizens and their organizations in issue campaigns to win concrete victories for consumers and strengthen ties between grassroots groups that share common concerns.

Methods of operation: Research, public education, lobbying, organizing, outreach and during each election cycle voter education

Constituency: Coalition of community, religious, labor, senior, farm and environmental groups

Recent issues and projects: ICAN works on environmental and consumer issues such as pollution prevention, safe and affordable energy, sustainable agriculture, health care for all and fair taxes.

Major publications: *ICAN News*; *IMPACT*

Funding: Public support (80%), affiliate dues and contributions (10%), other (10%)

Staff: 35
5 Office staff and 30 Field staff includes:
1 Executive Director
1 Financial Manager
2 Organizers
1 Data Manager
20-30 Canvassers

Work Week: 40-50 hours

Salary/year: $15,600 Canvasser (Recent College Graduate); $20,000 Organizer (Graduate with advanced degree)

Benefits: Health insurance, life insurance, paid vacation

Summer Employees: 30-40

Interns: Yes
Length: Semester
Duties: Organizing, canvassing, researching, fundraising
Remuneration: Volunteer

Jobs advertised: Newspapers and fliers

To apply: Contact Brad Lint, Executive Director or Geoffrey Hennies, Field Canvass Director or Lisa Waggoner, Phone Canvass Director (319)354-8116

IRONBOUND COMMUNITY CORPORATION
95 Fleming Avenue
Newark, NJ 07105
(201) 344-7210

Director: Vic DeLuca

Purpose: Empower people

Methods of operation: Research, lobbying, publications, community organizing, direct action

Recent issues and projects: Fight the siting of the world's largest sewage sludge incinerator

Major publications: Tri-lingual monthly newspaper: *Ironbound Voices*

Budget: $60,000

Funding: Foundations (80%), individual contributions (20%)

Staff: 3
Issue Expert
Organizer
Writer/Editor
Researcher

Work Week: 50-60 hours

Benefits: Health insurance (1/2), paid vacation

Part-Time Employees: 1

Volunteers: Yes

ISAR
1601 Connecticut Ave., NW, Suite 301
Washington, DC 20009
(202) 387-3034

Director: Eliza K. Klose

Purpose: ISAR is a small, nonprofit, nonpartisan service organization which works to improve Soviet-American relations by: promoting constructive alternatives to an adversarial relationship; identifying areas of mutual interest; opening channels of communication and dialogue; enlarging areas of common ground and cooperation; collaborating on exchanges in a broad range of fields; encouraging the study of Russian language, history and culture; and facilitating working relationships between individual Soviets and Americans.

Methods of operation: Publications, public education (50%), research (50%)

Constituency: Individuals, organizations, media, legislators concerned with Soviet-American relations

Recent issues and projects: ISAR serves primarily as a clearinghouse for Soviet-American exchange, providing information and answering questions from organizations, individuals, government offices and the press. We do a major part of our work through our publications, in particular our journal and our handbook. We also take part in behind-the-scenes efforts to bring Soviets and Americans together to discuss issues of mutual interest.

Major publications: *1990 Handbook on Organizations Involved in Soviet-American Relations*; *Surviving Together: A Journal on Soviet-American Relations*, triannual; *Hosting Soviet Visitors: A Handbook*

Budget: $200,000

Funding: Individual contributions, foundations

Staff: 9
4 Research and Production Assistants
1 Executive Director
1 Senior Associate
1 President and Founder, volunteer
1 Bookkeeper
1 Managing Editor

Staff openings/year: 1

Work Week: 55 hours

Salary/year: $18,000 (Recent College Graduate); $20,000 (Graduate with advanced degree)

Benefits: Health insurance, paid vacation

Summer Employees: 3

Volunteers: 1

Interns: 3
Length: One semester
Duties: Word processing, research, editing, responding to inquiries
Remuneration: None

To apply: Contact Tertia Speiser

ISLES, INC.

126 N. Montgomery Street
Trenton, NJ 08608
(609) 393-5656

Director: Martin Johnson

Purpose: Isles, Inc. is a nonprofit organization dedicated to community and environmental development in the Trenton, NJ region. Isles projects address the critical needs of food, housing, environmental education and improvement. Isles is also an advocate of community development and environmental improvement throughout New Jersey.

Methods of operation: Publications, community organizing, public education, training and technical assistance, housing construction

Constituency: Urban residents of all ages, mostly low or moderate income

Recent issues and projects: Recent projects include: The creation of the Cadwalader Park Environmental Education Center; The Trenton Neighborhood Tree Project; Children's Gardens; Isles Greening Program; Isles Affordable Housing Program; Scattered Site Housing Rehabilitation; Sales and Rental Programs; Home Ownership Repair and Maintenance Course; Wood Street Partnership; Operation Fatherhood; and The Youthbuild Program

Major publications: *IsleWorks*, newsletter; *The Grapevine Plant It for the Planet*, newsletter

Budget: $650,000

Funding: Government (50%), foundations (30%), direct mail (10%), individual contributions (10%)

Staff: 14
3 Organizers
2 Office Managers
1 Foundation Fundraiser
1 Bookkeeper/Accountant
5 Directors
1 Home Ownership Trainer
1 Construction Manager

Staff openings/year: 3-5

Work Week: 40 hours

Salary/year: $Varies (Recent College Graduate); $Varies (Graduate with advanced degree)

Benefits: Health insurance, paid vacation, life insurance, family leave

Part-Time Employees: 3

Summer Employees: 1-3

Volunteers: Varied

Interns: 5-7
Length: 8-12 weeks
Duties: Varied
Remuneration: Mostly unpaid

Jobs advertised: Local papers, *Community Jobs*

To apply: Please contact Martin Johnson, Executive Director

IT'S TIME ... INC.

139 Henry Street
New York, NY 10002
(212) 962-3069

Director: Anthony Johnson

Purpose: It's Time exists to empower low-income residents of the Lower East Side through tenant organizing, the preservation and development of low-income housing and social services to youth and senior citizens.

Methods of operation: Community organizing (50%), human services (45%), training and technical assistance (5%)

Constituency: Lower income, multi-ethnic population (especially Chinese-speaking) in Lower East Side

Recent issues and projects: Rent strikes and court actions to improve housing conditions and prevent displacement; fair housing law suits; rehabilitation of abandoned housing; coalition building around housing issues

Major publications: *Shining Youth Magazine*, written and illustrated by youth center members

Budget: $240,000

Funding: Government contracts (87%), foundations (9%), individual contributions (4%)

Staff: 10
4 1/3 Organizers
2 Directors/Managers/Organizers
1 1/2 Youth Program Staff
1/3 Custodian
1 Bookkeeper
2/3 Cook

Staff openings/year: 1

Work Week: 35 hours

Salary/year: $Varies (Recent College Graduate); $Varies (Graduate with advanced degree)

Benefits: Health insurance, paid vacation

Part-Time Employees: 5

Volunteers: 3

Interns: Yes
Length: 3 months
Duties: Varies with the program and individual
Remuneration: Volunteer

Jobs advertised: Full-time positions in housing and NYC area publications, and at universities with urban affairs and social work programs. Part-time positions at college and university placement offices and community newspapers.

To apply: Contact Tony Johnson, Executive Director

Remarks: It's Time Inc. is one of the few NYC housing organizations with both Spanish- and Chinese-speaking staff. It also has a history of long-tenured staff. Current staff include two community organizers with twenty years experience with It's Time. We are strongly based in the community, with the majority of staff members being local residents.

IZAAK WALTON LEAGUE OF AMERICA

1401 Wilson Boulevard, Level B
Arlington, VA 22209
(703) 528-1818

Other Offices: Minneapolis, MN

Director: Maitland Sharpe

Purpose: As defenders of the nation's soil, air, woods, waters and wildlife, the League pursues a broad range of conservation goals. These include: clean water, acid rain reduction, improve wildlife habitat, protection of natural areas, improve outdoor ethics, public land management and farm conservation.

Methods of operation: Research, lobbying, litigation, publications, community organizing, public education

Membership: Members come from all walks of life, and all share a fervent love of and commitment to the protection of America's outdoor heritage.

Recent issues and projects: (1) The League's Save Our Streams program now encompasses 1,200 local projects, groups and individuals who adopt and monitor streams. EPA chose the League's monitoring techniques and assistance for their National Stream Monitoring Day. (2) The League's Outdoor Ethics program and newsletter are the only such public awareness programs. The League campaigned for, and bought a helicopter for the U.S. Fish and Wildlife Service to halt poaching and baiting of Waterford. (3) Regional office in Minnesota has developed a constituency to promote energy conservation throughout the upper Midwest, and to build support for sustainable agriculture practices.

Major publications: Quarterly magazine: *Outdoor America*; quarterly newsletters: *Outdoor Ethics* and *Splash!*; *Tipsheet* sent to media

Budget: $1,544,908

Funding: Foundations (54%), members' dues (40%), individual contributions (3%)

Staff: 24
6 Typists
5 Issue Experts
3 Membership Services
3 Lobbyists
2 Writer/Editors
2 Foundation Fundraisers
1 Executive Director
1 Office Manager
1 Bookkeeper/Accountant

Staff openings/year: 1

Work Week: 40 hours

Benefits: Health insurance, life insurance, pension, paid vacation, long-term disability insurance

Part-Time Employees: 1

Interns: 1-2
Length: 2-3 months
Duties: Research and write articles for newsletter; assist with workshops; update database
Remuneration: Non-paying

Jobs advertised: Professional magazines and newsletters; *Washington Post*

To apply: Contact Ann Boswell, Executive Assistant/ Office Manager

JACKSON HOLE LAND TRUST

P.O. Box 2897
Jackson Hole, WY 83001
(307) 733-4707

Director: Leslie Mattson

Purpose: The Jackson Hole Land Trust works to preserve the scenic, ranching and wildlife values of Jackson Hole by assisting landowners who wish to protect their land in perpetuity.

Methods of operation: Research, fundraising, publications, direct action, public education, training and technical assistance

Membership: Local, national and international donors desiring to protect Jackson Hole

Recent issues and projects: Five properties were protected last year with conservation easements totaling over 800 acres. One of these properties became a town park.

Major publications: Biannual newsletter

Budget: $350,000

Funding: Individual contributions (90%), foundations (10%)

Staff: 7
1 Attorney
1 Office Manager
2 Issue Experts
1 Administrative Assistant
1 Bookkeeper/Accountant
1 Grassroots Fundraiser

Work Week: 40 hours

Interns: 1
Length: 3 months
Duties: Research projects, mapping, office support, fundraising, etc.
Remuneration: $200 per month for 20 hours per week

Jobs advertised: Through a variety of publications

To apply: Contact Creed Clayton

Remarks: Internships are available year-round

JAMESTOWN AUDUBON NATURE CENTER

1600 Riverside Road
Jamestown, NY 14701
(716) 569-2345

Other Offices: Olean, NY

Director: James A. Yaich

Purpose: Nature and environmental education

Methods of operation: Public education (90%), training and technical assistance (5%), research (2%), publications (2%), lobbying (1%)

Membership: 800 members mostly from throughout Western New York and Northwestern Pennsylvania

Recent issues and projects: Nature Center field trips, in-class lessons, after school nature clubs at school sites, summer nature day camp, residential camping, teacher workshops, public programs, etc.

Major publications: *Blue Bird Notes*, a membership newsletter

Budget: $200,000

Funding: Individual contributions (40%), foundations (40%), other (20%)

Staff: 5
1 Office Manager
1 Foundation Fundraiser
1 Bookkeeper/Accountant
1 Director
1 Assistant Director

Staff openings/year: 1

Work Week: 40 hours

Salary/year: $17,000 (Recent College Graduate); $19,000 (Graduate with advanced degree)

Benefits: Health insurance, pension, paid vacation, life insurance, credit union, family leave

Part-Time Employees: 6

Summer Employees: 2

Volunteers: 100

Interns: 1
Length: 3 months
Duties: Teacher-naturalists, tour guide
Remuneration: $100/month and help with finding housing

Jobs advertised: Local newspaper, trade journals

To apply: Contact James A. Yaich

JUDGE DAVID L. BAZELON CENTER FOR MENTAL HEALTH LAW

1101 15th Street, NW, Suite 1212
Washington, DC 20005
(202) 467-5730 Fax: (202) 223-0409

Director: Leonard S. Rubenstein

Purpose: The Judge David L. Bazelon Center for Mental Health Law is a national nonprofit advocacy organization. The Center was formed in 1972 as the Mental Health Law Project; its name was changed in March 1993 to honor the late Chief Judge of the United States Court of Appeals for the District of Columbia Circuit, David L. Bazelon, who had pioneered the field of mental health law with groundbreaking decisions spelling out the constitutional rights of mental patients.

Methods of operation: Research, litigation, publications, training and technical assistance, policy advocacy

Constituency: Lawyers, advocates, mentally/developmentally disabled persons and their families

Recent issues and projects: The Bazelon Center uses litigation and federal policy reform to define and uphold the legal rights of children, adults and elders with mental disabilities and to create approaches to meeting their needs that will assure them choice and dignity. Staff attorneys provide training and technical assistance to legal services, protection and advocacy, state ombudsman programs and other advocates for low-income individuals and families.

Major publications: The Center publishes issue papers, booklets, manuals and occasional newsletters explaining and interpreting major federal laws and regulations that protect the rights of and make resources available to children and adults with disabilities. A list of current publications is available.

Budget: $1,800,000

Funding: Foundations and individual contributions (65%), project-specific federal grants (20%), court-awarded attorney's fees and publication sales (10%), interest and other income (5%)

Staff: 18
4 Attorneys
3 Typists
2 Fundraisers
2 Children's Program Directors
1 Director
1 Policy Analyst/Government Relations
1 Writer/Editor
1 Paralegal
1 Office Manager
1 Bookkeeper/Accountant
1 Receptionist

Staff openings/year: 1

Work Week: 40 hours

Salary/year: $20,000 (Recent College Graduate);

$30,000 (Graduate with advanced degree)

Benefits: Health insurance, dental insurance, life insurance, pregnancy leave, paid vacation

Part-Time Employees: 2

Summer Employees: 2

Volunteers: 1

Interns: 1
Length: Semester
Duties: Assistance with legal research
Remuneration: Course credit

Jobs advertised: *Washington Post*; notices sent to all relevant legal/disability organizations and publications

To apply: Contact Leonard S. Rubenstein, Director

JUST HARVEST

120 East 9th Avenue
Homestead, PA 15120
(412) 464-0739

Director: Ken Regal, Joni Rabinowitz, Pete Harvey, Co-Directors

Purpose: To advocate for public policy changes on hunger issues and related economic justice concerns.

Methods of operation: Lobbying (40%), direct action (15%), research (15%), public education (10%), community organizing (10%), publications (10%)

Constituency: Concerned individuals involved in social justice/hunger concerns. Church-oriented and social service-oriented folk also. Membership of 800.

Recent issues and projects: (1) Local campaign to have National School Breakfast Program implemented in local school districts; (2) Research study on childhood hunger in Allegheny County; (3) Effort to win city policies to stop flight of supermarkets from inner cities

Major publications: Bimonthly newsletter: *Just Harvest News*, 6-8 pages

Budget: $85,000

Funding: Religious and grassroots (65%), individual contributions (25%), foundations (10%)

Staff: 5

Staff openings/year: 0-1

Work Week: 35-45 hours

Salary/year: $16,000 starting (Recent College Graduate); $Varies (Graduate with advanced degree)

Benefits: Health insurance, pregnancy leave, paid vacation

Volunteers: Yes

Interns: Occasionally, willing to accept applications
Length: Varies

Jobs advertised: Local networks; local papers

To apply: Contact Personnel Committee of Board of Directors

Remarks: We do "good works" for sure, but we are a small, community-based group which exists on a month-to-month basis. Our successes have far out-stripped the size of our organization, but we have a good, committed membership, 800 strong, and local and national organizations, which continue to believe in our work and respond to our requests for funds.

JUVENILE LAW CENTER

801 Arch Street, Suite 610
Philadelphia, PA 19107
(215) 625-0551

Director: Robert G. Schwartz

Purpose: The Juvenile Law Center is a nonprofit, public interest law firm which advances the rights of children involved with public agencies, by working for the reform and coordination of the child welfare, juvenile justice, mental health and public health care systems.

Methods of operation: Policy reform (50%), litigation (15%), research (10%), publications (10%), training and technical assistance (10%), public education (5%)

Constituency: Primarily children involved with public agencies

Recent issues and projects: Recent projects include: child welfare; family preservation; adoption reform; dependency representation; juvenile justice; detention overcrowding; conditions of confinement; bond financing of transitional social services; mental health; interagency coordination of services; implementation of entitlements

Major publications: Bi-monthly newsletter, judicial deskbook, child abuse manual, family preservation handbook, numerous fact sheet

Budget: $550,000

Funding: Foundations (66%), other (30%), individual contributions (4%)

Staff: 9
5 Attorneys
2 Paralegals
1 Office Manager
1 Executive Secretary

Staff openings/year: 1

Work Week: 40 hours

Salary/year: $17,500 (Recent College Graduate); $28,000 (Graduate with advanced degree)

Benefits: Health insurance, pension, paid vacation, life insurance, family leave

Part-Time Employees: None

Summer Employees: None

Volunteers: None

Interns: Yes
Length: 10-12 weeks
Duties: Legal research and writing (prefer 2nd year law students)
Remuneration: Fellowship funded - students arrange for their own funding

Jobs advertised: College and law school placement office job listings

To apply: Please contact Robert G. Schwartz, Executive Director

KALAMAZOO RIVER PROTECTION ASSOCIATION

917 South Park
Kalamazoo, MI 49001
(616) 345-8488

Director: Mary B. Powers

Purpose: The Kalamazoo River Protection Association is recognized by the United States Environmental Protection Agency as THE citizens representation on the Allied Paper Inc./Portage Creek/Kalamazoo River Superfund Site in Kalamazoo and Allegan counties in Michigan. KRPA has been awarded a $50,000 Technical Assistance Grant (TAG) to hire consultants to decipher and rebutt cleanup documents designed by the engineers representing the polluters on this Superfund site. KRPA has been called by other citizen superfund groups in the U.S.

Methods of operation: Public education (40%), direct action (20%), research (10%), lobbying (10%), publications (10%), training and technical assistance (10%)

Constituency: Property owners along river whose property is damaged; personal contacts

Recent issues and projects: Most of our time has been spent scrutinizing the Superfund and Area of Concern processes on the Kalamazoo River. KRPA has also spent considerable time focusing on the discharge processes of the UPJOHN Company.

Major publications: Quarterly newsletter: *Kalamazoo River Update*; issue press releases on positions regarding state policy on the Kalamazoo River; worked with *Sports Illustrated* (July 1989) to highlight the need to "Restore the River"

Budget: $50,000

Funding: Individual contributions (50%), foundations (50%)

Staff:
Volunteer Positions:
1 Press Aide
2 Issue Experts
2 Lobbyists

Part-Time Employees: 1

Volunteers: Yes

Interns: Periodically

To apply: Contact Mary B. Powers

KENTUCKIANS FOR THE COMMONWEALTH

P.O. Box 864
Prestonburg, KY 41653
(606) 886-0043

Other Offices: Carcassone, KY; Louisville, KY; London, KY

Director: Burt Lauderdale

Purpose: Statewide membership-based citizens organization which emphasizes leadership development and the development of strong local community groups

Methods of operation: Community organizing (85%), publications (10%), litigation (5%); also research, lobbying, and direct action

Membership: 2,500 members - varied; primarily low-income and working class

'ects: Landowners rights; 'ation; education; utilities; 'ces

. Monthly newspaper: ɔcales; annual report; annual study ..ship/control of coal production in the state: ɔ s *Mining Kentucky's Coal?*

Budget: $330,000

Funding: Foundations and churches (65%), individual contributions (25%), grassroots fundraising (10%)

Staff: 8
5 Organizers
1 Writer/Editor
1 Office Manager
1 Financial Manager

Staff openings/year: 1-2

Work Week: 40 + hours

Salary/year: $15,000 (Recent College Graduate); $Varies (Graduate with advanced degree)

Benefits: Health insurance, life insurance, pregnancy leave, pension, credit union, paid vacation, dental insurance

Part-Time Employees: 2

Summer Employees: 1-2

Volunteers: Lots

Interns: 1-2
Length: 3 months-1 year
Duties: Varied; mainly "special projects"
Remuneration: Very limited stipends; usually work through other intern programs

Jobs advertised: Through monthly newspaper, *Balancing the Scales*; *Community Jobs*; word of mouth

To apply: Contact Burt Lauderdale, Coordinator

KIDSNET
6856 Eastern Ave., NW, Suite 208
Washington, DC 20012
(202) 291-1400

Director: Karen Jaffe

Purpose: KIDSNET is a national nonprofit clearinghouse for children's radio and TV. They provide information in print and electronic format for people in the TV industry, educators and parents.

Methods of operation: Publications (80%), research (10%), public education (5%), training and technical assistance (5%)

Constituency: Educators, education associations, broadcast and cable programmers, and producers

Recent issues and projects: Ongoing research detailing programs currently on public, commercial and cable networks.

Major publications: Monthly bulletin with quarterly calendar and study guides

Budget: $250,000

Funding: Foundations (35%), other (65%)

Staff: 4
1 Organizer
1 Office Manager
1 Researcher
1 Foundation Fundraiser

Staff openings/year: 0-1

Work Week: 43 hours

Salary/year: $22,000 (Recent College Graduate); $Varies (Graduate with advanced degree)

Benefits: Health insurance, paid vacation

Part-Time Employees: None

Summer Employees: None

Volunteers: 2-3

Interns: 2-3
Length: 4 months
Duties: Assist research manager with monthly publication. Conducts research for weekly syndicate column. Offers general office assistance
Remuneration: Unpaid

Jobs advertised: Newspapers and trade journals

To apply: Contact Executive Director

Remarks: KIDSNET is a 10-year old national clearinghouse on children's electronic media. It is an information service, NOT a production company.

KIT CLARK SENIOR SERVICES
1500 Dorchester Avenue
Dorchester, MA 02122
(617) 825-5000

Director: Sandra K. Albright

Purpose: Services for one-third of Boston's elderly in nutrition, transportation, adult day care, social day care, home care, senior center, shelter, congregate house, alcohol and mental health.

Methods of operation: Human services (85%), community organizing (10%), public education (5%)

Constituency: Persons over 60 years old living in coastal Boston neighborhoods: East Boston, South End, South Boston, Boston, South Cove, Mattapan, Dorchester, Charlestown

Recent issues and projects: Most of their recent emphasis has been on housing projects for homeless elderly and their new community kitchen that prepares 3,000 daily meals for the elderly.

Budget: $5,500,000

Funding: Government (70%), individual contributions (15%), foundations (15%)

Staff: 160
Caseworkers
Bookkeepers/Accountants
Administrative Assistants
Drivers
Cooks
Mental Health Staff
Home Health Aides
Site Food Managers
Nurses
Aides

Staff openings/year: 10

Work Week: 40 hours

Salary/year: $20,000 (Recent College Graduate); $26,000 (Graduate with advanced degree)

Benefits: Health insurance, pension, paid vacation, pregnancy leave

Part-Time Employees: 108

Volunteers: 185

Interns: Vista and social workers
Remuneration: No funding available, but we will supervise

Jobs advertised: *Boston Globe*; professional journals

To apply: Contact Sandra Albright, Director

LA FRONTERA CENTER, INC.

502 West 29th Street
Tuscon, AZ 85713
(602) 884-9920

Director: Dr. Floyd H. Martinez

Purpose: To provide a network of accessible, coordinated, mental health, vocational rehabilitation and chemical dependency services that are responsive and relevant to the needs of a culturally diverse community.

Methods of operation: Human services (90%), public education (10%)

Recent issues and projects: Addition of major project to assist SMI; strong vocation rehabilitation programs; therapeutic day care; creation of a new foundation for fundraising

Major publications: *Behavioral Health*, quarterly newsletter

Budget: $11,000,000

Funding: Contracts (80%), foundations (15%), individual contributions (5%)

Staff: 250
2 Foundation Fundraisers
65 Counselors/Therapists
15 Day Care
95 Vocational Rehabilitation
73 Support Staff

Staff openings/year: 25

Work Week: 40 hours

Salary/year: $18-25,000 (Recent College Graduate); $25-30,000 (Graduate with advanced degree)

Benefits: Health insurance, pension, child care, paid vacation, life insurance, wellness program, family leave

Part-Time Employees: Yes

Volunteers: Yes

Interns: Yes
Length: Academic year
Duties: Counseling/Development

Jobs advertised: Local newspapers/jobline/in-house list

To apply: Please contact Jan Shuman, Director of Human Resources

Remarks: Serving Pima County and Southern Arizona since 1968, La Frontera Center is the largest provider of community-based, comprehensive behavioral health services in the state.

LABOR EDUCATION & RESEARCH PROJECT

7435 Michigan Avenue
Detroit, MI 48210
(313) 842-6262

Purpose: To bring together union activists at the grassroots level to develop a movement which can revitalize the labor movement.

Constituency: Union members and local officers who want to "put the movement back in the labor movement"

Recent issues and projects: National conferences of 1,000 activists; small training schools; books on current labor issues

Major publications: Monthly newsletter: *Labor Notes*, circulated to union activists nationwide

Budget: $300,000

Funding: Individual contributions, foundations, literature sales and subscriptions

Staff: 8
Organizers
Writers/Editors

Staff openings/year: 1

Work Week: 45 hours

Salary/year: $20,000 (Recent College Graduate); $Varies (Graduate with advanced degree)

Benefits: Health insurance, life insurance, pregnancy leave, paid vacation

Part-Time Employees: 1 Bookkeeper

Volunteers: Yes; sometimes

Interns: Willing to accept applications

Jobs advertised: Ads in *Labor Notes*; word of mouth

To apply: Contact Jane Slaughter

LABOR/COMMUNITY STRATEGY CENTER

3780 Wilshire Blvd., Suite 1200
Los Angeles, CA 90010
(213) 387-2800

Director: Eric Mann

Purpose: The Labor/Community Strategy Center is a long-term movement and a permanent institution of progressive activism in Los Angeles. The Strategy Center brings together organizers to analyze their work and develop campaigns to confront some of the structural problems facing us today.

Methods of operation: Community organizing (25%), public education (25%), direct action (20%), administration and fundraising (20%), research (10%)

Constituency: Community organizers, labor activists

Recent issues and projects: Recent projects include: Implementing a grassroots based regional "test case" boycott of Texaco tied internationally to the Ecuadorian Accion Ecologica's Texaco boycott; organizing a "bus-riders union" amongst L.A.'s 1.3 million bus riders that fights for a world-class bus-centered zero emission mass transit system built/manufactured by high-wage unionized labor

Major publications: Through Strategy Center publications, we distribute books, reports and films, including: *Taking On General Motors*; *LA's Lethal Air: New Strategies for Policy*; *Organizing*; and *Action and Reconstructing Los Angeles from the Bottom Up* by Eric Mann, and the award-winning film, "Tiger By the Trail."

Budget: $400,000

Funding: Foundations (70%), individual contributions (30%)

Staff: 8
5 Organizers
1 Administrator
1 Researcher
1 Director

Staff openings/year: 1

Work Week: 55 hours

Salary/year: $25,000+ (Recent College Graduate); $Varies (Graduate with advanced degree)

Benefits: Health insurance, pregnancy leave, pension, paid vacation

Volunteers: 100

Interns: Yes
Length: Flexible; minimum of 3 months
Duties: Research and organizing work
Remuneration: Small stipend negotiable

Jobs advertised: Community organizations; labor unions; word of mouth

To apply: Contact Georgia Hayashi, Administrator

Remarks: We particularly focus on Blacks, Latinos and Asians in Los Angeles, and encourage Blacks, Latinos and Asian women to apply for positions and internships.

LACASA OF GOSHEN, INC.

202 North Cottage Ave.
Goshen, IN 46526
(219) 533-4450

Director: Arden Shank

Purpose: To meet immediate needs in the low-income and hispanic communities and to empower these communities for self-development.

Methods of operation: Human services (45%), rental housing program (30%), community organizing (15%), public education (5%), research (5%)

Constituency: Local Christian churches

Recent issues and projects: Lack of adequate, affordable housing led to tenant organizing and advocacy, and a rental rehab program; inadequate local or state poor relief led to poor relief advocacy; growing Hispanic population led to immigration counseling; lack of home purchase information and alternative financing led to home buyer training.

Budget: $370,000

Funding: Individual contributions (50%), government (30%), United Way (10%), rent (10%)

Staff: 10
1 Carpenter
1 Executive Director
1 Business Manager
1 Development Coordinator
1 Receptionist/Secretary
1 Immigration Counselor
1 Emergency Assistance Counselor
1 Construction Manager
1 Tenant Development Counselor
1 Property Manager

Staff openings/year: 1-3

Work Week: 40 hours

Salary/year: $13,000 (Recent College Graduate); $15,000 (Graduate with advanced degree)

Benefits: Health insurance, paid vacation

Part-Time Employees: 5

Summer Employees: Yes

Volunteers: 200-250 year

Interns: None currently, but willing to accept applications

Jobs advertised: Local papers; church periodicals; Community Link/HandsNet Electronic Information Sharing Network

To apply: Contact Arden Shank, Executive Director

Remarks: LaCasa is a small, local organization working for social change in our community. We have low salaries; people work here because they really want to. We are also involved in statewide organizing on a number of issues.

LAKE MICHIGAN FEDERATION

59 East Van Buren Street, Suite 2215
Chicago, IL 60605
(312) 939-0838

Other Offices: Green Bay, WI; Milwaukee, WI; Muskegon, MI

Director: Christopher D. Knopf

Purpose: Clean up Lake Michigan; work for zero discharge of pollution; and educate public on these and shoreline/lake levels issues

Methods of operation: Public education (20%), direct action (20%), publications (20%), community organizing (20%), research (15%), lobbying (5%)

Constituency: Environmentalists, organizations, recreational users

Recent issues and projects: Toxic Hotspots (areas of concern); research/cleanup; Wetlands Mitigation research; *Great Lakes Environmental Education Kit* for grades K-8

Major publications: Quarterly publication: *Monitor*; *Citizens Guide to Cleaning Up Contaminated Sediments*; *Wetlands and Water Quality: How to Use Section 404 Permit Process*; *Great Lakes Environmental Education Kit* for grades K-8; *It's All Connected: Household Pollution Protection Kit* (videos, slideshow, brochures, pamphlets)

Budget: $490,000

Funding: Foundations (60%), government (20%), individual contributions (20%)

Staff: 10
1 Organizer
1 Writer/Editor
1 Office Manager
1 Researcher

1 Issue Expert

Staff openings/year: 1

Work Week: 40 hours

Salary/year: $22,000 (Recent College Graduate); $25,000 (Graduate with advanced degree)

Benefits: Health insurance, life insurance, paid vacation

Volunteers: Yes

Interns: Yes
Length: 3 months, part-time
Duties: Research, writing, fundraising

Jobs advertised: Through schools, organizations, periodicals, etc.

To apply: Contact Christopher D. Knopf

LAMBDA LEGAL DEFENSE AND EDUCATION FUND, INC.

666 Broadway, 12th Floor
New York, NY 10012
(212) 995-8585

Director: Kevin Cathcart, Executive Director

Purpose: To advance the rights of lesbians, gay men and people with HIV and to educate the public at large about discrimination against gay men and lesbians. Lambda pursues test-case litigation in all parts of the country, and in all areas of concern to gay men and lesbians.

Methods of operation: Litigation, research, publications, human services, direct action and public education

Constituency: Gay men, lesbians, sympathizers, lawyers

Recent issues and projects: Recent projects include: 1) Domestic partnership and family issues; 2) Gays in the military; 3) Battling anti-gay local and state wide ballot initiatives; 4) Health care reform

Major publications: *AIDS Update*; *Lambda Update*

Budget: $1,700,000

Funding: Individual contributions, direct mail (60%), foundations (22%), special events (16%), revenue (2%)

Staff: 20
8 Attorneys
2 Bookkeepers/Accountants
1 Paralegal
5 Administrative Assistants
1 Development Director
1 Executive Director
1 Director of Administration and Finance
1 Receptionist

Staff openings/year: 1-3

Work Week: 40 hours

Salary/year: $24,000 (Recent College Graduate); $30,000+ (Graduate with advanced degree)

Benefits: Health insurance, life insurance, paid vacation

Part-Time Employees: 1

Volunteers: Yes

Interns: 10
Length: Summer or semester
Duties: Research for cases; phone clinic for general public; providing literature on specific topics upon request
Remuneration: Stipend or wage

Jobs advertised: In New York gay press; *New York Times*; at law schools; word of mouth; press advisories

To apply: Contact Beatrice Dohrn for legal positions; Donald Huppert for all other positions.

LANCASTER PEACE EDUCATION PROJECT/AMERICAN FRIENDS SERVICE COMMITTEE

110 North Lime Street
Lancaster, PA 17602
(717) 393-1735

Director: Amina Smith

Purpose: Inform and educate youth, teachers and the community about nonviolent social change; educate on conscientious objection and alternative careers in peace and social change; sponsor a peace and justice community education program and speakers bureau; and maintain a peace and justice resource and lending library.

Methods of operation: Public education (50%), community organizing (30%), research (5%), direct action (5%), training and technical assistance (5%), publications (5%)

Constituency: Youth, teachers, community

Recent issues and projects: 1990 Freedom Ride for Youth; conflict resolution and nonviolence;

youth survey; youth directory; community public awareness program; prejudice reduction and conflict resolution. These programs help participants to evaluate behaviors and to identify the skills required for eliminating or modifying offending behaviors. Work focuses on empowering youth in peace and justice work, and encouraging them to seek educational and occupational advancement outside the military and military-related work.

Budget: $28,000

Funding: Individual contributions, foundations

Staff: 1
1 Director

Staff openings/year: 0-1

Work Week: 40-45 hours

Salary/year: $28,000 (Recent College Graduate); $Varies (Graduate with advanced degree)

Benefits: Health insurance, life insurance, pregnancy leave, pension, paid vacation

Volunteers: 3

Interns: Yes
Length: Summer; 2-3 months during year
Duties: Interviewing veterans; research; fundraising; youth leadership directory; compiling veterans speakers bureau and information packets
Remuneration: Funding is being sought

Jobs advertised: An affirmative action employer, they advertise in newspapers, civic organizations, churches and through the mail.

To apply: Contact Amina Smith, Director

LAND INSTITUTE

2440 East Water Well Road
Salina, KS 67401
(913) 823-5376

President: Wes Jackson

Purpose: The goal of study and research at the Land Institute is to help transform agriculture in order to protect the long-term ability of the earth to support a variety of life and culture.

Methods of operation: Public education (40%), research (40%), publications (20%)

Recent issues and projects: (1) Ongoing agro-ecological research in perennial polycultures; (2) internships in sustainable agriculture; (3) agricultural and environmental public policy

Major publications: *The Land Report*, a 40-page journal, 3 times/year; annual research report; *Altars of Unknown Stone*; articles by Institute staff

Budget: $650,000

Funding: Foundations (67%), individual contributions (33%)

Staff: 10
3 Researchers
2 3/4 Farm Operators
1/2 Grassroots Fundraiser
1 Writer/Editor
1 Bookkeeper/Accountant
1/2 Typist
1/2 Foundation Fundraiser

Staff openings/year: 2

Work Week: 40 hours

Salary/year: $12-15,000 (Recent College Graduate); $15-25,000 (Graduate with advanced degree)

Benefits: Health insurance, pregnancy leave, paid vacation

Part-Time Employees: 3

Volunteers: Yes

Interns: 8-10
Length: 10 months
Duties: Research, education, physical labor
Remuneration: Tuition scholarships provided + $139 week stipend

---

LAND STEWARDSHIP PROJECT

14758 Ostlund Trail North
Marine on St. Croix, MN 55047
(612) 433-2770

Other Offices: Lewiston, MN; Montevideo, MN

Director: Ron Kroese, Co-Founder

Purpose: Promote an ethic of stewardship toward farmland and to foster a more sustainable agriculture system through on-farm research and demonstration, citizen action education and public policy development

Methods of operation: Community organizing (50%), public education (30%), direct action (20%)

Constituency: Urban consumers and stewardship-minded farmers in the Upper Midwest

Recent issues and projects: LSP's staff and board

of directors rely heavily on constituents involvement to shape goals, strategies and work plans. Currently, LSP's work is divided into four programs: 1) Sustainable Agriculture Education Program; 2) Metro Farm Program; 3) Policy and Development Program 4) Outreach and Comprehensive Development Program

Major publications: *The Land Stewardship Letter*; *Soil and Survival*; *Reshaping the Bottom Line*; *Excellence in Agriculture* (book and video); *Planting in the Dust* (video)

Budget: $900,000

Funding: Foundations (80%), individual contributions (10%), churches (10%)

Staff:
9 Organizers
2 Office Managers
1 Press Aide
1 Foundation Fundraiser
1 Issue Expert
1 Bookkeeper/Accountant
1 Grassroots Fundraiser

Staff openings/year: Varies

Work Week: 40 hours

Salary/year: $20,000 (Recent College Graduate); $25,000 (Graduate with advanced degree)

Benefits: Health insurance, life insurance, maternity/ paternity leave, pension, tuition reimbursement, disability insurance, paid vacation

Part-Time Employees: 3

Summer Employees: 2

Volunteers: 15

Interns: 2
Length: 6 months
Duties: Field work/organizing
Remuneration: Some paid, some not

Jobs advertised: Newspaper; direct mail; *Community Jobs*

To apply: Contact George Boody, Managing Director

LATINO CIVIL RIGHTS TASK FORCE (LCRT)

1815 Adams Mill Road, NW
Washington, DC 20009
(202) 332-1053

Director: Pedro Asites

Purpose: The LCRTF promotes and defends the civil rights of Latinos in the Washington area; it implements its missions through community organizing, policy analysis, media strategies, advocacy and collaborative efforts.

Methods of operation: Community organizing (20%), research (15%), lobbying (10%), direct action (10%), public education (10%), publications (5%), training and technical assistance (5%)

Constituency: First generation immigrants

Recent issues and projects: Recent projects include: anti-immigrant legislation; chapter formation; annual conference; and policy papers

Major publications: *The Latino Blueprint for Action*; *El Boletin*, newsletter

Budget: $175,000

Funding: Foundations (99%), individual contributions (1%)

Staff: 3
1 Office Manager
1 Executive Director
1 Researcher

Work Week: 40 hours

Salary/year: $18,000 (Recent College Graduate); $30,000 (Graduate with advanced degree)

Benefits: Health insurance, paid vacation

Part-Time Employees: 1

Summer Employees: 1

Volunteers: 15+

Interns: Varies
Length: Summer or semester
Duties: Project related (media, legal, community organizing, voter registration)
Remuneration: Possible

Jobs advertised: Newspapers, word-of-mouth

To apply: Contact Pedro Aviles, Executive Director

LAWYERS ALLIANCE FOR NEW YORK

99 Hudson Street
New York, NY 10013
(212) 219-1800

Director: Allen R. Bromberger

Purpose: Low-income housing development and neighborhood preservation; legal services to nonprofit organizations. Lawyers Alliance is the leading source of corporate, tax and real estate legal services available on a pro bono basis to nonprofit, community development, and child care organizations in New York City. Lawyers Alliance provides these services through an in-house staff of 9 attorneys and a roster of over 400 volunteers from over 100 law firms in the city.

Methods of operation: Training and technical assistance, publications, direct action, fundraising, and volunteer placement

Constituency: Attorneys; nonprofit organizations

Major publications: *Advising Nonprofits*; *Getting Organized*

Budget: $1,000,000

Funding: Foundation and law firm contributions, individual contributions

Staff: 16
9 Attorneys
1 Attorney Recruitment Coordinator
1 Pro Bono Program Assistant
1 Office Manager
1 Director of Development
1 Development Assistant
2 Secretaries/Receptionists

Staff openings/year: 4-5

Work Week: 40-50 hours

Salary/year: $Varies (Recent College Graduate); $Varies (Graduate with advanced degree)

Benefits: Health insurance, life insurance, pregnancy leave, pension, paid vacation, transit vouchers

Part-Time Employees: 2

Summer Employees: 2-3

Volunteers: 1

Interns: 2-3
Length: 3-4
Duties: Law student interns assist attorneys on research and writing projects
Remuneration: School sponsored stipends

Jobs advertised: Organizational newsletter; newspapers; nonprofit listings

To apply: Contact Allen Bromberger, Executive Director

LAWYERS ALLIANCE FOR NUCLEAR ARMS CONTROL

43 Charles Street, Suite 3
Boston, MA 02114
(617) 547-9319

Director: Anthony P. Sager

Purpose: LANAC was incorporated in 1981 in Massachusetts as a charitable corporation for the purpose of educating the legal community and the public concerning nuclear weapons and policy, and conducting other educational scientific, cultural and charitable activities that will contribute to reducing the threat of nuclear war.

Methods of operation: Training and technical assistance (40%), research (20%), litigation (20%), publications (20%)

Membership: Practicing attorneys, as well as judges, law professors, law students and paralegals

Recent issues and projects: The national office and the 43 chapters across the country sponsor a wide variety of programs. Ongoing activities include the "Right to Know" litigation project, which engages volunteer lawyers in Freedom of Information Act suits to keep the public informed about our government's nuclear weapons policies and programs; annual meetings between Lawyers Alliance delegates and representatives from the Association of Soviet Lawyers, etc.

Major publications: Working papers and joint papers from the annual U.S.-Soviet conferences; newsletters; *Lawyers Alliance Issue Briefs*; fact sheets

Budget: $300,000

Funding: Individual contributions (65%), foundations (35%)

Staff: 4
3 Campaign Managers
1 Attorney/Foundation Fundraiser
1 Bookkeeper/Accountant (part-time)

Staff openings/year: 1

Work Week: 40 hours

Salary/year: $14,000 (Recent College Graduate); $Varies (Graduate with advanced degree)

Benefits: Health insurance, paid vacation

Part-Time Employees: 1

Volunteers: 2

Interns: 2
Length: 1 year
Duties: Office assistance, help with mailings and press releases, etc.
Remuneration: Work-study only

Jobs advertised: Locally in newspapers

To apply: Contact Elizabeth A. Wilson, Program Director

LAWYERS COMMITTEE ON NUCLEAR POLICY

666 Broadway, Room 625
New York, NY 10012
(212) 674-7790

Director: Alyn Ware

Purpose: LCNP, founded in 1981, is a national, nonprofit educational association of lawyers and legal scholars concerned with legal aspects of the nuclear weapons debate. LCNP supports global security and the abolition of nuclear weapons through the promotion and strengthening of nonviolent legal mechanisms for resolving international disputes. LCNP coordinates lawyers around the globe on the nuclear weapons issue, sponsors research and education on legal aspects of the nuclear arms race and provides probono legal advice and assistance to the disarmament movement.

Methods of operation: Research (20%), publications (20%), litigation (20%), public education (20%), training and technical assistance (15%), lobbying (5%)

Constituency: Lawyers and other professionals

Major publications: Quarterly newsletter; *NUKEPORT: The Navy's Shell Game*; *Statement on the Illegality of Nuclear Warfare*; *Defending Civil Resistance Under International Law*; *Legal Aspects on a Nordic Nuclear Weapon Free Zone*; *Nuclear Weapons and Scientific Responsibility*; *The World Count Project on Nuclear Weapons and International Law*; *Abolishing the War System*; *The World Count Project Report*

Budget: $80,000

Funding: Foundations (60%), individual contributions (30%), events and sales (10%)

Staff: 3
1 Attorney
1 Media Liaison
1 Director

Staff openings/year: 1

Work Week: 40 hours

Salary/year: $30,000 (Graduate with advanced degree)

Benefits: Health insurance, paid vacation, pregnancy leave

Part-Time Employees: 1

Summer Employees: 1

Volunteers: Yes

Interns: Yes
Length: 3-6 months
Duties: Varied
Remuneration: Varied

LAWYERS' COMMITTEE FOR CIVIL RIGHTS UNDER LAW

1450 G Street, NW, Suite 400
Washington, DC 20005
(202) 662-8600

Other Offices: Boston, MA; Chicago, IL; Philadelphia, PA; San Francisco, CA; Los Angeles, CA; Denver, CO

Director: Barbara R. Arnwine

Purpose: The Committee is a national organization committed to provision of quality legal services for poor and minority individuals on major civil and Constitutional rights cases, both through representation of clients in suits alleging unlawful racial discrimination and by influencing the development and application of civil rights law. Staff and volunteer attorneys represent clients in cases involving voting rights, employment discrimination, education, housing, and minority business enterprise, and coordinate legal representation for political detainees in Southern Africa.

Methods of operation: Research, litigation, publications, public education, training and technical assistance

Constituency: Impoverished and minority individuals

Recent issues and projects: As part of our efforts to develop and maintain good law in the civil rights area, we regularly file *amicus curiae* briefs in the U.S. Supreme Court when cases raising important civil rights issues are accepted by the Court. We have also been involved as *amicus* before federal circuit and state courts in cases involving voting rights, upholding affirmative action remedies in employment, fair and affordable housing and the constitutionality of a city ordinance requiring a city retirement system to divest itself of stock in companies doing business in South Africa. The Southern Africa Project established the Commission on Independence for Namibia to monitor the 7-month process leading up to Namibia's election of a Constituent Assembly.

Major publications: Quarterly newsletter: *Committee Report*; annual report; Southern Africa Project Annual Report

Budget: $4,500,000

Funding: Foundations (39%), UN Trust Fund (24%), court awarded fees (14%), lawyers/law firms (12%), churches, CFC, etc. (7%), corporations (3%), individual contributions (1%), direct mail (1.05%)

Staff: 28
Includes:
13 Attorneys
2 Paralegals
5 Secretaries
3 Bookkeepers/Accountants
1 Office Manager
2 Development Assistants
1 Receptionist
1 Development Director

Staff openings/year: 2

Work Week: 37.5 hours

Salary/year: $Varies (Recent College Graduate); $Varies (Graduate with advanced degree)

Benefits: Health insurance, life insurance, pregnancy leave, paid vacation

Part-Time Employees: 1-2

Summer Employees: 1-2

Interns: 6-8
Length: 2-3 months
Remuneration: Salary schedule is competitive with most public interest, nonprofit, legal organizations

Jobs advertised: Newspapers; magazines; other public interest groups

To apply: Contact Ruby Sherrod Knox, Deputy Director of Administration

LEAGUE OF CONSERVATION VOTERS

1707 L Street, NW, Suite 550
Washington, DC 20036
(202) 785-8683

Other Offices: Portsmouth, NH

President: Jim Maddy

Purpose: To help elect pro-environment candidates to the U.S. House of Representatives and the Senate

Methods of operation: Public education (30%), research (30%), publications (20%), development and membership activities (20%)

Constituency: People interested in changing the makeup of Congress

Recent issues and projects: *1989 National Environmental Scorecard* - rating members of Congress on environmental commitment and working with campaigns of pro-environment candidates

Major publications: *National Environmental Scorecards*, 1970-92; Election Reports

Budget: $1,000,000

Funding: Individual contributions from direct mail, canvassing, telephone solicitation, etc.

Staff: 55
1 Political Director
1 Research Associate
1 Communications Director
1 Vice President
1 President
1 Chief Financial Officer
1 Office Manager
40 Canvass Staff
5 Interns
1 Bookkeeper
1 Deputy Development Director
1 Membership Director

Staff openings/year: 5-10

Work Week: 50 hours

Salary/year: $Varies (Recent College Graduate); $Varies (Graduate with advanced degree)

Benefits: Health insurance, paid vacation

Summer Employees: No

Interns: 5
Length: Summer internships of 6 months
Duties: Research work on publications and for

campaigns
Remuneration: $850/month

To apply: For canvassing in New Hampshire, contact Jay Daly, Canvass Manager

LEAGUE OF RURAL VOTERS
212 Third Avenue North, Suite 300
Minneapolis, MN 55401
(612) 379-3892

Other Offices: Hartington, NE

Director: Julie Ristau

Purpose: The League of Rural Voters works to improve the quality of life in rural America by educating rural citizens to become active in the political process.

Methods of operation: Public education (50%), community organizing (40%), publications (10%)

Constituency: Farmers, rural citizens, people involved in sustainable agriculture issues and others who share our goals of improving the quality of life in rural America

Recent issues and projects: During the 1988 elections, the League organized Rural Voter '88, a nationally coordinated drive to bring informed rural voters to the polls on election day to make the rural vote count. Also published a booklet entitled *Crisis By Design: A Brief Review of U.S. Farm Policy.* The League is currently working to educate rural citizens about the GATT talks (General Agreement on Tariffs and Trade) which have the ominous potential to supersede the 1990 Farm Bill. Toward that end the League has made so called "Trading Our Futures?" which they are promoting widely as a tool to educate people about the GATT talks. The League is also in the process of creating a high school curriculum on the GATT to be used in rural classrooms.

Major publications: Newsletter: *The Rural Voter Network News*; booklet: *Crisis By Design: A Brief Review of U.S. Farm Policy*

Funding: Foundations (95%), individual contributions (5%)

Staff: 3
1 Executive Director
1 Program Coordinator
1 Administrative Assistant

Staff openings/year: 1

Work Week: 40 hours

Salary/year: $12-15,000 (Recent College Graduate); $15-20,000 (Graduate with advanced degree)

Benefits: Health insurance, paid vacation

Part-Time Employees: 1

Volunteers: Yes

Interns: 1
Length: Negotiable
Duties: Varies with individual skills, interests
Remuneration: Dependent on funds raised via grants

Jobs advertised: Newspaper; local publications; *Community Jobs*

To apply: Contact Julie Ristau, Director

LEAGUE OF WOMEN VOTERS
1730 M Street, NW
Washington, DC 20036
(202) 429-1965

President: Becky Cain

Purpose: A nonpartisan political organization that encourages the informed and active participation of citizens in government and influences public policy through education and advocacy.

Methods of operation: Research, lobbying, litigation, publications, direct action, public education, training and technical assistance

Membership: 105,000 women and men

Recent issues and projects: Current priorities are to advocate for the voter, tackling toxics, Campaign for a Safer World, child care and housing.

Major publications: Bimonthly magazine: *The National Voter*; reports and guides on how to be politically effective, election services, debates, government, international relations, natural resources, social policy and public relations

Budget: $5,000,000

Funding: Individual contributions, foundations, direct mail, member dues

Staff: 52
10 Issue Experts
6 Lobbyists
5 Bookkeeper/Accountants
3 Writer/Editors
2 Organizers
2 Foundation Fundraisers
1 Attorney

1 Office Manager
1 Press Aide

Staff openings/year: 10

Work Week: 35 hours

Salary/year: $Varies (Recent College Graduate); $Varies (Graduate with advanced degree)

Benefits: Health insurance, pregnancy leave, credit union, pension, paid vacation

Part-Time Employees: Yes

Volunteers: Yes

Interns: 1-2
Length: Summer
Remuneration: Through Connecticut College (Board)

Jobs advertised: *Washington Post*; other organizations

To apply: Contact Sandra Bentzman, Personnel Director

Remarks: There are 1200 Local and State Leagues.

LEARNING ALLIANCE: OPTIONS FOR EDUCATION AND ACTION

494 Broadway
New York, NY 10012
(212) 226-7171

Other Offices: Toronto, CANADA

Director: David Levine

Purpose: To provide access to information, skills and resources to help to encourage cooperative action on a wide range (personal, community and social issues) towards a just and sustainable society.

Methods of operation: Public education (70%), training and technical assistance (15%), community organizing (10%), research (5%)

Constituency: General public, mostly from NY metropolitan area

Recent issues and projects: Current issues include: Social Justice; Environmental Justice; Multiculturalism; Indigenous Issues; Compassionate Action Network; Art and Culture; Women's Issues; Popular and Adult Education; Youth Programming; and Holistic and Community Health

Major publications: Learning Alliance catalog and catalog of audiotapes of programs

Budget: $250,000

Funding: Program fees (75%), foundations (20%), individual contributions (5%)

Staff: 5
2 1/2 Organizers
1 Office Manager
1 Administrative Assistant
1/4 Foundation Fundraiser
1/4 Campaign Manager

Staff openings/year: 1

Work Week: 50 hours

Salary/year: $18,000 (Recent College Graduate); $Varies (Graduate with advanced degree)

Benefits: Health insurance, paid vacation

Part-Time Employees: 1

Summer Employees: No

Volunteers: 20

Interns: 4
Length: 1-3 months
Duties: Program development, graphic arts, public relations, community outreach
Remuneration: Depends on time commitment (usually travel)

Jobs advertised: Local papers, networking

To apply: Contact David Levine

LEE COUNTY COOPERATIVE CLINIC

530 West Atkins Boulevard
Marianna, AR 72360
(501) 295-5225

Other Offices: Madison, AR; Lakeview, AR

Director: John Eason

Purpose: To deliver out-patient medical care to residents at affordable prices. Lee County was and remains one of the poorest counties in the U.S. Since the Clinic's founding in 1969, Lee County has seen infant deaths cut more than half, and Lee residents now live longer because of better health care and health education programs.

Methods of operation: Human services (86%), community organizing (7%), lobbying (5%), research (2%)

Constituency: Eighty-percent of patients are at or below poverty level. Ninety-eight percent come from the eastern Arkansas area. Seventy-percent are Black.

Recent issues and projects: Departments include: Medical, Dental, Child Development, Nutrition, Pharmacy, Transportation, and Environmental.

Budget: $1,500,000

Funding: Federal government (80%)

Staff: 50
Including:
8 Nurses
7 Finance Administrators
6 Drivers
5 Typists
4 Providers
2 Caseworkers
2 Researchers
2 Bookkeeper/Accountants
1 Press Aide
1 Foundation Fundraiser

Staff openings/year: 2-4

Work Week: 40 hours

Salary/year: $Varies (Recent College Graduate); $Varies (Graduate with advanced degree)

Benefits: Health insurance, pension, life insurance

Part-Time Employees: 5

Volunteers: 1

Jobs advertised: Local and state newspapers

To apply: Contact Clifton Collier, Marketing Coordinator

LEGAL ACTION CENTER

153 Waverly Place
New York, NY 10014
(212) 243-1313

Other Offices: Washington, DC

Director: Paul N. Samuels

Purpose: Legal Action Center works to end discrimination against people with criminal histories, substance abuse histories and those afflicted with HIV/AIDS. Provides direct legal services to clients, helps human service agencies solve legal and policy problems and educate policymakers about the issues affecting the communities they serve.

Methods of operation: Legal services (25%), research (10%), litigation (10%), publications (10%), community organizing (10%), direct action (10%), public education (10%), training and technical assistance (10%), lobbying (5%)

Constituency: We serve ex-offenders, persons with histories of drug or alcohol dependence, people with HIV/AIDS and the agencies providing them with health and other human services

Recent issues and projects: The Center's focus currently is on national and local AIDS and drug policy, technical assistance for AIDS service agencies and legal services for people with AIDS.

Major publications: Bimonthly newsletter: *Of Substance*; *Action Watch*; *Confidentiality: A Guide to the New Federal Regulations*; *AIDS: A Guide to Legal and Policy Issues*; *How to Get and Clean Up Your New York State Rap Sheet* (Spanish version available)

Budget: $1,300,000

Funding: State contracts, earned income (70%), foundations (20%), individual contributions (10%)

Staff: 20
7 Attorneys
3 Paralegals
3 Legal Secretaries
3 Policy Directors/Associates
1 Business Manager
1 Office Manager
1 Receptionist
1 Office Assistant

Work Week: 40 hours

Salary/year: $20,000 (Recent College Graduate); $40,000 (Graduate with advanced degree)

Benefits: Health insurance, life insurance, pregnancy leave, paid vacation

Part-Time Employees: 2

Summer Employees: 3 law students

Jobs advertised: Newspapers; university career placement offices

To apply: Contact Jamie Johnson, Manager of Administration and Finance

LEGAL ACTION CENTER FOR THE HOMELESS

27 West 24th Street, Room 600
New York, NY 10010
(212) 529-4240

Director: Douglas Lasdon

Purpose: Direct advocacy through soup kitchen legal clinics, class action lawsuits, community education

Methods of operation: Research, litigation, publications, human services, training and technical assistance

Constituency: Homeless people

Recent issues and projects: Sued the Mass Transit Authority for banning begging as violation of First Amendment; sued major grocery store chains for unlawful limitations on recycling cans

Major publications: *Below the Safety Net*, a study of soup kitchen users; *Services to Youth After Leaving Foster Care*; *NYC's Public Bathroom Crisis*

Budget: $450,000

Funding: Foundations (70%), individual contributions (15%), other (15%)

Staff: 9
4 Paralegals
4 Attorneys
1 Receptionist/Information Coordinator

Staff openings/year: 0-1

Work Week: 40 hours

Salary/year: $Varies (Recent College Graduate); $Varies (Graduate with advanced degree)

Benefits: Health insurance, life insurance, paid vacation

Summer Employees: 4

Volunteers: Yes

Interns: Yes
Length: Varies
Duties: Direct services, advocacy, representing homeless people

To apply: Contact Doug Lasdon

LEGAL AID SOCIETY OF DAYTON

211 South Main Street, Suite 300
Dayton, OH 45402
(513) 228-8088

Director: Gary Weston

Purpose: To provide legal services to the poor, seniors and the disabled.

Methods of operation: Litigation (90%), training and technical assistance (7%), public education (3%)

Recent issues and projects: Federal class action to improve Medicaid services in county; federal class action to improve conditions for public housing residents

Budget: $1,000,000

Funding: Legal Services Corporation (50%), interest on lawyers trust accounts (30%), foundations (20%)

Staff: 28
Including:
10 Attorneys
4 Legal Secretaries
4 Paralegals
10 Administrative Support Staff

Staff openings/year: 2

Work Week: 37.5 hours

Salary/year: $21,000 (Graduate with advanced degree)

Benefits: Health insurance, life insurance, pregnancy leave, tuition reimbursement, paid vacation

Volunteers: 4

Jobs advertised: *Clearinghouse Review*; Ohio State Legal Services Reports and Ohio State Bar Association Report

To apply: Contact Ellis Jacobs, Attorney

LEGAL AID SOCIETY OF ROANOKE VALLEY

416 Campbell Ave., SW
Roanoke, VA 24016
(703) 344-2088

Other Offices: Lexington, VA

Director: Henry L. Woodwared, Esq.

Purpose: The program provides a combination of individual client service and impact litigation intended to change legal and economic structures which exploit or discriminate against the poor.

Methods of operation: Litigation (70%), public education (20%), lobbying (5%), community organizing (5%)

Constituency: We serve low-income people of southwestern Virginia, with a client base of 37,300

Budget: $671,000

Funding: Foundations, individual contributions, other

Staff: 15
6 Attorneys
3 Paralegals
1 Office Manager
5 Legal Secretaries

Staff openings/year: Varies

Work Week: 37.5 hours

Salary/year: $24,000 (Graduate with advanced degree)

Benefits: Health insurance, paid vacation, life insurance, credit union, dental insurance, tax-deferred annuity with employer contributions

Part-Time Employees: None

Summer Employees: 1-3

Volunteers: 4

Interns: Varies
Length: Semester or summer
Duties: Research, draft pleadings, investigate, represent in administrative hearings
Remuneration: Students must provide own funding

Jobs advertised: Legal publications

To apply: Contact David D. Beidler, Esq., Hiring Coordinator

Remarks: Our service area is located in the lower Blue Ridge, and features some of Virginia's best scenery and outdoor recreational opportunities. The Blue Ridge Parkway passes through the city, and the Appalachian Trail lies just outside. Roanoke is a prosperous and energetic railroad, manufacturing and medical center with a surprising diversity of arts, cultural and entertainment resources. A wide variety of housing choices, from urban apartments to rural farms, wi within easy access of program offices.

LEGAL ASSISTANCE FOR SENIORS

1611 Telegraph Avenue, Suite 905
Oakland, CA 94612
(510) 832-3040

Director: Orah I. Young

Purpose: Providing legal services to Alameda County seniors, including: income maintenance (Social Security, Supplemental Security Income), health care (Medicare, Medi-Cal), subsidized housing, elder abuse, incapacity issues and guardianship. Also counseling on Medicare and supplemental health insurance.

Methods of operation: Direct action (35%), public education (25%), community organizing, Health Insurance Counseling and Advocacy Program (15%), human services (15%), litigation (10%)

Constituency: Alameda County residents over 60 years of age

Recent issues and projects: Grandparent Guardianship Project to help grandparents and great grandparents obtain custody of children whose parents cannot or will not care for them and obtain benefits for the children

Budget: $325,000

Funding: State, federal, local (74%), foundations (18%), individual contributions (8%)

Staff: 11
3 Attorneys
2 Paralegals
2 Office Managers
1 Executive Director
1 Organizer
1 Bookkeeper/Accountant
1 Typist

Staff openings/year: 2

Work Week: 37.5 hours

Salary/year: $16,000 (Recent College Graduate); $24,000 (Graduate with advanced degree)

Benefits: Health insurance, pension, pregnancy leave, paid vacation

Part-Time Employees: 3

Volunteers: 4

Interns: Yes
Length: 3-4 months
Duties: Law clerk; research, client interviews, casework with attorney supervision
Remuneration: Volunteer

Jobs advertised: Newspapers; postings sent to legal and social service agencies, career counseling centers, law schools

To apply: Contact Orah I. Young, Director

LEGAL ASSISTANCE FOUNDATION OF CHICAGO

343 South Dearborn Street, Suite 700
Chicago, IL 60604
(312) 341-1070

Director: Sheldon H. Roodman

Purpose: Provides free legal services in civil cases to eligible individuals and groups.

Major publications: Newsletters; docket of major litigation

Budget: $10,000,000

Funding: Legal Services Corporation (75%)

Staff: 191
85 Attorneys
51 Clerical
34 Paralegals
21 Other (Non-attorney professionals, Intake Specialists, etc.)

Staff openings/year: 5-10

Work Week: 37.5 hours

Salary/year: $30,000

Benefits: Health insurance, life insurance, family leave, paid vacation

Part-Time Employees: 7

Volunteers: 2

Interns: 20-25 law students
Length: Summer

Jobs advertised: Law schools; newspapers; *Clearinghouse Review*

To apply: Contact John Bouman, Supervisory Attorney

LEGAL ASSISTANCE OF THE FINGER LAKES

1 Franklin Square, P.O. Box 487
Geneva, NY 14456
(315) 781-1465

Director: C. Kenneth Perri

Purpose: The Legal Assistance of the Finger Lakes provides free legal services to low-income people with civil legal problems in a five county rural area. Priorities include: public assistance; food stamps; medicaid; social security; unemployment insurance benefits; housing; and child support. Spouse abuse divorces and consumer cases are handled through a pro-bono program that we administer.

Methods of operation: Litigation (100%)

Constituency: Our clients are low-income members of the communities in the five rural counties that we serve. Approximately 36,000 people qualify.

Recent issues and projects: Successfully litigated challenge to statutory imposition of durational residency requirement for receipt of full home relief benefits by newcomers to New York State; presenting series of trainings to private attorneys on elder law issues.

Budget: $650,000

Funding: Government grants, United Way

Staff: 11
8 Attorneys
1 Office Manager
2 Administrative Assistants

Staff openings/year: 0-1

Work Week: 35 hours

Salary/year: $26,500 (Graduate with advanced degree)

Benefits: Health insurance, pension, paid vacation, life insurance, credit union

Part-Time Employees: 3

Summer Employees: None

Volunteers: 4

Interns: 4
Length: 4
Duties: Conduct initial interview of new clients and provide advocacy services to clients at administrative levels
Remuneration: Volunteers or students able to secure own funding

Jobs advertised: Local newspapers

To apply: Contact C. Kenneth Perri, Managing Attorney

LEGAL COUNSEL FOR THE ELDERLY

601 E Street, NW, Building A, 4th Floor
Washington, DC 20049
(202) 434-2120

Director: Wayne Moore

Purpose: LCE operates a full service law office in noncriminal matters for DC residents 60+ and houses the DC Long-Term Care Ombudsman Program. Most LCE programs are national and focus on legal services, long-term care ombudsman services, public benefits and protective services.

Methods of operation: Litigation, publications, public education, training and technical assistance

Recent issues and projects: Recent projects include: training in substantive law; 9 statewide legal hotlines; national volunteer lawyers project; testing new ways of providing legal services; support in guardianship issues and financial management

Major publications: *Disability Practice Manual, Protective Services Manual, Elder Law Forum,* newsletter, *Medicare Practice Manual, Planning for Incapacity, Organizing Your Future*

Funding: Local and federal government grants, AARP, Legal Services Corporation, foundations

Staff: 49
Includes:
Attorneys
Paralegals
Administrative Staff
Support Staff
Project Specialists

Staff openings/year: 2-5

Work Week: 35 hours

Salary/year: $31,600-35,375 (Recent College Graduate); $34,700 and up (Graduate with advanced degree)

Benefits: Health insurance, life insurance, pension, credit union, tuition reimbursement, parental leave, dental subsidy

Part-Time Employees: 12

Summer Employees: Yes

Volunteers: 50

Interns: Yes
Length: Semester
Duties: Assist in broad range of legal work
Remuneration: Stipend, work-study

Jobs advertised: Newspaper; selected mailings

To apply: For internships, contact Ms. Kathleen Harrigan; for attorney positions, contact Mr. Jan May; for writer, editor and trainer positions, contact Ms. Ann Crawley.

LEGAL ENVIRONMENTAL ASSISTANCE FOUNDATION

1115 North Gradsen Street
Tallahassee, FL 32303
(904) 681-2591

Director: B. Suzi Ruhl, J.D., M.P.H.

Purpose: Headquartered in Tallahassee, Florida, LEAF is a public interest law firm dedicated to defending our right to a pollution-free environment. LEAF shows citizens from Alabama, Florida and Georgia how to identify polluters, make a positive impact on government decisions and use the law constructively. LEAF does not charge for its services.

Methods of operation: Research, litigation, direct action, public education, training and technical assistance, publications

Membership: Membership consists primarily of those citizens to whom LEAF has provided services and those who are interested in protecting the South's environmental and public health.

Recent issues and projects: Successfully prevented the location of a hazardous waste facility in four rural north Florida counties; working with citizens to prevent the improper siting of a hazardous waste incinerator in Georgia

Major publications: Quarterly newsletter: *LEAF BRIEFS*

Budget: $500,000

Funding: Foundations (65%), individual contributions (35%)

Staff: 10
5 Attorneys
1 Program Director/Administrator
1 Development Director
1 Paralegal
1 Office Manager
1 Secretary

Staff openings/year: 0-1

Work Week: 40 hours

Salary/year: $Varies (Recent College Graduate); $Varies (Graduate with advanced degree)

Benefits: Health insurance, life insurance, pregnancy leave, pension, paid vacation

Part-Time Employees: 0

Volunteers: 2

Interns: No paid internship program at this time

Jobs advertised: Local paper and job service

To apply: Contact Cynthia Valencia, Vice President for Programs

LEGAL SERVICES CORPORATION OF IOWA

315 East Fifth Street, Suite 22
Des Moines, IA 50309
(515) 243-2151

Other Offices: Cedar Rapids, IA; Council Bluffs, IA; Dubuque, IA; Iowa City, IA; Mason City, IA; Ottumwa, IA; Sioux City, IA; Waterloo, IA

Director: Dennis Groenenboom

Purpose: LSCI provides free legal help to low-income people throughout the state. Types of cases handled include income maintenance, housing, family abuse, health care, individual rights, consumer and education.

Methods of operation: Litigation (90%), publications (5%), public education (5%)

Constituency: Free legal services are provided to low-income Iowans who meet income and asset criteria.

Recent issues and projects: LSCI is involved in class action lawsuits, as well as single client representation on all issues listed above.

Major publications: LSCI has a community legal education component which publishes over 40 "Know Your Rights" booklets on various legal topics.

Budget: $3,000,000

Funding: Government grants and contracts (90%), individual contributions (5%), United Ways/foundations (5%)

Staff: 79
48 Attorneys
9 Non-Attorney Professionals
22 Support Staff

Staff openings/year: 5-10

Work Week: 37.5 hours

Salary/year: $Varies (Recent College Graduate); $20,400 (Graduate with advanced degree)

Benefits: Health insurance, life insurance, paid vacation, pregnancy leave

Part-Time Employees: 4

Volunteers: 20-25

Interns: 8-10, usually through law school clinical programs
Length: 1 semester
Duties: Representation of clients, research, writing
Remuneration: None

Jobs advertised: Local, state and national publications

To apply: Contact Dennis Groenenboom, Executive Director

LEGAL SERVICES FOR CHILDREN, INC.

1254 Market Street, 3rd Floor
San Francisco, CA 94102
(415) 863-3762

Director: Christopher N. Wu

Purpose: Founded in 1975 as the nation's first and still only comprehensive direct service law firm solely for children and youth. Casework includes representing children in the areas of abuse and neglect, guardianship, emancipation, custody, special education and mental health.

Methods of operation: Litigation (75%), human services (15%), training and technical assistance (10%)

Constituency: Children and youth under age 18 in the San Francisco Bay Area

Recent issues and projects: Ongoing projects include: (1) Runaway and Status Offender Project, providing legal and related support services to runaway and "throwaway" children; (2) The Teamed Advocacy Project, utilizing teams of attorneys and social workers to advise and represent abused, neglected and handicapped children; (3) The Guardianship Project, providing advice and representation to children living with responsible nonparent caretakers; (4) The children's AIDS/HIV Project, providing comprehensive legal resources for children and their caretakers infected and/or affected by AIDS/HIV

Major publications: *The Child's Advocate* newsletter; *Guardianship Manual and Pamphlet*; *Emancipation*

Budget: $350,000

Funding: Government (30%), attorney fees (30%), foundations (25%), direct mail (10%), individual contributions (5%)

Staff: 8
3 Attorneys
2 Caseworkers
1 Office Manager
1 Typist
1 Bookkeeper/Accountant

Staff openings/year: 1-2

Work Week: 40 hours

Salary/year: $23,000

Benefits: Health insurance, pregnancy leave, paid vacation

Part-Time Employees: 2

Interns: 3
Length: 3 months
Duties: Law students and social work graduate students who assist attorneys and social workers in all aspects of practice
Remuneration: Usually working for school credit or funded by outside foundation

Jobs advertised: Notices sent to other legal and youth serving agencies; local classified ads; placement offices

To apply: Contact Christopher N. Wu, Executive Director

LEGAL SERVICES OF GREATER MIAMI

3000 Biscayne Blvd., Suite 500
Miami, FL 33137
(305) 576-0080

Director: Marcia K. Cypen

Purpose: The Legal Services of Greater Miami provides free civil legal assistance to persons with low-income in Dade and Monroe counties in areas of housing, public benefits, elder law, homeless, immigration, AIDS, family/juvenile, disaster legal assistance and community economic development.

Methods of operation: Litigation (85%), public education (10%), lobbying (5%)

Recent issues and projects: Current projects include: the Disaster Legal Assistance Project which provided free legal assistance to victims of Hurricane Andrew; AIDS Legal Advocacy Project which provides free civil legal assistance to HIV+ persons; and a homeless unit which provides free civil legal assistance to homeless individuals and families in Dade County

Budget: $6,000,000

Funding: Federal/state/local grants (95%), foundations (5%)

Staff: 105
54 Attorneys
10 Paralegals
1 Office Manager
2 Bookkeepers/Accountants
15 Secretaries
3 Administrative Assistants
8 Intake Paralegals
5 Receptionists/Switchboard Operators
5 Office Clerks
2 Computer Operations

Staff openings/year: 3

Work Week: 35 hours

Salary/year: $25,000 (Graduate with advanced degree)

Benefits: Health insurance, paid vacation, life insurance, credit union, dental insurance, disability insurance

Part-Time Employees: 5

Summer Employees: None

Volunteers: 20

Interns: 10-30
Length: Semester or summer
Duties: Client intake, legal research and writing, drafting pleadings, court appearances (certified interns)
Remuneration: Work-study, public interest grants or volunteers

Jobs advertised: Local newspapers, professional journals

To apply: Attorney applicants: Maria Soto, Senior Attorney. Support staff: Akilah Toure, Deputy Director

LEGAL SERVICES OF MIDDLE TENNESSEE, INC.

211 Union Street, Suite 800
Nashville, TN 37201
(615) 244-6610

Other Offices: Gallatin, TN; Clarksville, TN; Murfreesboro, TN

Director: Ashley T. Wiltshire, Jr.

Purpose: To enforce, enhance and defend the legal rights of low-income and elderly people. We provide legal advocacy and education to obtain necessities such as health care, housing, income, family safety, child support and access to basic goods and services.

Methods of operation: Litigation, lobbying, publications, public education, training and technical assistance

Constituency: Low-income and elderly

Major publications: Self-help pamphlets; *The Docket Report*; *Nursing Home Insurance*

Budget: $1,600,000

Funding: Government, individual contributions, foundations

Staff: 41
18 Support Staff
13 Attorneys
4 Paralegals
2 Bookkeepers/Accountants
1 Executive Director
1 Development Coordinator
1 Community Educator
1 Executive Secretary

Staff openings/year: 3

Work Week: 40 hours

Salary/year: $Varies (Recent College Graduate); $Varies (Graduate with advanced degree)

Benefits: Health insurance, pension, life insurance, credit union, paid vacation, dental insurance, long-term disability

Part-Time Employees: Yes

Volunteers: Yes

Interns: None currently, but willing to accept applications

Jobs advertised: For attorneys: *Clearinghouse Review*, law schools, National Legal Aid and Defenders Association; for support staff: locally

To apply: Contact Patricia M. Apuzzo, Executive Secretary

LEGAL SERVICES ORGANIZATION OF INDIANA MIGRANT FARMWORKER PROJECT

151 North Delaware Street, Suite 1800
Indianapolis, IN 46204
(317) 631-9410

Director: Nancy Hale

Purpose: Provide legal services (civil, not criminal) to migrant farmworkers in Indiana

Methods of operation: Litigation and legal advice (85%), public education (10%), publications (5%)

Constituency: Migrant farmworkers who work in Indiana

Recent issues and projects: Immigration, Social Security credits/tax issues; workplace issues (minimum wage violations, unpaid wages, etc.)

Budget: $121,000

Funding: Legal Services Corporation (100%)

Staff: 3
1 Director
1 Support Staff
1 Paralegal

Staff openings/year: 0-1

Work Week: 40+ hours

Benefits: Health insurance, life insurance, family leave, credit union, paid vacation, (not for summer employees)

Summer Employees: 2-3

Volunteers: Occasionally

Interns: None currently, but willing to accept applications

Jobs advertised: Notices sent to Hispanic/bilingual, contacts in Indiana

To apply: Contact Nancy Hale

ELECTORAL ACTION AP)

on Ave.
d, CT 06105
(203) 249-4620

Director: Lynn Ide

Purpose: Elect progressives to municipal, state and national office; recruit and train campaign workers; help member organizations make the most of their political power.

Methods of operation: Electoral organizing, coalition building, training and technical assistance

Constituency: LEAP is a coalition organization made up of labor unions, citizen groups, civil rights groups, environmentalists, and women's organizations.

Recent issues and projects: Helped to elect the first Black mayor of New Haven and Third Party city council members to Hartford City Council. Issues: tax reform, health care, reproductive rights, campaign finance reform

Budget: $200,000

Staff: 3

Work Week: 50 hours

Salary/year: $20,000

Benefits: Pregnancy leave, child care (a little higher salary), paid vacation

Part-Time Employees: 4

Summer Employees: 1-3

Volunteers: 1

Interns: 1-2
Length: 3-6 months
Duties: Organizing
Remuneration: Some paid, some unpaid, depending on need

To apply: Contact Lynne Ide, Director

LESBIAN MOTHERS NATIONAL DEFENSE FUND

P.O. Box 21567
Seattle, WA 98111
(206) 325-2643

Director: Jerry Sayward

Purpose: The Lesbian Mothers National Defense Fund is a volunteer resource network which fights discrimination against lesbian and bisexual mothers. The primary goal of LMNDF is to secure fair judgements in child custody/visitation disputes based on the best interests of the children. LMNDF provides information to judges, attorneys, expert witnesses, caseworkers and parents, so that they will recognize that sexual orientation has nothing to do with a woman's ability to effectively parent.

Methods of operation: Research, publications, community organizing, public education, training and technical assistance

Constituency: Lesbian and Bisexual mothers and their children

Recent issues and projects: Recent projects include: Lavender Ribbon Project, to raise public awareness of parents and children separated by bigotry; pamphlet series on issues for lesbian families; and "Adopt-A-Mother" project to help lesbian mothers in custody disputes

Major publications: *Mom's Apple Pie*, quarterly newsletter

Budget: $5,000

Funding: Individual contributions (100%)

Part-Time Employees: None

Summer Employees: None

Volunteers: 5

Interns: 2
Length: 10 weeks
Duties: Legal or psychological literature search, writing handbooks on special topics, grantwriting, public information
Remuneration: Reimbursement for expenses

Jobs advertised: College internship programs

To apply: Contact Jerry Sayward, Director

LIBRARY THEATRE, INC.

6925 Willow Street, NW
Washington, DC 20012
(202) 291-4800

Other Offices: Bethesda, MD; Hyattsville, MD

Director: Cherry Adler

Purpose: Library Theatre produces theatre and media programs to educate and entertain children and their families. Library Theatre uses its programming not only to enrich children culturally, but also to address social and educational issues. For example, Library Theatre's programs have focused on peer pressure, drug abuse, the importance of hard work in achieving success, overcoming disabilities and gender stereotypes, and other issues which concern children.

Methods of operation: Public education (90%), publications (10%)

Constituency: Elementary school-aged children, their teachers and families

Recent issues and projects: Books Alive and Summer Storybuilders touring reading motivation musicals; *Delia and the Demon* drug abuse prevention book; performance series for children

Major publications: Newsletter: *Library Theatre News*; *BOOKS ALIVE Classroom Guides*; *Delia and the Demon* drug abuse prevention book

Budget: $350,000

Funding: Earned income (50%), government and corporations (25%), foundations (15%), individual contributions (5%)

Staff: 6
4-8 Contracted Actors
2 Administrators
2 Issue Experts
1-2 Contracted Stage Managers
1 Office Manager
1 Foundation Fundraiser

Staff openings/year: 2

Work Week: 40-50 hours

Salary/year: $15,000 (Recent College Graduate); $18,000+ (Graduate with advanced degree)

Benefits: Health insurance, paid vacation

Part-Time Employees: Yes

Summer Employees: Yes

Volunteers: 20+

Interns: Yes
Length: Semester or summer
Duties: Varied
Remuneration: Varied

Jobs advertised: Classified ads and ads in cultural/ educational newsletters

To apply: Contact Mary Cichello Beck, Associate Director

LIFE OF THE LAND
19 Niolopa Place
Honolulu, HI 96817
(808) 595-3903

Manager: Annie Szvetecz

Purpose: LOL advocates for the environment with administrative, legislative and judicial initiatives, research and action.

Methods of operation: Public education (50%), lobbying (5%), litigation (25%), research (10%), direct action (10%)

Constituency: Hard-core environmentalists

Recent issues and projects: Water pollution law enforcement, overdevelopment/tourism, grassroots education program, native forests/biodiversity, shoreline protection and coral reefs

Major publications: Quarterly newsletter

Budget: $15,000

Funding: Individual contributions (100%)

Part-Time Employees: 1

Volunteers: Yes

Interns: Yes
Length: 1-3 months
Duties: Research issues, write reports/testimony/legislation, education program
Remuneration: Volunteer

Jobs advertised: Through local university

To apply: Contact Intern Coordinator

Remarks: One of Hawaii's earliest and most vocal environmental groups, Life of the Land is a small, effective group with a big reputation. Our Board of Directors consists of several lawyers, legislative lobbyists, planners and scientists who pursue projects, mostly independently, and on a volunteer basis. Interns focus on one issue, and have the chance to make a very real contribution towards a cleaner, healthier world.

LINCOLN FILENE CENTER
Tufts University
Medford, MA 02155
(617) 628-5000

Director: Professor Robert Hollister

Purpose: The Center's mission is to empower

people to participate in democratic institutions to their fullest potential.

Methods of operation: Research, publications, training and technical assistance, public education

Recent issues and projects: National Citizen Participation Development Project, funded by the Ford Foundation, research on citizen participation efforts in five cities translated into recommendations for further efforts. Global Action Network - computerized environmental information, education and communication system. Eyes on the Prize Institute, helping teachers incorporate the Eyes series into teaching about civil rights. Institute for Management and Community Development, a week-long summer institute convening community activists.

Major publications: *New England Environmental Network Newsletter*; *Directions for Democracy* forthcoming; *Teaching and Training about Nonprofit Boards*; *Quest for Funds: An Insider's Guide to Corporate and Foundation Funding*

Budget: $500,000

Funding: Courses (50%), foundations (35%), individual contributions (15%)

Staff: 6
4 Organizers
1 Office Manager
1 Director

Staff openings/year: 3 p-t

Work Week: 35 hours

Salary/year: $30,000 (Graduate with advanced degree)

Benefits: Health insurance, life insurance, pension, credit union, tuition reimbursement, paid vacation

Part-Time Employees: 6

Volunteers: 3

Interns: 6
Length: 1-2 semesters
Duties: Research, organizing conferences and training
Remuneration: University work-study money

Jobs advertised: Posted at the university. Listed in the *Boston Globe*.

To apply: Contact Robert M. Hollister, Director

LIVING STAGE THEATRE COMPANY

6th and Main Avenue, SW
Washington, DC 20024
(202) 554-9066

Director: Robert Alexander

Purpose: Living Stage is a nonprofit, professional theater company which utilizes improvisational theater techniques in a performance/workshop format. Works with groups of youth and adults in the inner city, helping them to rediscover their creativity, thereby helping them to make more positive life choices.

Methods of operation: Human services (90%), training and technical assistance (10%)

Recent issues and projects: Focus on Conflict Resolution; special project with the Mental Health Commission for emotionally disturbed youths; advocacy for the arts in drug/alcohol prevention; residency workshops

Major publications: *Improvisational Theater for the Classroom* curriculum guide; several videos on issues such as drug abuse, poverty, teenage motherhood, physical disabilities

Budget: $650,000

Funding: Individual contributions, foundations (60%), earned income (40%)

Staff: 17
5 Actor/Educators
5 Production Staff
4 Administrative Assistants
1 Musical Director
1 Director
1 Associate Director

Staff openings/year: 2-4

Work Week: 40-60 hours

Salary/year: $15,000 (Recent College Graduate); $17,000 (Graduate with advanced degree)

Benefits: Health insurance, pension, paid vacation, pregnancy leave

Part-Time Employees: 1

Summer Employees: 1-2

Volunteers: 2-3

Interns: 2-3
Length: 1 year
Duties: Varied

Remuneration: $75 per week

Jobs advertised: Production positions are advertised in local publications; acting positions, in national trade publications and mailings to training schools

To apply: For acting positions, contact Robert Alexander, Director; for administration, contact Catherine Irwin, Managing Director; for production, contact Kelly Jerome, Production Manager.

LIVINGSTON ECONOMIC ALTERNATIVES IN PROGRESS, INC. (LEAP)

P.O. Box 246, Old City Hall
Livingston, KY 40445
(606) 453-9800

Director: Bob Haduch

Purpose: LEAP is a community-based, nonprofit group made up of low-income Eastern Kentuckians working together to empower people of Rockcastle County area.

Methods of operation: Direct action (50%), training and technical assistance (30%), community organizing (20%)

Constituency: Low-income men and women in Rockcastle County, Kentucky

Recent issues and projects: Opportunities for Women, hands-on training for women in the area; Sweet Sorghum Project- farmers are encouraged to grow sweet sorghum instead of tobacco, since sorghum production does not involve the back-breaking labor, massive amounts of chemical fertilizer and potential health hazards of tobacco growing; members of the Central Appalachian Peoples Federal Credit Union; Heifer Project International, training in sound livestock and crop management techniques, and distributes sheep, milk goats and fruit trees to qualified low-income farm families; farmers market; community involvement

Budget: $100,000

Funding: Product sales (79%), foundations (20%), direct mail (1%)

Staff: 1
1 Executive Director

Work Week: 40-60 hours

Benefits: Health insurance, credit union

Part-Time Employees: 3

Volunteers: 1

Jobs advertised: Word of mouth; *Appalachian Reader*; *Community Jobs*; local newspapers

To apply: Contact Ina Taylor, Executive Director

Remarks: We hire local people exclusively.

LOS ANGELES REGIONAL FAMILY PLANNING COUNCIL, INC. (LARFPC)

3600 Wilshire Boulevard, Suite 600
Los Angeles, CA 90010
(213) 386-5614

Director: Margie Fites Seigle

Purpose: LARFPC is a private, nonprofit agency which serves as an umbrella agency for the delivery of government-subsidized family planning services in Los Angeles County. Receives state and federal funds and allocates them to agencies throughout the County which provides family planning-related care to low-income clients. It provides fiscal monitoring, quality assurance, training, data processing and other services to delegate agencies. They are committed to increasing the accessibility and availability of reproductive health services to all persons regardless of income.

Methods of operation: Research, human services, public relations, public education, training and technical assistance

Constituency: System-wide clients are mostly women, most of whom have incomes below 200% of the Federal Poverty Level. Seventy-percent are Hispanic, African-American or members of other ethnic groups.

Recent issues and projects: Because California now ranks #1 in teen births, and the numbers of teens with sexually-transmitted diseases is growing at an alarming rate, LARFPC has focused a great deal of attention on increasing the numbers of teens at our clinics. LARFPC is also currently conducting research studies on a new spermicide and a new condom, as well as on the side-effects of the IUD. They are also implementing a new program which will assess and implement ways that family planning agencies can better serve the disabled community.

Major publications: *Basic Health Worker Manual*, an introductory guide for family planning clinic workers; biannual brochure of educational programs; LARFPC library newsletter; annual report

Budget: $20,000,000

Funding: State and federal grants (100%)

Staff: 46
9 Secretaries
6 Managers
7 Trainers/Health Educators
5 Bookkeepers/Accountants
6 Researchers
5 Data Processors
5 Tech Assistance/Quality Assurance Staff
1 Assistant to the Executive Director
1 Human Resources Coordinator
1 Purchasing Person

Staff openings/year: 6

Work Week: 40 hours

Salary/year: $29-40,000 (Recent College Graduate); $33-55,000 (Graduate with advanced degree)

Benefits: Health insurance, life insurance, pregnancy leave, pension, credit union, paid vacation, tuition reimbursement, dental insurance, parking allowance

Part-Time Employees: 2

Summer Employees: Occasionally 1

Volunteers: 6

Interns: Yes; occasionally
Length: Depends on situation
Duties: Depends on situation
Remuneration: Federally funded Title 10 Intern Program, stipend available for graduate students

Jobs advertised: Newspaper; other community agency networking; Universities participating in intern programs

To apply: Contact Sima Michaels, Associate Director

LOS ANGELES WOMEN'S FOUNDATION

6030 Wilshire Boulevard, Suite 303
Los Angeles, CA 90036
(213) 938-9828

Director: Jean T. Conger

Purpose: The Los Angeles Women's Foundation is dedicated to reshaping the status of women and girls through responsive philanthropy. The Foundation provides grants, training and management assistance to community-based organizations serving women and girls in Los Angeles County.

Methods of operation: Grantmaking, research, public education, training and technical assistance

Constituency: Foundations, corporations and individuals interested in breaking down the barriers to women's self-sufficiency

Recent issues and projects: We have awarded over $1,000,000 in grants and have provided management assistance to over 250 organizations.

Major publications: Newsletter: *Voice*, published twice yearly; annual report

Budget: $670,000

Funding: Individual contributions, foundations, direct mail

Staff: 6
1 Executive Director
1 Program Director
1 Administrative Assistant
1 Development Director
1 Development Assistant
1 Community Outreach Coordinator

Staff openings/year: 1

Work Week: 40 hours

Salary/year: $28,000

Benefits: Health insurance, paid vacation

Part-Time Employees: 1

Volunteers: 300

Interns: 1-2
Length: 3 months minimum
Duties: Research on issues affecting women and girls
Remuneration: Unpaid; mileage reimbursement

Jobs advertised: Job announcements are sent to nonprofit organizations, to employment offices and to grantees. Occasionally advertise in newspapers.

To apply: Contact Jean Conger, Executive Director

LOS NINOS

9765 Marloni Drive, Suite 105
San Ysidro, CA 92173
(619) 661-6912

Other Offices: Calexico, CA

Director: Roque Barros

Purpose: To improve the quality of life for Mexican children and their families, and to simultaneously provide education on the benefits of self-help community development through cultural interaction.

Methods of operation: Public education (30%), training and technical assistance (30%), human services (20%), community organizing (10%), research (5%), publications (5%)

Constituency: Newsletter recipients and Education Program participants

Recent issues and projects: (1) Teach agriculture and ecology; (2) provide nutrition and health programs

Major publications: Newsletter, 4 times a year; Nutrition Manual; Agricultural Manual

Budget: $500,000

Staff: 60
4 Organizers
1 Executive Director
1 Office Manager
6 Field Experts
48 Promoters

Staff openings/year: 1

Work Week: 40 hours

Salary/year: $Varies (Recent College Graduate); $Varies (Graduate with advanced degree)

Benefits: Health insurance, pregnancy leave, paid vacation

Part-Time Employees: No

Interns: 2
Length: 1 year
Duties: Teaching and administrative
Remuneration: Free room and board, $50.00 stipend

Jobs advertised: Universities

To apply: Contact Graciela Cueva

LOUISIANA CONSUMERS LEAGUE

251 Florida Street, Suite 310
Baton Rouge, LA 70801
(504) 344-7416

Director: David Czernik

Purpose: The League's main purpose is public interest lobbying and consumer education. They represent consumers in the legislature. Their main issues are auto insurance reform, worker privacy rights, fair phone rates, health care access and credit consumer rights.

Methods of operation: Lobbying (30%), human services (20%), research (10%), publications (10%), community organizing (10%), public education (10%), direct action (5%), training and technical assistance (5%)

Constituency: Low to middle income consumers; professionals with consumer perspective; seniors

Recent issues and projects: (1) Insurance Reform Campaign - draft legislation to confront industry marketplace abuses, publish consumer insurance buying guides; (2) Worker Privacy Rights Project - research abuse of individual rights by corporations, draft legislation; (3) Assorted marketplace surveys; (4) Created Injured Workers Union to combat computer database blacklisting, unfair workers compensation law/system; (5) Citizens for Auto Reform; (6) Consumers Coalition for Realistic Insurance

Major publications: Newsletter: *Louisiana Consumer*; *Auto Insurance Consumer Buying Guide*; *Health Insurance Consumer Buying Guide*; *Toy Safety Consumer Buying Guide*; *Consumer Advocate's Guide to a Vulnerable Economy*; brochures on landlord/tenant issues, small claims court, information directory and Lemon Law information

Budget: $85,000

Funding: Individual contributions (60%), foundations (30%), direct mail (10%)

Staff: 1

Staff openings/year: 1

Work Week: 60 hours

Salary/year: $13,500 (Recent College Graduate); $16,000 (Graduate with advanced degree)

Summer Employees: 1-2

Volunteers: Yes

Interns: Yes; several throughout year
Length: 2-3 months
Duties: Project-oriented; established after consulting student with professor
Remuneration: No compensation, unless special grant or contribution allows

Jobs advertised: Informal network

To apply: Contact David Czernik, Executive Director

Remarks: Telephone canvassers/organizers are needed, with salary based on percentage of funds raised. College students who are willing to organize groups on campuses are needed. Will train organizers.

LULAC NATIONAL EDUCATIONAL SERVICE CENTERS (LNESC)

777 North Capitol Street, NE, Suite 305
Washington, DC 20002
(202) 408-0060

Other Offices: Los Angeles, CA; San Francisco, CA; Denver, CO; Corpus Christi, TX; Chicago, IL; Kansas City, MO; Miami, FL; Albuquerque, NM; Philadelphia, PA; Houston, TX

Director: Richard Roybal

Purpose: Nonprofit organization established to improve the educational condition of the Hispanic community in the United States. Works with both business and government to initiate educational programs at the local and national level. LULAC is the League of United Latin American Citizens.

Methods of operation: Human services (100%)

Constituency: 100,000 Hispanic U.S. citizens

Recent issues and projects: LNESC counsels 18,000 high school students each year at 10 service centers, encouraging them to go on to college; gives over $500,000 in scholarships; leadership seminars; and reading programs

Major publications: *Opportunity to Lead* newsletter for Hispanic Leadership Opportunity Program

Budget: $2,700,000

Funding: Government (60%), individual contributions (40%)

Staff: 69
40 Caseworkers
12 Office Managers
12 Administrative Assistants
2 Bookkeepers/Accountants
1 Talent Search Coordintor
1 Research Developer
1 Special Programs Coordinator

Staff openings/year: 10

Work Week: 40 hours

Salary/year: $16,000 (Recent College Graduate); $18,000 (Graduate with advanced degree)

Benefits: Health insurance, life insurance, paid vacation

Part-Time Employees: 11

Summer Employees: 5

Volunteers: 20

Interns: 2
Length: 3 months
Duties: Assist program coordinators
Remuneration: Non-paid

Jobs advertised: Newspaper; mailings to similar organizations

To apply: Contact Brent Wilkes, Special Programs Coordinator

Remarks: LNESC is service-oriented and does very little research and lobbying. We implement the largest Talent Search program funded by the Department of Education. LNESC offers concerned individuals an excellent opportunity to become directly involved in the advancement of Hispanic education.

LUTHERAN VOLUNTEER CORPS

1226 Vermont Avenue, NW
Washington, DC 20005
(202) 387-3222

Director: Christine Bekemeier

Purpose: The Lutheran Volunteer Corps is a one-year program whose purpose is to provide participants with experience working for social justice, living simply and living with others committed to justice. All jobs and living situations are based in the inner city.

Methods of operation: Depending on the placement, the volunteer could be involved in almost any of these activities: research, lobbying, litigation, publications, human services, community organizing, direct action, public education and training and technical assistance.

Constituency: Open to people of all Christian traditions over age 21. The 1993-94 Volunteer Corps ranges in age from 21 to 60.

Recent issues and projects: Placement agencies include: homeless shelters; health clinics; human rights and women's rights organizations; food banks; alternative schools; environmental, food policy and energy-related advocacy organizations; community organizing, refugee and sanctuary-related organizations; and soup kitchens, among others. Volunteers are placed in Baltimore, MD, Chicago, IL, Milwaukee, WI and Wilmington, DE, Washington, DC and St. Paul, Minneapolis.

Major publications: Tri-annual newsletter: *Esprit de Corps*; volunteers in publication-oriented agencies are often contributing members of their organization's written works.

Budget: $208,000

Funding: Foundations, individual contributions, churches

Staff: 5

Work Week: 40-45 hours

Part-Time Employees: 1

Volunteers: Entire corps (70)

Jobs advertised: National publications; various church avenues; national campus recruiting visits; local presentations

To apply: Contact Lisa Wenger, Recruitment Coordinator

Remarks: The LVC program runs from August to August each year. Applications for the program are available after the first of December and placement matches are completed by July 15th. Volunteers are matched with agencies through a mutual selection process of interviewing, and live with other volunteers for their program year. The shared living experience of the program is considered as important to the year as the workplace assignment.

MADRE

121 West 27th Street, Room 301
New York, NY 10001
(212) 627-0444

Director: Vivian Stromberg

Purpose: To connect women and children internationally through friendship and skills exchange and humanitarian aid and to understand the relationship between U.S. and abroad.

Constituency: Multicultural; cross-class; women and men

Recent issues and projects: Issues include women and children's human rights, development and empowerment. Recent projects include: Sisters Without Borders an international gender-based skills exchange; Youth Leadership Through the Arts, artist in residence program in the public schools; U.S. Women's Human Rights Program, initiating the development of a nationally coordinated U.S. women's human rights agenda; Voices of the Children, Voices de los Ninos, Children's Art Exhibit; and humanitarian aid and support for health centers, social services, educational projects in Central America, the Carribbean, the Middle East and other areas internationally

Major publications: Quarterly newsletter

Budget: $850,000

Funding: Direct mail (55%), foundations (25%), individual contributions (20%)

Staff: 6
1 Executive Director
3 1/2 Program Staff
1 Office Manager
1 Bookkeeper

Staff openings/year: 2

Work Week: 40+ hours

Salary/year: $23,500

Benefits: Health insurance, paid vacation

Part-Time Employees: Sometimes

Volunteers: Yes

Interns: Yes

Jobs advertised: Newspapers; posting job descriptions with organizations

To apply: Contact Vivian Stromberg, Executive Director

MADRES DE EAST LA

924 South Mott Street
Los Angeles, CA 90023
(213) 269-9898

Director: Juana B. Gutirrez

Purpose: Madres De East Los Angeles strives to advocate for jobs in the community and empower the community.

Methods of operation: Community organization (25%), direct action (25%), public education (25%), training and technical assistance (25%)

Constituency: East LA community

Recent issues and projects: Recent projects include: immunization for East LA children; lead poison awareness; and water conservation project.

Budget: $500,000

Funding: Government (100%)

Part-Time Employees: Yes

Summer Employees: Yes

Volunteers: Yes

Interns: None at the time

MAGIC ME, INC.

2521 North Charles Street
Baltimore, MD 21218
(410) 243-9066

Other Offices: Boston, MA; San Joaquin, CA; Hagerstown, MD; Clinton, MD; Warrensburg, MO; Wilmington, DE; Syracuse, NY; London, ENGLAND

Director: Alfred de la Cuesta

Purpose: MAGIC ME, Inc. engages at-risk middle school youth in long-term service-learning to the elderly and physically and mentally handicapped. The program strives to increase self-esteem, academic motivation, and sense of community.

Methods of operation: Human services (90%), training and technical assistance (10%)

Constituency: Private corporations and individuals from the local and national communities

Recent issues and projects: MAGIC ME, Inc. recently received a grant of $750,000 from the Corporation on National and Community Service. The grant gives AmeriCorps members living and educational stipends, and will allow thousands of students and seniors to benefit from MAGIC ME.

Major publications: Quarterly newsletter

Budget: $1,000,000

Funding: Government funds (60%), foundations (30%), individual contributions (10%)

Staff: 23
1 Office Manager
1 Press Aide
1 Bookkeeper
16 Caseworkers
1 Executive Director
1 National Training Director
1 Program Director

Staff openings/year: 2

Work Week: 40 hours

Salary/year: $20,000 (Recent College Graduate); $23,000 (Graduate with advanced degree)

Benefits: Health insurance, paid vacation, family leave

Part-Time Employees: None

Summer Employees: None

Volunteers: 250

Interns: 1
Length: 3 months
Duties: Variety of work, mostly administrative
Remuneration: Volunteer basis, food stipends have been given

Jobs advertised: Newspapers, professional journals

To apply: Please contact Alicia Hay, Coordinator of Public Information

MAINE LABOR GROUP ON HEALTH

P.O. Box V
Augusta, ME 04332-1042
(207) 622-7823

Director: P. Vincent O'Malley

Purpose: The Maine Labor Group on Health is dedicated to protecting the health and safety of Maine working people and their families. They provide worker educational programs and act as worker advocates within the health care and public policy arenas.

Methods of operation: Training and technical assistance (60%), advocacy (20%), research (15%), publications (5%)

Membership: Our membership includes organized labor, health professionals, and unorganized workers.

Recent issues and projects: The Maine Labor Group on Health was instrumental in the passage of Maine's toxics use reduction legislation. We are continuing our training programs in asbestos abatement, hazardous materials, and general health and safety.

Major publications: *Occupational Safety and Health Newsletter*, published at least quarterly, with special editions as needed

Budget: $150,000

Funding: Fees for service, grants

Staff: 3
2 Issue Experts
1 Office Manager

Staff openings/year: 1

Work Week: 40+ hours

Salary/year: $18,500 (Recent College Graduate); $23,000 (Graduate with advanced degree)

Benefits: Health insurance, pregnancy leave, pension, paid vacation

Part-Time Employees: 5

Summer Employees: 1

Volunteers: 2

Interns: None currently, but could be arranged

Jobs advertised: Local and statewide newspapers

To apply: Contact Diana White, Executive Director

Remarks: The Maine Labor Group on Health is organized; full-time employees will be required to join the Union as a condition of employment.

MAINE ORGANIC FARMERS AND GARDENERS ASSOCIATION

P.O. Box 2176
Augusta, ME 04338-2176
(207) 622-3118

Director: Nancy Ross

Purpose: (1) Help farmers and gardeners grow organic food; protect the environment; recycle natural resources; increase local food production; support rural communities; (2) Illuminate for consumers the connection between healthful food and the farming practices we encourage.

Methods of operation: Public education (64%), publications (12%), training and technical assistance (10%), certification (6%), research (5%), lobbying (3%)

Constituency: Organic farmers and gardeners; consumers; transitional farmers and gardeners

Recent issues and projects: Comprehensive state and national organic certification; food safety labeling; Common Ground Country Fair; Low Input Sustainable Agriculture research; farmer conference

Major publications: Bimonthly newspaper: *Maine Organic Farmer and Gardener*; technical bulletins and fact sheets on organic agricultural practices

Interns: Apprenticeships
Length: No minimum or maximum
Duties: On-farm apprenticeships
Remuneration: With farmer

To apply: Contact MOFGA office for an application

MAINE PEOPLE'S ALLIANCE

65 West Commercial Street
Portland, ME 04101
(207) 761-4400

Other Offices: Augusta, ME; Bangor, ME

Director: George A. Christie

Purpose: The Maine People's Alliance is a grassroots, multi-issue citizen group with a membership of 15,000 statewide. MPA carries on local and statewide issue campaigns which share the common theme of empowering low-income citizens, increasing citizen participation, and building broad-based, progressive coalitions.

Methods of operation: Community organizing (30%), public education (30%), research (10%), direct action (10%), publications (10%), lobbying (5%), training and technical assistance (5%)

Constituency: Statewide group with members in every county; projects benefit the disadvantaged and unorganized directly by empowering people and building coalitions for institutional change and social justice

Recent issues and projects: Our current projects cover affordable health care (Consumers for Affordable Health Care), toxic wastes (Maine Toxics Action Campaign), insurance reform (Campaign for Fair Rates and Equal Justice), and child care (Child Care Action Alliance).

Major publications: Newsletter: *The Alliance*; *Voting Index to the Maine State Legislature*

Budget: $282,000

Funding: Canvassing (43%), foundations (36%), telephone solicitation (3%), other (18%)

Staff: 12
6 Canvassers
4 Organizers
1 Phone Canvass Director
1/2 Bookkeeper/Accountant
3/4 Office Manager

Staff openings/year: 2

Work Week: 50 hours

Salary/year: $18,000 (Recent College Graduate); $Varies (Graduate with advanced degree)

Benefits: Health insurance, life insurance, paid vacation

Part-Time Employees: 2

Volunteers: 3

Interns: 1
Length: 3 months
Duties: Special publications, research projects
Remuneration: Stipends available

Jobs advertised: Newspapers; *Community Jobs*; networking

To apply: Contact George A. Christie, Executive Director

MANAGEMENT ASSISTANCE GROUP (MAG)

1835 K Street, NW, Suite 305
Washington, DC 20006
(202) 659-1963

Other Offices: Santa Barbara, CA

Director: Karl Mathiasen

Purpose: MAG counsels nonprofit, social-purpose groups that are wrestling with organizational problems or want insights into how to function more effectively.

Methods of operation: Organizational diagnosis, organizational planning, training and technical assistance

Constituency: Social change organizations

Recent issues and projects: Consults with groups on strengthening organizational structure, clarifying purpose and goals, dealing with management problems, strengthening financial management; conducts workshops on organizational development matters

Budget: $500,000

Funding: Client fees, foundation grants

Staff: 7
6 Consultants
1 Support Staff

Staff openings/year: 1

Work Week: 45-50 hours

Benefits: Health insurance, life insurance, family leave, retirement leave

Jobs advertised: Announcements sent to network of colleagues

To apply: Contact Jeannie Engel

MARYLAND CITIZEN ACTION COALITION

2300 North Charles Street
Baltimore, MD 21218
(301) 235-5588

Other Offices: Silver Spring, MD

Director: Arthur W. Murphy

Purpose: MCAC is a coalition-based organization that works legislatively and electorally on: utility rate reform, health care, insurance reform, community reinvestment and family leave/family policy. Major goals are to build coalitions, win concrete victories that affect people's lives, empower citizens on a grassroots level and affect the balance of power in the state.

Methods of operation: Lobbying (10%), community organizing and public education (25%), research (10%), publications (10%), direct action (30%), training and technical assistance (10%), human services (5%)

Recent issues and projects: Insurance reform; health care/legislative 1994 statewide elections in Maryland

Major publications: Quarterly newsletter sent to individual members across the state

Budget: $450,000

Funding: Individual contributions, canvassing, telephone solicitation (75%), foundations (20%), special events (5%)

Staff: 16
10-40 Canvassers
2 Field Managers
1 Canvass Director
1 Organizer
1 Office Manager
1 Bookkeeper/Accountant

Work Week: 40-45 hours

Salary/year: $15-17,000

Benefits: Health insurance, pregnancy leave, paid vacation

Part-Time Employees: Yes

Summer Employees: Yes

Interns: 3

Jobs advertised: Help wanted section of *Baltimore Sun* and *Washington Post*; campus recruitment; alternative publications

To apply: Canvass applicants should contact Sol Bey, Canvass Director

MARYLAND NEW DIRECTIONS, INC.

2220 North Charles Street
Baltimore, MD 21218
(410) 235-8800

Director: Rose Marie Coughlin

Purpose: MND has as its broad mission "to help people reach their employment potential."

Methods of operation: Human services, direct action (75%), training and technical assistance (15%), publications (5%), public education (5%)

Constituency: Local career changers; unemployed; underemployed

Recent issues and projects: Displaced Homemaker Project; Welfare to Work projects; counseling for inmates; technical assistance for programs serving women interested in non-traditional employment; literacy program

Major publications: Newsletter: *Directions*; *Job Interviewing Handbook*

Budget: $700,000

Funding: Grants (75%), fees for direct services (19.9%), corporate contributions (5%), individual contributions (.05%), foundations (.05%)

Staff: 22
15 Caseworkers
2 Office Managers
2 Foundation Fundraisers
1 Writer/Editor
1 Bookkeeper/Accountant
1 Issue Expert

Staff openings/year: 2

Work Week: 40 hours

Salary/year: $18,000 (Recent College Graduate); $20,000 (Graduate with advanced degree)

Benefits: Health insurance, life insurance, paid vacation

Part-Time Employees: 4

Volunteers: 3

Jobs advertised: Newspaper; word of mouth; job networks

To apply: Contact Pat Forster, Employment Coordinator

MARYLAND PUBLIC INTEREST RESEARCH GROUP (MARYPIRG)

3121 Saint Paul Street, Suite 26
Baltimore, MD 21218
(410) 467-0439

Other Offices: Baltimore, MD

Director: Daniel J. Pontious

Purpose: Through research, organizing and advocacy, we promote legislation and other initiatives to protect our health and environment from problems such as toxic pollution, the growing trash crisis and ozone layer depletion. We also oppose harmful and unfair consumer practices in the marketplace.

Methods of operation: Community organizing (30%), research (20%), lobbying (20%), public education (20%), publications (5%), training and technical assistance (5%)

Membership: 23,000 college students; 15,000 community members

Recent issues and projects: Worked to pass 1990 Clean Air Act. Have recently worked to strengthen Clean Water Act, pass a national bottle bill, reform the federal campaign finance system and require California's law emission vehicle program in MD to curb smog.

Major publications: Newsletters: *MARYPIRG Progression* and *PIRG Citizen Advocate*. Reports: *A Future Too Bright: A Report on Industrial Sources of Ozone Depleters in Maryland*; *Solutions, Not Pollution: A Report to the Prince Georges County Council on Solid Waste Management for the Future*; *Streamwalk Manual: A Field Guide to Clean Water*; *Maryland Tenants Handbook*

Staff: 5
4 Organizers
1 Executive Director

Staff openings/year: 2

Work Week: 60 hours

Salary/year: $14-18,500

Benefits: Health insurance, paid vacation

Part-Time Employees: 5-10

Summer Employees: 30-40

Volunteers: 30-50

Interns: 2-6
Length: 1 semester
Duties: Varied; topics include environment, consumer, hunger
Remuneration: No paid internships at this time

Jobs advertised: College career placement offices; newspapers; posters

To apply: Contact Daniel Pontious, Executive Director

MASSACHUSETTS CAMPAIGN TO CLEAN UP HAZARDOUS WASTE (MCCHW)

37 Temple Place
Boston, MA 02111
(617) 292-4821

Director: Matthew Wilson

Purpose: Since 1986, MCCHW has assisted more than 125 neighborhood groups fight toxic chemical and other environmental hazards in their communities. They work on the local level helping neighborhoods organize to pressure polluters and government bureaucrats to act on these issues.

Methods of operation: Community organizing (80%), training and technical assistance (10%), public education (5%), publications (5%)

Recent issues and projects: Annual "Toxics Action Conference" attracts over 250 local activists for a day of workshops, speeches, and planning sessions on tactics and skills for cleanup. They work on various campaigns in towns and cities across the state.

Major publications: Quarterly: *Clean Update*, an update on local community groups' work on cleanup of toxic waste sites in the state; release annual reports on new toxic waste sites in state and 500 largest toxic chemical users

Budget: $65,000

Funding: Grassroots fundraisers (40%), telephone solicitation (20%), direct mail (20%), canvassing (15%), foundations (5%)

Staff: 2
2 Organizers

Staff openings/year: 1

Work Week: 55 hours

Salary/year: $12,500 (Recent College Graduate); $16,000 (Graduate with advanced degree)

Benefits: Health insurance, paid vacation, college loan repayment plan

Volunteers: 3

Interns: 3
Length: 3 months

To apply: Contact Matthew Wilson, Director

MASSACHUSETTS CITIZEN ACTION

186 South Street
Boston, MA 02111
(617) 695-9441

Director: Cynthia Ward

Purpose: MCA is a statewide grassroots consumer organization of 85,000+ members, working for progressive social change through increasing citizen participation in the democratic process.

Methods of operation: Lobbying (30%), public education (30%), community organizing (25%), direct action (15%)

Membership: 85,000 low and middle income families throughout Massachusetts

Recent issues and projects: In 1988 MCA was successful in helping pass a pro-consumer bill that saves Massachusetts drivers $400 million, and forces the auto insurance industry to practice cost containment measures. MCA is active on the passage of state Family Leave legislation, in mobilizing consumer support for a corporate tax report right-to-know law, and on environmental issues.

Major publications: Monthly newsletter: *Citizen Action Alert*

Budget: $600,000

Funding: Individual contributions (90%), foundations (10%)

Staff: 6
2 Organizers
2 Office Managers
1 Grassroots Fundraiser
1 Campaign Manager

Staff openings/year: 1

Work Week: 50 hours

Benefits: Health insurance, pregnancy leave, paid vacation

Part-Time Employees: 30

Summer Employees: 40

Volunteers: 20

Interns: 2
Length: Minimum 3 months, to 1 year
Duties: Lobbying, researching, fundraising, staff support
Remuneration: Salary up to $1700/month

Jobs advertised: Regional news publications; school listings

To apply: Contact David Buchanan, Director of Development

Remarks: The internship program at MCA is geared towards people who have little or no experience in politics or fundraising, but who have an interest in learning on the job. Candidates need to be articulate, politically committed, be able to conduct research, and be willing to raise their salaries on the phone bank. This is an excellent opportunity to get involved in the fundamentals of grassroots organizing and lobbying.

MASSACHUSETTS COALITION FOR OCCUPATIONAL SAFETY AND HEALTH (MASSCOSH)

555 Amory Street
Jamaica Plain, MA 02130
(617) 524-6686

Other Offices: Hatfield, MA

Director: Nancy Lessin

Purpose: To assist unions and workers in the struggle for safe and healthy workplaces and a clean environment for all.

Methods of operation: Training and technical assistance (73%), public education (20%), publications (5%), research (1%), lobbying (1%)

Constituency: Unions, workers, occupational health professionals, environmentalists, labor attorneys

Recent issues and projects: Health and safety for health care workers; Reproductive Hazards in the Workplace Project; preventing occupational cancer; health and safety for hazardous waste workers; moving from the "right to know" to the power to act; strengthening health and safety committees; linking safe jobs and a clean environment; women's occupational health

Major publications: *MassCOSH News*; *Confronting Reproductive Hazards on the Job* to be published soon; many fact sheets

Budget: $150,000

Funding: Foundations (70%), program income (15%), individual contributions (10%), membership (5%)

Staff: 9
7 Occupational Health Specialists/
Labor Educators
1 Office Manager
1 Bookkeeper/Accountant

Work Week: 8-40 hours

Salary/year: $25,000

Benefits: Unpaid pregnancy leave, cafeteria benefits - 15% of salary

Part-Time Employees: 6

Volunteers: 100

Interns: Yes
Length: 3-6 months
Duties: Vary
Remuneration: Interns usually find own funding or course credits

Jobs advertised: Newspaper; COSH group list; other lists

To apply: Contact Nancy Lessin, Director

MASSACHUSETTS COALITION FOR THE HOMELESS

288 A Street
Boston, MA 02210
(617) 737-3508

Other Offices: Worcester, MA

Director: Sue Marsh

Purpose: The Massachusetts Coalition for the Homeless is an advocacy network of over 1400 members which works on behalf of our state's homeless children, women, and men. MCH initiates and supports public policies concerning housing, income maintenance programs, job and training programs, medical and mental health care, legal rights and services. The Coalition operates two statewide committees on policy issues as well as a Donations Clearinghouse, which provides furniture and appliances to shelters and newly resettled households.

Methods of operation: Direct services (Donations Assistance Program), lobbying, research, litigation, publications, human services, community organizing, public education

Recent issues and projects: Advocated for a rent supplement program for people who could not afford rent increases. In addition, an emergency relief program modeled for individuals after the program for families, was created. The Coalition is currently negotiating with public officials responsible for issues related to the homeless. The Coalition support reforms in housing development, community revitalization and public housing. They support changes in the welfare system to raise benefits for anyone on welfare to at least the poverty line.

Major publications: Quarterly newsletter: *Streetsmarts*

Budget: $550,000

Funding: Contracts (33%), grants (33%), special events, direct mail, dues (33%)

Staff: 11
6 Direct Service Program
4 Organizers
1 Administration

Staff openings/year: 0-1

Work Week: 40+ hours

Salary/year: $20,000

Benefits: Health insurance, paid vacation, pregnancy leave, tuition reimbursement, travel expenses

Part-Time Employees: 0

Volunteers: 100-150

Interns: yes
Length: 1-2 semesters
Duties: Varies

Jobs advertised: Newspapers (dailies)

To apply: Contact Sue Marsh; write only please, no phone calls

---

MASSACHUSETTS HALF-WAY HOUSES, INC.

P.O. Box 348, Back Bay Annex
Boston, MA 02117
(617) 437-1864

Director: J. Bryan Riley

Purpose: To provide residential and non-residential support services to ex-offenders (men and women, adults and juveniles) with the goal of achieving successful reintegration into the community after incarceration. MHHI has also recently started a new division, Community Strategies, which provides community based residential treatment to mentally retarded individuals.

Methods of operation: Human services, training and technical assistance

Budget: $4,500,000

Funding: Public contracts (85%), foundations (1%), individuals (14%)

Staff: 118
67 Caseworkers
19 Supervisory Staff
15 Executive Staff
9 Clerical Staff
3 Bookkeepers/Accountants
5 Other

Staff openings/year: 24

Work Week: 40 hours

Salary/year: $18,000

Benefits: Health insurance, life insurance, pregnancy leave, pension, credit union, paid vacation

Volunteers: 50

Interns: Yes
Length: 1 semester
Duties: Vary
Remuneration: Paid work-study

Jobs advertised: Local newspapers, employment agencies, etc.

To apply: Contact Personnel Coordinator

MASSACHUSETTS PUBLIC INTEREST RESEARCH GROUP (MASSPIRG)

29 Temple Place
Boston, MA 02111
(617) 292-4800

Director: Janet Domenitz

Purpose: MASSPIRG is a nonprofit, nonpartisan public interest research and advocacy organization. Established in 1971, MASSPIRG works to develop policy, coordinate grassroots campaigns, and win legislation to promote environmental preservation, consumer protection, safe energy and corporate and governmental responsibility.

Methods of operation: Lobbying (30%), research (20%), community organizing (15%), fundraising (15%), public education (13%), litigation (5%), publications (2%)

Membership: A diverse group of citizens and college students who want to make a difference on issues including the environment, consumer rights, safe energy, and corporate and government accountability

Recent issues and projects: Current campaign priorities include an initiative campaign for legislation to curb corporate spending on ballot campaigns, advocacy for state and federal clean air regulations, efforts to reduce reliance on nuclear energy and corporate campaigns to promote packaging reform. In the consumer area, they are working to increase access to child care and health insurance. Recent victories include the passage of toxics use reduction legislation in 1989, passage of a state Clean Air Act in 1990, and passage of a contractor licensing bill in 1992 which streamlines the clean up of hazardous waste dumpsites.

Major publications: *MASSCITIZEN* quarterly citizen members' report; *MASSPIRG Report* twice-annual update for student members and others. A range of consumer and environmental issue reports including: *Art of the Possible: The Feasibility of Recycling Standards for Packaging*; *A Mixed Bag: A Report on "User Fee" Programs for Solid Waste Management*; *Still Smoking: Massachusetts Over Reliance on Trash Incineration*; *For Their Eyes Only: The Insurance Industry and Consumer Privacy* to name a few.

Budget: $1,200,000

Funding: Individual contributions, foundations, direct mail, canvassing, telephone solicitation

Staff: 54
20 Organizers
6 Lobbyists
1 Writer/Editor
1 Attorney
5 Attorneys
2 Bookkeepers/Accountants
4 Administrative Staff
2 Senior Executive Staff
3 Campaign Managers
10 Citizen Outreach Directors

Work Week: 40-55 hours

Salary/year: $14,000 (Recent College Graduate); $24,000 (Graduate with advanced degree)

Benefits: Health insurance, paid vacation, paid sick leave, paid holidays, parental leave, college loan assistance program

Part-Time Employees: 10-20

Summer Employees: 200-250

Volunteers: 5-15

Interns: 10-15
Length: 10 weeks
Duties: Law and policy students work with the advocacy and litigation staff; opportunities for undergraduate interns available in variety of areas
Remuneration: Stipend of $500 for legal and policy interns; other interns are unpaid

Jobs advertised: Through local newspapers and national publications such as *Community Jobs*; through listings and interviews at college, graduate and law school career placement offices; through listings sent to other public interest organizations

To apply: Contact Janet Domenitz, Executive Director

Remarks: MASSPIRG has 30 other campus and community offices statewide. During the past 20 years, MASSPIRG has earned a reputation for taking strong, often controversial stands on such issues as safe energy, solid waste and toxics use reduction. Our staff, student members and citizen volunteers combined wage important and exciting public interest campaigns.

MASSACHUSETTS SENIOR ACTION COUNCIL (MSAC)

277 Broadway
Somerville, MA 02145
(617) 776-3100

Other Offices: Boston, MA; North Dartmouth, MA; Holyoke, MA; Greenfield, MA

Director: Geoffrey W. Wilkinson

Purpose: MSAC is a grassroots organization of low-income and minority senior citizens dedicated to the empowerment of seniors, enabling them to organize for progressive public policies.

Methods of operation: Community organizing (55%), research (15%), direct action (15%), training and technical assistance (10%), public education

(5%)

Constituency: Low-income and minority seniors

Recent issues and projects: Legislative victories: Banon Balance Billing of Medicare patients, Discharge Planning Act, Boston Security Ordinance. Major contracts with 6 major hospitals around the state and a statewide eyecare company.

Major publications: Bimonthly newspaper: *Senior Action Leader*; *Knowing Your Rights as a Medicare Patient* (16-page booklet)

Budget: $350,000

Funding: Foundations (62%), individual contributions (30%), telephone solicitation (8%)

Staff: 9
5 Organizers
1 1/2 Office Managers
1 Foundation Fundraiser
1 Grassroots Fundraiser
1/2 Bookkeeper

Staff openings/year: 2

Work Week: 45 hours

Salary/year: $17,000

Benefits: Health insurance, pregnancy leave, paid vacation

Part-Time Employees: 5

Volunteers: 100's

Interns: 1

Jobs advertised: Massachusetts papers and usually in *Community Jobs*

To apply: Contact Jim Wessler, Executive Director

MASSACHUSETTS TENANTS ORGANIZATION

14 Beacon Street, Room 809
Boston, MA 02108
(617) 367-6260

Director: Pamela Bender

Purpose: To preserve and expand tenants' rights; educate, assist and organize tenants and tenants groups; preserve and expand affordable rental housing opportunities.

Methods of operation: Research, lobbying, community organizing, direct action, public education, training and technical assistance

Constituency: Low and moderate income renters; racially diverse; geographically distributed

Recent issues and projects: Organizing tenants living in properties foreclosed on by banks; organizing tenants receiving state rental subsidies; and low-income tenant leadership development program

Major publications: Quarterly newsletter: *The Massachusetts Tenant*

Budget: $130,000

Funding: Foundations (70%), individual contributions (30%)

Staff: 3
2 Organizers
1 Director

Staff openings/year: 1

Work Week: 40+ hours

Salary/year: $20,000

Benefits: Health insurance, pregnancy leave, paid vacation

Part-Time Employees: 2

Volunteers: 100

Interns: Yes
Length: 4 months
Duties: Varied, depending on interests, projects
Remuneration: Prefer cost free; top is $50-75 per week

Jobs advertised: Through organizational networks; daily newspapers

To apply: Contact Pamela Bender, Executive Director

MEADOWCREEK PROJECT, INC.

P.O. Box 100
Fox, AR 72051
(501) 363-4500

Purpose: The Meadowcreek Project is an environmental education center.

Methods of operation: Public education, training and technical assistance, conferences, workshops, publications, demonstrations, and internships

Constituency: Wide variety

Recent issues and projects: Environmental education: alternative and renewable energy, sustainable agriculture, applied ecology.

Demonstrations in energy include passive/active solar systems, photovoltaics, solar batch water heaters, solar ovens, water distiller, energy strategies together with resource conservation methods. Organic gardening techniques are demonstrated including ecological pest control, planned cropping systems, low-maintenance landscaping, and minimal external resource inputs. Programs are designed for school age students, college students, business professionals, as well as the general public on environmental topics. Conferences are 1-14 days long.

Major publications: *KCSA* newsletter

Funding: Individual contributions, grants, foundations

Staff: 15
2 Administration
3 Program
5 Support
4 Horticulture
1 Energy

Staff openings/year: 1

Work Week: 40 hours

Benefits: Health insurance, paid vacation, housing

Part-Time Employees: 6

Summer Employees: 6

Volunteers: Yes

Interns: 5 per year
Length: 10 weeks
Duties: Topics ranging from agriculture to architecture
Remuneration: $950 tuition/$15 a week stipend and room

Jobs advertised: Nationally through publications, universities, etc.

To apply: For internships and volunteer positions, contact Cindy Elliott for application

Remarks: Meadowcreek has a spring and fall leadership development internship in sustainable living, which includes readings and discussions, practical workshops, individual and group projects, field trips, research and hands-on work in the areas of energy, agriculture, forestry and rural development.

MEDIA ACCESS PROJECT

2000 M Street, NW, Suite 400
Washington, DC 20036
(202) 232-4300

Director: Andrew Jay Schwartzman

Purpose: Public interest law firm which represents the rights of the listening and viewing public to receive information.

Methods of operation: Litigation (80%), speaking at conventions (8%), research (5%), fundraising (5%), lobbying (1%), public education (1%)

Constituency: Civil rights, civil liberties, environmental and consumer groups; unions and other labor organizations; some individuals

Recent issues and projects: Litigation to restore support of the Fairness Doctrine; Brief in Supreme Court in support of 1992 Cable Acts; Litigation v. Congressional ban on "indecent" programming; Challenge to over-the-air home shopping stations

Major publications: *Changing America: Blueprints for A New Administration* (1992)

Budget: $150,000

Funding: Foundations (98-99%), individual contributions (1%), attorneys' fees (0-1%)

Staff: 3
2 Attorneys
1 Office Manager

Staff openings/year: 0-1

Work Week: 45 hours

Salary/year: $Varies (Recent College Graduate); $Varies (Graduate with advanced degree)

Benefits: Health insurance, life insurance, pregnancy leave, paid vacation

Summer Employees: 1-2

Volunteers: 1

Interns: 3
Length: 1 semester or summer
Duties: Write pleadings, briefs; attend meetings, oral arguments, Congressional hearings; some research
Remuneration: Summer interns paid a stipend. Semester interns given full semester's credit for 40 hours a week

Jobs advertised: Law school placement offices; *Legal Times*; National and Federal Job Reports;

minority placement organizations

To apply: Contact Gigi B. Sohn, Staff Attorney

MEDIA ALLIANCE

Fort Mason Center, Building D
San Francisco, CA 94123
(415) 441-2557

Director: Ann Wrixon

Purpose: Working to promote a more democratic and humane society by protecting freedom of speech and freedom of the press; holding the media accountable for the breadth of its hiring practices and the integrity of its products; and to provide a sense of community for media workers

Methods of operation: Research, publications, community organizing, public education, training and technical assistance

Constituency: Progressive media professionals

Recent issues and projects: Bay Area Censored (top underreported stories in the Bay Area); Annual Awards Ceremony; magazine fair for freelance writers; panel discussions on First Amendment issues; media studies

Major publications: Bimonthly media review: *MediaFile*; *Media How-To Notebook*; *How to be Happily Employed in the San Francisco Bay Area*; *People Behind the News*; *Freelance Markets ... A Guide to Bay Area Publications*

Budget: $425,000

Funding: Individual contributions, members (90%), foundations (10%)

Staff: 8
1 Computer Alliance Staff
1 Executive Director
1 Program Director
1 Office Manager
1 Writer/Editor (part-time)
1 Membership Services Manager
1 Bookkeeper/Accountant (part-time)
1 Program Assistant

Staff openings/year: 1-2

Work Week: 40 hours

Benefits: Health insurance, credit union, paid vacation

Part-Time Employees: 4

Volunteers: Yes; dozens

Interns: Yes; several
Length: 2-4 months
Remuneration: No $; college credit available

Jobs advertised: Through local media and newsletters

To apply: For internships, contact Dan Kalb. For staff positions, contact Ann Wrixon

MEDIA COALITION

1221 Ave. of the Americas, 24th Floor
New York, NY 10020
(212) 768-6770

Director: Christopher Finan

Purpose: The Media Coalition is an association that defends the First Amendment right to produce and sell books, magazines, recordings and videotapes; and defends the public's right to have access to the broadest possible range of opinion and entertainment.

Methods of operation: Research, lobbying, litigation, publications, direct action, public education

Membership: Coalition that represents most of the booksellers, book and periodical publishers, periodical wholesalers and distributors, recording producers and recording and video retailers in the U.S.

Recent issues and projects: The Media Coalition is presently involved in fighting censorship of "violent" works at both the state and federal levels.

Major publications: *The Rise of a Feminist Censor*, 1983-1993; *The Reverend Donald E. Wildman's Crusade for Censorship*, 1977-1992

Budget: $350,000

Staff: 2
Responsibilities include:
Organizing
Writing/Editing
Researching
Fundraising
Administrative
Bookkeeping

Work Week: 40 hours

Benefits: Health insurance, pension

Part-Time Employees: None

Summer Employees: None

Volunteers: None

Interns: No formal program
Length: No set length
Duties: Research, administrative, organizing, fundraising, etc.
Remuneration: Expenses only

Jobs advertised: Newspapers

To apply: Contact Christopher H. Finan, Executive Director

MEDIA NETWORK

39 West 14th Street #403
New York, NY 10011
(212) 929-2663

Director: Don Derosby

Purpose: Media Network is a national membership organization committed to the development and use of alternative media to promote social change. They promote the development and use of alternative media.

Methods of operation: Publications (100%)

Constituency: Producers, universities, libraries

Recent issues and projects: We research and publish directories listing new media titles addressing pressing social themes. Send for a listing of Media Network's most recent publications.

Major publications: *Immediate Impact*, a quarterly newsletter

Budget: $200,000

Funding: Foundations (100%)

Staff: 4

Staff openings/year: 0

Work Week: 40 hours

Salary/year: $Varies (Recent College Graduate); $Varies (Graduate with advanced degree)

Benefits: Health insurance

Part-Time Employees: None

Summer Employees: None

Volunteers: Yes

Interns: Yes
Length: Flexible
Remuneration: Non-paid

To apply: For internships contact Ilana Navaro, Outreach Coordinator

MEDIA WATCH

P.O. Box 618
Santa Cruz, CA 95061-0618
(408) 423-6355

Director: Ann J. Simonton

Purpose: MEDIAWATCH is dedicated to helping people become more critical consumers of all forms of mass media. MediaWatch promotes anti-censorship and free speech for all individuals, no matter their gender, age, race, class, ethnicity or sexual orientation.

Methods of operation: Public education (50%), publications (30%), direct action (20%)

Constituency: Diverse, feminist - national as well as international

Recent issues and projects: Major projects include: the distribution of our two highly acclaimed educational videos; boycotts of companies that promote sexism, racism and violence; exposing how the term "free speech" is used to silence those who don't have the same access to free speech that advertisers, pimps and pornographers do.

Major publications: *Media Watch/Action Agenda*, newsletter; videos: *Don't Be TV: Television Victim* and *Warning Media May Be Hazardous To Your Health*

Budget: $40,000

Funding: Publication sales (80%), individual contributions (20%)

Staff:
1 Organizer
2 Writers/Editors
1 Office Manager
2 Bookkeepers/Accountants

Staff openings/year: 1

Work Week: 40 hours

Part-Time Employees: None

Summer Employees: None

Volunteers: 5

Interns: 2
Length: 1-2 months
Duties: Office management, writing, researching, fundraising

Remuneration: None

To apply: Ann J. Simonton

Remarks: Our staff consists mainly of volunteers.

MEDICARE ADVOCACY PROJECT, INC. (MAP)

520 S. Lafayette Park Place, Suite 214
Los Angeles, CA 90057
(213) 383-4519

Director: Geraldine Dallek

Purpose: To assist seniors in Los Angeles County with Medicare and related health care problems/issues. MAP strives to ensure that all Medicare beneficiaries receive their health care free of impediments and barriers. While education, counseling and advocacy services are offered primarily to Los Angeles County residents, it is hoped that MAP's aggressive pursuit of reform and accountability will profit Medicare beneficiaries nationwide.

Methods of operation: Direct action (40%), public education (15%), lay advocate training and supervision (15%), litigation (10%), training and technical assistance (10%), research (5%), publications (5%)

Constituency: Our client base is primarily those 65+ or those under 65 who are Medicare disabled.

Recent issues and projects: MAP specializes in Medicare, Medigap, LTC, HMO and related areas of vital concern to seniors, caregivers and other Medicare beneficiaries. To supplement individual advocacy and representation, the MAP legal staff is actively involved in initiating and co-counseling on impact litigation. Impact cases successfully concluded during the 1989-90 fiscal period include: William vs. Sullivan, a class action lawsuit to ensure federal enforcement of Part B, limiting charges (case settled). The issues and cases came to light through direct client advocacy and representation.

Major publications: Every year MAP produces consumer-oriented flyers and brochures on various issues. MAP also produces a training manual primarily intended for in-house training and lay advocate training.

Budget: $700,000

Funding: Government grants (84%), foundations (15%), individual contributions (1%)

Staff: 14
4 Paralegals
2 Attorneys
1 Director of Community Education
1 Volunteer Coordinator
1 Director of Volunteers
1 Office Manager
4 Secretaries

Staff openings/year: 1-2

Work Week: 40 hours

Salary/year: $23,000 (Recent College Graduate); $24,000 (Graduate with advanced degree)

Benefits: Health insurance, pregnancy leave, paid vacation, credit union, dental/TDA

Part-Time Employees: 2

Volunteers: 60 lay counselors

Interns: Two currently, but willing to accept applications
Duties: Developing program for law student(s) to aid in impact litigation efforts and direct representation, such as administrative hearings

Jobs advertised: Newspaper; mailings; newsletters

To apply: Contact Geraldine Dallek, Executive Director

MEIKLEJOHN CIVIL LIBERTIES INSTITUTE

P.O. Box 673
Berkeley, CA 94701
(510) 848-0599

Director: Ann Fagan Ginger

Purpose: Meiklejohn Civil Liberties Institute is a center for peace law, an information clearinghouse on social change, a publisher, a training center, and a repository of history. Founded in 1965, it has become part of the infrastructure of the peace and justice community, empowering people to protect and expand their rights under the law. The U.S. Human Rights Project works on the enforcement in the U.S. of the newly-ratified International Covenant on civil and political rights

Methods of operation: Research (40%), publications (40%), public education (10%), community organizing (10%)

Constituency: 8,000 name national mailing list

Major publications: *Human Rights and Peace Law Docket: 1945-1991*; *The Cold War Against Labor,*

Ginger and Christians, editors; *The National Lawyers Guild: From Roosevelt Through Reagan*, Ginger and Tobin, editors; *Human Rights Organizations and Periodicals Directory, 7th edition 1993; News from MCLI* newsletter

Budget: $100,000

Funding: Individual contributions, foundations

Staff openings/year: 1-2

Work Week: 40 hours

Part-Time Employees: 3

Summer Employees: Yes

Volunteers: 6

Interns: Yes
Length: 3 months

Jobs advertised: Flyers; word of mouth

To apply: Contact Ann Fagan Ginger, Executive Director

Remarks: Staff earn $10 per hour.

MENTAL HEALTH ASSOCIATION OF MINNESOTA

2021 East Hennepin Avenue
Minneapolis, MN 55413
(612) 331-6840

Other Offices: Duluth, MN

Director: Kathleen Kelso

Purpose: To improve the quality of life of persons with mental illness and to promote mental health for all people

Methods of operation: Client advocacy (100%), involving lobbying (50%), public education (35%), direct action (10%), publications (5%)

Recent issues and projects: Reducing the size of state hospital system, seeking increase in funding for community services. Seeking equity in health care coverage.

Major publications: Quarterly newsletter: *Focus*

Budget: $385,000

Funding: United Way (65%), contributions (25%)

Staff: 6
1 Foundation Fundraiser
3 Client Advocates
1 Lobbyist
1 Office Manager

Staff openings/year: 0-1

Work Week: 40 hours

Salary/year: $21,000

Benefits: Health insurance, life insurance, family leave, pension, paid vacation, dental insurance

Volunteers: 40

Interns: Yes
Length: School sequence
Duties: Same as full-time advocates
Remuneration: Expenses only

Jobs advertised: Word of mouth

To apply: Contact Kathleen Kelso, Executive Director

METROPOLITAN COUNCIL ON HOUSING

102 Fulton Street, Room 302
New York, NY 10038
(212) 693-0550

Director: Gloria Sukenick, Chair

Purpose: A membership tenant union, New York City-wide in scope. Organizes tenants in groups where they live to protect their rights and correct conditions; work on legislation; organize rent strikes, demonstrations, etc.; testify at hearings; go to court with groups of tenants.

Methods of operation: Community organizing (50%), direct action (10%), lobbying (10%), litigation: Housing Court regarding rent strikes (10%), publications (10%), answer telephones 3 days a week for anyone wanting information on tenant problems (10%)

Membership: Tenants

Recent issues and projects: (1) Effort to get anti-warehousing law to prevent landlords from keeping thousands of apartments empty (called "warehousing") in the face of homelessness; (2) effort to change Major Capital Improvement (MCI) law allowing widespread increases for building-wide maintenance not truly "improvement" (e.g. new furnace, new roof, new windows)

Major publications: Newspaper: *Tenant*, 8 pages, 11 issues/year; fact sheets; published *Housing in the Public Domain: The Only Solution* (1978)

Budget: $140,000

Funding: Membership dues, individual

contributions

Staff: 3
3 Organizers

Salary/year: $15,000

Benefits: Health insurance

Part-Time Employees: 2

Volunteers: Yes

Interns: None currently, but willing to accept applications

Jobs advertised: Word of mouth; tenant publications

To apply: Contact Jenny Laurie, Vice-Chair

MEXICAN AMERICAN LEGAL DEFENSE AND EDUCATIONAL FUND (MALDEF)

634 South Spring Street, 11th Floor
Los Angeles, CA 90014
(213) 629-2512

Other Offices: San Francisco, CA; Washington, DC; San Antonio, TX; Chicago, IL; Sacramento, CA; Fresno, CA; Santa Ana, CA; Detroit, MI

President: Antonia Hernandez, President and General Counsel

Purpose: To promote and protect the civil rights of U.S. Latinos through class action litigation, advocacy and community education

Methods of operation: Lobbying, litigation, publications, direct action, public education, leadership development

Recent issues and projects: Immigrant's rights and parental leadership

Major publications: *MALDEF Newsletter*; *Leading Hispanics*

Budget: $4,300,000

Funding: Individual contributions, foundations, corporations

Staff: 60
20 Attorneys
2 Human Resources Administrators
3 Grassroots Fundraisers
1 Foundation Fundraiser
2 Bookkeepers/Accountants
5 Paralegals
16 Secretaries
7 Leadership Development
1 Communications Generalist
3 Policy Analysts

Staff openings/year: 2-3

Work Week: 40+ hours

Benefits: Health insurance, life insurance, paid vacation

Volunteers: Yes

Interns: Yes
Length: 3 months
Duties: Law clerks; public relations interns
Remuneration: None; volunteer

To apply: Contact Alba Hernandez, Personnel Associate

MICHIGAN AVENUE COMMUNITY ORGANIZATION (MACO)

6608 Michigan Avenue
Detroit, MI 48210
(313) 898-5000

Director: Bonnie Yost

Purpose: To empower residents of the 5-square-mile MACO neighborhood in order to secure measures from traditional power centers that will sustain viability of their low-income, multi-ethnic neighborhood. Also a housing development program.

Methods of operation: Community organizing (80%), direct action (5%), public education (5%), training and technical assistance (5%), publications (5%)

Constituency: Low to moderate income; Polish, Hispanic, black residents; 25% are seniors

Recent issues and projects: Housing Vacancy Campaign aimed at expediting demolitions of arson-likely abandoned homes while seeking policy changes to prevent vacancy; Housing Rehabilitation Project that uses Community Development Block Grant (CDBG) funds to repair owner-occupied homes and rehabilitates vacant structures.

Major publications: *MACO News*, 10 times/year

Funding: Foundations (50%), corporate contributions (40%), grassroots campaign (10%)

Staff: 10
4 Housing Development Staff

3 Organizers
1 Office Manager
1 Bookkeeper/Accountant
1/2 Writer/Editor
1/2 Foundation Fundraiser
1/2 Grassroots Fundraiser

Staff openings/year: 2

Work Week: 50 hours

Salary/year: $18,000 (Recent College Graduate); $20-25,000 (Graduate with advanced degree)

Benefits: Health insurance, life insurance, paid vacation, comp time

Part-Time Employees: 3

Volunteers: Yes

Interns: None currently, but willing to accept applications

Jobs advertised: *Community Jobs*; Detroit newspapers

To apply: Contact Mary Madigan, Lead Organizer

MICHIGAN LEAGUE FOR HUMAN SERVICES

300 North Washington Square, Suite 401
Lansing, MI 48933
(517) 487-5436

President: Ann Marston

Purpose: The League is a statewide citizens organization engaged in research, public information, general education and advocacy on issues related to the provision of basic needs for the state's low-income citizens.

Methods of operation: Public education (27%), management (15%), human services (15%), research (11%), training and technical assistance (10%), community organizing (10%), government commissions and task forces (10%), lobbying (2%)

Constituency: Human services professionals, labor, United Way, business, industry, academia, low-income citizens

Recent issues and projects: Analysis of the impact of ending government assistance in Michigan; development of county-by-county data on children at risk in Michigan, *Kids Count*

Major publications: *Michigan's Children: Is the State's Future in Jeopardy?*; *Reassessing Michigan's Energy Assistance Programs*; *The Helping Handbook*

Budget: $750,000

Funding: United Way (70%), publications, membership (30%)

Staff: 16
6 Issue Experts/Researchers/Lobbyists
3 Secretaries (part-time)
1 Insurance Specialist (part-time)
2 Secretaries/Receptionists
1 Bookkeeper/Accountant
1 Management Support Specialist
1 File Clerk (part-time)
1 Librarian (part-time)

Work Week: 37.5 hours

Salary/year: $24,000 (Recent College Graduate); $27-30,000 (Graduate with advanced degree)

Benefits: Health insurance, life insurance, pregnancy leave, pension, paid vacation, disability insurance, sick leave

Part-Time Employees: 6

Volunteers: Yes

Interns: Yes
Length: Two terms
Duties: Assist with programmatic, issue work
Remuneration: Small stipend to cover mileage or parking

Jobs advertised: Announcement circulated among agency constituency and ads placed in major daily papers

To apply: Contact Ann Marsten, President/CEO

MICHIGAN MIGRANT LEGAL ASSISTANCE PROJECT, INC.

49 Monroe Center, NW, Suite 3A
Grand Rapids, MI 49503-2933
(616) 454-5055

Other Offices: Berrigen Springs, MI

Director: Gary N. Gershon

Purpose: Provide civil legal services to migrant and seasonal farmworkers in Michigan in areas of civil rights, employment, housing, public benefits, health, consumer and education

Methods of operation: Litigation (50%), research (20%), human services (18%), public education (10%), publications (1%), lobbying (1%)

Constituency: Migrant and seasonal farmworkers

and dependents

Recent issues and projects: Ramirez v. Immigration and Naturalization Service (Class, 4th Amendment INS); Velasquez v. Michigan Senate (field sanitation, separation of powers); DeBruyn Produce Company v. Romero et al (whether state landlord tenant law applies to migrant labor camps); Rodriquez v. Berry Brook Farms (Migrant Seasonal Agricultural Worker Protection Act, classes); Van Buren Intermediary School District Parent Advisory Committee vs. Ruiz and Board of Education (State compliance with migrant education statutes and regulations)

Major publications: Newsletter: *Bajo*

Budget: $550,000

Funding: Legal Services Corporation (92%), foundations (7%), direct mail (1%)

Staff: 12
6 Attorneys
4 Secretaries
1 1/2 Paralegal
1 Office Manager

Staff openings/year: 1-2

Work Week: 37.5 hours

Salary/year: $20,000+ attorney

Benefits: Health insurance, life insurance, pregnancy leave, paid vacation, pension: employee contributory/tax sheltered annuity

Part-Time Employees: 5

Summer Employees: 5, as above

Jobs advertised: Newspapers; Clearinghouse for Legal Services; law schools

To apply: Contact Gary Gershon

MID-PENINSULA CITIZENS FOR FAIR HOUSING

457 Kingsley Avenue
Palo Alto, CA 94301
(415) 327-1718

Director: Beverly Lawrence

Purpose: To secure for all individuals in the local community and in the state equal opportunity to purchase or rent property wherever they choose.

Methods of operation: Counseling, referral, lobbying

Constituency: Clients are homeseekers, tenants, managers; all people who need help in securing their rights in housing

Recent issues and projects: Eliminating discriminatory housing practices

Budget: $200,000

Staff openings/year: 1

Work Week: 40 hours

Salary/year: $17,500-24,000

Benefits: Health insurance

Volunteers: Yes

Interns: Yes
Length: Summer or semester
Remuneration: Work-study

Jobs advertised: Newspapers

To apply: Contact Beverly Lawrence, Director

MID-VALLEY WOMEN'S CRISIS SERVICE

795 Winter Street, NE
Salem, OR 97301
(503) 378-1572

Other Offices: Portland, OR

Director: Vietta Helmle

Purpose: To provide crisis intervention and support services to victims of domestic violence, rape and incest.

Methods of operation: Human services (75%), public education (10%), publications (5%), training and technical assistance (5%), community organizing (4%), lobbying (1%), 24-hour hotline

Recent issues and projects: Expanded newsletter on domestic violence, rape and pornography

Major publications: Quarterly newsletter

Budget: $250,000

Funding: Government (64%), foundations (1%), individual contributions (35%)

Staff: 7
4 1/3 Caseworkers
1 Organizer
1 Office Manager
1 Issue Expert

Staff openings/year: 1

Work Week: 40 hours

Salary/year: $18,000 (Recent College Graduate); $22,000 (Graduate with advanced degree)

Benefits: Health insurance, pregnancy leave, paid vacation, housing for 1 staff, board for 1 staff

Part-Time Employees: 3

Volunteers: 40

Interns: 6 per year
Length: 6 months
Duties: Same as paid staff

Jobs advertised: Newspaper; other similar programs; colleagues; community organizers

To apply: Contact Vietta Helmle, Director

MIDDLE EAST RESEARCH & INFORMATION PROJECT (MERIP)

1500 Massachusetts Avenue, NW, Suite 119
Washington, DC 20005
(202) 223-3677

Director: Peggy Hutchison, Publisher

Purpose: To provide a critical and independent source of information on pressing and controversial political and economic developments in the Middle East, from the Palestinian uprising to the spiraling arms race, from women's rights to Islam and politics, with a special eye to U.S. policy.

Methods of operation: Publications (80%), public education (10%), research (10%)

Constituency: Middle East studies scholars and students, journalists, peace movement, unionists, interested public

Recent issues and projects: Publication of a bimonthly magazine, *Middle East Report*; publication of a special series of human rights reports: *Academic Freedom, Press Freedom, Women's Rights, Religious Freedoms*

Major publications: *Middle East Report*, a bimonthly magazine

Budget: $330,000

Funding: Individual contributions (33%), foundations (33%), subscriptions and sales (33%)

Staff: 5
1 Editor
1 Publisher
1 Circulation Manager
1 Administrative Assistant (half-time)
1 Assistant Editor

Staff openings/year: 0-1

Work Week: 35-40 hours

Salary/year: $18,000 (Recent College Graduate); $20-30,000 (Graduate with advanced degree)

Benefits: Health insurance, life insurance, pregnancy leave, paid vacation

Volunteers: 3

Interns: 3
Length: Semester; 6-12 months preferred
Duties: Circulation/promotion or editorial assistance
Remuneration: Unpaid; college credit may be arranged

Jobs advertised: Word of mouth; notices to other Middle East and peace groups; local papers; *Community Jobs*

To apply: Contact Peggy Hutchinson

MIDWEST ACADEMY

225 West Ohio Street, Suite 250
Chicago, IL 60610
(312) 645-6010

Director: Jacquelyn A. Kendall

Purpose: Dedicated to enabling people and organizations of low and moderate income people to win concrete benefits, develop a sense of their own power, and alter the relations of power in order to build a more just and humane society.

Methods of operation: Training and technical assistance

Constituency: Staff and leaders working in social change organizations; nationwide

Recent issues and projects: Community organizing; coalition building; annual retreat; consulting and training; senior citizen, minority, neighborhood, union, women, environmental and toxic waste issues; health care

Major publications: *Midwest Academy Organizing Manual*; *Citizen Action and the New American Populism*; *Lives Matter: A Handbook for Christian Organizing*; *Direct Action Organizing* manuals

Budget: $300,000

Funding: Fees from consulting and training, foundations, donations

Staff: 5
2 Administrators
2 Trainers
1 Executive Director

Staff openings/year: 1

Work Week: 50 hours

Salary/year: $15,000 (Recent College Graduate); $20,000 (Graduate with advanced degree)

Benefits: Health insurance, life insurance, paid vacation

Summer Employees: Yes

Volunteers: Yes

Interns: Yes
Length: Flexible
Duties: Flexible

Jobs advertised: Newspapers; social change newsletters; word of mouth

To apply: Contact Arlette Slachmuylder, Training Administrator

---

MIDWEST CENTER FOR LABOR RESEARCH

3411 West Diversey, Suite 10
Chicago, IL 60647
(312) 278-5418

Director: Dan Swinney

Purpose: A nonprofit consulting group. We offer a wide variety of economic development services, specializing in the retention of industrial employment.

Methods of operation: Research (50%), training and technical assistance (30%), community organizing (10%), publications (5%), public education (5%)

Constituency: Labor organizations, government agencies, community organizations and church groups

Recent issues and projects: (1) Anti-plant closing campaigns; (2) develop labor/community coalitions; (3) conduct workshops and seminars on job retention issues

Major publications: *Labor Research Review*; *Early Warning Manual*; quarterly newsletter

Budget: $400,000

Funding: Foundations (50%), individual contributions (15%), other (35%)

Staff: 10
2 Organizers
1 Executive Director
2 Secretaries
1 Office Manager
1 Researcher
1 Assistant Research Director
1 Development Director
1 Research Director

Staff openings/year: 1

Work Week: 40 hours

Salary/year: $24,000 (Recent College Graduate); $30,000 (Graduate with advanced degree)

Benefits: Health insurance, life insurance, pregnancy leave, tuition reimbursement, paid vacation

Part-Time Employees: 4

Summer Employees: Yes

Volunteers: 1

Interns: Yes
Length: 2 months
Duties: Gathering and assembly of research projects
Remuneration: Stipend paid by institution, if possible

Jobs advertised: Direct mailings; word of mouth

To apply: Contact Jacqui Johnson, Office Manager

MIDWEST IMMIGRANT RIGHTS CENTER

327 South LaSalle Street, Suite 1400
Chicago, IL 60604
(312) 435-1960

Director: Roy Petty

Purpose: The Midwest Immigrant Rights Center and the Immigrant and Community Services Department of Travelers and Immigrants Aid provides free or low cost legal representation to immigrants and refugees through direct service or pro bono attorneys. Our goal is to counsel and refer social service needs for eligible clients.

Methods of operation: Legal representation (80%), public education (20%)

Funding: Foundation and corporate grants (20%), direct individual and United Way donations (80%)

Staff: 19

10 Caseworkers
4 Attorneys
4 Typists
1 Pro Bono Coordinator

Staff openings/year: 1

Work Week: 40 hours

Summer Employees: 2

Volunteers: 200

Interns: 2
Length: 10 weeks
Remuneration: Public Interest Law Institute

Jobs advertised: Local and national publications

To apply: Contact Esther Lopez

MIDWEST WOMEN'S CENTER

828 S. Wasbash, Suite 200
Chicago, IL 60605
(312) 922-8530

Director: Laurina E. Uribe

Purpose: MWC enables women to achieve self-sufficiency and economic and political parity by providing the opportunities and resources to fully participate in and contribute to society.

Methods of operation: Employment and training (70%), research (10%), coalition work (10%), lobbying (5%), publications (5%)

Recent issues and projects: Employment and Training Projects: General Information Clerk, an 18-week program; WOMEN CAN, a 10-month carpentry and building maintenance program; Working Knowledge Literacy Program; Construction/Industrial Services, an 18-week program; and Stepping Up, a 2 week career exploration.

Major publications: Newsletter: *Connection*, describes agency happenings and is published 4 times/year; *The Advocate*, an issue-specific quarterly on policy and advocacy

Budget: $1,100,000

Funding: Government (50%), corporations and events (25%), foundations (15%), United Way (10%), individual contributions (5%)

Staff: 22
3 Program Managers
3 Literacy Specialists
1 Computer Instructor
3 Non-Traditional Instructors
3 Counselors
1 Development Assistant
1 Secretary
1 Receptionist
1 Director of Finance
1 Accounting Assistant
1 Office Manager
1 Director of Communications
1 Recruiter
1 Intake Specialist

Staff openings/year: 5

Work Week: 35 hours

Salary/year: $18,000 (Recent College Graduate); $22,000 (Graduate with advanced degree)

Benefits: Health insurance, pregnancy leave, paid vacation, $200/year staff development support

Volunteers: Yes

Interns: 2-5
Length: Intern's availability
Duties: Various (literacy; media development; library; research)
Remuneration: No support available

Jobs advertised: Local press; job announcements sent to pertinent organizations

To apply: Contact Marcia Medem, Director of Administration

MIGIZI COMMUNICATIONS, INC.

3123 East Lake Street, Suite 200
Minneapolis, MN 55406
(612) 721-6631

Other Offices: New York, NY

Director: Laura Waterman Wittstock

Purpose: To provide balanced coverage of Native news and information to the Native and general public, to train Native journalists, and educate elementary, secondary and adult students in a communications related setting.

Methods of operation: Training and technical assistance (50%), independent radio programming (15%), public education (5%), community organizing (5%), publications (5%), research (5%), human services (14%), direct action (1%)

Constituency: American Indians and others interested in news, journalism and media

Recent issues and projects: Award-winning radio

documentary on multi-cultural America; publication of *The Cloud Family* language arts materials, which include 8 radio plays; development of new methods in adult education which stress behavioral/attitudinal change, creation of new youth leadership center, including annual European student tours

Major publications: Radio programs available on cassette for individual listeners; *Communicator* monthly newsletter, with regular features on nonprofit and race topics; periodic reports on the status of Native-owned radio stations

Budget: $700,000

Funding: Government grants (65%), foundations (25%), fees (5%), individual contributions (5%)

Staff: 9
4 Teachers
1/2 Writer/Editor
1/2 Office Manager
1 Fundraiser
1/2 Issue Expert
1/2 Bookkeeper/Accountant
1/2 Radio Executive Producer
2 Youth Specialists

Staff openings/year: 1

Work Week: 40 hours

Salary/year: $25,000 (Recent College Graduate); $30,000 (Graduate with advanced degree)

Benefits: Health insurance, life insurance, pension, paid vacation

Part-Time Employees: 2

Volunteers: 15

Interns: 1
Length: 13 weeks
Duties: Radio production: traffic, management, production, engineering
Remuneration: Training support if eligible; otherwise no tuition charge

Jobs advertised: Radio trade journals; daily newspapers; Native newspapers; announcements sent to universities and programs

To apply: Send letter and resume to Vicki Cain

Remarks: MIGIZI is dedicated to the promotion of Native participation in the media as a means of balancing information received by the American and world public on Natives, and to promote the advancement of Natives in communications-related careers. Media-related education is provided to high school students for credit and to elementary students to introduce them to the tools of the business. Our award-winning documentaries serve as models for students to learn from.

MIGRANT LEGAL ACTION PROGRAM

2001 S Street, NW, Suite 310
Washington, DC 20009
(202) 462-7744

Director: Roger C. Rosenthal

Purpose: MLAP is a national legal services support center which provides representation to this nation's migrant and seasonal farmworkers.

Methods of operation: Legal research (40%), litigation (38%), publications (15%), training and technical assistance (3%), legislative and administrative monitoring (3%), lobbying (1%)

Constituency: Farmworker clients; support to legal services field programs

Recent issues and projects: MLAP provides support to migrant legal services field programs and farmworkers organizations nationwide and engages in litigation and some administrative and legislative work.

Budget: $700,000

Funding: Legal Services Corporation (95%), foundations (5%)

Staff: 9
4 Attorneys
2 Secretaries
1 Law Librarian
1 Office Manager
1 Bookkeeper/Accountant (part-time)

Staff openings/year: 0-1

Work Week: 35-50 hours

Salary/year: $Varies (Recent College Graduate); $Varies (Graduate with advanced degree)

Benefits: Health insurance, paid vacation, life insurance, pregnancy leave, disability insurance, dental insurance, sick leave, compensatory time

Part-Time Employees: 1

Volunteers: 1-6

Interns: 4-5 law clerks; 1-2 undergraduates
Length: Summer or school semester
Duties: Research and writing for law clerks; assistance on a variety of tasks for undergraduate interns

Remuneration: We urge students to try to find their own source of funding.

Jobs advertised: School placement offices; various publications

To apply: Contact Roger Rosenthal, Executive Director

MILITARY TOXICS PROJECT
P.O. Box 845
Sabattus, ME 04280
(207) 375-8482

Other Offices: San Francisco, CA

Director: Cathy Hinds

Purpose: The Military Toxics Project is a national network of grassroots groups working to promote safe remediation technologies of hazardous waste, increase controls of toxic releases and organize around pollution prevention at Department of Defense installations.

Methods of operation: Community organizing (50%), public education (20%), training and technical assistance (20%), research (10%)

Constituency: Civilian base workers, unions, military, veterans, community groups, scientists

Recent issues and projects: Recent projects include 4 national campaign networks around base closure, depleted uranium, chemical weapons and convention munitions. MTP is actively working in a number of other areas such as RABs, impact of Department of Defense on Native American lands, electromagnetic weaponry and Department of Defense contractor pollution.

Major publications: *Touching Bases*, newsletter; reports

Funding: Foundations (95%), individual contributions (5%)

Staff: 2

Staff openings/year: 1

Work Week: 40-50 hours

Salary/year: $18,000 (Recent College Graduate); $30,000 (Graduate with advanced degree)

Benefits: Health insurance, paid vacation, dental insurance, tuition reimbursement

Part-Time Employees: 2

Summer Employees: None

Volunteers: None

Interns: Willing to accept applications

Jobs advertised: Through statewide job services, newspapers and by mail to other organizations

To apply: Contact Cathy Hinds, Director

MILWAUKEE PEACE EDUCATION/RESOURCE CENTER
2437 N. Grant Blvd.
Milwaukee, WI 53218
(414) 445-9736

Director: Jacqueline Haessly

Purpose: Provide educational resources and consultations on topics of peace, social justice, and global awareness education; develop resources such as books, manuals, videos and tapes on peace topics.

Methods of operation: Research (20%), publications (35%), public education (30%), training and technical assistance (15%)

Recent issues and projects: Developing peace talks publications and videos; coordinating 1994 International Year of the Family

Major publications: *Learning to Live Together, Peacemaking for Families, What Shall We Teach Our Children?, Promise and Possibility, When the Canary Stops Singing: Women's Voices for Transforming Business*

Funding: Sale of products (100%)

Staff: 2
2 Writers/Editors
1 Office Manager/Issue Expert/Accountant

Work Week: 30 hours

Summer Employees: 1

Volunteers: 5

Interns: 2 - 3
Length: 3 months to 1 year
Duties: Office management; training programs; financial/accounting; research; librarian
Remuneration: Stipend + free room and board

Jobs advertised: Peace newsletters, local colleges

To apply: Contact Jacqueline Haessly, Director

MINERAL POLICY CENTER

1612 K Street, NW, Suite 808
Washington, DC 20006
(202) 887-1872

Other Offices: Durango, CO; Bozeman, MT

President: Philip M. Hocker

Purpose: The Center is a growing national nonprofit environmental organization founded in 1988 that works in cooperation with local citizens around the country to protect their environment from damage caused by mining.

Methods of operation: Research, lobbying, publications, community organizing, public education, training and technical assistance

Constituency: Citizens concerned about the impacts of mining in their communities; other organizations focused on public lands issues; and taxpayers outraged by the continued giveaway of public lands

Recent issues and projects: The organization works primarily on the reform of the 1872 Mining Law

Major publications: *Clementine*; *Canary Calls*; *Burden of Guilt*; *Golden Patents, Empty Pockets*; *States Rights, Miners Wrongs*; *Mining Conservation Directory*

Funding: Individual contributions, foundations

Staff: 11
2 Organizers
2-3 Writers/Editors
1 Attorney
1 Office Manager
2 Researchers
2 Lobbyists
2 Foundation Fundraisers
3 Issue Experts
1 Bookkeeper/Accountant
(some functions crossover)

Staff openings/year: 1-2

Work Week: 40 hours

Salary/year: $Varies (Recent College Graduate); $Varies (Graduate with advanced degree)

Benefits: Health insurance, paid vacation

Part-Time Employees: None

Summer Employees: None

Volunteers: None

Interns: 1-2
Length: 3-6 months
Duties: Research, routine clerical work, assist program staff
Remuneration: Paid

Jobs advertised: *The Washington Post*, *Environmental Career Opportunities*, organizational mailings

MINNEAPOLIS TELECOMMUNICATIONS NETWORK

125 SE Main Street
Minneapolis, MN 55414
(612) 331-8575

Director: Anthony Riddle

Purpose: Minneapolis Telecommunications Network is the cable access center in Minneapolis. They train 400 people every year to use and create programs which promote free speech, communication within cultures, education to the general public about neighborhoods and other cultures. They run 5 major channels on the cable system, have two large studios, eleven edit suites and broadcast quality cameras and equipment for checkout. All of the equipment, studios and editing is available free of charge for a one year membership fee of $30. They create approximately 22,000 hours of programming through volunteers each year.

Methods of operation: Training and technical assistance (40%), community organizing (30%), public education (20%)

Constituency: Inner City Minneapolis individuals and organizations

Recent issues and projects: MTN is also setting up a community network focused on nonprofits, government agencies and the setting up of public access terminals for Minneapolis. Their focus is to make sure that nonprofit and government information is available on the net. They will, however be training individuals in the use of computers and how to use the Internet. They are also working with the Twin Cities Freenet for individual access.

Budget: $650,000

Funding: Government funding (85%), foundations (10%), individual contributions (5%)

Staff: 15

1 Lobbyist
1 Administrative Assistant
1 Fundraiser
1 Office Manager
1 Bookkeeper/Accountant

Staff openings/year: 2

Work Week: 40 hours

Salary/year: $18,000 (Recent College Graduate); $Varies (Graduate with advanced degree)

Benefits: Health insurance, life insurance, family leave, vacation

Part-Time Employees: 7

Summer Employees: None

Volunteers: 500

Interns: 3-5
Length: 3 months
Duties: Depends on the department, ideally teaching, studio and video production. None are set up to be receptionists or gopher positions.
Remuneration: None

Jobs advertised: Through community papers, dailies and word of mouth

To apply: Please contact Tamara Blaschko, Development Specialist

MINNESOTA CITIZENS' ORGANIZATIONS ACTING TOGETHER (COACT)

2233 University Ave., West, Suite 300
St. Paul, MN 55114
(612) 645-3733

Other Offices: Duluth, MN; Little Falls, MN; Rochester, MN

Director: Jon Youngdahl

Purpose: Organize low and moderate income people in cities and rural areas to gain power to create progressive social change.

Methods of operation: Fundraising, administration, management, public education, research, lobbying

Constituency: Low and moderate income people in all parts of the state

Recent issues and projects: Single-payer health care reform and fair family farm policies

Major publications: Quarterly: *Minnesota COACT News*

Budget: $1,000,000

Funding: Individual contributions by door-to-door canvassing and telephone canvassing, special fundraising events and support via grants from foundations

Staff: 15

Staff openings/year: 1-2

Work Week: 50 hours

Salary/year: $15,600 - 25,000

Benefits: Health insurance, life insurance, paid vacation, sick days and holidays.

Part-Time Employees: 25-35

Volunteers: 2

Interns: Yes
Length: 3 months
Duties: Arranged by intern
Remuneration: Pay mileage and expenses

Jobs advertised: *Community Jobs*, local newspapers, fliers

To apply: Contact Jon Youngdahl

MINNESOTA INSTITUTE FOR SUSTAINABLE AGRICULTURE

1991 Buford Circle, 411 Borlaug Hall
St. Paul, MN 55108-1013
(612) 625-8235

Director: Dr. Donald L. Wyse

Purpose: MISA is a joint venture between the University of Minnesota's College of Agriculture and the Sustainers Coalition. The purpose of MISA is to bring together the interests of the agriculture community in a cooperative effort to develop and promote sustainable agriculture.

Methods of operation: Research team formation (50%), public education (30%), community organizing (20%)

Membership: 40-member joint seminar, representing the University of Minnesota and Sustainers Coalition. Also the constituency of the State of Minnesota

Recent issues and projects: Funding of three sustainable agriculture research projects: Biological, Financial and Social Monitoring to Develop Highly Sustainable Farming Systems; Sustainable Dairy Farming; and Graduate School Program for a total of approximately $250,000. Also sustainable agriculture seminar series.

Budget: $250,000

Funding: University of Minnesota, College of Agriculture (100%)

Staff: 3
1 Organizer
1 Office Manager
1 Issue Expert

Staff openings/year: 0-3

Work Week: 40 hours

Salary/year: $Varies (Recent College Graduate); $Varies (Graduate with advanced degree)

Benefits: Health insurance, pension, paid vacation, life insurance, credit union, family leave, tuition reimbursement

Part-Time Employees: No

Summer Employees: No

Volunteers: No

Interns: No intern program, willing to accept applications

Jobs advertised: National advertisements and mailings to sustainable agricultural organizations and universities

To apply: Contact Dr. Donald L. Wyse, Executive Director

MINNESOTA PROJECT

1885 University Ave. West, Suite 315
St. Paul, MN 55104
(612) 645-6159

Other Offices: Canton, MN

Director: Beth E. Waterhouse

Purpose: The Minnesota Project is a nonprofit organization working to strengthen rural communities. Founded in 1979, they work with leaders in rural areas as they build their capacity to resolve their own issues of sustainability and natural resource management. They currently focus their mission, values and project work in five basic areas: groundwater protection; sustainable agriculture; recycling market development; pollution prevention; and river protection. In each area they develop citizen involvement and leadership as well as initiate policies that are feasible and community connected. The Minnesota Project is known for its ability to act as a convener and collaborator, sometimes between unlikely partners.

Methods of operation: Public education (40%), training and technical assistance (30%), community organizing (20%), publications (10%)

Constituency: Rural communities in Minnesota

Recent issues and projects: We are working on or have completed the following projects: the reauthorization of the Clean Water Act; formulating program recommendations for the 1995 Farm Bill; leading an interdisciplinary team of state agency staff and University of Minnesota faculty, to develop a process for the widespread implementation of comprehensive farm planning; conducting national case-study research on rural cooperative marketing of recyclable materials; assisted in the formation of the Cooperative Marketing Network, which has created a database and a peer-match directory as well as a national status report on cooperative marketing efforts for recyclables; and serve on the steering committee of Water Quality 2000

Major publications: Please write for publications list

Budget: $300,000

Funding: Foundations (78%), government contracts (11%), individual contributions (8%)

Staff: 5
1 Organizer
1 Writer/Editor
1/2 Lobbyist
1 Foundation Fundraiser
1 Typist
1/2 Bookkeeper/Accountant

Staff openings/year: 1/2

Work Week: 45 hours

Salary/year: $22,000 (Recent College Graduate); $32,000 (Graduate with advanced degree)

Benefits: Health insurance, paid vacation, life insurance, long term disability

Part-Time Employees: 1

Summer Employees: None

Volunteers: Yes

Interns: Varies
Length: 3 months
Duties: Varies
Remuneration: Paid or unpaid

MINNESOTA PUBLIC INTEREST RESEARCH GROUP

2512 Delaware Street, SE
Minneapolis, MN 55414
(612) 627-4035

Other Offices: Duluth, MN; Minneapolis, MN; Morris, MN; Northfield, MN; St. Paul, MN

Director: Heather Cusick

Purpose: The state's largest and fastest growing environmental and consumer organization, and the first incorporated state PIRG, MPIRG is a nonpartisan organization directed by students and working to promote the public interest through research and policy development, legislative advocacy, impact litigation, and grassroots organizing.

Methods of operation: Research (20%), lobbying (20%), litigation (10%), community organizing (10%), public education (20%)

Membership: Minnesota college students on 9 campuses throughout the state

Recent issues and projects: Legislative support of reuse, recycled paper procurement and environmental labelling. Establishment and maintenance of the state's materials and exchange network. Radon education and policy advocacy. Legal and legislative opposition to nuclear power and waste storage and promotion of conservation, efficiency and renewables. Legislative and administrative support of sustainable forest management and planning. Promotion of avenues for citizen involvement.

Major publications: *Statewatch* (newsletter)

Budget: $400,000

Funding: Student membership fee (60%), canvassing (23%), program service fee (8%), grants (8%), telephone solicitation (1%)

Staff: 15
5 Organizers
1 Attorney
2 Researchers
2 Issue Experts
3 Grassroots Fundraisers
1 Executive Director
1 Administrative Director
1/2 Bookkeeper/accountant
5-50 Canvassers (varies)

Staff openings/year: 1-5

Work Week: 40-60 hours

Salary/year: $13,200 (Recent College Graduate); $18,100 (Graduate with advanced degree)

Benefits: Health insurance, child care, paid vacation, pregnancy leave, family leave, internal/external staff trainings

Part-Time Employees: 5-15

Summer Employees: 5-50

Volunteers: 300-500

Interns: 5-25
Length: 3 - 9 months
Duties: Assist one program advocate with duties and work on one special project
Remuneration: Principally academic credit but also stipend, fellowship and work study

Jobs advertised: Postings with career, intern and departmental offices and related state and national groups as well as advertisements in newspapers and *Community Jobs*

To apply: Contact Dave Anderson, Administrative Director

MINNESOTA TENANTS UNION

1513 East Franklin Avenue East
Minneapolis, MN 55404
(612) 871-2701

Director: Kirk Hill

Purpose: The Tenants Union provides individual advocacy services to tenants with landlord problems, does public education on tenants rights and housing issues and works on related public policy issues.

Methods of operation: Human services (80%), publications (10%), research (3%), public education (2%)

Constituency: Minneapolis area tenants, predominantly low/moderate income

Recent issues and projects: Special emphasis on property tax issues. Publishes a newspaper on tenant issues. Projects include work on courts, housing codes, evictions.

Major publications: Newspaper: *Tenant Inquirer*; tenants rights handbook: *Know Your Rights*

Budget: $35,000

Funding: Individual contributions (60%), government (30%), foundations (5%), direct mail (5%)

Staff: 1
1 Director

Work Week: 50 hours

Benefits: Health insurance, paid vacation

Volunteers: Yes

Interns: Yes
Length: Determined by project

Jobs advertised: Local papers

To apply: Contact Kirk Hill

MISSISSIPPI CIVIL LIBERTIES UNION

P.O. Box 2242
Jackson, MI 39225-2242
(601) 355-6464

Director: Virginia L. Watkins

Purpose: MCLU is a private, nonprofit membership organization, dedicated to the protection and promotion of The Bill of Rights of the U.S. Constitution.

Methods of operation: Fundraising (45%), lobbying (10%), litigation (10%), direct action (10%), public education (10%), research (5%), publications (5%), human services (5%)

Recent issues and projects: Recent issues include: Pro-choice; school prayer; First Amendment; public access to state sealed records. Projects include: public education; Annual Art and Adventure Auction; Annual Dinner and various CLE's.

Major publications: MCLU produces four newsletters a year. Through sponsors and contributors, have had several books written in dedication to MCLU.

Budget: $80,000

Funding: Subsidy (50%), auction (20%), direct mail (10%), individual contributions (10%), foundations (5%), telephone solicitation (5%)

Staff:
2 Organizers
2 Writers/Editors
1 Attorney
1 Office Manager
2 Researchers
1 Lobbyist
2 Foundation Fundraisers
2 Administrative Assistant
1 Bookkeeper/Accountant
2 Grassroots Fundraisers

Staff openings/year: Varies

Work Week: 40-60 hours

Salary/year: $Varies (Recent College Graduate); $Varies (Graduate with advanced degree)

Benefits: Health insurance, pension, paid vacation, life insurance, pregnancy leave

Part-Time Employees: No

Summer Employees: No

Volunteers: Varies

Interns: Varies
Length: 3 months
Duties: Varies
Remuneration: Most interns have located their own sponsors

Jobs advertised: Major newspapers, law schools, word of mouth

To apply: Contact Virginia L. Watkins, Executive Director

Remarks: MCLU members typically do not believe in all we do. They often support us in one cause of action. But the basic premise remains the same; they understand that if it is not for one, it's for none.

MISSOURI PUBLIC INTEREST RESEARCH GROUP (MOPIRG)

4069 1/2 Shenandoah Avenue
St. Louis, MO 63110
(314) 772-7710

Other Offices: Kansas City, MO

Director: Beth Zilbert

Purpose: To represent the public interest before the legislature, through the media and through the courts. Issues are environmental.

Methods of operation: Student development and empowerment through community organizing (50%), lobbying (20%), research (10%), public education (10%), publications (5%), litigation (3-5%)

Membership: 30,000 citizen members ranging in age, socio-economic and political affiliation; 11,000

student members from two St. Louis area campuses

Recent issues and projects: Passed the Missouri Safe Drinking Water Act; registered 4,000 students to vote; published recycling handbook; set up a tenants' rights hotline; working to establish an office of insurance consumer advocate; stop illegal toxic pollution; prevent future contamination

Major publications: *Testing the Waters: A Consumers Guide to Choosing and Protecting Drinking Water*; *Recycling Guide*; *Tenants' Rights Handbook*; quarterly newsletter

Budget: $90,000

Funding: Canvassing (45%), student chapters (45%), fundraisers (5%), foundations (3%), individual contributions (2%)

Staff: 6
10 Canvassers - winter
50 Canvassers - summer
2 Organizers
1 Lobbyist
1 Executive Director
1 Campaign Director
1 Assistant Director

Staff openings/year: 3

Work Week: 60 hours

Salary/year: $12,000 (Recent College Graduate); $13,000+ (Graduate with advanced degree)

Benefits: Health insurance, paid vacation, pregnancy leave, college loan assistance

Part-Time Employees: 5 canvassers

Summer Employees: Yes; canvassers

Volunteers: Yes

Interns: Yes: media, tenants' rights, legislative research
Length: 1 semester
Duties: Research, answering constituent calls, setting up press conferences, writing press releases
Remuneration: Negotiable

Jobs advertised: Newspapers; campus career placement offices

To apply: Contact Beth Zilbert, Executive Director

MONTANA COMMUNITY SHARES

713 South Black #3
Bozeman, MT 59715
(406) 587-1770

Other Offices: Helena, MT

Director: Bob Nichol

Purpose: A federation of environmental, women's, human rights, health advocacy and human rights programs formed to raise money through employer payroll deduction charitable giving programs.

Methods of operation: Community organizing (50%), research (10%), lobbying (10%), public education (10%), training and technical assistance (10%)

Constituency: Progressive statewide advocacy programs

Recent issues and projects: Recent projects include a fall workplace-giving charitable campaign

Major publications: Semi-annual newsletter

Budget: $120,000

Funding: Individual contributions (70%), foundations (25%), direct mail (5%)

Staff: 1
Executive Director (2/3rds time)

Staff openings/year: 1-2

Work Week: 40 hours

Benefits: Health insurance, paid vacation

Part-Time Employees: 2

Summer Employees: 1-2

Volunteers: 50 +

Interns: 1-2
Length: 3 months
Duties: Assist in development of strong workplace campaign committees
Remuneration: $500 a month

To apply: Contact Bob Nichol, Executive Director

MONTANA ENVIRONMENTAL INFORMATION CENTER

Box 1184
Helena, MT 59624
(406) 443-2520

Director: James Jensen

Purpose: To protect and enhance Montana's natural environment.

Methods of operation: Lobbying (40%), research (20%), public education (20%), publications (10%), community organizing (10%)

Constituency: Individuals and families in Montana

Recent issues and projects: Hazardous waste, cyanide heap leach gold mining, water quality, environmental policy, energy conservation, air quality

Major publications: Quarterly newsletter: *Down to Earth*; *Capitol Monitor* biweekly legislative bulletin

Budget: $90,000

Funding: Individual contributions (60%), foundations (30%), direct mail (5%), other (5%)

Staff: 3

Staff openings/year: 1

Work Week: 40 hours

Salary/year: $18,000 (Recent College Graduate); $Varies (Graduate with advanced degree)

Benefits: Health insurance, paid vacation, pregnancy leave

Part-Time Employees: 1

Volunteers: 15

Interns: 1
Length: 3 months
Duties: Varied
Remuneration: $500 per month

Jobs advertised: Newspapers; mailing of announcements

To apply: Contact James Jensen, Executive Director

MONTANA PEOPLE'S ACTION
208 East Main Street
Missoula, MT 59802
(406) 728-5297

Other Offices: Billings, MT; Great Falls, MT

Director: Jim Fleischmann

Purpose: To empower low and moderate income Montanans through community organizing and direct action on issues which members and constituents have identified.

Methods of operation: Community organizing, direct action, public education

Constituency: Low and moderate income Montanans

Recent issues and projects: Forced 4 banks in 3 separate communities to halt the redlining of low-income neighborhoods and to loan an increase of $20 million to those areas

Major publications: Quarterly newsletter

Budget: $160,000

Funding: Foundations (35%), canvassing (35%), events, dues, etc. (30%)

Staff: 10
5 Organizers
4 Canvassers
1 Office Manager

Staff openings/year: 2-4

Work Week: 50 hours

Salary/year: $16,000

Benefits: Health insurance, paid vacation

Summer Employees: 10+

Interns: Yes
Length: 1 quarter of academic year
Duties: Varied

Jobs advertised: *Community Jobs*; local newspapers; mailings to public interest groups

To apply: Contact Jim Fleischmann, Director

Remarks: Over the last 5 years, MPA has established itself as one of the most effective grassroots low-income organizations in the west. A result of this is that the organization is increasingly providing training and technical assistance to emerging constituency-based organizations (disabilities groups, Native American organizations, and others). MPA is also increasingly involved in coalition strategies and was a founding member of the Montana Community Labor Alliance, a coalition of 11 progressive labor and community organizations in Montana.

MONTANA WILDLIFE FEDERATION
P.O. Box 1175
Helena, MT 59624
(406) 449-7604

Director: Tony Jewett

Purpose: To work for the protection, enhancement and conservation of Montana's wildlife resource, the habitat upon which it depends. To advocate recreational activities for the general public in conjunction with their resources.

Methods of operation: Public education (30%), direct action (20%), community organizing (20%), publications (10%), lobbying (10%), research (5%), litigation (5%)

Membership: Grassroots sportspeople, both residents and non-residents of Montana from all walks of life.

Recent issues and projects: Recent projects include: National Clean Water Act; public land access; fisheries maintenance; mining reform; private land/public wildlife efforts; subdivision reform; game farming reform; wilderness designation

Major publications: *Montana Wildlife*, a bi-monthly newsletter

Budget: $400,000

Funding: Individual contributions (40%), foundations (20%), telephone solicitation (20%)

Staff: 4
1 Organizer
1 Office Manager
1 Lobbyist
1 Grassroots Fundraiser

Staff openings/year: 0-1

Work Week: 50 hours

Salary/year: $Varies (Recent College Graduate); $Varies (Graduate with advanced degree)

Benefits: Health insurance, paid vacation

Part-Time Employees: 4

Volunteers: 30

Interns: 2
Length: 3 months
Duties: Depends on season; primarily state legislature lobby
Remuneration: Small stipend

Jobs advertised: In newspapers of the state and job service

MONTHLY REVIEW FOUNDATION

122 West 27th Street
New York, NY 10001
(212) 691-2555

Director: Board of Directors

Purpose: An independent socialist publishing house. They publish a monthly magazine and 15-20 books each year. The audience is the university and graduate school level. They publish non-fiction with few exceptions.

Methods of operation: Publications (100%)

Constituency: For books, largely college and university course adoptions

Recent issues and projects: Economics, politics, sociology, feminism, third world, labor, ecology, socialism and marxism

Major publications: Monthly magazine: *Monthly Review*; books

Budget: $900,000

Staff: 10
3 Editors
3 Order Department
1 Book Production
1 Subscription Department
1 Bookkeeper/Accountant
1 Rights and Permissions

Staff openings/year: 0-1

Work Week: 40 hours

Benefits: Health benefits through U.S. Health Care and paid vacation

Part-Time Employees: 5

Interns: 1
Length: 3 months-1 year
Duties: General office work; proofreading; some research
Remuneration: None unfortunately

Jobs advertised: Through advertising

To apply: Contact Susan Lowes or Judy Ruben.

MOTHER JONES MAGAZINE

731 Market Street, Suite 600
San Francisco, CA 94103
(415) 558-8881

Director: Jeffrey Klein, Editor and Jay Harris, Publisher

Purpose: *Mother Jones* is a progressive journal of politics and the arts, with a particular interest in investigative reporting.

Methods of operation: Publications (90%), research (10%)

Constituency: The average *Mother Jones* reader is in his or her late thirties; 93-4% college educated; 45% women; 55% men; high degree of social/political involvement

Recent issues and projects: The magazine's key interests include the environment, civil liberties, campaign finance reform, violence, peace, education, health security, and the media

Major publications: *Mother Jones*

Budget: $4,000,000

Funding: Circulation, advertising (70%), individual contributions (28%), foundations (2%)

Staff: 15
4 Writers/Editors
1 Bookkeeper/Accountant
2 Circulation Professionals
3 Advertising Sales
2 Researchers
1 Office Manager
1 Foundation Fundraiser
1 Press Aide

Staff openings/year: 1-2

Work Week: 35 hours

Salary/year: $16,000 (Recent College Graduate); $24,000 (Graduate with advanced degree)

Benefits: Health insurance, pregnancy leave, paid vacation

Part-Time Employees: 4

Volunteers: Yes

Interns: Yes
Length: 4 months
Duties: Fact checking; research; reading unsolicited manuscripts
Remuneration: Travel expenses

Jobs advertised: Depends on job

To apply: Depends on position

MOTHERS AGAINST DRUNK DRIVING (MADD)

511 E John Carpenter Fwy., Suite 700
Irving, TX 75062
(214) 744-6233

Director: H. Dean Wilkerson, Executive Director

Purpose: To stop drunk driving and to support victims of this violent crime.

Methods of operation: Research, lobbying, publications, human services, community organizing, public education, training and technical assistance

Constituency: Victims of impaired driving crashes and their allies

Recent issues and projects: Problems of underage drinking and its consequences, responsible beverage advertising, constitutional amendments for crime victims rights, lower legal limits of blood alcohol content for DWI/DUI offenses

Major publications: Quarterly newsletter, *MADD in Action*; *MADDvocate*, a biannual publication dealing with victim issues, etc.; Victim Issues brochures, Student Library materials

Budget: $45,000,000

Funding: Individuals, corporations and foundations

Staff: 56
29 Professional Staff
27 Support Staff

Staff openings/year: 10

Work Week: 40 hours

Salary/year: $Varies (Recent College Graduate); $Varies (Graduate with advanced degree)

Benefits: Health insurance, pregnancy leave, pension, paid vacation

Part-Time Employees: Yes

Volunteers: Yes

Jobs advertised: Newspapers and employment agencies

To apply: Contact Debbie Pendergrass

Remarks: We have 400 chapters in 48 states, Australia, England, New Zealand and Canada.

MOUNT CARMEL HOUSE

471 G Place, NW
Washington, DC 20001
(202) 289-6315

Director: Sr. Rosa Alvarez

Purpose: The Mount Carmel House's primary goals are to provide clean, safe, dignified shelter for homeless women, and to provide services that help them move toward independence.

Methods of operation: Human services (95%), public education (3%), publications (2%)

Recent issues and projects: Mount Carmel has expanded their educational day program. They are currently offering a variety of seminars and courses to help residents regain their independence. They continue to advocate on behalf of the homeless population.

Major publications: Quarterly: *Mount Carmel House Newsletter*; the pamphlet *Faces and Reflections*, about the personal experiences of the homeless

Budget: $220,000

Funding: Individual contributions (65%), Catholic charities (30%), foundations (5%)

Staff: 8
1 Assistant Administrator
1 Day Program/Volunteer Coordinator
1 Substance Abuse Counselor
1 Case Worker
1 House Manager
3 Night Managers
1/2 Staff Aide

Staff openings/year: 3

Work Week: 40 hours

Salary/year: $13,000 (Recent College Graduate); $16,000 (Graduate with advanced degree)

Benefits: Health insurance, pension, pregnancy leave, paid vacation

Part-Time Employees: 3

Summer Employees: Yes; as needed

Volunteers: 100

Interns: 1
Length: 1 year or less
Duties: General work with women; others according to skills
Remuneration: Individually negotiated

Jobs advertised: Newspaper; local justice networks

To apply: Contact Sr. Rosa Alvarez, Coordinator

MUTUAL HOUSING ASSOCIATION OF NEW YORK, INC. (MHANY)

845 Flatbush Avenue
Brooklyn, NY 11226
(718) 693-9100

Director: Lawson Shadburn

Purpose: Rehabilitation of abandoned housing and placement of families into that housing

Methods of operation: Construction, acquisition of properties (30%), training and technical assistance (20%), direct action (20%), human services (15%), community organizing (15%)

Constituency: Low-moderate income; mostly minorities

Budget: $590,000

Funding: Foundations (35%), development and management fees (65%)

Staff: 8
1 Construction Coordinator
3 Property Managers
2 Executive
1 Bookkeeper
1 Organizer

Staff openings/year: 1-2

Work Week: 50 hours

Salary/year: $12-34,000

Benefits: None

Summer Employees: 1

Volunteers: Yes; membership

Interns: 1
Length: 3 months
Duties: Various; property management, proposal writing

Jobs advertised: Local newspaper

To apply: Contact Nan Wilson, Director of Operations

MY SISTER'S PLACE

P.O. Box 29596
Washington, DC 20017-0796
(202) 529-5991

Director: Betty Mathews, Executive Director

Purpose: My Sister's Place provides a hotline and shelter for battered women and their children as well as public education and advocacy.

Methods of operation: Human services (90%), public education (10%)

Constituency: Broad-based constituency of persons concerned with violence, especially against women and children

Recent issues and projects: My Sister's Place has added transitional housing to our shelter program, to extend the period of time in which a woman departing the shelter may continue to work to establish a solid independence from her abuser. They have also begun a youth outreach component by creating the Teen Advocacy program and extending the Children's Advocacy program beyond the shelter into the community. By reaching young women and men at an earlier age, they increase the likelihood of interrupting the intergenerational cycle of violence in their lives.

Budget: $600,000

Staff: 10
1 Job/Housing Coordinator
1 Direct Services Coordinator
1 Women's Advocate
1 Volunteer Coordinator/Community Organizer
1 Development Coordinator
1 Child Advocate
1 Administrative Assistant
1 Facilities Manager
1 Community Education Coordinator
1 Overnight House Coordinator

Work Week: 40+ hours

Salary/year: $20,000 (Recent College Graduate); $Varies (Graduate with advanced degree)

Benefits: Health insurance, paid vacation

Part-Time Employees: 1

Volunteers: 100+

Interns: 1-5
Length: 6 months
Duties: Varies with interns
Remuneration: Depends; most are students and receive no pay

Jobs advertised: *Washington Post*, other social service agencies, *Community Jobs*

To apply: Contact the Program Director

NAACP LEGAL DEFENSE & EDUCATIONAL FUND - LOS ANGELES

315 W 9th Street, Suite 208
Los Angeles, CA 90025
(213) 624-2405

Other Offices: New York, NY

Director: Elaine Jones

Purpose: The NAACP undertakes Civil Rights Impact litigation and advocacy in a variety of discrimination areas including: education, housing, voting rights, employment, health, environmental justice, poverty and criminal justice.

Methods of operation: Litigation (85%), training and technical assistance (15%)

Constituency: African American community and other communities of color

Recent issues and projects: Since its founding in 1988, the Western Regional Office has undertaken litigation in the areas of voting rights for LA County, police misconduct in South Central, LA, access to health care for the minority in Contra Costa County, housing discrimination in LA, disproportionate allocation of resources in probation services, employment discrimination within the Los Angeles Police Department and state requirements for the testing of poor children for lead poisoning.

Major publications: *LDF Annual Report*; *Capital Punishment/Criminal Justice Newsletter*; *Our Earth Matters: An Environmental Newsletter*

Budget: $9,500,000

Funding: Individual contributions, foundations, direct mail

Staff: 9
5 Attorneys
1 Paralegal
3 Administrative Assistants

Staff openings/year: 1

Work Week: 40 hours

Salary/year: $22,000

Benefits: Health insurance, pension, paid vacation, life insurance, family leave

Part-Time Employees: None

Summer Employees: None

Volunteers: 1

Interns: 5
Length: 10-15 weeks
Duties: Legal research, drafting documents, participate in all aspects of litigation
Remuneration: Interns must bring own funding

NAACP LEGAL DEFENSE & EDUCATIONAL FUND, INC.

99 Hudson Street, 16th Floor
New York, NY 10013
(212) 219-1900

Other Offices: Los Angeles, CA; Washington, DC

Director: Elaine R. Jones, Director-Counsel

Purpose: Bring civil rights litigation on behalf of African Americans in areas of employment, housing, voting, education, health care, poverty and justice and capital punishment.

Methods of operation: Litigation (80%), research (5%), lobbying (5%), community organizing (5%), scholarships (5%)

Constituency: African Americans

Recent issues and projects: Low-income housing; higher education; employment discrimination; capital punishment

Major publications: Quarterly newsletter: *Equal Justice*; annual report

Budget: $9,000,000

Funding: Individual contributions (60%), foundations (20%), legal fees (20%)

Staff: 75
25 Attorneys
20 Typists
6 Paralegals
6 Bookkeepers/Accountants
5 Grassroots Fundraisers
4 Office Managers
2 Issue Experts
2 File Clerks
1 Researcher
1 Press Aide
1 Foundation Fundraiser
1 Receptionist
1 Director of Scholarship Program

Staff openings/year: 2-4

Work Week: 35-50 hours

Salary/year: $20,000 (Recent College Graduate); $29,000 (Graduate with advanced degree)

Benefits: Health insurance, life insurance, pregnancy leave, pension, paid vacation

Part-Time Employees: 3

Summer Employees: 20

Interns: 2-3
Length: 1 semester
Duties: Law clerk
Remuneration: Work-study

Jobs advertised: Legal positions advertised in law school employment offices; other positions in newspapers

To apply: For staff lawyer positions, contact Julius L. Chambers, Director-Counsel; for legal internships, contact the Law Student Selection Committee; for clerical positions, contact Donna Gloeckner, Office Administrator.

NATIONAL ABORTION FEDERATION

1436 U Street, NW, Suite 103
Washington, DC 20008
(202) 667-5881

Director: Sylvia Stengle, MPH

Purpose: NAF is the national professional association of abortion providers. Our mission is to enhance the quality and accessibility of abortion care. We set standards for quality care, work to enhance public understanding of issues surrounding abortion, and advocate for women and providers.

Methods of operation: Public education (25%), training and technical assistance (20%), publications (15%), human services (15%), research (10%), health care services support - legal clearinghouse, guidance on response to violence, etc. (15%)

Membership: Abortion providers and their supporters in the United States, its territories, and Canada

Recent issues and projects: The Access Initiative is NAF's effort to address the shortage of physicians to provide abortion services through expansion of training opportunities, recruitment and mentoring programs, and other projects. The Truth About Abortion Campaign creates and distributes fact sheets and issue papers.

Major publications: *The Model Pleadings Book for Abortion Providers; Who Will Provide Abortions?* (a joint report with ACOG); *The Truth About Abortion* fact sheet series; *Unsure About Your Pregnancy? A Guide to Making the Right Decision for You; Having an Abortion? Your Guide to Good Care*; and many others

Budget: $1,000,000

Funding: Foundations (40%), membership fees (34%), meeting revenues (19%)

Staff: 13
4 Program Support
1 Office Manager
1 Lobbyist
1 Press Aide
1 Foundation Fundraiser
1 Training Expert
1 Issue Expert
1 Computer Staff
1 Group Purchasing Manager

Staff openings/year: 4

Work Week: 40 hours

Salary/year: $18-22,000 (Recent College Graduate); $Varies (Graduate with advanced degree)

Benefits: Health insurance, pension, paid vacation, life insurance, pregnancy leave

Part-Time Employees: 1

Summer Employees: 1-2

Volunteers: None

Interns: 2
Length: 3 months
Duties: Respond to callers on national toll-free abortion information/referral hotline
Remuneration: Salary

Jobs advertised: Varies among the following: *Washington Post, Roll Call, Opportunities in Public Affairs, Community Jobs*, ASAE listings, Women's Information Network

To apply: Contact Tamalynn McGowan, Director of Finance and Administration

NATIONAL ABORTION RIGHTS ACTION LEAGUE (NARAL)

1156 15th Street, NW, Suite 700
Washington, DC 20005
(202) 408-4600

President: Kate Michelman

Purpose: To develop and sustain a constituency that effectively uses the political process at the state and national level to guarantee every woman in the U.S. the right to choose and obtain a legal abortion.

Methods of operation: Research, lobbying, publications, community organizing, public education, training and technical assistance

Constituency: Pro-choice activists

Recent issues and projects: Ongoing grassroots organizing and lobbying efforts.

Major publications: Newsletter: *NARAL News*; *A Legislative Update*; *Who Decides? A Reproductive Rights Issues Manual*; *Who Decides? A State by State Review of Abortion Rights in America*; *Annual Congressional Voting Records*

Budget: $3,500,000

Funding: Individual contributions, foundations, direct mail, telephone solicitation

Staff: 34
7 Grassroots Organizers
5 Political
5 Legal/Research
6 Finance/Administrative
6 Development
3 Executive
2 Communications

Staff openings/year: 3-5

Work Week: 37.5 hours

Salary/year: $19,000 (Recent College Graduate); $22,000 (Graduate with advanced degree)

Benefits: Health insurance, life insurance, pregnancy leave, pension, paid vacation, long-term disability

Part-Time Employees: 0

Volunteers: Yes

Interns: Yes
Length: Flexible
Duties: Research and support work on special projects
Remuneration: Unpaid and paid

Jobs advertised: Newspaper ads and pro-choice network

To apply: Contact Human Resources

Remarks: NARAL has 40 affiliate organizations nationwide.

NATIONAL AIDS NETWORK

2033 M Street, NW, Suite 800
Washington, DC 20036
(202) 293-2437

Director: Eric Engstrom

Purpose: The National AIDS Network provides leadership, information and support to community-based AIDS education and service providers.

Methods of operation: Public education, training and technical assistance, community organizing, publications

Constituency: 650 community-based organizations providing AIDS education and services; health departments

Recent issues and projects: We are currently organizing our National conference for managers of AIDS organizations and programs.

Major publications: Newsletters: *Network News*, *Multi-Cultural NOTES*; series of technical assistance packages on food programs, volunteer management and buddy programs

Budget: $1,400,000

Funding: Foundations (60%), memberships, government contracts, corporate support (39%), individual contributions (1%)

Staff: 17
3 National-Community AIDS Partnership
2 Issue Experts
2 Foundation Fundraisers
1 Writer/Editor
1 Researcher
1 Office Manager
1 Executive (on loan)
1 Organizer
1 Membership Services
1 Information and Referral
1 Press Aide
1 Bookkeeper/Accountant
1 Typist

Staff openings/year: 1

Work Week: 45 hours

Salary/year: $Varies (Recent College Graduate); $Varies (Graduate with advanced degree)

Benefits: Health insurance, life insurance, pregnancy leave, paid vacation

Part-Time Employees: 3

Interns: Yes
Length: 3 months
Duties: Depends on program in which intern chooses to work; writing, research
Remuneration: No stipend

Jobs advertised: Through major daily newspapers and targeted mailings

To apply: Contact Eric Engstrom, Executive Director, for staff positions; contact Anne Lewis for internships

---

NATIONAL ALLIANCE FOR THE MENTALLY ILL

2101 Wilson Boulevard, Suite 302
Arlington, VA 22201
(703) 524-7600

Director: Laurie M. Flynn

Purpose: NAMI is a self-help organization of people with mental illness, their families and friends. It provides emotional support and information on the biological nature of serious mental illness through local family support groups, advocates for better treatment and community services, promotes research on causes and treatments of serious mental illness and seeks to eliminate the stigma associated with these disorders.

Methods of operation: Public education (60%), training and technical assistance (25%), human services (5%), publications (5%), direct action (5%)

Constituency: Families and friends of people with serious mental illness and those persons themselves

Recent issues and projects: Teleconference on Depressive Illness to over 100 colleges and universities (February 13, 1990); Patty Duke testified before Congressional hearing on need for research funds; presentation to Congress of over 400,000 signatures in support of increased funding to National Institute of Mental Health; a reception honoring Congressional leaders with strong records on mental illness issues (April 1990); 1990 Annual Meeting held in Chicago July 18-22.

Major publications: National newsletter: *The*

Advocate; newsletters of the Consumer Council (*The Alliance*), of the Sibling and Adult Children's Network (*The Bond*), of the Forensic Network (*Forensic Monitor*), of the Religious Outreach Network (*Lumen*), and of the Curriculum and Training Network. Also *Care of the Seriously Mentally Ill: A Rating of State Programs.*

Budget: $2,200,000

Funding: Individual contributions (75%), foundations (15%), other (10%)

Staff: 23
Including:
3 Campaign Managers
3 Typists
3 Advocates
2 Bookkeeper/Accountants
1 Office Manager
1 Foundation Fundraiser
1 Caseworker
1 Grassroots Fundraiser

Staff openings/year: 2

Work Week: 35-50 hours

Salary/year: $15-25,000

Benefits: Health insurance, pension, paid vacation, life insurance, pregnancy leave

Part-Time Employees: 2

Volunteers: 30

Interns: Yes
Length: 1-5 months

Jobs advertised: *Washington Post*

To apply: Contact Lynn Dorton, Director of Administration and Management

Remarks: There are over 900 local and state NAMI affiliates nationwide, in all 50 states.

NATIONAL ASSEMBLY OF VOLUNTARY HEALTH AND SOCIAL WELFARE ORGANIZATION

1319 F Street, NW #601
Washington, DC 20004
(202) 347-2080

Director: Gordon Raley

Purpose: The National Assembly is an association of 40 national health and human service organizations. The National Assembly provides opportunities for its members to network and provides forum for focusing on mutual programs and policy goals.

Methods of operation: Research (10%), lobbying (10%), publications (10%), public education (10%), training and technical assistance (10%), human resource development (10%), conference and meeting networking (10%)

Membership: National human service organizations including national health and national youth servicing organizations

Recent issues and projects: The National Assembly convenes: 1)professional support groups for management personnel of health and human service organizations; 2) Public Policy groups; 3) The National Collaboration for youth, an affinity group of the National Assembly including 15 national youth service organizations.

Budget: $500,000

Funding: Foundations, member dues

Staff: 5
1 Office Manager
1 Researcher
1 Coordinator, Membership Activities
1 Research Assistant
1/2 Newsletter Editor
1/2 Director of Human Resource

Staff openings/year: 1

Work Week: 35 hours

Salary/year: $23,000 (Recent College Graduate); $24,000 (Graduate with advanced degree)

Benefits: Health insurance, pension, paid vacation, life insurance

Part-Time Employees: None

Summer Employees: None

Volunteers: Yes

Interns: 2
Length: 2-3 months
Duties: Assist in writing articles for newsletter, assist in conducting policy research for program research.
Remuneration: Varies

Jobs advertised: Through national organizations that are members and human service Newsletters and Journals

To apply: Please contact Gordon Raley, Executive Director

NATIONAL ASSOCIATION FOR PUBLIC INTEREST LAW (NAPIL)

1118 22nd Street, NW, Third Floor
Washington, DC 20037
(202) 466-3686

Director: Kathleen A. Welch

Purpose: NAPIL is a national coalition of law student organizations that offer grants and other forms of assistance to students and recent graduates engaged in public interest employment. Law students formed NAPIL in 1986 to educate and prepare future lawyers to recognize the inequities that exist in our legal system and to dedicate their professional lives to the development of a more just society. As a clearinghouse and public education and training center, NAPIL works with our member organizations to create public interest legal employment and training opportunities, remove the economic barriers that confront future public interest lawyers, and provide informational and inspirational resources for public service work.

Methods of operation: Training and technical assistance (30%), publications (25%), public education (20%), community organizing (15%), research (10%)

Constituency: NAPIL is a coalition of law students and public interest organizations across the country.

Recent issues and projects: Income sharing programs; loan repayment assistance programs; improved public interest placement resources; annual conference and career fair bringing together hundreds of law students, public interest practitioners and law school administrators; national post-graduate fellowship program, summer legal corps, regional law student trainings and income sharing groups

Major publications: *NAPIL Directory of Public Interest Legal Internships*; *NAPIL Fellowships Guide*; *Loan Repayment Assistance Program Report*; *An Action Manual for Loan Repayment Assistance*; *The NAPIL Connection* newsletter; *NAPIL Public Interest Career Resource Guide*

Budget: $100,000

Funding: Student organizations, publications (50%), foundations (50%)

Staff: 7
1 Executive Director
1 Organizer
1 Public Interest Clearinghouse Coordinator
1 Foundation Fundraiser
1 Fellowship Project Director
1 Fellowship Program Associate
1 Office Manager/Program Associate

Staff openings/year: 2

Work Week: 40-50 hours

Salary/year: $17,000 (Recent College Graduate); $23,000 (Graduate with advanced degree)

Benefits: Health insurance, paid vacation, loan forgiveness

Summer Employees: 2-4

Volunteers: Yes

Interns: Yes
Length: Summer or semester
Duties: Research, writing, press work, conference organizing
Remuneration: Matching grants provided in some instances

Jobs advertised: *Community Jobs*; public interest job boards; ACCESS: Networking in the Public Interest; school career services; *Opportunities in Public Affairs*

To apply: Contact Kathleen A. Welch for permanent positions and Internship Coordinator for internships

NATIONAL ASSOCIATION FOR THE ADVANCEMENT OF COLORED PEOPLE (NAACP)

4805 Mt. Hope Drive
Baltimore, MD 21215-3297
(410) 358-8900

Other Offices: Washington, DC

Director: Earl Shinhoster (Acting Director)

Purpose: To insure the political, educational, social and economic equality of black citizens; to achieve equality of rights and eliminate race prejudice among people of the U.S.; to eliminate racial discrimination

Methods of operation: Litigation, lobbying, research

Recent issues and projects: Access to quality education for minorities; enforcement and protection of civil rights laws; minority voter registration and education; economic empowerment; Fair Share Program; Back to School/Stay in School Program;

Afro-Academic, Cultural and Scientific Olympics (ACT-SO); legal action against discrimination in employment and other areas; the black family

Major publications: *CRISIS Magazine*, monthly; annual report; occasional papers on issues

Funding: Individual contributions, foundations

Staff: 120
43 Clerks/Secretarial
33 Professional/Administrative Support
9 Organizers
9 Attorneys
7 Program Directors
7 Bookkeepers/Accountants
4 Lobbyists
4 Writers/Editors
2 Foundation Fundraisers
2 Press Aides
1 Paralegal
1 Office Manager

Staff openings/year: 4

Work Week: 37.5 hours

Salary/year: $22-25,000

Benefits: Health insurance, life insurance, pregnancy leave, pension, paid vacation

Part-Time Employees: 1

Volunteers: Yes

Interns: 3-4
Length: 3 months
Duties: Research and writing, usually in the Legal Department
Remuneration: College/university subsidies; stipend from the Association

Jobs advertised: Newspapers, *The CRISIS*, school placement offices

To apply: Contact Ms. Earlene Bollin, Director of Personnel

Remarks: The officers of the 2,200 NAACP branches across the country are volunteers.

NATIONAL ASSOCIATION FOR THE LEGAL SUPPORT OF ALTERNATIVE SCHOOLS

P.O. Box 2823
Sante Fe, NM 87501
(505) 471-6928

Director: Ed Nagel, Coordinator

Purpose: NALSAS is a national information and legal service center designed to research, coordinate and support legal actions involving nonpublic educational alternatives. Challenges compulsory attendance laws as violative of First Amendment rights and other state controls as noncompulsory learning arrangements. NALSAS helps interested persons and organizations locate/evaluate/create viable alternatives to traditional schooling approaches.

Methods of operation: Research, litigation, publications, organizing, public education

Constituency: Teachers, lawyers, parents, educators

Major publications: Newsletter: *Tidbits*

Budget: $6,000

Funding: Membership fees, contributions

Staff: 3

Staff openings/year: 1

Work Week: 40+ hours

Salary/year: $Varies (Recent College Graduate); $Varies (Graduate with advanced degree)

Benefits: Child care, pregnancy leave

Part-Time Employees: Yes

Volunteers: Yes

Interns: Yes
Length: 3 months
Duties: Office work, research, community service, cleaning
Remuneration: Room and board (food stamps)

Jobs advertised: Word of mouth

To apply: Contact Ed Nagel, Coordinator

Remarks: Salary consists of room and board.

NATIONAL ASSOCIATION OF ARTISTS' ORGANIZATIONS

918 F Street, NW
Washington, DC 20004
(202) 347-6350

Director: Charlotte R. Murphy, Executive Director

Purpose: Dedicated to serving and promoting artists' nonprofit organizations and the art they support and present. We promote artistic freedom.

Methods of operation: Direct action (40%), lobbying (20%), research (10%), publications

(10%), community organizing (10%), public education (10%)

Constituency: Artists' organizations (national), museums, galleries, theaters, arts centers, individual artists and arts supporters nationwide

Recent issues and projects: Campaign against censorship in the arts; multi-site collaborations; directory - artist organization resource and information; membership; comprehensive organizational assistance for artists' organizations

Major publications: *NAAO Directory*; *NAAO Bulletin*, quarterly; newsflashes; etc.

Budget: $357,330

Funding: Individual contributions (50%), foundations (50%)

Staff: 2
1 Executive Director
1 Assistant Director

Staff openings/year: 2

Work Week: 50 hours

Part-Time Employees: 1

Interns: 2
Length: 1-2 semesters
Duties: Edit bulletin; answer correspondence, telephones; do mailings, errands; disseminate information

Jobs advertised: Publications, ads, etc.

To apply: Contact Charlotte R. Murphy, Executive Director

NATIONAL ASSOCIATION OF NEIGHBORHOODS

1651 Fuller Street, NW
Washington, DC 20009
(202) 332-7766

Director: Deborah Crain

Purpose: NAN is a multi-issue constituency made up of over 2,000 community-based organizations and small businesses in 38 states. NAN members work locally to improve the quality of life in our nation's neighborhoods and to promote social and economic development.

Methods of operation: Community organizing, training and technical assistance

Constituency: Over 2,000 community-based organizations

Recent issues and projects: (1) Neighborhood Based Service Delivery Project: to develop and improve the skills of community-based organizations to provide essential services to their neighborhoods. (2) Public Transportation Entrepreneurial Services Project: to stimulate the development of creative small business ventures that will supplement current public transit systems and respond to the unmet transportation needs of inner-city and suburban areas. (3) Leadership Training Institute. (4) Environmental

Major publications: *NAN Bulletin*, quarterly; *Building Neighborhood Organizations*; *NAN Handbook on Reinvestment Displacement*; *Neighborhood Economic Enterprises*; *How to Start a Neighborhood Weatherization Co-op*

Funding: Government grants (50%), individual contributions (25%), foundations (25%)

Staff: 5
1 Organizer
1 Foundation Fundraiser
1 Administrator
1 Bookkeeper/Accountant
1 Secretary

Staff openings/year: 1

Work Week: 40 hours

Benefits: Health insurance, life insurance, pregnancy leave, paid vacation

Summer Employees: 1

Volunteers: 1-2

Jobs advertised: Newspaper ads

To apply: Contact Althea Gatewood, Administrator

NATIONAL ASSOCIATION OF PARTNERS IN EDUCATION

209 Madison Street, Suite 401
Alexandria, VA 22301
(703) 836-4880

Director: Daniel W. Merenda

Purpose: NAPE is the only national membership organization devoted solely to the mission of providing leadership in the formation and growth of effective partnerships that ensure success for all students. NAPE defines "partnership in education" as a collaborative effort between a school(s) or school district(s) and one or more community organizations with the purpose of improving the academic and personal growth of America's youth.

: Training and technical
cations (25%), community
:t action (5%), public

hip Directors, educators,
makers

Recent issues and projects: Recent projects include: Ambassadors for Education - School Smart Citizens; Ideals-Service-Learning Project; Virginia Project - Integrating Comprehensive Services into the Curriculum

Major publications: Monthly newsletters on education issues, books and manuals on topics including partnerships for school dropout prevention, intergeneration volunteers, etc.

Budget: $1,200,000

Funding: Individual contributions, foundations, membership

Staff:
2 Desktop Publishers
1 Office Managers
1 Foundation Fundraiser
1 Administrative Assistant
1 Public Relations, Membership Coordinator
1 Manager Computer Systems

Staff openings/year: 1-2

Work Week: 60 hours

Salary/year: $19,000 (Recent College Graduate); $27,000 (Graduate with advanced degree)

Benefits: Health insurance, paid vacation, life insurance

Summer Employees: Sometimes

Volunteers: 2

Interns: 1
Length: Semester, summer
Duties: Public relations intern, special project intern

Jobs advertised: *Washington Post*

To apply: Please contact Marilyn Capretta, Office Manager

NATIONAL ASSOCIATION OF PEOPLE WITH AIDS

1413 K Street, NW, 7th Floor
Washington, DC 20005
(202) 898-0414

Director: William Freeman

Purpose: NAPWA is dedicated to improving the lives of people with HIV/AIDS at home, in the community and in the workplace. NAPWA serves as a national information resource and "voice" for the needs and concerns of all Americans infected and affected by HIV.

Methods of operation: Public education (50%), training and technical assistance (20%), publications (10%), community organizing (10%), lobbying (10%)

Constituency: AIDS service organizations, businesses, individual and community-based organizations. Our constituency is everyone infected and affected by HIV.

Major publications: *Medical Alert*; *The Active Voice*; *HIV in America: A Profile of the Challenges Facing Americans Living With AIDS*

Funding: Foundations (60%), individual contributions (40%)

Staff: 21
2 Writers/Editors
1 Attorney
1 Office Manager
1 Lobbyist
1 Foundation Fundraiser
6 Issue Experts
2 Administrative Assistants
6 HIV Educators

Staff openings/year: 2

Work Week: 40 hours

Salary/year: $24,000 (Recent College Graduate); $30,000 (Graduate with advanced degree)

Benefits: Health insurance, paid vacation, life insurance

Part-Time Employees: 2

Summer Employees: None

Volunteers: 2

Interns: 1
Length: 6 months
Duties: Varies
Remuneration: Small Stipend

Jobs advertised: Local and national newspapers; gay and lesbian newspapers; networking with other organizations

To apply: Contact Director of Finance

NATIONAL ASSOCIATION OF RAILROAD PASSENGERS (NARP)

900 Second Street, NE, Suite 308
Washington, DC 20002
(202) 408-8362

Director: Ross Capon

Purpose: Improving the quality and quantity of all types of rail passenger service in the U.S. Helping freight railroads get a "fair deal" from the government, especially by means of forcing big trucks to pay the full cost of the damage they do to highways. Working with environmental organizations and other natural allies.

Methods of operation: Research, public education, publications, lobbying

Membership: 11,500 dues-paying individuals

Recent issues and projects: Their Campaign for New Transportation Priorities, established in 1986, focuses on the broader issues noted above, especially adequate funding of mass transit and the fight for a federal/weight-distance tax on trucks. NARP also testifies annually before the House Appropriations Subcommitte on Transportation and at all House and Senate authorization hearings.

Major publications: *NARP News*, published 11 times/year

Budget: $325,000

Staff: 4
2 Writers/Lobbyists/Press Aides
1 Membership Director
1 Administrative Assistant

Work Week: 40 hours

Benefits: Health insurance, life insurance, pension, paid vacation

Part-Time Employees: 2

Jobs advertised: *Washington Post*

To apply: Contact Ross Capon, Executive Director

NATIONAL ASSOCIATION OF SERVICE AND CONSERVATION CORPS (NASCC)

666 11th Street, NW, Suite 500
Washington, DC 20001
(202) 737-6272

Director: Kathleen Selz, Executive Director

Purpose: Nonprofit education association made up of conservation and service corps operating in states and cities. Serves as information exchange network for members concerning conservation corps administration and management, promotes conservation and service values among staff and corpsmembers, offers technical assistance to those interested in launching new corps, and promotes establishment of federal, state and local programs.

Constituency: State and local conservation corps and service corps

Recent issues and projects: NASCC sponsors an annual national conference and regional seminars and workshops for youth corps advocates and related youth service programs.

Major publications: Quarterly newsletter: *Youth Can!*; *A Conservation and Service Corps Workbook*; *Urban Conservation and Service Corps Programs* reports; job announcements; *Profiles*

Funding: Foundations (90%)

Staff: 5
1 Member Services Director
1 Technical Assistance Director
1 Office Manager
1 Public Policy Director
1 Director, Special Projects

Work Week: 40 hours

Salary/year: $Varies (Recent College Graduate); $Varies (Graduate with advanced degree)

Benefits: Health insurance, life insurance, pregnancy leave, paid vacation

Interns: Yes
Length: Summer/School Year
Duties: Work on specific projects
Remuneration: Stipend

Jobs advertised: Newspapers; local publications; environmental/conservation network

To apply: Contact the Office Manager

NATIONAL AUDUBON SOCIETY

700 Broadway
New York, NY 10003
(212) 979-3100

Other Offices: Anchorage, AK; Washington, DC; Minneapolis, MN; Santa Fe, NM; Boulder, CO; Tallahassee, FL; Austin, TX; Camp Hill, PA; Columbus, OH; Olympia, WA; Miami, FL

Purpose: The National Audubon Society is a conservation and environmental organization whose mission is to: (1) conserve native plants and animals and their habitats; (2) protect life from pollution, radiation, and toxic substances; (3) further the wise use of land and water; (4) seek solutions for global problems involving the interaction of population, resources, and the environment; and (5) promote rational strategies for energy development and use, stressing conservation and renewable energy sources.

Methods of operation: Research, education, lobbying, litigation, publications, community organizing

Major publications: *Audubon Magazine*; *American Birds Magazine*; *Activist*; *Audubon Adventures*; *Audubon*

Funding: Individual contributions, foundations, direct mail, telephone solicitation

Staff: 350
Including:
Senior Managers
Middle Managers
Fundraisers
Researchers
Lobbyists
Public Affairs Staff
Accountants
Secretaries

Staff openings/year: 10

Work Week: 35 hours

Salary/year: $20,000 (Recent College Graduate); $25,000 (Graduate with advanced degree)

Benefits: Health insurance, life insurance, pregnancy leave, pension, paid vacation

Part-Time Employees: 30

Summer Employees: 30

Volunteers: Yes

Interns: 10
Length: 3 months
Remuneration: Housing and stipend

Jobs advertised: Newspaper; environmental listings

To apply: Contact Morag Rollins, Director of Human Resources

NATIONAL BLACK CHILD DEVELOPMENT INSTITUTE

1023 15th Street, NW
Washington, DC 20005
(202) 387-1281 Fax: (202) 234-1738

Director: Evelyn K. Moore

Purpose: The National Black Child Development Institute is dedicated to improving the quality of life for African American children, youth and families in the areas of education, child care, health and child welfare. NBCDI and its affiliate network consists of 42 chapters in 23 states.

Methods of operation: Human services (20%), publications (15%), training and technical assistance (15%), research (10%), lobbying (10%), community organizing (10%), direct action (10%), public education (10%)

Membership: Child advocates, human service providers, educators, parents

Recent issues and projects: Recent projects include: The Spirit of Excellence Parent Empowerment Project, a program working with low-income African American families in Washington, DC to improve parenting through self development, mentoring and parenting training; The Spirit of Excellence Each One, Reach One, an educational-enrichment program that works to improve academic competency and performance, and self-esteem

Major publications: *Child Health Talk*, a quarterly newsletter that covers health-related issues that affect children; *The Black Child Advocate*, a quarterly newsletter that covers public policy and legislation; *Paths to African American Leadership Positions in Early Childhood Education*, a research study; annual calendar of African American children; Spirit of Excellence resource guides

Budget: $1,800,000

Funding: Individual contributions (50%), foundations (20%), direct mail (15%)

Staff: 17

3 Caseworkers
2 Organizers
2 Typists
1 Writer/Editor
1 Office Manager
1 Press Aide
1 Foundation Fundraiser
1 Issue Expert
1 Bookkeeper/Accountant
1 Director for Program Development
1 Meeting Planner
1 Program Associate
1 Office Assistant

Work Week: 40 hours

Volunteers: 33

Interns: 2
Length: Yearly
Duties: Fundraising, public relations, research, administrative support
Remuneration: On an individual basis

Jobs advertised: Newspaper

To apply: Contact Sherry Deane, Deputy Executive Director

NATIONAL BLACK WOMEN'S HEALTH PROJECT
1237 Ralph D. Abernathy Blvd., SW
Atlanta, GA 30310
(404) 758-9590 (800) ASK-BWHP

Other Offices: Washington, DC

Director: Cynthia Newbille

Purpose: The NBWHP, founded in 1981 by MacArthur Award winner Byllye Y. Avery, provides wellness education and services, self-help group development and health information and advocacy for African-American women and their families. The NBWHP continues to challenge America and champion the cause of affordable, equitable and quality healthcare for Black women, their families and communities. The organization has been a tireless and determined voice on the issues of Black women's health for over a decade.

Recent issues and projects: The NBWHP is taking the lead in empowering black women to improve our collective wellness. NBWHP's accomplishments over the last year reflect our continued focus on the promotion of Black women's wellness. These accomplishments include: increased national membership; the launching of a health promotion initiative, Walking for Wellness, to engage Black women in a structured walking program; the spearheading of a national campaign for abortion and reproductive equity (so as to insure poor women's access to safe and affordable abortions); an annual conference on women's health held in Detroit, Michigan which was attended by over 650 women from around the country and the world; and the establishment of a Women of Color Coalition.

Major publications: Quarterly newsmagazine: *Vital Signs*

Budget: $1,426,916

Funding: Foundations (80%), program services (10%), government grants (5%), NUSA (3%), membership (2%)

Staff: 20
10 Organizers
4 Typists
2 Office Managers
2 Bookkeepers/Accountants
1 Foundation Fundraiser
1 Grassroots Fundraiser

Staff openings/year: 5

Work Week: 60 hours

Salary/year: $18,000 (Recent College Graduate); $Varies (Graduate with advanced degree)

Benefits: Health insurance, life insurance, paid vacation, opportunity to work with Black women

Part-Time Employees: 2

Volunteers: 10

Interns: Yes
Length: 6 months
Duties: Research, writing, organizing
Remuneration: Case-by-case basis

Jobs advertised: Newspaper; networks

To apply: Contact Loretta Ross, Program Director

NATIONAL CAMPAIGN FOR A PEACE TAX FUND
2121 Decatur Place, NW
Washington, DC 20008
(202) 483-3751

Director: Marian C. Franz

Purpose: NCPTF works for legislation that would make it possible for persons religiously, morally, or ethically opposed to supporting war to have the military portion of their taxes go into a trust fund for projects that enhance peace.

Methods of operation: Lobbying (50%), public education (30%), publications (20%)

Constituency: Those conscientiously opposed to having their taxes supporting the military, and those in sympathy with their plight

Recent issues and projects: Lobbying in DC and grassroots campaign for U.S. Peace Tax Fund Bill. Coordinated testimony for a Congressional hearing on the U.S. Peace Tax Fund Bill. Produced and distributed video about conscience and taxes.

Major publications: Quarterly newsletter

Budget: $130,000

Funding: Individual contributions (90%), churches (10%)

Staff: 3
1 Lobbyist
1 Office Manager
1/2 Organizer
1/2 Grassroots Fundraiser

Staff openings/year: 1

Work Week: 40 hours

Salary/year: $17,000 (Recent College Graduate); $Varies (Graduate with advanced degree)

Benefits: Health insurance, paid vacation, pregnancy leave

Part-Time Employees: 2

Interns: None at this time

Jobs advertised: Through newsletter, organizations and colleges

To apply: Contact Marian Franz, Executive Director

NATIONAL CAMPAIGN FOR FREEDOM OF EXPRESSION

1402 3rd Ave. #421
Seattle, WA 98101
(206) 340-9301

Other Offices: Washington, DC

Director: David Mendoza

Purpose: NCFE is an education and advocacy network of artists, arts organizations and the public, founded to fight censorship and to protect and extend the First Amendment right to freedom of artistic expression. NCFE is committed to the understanding that a true democracy must afford the right of free artistic expression to all, including those who might be censored because of class, race, gender, religion, sexual orientation and all other forms of invidious discrimination. NCFE also works on behalf of the public, who we believe has the right to access of free expression, including the right to determine for themselves what they choose to read, see, hear, believe.

Methods of operation: Research, lobbying, litigation, publications, community organizing, public education, media education/advocacy

Membership: Artists, gallery owners, arts organizations, audience members

Recent issues and projects: NCFE is currently working on the following projects: Communication and education; media advocacy; grass roots and coalitions; legal offense; and advocacy

Major publications: *Bulletin*, an 8-page quarterly; produces video-tapes; issue pamphlets

Budget: $250,000

Funding: Foundations (85%), individual contributions (15%), direct mail (5%)

Staff: 3
1 Organizer
2 Office Managers
1/2 Foundation Fundraiser

Staff openings/year: 2

Work Week: 40 hours

Salary/year: $22,000 (Recent College Graduate); $26,000 (Graduate with advanced degree)

Benefits: Health insurance

Part-Time Employees: 3

Summer Employees: 2

Volunteers: Varies

Interns: 1
Length: 3 months
Duties: Varies
Remuneration: Depends on organization/sponsor

Jobs advertised: Word of mouth

To apply: Contact the office

NATIONAL CAUCUS AND CENTER ON BLACK AGED, INC.

1424 K Street, NW, Suite 500
Washington, DC 20005
(202) 637-8400

Other Offices: Atlanta, GA; Chicago, IL; Baltimore, MD; Cleveland, OH; Philadelphia, PA; Raleigh, NC; Stuttgart, AZ

President: Samuel J. Simmons

Purpose: NCBA's number one priority is improvement in the quality of life for African American elderly, especially those who are of low-income. Our goals in achieving that aim are: the elimination of poverty for all elderly Americans; improving the status of health and quality of life for African American seniors; increasing minority participation in programs and services for the aged; providing training and professional development opportunities for persons who work in the aging field, especially minority professionals and those who work with the African American aged.

Methods of operation: Lobbying, publications, human services, direct action, public education, training and technical assistance

Constituency: Senior citizens and advocates for the elderly

Recent issues and projects: Health Care Reform Video

Major publications: *Golden Page Newsletter* published quarterly

Budget: $1,700,000

Funding: Federal Grants (99%), other (1%)

Staff: 26
1 Writer/Editor
1 Attorney
1 Office Manager
1 Lobbyist
4 Issue Experts
6 Administrative Assistants
8 Bookkeepers/Accountants
2 Enrollees

Staff openings/year: 1

Work Week: 37.50 hours

Benefits: Health insurance, pension, paid vacation

Part-Time Employees: 2

Summer Employees: None

Volunteers: None

Interns: 7
Length: One year
Duties: Nursing Home Administrator internship only, via our Minority Training and Development Program in long-term care
Remuneration: Interns paid monthly stipend of $1,200 plus $350 allowance for licensure exams/materials

Jobs advertised: Local newspapers

To apply: Please contact Samuel J. Simmons, President/CEO

NATIONAL CENTER FOR APPROPRIATE TECHNOLOGY

P.O. Box 3838, 3040 Continental Drive
Butte, MT 54702
(406) 494-4572

Other Offices: Fayetteville, AR

Director: Ron Kroese

Purpose: The National Center for Appropriate Technology supports and encourages development of technologies and community processes which conserve natural resources and provide opportunities for sustainable economic development so that low-income families can become more self-reliant and live with decency and dignity in a safe and healthy environment.

Methods of operation: Public education (35%), training and technical assistance (35%), research (25%), publications (5%)

Recent issues and projects: Recent projects include: a national sustainable agriculture hot line which provides technical assistance to 10,000-12,000 farmers ranches, etc. interested in adopting sustainable agricultural products

Major publications: *Appropriate Technology Voice*, newsletter

Budget: $2,000,000

Funding: County and contracts (95%), state (5%)

Staff: 23
3 Writers/Editors
3 Office Managers
12 Issue Experts/Research
3 Administrative Assistants
2 Bookkeepers/Accountants

Staff openings/year: 3

Work Week: 40 hours

Salary/year: $19,000 (Recent College Graduate); $25,000 (Graduate with advanced degree)

Benefits: Health insurance, pension, paid vacation, life insurance, family leave, tuition reimbursement, employee assistance program

Part-Time Employees: 20

Summer Employees: 1

Volunteers: None

Interns: Yes
Length: 3-6 months

Jobs advertised: National newspapers, professional journals/periodicals, affirmative action publications

To apply: Contact Jeanne Weiss, Personnel Specialist

NATIONAL CENTER FOR EMPLOYEE OWNERSHIP

2201 Broadway, Suite 807
Oakland, CA 94612
(415) 272-9461

Director: Corey Rosen

Purpose: National nonprofit membership/research organization to provide information, conduct conferences and meetings, publish handbooks, and work with researchers on employee ownership.

Methods of operation: Public education (25%), publications (25%), conferences, workshops (25%), research (15%), media work (10%)

Membership: 1,700 members: half businesses, half consultants, academics, unions, public officials, etc.

Recent issues and projects: Research on Employee Stock Ownership Plan-led Leveraged Buyouts (LBO's); series of introductory workshops on employee ownership; began project to create international resource guide on employee ownership

Major publications: *Employee Ownership Report*, bimonthly; *Journal of Employee Ownership Law and Finance*; *Employee Ownership Reader*; *Model Employee Stock Ownership Plan (ESOP)*; and several others

Budget: $475,000

Funding: Conferences/workshops (50%), memberships (30%), publications (20%)

Staff: 8
5 Issue Experts
1 Writer/Editor
1 Attorney
1 Office Manager

Staff openings/year: 1-2

Work Week: 40-45 hours

Salary/year: $24,000 +bonus

Benefits: Health insurance, paid vacation

Part-Time Employees: 1

Interns: 1
Length: 3-5 months
Duties: Research
Remuneration: Minimum wage

Jobs advertised: Word of mouth, *Community Jobs*

To apply: Contact Corey Rosen

NATIONAL CENTER FOR ENVIRONMENTAL HEALTH STRATEGIES

1100 Rural Avenue
Voorhees, NJ 08043
(609) 429-5358

Director: Mary Lamielle

Purpose: NCEHS provides educational, research and advocacy services in environmental illness and environmental health issues with a focus on chemical sensitivities. NCEHS promotes awareness of health effects of chemical and environmental pollutants through informational educational, technical and referral services for professionals, the public and those with chemically-induced illnesses. NCEHS encourages national and grassroots activism with a dedication to the development and implementation of programs, products, policies and strategies to assist chemical victims and protect public health.

Methods of operation: Research, lobbying, publications, human services, community organizing, direct action, public education, training and technical assistance

Constituency: Professionals (medical, legal, research, government officials); general public; those with chemical sensitivities

Recent issues and projects: (1) Amendments in the Indoor Air Quality Act that address multiple chemical sensitivities; (2) initiated and served peer review for major report on chemical sensitivities commissioned by New Jersey Department of Health; (3) campaign for recognition of chemical sensitivity as a disability; (4) workplace accommodations; (5) campaign to seal fragrance samples in mail and magazines

Major publications: Quarterly newsletter: *The Delicate Balance*; *Chemical Sensitivity*, an initiated study by Nicholas A. Ashford, Ph.D., J.D. and Claudia S. Miller, M.D., M.S., commissioned by the New Jersey Department of Health

Budget: $30,000

Funding: Individual membership/subscription (75%), donations (25%)

Staff: 1
1/2 Director

Work Week: 60 hours

Salary/year: $Varies

Part-Time Employees: 2

Summer Employees: 1

Volunteers: 5

Interns: Yes
Duties: Several potential areas: research, manage telephone clearinghouse, writing/editorial for newsletter, business/financial, bookkeeping, grants
Remuneration: Volunteer; small stipend

To apply: Contact Mary Lamielle, Director

NATIONAL CENTER FOR FAIR & OPEN TESTING (FAIRTEST)

342 Broadway
Cambridge, MA 02139-1802
(617) 864-4810

Director: Pamela Zappardino

Purpose: FairTest is a public education and advocacy organization working to end the abuses, misuses and biases of standardized testing and make certain that the evaluation of students and workers is fair, open, accurate and educationally sound.

Methods of operation: Public education, advocacy, publications, research, training and technical assistance

Constituency: Educators, civil rights activists, parents and others interested in the impact of standardized tests on U.S. society

Recent issues and projects: FairTest undertakes work in three major areas: K-12 Testing, University Admissions Tests and Employment Tests. Recent projects include public education and advocacy around national testing and attempts to make the National Merit Scholarships fairer for women and minorities.

Major publications: *FairTest Examiner*, quarterly; *Fallout From the Testing Explosion*; *Sex Bias in College Admissions Tests: Why Women Lose Out*; *Beyond Standardized Tests*; *Standardized Tests and Our Children*

Budget: $350,000

Funding: Foundations, individual contributions, publication sales

Staff: 4
1 Office Manager
2 Issue Experts
1 Administrative Assistant

Staff openings/year: 0-1

Work Week: 40 hours

Salary/year: $19,000 (Recent College Graduate); $Varies (Graduate with advanced degree)

Benefits: Health insurance, paid vacation, family leave

Part-Time Employees: 3

Summer Employees: 1

Volunteers: 2

Interns: Yes
Length: 2 months or 1 semester
Duties: Variety of projects available, a recent intern researched challenges to testing abuses.
Remuneration: Small stipend/work study

Jobs advertised: *Community Jobs*; *Boston Globe*; *Bay State Banner*

To apply: Contact Karen Orton, Administrative Assistant

NATIONAL CENTER FOR SERVICE LEARNING IN EARLY ADOLESCENCE

25 West 43rd Street, Suite 612
New York, NY 10036
(212) 642-2946

Director: Alice L. Halsted

Purpose: The National Center for Service Learning in Early Adolescence works to make service learning a possibility for every person. Service learning, the pairing of meaningful work and structured reflection, provides early adolescents with opportunities to effect change in themselves and in their communities. The Center assists schools and agencies in meeting the developmental needs of young adolescents through program development, research, advocacy and information sharing.

Methods of operation: Publications (30%), training and technical assistance (30%), research (20%)

Constituency: Educators, youth workers and people interested in service learning.

Recent issues and projects: Recent major projects include: the development of the Field Associates Network, the Clearinghouse, a new Helper model - Community Problem Solvers and new guides - Learning Helpers: A Guide to Training and Reflection and Student Evaluators: A Guide to implementation.

Major publications: *Learning Helpers: A Guide to Training and Reflection*; *The Partners Program: A Guide for Teachers and Program Leaders*; *Reading, Writing and Reviewing: Helpers Promoting Reading*; *Reflection: The Key to Service Learning*

Budget: $700,000

Funding: Foundations (90%), contracts, fees, sales (10%)

Staff: 4
1/2 Office Manager
2 Trainers
1 Administrative Assistant
1/2 Curriculum Development

Staff openings/year: 1.5

Work Week: 35 hours

Salary/year: $22,000 (Recent College Graduate); $26,000 (Graduate with advanced degree)

Benefits: Health insurance, pension, paid vacation

Part-Time Employees: None

Summer Employees: None

Volunteers: None

Interns: None, but willing to accept applications

Jobs advertised: Newspapers, word-of-mouth, college employment centers

NATIONAL CENTER FOR URBAN ETHNIC AFFAIRS

P.O. Box 20, Cardinal Station
Washington, DC 20064
(202) 232-3600

Director: John Kromkowski

Purpose: The National Center for Urban Ethnic Affairs is a nonprofit research and education institute that has sponsored and published many books and articles on ethnic relations, urban affairs and economic revitalization.

Methods of operation: Publications (35%), community organizing (25%), research (25%), training and technical assistance (15%)

Recent issues and projects: NCUEA is a national organization founded in 1970 to develop neighborhood programs and policies in older cities, particularly for neighborhoods founded by immigrants. NCUEA runs the Neighborhood Economic Revitalization program. The program provides on-site technical assistance to neighborhoods, organizations, municipally sponsored projects and nonprofit community development corporations. The NCUEA team offers assistance in planning, organizing, funding, marketing, promotions and packaging. It also provides assistance in traditional and multi-cultural education, ethnic festivals, and is involved in matters of international urbanization. It publishes studies on successful nonprofit housing ventures.

Major publications: Send for publications list

Jobs advertised: Contact John Kromkowski

NATIONAL CENTER FOR YOUTH LAW (NCYL)

114 Sansome Street, 9th Floor
San Francisco, CA 94104-3820
(415) 543-3307

Director: John Francis O'Toole, III

Purpose: NCYL, a national support center, provides assistance on juvenile law to legal services attorneys and child advocates throughout the country. NCYL's services include training and technical assistance, litigation assistance, consultation and publications. NCYL seeks to improve the quality of life for low-income and vulnerable children in the United States.

Methods of operation: Training and technical assistance (50%), litigation (40%), publications (10%)

Constituency: Legal services lawyers, child advocates, public defenders

Recent issues and projects: NCYL works on the issues of abuse, neglect and termination of parental rights; foster care; housing discrimination against families with children; child and adolescent health; children and youth living in institutions; and public benefits for children

Major publications: Bimonthly journal: *Youth Law News*

Budget: $1,400,000

Funding: Legal Services Corporation (55%), attorney fees (22%), foundations (14%), California Legal Services Trust Fund (13%)

Staff: 17
8 Attorneys
3 Legal Secretaries
1 Receptionist
1 Administrator
1 Editor
1 Development Director
1 Paralegal
1 Health Policy Analyst

Staff openings/year: 1

Work Week: 37.5 hours

Salary/year: $Varies (Recent College Graduate); $Varies (Graduate with advanced degree)

Benefits: Health insurance, life insurance, pregnancy leave, pension, child care, paid vacation

Part-Time Employees: 1

Volunteers: 3

Interns: 5
Remuneration: Interns need special financial arrangements

Jobs advertised: *Youth Law News*; *Clearinghouse Review*; local newspapers; mailings to all legal services programs

To apply: Contact John Francis O'Toole

NATIONAL CENTER ON WOMEN AND FAMILY LAW

799 Broadway, Suite 402
New York, NY 10003
(212) 674-8200

Director: Laurie Woods

Purpose: To assist attorneys and advocates for poor women on family law issues

Methods of operation: Training and technical assistance (60%), publications (30%), litigation (10%)

Constituency: Advocates for women's interests; legal services attorneys

Recent issues and projects: Battery, child custody, child support enforcement, child sexual abuse

Major publications: *Custody Litigation on Behalf of Battered Women*; *Protecting Confidentiality*; *Battery: The Facts*; *The Women's Advocate*; *Child Support: A National Disgrace*

Budget: $250,000

Funding: Legal Services Corporation (70%), foundations (30%)

Staff: 6
3 Attorneys
1 Secretary
1 Clerical Assistant
1 Bookkeeper/Accountant

Staff openings/year: 0-1

Work Week: 35 hours

Salary/year: $Varies (Recent College Graduate); $Varies (Graduate with advanced degree)

Part-Time Employees: 1

Summer Employees: 2

Volunteers: 7

Interns: Yes

Jobs advertised: *Clearinghouse Review*, circulation of announcement to other public interest offices, *New York Times*

To apply: Contact Laurie Woods, Director

NATIONAL CENTRAL AMERICA HEALTH RIGHTS NETWORK, INC. (NCAHRN)

853 Broadway, Room 416
New York, NY 10003
(212) 420-9635

Director: Louise Cohen

Purpose: NCAHRN sponsors a wide range of activities to promote health in Central America. Also to educate people in the U.S. on the impact of poverty and U.S. intervention in Central America through the perspective of health and to work towards a more humane foreign policy.

Methods of operation: Human services (50%), networking with local groups (30%), public education (10%), publications (10%)

Constituency: Health professionals and others concerned with health

Recent issues and projects: Nicaragua: work-study tours on health; El Salvador: advocating for respect for medical neutrality rights of health workers and civilians; emergency medical relief projects

Major publications: Quarterly magazine: *LINKS: Health and Development Report*; periodic reports on health rights in Central American countries

Budget: $120,000

Funding: Individual contributions (60%), direct mail (20%), foundations (5%), other (15%)

Staff: 2
1 Organizer
1 Grassroots Fundraiser

Work Week: 40 hours

Salary/year: $20,000 (Graduate with advanced degree)

Benefits: Health insurance, pregnancy leave, paid vacation

Part-Time Employees: 1

Volunteers: 3-4

Interns: 1-2
Length: 3 months
Duties: Assisting with national projects
Remuneration: Voluntary

Jobs advertised: *New York Times*; *The Guardian*

To apply: Contact Louise Cohen

NATIONAL CITIZENS' COALITION FOR NURSING HOME REFORM

1424 16th Street, NW, Suite L-2
Washington, DC 20036
(202) 797-0657

Director: Elma Holder

Purpose: Consumer-based organization of local and state member groups and individuals, working to improve health care and quality of life for nursing home residents. They work for quality medical care; exercise of residents' rights and self-determination; resident and family access to community services, community advocates and ombudsman programs; training and improved working conditions and wages for nurse aides and other caregivers; and reintegration of residents into community life.

Methods of operation: Community organizing (15%), public education (15%), training and technical assistance (15%), publications (15%), research (10%), lobbying (10%), human services (10%), direct action (10%)

Constituency: 1.9 million nursing home residents, plus their friends and families

Recent issues and projects: (1) Coordination of the Campaign for Quality Care with over 50 national organizations to assure full implementation of the 1987 Nursing Home Reform Law; (2) Efforts to assure that nursing homes and their residents are included in national public policy development; (3) Operation of an information clearinghouse to assist the public in improving nursing home conditions in their communities and states; and (4) Cooperative work with National Association of State Units on Aging to improve ombudsman resources.

Major publications: Newsletter: *Quality Care Advocate*, published 6 times a year; *A Consumer Perspective on Quality Care*, a 1985 report based on interviews with nursing home residents across the country; *Nursing Home Care - Critical Determinants of and Impediments to Quality*, a paper outlining a "total community approach" to improving nursing homes

Budget: $400,000

Funding: Foundations, grants, contracts (62%), annual meeting (18%), membership (12%), direct mail (2.5%)

Staff: 6
2 Issue Experts/Lobbyists
1 Researcher

1 Writer/Editor
1 Organizer
1 Support Staff
1/2 Office Manager
1/2 Membership
1/2 Foundation/Grassroots Fundraiser
1/6 Bookkeeper/Accountant

Staff openings/year: 1

Work Week: 40 hours

Salary/year: $18,000 (Recent College Graduate); $21,000 (Graduate with advanced degree)

Benefits: Health insurance, paid vacation

Part-Time Employees: 4

Summer Employees: 1

Volunteers: 1

Interns: 3
Length: 16 weeks
Duties: Assist in Clearinghouse activities
Remuneration: Negotiable

Jobs advertised: Newsletters; newspapers; university programs

To apply: Contact Cyma Heffter, Development Coordinator

NATIONAL CIVIC LEAGUE

1445 Market Street, Suite 300
Denver, CO 80202
(303) 571-4343

President: John Parr

Purpose: The National Civic League works as a convener to communities interested in collaborative projects to improve the quality of life within their community.

Methods of operation: Training and technical assistance (50%), publications (20%), community organizing (20%), research (10%)

Membership: Individuals, organizations and institutions from all sectors

Recent issues and projects: American Renewal initiative is a new movement in the U.S. NCL will serve as a catalyst and convener to build a national network of organizations, institutions and individuals from all sectors to work toward the goal of improving America's communities.

Major publications: *National Civic Review*; *Civic Action Newsletter*

Budget: $2,500,000

Funding: Individual contributions and foundations

Staff: 25
2 Writers/Editors
1 Office Manager
1 Researcher
1 Foundation Fundraiser
6 Administrative Assistants
1 Bookkeeper/Accountant
7 Program Managers
3 Officers
3 Researchers

Work Week: 40 hours

Salary/year: $20,000 (Recent College Graduate); $25,000 (Graduate with advanced degree)

Benefits: Health insurance, pension, paid vacation, life insurance

Part-Time Employees: 1

Summer Employees: None

Interns: 4
Length: 6 months
Duties: Research

Jobs advertised: Newspapers

To apply: Contact Renee Castillo, Office Administrator

NATIONAL CLEARINGHOUSE ON MARITAL AND DATE RAPE

2325 Oak
Berkeley, CA 94708
(510) 524-1582

Director: Laura X

Purpose: The only comprehensive source for up-to-date information on legislation, cases - criminal and sociological - and attitudes condoning and supporting the targeting of women and children for abuse.

Methods of operation: Public education (30%), research (15%), lobbying (10%), litigation (10%), training and technical assistance (10%), publications (5%), human services (5%), information and referral (5%), direct action (5%), community organizing (5%)

Constituency: Students, senior citizens, unemployed, faculty, researchers, writers, media, librarians, counselors, attorneys, law enforcement, legislators, clergy, prosecutors, rape crisis centers, etc.

Recent issues and projects: Ongoing effort to have marital and date rape declared a crime in every state. Works with the enforcement of date and marital rape laws and monitors proposed bills. Tours on college campuses to promote awareness of the social, legal, political, religious, philosophical and psychological meaning of date/marital rape.

Major publications: Date/marital rape brochure; state law charts; prosecution statistics; bibliographies

Budget: $40,000

Funding: Individual contributions (60%), speakers fees and telephone consultations (30%), telephone solicitation (10%)

Staff:
All part-time volunteer including:
3 Issue Experts
3 Researchers
2 Press Aides
1 Office Manager
1 Organizer
1 Lobbyist
1 Bookkeeper/Accountant
1 Writer/Editor

Staff openings/year: 1-2

Work Week: 4-40 hours

Salary/year: $6-7,000

Benefits: Negotiable schedule, 5:00 am-10:00 pm, 7 days a week

Part-Time Employees: 2-4

Summer Employees: 2-4

Volunteers: 5-10

Interns: 5-10
Length: 1-3 months
Duties: Monitoring legislation and cases, information and referral, outreach
Remuneration: Small stipend for local transportation, etc.

Jobs advertised: Newspapers; intern directory

To apply: Contact Laura X

Remarks: No funding, but fun! All of our positions are part-time and the majority of our positions are volunteer, because funding has not been available for rape prevention efforts.

NATIONAL COALITION AGAINST CENSORSHIP

275 7th Avenue, 20th Floor
New York, NY 10001
(212) 807-6222

Director: Leanne Katz

Purpose: A coalition of 42 national nonprofit organizations dedicated to defense of the First Amendment and freedom of expression.

Methods of operation: Public education (60%), publications (20%), community organizing (20%)

Constituency: National nonprofit organizations, interested individuals across the country

Major publications: 5x/yr newsletter; *Meese Commission Exposed*; *Books On Trial*; *The Sex Panic*; *Editorial Memorandum on Women, Censorship and "Pornography"*

Budget: $220,000

Funding: Individual contributions (35%), participating groups (25%), foundations, direct mail (20%), corporate and union (20%)

Staff: 4
1/2 Organizer
1/2 Writer/Editor
1/2 Office Manager
1/2 Issue Expert
1/2 Typist
1/2 Grassroots Fundraiser
1 Communications Coordinator

Work Week: 35 hours

Salary/year: $Varies (Recent College Graduate); $Varies (Graduate with advanced degree)

Benefits: Health insurance, life insurance, paid vacation

Part-Time Employees: 3

Summer Employees: Yes

Volunteers: Yes

Interns: Yes

Jobs advertised: Publicly and through college placement offices

To apply: Contact Leanne Katz, Executive Director

NATIONAL COALITION AGAINST DOMESTIC VIOLENCE

P.O. Box 18749
Denver, CO 80218
(303) 839-1852

Director: Rita Smith, Program Coordinator

Purpose: The National Coalition Against Domestic Violence is the only national organization of grassroots shelter and service programs for battered women. They are a membership organization providing national systems advocacy and technical assistance for constituents. They seek to end personal and societal violence in the lives of women and their children.

Methods of operation: Lobbying (10%), publications (10%), community organizing (20%), public education (40%), training and technical assistance (20%)

Constituency: Individuals, programs, and state coalitions serving battered women and their children

Recent issues and projects: Updating national directory of domestic violence support programs in the U.S.; holding a national conference for battered women and their advocates during the summer of 1994; public policy work on the Violence Against Women Act; media campaign to increase violence awareness.

Major publications: Newsletters: *The Voice* and *The Bulletin*; *Guidelines for Mental Health Practitioners*; *Naming the Violence: Speaking Out About Lesbian Battering*; *National Directory of Shelters and Programs*

Budget: $374,000

Funding: Individual contributions (10%), membership (25%), direct mail (5%), foundations (10%), product sales (25%), CFC campaigns (25%)

Staff: 1
1 Office Manager

Staff openings/year: 1

Work Week: 40+ hours

Salary/year: $20,800 (Recent College Graduate); $25,000 (Graduate with advanced degree)

Benefits: Health insurance, paid vacation

Part-Time Employees: 4

Volunteers: 15

Interns: Varies
Length: 3-6 months
Duties: Varies, possibilities of public policy research, fundraising activities, public education projects, media campaigns
Remuneration: None

Jobs advertised: National newspapers, mailings to other organizations, through member network

To apply: Contact Rita Smith, Coordinator

NATIONAL COALITION AGAINST THE MISUSE OF PESTICIDES (NCAMP)

530 Seventh Street, SE
Washington, DC 20003
(202) 543-5450

Director: Jay Feldman

Purpose: NCAMP is a nonprofit membership organization that was formed in 1981 to serve as a national network committed to pesticide safety and the adoption of alternative pest management strategies which reduce or eliminate a dependency on toxic chemicals. The organization's primary goal is to effect change through local action, assisting individuals and community-based organizations to stimulate discussion on the hazards of toxic pesticides.

Methods of operation: Public education, community organizing, research, publications, litigation, human services

Recent issues and projects: Working on pesticide reform legislation to protect the public with regard to health effects and the implementation of public policies to protect consumers. NCAMP holds an annual forum in Washington, DC, bringing people together from across the country, providing an important opportunity to exchange information on critical issues pertaining to pesticide hazards and non-chemical and least toxic methods of pest control.

Major publications: Magazine: *Pesticides and You*, 4 times/year; *The Technical Report*, a monthly 4-page news brief; *Least Toxic Control of Pests*; *NCAMP's Pesticide Chemical Fact Sheets*; other brochures and booklets available, please write for a publications list

Budget: $300,000

Funding: Foundations (75%), individual contributions (25%)

Staff: 4

2 Writers/Editors
2 Information Assistants

Work Week: 50-60 hours

Salary/year: $18,000 (Recent College Graduate); $22-27,000 (Graduate with advanced degree)

Benefits: Health insurance, paid vacation, pregnancy leave, tuition reimbursement (depending on class)

Part-Time Employees: 3

Interns: Yes
Length: 2 months minimum to 6 months+
Duties: Library research, attend public meetings, answer information requests
Remuneration: Depending on funding, a minimal stipend is available

Jobs advertised: Mailings to regional and local organizations and universities, newspaper listings, job postings through "job centers"

To apply: Contact Jay Feldman

NATIONAL COALITION FOR THE HOMELESS

1621 K Street, NW, Suite 1004
Washington, DC 20006
(202) 775-1322

Other Offices: New York, NY

Director: Fred Karnas, Jr.

Purpose: The National Coalition for the Homeless is a federation of individuals, agencies and organizations working to address and end homelessness through a multi-level strategy of securing rights, services and housing for homeless people.

Methods of operation: Lobbying (20%), research (10%), litigation (10%), publications (10%), human services (10%), community organizing (10%), direct action (10%), public education (10%), training and technical assistance (10%)

Constituency: Individuals, agencies and organizations who have an interest in homelessness and low-income housing issues

Recent issues and projects: Successful design, introduction and passage of rural homelessness bill; Sponsorship of the "You Don't Need a Home to Vote" national voter registration campaign for homeless people; Lobby successfully for reauthorization of the McKinney Act programs; Setting up and nurturing state and local coalitions to deal with homelessness issues

Major publications: The NCH publishes a free, monthly newsletter called the *Safety Network.* The NCH also publishes a number of reports on homeless and low-income housing issues. Contact the NCH for a free publications list.

Budget: $550,000

Funding: Individual contributions (90%), foundations (10%)

Staff: 8
1 Director
2 Policy Analysts
1 Organizer
2 Information Specialists
1 Business Manager
1 Secretary/Receptionist

Staff openings/year: 1-2

Work Week: 40-50 hours

Salary/year: $25,000

Benefits: Health insurance, life insurance, paid vacation

Part-Time Employees: 1-2

Summer Employees: 0-2

Volunteers: 5

Interns: 4-6
Length: 3-6 months
Duties: Research and writing for NCH projects
Remuneration: None; college credit available

Jobs advertised: Word of mouth, establishment press and alternative press

To apply: Contact Fred Karnas, Director

NATIONAL COALITION FOR UNIVERSITIES IN THE PUBLIC INTEREST

1801 18th Street, NW
Washington, DC 20009
(202) 234-0041

Other Offices: Boston, MA

Director: Leonard Minsky

Purpose: Keeping universities honest.

Constituency: University faculty, students

Recent issues and projects: Scientific fraud;

conflict of interest; racism; sexism; the economy

Budget: $100,000

Funding: Foundations (75%), individual contributions (25%)

Staff: 1

Work Week: 90 hours

Salary/year: $10,000

Benefits: Health insurance

Summer Employees: Yes

NATIONAL COALITION OF ALTERNATIVE COMMUNITY SCHOOLS

P.O. Box 15036
Santa Fe, NM 87506
(505) 474-4312

Director: Kate Kerman, Chair; Ed Nagel, Natl Office Manager

Purpose: NCACS is a nonprofit, national coalition of schools, groups and individuals dedicated to providing children (and adults) with the kind of personalized and yet globally-oriented education we all need to successfully cope with, and change for the better, the society in which we live.

Methods of operation: Networking, research, publications, community organizing, public education

Constituency: Alternative schools and schoolers; homeschoolers; alternative colleges; people interested in educational change

Recent issues and projects: Keeping this diverse group connected and organizing conferences and publications is a major project. They update their directory, and are planning a catalog of products and services available in the alternative education area. Individual member schools have lots of projects; they serve as a network for these schools.

Major publications: *NCACS News* 4 times a year; *SKOLE*, an educational journal, 2 times a year; *National Directory of Alternative Schools*, updated periodically and completely redone every 2 years

Budget: $30,000

Funding: Sales of publications

Staff: 1
Part-time employees perform tasks of:
Organizer
Writer/Editor
Office Manager
Foundation Fundraiser
Issue Expert
Typist
Bookkeeper/Accountant

Interns: Yes; some schools have intern programs
Duties: Different for different situations

Jobs advertised: *NCACS News*

To apply: Contact Ed Nagel, National Office Manager

Remarks: NCACS doesn't hire much, but we do serve as a network for alternative schools of all kinds who do hire personnel and we try to be a bulletin board to connect people looking for jobs in alternative education situations with schools looking for people.

NATIONAL COALITION ON BLACK VOTER PARTICIPATION, INC.

1101 14th Street, NW, Suite 925
Washington, DC 20005
(202) 898-2220

Director: Sonia Jarvis

Purpose: The National Coalition's principle goal is to increase minority participation in the American political system through voter registration and education programs.

Methods of operation: Community organizing (40%), research (20%), public education (20%), training and technical assistance (15%), publications (5%)

Membership: The Coalition is composed of 86 National Member Organizations with diverse backgrounds.

Recent issues and projects: (1) Operation Big Vote: grassroots coalitions conduct intensive voter education, registration and get-out-the-vote activities while bringing together a broad cross section of the community. There are more than 70 Operation Big Vote coalitions operating in 29 states. (2) Information Resource Center: analyzes voting statistics and patterns, monitors federal and state election reform initiatives and other electoral activities across the country. (3) Training and Technical Assistance: regional workshops, seminars and meetings on voter registration techniques. (4) Public Service Announcement Project. (5) Black Women's Roundtable: addressing the issues surrounding the 1990 Census and preparing for upcoming local, state and Congressional races.

Major publications: Quarterly newsletter

Budget: $300,000

Funding: Foundations (60%), individual contributions (30%), member contributions (10%)

Staff: 4
1 Executive Director
1 Deputy Director
1 Organizer
1 Issue Expert
1/2 Office Manager
1/2 Bookkeeper/Accountant

Staff openings/year: 1

Work Week: 40 hours

Salary/year: $20,000 (Recent College Graduate); $27,000 (Graduate with advanced degree)

Benefits: Health insurance, life insurance, pregnancy leave, tuition reimbursement, paid vacation

Volunteers: Yes

Interns: 2 per semester
Length: 1 year
Duties: Send for student intern job description
Remuneration: Hourly rate

Jobs advertised: University referral services

To apply: Contact Leslie Norris McFarland, Deputy Director

Remarks: The Coalition's yearly budget is $600,000 during election years.

NATIONAL COALITION TO ABOLISH THE DEATH PENALTY

1325 G Street, NW, Lower Level
Washington, DC 20005
(202) 797-7090

Other Offices: Liberty Mills, IN

Director: Ms. Leigh Dingerson

Purpose: The NCADP is a coalition of organizations which share a common opposition to the death penalty. It is the only national group solely dedicated to abolishing capital punishment in the U.S.

Methods of operation: Public education (50%), research (10%), assistance and support to state coalitions (10%), legislative monitoring (5%), lobbying (5%), training and technical assistance (5%), publications (5%)

Constituency: Formal membership is through organizations. Supporters and activists include lawyers, family members of those under death sentences, family members of murder victims, church members, etc.

Recent issues and projects: The Coalition is an information clearinghouse on general topics; co-sponsored a 400 mile "Pilgrimage for Abolition" in Florida and Georgia; monitor legislation relating to racism and injustice in the death penalty.

Major publications: Membership newsletter: *Lifelines*, 4 times per year; *The Execution Alert* action letter around scheduled executions

Budget: $240,000

Funding: Individual contributions (60%), direct mail (25%), foundations (10%), telephone solicitation (5%)

Staff: 3
1 Organizer
1 Grassroots Fundraiser
1/3 Bookkeeper/Accountant
1/3 Office Manager
1/3 Writer/Editor

Staff openings/year: 1-2

Work Week: 45-50 hours

Salary/year: $27,000

Benefits: Health insurance, life insurance, pregnancy leave, child care, paid vacation, participation in a "cafeteria plan," paid sabbatical every fifth year

Part-Time Employees: 1

Summer Employees: 0

Volunteers: 1-3

Interns: 1-2
Length: 2-3 months, flexible
Duties: Special projects such as legislative monitoring
Remuneration: We can sometimes afford a small stipend.

Jobs advertised: Within the movement and through local free listings. They encourage folks to contact them and apply on an ongoing basis. They bring people on as funding becomes available.

To apply: Contact Leigh Dingerson, Director

Remarks: We strongly encourage people of color

to apply.

NATIONAL COALITION TO END RACISM IN AMERICA'S CHILD CARE SYSTEM, INC.

22075 Koths
Taylor, MI 48180
(313) 295-0257

Director: Carol Coccia

Purpose: To coordinate efforts throughout the country to educate, publicize and use legal means to assure that no child is denied services on the basis of race. They help the thousands of children, minority and handicapped mostly, who are being shortchanged by the system which is getting paid to help them. They have given the truly concerned workers within the system a place to direct folks without jeopardizing their jobs, as was the case previously.

Methods of operation: Direct action (60%), publications (25%), public education (5%), training and technical assistance (5%)

Constituency: Individuals and organizations interested in children caught up in the child care system. This would include potential foster or adoptive parents, politicians, social workers, etc.

Recent issues and projects: The Coalition has filed civil rights complaints against the states of Illinois, Washington, Minnesota, Michigan and New York. Agreements have been reached in all states except MN. They have also filed a suit in federal court in Michigan alleging unconstitutional use of race and won! They will also be publishing the national survey of all state laws regarding race in the placement of children in the near future.

Major publications: Quarterly newsletter: *The Children's Voice*

Funding: Individual contributions

Staff:
Volunteer Organization

Volunteers: Yes

NATIONAL COMMITTEE AGAINST REPRESSIVE LEGISLATION (NCARL)

1313 West 8th Street, #313
Los Angeles, CA 90017
(213) 484-6661

Other Offices: Washington, DC; Chicago, IL; San Francisco, CA; Seattle, WA; Portland, OR; Missoula, MT; Boston, MA; Miami, FL; Madison, WI; Louisville, KY; White Plains, NY

Director: Frank Wilkinson, Executive Director Emeritus

Purpose: To educate the Congress, and mobilize and educate the public on pending legislation and other government action that infringes on First Amendment rights of speech, press, assembly and association. In particular, to seek to limit FBI actions to investigation of criminal activity rather than political thought; and to educate the public on the inherent illegality and danger of unchecked covert action as government policy.

Methods of operation: Public education (40%), publications (30%), research (10%), lobbying (10%), training and technical assistance (10%)

Constituency: Nationwide support from campuses to retirement homes. Often civil liberties activists, community activists

Recent issues and projects: Petition to Congress to stop political spying and disruption by the FBI; CIA Off Campus Campaign - part of a larger education effort to publicize the effects of covert operations by the federal government

Major publications: Newsletter: *The Right to Know and the Freedom to Act*; *FBI Petition News*; *CIA Off Campus Handbook*; *The FBI vs. the First Amendment* report; *The FBI vs. Black Voting Rights* pamphlet

Budget: $100,000

Funding: Individual contributions (70%), foundations (30%)

Staff: 3
1 Computer Specialist, Los Angeles
1 Washington Representative, DC Office
1 National Speaker/Organizer

Staff openings/year: 1

Work Week: 30 hours

Salary/year: $16,000 part-time (Recent College Graduate); $18,000 part-time (Graduate with advanced degree)

Benefits: Health insurance, pregnancy leave, paid vacation, partial tuition reimbursement

Part-Time Employees: 3

Volunteers: Yes

Interns: 1
Length: 2-4 months usually; negotiable
Duties: Washington Office: attend and report on Congressional hearings; research and write on focal issues; assist in coalition building
Remuneration: Unpaid, but office expenses paid

Jobs advertised: *Community Jobs*; *The Nation*; word of mouth

To apply: In DC contact Kit Gage, Washington Representative, NCARL, 3321 12th St., NE, Washington, DC 20017. In Chicago, contact the Chicago Committee to Defend the Bill of Rights, 5232 S. Plymouth, #800, Chicago, IL 60605.

NATIONAL COMMITTEE FOR RESPONSIVE PHILANTHROPY

2001 S Street, NW, Suite 620
Washington, DC 20009
(202) 387-9177

Director: Robert O. Bothwell

Purpose: To expand the public accountability, accessibility and grantmaking responsiveness of foundations, corporate philanthropy, United Ways, and other workplace charity drives to minorities, women, disabled, other victims of discrimination, plus consumer and environmental activists.

Methods of operation: Research (25%), public education (15%), training and technical assistance (15%), community organizing (10%), direct action (10%), publications (10%), lobbying (5%)

Constituency: Local and national progressive nonprofit organizations

Recent issues and projects: Helped organize over 40 alternatives to United Way, and helped these and other progressive nonprofits raise $150 million in workplace donations in 1992. Evaluating community foundations' responsiveness to the disadvantaged and corporate philanthropy's responsiveness to minorities.

Major publications: Quarterly newsletter: *Responsive Philanthropy*; *Charity at the Workplace* (1992); *Community Foundations: Unrealized Potential for the Disadvantaged* (1989); *Rightwing Influence on Corporate Giving* (1990); *Burgeoning Conservative Think Tanks* (1991)

Budget: $854,000

Funding: Foundations, corporate and church grants, member dues, nonprofit contributions and contracts, publication sales and conference fees and individual contributions

Staff: 8
1 Executive Director
1 Administrative Assistant
1 Director of Field Operations
1 Associate Director, Workplace Fundraiser
1 Director, Foundation Responsiveness Proj.
1 Assistant Director/Development
1 Assistant to the Director
1 Acting Research Director

Staff openings/year: 2

Work Week: 40-45 hours

Salary/year: $7,200-15,000 (Recent College Graduate); $Varies (Graduate with advanced degree)

Benefits: Health insurance, life insurance, pension, pregnancy leave, paid vacation, disability insurance

Part-Time Employees: 7 Consultants

Interns: 4
Length: 3 to 15 months
Duties: Research, administrative, media activism, lobbying
Remuneration: $6.00 an hour for college grads. for first 6 months; $8.00 an hour thereafter

Jobs advertised: *Community Jobs*, sometimes *Washington Post*, our mailing list

To apply: Contact Assistant to the Director

NATIONAL COMMITTEE ON PAY EQUITY

1201 16th Street, NW, Suite 420
Washington, DC 20036
(208) 822-7304

Director: Ms. Claudia E. Wayne

Purpose: NCPE is a coalition of labor, women's and civil rights organizations and individuals working together to eliminate sex- and race-based discrimination.

Methods of operation: Public education (33%), training and technical assistance (16%), research

(15%), publications (15%), advocacy (10%), fundraising (6%)

Membership: Members include individuals who are interested in working to achieve pay equity, and labor, and women's and civil rights organizations which endorse pay equity.

Recent issues and projects: NCPE works to achieve pay equity for women and people of color through public education, grassroots organizing, coalition building, serving as a clearinghouse and providing technical assistance

Major publications: In 1989, NCPE released *Pay Equity Activity in the Public Sector 1979-1989*; *NCPE: A Decade of Working for Economic Justice*; and two issues of *Newsnotes*, NCPE's newsletter

Budget: $250,000

Funding: Membership, honoraria, interest (50%), foundations (40%), individual contributions (10%)

Staff: 5
1 Executive Director
1 Researcher/Writer/Editor
1 Office Manager
1 Membership and Foundation Fundraiser
1 Typist/Secretary

Staff openings/year: 0-1

Work Week: 35 hours

Salary/year: $25,200 (Recent College Graduate); $25,200-29,000 (Graduate with advanced degree)

Benefits: Health insurance, pension, paid vacation, life insurance, pregnancy leave

Volunteers: 1 + task forces

Interns: 2
Length: Semester or summer
Duties: Work closely with program or development coordinator
Remuneration: $800 full-time per semester and $400 part-time

Jobs advertised: Through *Newsnotes* and member organizations' newsletters and newspapers

To apply: Contact Lisa Hubbard

NATIONAL COMMUNITY ACTION FOUNDATION
2100 M Street, NW, Suite 604 A
Washington, DC 20037
(202) 775-0223

Director: David Bradley

Purpose: The National Community Act
Foundation represents interests of comm
agencies before Congress and the execut

Methods of operation: Lobbying (70%), research (25%), publications (3%), training and technical assistance (2%)

Membership: 1,000 Community Action Agencies and state and regional associations

Recent issues and projects: Recent projects include: Community Services Block Grant (CSBG); Low-income Home Energy Assistance Program (LIHEAP); homeless; weatherization; lobbying

Major publications: Newsletter

Budget: $500,000

Funding: Individual contributions (90%), conference (10%)

Staff: 5
2 Lobbyists
1 Researcher
1 Administrative Assistant
1 Office Manager
1/2 Typist

Staff openings/year: 1

Work Week: 40 hours

Salary/year: $23,000 (Recent College Graduate); $27,000 (Graduate with advanced degree)

Benefits: Health insurance, life insurance, paid vacation, pregnancy leave, tuition reimbursement

Part-Time Employees: 1

Interns: 1
Length: 1 week
Duties: Professional internships for employees of CAA's
Remuneration: No financial assistance available

Jobs advertised: Word-of-mouth, newspaper

To apply: Contact David Bradley or Betty Weiss

NATIONAL COMMUNITY EDUCATION ASSOCIATION
3929 Old Lee Highway, Suite 91-A
Fairfax, VA 22030
(703) 359-8973

Director: Starla Jewell-Kelly

Purpose: The purpose of the National Community Education Association is to provide the tools and knowledge for lifelong learning; parent and community involvement in education; community use of schools; leadership training for community members and improving quality of life in a community through education and training.

Methods of operation: Public education (60%), publications (20%), training and technical assistance (20%)

Constituency: Community educators in local school districts, universities and community colleges

Recent issues and projects: Recent projects include: new textbook *Legislation for Federal Funding for Community Schools*; interagency collaboration to provide full service schools; and an annual national conference

Major publications: *Community Education Today*, newsletter; *Community Education Journal*

Budget: $570,000

Funding: Membership (43%), foundations (28%)

Staff: 4
1 Writer/Editor
1 Office Manager
1 Organizer/Fundraiser/Issue Expert/Lobbyist
1 Executive Director

Staff openings/year: 1

Work Week: 60 hours

Salary/year: $20,800 (Recent College Graduate); $31,200 (Graduate with advanced degree)

Benefits: Health insurance, paid vacation, life insurance, family leave

Part-Time Employees: 1

Summer Employees: None

Volunteers: Varies

Interns: 1
Length: One semester
Duties: Varies with interns area of interest and skills
Remuneration: $500 a month plus transportation costs

Jobs advertised: *The Washington Post* and *The Chronicle of Higher Education*

To apply: Contact Starla Jewell-Kelly

Remarks: We experience limited turnover. Current staff have been here 4-6 years. We do expect one part-time position to open this year.

NATIONAL COMMUNITY REINVESTMENT COALITION

1875 Connecticut Ave., NW, Suite 1010
Washington, DC 20009
(202) 986-7898

Director: John Taylor

Purpose: Increase access to credit and asset accumulation in low-income, minority and underserved urban and rural communities.

Methods of operation: Research (30%), publications (30%), public education (30%), training and technical assistance (10%)

Recent issues and projects: Current projects include: community development; fair housing; civil rights; community reinvestment, labor and religious rights

Major publications: *Reinvestment Works*, newsletter; *NCRC Compendium*; *Sourcebook*; *Agreements Catalogue and Directory*; *Research Agenda Planning Resource*

Budget: $380,000

Funding: Foundations (90%), individual contributions (10%)

Staff: 4
1 Office Manager
1 President and CEO
1 Vice President
1 Membership Director

Staff openings/year: 1-2

Work Week: 40 hours

Salary/year: $20,000 (Recent College Graduate); $25,000 (Graduate with advanced degree)

Benefits: Health insurance, pension, paid vacation, life insurance, family leave

Part-Time Employees: 2

Summer Employees: None

Volunteers: 2

Interns: 2
Length: 3 months
Duties: Work on legislative and research projects
Remuneration: None

Jobs advertised: Through community-based networks and *The Washington Post*

To apply: Contact John Taylor

Remarks: NCRC is the largest community reinvestment groups in the U.S. with over 420 member organizations.

NATIONAL CONGRESS OF NEIGHBORHOOD WOMEN

249 Manhattan Avenue
Brooklyn, NY 11211
(718) 388-6666

Purpose: To provide a voice for poor and working class concerns. To strengthen women's leadership roles in our neighborhoods by giving support, information, training, and recognition for their work. To encourage an emerging women's consciousness with the multi-racial character of the communities in which they live.

Methods of operation: Organizing, public education, training and technical assistance

Constituency: Poor and working class women throughout the community

Recent issues and projects: Housing; health; unemployment; community-based college programs and high school equivalency programs; vocational counseling; job referral services

Funding: Foundations

Staff: 15
Includes:
1 Education Coordinator
1 Fiscal Officer
Vocational Counselors
Program Directors

Staff openings/year: 1-2

Salary/year: $16-22,000

Benefits: Health insurance, paid vacation

Volunteers: Yes

Interns: None currently, but willing to accept applications

Jobs advertised: Local and citywide press; word of mouth; announcements sent to other groups

To apply: Contact Elaine Carpinelli

NATIONAL CONSUMER LAW CENTER

11 Beacon Street
Boston, MA 02108
(617) 523-8010

Other Offices: Washington, DC

Director: Willard P. Ogburn

Purpose: A legal services national support center, providing legal and technical assistance to lawyers representing low-income clients on consumer and energy issues and providing direct representation to low-income clients on these issues in cases of national scope

Methods of operation: Research, lobbying, litigation, publications, training and technical assistance

Constituency: Legal services attorneys and other low-income consumer advocates; nationwide

Recent issues and projects: Advocated federal weatherization assistance programs for low-income people; reform of state credit consumer protection acts; utility rate work; home equity lending policies; delivery mechanisms for low-income energy programs

Major publications: Newsletter: *NCLC Reports*; *Energy Update*; 10-volume consumer law practice series

Budget: $2,000,000

Funding: Legal Services Corporation, private foundations, other

Staff: 22
Includes:
Attorneys and other professionals
Support Staff

Staff openings/year: 1-2

Part-Time Employees: Yes

Volunteers: Yes

Interns: Yes
Length: 2-6 months
Duties: Research
Remuneration: Stipend available

Jobs advertised: Professional journal: *Clearinghouse Review*

To apply: Contact office

NATIONAL CONSUMERS LEAGUE
815 15th Street, NW, Suite 928
Washington, DC 20005
(202) 639-8140

Director: Linda Golodner

Purpose: NCL is a private, nonprofit membership organization. Since 1899, NCL's three-pronged approach of research, education and advocacy has made it an effective representative and source of information for consumers and workers.

Methods of operation: Public education (25%), direct action (20%), research (15%), publications (15%), community organizing (10%), lobbying (5%), human services (5%)

Constituency: NCL's public and members are nurses, students, steelworkers, teachers, retired people, professionals, etc.

Recent issues and projects: National Fraud Information Center, telemarketing fraud, child labor, privacy, food and drug safety, airline safety, financial services, insurance and health care issues

Major publications: Bimonthly newsletter: *NCL Bulletin*; *Quarterly*, a quarterly newsletter on telemarketing fraud; *Child Labor Monitor* and quarterly newsletter on exploitation of children in the workplace; series of consumer health care guides

Budget: $1,000,000

Funding: Individual contributions (20%), foundations (20%), other contributions (50%), publication sales (10%)

Staff: 15
Including:
Program Directors
Public Policy Experts
Public Affairs
Support Staff

Staff openings/year: 1-2

Work Week: 40+ hours

Salary/year: $16,000 (Recent College Graduate); $Varies (Graduate with advanced degree)

Benefits: Health insurance, pension (deferred annuity plan available), paid vacation

Part-Time Employees: 4

Volunteers: 1-2

Interns: 2-3
Length: Summer or semester
Duties: Responsible for working with staff on a specific project, usually research, writing, congressional and agency contact.
Remuneration: Varies with each intern

Jobs advertised: Through the public interest network

To apply: Contact Sara Cooper, Executive Assistant to the President

NATIONAL COUNCIL OF SENIOR CITIZENS
925 15th Street, NW
Washington, DC 20005
(202) 347-8800

Director: Lawrence T. Smedley

Purpose: To advocate on behalf of senior citizens.

Methods of operation: Research, lobbying, publications, organizing

Membership: 5 million

Recent issues and projects: National health plan; Medicare reform; Social Security reform issues; Supplemental Security Income outreach; low-income energy assistance; run a government-funded employment project; manage housing projects for the elderly; electoral involvement; rate Congressional voting records annually

Major publications: *Senior Citizen News*; *Voting Record*

Budget: $750,000

Funding: Membership dues, government grants, union contributions

Staff: 100
Including:
3 Writer/Editors
2 Organizers

Staff openings/year: 2

Work Week: 40 hours

Salary/year: $Varies (Recent College Graduate); $Varies (Graduate with advanced degree)

Benefits: Health insurance, life insurance, pregnancy leave, pension, credit union, family leave

Interns: None currently, but willing to accept applications

Jobs advertised: In-house

To apply: Contact Hugh Layden

NATIONAL COUNCIL ON THE AGING, INC.

600 Maryland Avenue, SW, West Wing 100
Washington, DC 20024
(202) 479-1200

Other Offices: Los Angeles, CA; New York, NY

President: Dr. Daniel Thursz, ACSW

Purpose: NCOA serves as a national source of information, training, technical assistance, advocacy and research on every aspect of aging. NCOA forms cooperative relationships with government, business, private foundations, and other funding sources to demonstrate the validity of new ideas and services, to educate the public and professionals about them, and to anticipate the signal challenges and opportunities of the future.

Methods of operation: Research, lobbying, member services, publications, public education, training and technical assistance

Constituency: Individuals, voluntary agencies, associations, business organizations, labor unions, and others united by the common commitment to improve the lives of older Americans

Recent issues and projects: New Directions training program; National Association of Older Worker Employment Services; National Center on Rural Aging; National Institute of Senior Centers; National Institute on Senior Housing; National Institute on Adult Daycare; National Institute on Community-based Long-term Care; National Voluntary Organizations for Independent Living for the Aging; Family Caregivers of the Aging; Long-Term Care CHOICES; National Center for Health Promotion and Aging; Project Independence; Facing Our Future; Team Work program; Discovery Through the Humanities program; Travelers Geriatric Fellowship Program; Senior Community Service Employment Program; Prime Time Productivity program

Major publications: *Perspective on Aging*; *Current Literature on Aging*; NCOA *Networks*; a number of brochures available on topics of interest to older Americans and service providers; publications catalogue available upon request

Budget: $40,000,000

Funding: Government grants and contracts (92.4%)

Staff: 94

Work Week: 35 hours

Salary/year: $20,000

Benefits: Health insurance, life insurance, pregnancy leave, pension, tuition reimbursement, paid vacation

Part-Time Employees: 12

Summer Employees: Rarely

Volunteers: 40

Interns: 4
Length: 3 months
Duties: Varies
Remuneration: None

Jobs advertised: *Washington Post*; 100 minority agencies; networking; word of mouth

To apply: Contact the Senior Personnel Manager

NATIONAL EMERGENCY CIVIL LIBERTIES COMMITTEE

175 5th Avenue
New York, NY 10010
(212) 673-2040

Director: Edith Tiger

Purpose: To uphold the Bill of Rights and the Constitution and litigate test cases of any infringements thereof.

Methods of operation: Research, litigation, publications

Constituency: Professionals and progressives; nationwide

Recent issues and projects: Haitian refugees; right to travel; right to run advertisements; the right to know; against censorship; strong support for the First Amendment

Major publications: *Rights*; *Bill of Rights Journal*

Budget: $300,000

Funding: General public

Staff: 12
Plus attorneys on retainer

Staff openings/year: 0-1

Work Week: 40 hours

Salary/year: $Varies (Recent College Graduate);

$Varies (Graduate with advanced degree)

Benefits: Health insurance

Volunteers: Yes

Interns: Yes; undergraduates and law students
Length: Summer
Remuneration: Work-study

Jobs advertised: Through our network

To apply: Contact Director

NATIONAL ENVIRONMENTAL POLICY & LAW CENTER - LITIGATION CENTER

29 Temple Place
Boston, MA 02111
(617) 422-0880

Other Offices: Ann Arbor, MI

Director: Charles C. Caldart

Purpose: The Litigation Center takes legal action against polluters - winning court orders that stop illegal discharges, securing major fines where appropriate and working out settlements that direct money to environmental preservation project.

Methods of operation: Litigation (100%)

Recent issues and projects: Deal primarily with Clean Water Act violations. Recent litigation includes cases in Washington, California, Michigan, Ohio, Illinois, Massachusetts and New Jersey. Work closely with Environment Law Clinic at Rutgers University and private firms

Major publications: *The National Environmental Law Center* quarterly newsletter to members

Funding: Individual contributions, direct mail, canvassing

Staff: 5
4 Attorneys
1 Office Manager/Paralegal/Researcher

Work Week: 40 hours

Benefits: Health insurance, paid vacation, family leave, student loan repayment assistance

Part-Time Employees: None

Summer Employees: None

Volunteers: None

Interns: 2-4
Length: 10 weeks in summer
Duties: Legal support, legal research, drafting memoranda, pleading and briefs, pre and post complaint investigation
Remuneration: $500 stipend

Jobs advertised: *Community Jobs, Job Seeker, Environmental Career Opportunities*

To apply: Contact Diane Silva, Office Administrator

NATIONAL FAMILY FARM COALITION

110 Maryland Avenue NE #205
Washington, DC 20002-5626
(202) 737-2215

Director: Susan Denzer

Purpose: Goals: bring about progressive agriculture policy reforms that will strengthen family farm-based sustainable agriculture, protect the environment, and bring vitality back to rural America. Purpose: provide an organizational structure for diverse grassroots groups to work together on federal policy and national issues.

Methods of operation: Public education (40%), training and technical assistance (30%), lobbying (20%), research (10%)

Constituency: Grassroots farm and rural advocacy organizations; individuals who support family farm agriculture

Recent issues and projects: Policy advocacy on the 1990 Farm Bill; campaign to address rapid concentration in livestock industry; national coordination of groups fighting the adoption of Bovine Growth Hormone; uniting family dairy farmers across regions to bring dairy policy reform; opposition to U.S. position on agriculture at GATT. They have recently launched a Pure Milk Campaign, which is building support from urban consumers.

Major publications: Quarterly newsletter

Budget: $250,000

Funding: Foundations (90%), individual contributions (5%), member dues (5%)

Staff: 3
1 Organizer
1 Lobbyist
1 Writer/Editor
1 Bookkeeper/Accountant (part-time)

Staff openings/year: 1

Work Week: 50 hours

Salary/year: $18-20,000 (Recent College Graduate); $26,000 (Graduate with advanced degree)

Benefits: Health insurance, pregnancy leave, paid vacation

Part-Time Employees: 2

Summer Employees: 1

Volunteers: 1

Interns: 2
Length: 3-6 months
Duties: 1/2 programmatic, depending on interest of intern; 1/2 staff support
Remuneration: Variable; stipend offered dependent on need and cash flow

Jobs advertised: *Community Jobs*; mail out job announcements in DC area

To apply: Contact Jane Kochersperger, Information and Outreach Coordinator

Remarks: The organization is led and controlled by grassroots farmers and ranchers. Staff of the 40 member organizations has a diverse and impressive array of experience with community organizing on rural and natural resource issues. The Coalition works on issues through committees of farmer representatives such as: Agriculture Policy, Dairy, Sustainable Agriculture, Farm Credit, Trade, Corporate Accountability.

NATIONAL FAMILY PLANNING AND REPRODUCTIVE HEALTH ASSOCIATION (NFPRHA)

122 C Street, NW, Suite 380
Washington, DC 20001-2109
(202) 628-3535

President: Judith M. DeSarno

Purpose: NFPRHA is dedicated to improving and expanding the delivery of family planning and reproductive health services and programs throughout the United States.

Methods of operation: Public education (80%), publications (10%), lobbying (5%), litigation (5%)·

Constituency: Family planning providers; state, county, local health departments; hospital-based clinics; affiliates of Planned Parenthood; family planning councils; health care professionals and consumers; clinics

Recent issues and projects: Legislative/advocacy efforts to reauthorize federal family planning programs; legal efforts to prevent damaging changes in federal regulation; inclusion in health care reform; annual meetings drawing together individuals and organizations involved in family planning and reproductive health care

Major publications: *NFPRHA News*; *NFPRHA Report*; *NFPRHA Alert*; *NFPRHA Report Line*, a hotline of family planning news

Budget: $850,000

Funding: Foundations (62%), membership (24%)

Staff: 9
2 Lobbyists
1 Foundation Fundraiser
1 President/CEO
1 Director for Membership
1 Director of Administration and Finance
1 Associate Assistant
1 Director of Service Delivery
1 Membership and Meetings Associate

Work Week: 37.5 hours

Salary/year: $Varies (Recent College Graduate); $Varies (Graduate with advanced degree)

Benefits: Health insurance, pension, life insurance, paid vacation

Interns: None currently, but willing to accept applications

Jobs advertised: Send out position announcement to other health organizations; *Washington Post* classifieds

To apply: Contact Megan Jackson, Director of Administration

NATIONAL FARMERS UNION

10065 East Harvard Avenue
Denver, CO 80231
(303) 337-5500

Other Offices: Washington, DC

President: Leland H. Swenson

Purpose: To foster a better standard of living and way of life for family farmers and rural Americans through cooperation, education and legislation.

Methods of operation: Lobbying (30%), public education (20%), publications (20%), human services (10%), community organizing (10%), litigation (5%)

Constituency: Family farmers and other rural citizens

Recent issues and projects: Legislative, communications and education work on family farm issues. Similar work has been done in 1989 on futures trading reform, agricultural credit issues, rural development, health care, trade, etc. International Exchange Programs

Major publications: *Washington*, newsletter

Budget: $2,000,000

Staff: 28
3 Lobbyists
2 Field Staff
3 Vice Presidents
1 National Secretary
1 Librarian
2 Office Managers
2 Bookkeepers/Accountants
4 Program Coordinators
2 Membership Assistants
4 Administrative Assistants
2 Office Managers

Staff openings/year: 1

Work Week: 40 hours

Salary/year: $Varies (Recent College Graduate); $Varies (Graduate with advanced degree)

Benefits: Health insurance, life insurance, pregnancy leave, pension, credit union, paid vacation

Part-Time Employees: 1

Summer Employees: 3

Interns: None currently, but willing to accept applications

To apply: Contact Leland H. Swenson, President

NATIONAL GAY AND LESBIAN TASK FORCE

1734 14th Street, NW
Washington, DC 20009
(202) 332-6483

Director: Ms. Torie Osborn

Purpose: National lobbying, organizing, educating and mobilizing for gay and lesbian civil rights and expedient, responsive federal AIDS policy.

Methods of operation: Community organizing (25%), lobbying (25%), research (10%), direct action (10%), publications (10%), public education (10%), training and technical assistance (10%)

Constituency: Gay, lesbian and heterosexual supporters of all ages and ethnicities

Recent issues and projects: Anti-Violence Project; Family/ Domestic Partnership Project; Gays in the Military Project; Sodomy Law Reform Project; Campus Organizing Project; Legislative Project; and Public Information/Education Project

Major publications: Quarterly newsletter: *Task Force Report*; annual *Gay Violence and Victimization Report*; civil rights brochure; monthly *Activist Alert*

Budget: $1,000,000

Funding: Direct mail (33%), individual contributions (31.9%), events (30%), foundations (5%)

Staff: 12
1 Lobbyist
1 Director of Special Projects
1 Office Manager
1 Senior Accountant
1 Receptionist
1 Operations Manager
1 Development Assistant
1 Volunteer/Intern Coordinator
1 Acting Executive Assistant
1 Publications Assistant
1 Executive Director
1 Executive Assistant

Staff openings/year: 1-2

Work Week: 50 hours

Salary/year: $25,000 (Recent College Graduate); $30,000 (Graduate with advanced degree)

Benefits: Health insurance, life insurance, pregnancy leave, paid vacation, dental

Part-Time Employees: Yes

Volunteers: 30

Interns: 4
Length: 1-3 months
Duties: Program and project work; administrative
Remuneration: None

Jobs advertised: Gay and lesbian press; postings in other progressive organizations; mailings

To apply: Contact Peri Jude Radecic, Deputy Director of Public Policy

NATIONAL HEAD START ASSOCIATION

201 N. Union Street, Suite 320
Alexandria, VA 22314
(703) 739-0875

Director: Sara M. Greene

Purpose: To nurture and to advocate for children and families; to provide the Head Start community the opportunity of expressing concerns; to define strategies on pertinent issues affecting Head Start; to serve as an advocate for Head Start programs; to provide training and professional development opportunities for the Head Start Community; and to develop a networking system with other organizations whose efforts are consistent with the National Head Start Association

Methods of operation: Research, lobbying, publications, training and technical assistance

Constituency: Parents, directors, staff and friends of local Head Start Program

Recent issues and projects: Recent project includes: Head Start reauthorization and appropriations for the next 4 years

Major publications: *NHSA Journal*; *Silver Ribbon Panel* report; newsletter; advocacy kit

Budget: $2,000,000

Funding: Individual contributions, foundations, fundraising

Staff: 16
5 Organizers
2 Writers/Editors
1 Office Manager
1 Researcher
2 Lobbyists
4 Administrative Assistants
1 Bookkeeper/Accountant
1 Partnership Director
2 Public Relations Director
3 Conference Coordinators

Staff openings/year: 1

Work Week: 70 hours

Salary/year: $24,000 (Recent College Graduate); $30,000 (Graduate with advanced degree)

Benefits: Health insurance, pension, paid vacation, life insurance, pregnancy leave, tuition reimbursement

Part-Time Employees: None

Summer Employees: None

Volunteers: Yes

Interns: Yes
Length: Summer months only
Duties: Research, administrative
Remuneration: Paid by the university

Jobs advertised: Newspaper

To apply: Contact Leslie Roberts, Office Manager

NATIONAL HEALTH LAW PROGRAM, INC.

2639 South La Cienega Blvd.
Los Angeles, CA 90034
(310) 204-6010

Other Offices: Washington, DC

Director: Laurence M. Lavin

Purpose: NHLP attorneys work on a wide range of health care issues affecting the poor, primarily assisting legal services attorneys and non-Legal Services Corporation (LSC) attorneys representing LSC-eligible clients.

Recent issues and projects: Health advocate

Budget: $830,000

Funding: Legal Services Corporation/Legal Services Trust Fund (89%), foundations (10%), individual contributions (1%)

Staff: 13
8 Attorneys
3 Administrative Assistants
1 Office Manager
1 File Clerk

Work Week: 37.5 hours

Salary/year: $26,500

Benefits: Health insurance, life insurance, pension, paid vacation

Part-Time Employees: 2

Summer Employees: 2-3

Jobs advertised: *Los Angeles Times*; state and local bar associations

To apply: Contact Karen Anthony, Administrator

NATIONAL HISPANA LEADERSHIP INSTITUTE

1816 Jefferson Place, NW, Suite 007
Washington, DC 20036
(202) 466-6732

Director: Nancy Leon

Purpose: The National Hispana Leadership Institute's purpose is to increase the number of Hispanic women in key policy and decision making positions, Boards and Commissions and to develop a national support network of Hispanic women.

Methods of operation: Training and technical assistance (60%), alumnae association (20%), research (10%), publications (10%)

Constituency: Hispanic women leaders

Recent issues and projects: Fellowship project focussing on leadership and mentoring

Major publications: *NHLI News*, quarterly newsletter; 5-year anniversary report

Budget: $400,000

Funding: Tuition/fees, foundations

Staff: 3
1 Executive Director
1 Coordinator
1 Clerical Support

Work Week: 40 hours

Salary/year: $20,000 (Recent College Graduate); $28,000 (Graduate with advanced degree)

Benefits: Health insurance, paid vacation, dental insurance

Part-Time Employees: 1

Summer Employees: None

Volunteers: None

Interns: None currently, willing to accept application

Jobs advertised: Word-of-mouth, *Hispanic Link*

To apply: Contact Magda Candelaria, Coordinator

Remarks: The National Hispana Leadership Institute was founded in 1987 to ensure that Hispanic women are included at the highest levels of decision making, particularly in the national arena. The Institute's mission is to prepare Hispanas with a distinguished record of community service to realize their leadership capabilities, promote the advancement of the Hispanic community and create a national network of Hispanic women. The program includes four one-week leadership development seminars which span nine months and four cities.

NATIONAL HISPANIC COUNCIL ON AGING

2713 Ontario Road, NW
Washington, DC 20009
(202) 745-2521

Director: Dr. Marta Sotomayor

Purpose: The National Hispanic Council on Aging is a membership based, non-profit, tax-exempt organization that promotes the well being of the Hispanic elderly through demonstration projects, research, policy analysis, training, development of educational and informational resources.

Methods of operation: Research ((10%), lobbying (10%), litigation (10%), publications (10%), human services (10%), community organizing (10%), direct action (10%), public education (10%), training and technical assistance (20%)

Recent issues and projects: Promotes the sharing of resources, the establishment of linkages with other organizations and collaborative projects on behalf of the Hispanic elderly. The NHCoA carries out most of its activities through its membership and local Chapters, affiliates and organizational members.

Major publications: Newsletter

Staff: 4
Following positions are shared:
Organizing
Writer/Editor
Office Manager
Researcher
Lobbyist
Press Aide
Foundation Fundraiser
Issue Expert
Grassroots Fundraiser

Work Week: 40 hours

Benefits: Health insurance, life insurance, family leave

Part-Time Employees: 1

Summer Employees: 1

Volunteers: 3

Interns: None, but willing to accept applications

Jobs advertised: Newspapers, newsletters

To apply: Contact Dr. Marta Sotomayor

NATIONAL HISPANIC MEDIA COALITION

5400 E. Olympic Blvd., Suite 250
Los Angeles, CA 90022
(213) 726-7690

Director: Esther Renteria, National Chair

Purpose: The National Hispanic Media Coalition works to improve the image and employment of Hispanic Americans in radio, television and film.

Methods of operation: Public education (41%), training and technical assistance (20%), litigation (20%), research (10%), lobbying (5%), publications (1%), human services (1%)

Constituency: Comprised of 150 Hispanic American, Puerto Ricans, Mexican American, Cuban American organizations throughout the United States which represent various professional groups

Recent issues and projects: NHMC constantly battles the resurgence of racism. Especially in talk radio which has really degenerated into "Hate" radio as far as race baiting and immigrant bashing.

Major publications: *Positive Images*, newsletter

Budget: $100,000

Funding: Member Oganizations (100%)

Staff: 2
1 Office Manager
1 Issue Expert

Staff openings/year: 1

Work Week: 40 hours

Salary/year: $25,000 (Recent College Graduate); $35,000 (Graduate with advanced degree)

Benefits: Health insurance

Part-Time Employees: None

Summer Employees: None

Volunteers: 25

Interns: 1
Length: Summer
Duties: Varies

Jobs advertised: In newsletters

To apply: Please contact Esther Renteria

NATIONAL HOUSING INSTITUTE/SHELTERFORCE

439 Main Street
Orange, NJ 07050
(201) 678-3110

Director: Patrick Morrissy

Purpose: To increase public understanding of the housing crisis, and to increase public awareness of potential solutions. These goals will be achieved by concentrating on the media's coverage of housing issues, and by publicizing the successes of the housing movement.

Methods of operation: Training and technical assistance (30%), public education (30%), publications (30%), research (10%)

Recent issues and projects: National poll on housing attitudes; Atlanta House at the 1988 Democratic Convention; building a national housing campaign; Housing Now! march

Major publications: *Shelterforce*, a bimonthly national magazine of the housing movement

Budget: $150,000

Funding: Foundations (50%), individual contributions (40%), subscriptions (10%)

Staff: 2
1/2 Writer/Editor
1/2 Organizer
1/2 Foundation Fundraiser
1/2 Campaign Manager

Staff openings/year: 1

Work Week: 40 hours

Salary/year: $16-18,000 (Recent College Graduate); $18-22,000 (Graduate with advanced degree)

Benefits: Health insurance, paid vacation

Part-Time Employees: 1

Volunteers: Yes

Interns: Yes
Length: Term-related or summer
Duties: Writing/editing bimonthly magazine; developing technical assistance manuals and seminars
Remuneration: Volunteer preferred; small stipend possible depending on qualifications

Jobs advertised: ACCESS: Networking in the Public Interest; local papers; *Shelterforce*

To apply: Contact David Steinglass

NATIONAL IMMIGRATION FORUM

220 I Street, NE
Washington, DC 20017
(202) 544-0004

Director: Frank Sharry

Purpose: To fight discrimination and exploitation of refugees and immigrants and also addresses ethnic and racial tensions between these newcomers and current residents.

Methods of operation: Public education (75%), publications (10%), research (5%), lobbying (5%), training and technical assistance (5%)

Constituency: National, regional and local organizations working on immigration and refugee related issues

Major publications: *Golden Door*; *Advocacy Matters*

Budget: $1,000,000

Funding: Foundations (90%), other (10%)

Staff: 12
1 Attorney
1 Office Manager
1 Press Aide
1 Foundation Fundraiser
7 Issue Experts
1 Typist

Staff openings/year: 1-2

Work Week: 40 hours

Salary/year: $24,000 (Recent College Graduate); $40,000 (Graduate with advanced degree)

Benefits: Health insurance, pension, paid vacation, family leave

Part-Time Employees: 1

Summer Employees: None

Volunteers: None

Interns: 3
Length: Semester
Duties: Clerical and policy
Remuneration: Usually $1,000 a semester

Jobs advertised: *Washington Post*; *Opportunities in Public Affairs*

To apply: Please contact Laura Garcia Melendez, Office Manager

NATIONAL IMMIGRATION PROJECT OF THE NATIONAL LAWYERS GUILD

14 Beacon Street, Suite 506
Boston, MA 02108
(617) 227-9727

Director: Dan Kesselbrenner

Purpose: Protect, defend and expand civil and human rights of all immigrants in U.S. documented and undocumented.

Methods of operation: Training and technical assistance (75%), publications (15%), public education (10%)

Membership: Progressive advocates (lawyers, legal workers, law students and agencies) for immigrants rights.

Recent issues and projects: Recent projects include: Assisting battered immigrant women; HIV and Immigrants; border violence; Haitian asylum; children in detention; non-citizen criminal offenders; and ideological visa denials.

Major publications: Quarterly *Immigration* newsletter; *Immigration Law and Crimes*; *Immigration Law and Defense*; *Immigration Act of 1990 Handbook*; *Immigration Law and the Family*

Budget: $200,000

Funding: Royalties (60%), foundations (30%), individual contributions (10%)

Staff: 3
1 Attorney/Issue Expert
1 Office Manager
1 Foundation Fundraiser/Issue Expert

Staff openings/year: 0-1

Work Week: 35-50 hours

Salary/year: $Varies (Recent College Graduate); $Varies (Graduate with advanced degree)

Benefits: Health and dental insurance, paid vacation, life insurance, sick leave, bereavement leave, paid sabbatical

Part-Time Employees: None

Summer Employees: None

Volunteers: 1-3

Interns: 1-3
Length: Semester to year or summer
Duties: Research, writing, work on education project or training materials
Remuneration: Work study program, or possible school credit for independent study or classwork

To apply: Contact Mona Dahan

Remarks: We are a national back-up center for advocates; we are also a membership organization with 500 members. We are a union shop and and are a project of the National Lawyers Guild, although we are independently funded.

NATIONAL INDIAN HEALTH BOARD, INC.

1385 South Colorado Blvd., Suite A-708
Denver, CO 80222
(303) 759-3075

Director: Gordon Belcourt

Purpose: Indian Health advocacy for American Indian and Alaska Native Tribes across the country.

Methods of operation: Community organizing (30%), publications (20%), training and technical assistance (20%), public education (15%), community networking (15%)

Constituency: Tribal health representatives selected by Tribal groups

Recent issues and projects: Major projects and issues have to do with legislation impacting Indian health: maintaining communications with Tribes relative health issues as well as legislation; health care facilities and manpower; networking with other national and regional Indian organizations on Indian health issues; and providing information to non-Indian agencies/organizations relative to Indian Health.

Major publications: *NIHB REPORTER*, quarterly issues with 3 special publications

Budget: $300,000

Staff: 4
1 Writer/Editor
1 Office Manager
1 Typist
1 Bookkeeper/Accountant

Work Week: 40 hours

Salary/year: $25,000 (Recent College Graduate); $30,000 (Graduate with advanced degree)

Benefits: Health insurance, pension, paid vacation, family leave

Part-Time Employees: None

Summer Employees: None

Volunteers: 2

Interns: None

Jobs advertised: Through newspapers and flyers in the community

To apply: Please contact Gordon Belcourt or Cynthia Ligtenberg

NATIONAL INDIGENOUS YOUTH LEADERSHIP PROJECT, INC. (NIYLP)

650 Vanden Bosch
Gallop, NM 87301
(505) 722-9176

Other Offices: Albuquerque, NM; Zuni, NM

Director: McClellan Hall

Purpose: To develop the leadership capabilities of Native youth; to enable these youth to become contributors to their communities and the larger society.

Methods of operation: Community organizing, leadership development, outdoor adventure activities, service learning, training, community development in Native Communities

Constituency: Native American communities with emphasis on youth development

Recent issues and projects: Recent projects include: Hosted the National Service Learning Conference, March 1994; Conducted the 9th session of the NIYLP Pathfinder Camp, June 1994; and Hosting the 12th annual National Indigenous Youth Camp, July 1994

Major publications: *Something Shining, Like Gold, But Better*, a program leader's manual; several articles in *Journal of Navajo Education* and *New Designs for Youth*

Budget: $400,000

Funding: Federal grants (65%), foundations (35%)

Staff: 5
1 Office Manager
3 Youth Workers

1 Executive Director

Staff openings/year: 0-1

Work Week: 40 hours

Salary/year: $22,000 (Recent College Graduate); $25,000 (Graduate with advanced degree)

Benefits: Health insurance, retirement

Part-Time Employees: 10

Summer Employees: 5-10

Volunteers: 5-10

Interns: None, but willing to accept applications

Jobs advertised: Newspapers, word-of-mouth

To apply: Contact McClellan Hall, Director

NATIONAL INSTITUTE FOR CITIZEN EDUCATION IN THE LAW (NICEL)

711 G Street, SE
Washington, DC 20003
(202) 546-6644

Director: Edward O'Brien and Jason Newman, Co-Directors

Purpose: Increasing citizen understanding of law and the American legal system

Methods of operation: Training and technical assistance (50%), publications (25%), public education (25%)

Constituency: Students (K-12), law students, teachers, lawyers, legal community

Recent issues and projects: Recent projects include: mediation; and drug abuse prevention education

Major publications: *Street Law* - high school practical law text; *Excel in Civics: Lessons in Citizenship*; *Law and the Consumer*; *Teens, Crime and the Community*, an 11-lesson curriculum; *Teaching Today's Constitution*, a 10-lesson curriculum

Budget: $1,200,000

Funding: Federal/DC government, royalties (100%)

Staff: 20
14 Attorneys
2 Writers/Editors
2 Support Staff
1 Development/Finance
1 Office Manager

Staff openings/year: 1

Work Week: 35-40 hours

Salary/year: $22-25,000

Benefits: Health insurance, life insurance, pregnancy leave, pension, paid vacation, disability

Part-Time Employees: 1

Interns: 1-2
Length: Summer or year round
Duties: Researching, writing, project coordination
Remuneration: Stipend possible

Jobs advertised: *Washington Post* and other area newspapers; newsletter

To apply: Contact Edward O'Brien, Co-Director

NATIONAL INSTITUTE FOR DISPUTE RESOLUTION

1726 M Street, NW, Suite 500
Washington, DC 20036
(202) 466-7464

President: Margery Baker

Purpose: NIDR's mission is: to promote the development of fair, effective and efficient conflict resolution process and progress; to foster the use of such processes and programs in new areas; and to stimulate innovative approaches to the productive solution of future conflict.

Methods of operation: Training and technical assistance (40%), public education (30%), publications (30%)

Constituency: Community mediation centers; individual mediators; public sectors; universities

Recent issues and projects: Recent projects include: youth violence; health care; court-based mediation programs; international environmental policy and law

Major publications: *Forum*, monthly journal; *NIDR News*, bi-monthly newsletter; special reports and teaching materials

Budget: $2,000,000

Funding: Foundations (95%), publications (5%)

Staff: 10
1 Writer/Editor
1 Office Manager
1 Researcher

1 Foundation Fundraiser
4 Issue Experts
1 Secretary
1 Bookkeeper/Accountant

Staff openings/year: 2

Work Week: 40 hours

Salary/year: $25,000

Benefits: Health insurance, pension, paid vacation, life insurance

Part-Time Employees: 2

Summer Employees: 2

Interns: 2
Length: 2 to 3 months
Duties: Research, information support
Remuneration: Varies

Jobs advertised: Newsletters, newspapers

NATIONAL LAWYERS GUILD SUMMER PROJECTS COMMITTEE

55 Avenue of the Americas
New York, NY 10013
(206) 966-5000

Purpose: (1) To meet the legal, educational and political needs of progressive community organizations and the people they serve; and (2) to provide law students and legal workers with direct experience in public interest law, encouraging careers in this field of legal work.

Methods of operation: Litigation (60%), community organizing (20%), public education (20%)

Recent issues and projects: Works for voting rights for Blacks in the South; for union democracy in the Teamsters Union; against the death penalty and inhumane prison conditions; for women's economic, political and reproductive rights; for workplace health and safety; for the rights of farmworkers and refugees from Central America; and in support of farmers facing foreclosure.

Major publications: An annual *Summer Projects* brochure describing the internships comes out each December

Interns: 20-30
Length: 10 weeks
Duties: Legal research and writing; community education and organizing; administrative hearings
Remuneration: $2,000 stipend for 10 weeks

Jobs advertised: Through our annual *Summer Projects* brochure, which is issued each December and sent to over 180 law school placement offices and all National Lawyers Guild chapters throughout the country. Applications must be postmarked by February 1.

To apply: Contact the Director, Summer Projects Committee

NATIONAL LEADERSHIP COALITION ON AIDS

1730 M Street, NW, Suite 905
Washington, DC 20036
(202) 429-0930

President: B.J. Stiles

Purpose: The mission of the National Leadership Coalition on AIDS is to marshal the collective resources of business and labor to prevent and combat the spread of HIV disease through effective workplace AIDS education, policies and practices.

Methods of operation: Publications (30%), human services (20%), direct action (20%), training and technical assistance (20%), public education (10%)

Constituency: Businesses, labor unions, academics, trade associations, voluntary organizations, health and safety organizations and concerned individuals

Recent issues and projects: Recent projects include: provided the first and only guidelines for managing TB and HIV infection in the general workplace; provided the results of a national survey of 2000 working Americans and their opinions on AIDS; compiled and distributed the case studies of 10 U.S. employers and their employees with HIV infection and AIDS and how they worked together to shape accommodations to help them keep productive and on the job as long as they wanted to do so.

Major publications: *Managing TB and HIV Infection in the General Workplace*; *Employee Attitudes About AIDS: What Working Americans Think*; *Accommodating Employees With HIV Infection and AIDS: Case Studies of Employer Assistance*

Budget: $662,000

Funding: Individual contributions (33%), foundations (33%), Center for Disease Control (33%)

Staff: 8
2 Organizers

1 Office Manager
1 Researcher
1 Press Aide
1 Canvasser
1 Issue Expert
1 Bookkeeper/Accountant

Staff openings/year: 1-2

Work Week: 45 hours

Salary/year: $23,000 (Recent College Graduate); $28,000 (Graduate with advanced degree)

Benefits: Health insurance, pension, paid vacation, life insurance, family leave

Part-Time Employees: None

Summer Employees: None

Volunteers: 2-4

Interns: None, but willing to accept applications

Jobs advertised: *Washington Post*, word-of-mouth

To apply: Contact Patrick May, Director of Communications

NATIONAL LEGAL AID AND DEFENDER ASSOCIATION

1625 K Street, NW, Suite 800
Washington, DC 20006
(202) 452-0620

Director: Clinton Lyons

Purpose: Private, nonprofit, national membership organization dedicated to developing and supporting high quality legal help for poor people in America.

Methods of operation: Training and technical assistance, public education, publications, research, lobbying, litigation. NLADA provides no direct representation of clients in need of civil and defender legal services.

Constituency: Individual lawyers; clients; members of public; organizations/individuals in professions that provide civil and criminal representation for poor persons; bar association; civil rights/liberties groups

Recent issues and projects: Technical assistance and training for providers of legal assistance; standards development to guide providers in delivering high quality legal services; national pilot projects to develop advanced techniques and systems for legal services; advocating for civil and defender legal services; building support for legal assistance for poor people among public officials, the organized bar, individual attorneys, business organizations and others

Major publications: *The Cornerstone*; *Capital Report*; *The Directory of Legal Aid and Defender Offices*

Budget: $2,500,000

Funding: Dues (52%), training (18%), foundations (20%), corporate and individual contributions (10%), publications/subscriptions (2%)

Staff: 23
8 Attorneys
7 Administrative Assistants
1 Director, Conference and Training
1 Director, Government Relations
1 Director, Finance and Administration
1 Executive Assistant
1 Receptionist
1 Accountant
1 Press Secretary
1 Office Manager

Work Week: 37.5 hours

Salary/year: $Varies (Recent College Graduate); $Varies (Graduate with advanced degree)

Benefits: Health insurance, life insurance, pregnancy leave, paid vacation

Interns: Yes
Length: Semester
Duties: Membership services and communications

Jobs advertised: Newspaper; announcements to legal services community

To apply: Contact Aurea Ortiz, Office Manager

Remarks: Unsolicited resumes are discouraged. Please contact NLADA for information on current vacancies.

NATIONAL LEGAL CENTER FOR THE MEDICALLY DEPENDENT & DISABLED, INC.

50 South Meridian, Suite 605
Indianapolis, IN 46204-3541
(317) 632-6245

Other Offices: Terre Haute, IN

President: James Bopp, Jr.

Purpose: To provide legal assistance to legal services attorneys and other counsel representing low-income persons with disabilities subject to discriminatory denial of life-sustaining care.

Methods of operation: Research (25%), publications (25%), training and technical assistance (25%), litigation (15%), public education (10%)

Constituency: Low-income persons with disabilities requiring life-sustaining care

Recent issues and projects: Filed amicus brief on behalf of disabilities groups in Cruzan "right to die" case urging U.S. Supreme Court to uphold comatose person's right to receive life-support unless clearly waived by person prior to incapacitating condition.

Major publications: Quarterly journal: *Issues in Law and Medicine*

Budget: $430,000

Funding: Legal Services Corporation (99%), foundations (1%)

Staff: 8
4 Attorneys
2 Typists
1 Writer/Editor
1 Office Manager

Work Week: 40 hours

Salary/year: $Varies (Recent College Graduate); $22,000 (Graduate with advanced degree)

Benefits: Health insurance, paid vacation

Part-Time Employees: Yes

Interns: 2-5
Length: Summer
Duties: Research, writing
Remuneration: Housing

Jobs advertised: Legal services publications, law school placement offices, various national publications, disability groups

To apply: Contact James Bopp, Jr., President

NATIONAL LOW-INCOME HOUSING COALITION AND INFORMATION SERVICE

1012 14th Street, NW, 12th Floor
Washington, DC 20005
(202) 662-1530

Director: Cushing N. Dolbeane

Purpose: To provide decent housing, suitable environments, adequate neighborhoods, and freedom of housing choice for low-income people. The Coalition works toward these goals through lobbying Congress and the Administration for better, sufficiently funded housing programs and through publications to inform people of housing legislation.

Methods of operation: Lobbying, publications, public education

Constituency: Individuals, coalitions and nonprofit housing providers who represent tenant, labor, church, minority and other interests; located in all 50 states and territories

Recent issues and projects: "Two Cents More for Housing" campaign, which advocates two cents more of every federal tax dollar for housing; legislative push for a major housing bill to be passed in 1990

Major publications: Monthly newsletter: *Roundup*; *A Place to Call Home*, a profile of low-income housing in America

Budget: $500,000

Funding: Membership contributions, subscriptions, foundation grants

Staff: 15
8 Program Staff
4 Administrative Staff
2 Lobbyists
1 Director

Staff openings/year: 2-3

Work Week: 50-60 hours

Benefits: Health insurance, life insurance, paid vacation, all federal holidays, sick leave

Interns: 2-3
Length: Semester or summer
Duties: Varies depending upon position
Remuneration: Stipend

Jobs advertised: College intern guides; advertise in *Community Jobs*; word of mouth through housing network

To apply: Contact Francis Williams, Administrative Assistant

Remarks: Housing is getting a lot of attention these days, so unfortunately we have to turn away many talented people. We don't have as many openings or as much space as we would like.

NATIONAL MINORITY AIDS FOUNDATION

300 Eye Street, NE, Suite 400
Washington, DC 20002
(202) 544-1076

Director: Paul Kawata

Purpose: Develop and guide national public policy initiatives on HIV/AIDS infection in communities of color. Provides technical assistance on organizational development to CRO's, creates forums to address new critical issues for our community. We co-sponsor the annual National Skills Building Conference.

Methods of operation: Lobbying, publications, community organizing, public education, training and technical assistance, conferences

Membership: Around 500 community based AIDS organizations

Major publications: *The Impact of HIV on Communities of Color: A Blueprint for the nineties*; *Update*

Budget: $1,500,000

Funding: Government grants (33%), foundations (33%), individual contributions (33%)

Staff: 22
2 Writers/Editors
4 Office Managers
3 Lobbyists
1 Press Aide
2 Foundation Fundraisers
3 Issue Experts
3 Technical Assistants
2 Bookkeepers/Accountants

Staff openings/year: 5

Work Week: 40 hours

Salary/year: $20,000 (Recent College Graduate); $25,000 (Graduate with advanced degree)

Benefits: Health insurance, pension, paid vacation, life insurance, family leave

Part-Time Employees: 1

Interns: 1
Length: 6 months
Duties: Varies depending on projects and interests
Remuneration: Stipend

Jobs advertised: Ads in local papers

To apply: Please contact Paul Kawata, Executive Director

NATIONAL NATIVE AMERICAN AIDS PREVENTION CENTER

3515 Grand Avenue #100
Oakland, CA 94610
(510) 444-2051

Other Offices: Minneapolis, MN; Oklahoma City, OK

Director: Ron Rowell

Purpose: Resource to Native communities and to support community efforts by providing education and information services and training/technical assistance; offer case management and client advocacy services to Native Americans with HIV infection

Methods of operation: Training and technical assistance (34%), publications (33%), case management (33%)

Recent issues and projects: Recent projects include: completed training of trainers in Albuqueque,NM in 7/94; Continuing technical assistance to the NW region; getting a new award for a Wellness Center in Oklahoma City

Major publications: *Seasons in the Wind*

Budget: $2,000,000

Funding: Federal Government (100%)

Staff: 16
4 Organizers
2 Writer/Editors
1 Office Manager
1 Typist
2 Bookkeepers/Accountants
3 Caseworkers
1 Program Assistant
1 Evaluation Specialist

Work Week: 37.50 hours

Salary/year: $25,000 (Recent College Graduate); $32,000 (Graduate with advanced degree)

Benefits: Health insurance, paid vacation

Part-Time Employees: 2

Summer Employees: None

Volunteers: None

Interns: None

Jobs advertised: Newspapers, newsletters

To apply: Please send resumes to the Fiscal Department in Oakland, CA

NATIONAL NEIGHBORHOOD COALITION

810 First Street, NE, Third Floor
Washington, DC 20002
(202) 289-1551

Director: Bud Kanitz

Purpose: Serves as an informational and educational clearinghouse on national public policies and federal programs that help or hurt inner-city neighborhoods in the U.S.

Methods of operation: Public education (40%), publications (30%), community organizing (10%), public policy (10%), research (7%), lobbying (3%)

Constituency: National and regional nonprofit organizations that work with inner-city neighborhood groups or on inner-city issues

Recent issues and projects: Monthly information forums held on the first Thursday of each month at noon. Issues: low-income housing and community development, community reinvestment banking

Major publications: *Monthly Information Report*: includes minutes of the previous Information Forum, calendar of conferences, new publications, and job openings

Budget: $90,000

Funding: Foundations (83%), membership dues (15%), individual contributions (2%)

Staff: 1
1 Organizer
1/10 Writer/Editor
1/20 Foundation Fundraiser
1/20 Bookkeeper/Accountant

Work Week: 45 hours

Benefits: Health insurance, life insurance, pension, paid vacation

Part-Time Employees: 3 consultants

Jobs advertised: *Community Jobs*

To apply: Contact Bud Kanitz, Executive Director

NATIONAL ORGANIZATION FOR THE REFORM OF MARIJUANA LAWS (NORML)

1001 Connecticut Ave., NW, Suite 1119
Washington, DC 20036
(202) 483-5500

Director: Richard Cowan

Purpose: Education on effects of marijuana and advocacy of decriminalization of marijuana laws; legal referrals

Methods of operation: Public education (60%), research (10%), litigation (10%), training and technical assistance (10%), lobbying (5%), publications (5%)

Constituency: Marijuana decriminalization advocates

Recent issues and projects: Suit before Drug Enforcement Administration (DEA) to allow use of marijuana for medical purposes; civil liberties issues involving illegal searches, arrests.

Major publications: Newsletter: *Active Resistance Potpourri/Ongoing Briefing*

Budget: $250,000

Funding: Individual contributions (60%), direct mail (20%), tours, concerts (20%)

Staff: 8
1 Organizer
1 Writer/Editor
1 Attorney
1 Office Manager
1 Researcher
1 Press Aide
1 Issue Expert
1 Bookkeeper/Accountant

Staff openings/year: 1

Work Week: 40 hours

Salary/year: $18,000 (Recent College Graduate); $Varies (Graduate with advanced degree)

Benefits: Paid vacation, some paid holidays

Part-Time Employees: 1-3

Summer Employees: 1-2

Volunteers: 10-15

Interns: 1
Length: 3 months
Duties: Answer telephones, office work, various

interesting projects
Remuneration: $5+/hour

Jobs advertised: Word of mouth; membership newsletter

To apply: Contact Donald Fiedler

Remarks: We are looking for individuals who agree that marijuana should be decriminalized, and are willing to work hard on a broad range of projects with a great deal of responsibility. We have over 25 chapters around the country.

NATIONAL ORGANIZATION FOR WOMEN (NOW)

1000 16th Street, NW, Suite 700
Washington, DC 20036
(202) 331-0066

President: Patricia Ireland

Purpose: NOW is dedicated to making legal, political, social and economic change in our society in order to achieve the goal of bringing women into participation in the mainstream of American society now and to exercise full rights and responsibilities in truly equal partnership with men.

Methods of operation: Community organizing (30%), direct action (30%), public education (20%), training and technical assistance (10%), lobbying (5%), litigation (5%)

Constituency: Progressive; multiracial; predominantly female

Recent issues and projects: NOW's principle focus at this time is protecting women's reproductive freedom by guaranteeing safe and legal abortion and birth control. Other issues include obtaining passage of the ERA, achieving economic equality, promoting lesbian and gay rights, eliminating racism, promoting quality child care and advancing the feminization of power. Recent projects include Women's Equality/Women's Rights March and Rally, Freedom Caravan for Women's Lives, Stand Up for Women and Global Feminism.

Major publications: *NOW Times*; *NOW LDEF Reproductive Rights Resource Manual*; *Stand Up for Women Action Manual to Combat Operation Rescue*

Budget: $10,000,000

Funding: Individual contributions, direct mail

Staff: 35
8 Administrative
5 Issue Experts
4 Membership Services
3 Press Aides
3 Bookkeepers/Accountants
3 Organizers
2 Attorneys
2 Direct Mail Specialists
1 Writer/Editor
1 Office Manager
1 Typist
1 Retail
1 Intern/Volunteer Coordinator

Staff openings/year: 37.5

Work Week: 5 hours

Salary/year: $18,000 (Recent College Graduate); $25,000 (Graduate with advanced degree)

Benefits: Health insurance, life insurance, dental insurance, pregnancy leave, paid vacation

Part-Time Employees: 1-5

Volunteers: 25

Interns: 5-10
Length: 3-4 months
Duties: Research, writing, administrative and project support, direct action
Remuneration: Unpaid

Jobs advertised: *NOW National Times*; word of mouth; newspaper advertisements

To apply: Contact the Intern/Volunteer Coordinator

NATIONAL ORGANIZERS ALLIANCE (NOA)

130 11th Street, NE
Washington, DC 20021
(202) 543-6603

Director: Kim Fellner (Coordinator)

Purpose: NOA's goals are 1) to forge a supportive "congregation" of community, union and issues organizers and develop connections and context to unify our work for social and economic justice; 2) To pursue work standards benefits that let organizers make a life, and a living, for the long haul; 3) create structures that teach and carry on a tradition of organizing as a calling and profession.

Methods of operation: Research (10%), community organizing (70%), publications (10%), public education (10%)

Membership: People whose paid work is

organizing or directly supports organizing

Recent issues and projects: Our first gathering will take place August 14, 1994 which will be part of our goal of building a community of organizers. Also working on a multiple employer protable pension for a social economic justice movement.

Major publications: *The Ark*, a quarterly newsletter

Budget: $135,000

Funding: Foundations (85%), membership (10%), individual contributions (5%)

Staff: 2
1 Organizer
1 "Jill of all Trades"

Staff openings/year: ?

Work Week: 50 hours

Salary/year: $22,000

Benefits: Health insurance, pension, paid vacation

Part-Time Employees: No

Summer Employees: Not yet

Volunteers: Not yet

Interns: Too New
Length: Willing to accept applications

To apply: Please contact Kim Fellner

NATIONAL PUBLIC RADIO

2025 M Street, NW
Washington, DC 20036
(202) 822-2000

President: Douglas J. Bennet

Purpose: To work in partnership with the member stations to inform, invigorate and challenge the American public by fostering a deeper understanding and appreciation of events, ideas and cultures.

Methods of operation: Producing radio network

Membership: 387 public radio stations

Recent issues and projects: Twentieth Anniversary

Major publications: *All Things Considered* and *Morning Edition* programs

Budget: $37,000,000

Funding: Membership dues (80%), foundations, corporations (20%)

Staff: 430
250 Writer/Editors and On-Air Talent
75 Engineers
40 Administrative Assistants
40 Managers
10 Foundation Fundraisers
10 Bookkeepers/Accountants
5 Attorneys

Staff openings/year: 30

Work Week: 40 hours

Salary/year: $18,000

Benefits: Health insurance, life insurance, pregnancy leave, pension, credit union, paid vacation

Part-Time Employees: Yes

Summer Employees: Yes

Volunteers: Yes

Interns: Yes
Length: 6 weeks
Duties: Vary
Remuneration: $200 per week

Jobs advertised: Press

To apply: Contact the Personnel Department

NATIONAL RAINBOW COALITION

P.O. Box 27385
Washington, 20005
(202) 728-1180 Fax: (202) 728-1192

Director: Angela Davis

Purpose: The National Rainbow Coalition is multi-racial, multi-issue national organization, founded by Reverend Jesse L. Jackson. Our mission it to move our nation and the world towards social, racial and economic justice. We embrace and seek to fulfill the democratic promise of America. We seek to do so by forming a mighty coalition across ancient barriers of race, gender, and religion, so that, together, all the old minorities will form the new majority. Our methods include legislation, litigation, registration, demonstration, and independent political action.

Recent issues and projects: The Rainbow's current projects include: Reclaim Our Youth, Rebuild and Reinvest in America, DC Statehood, Labor Law Reform, Rainbow Commission for Fairness in Athletics, Voter Registration and Voting Rights.

Staff:

4 Directors

To apply: Contact Angela Davis

NATIONAL RECYCLING COALITION, INC.

1101 30th Street, NW, Suite 305
Washington, DC 20007
(202) 625-6406

Director: Marsha L. Rhea

Purpose: Association of professional recyclers, businesses involved in recycling, environmental organizations and individuals who promote recycling. They provide technical assistance and a recyclers network for information on recycling.

Methods of operation: Research, community organizing, publications, direct action, training and technical assistance

Constituency: Professional recyclers, businesses involved in recycling, environmental organizations and individuals who promote recycling

Recent issues and projects: (1) Establishment of the Recycling Advisory Council: a council comprised of four sectors (public, environmental, businesses involved in recycling, and other business and industry). This council will research different recycling issues, their implications for the population and affected industry, and take an issue stand. (2) Peer Match Program: a program designed to assist in the establishment of recycling programs (community, governmental).

Major publications: Quarterly newsletter: *The Connection*

Budget: $1,400,000

Funding: Individual contributions (45%), donor solicitation (45%), foundations (10%)

Work Week: 40 hours

Benefits: Health insurance, pension, life insurance, paid vacation

Interns: 3-4
Length: Still in developmental stage
Duties: Research; development of library

Jobs advertised: Depends on the job. Possibly *Resource Recycler*, *BioCycle*, *Waste Age* or *Washington Post*

To apply: Send resume, cover letter to Susan Medick

NATIONAL RESOURCE CENTER FOR CONSUMERS OF LEGAL SERVICES

Tabb House, Main Street, P.O. Box 340
Gloucester, VA 23061
(804) 693-9330

Other Offices: Washington, DC

Director: William A. Bolger

Purpose: Nonprofit research and education group working to improve the legal system, particularly the delivery of legal services to individuals, by promoting preventive law and legal services plans.

Methods of operation: Publications (28%), research (20%), public education (20%), training and technical assistance (20%), lobbying (2%)

Constituency: People and organizations interested in legal services plans

Recent issues and projects: Encourage and assist groups to set up legal services plans; help plans work better; fight bar association rules that harm the public; encourage telephone access lines, paralegals, self-help law and a more flexible, responsive system. Also administer a free national legal services plan sponsored by AFL-CIO.

Major publications: Biweekly newsletter: *Legal Plan Letter*; monthly newsletter: *Serviceline*; *1988 National Legal Fee Survey*; *Free Legal Services Plans*; over 200 other short publications; preventive law article series

Budget: $150,000

Funding: Membership dues, publication sales, contracts for services (100%)

Staff: 2
1 Office Manager
1 Writer/Editor

Staff openings/year: 0-1

Work Week: 40 hours

Salary/year: $18,000

Benefits: Health insurance, paid vacation, very flexible scheduling

Part-Time Employees: 3

Summer Employees: 1

Interns: None currently, but willing to accept applications

Jobs advertised: Usually word of mouth or local paper

NATIONAL SAFE KIDS CAMPAIGN

Children's Nat'l. Med. Ctr., 111 Michigan Ave., NW
Washington, DC 20010-2970
(202) 884-4993

Director: Heather Paul

Purpose: To prevent unintentional childhood injuries which is the leading killer and disabler in America. The campaign addresses unintentional injuries to children through age 14 in the following major risk areas: traffic injuries, fires and burns, drownings, poisoning and choking.

Methods of operation: Public education (35%), community organizing (30%), publications (15%), research (10%), training and technical assistance (10%)

Recent issues and projects: SAFE KIDS America is the largest injury prevention outreach program in the nation's history. Current projects include: SAFE KIDS Cycle Smart, a bicycle safety program; National SAFE Kids Week 1994; and the SAFE KIDS Summit.

Major publications: *Campaign Update*

Budget: $1,600,000

Funding: Sponsors (70%), foundations and government grants (30%)

Staff: 20
3 Organizers
1 Writer/Editor
1 Office Manager
3 Public Policy Advocates
3 Media Specialists
1 Foundation Fundraiser
3 Issue Experts
1 Receptionist
1 Campaign Manager
3 Administrative Assistants

Staff openings/year: 1

Work Week: 40 hours

Salary/year: $35,100 (Recent College Graduate); $50,000 (Graduate with advanced degree)

Benefits: Health insurance, pension, paid vacation, life insurance, credit union

Part-Time Employees: None

Summer Employees: None

Volunteers: Yes

Interns: 1-4
Length: 3-6 months
Duties: Depends on department
Remuneration: Small stipend or unpaid

Jobs advertised: Newspapers; through Children's National Medical Center, Human Resources Department

To apply: Heather Paul, Executive Director

NATIONAL SAFE WORKPLACE INSTITUTE

3008 Bishops Ridge
Monroe, NC 28110
(704) 289-6061

Director: Joseph A. Kinney

Purpose: We work to advance safety and health in our workplace. This includes examining government and corporate policies and programs. We also spend much time on responding to press calls.

Methods of operation: Research, direct action, public education, training and technical assistance

Recent issues and projects: (1) Education: NSWI issues periodic reports, participates in conferences, supports investigative and interpretive journalism, and engages in other efforts to increase awareness of occupational safety and health issues. (2) Research: NSWI researches a variety of public and private sector issues - government accountability, business practices, emerging trends and further injury and illness reduction efforts. (3) Intervention: NSWI intervenes in specific circumstances to help further injury and illness reduction objectives.

Major publications: *Unmet Needs: Making American Work Safe for the 1990s*; *Unintended Consequences: The Failure of OSHA's Megafine Strategy*; *Faces: The Toll of Workplace Death on American Families*; *Safer Work: Job Safety and Health Challenges for the Next President and Congress*; *Failed Opportunities: The Decline of U.S. Job Safety in the 1980s*

Budget: $141,000

Funding: Foundations (80%), individual contributions (10%), publications (10%)

Staff: 3
Including:

Writer/Editor
Researcher
Foundation Fundraiser
Issue Expert
Caseworker

Staff openings/year: 4

Work Week: 50+ hours

Salary/year: $17,000 (Recent College Graduate); $22,000 (Graduate with advanced degree)

Benefits: Flexible benefits package

Part-Time Employees: Yes

Summer Employees: Yes

Interns: Yes
Length: 3 months
Duties: Depends on individual skills, goals of intern, and Institute's requirements
Remuneration: All interns are paid

Jobs advertised: Newspapers; student publications; through university placement offices

To apply: Contact Joseph A. Kinney, Executive Director

NATIONAL SECURITY ARCHIVE

1755 Massachusetts Ave., NW, Suite 500
Washington, DC 20036
(202) 797-0882

Director: Thomas S. Blanton

Purpose: Since its inception in 1985, the Archive's primary goal has been to document recent U.S. policy and to enrich public debate on the often hidden process of national security decision making. Through its collection, analysis and publication of previously classified government documents, the Archive is able to reconstruct U.S. policymaking on a variety of foreign, defense and intelligence issues and capture how government decisions are made.

Methods of operation: Research, litigation, publications, public education, training and technical assistance

Constituency: A wide range of researchers, journalists, scholars, students, etc.

Recent issues and projects: Current priority projects include U.S. policy on the following: nuclear history; Southern Africa; Persian Gulf; Cuba; international aspects of the war on drugs; Eastern Europe; human rights; and Japan. Additionally, their Freedom of Information project litigates several cases each year on access to information issues.

Major publications: *El Salvador: The Making of U.S. Policy*, 1977-1984; *The Iran-Contra Affair: The Making of a Scandal*, 1983-1988; *Iran: The Making of U.S. Policy*, 1977-1980; *The Cuban Missile Crisis*, 1962; *The U.S. Intelligence Community*, 1947-1989; *The Philippines: U.S. Policy During the Marcos Years*, 1965-1986; *Afghanistan: The Making of U.S. Policy*, 1973-1990; *Nicaragua: The Making of U.S. Policy*, 1978-1990; *South Africa: The Making of U.S. Policy*, 1962-1989

Budget: $1,000,000

Funding: Individual contributions, foundations, publications

Staff:
1 Attorney
Researchers
Librarians

Staff openings/year: 0-2

Work Week: 40 hours

Salary/year: $Varies (Recent College Graduate); $Varies (Graduate with advanced degree)

Part-Time Employees: 6

Summer Employees: None

Volunteers: None

Interns: 6-10 a semester
Length: Summer or semester
Duties: Archival and library research; building chronologies of events; helping obtain, order and catalog government documents; assist w/data entry
Remuneration: Unpaid

Jobs advertised: Local schools, newspapers, organizations

To apply: Contact Lynne Quinto, Administrator

NATIONAL SENIOR CITIZENS LAW CENTER

1815 H Street, NW, Suite 700
Washington, DC 20006
(202) 887-5280

Director: Burton D. Fretz

Purpose: NSCLC is a national legal services support center which focuses on the legal problems of the elderly poor.

Methods of operation: Litigation (30%), responding to requests for assistance from legal services attorneys (30%), research (10%), publications (10%), training and technical assistance (10%)

Constituency: Generally attorneys funded by the Legal Services Corporation and the Administration on Aging

Recent issues and projects: NSCLC undertakes all forms of advocacy covering various areas of the law including Social Security, Supplemental Security Income (SSI), Medicare, Medicaid, private pensions, age discrimination, home care and nursing homes.

Major publications: NSCLC has two regular publications: *Washington Weekly* and the *Nursing Home Letter.* In addition, NSCLC regularly publishes manuals and articles.

Budget: $1,400,000

Funding: Government grants (90%), foundations (10%)

Staff: 20
11 Attorneys
3 1/2 Legal Secretaries
2 Administrative Assistants
2 Receptionists/Clerks
1 Bookkeepers/Accountants
1/2 Writer/Editor

Staff openings/year: 2

Work Week: 35 hours

Salary/year: $Varies (Recent College Graduate); $Varies (Graduate with advanced degree)

Benefits: Health insurance, life insurance, pension, paid vacation

Part-Time Employees: 3

Interns: 2, through law school programs
Length: 3-6 months
Duties: Law Clerk
Remuneration: Usually none

Jobs advertised: Mostly through the public interest bar, newsletters and mailings

To apply: Contact Neal S. Dudovitz, Deputy Director

NATIONAL SOCIETY FOR EXPERIENTIAL EDUCATION

3509 Haworth Drive, Suite 207
Raleigh, NC 27609
(919) 787-3263

Director: Allen Wutzdorff

Purpose: NSEE's goals are to: advocate for the effective use of experiential learning throughout the educational system and the larger community; disseminate information on principles of good practice and on the innovations in the field; enhance professional growth and leadership development in the field; encourage the development and dissemination of related research and theory

Methods of operation: Publications, public education, training and technical assistance

Constituency: Faculty and staff at educational institutions interested in experiential education

Major publications: *The National Directory of Internships*; *Combining Service and Learning: A Resource Book for Community and Public Service*; *Strengthening Experiential Education within Your Institution*; *The Experienced Hand: A Student Manual for Making the Most of an Internship*; *The NSEE Quarterly*

Budget: $302,000

Funding: Individual memberships, publications, conference fees

Staff: 7
3 Administrative Staff
4 Program Staff

Staff openings/year: 0-1

Work Week: 40 hours

Salary/year: $Varies (Recent College Graduate); $Varies (Graduate with advanced degree)

Benefits: Health insurance, pension, paid vacation, family leave

Part-Time Employees: 1

Summer Employees: 1

Volunteers: None

Interns: 1
Length: 3 months
Duties: Depends upon interns qualifications

Jobs advertised: Local newspapers and through mailings to members

To apply: Please contact Annette Wofford

NATIONAL STUDENT CAMPAIGN AGAINST HUNGER AND HOMELESSNESS

29 Temple Place, Fifth Floor
Boston, MA 02111-9907
(617) 292-4823

Director: Jennifer Jones

Purpose: A national nonprofit organization dedicated to providing immediate relief to the hungry and homeless and providing long-term solutions to the problems which keep them impoverished by helping students put their concern into action. NSCAHH is guided by the belief that students have a unique opportunity to make a difference in our society.

Methods of operation: Training and technical assistance (55%), publications (15%), community organizing (15%), public education (10%), research (5%)

Constituency: High schools, colleges, universities, regional and national organizations concerned with involving youth in community service, the hunger and homelessness problems and social change

Recent issues and projects: Leading the annual spring Hunger Cleanup, which involved 10,000 students in completing community work projects and raising $170,000 for the impoverished; leads Leadership Conference for student activists and college administrators; supports Campus Hunger and Homelessness Week; publishes an *Opportunities Catalog*, listing domestic and international volunteer and work internships and jobs

Major publications: Quarterly newsletter: *Students Making a Difference*; *Going Places: A Guide to Domestic and International Internships, Jobs and Travel Opportunities*; *Hunger and Homelessness Action Handbook*; *Hunger Cleanup Manual*

Budget: $105,000

Funding: Individual contributions (65%), special events (15%), foundations (10%), publications (5%), direct mail (5%)

Staff: 4
3 Organizers
1 Campaign Manager

Staff openings/year: 2

Work Week: 55 hours

Salary/year: $14,500 (Recent College Graduate); $16,500 (Graduate with advanced degree)

Benefits: Health insurance, pregnancy leave, paid vacation, student loan assistance program

Volunteers: 5

Interns: 3
Length: 6 months
Duties: Includes research, writing, membership correspondence, graphic design and computer entry
Remuneration: None at present time. Course credit can be arranged.

Jobs advertised: Network; *Community Jobs*; Public Interest Research Groups; local newspaper and newsletters of other organizations working in related fields

To apply: Contact Jennifer Coken, Campaign Director

Remarks: NSCAHH was founded in 1985 by the Public Interest Research Groups (PIRGs) in cooperation with USA for Africa. It has grown to become the largest network of student hunger and homelessness activists in the country, working with 600 schools in 45 states. Entry level positions are available; individuals with organizing experience are encouraged to apply. Applicants must be motivated and committed to working for social change.

NATIONAL STUDENT NEWS SERVICE

116 New Montgomery Street, Suite 530
San Francisco, CA 94105
(415) 543-2089

Director: J. Bonasia

Purpose: To increase student news coverage, broadly defined over the ideological spectrum, by operating a wire service for college newspapers. In disseminating news about student campaigns to improve campuses and society, they hope to encourage further activism.

Methods of operation: Publications, public education

Constituency: College newspapers, student government associations, student activism organizations

Recent issues and projects: We are publishing 20 editions in the academic year with subscribers on 200 college campuses. Our aggregate audience is one million students. We also serve as a network for our members and for student activism organizations, supplying contacts and media outlets.

Budget: $30,000

Funding: Foundations (25%), membership/subscriptions (75%)

Staff: 1
1 Writer/Editor

Staff openings/year: 1

Work Week: 50+ hours

Salary/year: $14-16,000 (Graduate with advanced degree)

Benefits: Health insurance, paid vacation, parental leave, tuition reimbursement

Volunteers: 3-4

Interns: 3-4
Length: Academic semester
Duties: Reporting, writing, research, membership outreach, marketing
Remuneration: $125/month stipend available for full-time; other arrangements may be available for part-time

Jobs advertised: *Community Jobs*; local papers; college campus recruiting; notices sent to other organizations

To apply: Contact J. Bonasia, Director

NATIONAL TRAINING AND INFORMATION CENTER

810 North Milwaukee Avenue
Chicago, IL 60622-4103
(312) 243-3035

Director: Gale Cincotta

Purpose: To empower low-income neighborhood people to have input into decisions that affect their lives.

Methods of operation: Research, direct action, community organizing, publications, training and technical assistance

Constituency: Low-income people

Major publications: Quarterly newsletter: *NTIC Reports*; *Disclosure*, 6 times a year; occasional organizing and issue manuals

Budget: $900,000

Funding: Foundations, corporate, government

Staff: 18
9 Issue Experts
4 Organizers
2 Typists
1 Writer/Editor
1 Office Manager
1 Bookkeeper/Accountant

Staff openings/year: 2-3

Work Week: 50 hours

Salary/year: $Varies (Recent College Graduate); $Varies (Graduate with advanced degree)

Benefits: Health insurance, life insurance, pregnancy leave, paid vacation, long-term disability

Part-Time Employees: 2

Interns: Yes
Length: 3-6 months
Duties: Depends on intern's interests and skills
Remuneration: Depends on funding situation

Jobs advertised: Usually word of mouth

To apply: Contact Shel Trapp, Staff Director

NATIONAL URBAN LEAGUE, INC.

500 East 62nd Street
New York, NY 10021
(212) 310-9000

President: John E. Jacob

Purpose: NUL's mission is to assist African Americans in the achievement of social and economic equality. Success in this mission will be measured by progressive narrowing of the gaps that separate African Americans from other Americans, leading to parity on such crucial areas as educational attainment, employment and economic self-sufficiency.

Methods of operation: Advocacy, research, human services, community organizing, publications, public education, training and technical assistance

Recent issues and projects: Include the National Education Initiative; Employment and Training; Comprehensive Youth Development Program; AIDS Initiative; Stop the Violence Clearinghouse; Adolescent Pregnancy Prevention and Parenting; Senior Environmental Employment Program; Seniors in Community Service Program; Black Executive Exchange Program (BEEP)

Major publications: Annual Report: *The State of*

Black America; *Urban League News*, quarterly; research papers; *Urban League Review*, journal produced in the DC office; *Runta* fact sheet (DC office)

Budget: $27,000,000

Funding: Corporations, foundations, individuals, labor, private contributions, government grants

Staff: 200
Includes:
Social Workers
Economists
Administrators
Support Staff

Work Week: 40 hours

Benefits: Health insurance, life insurance, pension, credit union, paid vacation

Part-Time Employees: Yes; consultants

Summer Employees: Yes

Volunteers: 30,000+ nationwide

Interns: Yes
Length: Summer
Duties: Program assistance
Remuneration: Stipend

Jobs advertised: Internally

To apply: Contact Human Resources Department

Remarks: The NUL research department is part of the Washington operations office, located at 1111 14th Street, NW, 6th Floor, Washington, DC 20005. The Urban League has 113 affiliates in 34 states.

NATIONAL VETERANS LEGAL SERVICES PROJECT, INC.

2001 S Street, NW, Suite 610
Washington, DC 20009
(202) 265-8305

Director: David F. Addlestone, Barton F. Stichman, Co-Directors

Purpose: NVLSP is a national support center in the area of veterans law and policy, providing information, referrals, publications, training and litigation assistance to veterans and veterans advocates.

Methods of operation: Litigation (40%), publications (30%), training and technical assistance (20%), research (5%), public education (5%)

Constituency: Veterans and their dependents, veterans advocates

Recent issues and projects: Successfully litigated against the Department of Veterans Affairs, forcing them to revise their rules governing compensation to Vietnam veterans based on exposure to dioxin; representation of veterans in the new U.S. Court of Veterans Appeals

Major publications: *The Veterans Advocate*, a monthly newsletter providing current information in the area of veterans law; *Veterans Benefits Manual*, a 1300-page practice manual; *Military Discharge Upgrading*, a 700-page practice manual

Budget: $2,000,000

Funding: Foundations/Agent Orange Fund (40%), fee awards, Legal Services Corporation, contract work (40%)

Staff: 28
12 Attorneys
4 Paralegals
2 Typists
4 Law Clerks
4 Controller/Office Manager/Bookkeeper/Devel.
1 Receptionist
1 Office Clerk

Staff openings/year: 2

Work Week: 40-50 hours

Salary/year: $Varies (Recent College Graduate); $28,000 (Graduate with advanced degree)

Benefits: Health insurance, life insurance, pension, paid vacation, pregnancy leave

Part-Time Employees: 4-6 law clerks

Volunteers: Yes

Interns: 4
Length: 1 year
Duties: Law school student internship: litigation, law clerk
Remuneration: $12.00 an hour paid internship

Jobs advertised: Law school placement offices; Bar Association; *Clearinghouse Review*

To apply: Contact David F. Addlestone or Barton F. Stichman

NATIONAL WILDLIFE FEDERATION

1400 16th Street, NW
Washington, DC 20036-2266
(202) 797-6800

Other Offices: Anchorage, AK; Ann Arbor, MI; Missoula, MT; Bismarck, ND; Boulder, CO; Atlanta, GA; Montpelier, VT; Austin, TX; Portland, OR

President: Jay D. Hair

Purpose: NWF's goal is to be the nation's most responsible and effective conservation education organization promoting the wise use of natural resources and the protection of the global environment.

Methods of operation: Lobbying, litigation, publications, public education, direct action, research

Membership: Approximately 5 million members and supporters from varied demographic groups

Recent issues and projects: Endangered Species Act; Ancient Forests; Great Lakes Initiative; Range-Land Reform

Major publications: *National Wildlife*; *International Wildlife*; *Ranger Rick*; *Your Big Backyard*

Budget: $90,000,000

Funding: Nature education materials (40%), memberships (17%), individual contributions (15%), youth memberships (14%), other (6%)

Staff: 650
Including:
35 Writer/Editors
20 Bookkeepers/Accountants
12 Attorneys
7 Issue Experts
6 Lobbyists
5 Researchers
4 Organizers
2 Paralegals
2 Press Aides
2 Foundation Fundraisers
1 Office Manager

Staff openings/year: 20

Work Week: 40 hours

Salary/year: $23,000 (Recent College Graduate); $30,000 (Graduate with advanced degree)

Benefits: Health insurance, life insurance, pregnancy leave, tuition reimbursement, tax deferred annuity, paid vacation, credit union

Part-Time Employees: 10

Volunteers: 20

Interns: 40
Length: 6 months
Duties: Research, lobbying, and administrative work
Remuneration: Have both paid and volunteer interns

Jobs advertised: Newspaper

To apply: For internships, contact Nancy Hwa, Administrative Coordinator

NATIONAL WILDLIFE FEDERATION - CAMPUS OUTREACH PROGRAM (COOL IT!)

1400 16th Street, NW
Washington, DC 20036
(202) 797-5435

Other Offices: Atlanta, GA; Portland, OR; Ann Arbor, MI

Director: Nick Keller

Purpose: COOL IT's campus outreach mission is to establish environmentally sound practices on college campuses by promoting leadership and action within the campus community. They offer a variety of resources to students, faculty and administrators

Methods of operation: Campus-based environmental organizing (70%), publications (20%), training and technical assistance (10%)

Membership: College students, faculty and administrators

Recent issues and projects: COOL IT! currently has 157 registered projects, and that number will increase in January and February. Projects range from schools working on setting up a recycling program to schools working on environmental justice issues.

Major publications: *Cool it! Connection* newsletter; annual *Project Directory*; issue packets (14 different issues)

Budget: $243,000

Funding: Part of the National Wildlife Foundation's budget

Staff: 4

1 Office Manager
1 Director
1 Environmental Equity Coordinator
1 Special Projects Coordinator & Environmental Audit Specialist

Staff openings/year: 4

Work Week: 40 hours

Salary/year: $Varies (Recent College Graduate); $Varies (Graduate with advanced degree)

Benefits: Health insurance, pension, paid vacation, life insurance, credit union

Part-Time Employees: No

Summer Employees: No

Volunteers: 1

Interns: 4
Length: 10 months
Duties: Organizing and writing
Remuneration: $270 a week

Jobs advertised: Word of mouth; small, directed mail-outs; newsletter; inter-net; conferences

To apply: Contact Chris Soto, Office Manager

NATIONAL WILDLIFE FEDERATION ROCKY MOUNTAIN NATURAL RESOURCES CENTER

2260 Baseline, Suite 100
Boulder, CO 80309
(303) 786-8001

Director: Thomas D. Lustig, Esq.

Purpose: (1) Advocating natural resource protection in a five-state Rocky Mountain region; (2) providing no-cost legal representation to deserving citizens and citizen groups with meritorious resource issues and no means for securing legal assistance; (3) providing clinical program for Colorado University law students in environmental law; and (4) providing natural resource seminars to CU law students

Methods of operation: Research, litigation, public education

Constituency: 5.8 million members and supporters of NWF

Recent issues and projects: Litigation regarding wildlife protection, water resources protection, ski development, public lands

Staff: 10
1 Western Division Staff Director
1 Senior Attorney
2 Staff Attorneys
1 Regional Executive
1 Scientist
1 Development Director
1 Endangered Species Campus Coordinator
1 Office Manager
1 Administrative Assistant

Work Week: 40 hours

Benefits: Health insurance, life insurance, pension, paid vacation

Interns: Yes; law students only
Length: 6-8 weeks in summer

Remarks: There are 6 other NWF Natural Resources Clinics, in Ann Arbor, MI, Missoula, MT, Portland, OR, Bismarck, ND, Atlanta, GA and Montpelier, VT.

NATIONAL WOMEN'S HEALTH NETWORK

1325 G Street, NW, LLB
Washington, DC 20005
(202) 347-1140

Director: Cynthia Pearson, Acting Director

Purpose: To advocate for better health policies for women and to provide information to individual women to enable them to have more control over health decisions.

Methods of operation: Human services (40%), publications (25%), research (20%), public education (10%), lobbying (5%), clearinghouse

Constituency: Women interested in health issues; many work in health

Recent issues and projects: Promoting low fat diet; strategy guide to direct action abortion tactics; hormone education campaign; monitoring approval of new contraceptives

Major publications: Bimonthly: *The Network News*; *Abortion Then and Now: Creative Responses to Restricted Access*; *Taking Hormones and Women's Health: Choices, Risks and Benefits*

Budget: $350,000

Funding: Individual contributions (80%); foundations (10%), publications (10%)

Staff: 4
1 Executive Director

1 Issue Expert
1 Bookkeeper/Accountant
1 Office Manager

Staff openings/year: 0-1

Work Week: 40-50 hours

Salary/year: $18,000

Benefits: Health insurance, pregnancy leave, paid vacation

Part-Time Employees: 4

Volunteers: Yes

Interns: 4
Length: 3 months
Duties: Maintain clearinghouse; work with issue experts
Remuneration: No stipend available

Jobs advertised: *Washington Post*; women's papers

To apply: Contact Lorette Woodard, Office Manager

NATIONAL WOMEN'S LAW CENTER

1616 P Street, NW, Suite 100
Washington, DC 20036
(202) 328-5160

President: Nancy Duff Campbell and Marcia D. Greenberger, Co-Presidents

Purpose: Since 1972, the Center has been working to develop and protect women's rights. The goal is to affect public and private sector policies and practices to better reflect the needs and rights of women.

Methods of operation: Research, lobbying, litigation, publications, public education, training and technical assistance

Constituency: Women, with a focus on low-income women

Recent issues and projects: NWLC's major project areas include family support (child and adult dependent care, child support enforcement), income security (public assistance, Social Security, tax policy), employment (civil rights, minimum wage, fringe benefits), education (civil rights, vocational education), reproductive rights and health (including national health care reform).

Major publications: Newsletter: *National Women's Law Center Update*, published 3-4 times/year; many issue reports and articles on topics of child and adult dependent care, child support enforcement, education, employment, income security, taxes, and women's rights. Send for a publications list.

Budget: $2,000,000

Funding: Foundations (65%), individual contributions, direct mail (26%), other (9%)

Staff: 19
7 Attorneys
4 Secretaries
1 Clerk
1 Receptionist
1 Office Manager
1 Issue Expert
2 Fundraisers
1 Press Aide
1 Bookkeeper/Accountant

Work Week: 37.5 hours

Salary/year: $Varies (Recent College Graduate); $Varies (Graduate with advanced degree)

Benefits: Health insurance, life insurance, pregnancy leave, pension, child care, paid vacation

Part-Time Employees: 0

Summer Employees: 2

Interns: 2
Length: Summer/semester of law school
Duties: Law clerk
Remuneration: Work-study or equivalent for summer students; otherwise receive only course credit

Jobs advertised: *Washington Post*; circulated announcements; specialized publications

To apply: Contact Frances Thomas, V.P. Administration and Finance

NATIONAL WOMEN'S POLITICAL CAUCUS

1275 K Street, NW, Suite 750
Washington, DC 20005
(202) 898-1100

Director: Harriett Woods, President and Jody Newman, Ex. Director

Purpose: The National Women's Political Caucus is the only bipartisan grassroots membership organization dedicated to increasing the number of women in elected and appointed political office. The Caucus identifies, recruits, trains and supports pro-choice women to run for political office at all levels of government, regardless of party. In addition to the national office based in Washington, D.C., there are over 300 NWPC chapters across the country.

Constituency: Mostly women, of every ethnic, racial and socioeconomic group from across the nation

Recent issues and projects: Major issues are reproductive rights for women, children and dependent care initiatives and equal rights. Major political projects centered around the election of pro-choice women in federal and statewide elections and the Coalition for Women's Appointments. Other projects have included developing trainings for corporate and elected women, political campaign trainings for women as well as annual fundraising events.

Major publications: *Women's Political Times*, published quarterly; *The Directory of Elected Women Officials*; *Factsheet on Women's Political Progress*; *Campaigning to Win*

Budget: $1,500,000

Funding: Individual contributions, foundations, direct mail, corporate contributions

Staff: 13
1 Political Director
1 Field Director
1 Membership Director
1 Membership Director
1 Communications Director
1 Training/Convention Director
1 Development Director
1 Office Manager
1 Bookkeeper
1 Executive Assistant
2 Programs Assistants
1 Receptionist/Staff Assistant

Staff openings/year: Varies

Work Week: 35 hours

Salary/year: $20,000 (Recent College Graduate); $25,000 (Graduate with advanced degree)

Benefits: Health insurance, life insurance, pregnancy leave, pension, paid vacation

Part-Time Employees: None

Volunteers: Yes

Interns: 6-12
Length: 1 semester
Duties: Research, writing, assisting in specific departments, administrative/clerical
Remuneration: None

Jobs advertised: In newspapers and with other nonprofits

To apply: Contact Jody Newman, Executive Director

NATIONAL YOUTH LEADERSHIP COUNCIL (NYLC)
1910 West County Road B
St. Paul, MN 55113
(612) 631-3672

Director: James C. Kielsmeier

Purpose: NYLC works to develop service oriented youth leaders by supporting individuals, organizations and communities that encourage youth service and leadership.

Methods of operation: Training and technical assistance (35%), direct action (25%), publications (20%)

Recent issues and projects: Recent projects include: annual 7 day leadership training camp for youth; and an alternative summer school model for teachers, college and high school students using service-learning called Walkabout

Major publications: *The Generator*, semi-annual journal on service learning; *Update Newsletter*

NATIVE AMERICAN RIGHTS FUND
1506 Broadway
Boulder, CO 80302
(303) 447-8760

Other Offices: Anchorage, AK; Washington, DC

Director: John Echohawk

Purpose: Nonprofit legal defense fund for Native Americans. NARF's work involves issues relating to the preservation of tribal existence, the protection of tribal natural resources, the promotion of human rights, the accountability of governments, and the development of Indian law.

Methods of operation: Research (85%), litigation (9.5%), training and technical assistance (5%), lobbying (2.5%), publications (1.5%), public education (1.5%)

Constituency: Native American tribes and individuals nationwide

Recent issues and projects: NARF successfully represented the Nome Eskimo Community in stopping the illegal taxation of its tribal property by the city of Nome; in State of Alaska v. Native Village of Venetie, a federal appeals court held that the tribal status of Alaska Native villages was to be determined according to the same federal Indian law principles applicable to tribes elsewhere in the U.S.; in Cheyenne-Arapaho Tribe v. United States, the federal district court held that the Bureau of Indian Affairs breached its trust responsibility when it tried to extend the terms of three tribal oil and gas leases at below market rates without tribal consent; etc.

Major publications: *NARF Legal Review*; annual report

Budget: $6,000,000

Funding: Individual contributions, foundations, direct mail

Staff: 43
16 Attorneys
2 Researchers
5 Bookkeeper/Accountants
2 Office Managers
3 Administrative Assistants
2 Librarians
2 Library Staff
3 Foundation Fundraisers
1 Paralegal
1 Writer/Editor
2 Legal Secretaries
1 Receptionist
1 Copy Coordinator/Mail Clerk
2 Clerks

Staff openings/year: 1-2

Work Week: 40 hours

Salary/year: $25,000 attorney (Recent College Graduate); $35,000 (Graduate with advanced degree)

Benefits: Health insurance, life insurance, pregnancy leave, credit union, job-related tuition reimbursement, paid vacation

Part-Time Employees: 1

Summer Employees: 4-5

Volunteers: 1

Interns: 1
Length: 3 months
Duties: Law clerk
Remuneration: Salary and leave benefits

Jobs advertised: Newspapers

To apply: Contact Rose Brave

NATIVE AMERICANS FOR A CLEAN ENVIRONMENT

P.O. Box 1671
Tahlequah, OK 74465
(918) 458-4322

Director: Vickie McCullough

Purpose: The main focus is nuclear issues. They work on increasing public awareness on the health hazards of hazardous, toxic, and chemical wastes. They also focus on environmental education in the school systems, universities and civic organizations.

Methods of operation: Litigation, publications, human services, community organizing, direct action (50%), research (25%), public education (25%)

Constituency: Open membership

Recent issues and projects: Uranium Tetrafloride spill by Sequoyah Fuels Corp.; Transportation of Nuclear/Hazardous Waste Task Forces; incineration on Tribal Lands. They target Tribal environmental issues.

Major publications: *NACE Newsletter*

Budget: $100,000

Funding: Foundations (75%), membership (15%), individual contributions (10%)

Staff: 2
1 Organizer
1 Bookkeeper/Accountant

Staff openings/year: 1

Work Week: 40 hours

Salary/year: $12,000 (Recent College Graduate); $Varies (Graduate with advanced degree)

Benefits: Life insurance, paid vacation

Part-Time Employees: 1

Volunteers: 15

Interns: Yes
Duties: Clerical, some computer
Remuneration: Work-study programs

Jobs advertised: Newspapers, groups, recommendations

To apply: Contact Vickie McCullough, Executive Director

Remarks: We are a national organization and have an open membership, regardless of race, religion or gender. We like to deal with sincere, creative, and environmentally concerned citizens. We like hard workers and lots of dedication. Even though this job doesn't pay anything, it does give us self worth.

NATURAL RESOURCES COUNCIL OF MAINE

271 State Street
Augusta, ME 04330-6900
(207) 622-3101

Director: Everett B. Carson

Purpose: The Council is a nonprofit environmental advocacy organization which works to protect, conserve and improve Maine's natural and human environment through legal defense, lobbying and education.

Methods of operation: Litigation, research, publications, public education, lobbying, training and technical assistance

Membership: 7,000 members; basic member dues are $20 individual/$30 family

Recent issues and projects: Growth management legislation; solid waste legislation; energy conservation; air and water quality

Major publications: Monthly newsletter/bulletin; reports on particular issues

Budget: $1,200,000

Funding: Direct mail (35%), foundations (34%), individual contributions (29%), events (2%)

Staff: 22
5 Attorneys
2 Foundation Fundraisers
3 Administrative Assistants
1 Executive Director
1 Legislative Director
1 Writer/Editor
1 Business Manager
1 Paid Intern
1 Land Use Planner
1 Bookkeeper/Accountant
1 Public Relations Manager
1 Staff Scientist
1 General Counsel
1 Computer Coordinator
1 Development Director

Staff openings/year: 1-2

Work Week: 40 hours

Salary/year: $20,000 (Recent College Graduate); $25-30,000 (Graduate with advanced degree)

Benefits: Health insurance, life insurance, birth/adoption leave, pension, paid vacation

Part-Time Employees: None

Volunteers: 5-10

Interns: 2
Length: 3 months-1 year
Duties: Legal research/writing; factual research/writing
Remuneration: Unpaid internships

Jobs advertised: Law school publications (interns); newspaper; word of mouth

To apply: For legal internships/lawyer positions, contact Catherine Johnson. For other positions, contact Susan Adams.

NATURAL RESOURCES DEFENSE COUNCIL (NRDC)

40 West 20th Street
New York, NY 10011
(212) 727-2700

Other Offices: Washington, DC; San Francisco, CA; Los Angeles, CA; Honolulu, HI

Director: John H. Adams

Purpose: To protect America's endangered natural resources and to improve the quality of the environment. Projects combine monitoring and working with government agencies, scientific research, litigation, and citizen education.

Methods of operation: Research, lobbying, litigation, publications, organizing, public education, technical assistance

Constituency: Educated and concerned conservationists nationwide

Recent issues and projects: Energy policy and nuclear safety; toxic substances; air and water pollution; urban environment; land use, including public lands and wilderness; agricultural policy and forestry; coastal management; endangered species; and the international environment

Major publications: *AMICUS Journal*

Budget: $15,000,000

Funding: Membership, private foundations

Staff: 140
54 Support Staff
36 Attorneys
17 Resource Specialists
13 Development
11 Scientists
7 Membership and Public Education
3 Accounting

Staff openings/year: 6-10

Work Week: 40 hours

Salary/year: $20-30,000

Benefits: Health insurance, pension, dental insurance, life insurance, pregnancy leave, paid vacation

Part-Time Employees: Yes

Volunteers: Yes

Interns: Yes
Length: 2-3 months
Duties: Depend on type of internship: legal, scientific, etc.
Remuneration: Stipend

Jobs advertised: Classifieds; word of mouth; Environmental Consortium for Minority Outreach

To apply: Contact Sandy Kolakowski, Office Administrator. Minority applicants are encouraged to apply.

NATURE CONSERVANCY

1815 North Lynn Street
Arlington, VA 22209
(703) 841-5300

President: John Sawhill

Purpose: Preservation of global biological diversity (rare plants, animals, and natural communities). The Nature Conservancy is an international environmental organization.

Methods of operation: Protection, fundraising, general and administration, stewardship, identification, membership development, membership services, other

Constituency: Concerned individual citizens; corporations and private businesses. The Conservancy also works closely with certain universities on research projects and with other environmental groups.

Recent issues and projects: Connecticut River Protection Campaign; Delaware Bay and Basin Campaign, efforts to protect hundreds of key sites in several states for two critically important natural systems; debt-for-nature swaps (Ecuador, others); hundreds of land/species protection projects completed every year, of all kinds

Major publications: *The Nature Conservancy Magazine* (a bimonthly membership publication); *Katharine Ordway: The Lady Who Saved the Prairies* (hardcover book)

Budget: $81,700,000

Funding: Individual contributions, foundations, direct mail

Staff: 831
Including:
80 Fundraisers and Membership Programs
50 Life Scientists
15 Attorneys
10 Bookkeeper/Accountants
9 Office Managers
4 Lobbyists
4 Writer/Editors

Staff openings/year: 400

Work Week: 35 hours

Salary/year: $18,000

Benefits: Health insurance, life insurance, dental insurance, tuition reimbursement, paid vacation, long-term disability, parental leave, savings and retirement plan, tax-deferred annuity plan, accident insurance, etc.

Part-Time Employees: 94

Summer Employees: Yes

Volunteers: Low 100,000's

Interns: Yes
Length: Throughout year; summer mostly
Remuneration: Payment is either a fixed amount for the internship period, or an hourly rate.

Jobs advertised: Newspaper classified advertisements; internal "Personnel Memo;" *Environmental Opportunities*; *Job Seeker*

To apply: Contact Personnel and Administration

Remarks: There are more than 50 field offices of the Nature Conservancy, covering every state.

NE CHAPTER OF THE SIERRA CLUB

3801 Calvert Street
Lincoln, NE 68506
(402) 488-4460

Director: Jim Cole

Purpose: To protect and enjoy the states, nation and world resources, forests, waters, wildlife and wilderness.

Methods of operation: Lobbying (75%), public education (15%), litigation (5%), direct action (3%), publications (2%)

Membership: Mainly people from Lincoln and Omaha

Recent issues and projects: To create a sustainable agriculture. To establish the First National Park in the State of Nebraska.

Major publications: A quarterly published newspaper *Nebraska Sierran*

Budget: $22,000

Funding: Individual contributions (75%), direct mail (10%), telephone solicitation (5%), other (5%)

Staff: 1
1 Lobbyist

Work Week: Varies hours

Volunteers: 1500

Interns: No, but willing to accept applications

To apply: Please send a letter to the office

NEBRASKA CIVIL LIBERTIES UNION

P.O. Box 81455, 315 9th Street, Suite 213
Lincoln, NE 68501
(402) 476-8091

Director: Maralyn Cragun

Purpose: Represents those persons whose civil liberties have been infringed upon. Education and legislation to promote civil liberties.

Methods of operation: Litigation (20%), public education (20%), research (10%), lobbying (10%), publications (10%), human services (10%), community organizing (10%), direct action (10%)

Constituency: Very diverse, all educational and political backgrounds. Anyone interested in preserving the Bill of Rights.

Recent issues and projects: NCLU is working to include "sexual orientation" in Nebraska Fair Employment Act to prohibit employee termination based on sexual orientation. They are challenging federal sentencing guidelines and dress codes in high schools.

Major publications: Quarterly newsletter

Budget: $92,600

Funding: National office (58%), individual contributions (42%)

Staff: 2
1 Executive Director
1 Assistant Director

Staff openings/year: 1

Work Week: 40 hours

Salary/year: $25,000 (Recent College Graduate); $30,000 (Graduate with advanced degree)

Benefits: health insurance, pension, paid vacation, life insurance

Part-Time Employees: None

Summer Employees: None

Volunteers: 4-6

Interns: 2-4
Length: Semester
Duties: Review and maintain case files, research
Remuneration: None

Jobs advertised: Local newspapers; *Omaha World Herald*; *Lincoln Journal*; *Nuestro Mundo*

To apply: Contact Maralyn Cragun, Executive Director

NEIGHBOR TO NEIGHBOR

2601 Mission Street, Suite 400
San Francisco, CA 94110-3111
(415) 824-3355

Other Offices: New York, NY; Washington, DC; Boston, MA; Los Angeles, CA; Chicago, IL; Hartford, CT

Director: Glen Schneider

Purpose: Through grassroots organizing, Neighbor to Neighbor is committed to economic justice and human rights both at home and abroad.

Methods of operation: Community organizing,

lobbying, research

Constituency: People who want our democratic values reflected in our foreign policy and domestic policy

Recent issues and projects: Lobby Congress to end funding Contras in Nicaragua. Lobby Congress to stop funding fascist dictatorship in El Salvador. Lobby Congress to enact a Canadian-style, single-payer healthcare reform.

Major publications: *Faces of War* video; newsletter to donors

Budget: $1,062,323

Funding: Individual contributions, telephone solicitation, direct mail, foundations

Staff: 23
1 Executive Director
1 Special Gift Fundraiser
15 Organizers
1 Membership Director
1 Lobbyist
1 1/2 Bookkeeper
1/2 Administrative Director
2 Administrative Assistants

Staff openings/year: 10

Work Week: 40-50 hours

Salary/year: $20,064-25,724

Benefits: Health insurance, pregnancy leave, paid vacation

Part-Time Employees: 3

Volunteers: About 200

Interns: 3-5
Length: 2-3 months
Duties: Research, writing, organizing
Remuneration: Stipend

Jobs advertised: Local publications

To apply: Contact Glen Schneider, Organizing Director, for organizing positions; contact Robyn Berry, Administrative Director, for other positions.

NEIGHBORHOOD OPEN SPACE COALITION

72 Reade Street
New York, NY 10007
(212) 513-7555

Director: Anne McClellan

Purpose: Neighborhood Open Space is a working partnership of over 125 member organizations dedicated to enhancing the quality of life for all New Yorkers by expanding and protecting New York City's parks and open spaces through research, planning and advocacy.

Methods of operation: Training and technical assistance (20%), direct action (35%), research (20%), publications (5%), community organizing (20%)

Membership: Technical, grassroots and corporate group members and individuals

Recent issues and projects: Spearheading movement to create 400-mile greenway system in New York City. Advocate for increases to parks department budget. Research and publish monographs providing an overview of the benefits that parks and open spaces bring to real estate values, public health, energy conservation, air quality, storm water retention, and the city's image. Work on the Brooklyn/Queens Greenway, Summer Youth Program, the West Side Waterfront Park, and a harbor park at Brooklyn Piers 1-6.

Major publications: *Open Space and the Future of New York*; *The Struggle for Space*; *The Brooklyn Queens/Greenway: A Feasibility Study*; *A New Vision for the West Side Waterfront*; *The Brooklyn/Queens Greenway*; *A Design Study*; *Urban Open Space*; *An Investment That Pays: Real Estate Values*

Budget: $300,000

Funding: Foundations, corporations

Staff: 4
1 Executive Director
1 Office Manager
1 Researcher
1 Issue Expert

Staff openings/year: 1

Work Week: 50 hours

Salary/year: $18,000 (Recent College Graduate); $21,000 (Graduate with advanced degree)

Benefits: Health insurance, life insurance, pregnancy leave, paid vacation

Part-Time Employees: 3

Summer Employees: 1

Interns: 25
Length: Programs of 2 and 9 months

Jobs advertised: Newspapers, job descriptions mailed to key organizations

NETWORK

806 Rhode Island Avenue, NE
Washington, DC 20018
(202) 526-4070

Director: Kathy Thornton, RSM

Purpose: NETWORK is a national Catholic social justice lobby. Through engagement in the national, state and Congressional district levels, NETWORK educates, organizes and lobbies to influence the formation of national public policy from the viewpoint of the economically-marginalized in society.

Methods of operation: Lobbying, public education, publications

Recent issues and projects: Citizens' Budget Campaign to work for fairness in national funding; tracking and lobbying on legislation regarding peace, disarmament, against foreign military aid for the Contras in Nicaragua, El Salvador, Guatemala, Philippines, and for domestic social programs; Federal budget work with the Citizen's Budget Campaign, health care reform; economic conversion; housing; the Philippines and Central America; alternative feminist management style

Major publications: Periodical: *NETWORK Connection: People Lobbying for Justice*, print and audio cassette resources on justice issues

Budget: $750,000

Funding: Individual contributions, membership dues

Staff: 10
2 Lobbyists
2 Office Managers
1 Administrator/Public Relations
1 Organizer
1 Development Coordinator
1 Researcher
1/2 Foundation Fundraiser
1 Bookkeeper/Accountant

Staff openings/year: 1

Work Week: 40-50 hours

Salary/year: $26,400

Benefits: Health insurance, paid vacation

Part-Time Employees: 1

Volunteers: Yes

Interns: 3
Length: Academic semester or summer
Duties: Work with full-time staff assisting lobbyists, organizers and education coordinators. February 15th is the application deadline for interns
Remuneration: No stipend available; cite for academic credit

Jobs advertised: In the *NETWORK* publication

To apply: Contact Kathy Thornton, RSM (minority applicants are encouraged to apply)

Remarks: We also have an Associate Program available: full-time with job responsibilities including assisting lobbyists, organizers and education coordinator - 10 months, from September to June; $500/month stipend/ application deadline is February 15th.

NETWORK IN SOLIDARITY WITH THE PEOPLE OF GUATEMALA (NISGUA)

1500 Massachusetts Ave., NW, Suite 241
Washington, DC 20005
(202) 223-6474

Director: Michael Willis

Purpose: (1) To educate the public about Guatemala; (2) To build solidarity with grassroots organizations in Guatemala; (3) To provide material support for Guatemalan grassroots organizations working for peace and justice in Guatemala; (4) to provide a Rapid Response Network in order to respond to human rights emergencies; (5) To pressure Congress to end military aid to Guatemala.

Methods of operation: Community organizing (25%), direct action (25%), public education (25%), raise material aid for grassroots in Guatemala, organizing tours for popular leaders, organizing meetings and conferences (15%), publications (10%)

Constituency: Small but highly committed constituency. Membership is national; generally members have knowledge/direct experience with Guatemala, or Central American issues.

Recent issues and projects: (1) Grassroots Guatemala Campaign: NISGUA and its committees raised over $30,000 in 1989 on behalf of the popular movement in Guatemala; (2) Campaign to end military aid to Guatemala: NISGUA and its committees pressured Congress last year to end military aid to Guatemala. The results: military aid was capped at $9 million for fiscal year 1990 and restricted to non-lethal aid. (3) Tour of 3 leaders of popular movement in Guatemala during fall of 1989 in Midwest and on East and West Coasts.

Major publications: Quarterly newsletter: *Report on Guatemala*, 16 pages. Monthly newsletter: *Human Rights Update. Legislative Update* on Congressional policy concerning Guatemala, 6 per year.

Budget: $120,000

Funding: Resource sales, local events (35%), individual contributions (20%), foundations (20%), direct mail (20%), telephone solicitation (5%)

Staff: 3
1 Volunteer, Rapid Response Network
1 Volunteer, Editor/Organizer
1/2 Organizer
1/2 Campaign Manager
1/3 Writer/Editor
1/3 Office Manager
1/3 Foundation Fundraiser
1/3 Issue Expert
1/3 Grassroots Fundraiser
1/3 Bookkeeper/Accountant

Staff openings/year: 1-2

Work Week: 50-60 hours

Salary/year: $11,000

Benefits: Health insurance, paid vacation, pregnancy leave

Volunteers: 3

Interns: Yes
Length: Any length of time
Duties: Varies; some examples are to assist in fundraising, organizing, human rights rapid response, provide staff support, tours, correspondence
Remuneration: None

Jobs advertised: Publications such as *Community Jobs*, *In These Times* and *The Guardian*

To apply: Contact Joe Gorin, National Coordinator

Remarks: NISGUA has 250 committees nationwide.

NETWORK OF LOCAL ART AGENCIES OF WASHINGTON STATE

P.O. Box 1548
Olympia, WA 98507-1548
(206) 705-1183 fax: (206)705-2867

Director: Donovan Michael Gray

Purpose: The mission of NLAAWS is to foster cultural development within local communities throughout Washington. The mission is approached through the following organizational goals: to advocate on behalf of local arts agencies; to be an effective communications link and resource for members; to foster the professional development of local arts agencies; to support research and development for new paradigms; to insure that NLAAWS is a viable and dynamic statewide organization.

Methods of operation: Training and technical assistance (25%), direct action (20%), publications (15%), public education (15%), research (10%), community organizing(10%), lobbying (5%)

Membership: Individuals and organizations interested in community cultural development

Recent issues and projects: Statewide arts congress; assisting in restructuring the Washington State Arts Commission into a more grassroots, community-oriented agency, including conducting ten town meetings around the state to lay a planning foundation for this change; technical assistance program through training and subsidizing of "peers," e.g., everyday cultural workers to assist like agencies in the state

Major publications: Quarterly newsletter, monthly *updates*, cultural planning documents for specific client groups

Budget: $180,000

Funding: Grants (40%), earned income (40%), memberships (7%), individual contributions (2%), foundations (1%)

Staff: 1
1 Executive Director

Staff openings/year: 0-1

Work Week: 60 hours

Salary/year: $20,000 (Recent College Graduate); $30,000 (Graduate with advanced degree)

Benefits: Health insurance, family leave, vacation

Part-Time Employees: None

Summer Employees: None

Volunteers: None

Interns: None currently, but starting internship program
Length: 1-3 school quarters
Remuneration: Negotiable - probably $500/quarter

Jobs advertised: Locally

To apply: Contact Donovan Gray, Executive Director

NETWORK, INC.

300 Brickstone Square, Suite 900
Boston, MA 01810
(508) 470-1080

Other Offices: Washington, DC; Burlington, VT; San Juan, PR

President: David P. Crandall

Purpose: Provide support for school improvement efforts and other organizational change. Work to empower clients to achieve their improvement goals. Use existing knowledge, research, solutions, resources toward quality and equity in education.

Methods of operation: Training and technical assistance (50%), human services (20%), research (15%), publications (10%), lobbying (5%) all for public education

Constituency: Local schools; other education and education-related organizations

Recent issues and projects: The Regional Educational Laboratory serving New England, New York, Puerto Rico and the U.S. Virgin Islands; the National Center for Improving Science Education; the Center for Effective Communications; Ford Academy of Manufacturing Sciences

Major publications: Newsletter: *The Cutting Edge*; *Making Change for School Improvement: The Change Game*; equity publications; reports and research findings

Budget: $5,000,000

Funding: Federal grants and contracts (85%), direct client support (10%), foundations (5%)

Staff: 110
42 Issue Experts
30 Trainers/Technical Assistance Providers
16 Researchers
5 Writers/Editors
5 Typists
6 Bookkeepers/Accountants
3 Fundraisers
2 Office Managers
1 Lobbyist

Staff openings/year: 1-20

Work Week: 45 hours

Salary/year: $26,000 (Recent College Graduate); $34,000 (Graduate with advanced degree)

Benefits: Health insurance, life insurance, family leave, pension, paid vacation, tuition reimbursement, employee assistance plans, health development

Part-Time Employees: 10

Summer Employees: 5

Interns: 2
Length: 6 months
Duties: Associate to training, technical assistance personnel
Remuneration: Varies

Jobs advertised: Newspapers; professional publications; information to sister organizations; Division of Employment Security; internally

To apply: Contact David Crandall, Director, or Saleha A. Walsh, Personnel Director

NEVADA DESERT EXPERIENCE

P.O. Box 4487
Las Vegas, NV 89127-0487
(702) 646-4814

Other Offices: Oakland, CA

Director: Pamela Meidell and Jonathan Parfrey, Co-Directors

Purpose: Faith-based resistance to nuclear weapons testing through prayer, dialogue and nonviolent direct action.

Methods of operation: Community organizing (30%), public education (20%), direct action (20%), research (10%), lobbying (10%), publications (10%)

Constituency: Various denominational and religious groups

Recent issues and projects: Annual Lenten Desert Experience - 47 day series of events; Hiroshima Nagasaki actions in August

Major publications: Quarterly newsletter: *Desert Voices*

Budget: $80,000

Funding: Individual contributions (50%), foundations (25%), direct mail (15%), religious groups (10%)

Staff: 2
1 1/3 Organizers
1/3 Grassroots Fundraiser
1/4 Office Manager
1/5 Bookkeeper/Accountant

Staff openings/year: 1

Work Week: 40 hours

Salary/year: $14,000

Benefits: Paid vacation, housing

Volunteers: Yes; 10 part-time

Interns: 1
Length: 3 months
Duties: General office; organizing
Remuneration: Room, board, plus $150/month

Jobs advertised: Newsletter; mail list

To apply: Contact Pamela Meidell or Jonathan Parfrey, Co-Directors

NEW HAMPSHIRE CITIZEN ACTION

Concord Center, P.O. Box 319, 10 Ferry Road, Suite 438
Concord, NH 03301
(603) 225-2097

Director: Karen Hicks

Purpose: NHCA is a statewide public interest group which works on consumer, environmental, health care and good government issues. They are an affiliate of the national progressive organization, Citizen Action.

Methods of operation: Community organizing (50%), lobbying (25%), research (5%), publications (5%), direct action (5%), public education (5%), training and technical assistance (5%)

Constituency: Average New Hampshire citizens; 15,000 member families

Recent issues and projects: NHCA has worked for the development and implementation of a plan for access to health care for the uninsured, which may be established this spring. Starting in late 1989, they began a tax reform campaign.

Major publications: *NHCA Voting Index: A Guide to the New Hampshire Legislature* (annual); *NH Citizen Action News*; *Consumer Report on Taxes in New Hampshire*

Budget: $150,000

Funding: Foundations (40%), telephone solicitation (30%), individual contributions (10%)

Staff: 1
5 Phone Canvassers (part-time)
1 Organizer (part-time)

Work Week: 48 hours

Salary/year: $20,000 (Recent College Graduate); $22,000 (Graduate with advanced degree)

Benefits: Health insurance, pregnancy leave, paid vacation

Part-Time Employees: 4

Summer Employees: Maybe

Volunteers: Sometimes

Interns: 1
Length: 8 months
Duties: As organizational priorities and educational goals coincide
Remuneration: Expense reimbursement

Jobs advertised: Newspaper ads; allied organizations

To apply: Contact Karen Hicks, Director

NEW HAMPSHIRE PUBLIC DEFENDER

117 North State Street
Concord, NH 03301
(603) 224-1236

Director: Michael Skibbie

Purpose: NHPD is a private nonprofit corporation whose principal mission is to provide the most creative and aggressive legal representation possible to each of its indigent clients charged with homicides, felonies, misdemeanors and juvenile delinquency.

Methods of operation: Litigation (100%)

Funding: State of New Hampshire (100%)

Staff: 129
79 Attorneys
9 Office Managers
16 Administrative Assistants
2 Bookkeepers/Accountants
23 Investigators

Staff openings/year: 10

Work Week: 40+ hours

Salary/year: $29,260 (Graduate with advanced degree)

Benefits: Health insurance, paid vacation, life insurance, family leave, retirement, dental and vision

Part-Time Employees: 4 (support staff)

Summer Employees: 14

Volunteers: Varies

Interns: Varies
Length: Summer - 10 weeks
Duties: Legal research, drafting, memoranda and motions, case investigation, observing client interviews, court hearings and trials
Remuneration: $250/wk for 10 weeks

Jobs advertised: Notices to law schools; NALPLine; On-campus interviews at selected law schools; NAPIL Public Interest Job Fair; and other directories

To apply: Please contact Lawrence A. Vogelman, Deputy Director

Remarks: Staff Attorney positions will begin in the Fall of 1996. Application deadline is December 1, 1995. Summer Intern applications deadline is January 1, 1995.

NEW HAVEN LEGAL ASSISTANCE ASSOCIATION, INC.

426 State Street
New Haven, CT 06510-2018
(203) 777-4811

Other Offices: Derby, CT; West Haven, CT

Director: Patricia Kaplan

Purpose: To provide high quality legal services to persons unable to obtain counsel due to income, age, discrimination or other barriers

Methods of operation: Litigation (85%), public education (15%)

Constituency: Low-income, elderly and disabled persons in New Haven County

Recent issues and projects: Homelessness Project; Family Support Project; Child Law Unit; Housing and Community Development Unit; Disability Law Unit; Community Legal Education Program

Budget: $3,000,000

Staff: 48
24 Attorneys
7 Secretaries
8 Paralegals
4 Caseworkers
1 Bookkeeper/Accountant
1 Administrative Assistant
1 Development Officer
1 Receptionist
1 Controller

Work Week: 35-40 hours

Salary/year: $32,000 (Graduate with advanced degree)

Benefits: Health insurance, life insurance, credit union, pregnancy leave, paid vacation

Part-Time Employees: 4

Summer Employees: Yes

Volunteers: Yes

Interns: Yes
Length: 3-12 months
Duties: Client interviewing, fact investigation, legal research

Jobs advertised: Newspapers; legal services publications

To apply: Contact Patricia Kaplan, Executive Director

NEW JERSEY CITIZEN ACTION (NJCA)

400 Main Street
Hackensack, NJ 07601
(201) 488-2804

Other Offices: New Brunswick, NJ; Trenton, NJ; Woodbury, NJ; Collings Wood, NJ

Director: Phyllis Salowe-Kaye

Purpose: Founded in 1982, NJCA is a statewide citizen coalition working on social and economic justice issues in New Jersey. Their purpose is to increase citizen participation in the democratic process. Issues we have worked on include toxics, chemical right-to know, fair banking, affordable housing and health care, insurance reform, and issues affecting today's working families, such as family leave.

Methods of operation: Lobbying (25%), community organizing (25%), direct action (25%), public education (25%)

Membership: 95 affiliated organizations - labor, community, religious, senior citizen, tenants, housing advocate, etc. and 100,000 individual members statewide

Recent issues and projects: Housing: negotiated agreements with major banks in New Jersey to make $1 billion available for low and moderate income housing and funding to nonprofit housing development corporations. Working to get national health care legislation passed.

Major publications: Newsletter published 3 times/year; monthly update sent to members

Budget: $600,000

Funding: Foundations, canvassing, telephone solicitation, membership

Staff:
30-50 Canvassers
4 Organizers
3 Office Managers
1 Foundation Fundraiser
1 Bookkeeper/Accountant
1 Grassroots Fundraiser
3 Special Projects

Staff openings/year: 5-10

Work Week: 40-50 hours

Salary/year: $18,000 (Recent College Graduate); $Varies (Graduate with advanced degree)

Benefits: Health insurance, pregnancy leave, paid vacation, sick and personal days

Part-Time Employees: 2

Summer Employees: Yes, many canvassers

Volunteers: 4

Interns: 6
Length: 1 semester, but can be longer
Duties: Support work for organizers, varies with needs of organization
Remuneration: College credit, sometimes expenses

Jobs advertised: Newspapers and through our affiliated organizations

To apply: Contact Phyllis Salowe-Kaye, Executive Director

NEW JERSEY PUBLIC INTEREST RESEARCH GROUP (NJPIRG)

103 Bayard Street
New Brunswick, NJ 08901
(201) 247-4606

Other Offices: Trenton, NJ; Newark, NJ; Camden, NJ; Ridgewood, NJ; Morristown, NJ; Westfield, NJ

Director: Kenneth Ward

Purpose: NJPIRG work is conducted with three goals in mind: to develop innovative solutions to the social, political and environmental problems which confront us; to engage in sophisticated and forceful advocacy to advance those solutions; and to increase the size of our organization and help strengthen the general public interest community in order to overcome opposition from special interests opposed to our vision of the future.

Methods of operation: Lobbying (30%), research (25%), public education (25%), lobbying (20%)

Constituency: 70,000 citizens and students

Recent issues and projects: NJPIRG leads the Campaign for Clean Water, CAR (Consumer Auto Revolt), and the Pollution Prevention Project. NJPIRG organized events to commemorate the 20th anniversary of Earth Day, and has filed over 50 lawsuits against major industrial polluters in New Jersey.

Major publications: *Citizen Alert*, with 40,000 circulation, published triannually; *Polluters Playground: An Investigation of Clean Water Violations in New Jersey*; *Toxics in Bergen County*; *Ozone: New Jersey's Air Quality at Risk*; *A Prescription for Lowering Medical Costs: A Comparison Study of Prescription Drug Prices in New Jersey*; *ATV's and Children: Still at Risk*

Funding: Individual contributions, foundations, direct mail, canvassing, telephone solicitation, campus chapters

Staff: 29
7 Campus Program Staff
5 Campaign Organizers
5 Grassroots Fundraisers
3 Lobbyists
3 Issue Experts
2 Office Managers
2 Bookkeepers/Accountants
1 Attorney
1 Writer/Editor

Staff openings/year: 8-10

Work Week: 50 hours

Salary/year: $15,000 (Recent College Graduate); $19,000 (Graduate with advanced degree)

Benefits: Health insurance, pregnancy leave, paid vacation, dental, subsidized vacation, student loan payment

Part-Time Employees: 20 from Sept-May

Summer Employees: 150 part-time

Volunteers: 100+

Interns: 30 per semester
Length: 1 semester
Duties: Assistant to full-time staff lobbyists, researchers, campaign
Remuneration: Limited basis

Jobs advertised: Newspapers; career placement office

To apply: Contact Administrator

Remarks: NJPIRG has been described as a "scrappy advocate" for the public interest, a sobriquet of which we are proud. In the corridors of the statehouse, in courtrooms, on newspaper pages and on TV, NJPIRG staff are forceful, knowledgeable and tough leaders. The organization chooses issues which challenge and change the routine of "business of usual" in the Garden State. We believe in participatory democracy and lead the fight to win binding initiative and referendum for New Jersey. We believe that polluters should be punished, and have won over 30 lawsuits against major corporations for illegal water pollution. The major drives for environmental preservation, consumer protection and vital democracy in New Jersey are likely to be led by NJPIRG.

NEW MEXICO ADVOCATES FOR CHILDREN & FAMILIES

P.O. Box 26666
Albuquerque, NM 87125
(505) 841-1710

Director: Phil Davis

Purpose: Statewide nonpartisan, non-profit advocacy organization, dedicated to making the rights and needs of children and families a priority in New Mexico and the subject of intense thought, debate and action by all policy and decision makers.

Methods of operation: Public education (35%), lobbying (20%), community organizing (15%), training and technical assistance (15%), publications (10%), direct action (5%)

Membership: Individuals, social service providers, civic organizations, educators, healthcare professionals, businesses

Recent issues and projects: Recent projects include: Kids Count, project gathering statistics on the well-being of children, youth and families in New Mexico; Youth Public Policy and Leadership project; Youth Driven project identifying issues impacting NM youth and policy development/action plans to address issues.

Major publications: Quarterly Newsletter

Budget: $275,000

Funding: Foundations (80%), individual contributions (10%), organizations (10%)

Staff: 6
1 Lobbyist
1 Foundation/Grassroots Fundraiser
2 Program Directors
1 Secretary
1 Executive Director

Staff openings/year: 1

Work Week: 40 hours

Salary/year: $25,000 (Graduate with advanced degree)

Benefits: Health insurance, paid vacation, life insurance

Part-Time Employees: None

Summer Employees: None

Volunteers: 3

Interns: None, but willing to accept applications

Jobs advertised: Newspapers

To apply: Contact Phil Davis

NEW MEXICO PUBLIC INTEREST RESEARCH GROUP (NMPIRG)

Box 66, Student Union Building,
University of New Mexico
Albuquerque, NM 87131
(505) 277-2757

Director: Sara Sharer

Purpose: To promote social, economic, and political empowerment; to conduct research and advocacy on a variety of consumer and environmental issues; to educate the public and to serve as a public resource.

Methods of operation: Public education (20%), lobbying (15%), publications (15%), community organizing (15%), human services (10%), training and technical assistance (10%), research (10%), direct action (5%)

Constituency: UNM students; 6,000 citizen members in New Mexico

Recent issues and projects: Passage of Solid Waste Act in 1990; helped initiate major groundwater protection program in Albuquerque;

voter registration; state-wide grassroots campaign for single-payer health care reform; participant in statewide child care coalition; landlord hotline rental reform legislation

Major publications: Quarterly newsletter: *New Mexico PIRG Reports*; consumer guides and surveys

Budget: $65,000

Funding: Student fees (50%), canvassing (40%), foundations (10%)

Staff: 3
1 Director
1 Co-Director
1 Assistant Director
20 Canvassers (summer only)
1 Lobbyist (during session)

Staff openings/year: 1

Work Week: 50 hours

Salary/year: $15,000

Benefits: Tuition reimbursement, paid vacation, health insurance, dental insurance and maternity leave

Part-Time Employees: 5

Summer Employees: 20

Volunteers: 5-25

Interns: 2-3 per semester
Length: 1 semester
Duties: Generally focused on specific research project; available to undergraduate and graduate students
Remuneration: Stipend sometimes available

Jobs advertised: Classified ads in major state newspapers; through other PIRGs; occasionally in *Community Jobs*

To apply: Contact the Director

Remarks: After 20 years of slow but regular growth, New Mexico PIRG is poised to begin harvesting the fruits of those long labors. An established identity, several recent victories, and a growing concern among the state's citizens about social, economic and environmental decline have positioned New Mexico PIRG to serve as an important political force in the state. New Mexico PIRG is located on the 25,000 student University of New Mexico campus, in the heart of the state's largest city. The state's geographic, climatic and cultural diversity have earned it the title of the Land of Enchantment, and we hope to keep it that way.

NEW PAGES PRESS

P.O. Box 438
Grand Blanc, MI 48439
(313) 743-8055

Director: Casey Hill, Publisher

Purpose: To review books and periodicals from alternative publishers, giving librarians, booksellers and readers access to alternatives in print. Their main interests are political, economic and social change; environment, women's issues, media, culture.

Constituency: Librarians, booksellers and independent publishers, nationwide

Major publications: *New Pages: Alternatives in Print and Media*

To apply: Contact office

Remarks: We are always looking for writers, especially book reviewers.

NEW YORK ASIAN WOMEN'S CENTER

39 Bowery, Box 375
New York, NY 10002
(212) 941-1192

Director: Patricia Eng, Executive Director

Purpose: To provide direct services to battered women and rape survivors in the Asian communities; to promote public understanding on issues related to violence against women and public support for survivors of violence and for community-based programs; and to organize women and the Asian communities for social change.

Methods of operation: Human services (50%), public education (20%), community organizing (20%), training and technical assistance (10%)

Constituency: Asian women

Recent issues and projects: (1) Establishment of Asian Safe Homes Network and Safe Apartments Program; (2) Asian battered women support network; (3) technical assistance for new Asian groups working with battered women

Budget: $400,000

Funding: Foundations (30%), government grants (60%), individual contributions (10%)

Staff: 6

Staff openings/year: 0-1

Work Week: 45-50 hours

Salary/year: $25,000+ (Recent College Graduate); $30,000+ (Graduate with advanced degree)

Benefits: Health insurance, paid vacation

Volunteers: 75

Interns: 2
Length: One full academic year minimum
Duties: Counseling, advocacy, community education and organizing, volunteer coordination, research
Remuneration: Work-study stipends

Jobs advertised: Asian community papers; English press; college/graduate school recruitment; word of mouth

To apply: Contact Volunteer Coordinator

NEW YORK CITIZENS UTILITY BOARD

146 Washington Ave.
Albany, NY 12210
(518) 426-4282

Director: Robert Ceisler

Purpose: To challenge unfair utility rates and practices of telephone, gas and electric companies.

Methods of operation: Litigation (50%), research (20%), public education (20%), lobbying (10%)

Constituency: Residential utility customers of New York State

Major publications: Reports and quarterly newsletter

Budget: $500,000

Funding: Foundations (50%), direct mail (50%)

Staff: 3

Staff openings/year: 1

Work Week: 50 hours

Salary/year: $18,000 (Recent College Graduate); $Varies (Graduate with advanced degree)

Benefits: Health insurance, paid vacation, credit union

Part-Time Employees: 2

Summer Employees: 2

Interns: Yes
Length: 3-6 months, summer, semester
Duties: Vary with project assignment
Remuneration: Course credit, stipend

To apply: Contact the director

NEW YORK CITY SCHOOL VOLUNTEER PROGRAM, INC.

443 Park Avenue South, 9th Floor
New York, NY 10016
(212) 213-3370

Director: Susan Edgar

Purpose: The New York City School Volunteer Program, Inc. is a nonprofit corporation that recruits, trains and places volunteers as tutors of students in pre-kindergarten through 12th grade in New York City public schools. School volunteers are placed in all five boroughs and tutor at the school sites during the day. Evening assignments in high school are available.

Methods of operation: Public education (100%)

Constituency: 5,100 volunteers: 50% parents; 26% older adults; 10% students; 6% other

Recent issues and projects: Projects: Teens as School Volunteer Tutors, Junior Booktalk, Cultural Resources, Integrated High School. Issues: help needy public school children improve their English, math and reading skills by providing trained volunteers as tutors and mentors to the youngsters.

Major publications: Newsletters: *SVP Bulletin* and *School Volunteer Update*; annual report

Budget: $1,603,210

Funding: Foundations (43%), corporations (17%), benefits (9%), individual contributions (16%), New York City Board of Education (10%), New York State Discretionary Grant (.6%), interest from investments (8.7%), Fund for the Future (4.7%)

Staff: 44
28 Organizers
5 Typists
1 Executive Director
2 Foundation Fundraisers
2 Bookkeepers/Accountants
1 Press Aide
5 Other Assistants

Staff openings/year: Varies

Work Week: 35 hours

Salary/year: $21,000

Benefits: Health insurance, paid vacation

Part-Time Employees: 17

Volunteers: 12

Jobs advertised: Newspaper classified ads

To apply: Contact Walter Brock, Office Manager

NEW YORK GROUP AGAINST SMOKING POLLUTION (GASP)

7 Maxine Avenue
Plainview, NY 11803
(516) 938-0080

Director: Rhoda Nichter

Purpose: To educate the public and legislators as to the hazards of tobacco smoke to smokers and nonsmokers of all ages.

Methods of operation: Lobbying, publications, community organizing, direct action, public education

Constituency: Nonsmokers and smokers seeking information on quitting

Recent issues and projects: Obtained legislation restricting smoking in public places on the county level and in New York state. Current project is to get smoking banned on international flights and in the workplace.

Major publications: *Guide to a Smoke-Free Workplace*; newsletter

Funding: Individual contributions

Staff:
All volunteer

Volunteers: 2

NEW YORK PUBLIC INTEREST RESEARCH GROUP, INC. (NYPIRG)

9 Murray Street
New York, NY 10007-2272
(212) 349-6460

Other Offices: Buffalo, NY; Syracuse, NY; Cortland, NY; Binghamton, NY; Albany, NY; New Paltz, NY; Purchase, NY; Oswego, NY; Huntington, NY; Stony Brook, NY; Garden City, NY; New Paltz, NY; Old Westbury, NY; Washington, DC. There are 8 other NYPIRG offices in NY

Director: Jay Halfon

Purpose: NYPIRG is New York state's largest consumer and environmental advocacy organization. They work with students and other citizens to advocate for a cleaner environment, consumer protection, fair and open government, mass transit, quality health care, better funding for higher education and other issues of social justice.

Methods of operation: Research, lobbying, student organizing, litigation, publications, community organizing, public education, training and technical assistance, legal action

Membership: Twenty member college and university campuses serving more than 100,000 students and 85,000 citizen members

Recent issues and projects: NYPIRG leads the fight to promote waste reduction and recycling over incineration, and helped close an incinerator in downtown Albany earlier this year. NYPIRG has recently played a key role in passage of statewide anti-tobacco, lead poisoning prevention, and toxics laws. They have also successfully pushed for increased higher education funding.

Major publications: *NYPIRG Agenda*, quarterly newsletter; periodic surveys of mass transit in New York City, a five-times yearly newsletter; *CouncilWatch,* which details events at New York City Hall; and a guide to lead poisoning prevention, *Get the Lead Out.* Recently published reports that survey car rental discrimination, slow clean up of state Superfund sites, pollution threats in New Cassel, and much more.

Budget: $4,000,000

Staff: 98
25 Organizers

22 Program Staff Members
5 Fuel Buyers Group Staff Members
5 Accounting Staff Members
1 Office Manager
1 Receptionist
3 Graphics and Printing Staff
1 Writer/Editor
Canvass Directors (24 in summer/6 off season)
20 Telephone Outreach Staff
Canvassers (250 in summer/30 off season)
2 Computer Professionals

Staff openings/year: 15

Work Week: 50+ hours

Salary/year: $15,000 (Recent College Graduate); $15-20,000 (Graduate with advanced degree)

Benefits: Health insurance, life insurance, pregnancy leave, paid vacation

Part-Time Employees: Yes

Summer Employees: 100s

Volunteers: Yes

Interns: 6-12
Length: 1 semester or summer
Duties: Legislative, research, organizing
Remuneration: Stipends available under certain circumstances, credit available

Jobs advertised: Classified ads, materials distributed to career placement offices on college campuses, postings at other organizations

To apply: Contact Jay Halfon, Executive Director

NEW YORK STATE TENANT AND NEIGHBORHOOD COALITION

505 Eighth Ave., 24th Floor
New York, NY 10018
(212) 695-8922

Other Offices: Albany, NY; Syracuse, NY; Rochester, NY

Purpose: Advocacy and lobbying for tenant rights and tenant protection laws, and to pressure regulatory agencies to enforce such laws; coordinate campaigns around various issues; act as watchdog on government agencies

Methods of operation: Community organizing (30%), lobbying (30%), public education (20%), direct action (15%), research (5%)

Membership: 120+ organizations and 2,000+ individual members from all parts of the state, all concerned about tenant rights

Recent issues and projects: Successful campaign to incorporate anti-eviction protections into rent control laws to cover family members and "non-traditional" family members including lesbians and gay men; currently working to stop loss of low and moderate income government-assisted housing, and to strengthen co-op/condo conversion protections

Major publications: Newsletter: *Tenants and Neighbors*

Budget: $50,000

Funding: Individual contributions (60%), organizational dues (25%), grassroots funding (i.e. raffles) (15%)

Staff: 2
1 Lobbyist
1 Director

Work Week: 40-50 hours

Salary/year: $Varies (Recent College Graduate); $Varies (Graduate with advanced degree)

Volunteers: 25-30

Interns: None currently, but willing to accept applications

To apply: Contact the Director

NICARAGUA - U.S. FRIENDSHIP OFFICE

225 Pennsylvania Ave. SE, 3rd Floor
Washington, DC 20003
(202) 546-0915

Other Offices: '

Director: Rita d'Escoto Clark

Purpose: To educate North American about the reality of Nicaragua and to foster development and friendship through personal relationships between U.S. and Nicaraguan citizens and communities.

Methods of operation: Public education (40%), community organizing (15%), human services (10%), training and technical assistance (10%), researcher (10%), lobbying (10%)

Constituency: Friends of Nicaragua, religious groups, former volunteers, supporters of peace and justice in Central America

Recent issues and projects: Principal sponsor of

the July 1994 Sister-City Conference in Managua, Nicaragua. Sponsor the U.S. speaking tours of Nicaraguan leaders, including former President Daniel Ortega. Serve as liaison for the Technical Assistance Program in which U.S. volunteers work in Nicaragua on community development project.

Budget: $67,000

Funding: Individual contributions (50%), direct mail (40%), foundations (10%)

Staff: 2

Staff openings/year: 1

Work Week: 40 hours

Salary/year: $16,000 (Recent College Graduate); $20,000 (Graduate with advanced degree)

Benefits: Health insurance, paid vacation

Part-Time Employees: None

Summer Employees: None

Volunteers: 5-10

Interns: 2-3
Length: 3-6 months
Duties: Coordinating the technical assistance program, helping with mailings, helping with general office correspondence

To apply: Please contact Rita d'Escoto Clark, Director

NORTH AMERICAN CONGRESS ON LATIN AMERICA (NACLA)

475 Riverside Drive, Room 454
New York, NY 10115-0122
(212) 870-3146

Director: Pierre M. LaRamee

Purpose: Publish bi-monthly magazine, *NACLA Report on the Americas*, on politics, economics and social issues of Latin America, the Caribbean, and United States relations with the region.

Methods of operation: Research (33%), publications (33%), public education (33%)

Membership: Academics, activists, religious community, policymakers

Recent issues and projects: Published issues on women, U.S. policy, economic policy, Central America, Latinos in the U.S. and immigration.

Major publications: *NACLA Report on the Americas*

Budget: $400,000

Funding: Subscription and literature sales (50%), individual contributions (40%), foundations (10%)

Staff: 4
2 Writers/Editors
1 Business Manager
1 Executive Director

Staff openings/year: 0-1

Work Week: 35 hours

Salary/year: $20,000 (Recent College Graduate); $24,000 (Graduate with advanced degree)

Benefits: Health insurance, life insurance, family leave, paid vacation, congenial atmosphere

Part-Time Employees: 2

Volunteers: 2-5

Interns: 2-5
Length: 3 months
Duties: Editorial, clerical, artistic
Remuneration: None

Jobs advertised: Classified ads; mailings

To apply: Contact Pierre LaRamee

NORTH AMERICAN STUDENTS OF COOPERATION (NASCO)

P.O. Box 7715
Ann Arbor, MI 48107
(313) 663-0889

Director: Robert Cox

Purpose: A bi-national (U.S. and Canada) nonprofit organization that provides education and training to student-owned and operated cooperatives.

Methods of operation: Training and technical assistance (40%), development (30%), publications (15%)

Membership: Primarily campus-based, student-owned co-ops

Recent issues and projects: Major projects include: the development of new student co-ops; the annual Cooperative Education and Training Institute; and the Cooperative Internship Network

Major publications: Newsletter: *NASCO Newsbriefs* (10 times a year); publications catalogue (semiannually); *The NASCO Guide to Campus Cooperatives in North America* (every 2 years); *NASCO Guide to Cooperative Careers*

Budget: $190,000

Funding: Member dues (40%), Cooperative Education and Training Institute (30%), development (30%)

Staff: 3
3 Trainers/Educators

Staff openings/year: 1-2

Work Week: 40-45 hours

Salary/year: $18,000

Benefits: Health insurance, life insurance, pregnancy leave, credit union, child care, paid vacation

Interns: 1-2
Length: Summer
Duties: Past internships have included designing and piloting an education program for a student co-op and assisting with the CCA Institute
Remuneration: All internships offer enough to cover room and board and a small monthly stipend.

Jobs advertised: Through press releases; *Community Jobs*; etc.

To apply: Those interested in the Internship Network should write or call the Director of Member Services for an application. Applying is free for all NASCO members. There is a $10 administrative fee for all non-members.

Remarks: NASCO's job openings are generally filled by someone from the student co-op movement. However, our organization does have a member service called the Cooperative Internship Network, to help student co-opers find summer internships with established co-ops and cooperative organizations. Many students who were active in co-ops during college have a difficult time starting a career in co-ops after graduation because of a lack of experience. Through the Internship Network, students gain experience and knowledge about the cooperative movement, and the internship hosts receive enthusiastic, inexpensive summer help.

NORTH CAROLINA CENTER FOR PUBLIC POLICY RESEARCH

5 West Hargett Street, Suite 701, P.O. Box 430
Raleigh, NC 27602
(919) 832-2839

Director: Ran Coble

Purpose: (1) To evaluate state government programs; (2) to conduct research on public policy issues of statewide significance; (3) to educate the public about policy issues facing the state; (4) to enhance the accountability of elected officials to the state's citizens; and (5) to have the Center's research affect policy.

Methods of operation: Research (33%), publications (30%), public education (30%), lobbying (7%)

Constituency: Citizens who are interested in promoting government accountability, who have an interest in particular policy issues or public policy in general, and who want to support an independent analysis

Recent issues and projects: (1) The remaining life of every landfill in the state, local recycling efforts and state solid waste policy; (2) disparities in school finances among rich and poor school districts in North Carolina; (3) campaign finance disclosure; (4) how public universities evaluate and reward good teaching; (5) ways to increase voter participation

Major publications: Quarterly magazine: *North Carolina Insight*; bi-monthly newsletter: *From the Center Out*; book-length research reports; guide to the legislature (biennial); video cassettes of public affairs specials on the statewide public television network

Budget: $450,000

Funding: Foundations (68%), corporate contributions (18%), individual contributions (9%), sales of publications and other (5%)

Staff: 8
2 Writer/Editors
2 Researchers
1 Executive Director/Attorney
1 Fundraiser
1 Bookkeeper/Accountant/Personnel Manager
1 Typist
1/2 Membership Development

Staff openings/year: 1

Work Week: 40 hours

Salary/year: $Varies (Recent College Graduate); $Varies (Graduate with advanced degree)

Benefits: Health insurance, life insurance as disability policy, pregnancy leave, contribution to retirement, paid vacation

Part-Time Employees: Sometimes

Interns: 2 in summer, 2 during rest of year
Length: 10 weeks
Duties: Research and writing

Remuneration: $200/week

Jobs advertised: Newspaper, word-of-mouth, through nonprofit directors' group meetings

To apply: Contact Nancy Rose, Administrative Assistant

Remarks: NC Center research has influenced governmental actions in North Carolina, including; (1)The decision to create a State Environmental Index, which would make regular evaluations of the state's air and water quality, land use, and handling of wastes; (2) The incorporation of hospital financial information into the North Carolina Medical Database for use by health care consumers in North Carolina; (3) Appropriation of funds to small or poor school districts to equalize funding; (4) Authority for courts to appoint temporary managers for nursing homes which consistently have problems

NORTH CAROLINA OCCUPATIONAL SAFETY AND HEALTH PROJECT (NCOSH)

P.O. Box 2514
Durham, NC 27715
(919) 286-9249

Director: Vacant at publication date

Purpose: NCOSH's mission is to provide all North Carolina workers, from the trenches to the offices, with technical assistance, training and advice on work-related safety and health hazards. NCOSH mobilizes its supporters to build coalitions with other groups of similar interests to enforce existing laws and pass new laws to make the workplace safer and healthier.

Methods of operation: Training and technical assistance (40%), public education (20%), publications (20%), research (10%), lobbying (5%), community organizing (5%)

Constituency: Labor unions, workers, and health and legal professionals in North Carolina

Recent issues and projects: Led a public education project about the crisis of repetitive motion illness in North Carolina; help unions and community organizations organize to fight pollution. NCOSH is currently leading the struggle to increase fines for employers violating safety and health regulations.

Major publications: Quarterly newsletter: *NCOSH Health and Safety News*; annual report; *Workers' Compensation for Repetitive Motion Illness in North Carolina: A Lawyer's Guide*; *Workers' Compensation Handbook*; *Right-to-Know Handbook*; yearly report on occupational death in North Carolina

Budget: $150,000

Funding: Foundations (60%), individual contributions (15%), union membership (10%), telephone solicitation (10%), direct mail (5%)

Staff: 5
1 Director
1 Fundraising/Volunteer Development (p-t)
1 Organizer
1 Training Coordinator
1 Bookkeeper

Staff openings/year: 1

Work Week: 45 hours

Salary/year: $20,000 (Recent College Graduate); $26,000 (Graduate with advanced degree)

Benefits: Health insurance, life insurance, paid vacation, personal leave, comp time

Part-Time Employees: 2

Volunteers: 40 per year

Interns: Yes
Length: 1 semester
Duties: Issue research, development of training materials and publications
Remuneration: $1,000 stipend for Lawyers Guild interns; others negotiable

Jobs advertised: Local newspapers; notices mailed to other safety and health advocacy groups around the country; *Community Jobs*

To apply: Contact the Director

NORTH CAROLINA STUDENT RURAL HEALTH COALITION

P.O. Box 92218
Durham, NC 27708
(919) 684-5880

Other Offices: Rocky Mount, NC

Director: Steve Bader

Purpose: To provide assistance to the grassroots people's health movement in North Carolina; and to expose students to ways they can contribute to this movement.

Methods of operation: Training and technical assistance (50%), community organizing (35%), research (5%), publications (5%), public education (5%)

Constituency: Working class communities, mostly African-American, in North Carolina's Black Belt

Recent issues and projects: Their major work is focussed around development of People's Health Clinics, as well as providing assistance for workers organizing for better health conditions. We have four medical chapters providing assistance to the clinics, an undergraduate chapter raising money to support an organizer and providing an internship program and an occupational health working group.

Major publications: Quarterly newsletter; annual report

Budget: $150,000

Funding: Canvassing (30%), private foundations (31%), state/university administration, student government and work-study (22%), direct mail (11%), church foundations (6%)

Staff: 6
3 Organizers
3/4 Director
1/4 Foundation Fundraiser
1/4 Grassroots Fundraiser
1/4 Typist/Bookkeeper
1/4 Office Manager
1 1/2 Chapter Organizers

Staff openings/year: 1 - 3

Work Week: 40 hours

Salary/year: $13-19,000

Benefits: Health and life insurance, paid vacation, unemployment insurance, workers' compensation

Part-Time Employees: Yes

Volunteers: 100+

Interns: 3-6
Length: 10-12 weeks, summer
Duties: Support development of People's Clinics and community organizing; investigative research; speakers services; training workshops
Remuneration: Most students are from the area or go to school here; they raise stipends with the Coalition's help

Jobs advertised: *Community Jobs*; *ACCESS*: Networking in the Public Interest; local activist networks; national organizing networks; local publications

To apply: Contact Steve Bader, Director

NORTH SHORE COMMUNITY ACTION PROGRAMS

98 Main Street
Peabody, MA 01960
(508) 531-0767

Director: Daniel LeBlanc

Purpose: Anti-poverty organization dedicated to empowering low-income people so as to enable them to become self-sufficient.

Methods of operation: Human services (80%), community organizing (10%), lobbying (4%), research (2%), public education (2%), training and technical assistance (2%)

Constituency: Low-income residents of Beverly, Danvers, Peabody and Salem, Massachusetts

Recent issues and projects: Homeless advocacy; anti-displacement organizing in Salem; rent review campaign; welfare rights; investment analysis; energy programs; elder home care; Head Start

Major publications: 1990-92 Strategic Plan, which analyzed low-income needs and action plan

Budget: $4,000,000

Funding: State and federal government grants (93%), foundations (5%), individual contributions (2%)

Staff: 117
40 Teachers
40 Homemakers
20 Caseworkers
6 Clerks
3 Energy Conservation Specialists
3 Organizers
2 Bookkeeper/Accountants
1 Office Manager
1 Researcher
1 Typist

Staff openings/year: 20

Work Week: 35 hours

Salary/year: $21,000 (Recent College Graduate); $23,000 (Graduate with advanced degree)

Benefits: Health insurance, life insurance, pregnancy leave, paid vacation

Part-Time Employees: 20

Volunteers: 1

Jobs advertised: Local newspapers; *Boston Globe*; mailings

To apply: Contact Nancy Sullivan, Director of Community Outreach

NORTHEAST - MIDWEST INSTITUTE

218 D Street, SE
Washington, DC 20003
(202) 544-5200

Director: Dick Munson

Purpose: To enhance the economic vitality and environmental quality in the Northeast and Midwest.

Methods of operation: Research, lobbying

Recent issues and projects: Recent projects include pollution prevention; industrial site cleanup; worker retraining; trade; and sediment management

Major publications: *Northeast-Midwest Economic Review*; *The Great Lakes Congressional Report*

Budget: $1,200,000

Funding: Foundations (100%)

Staff: 14
1 Writer/Editor
1 Office Manager
1 Press Aide
10 Issue Experts
1 Bookkeeper/Accountant

Staff openings/year: 1

Work Week: 40 hours

Salary/year: $Varies (Recent College Graduate); $Varies (Graduate with advanced degree)

Benefits: Health insurance, pension, paid vacation, life insurance, pregnancy leave, tuition reimbursement

Part-Time Employees: None

Summer Employees: None

Interns: 5-8
Length: 2-3 months
Duties: Work with policy analysts on legislative issues

Jobs advertised: Mailings to other groups and newsletters

To apply: Contact Jennifer Olmstead

NORTHEAST CITIZEN ACTION RESOURCE CENTER (NECARC)

621 Farmington Ave.
Hartford, CT 06105
(203) 525-3688

Director: Marc Caplan

Purpose: To assist grassroots citizen action organizing, building broad-based coalitions, and the coordination of regional issue campaigns.

Methods of operation: Community organizing (40%), training and technical assistance (35%), research (20%)

Constituency: Organizations and individuals active in progressive issues through organizing

Recent issues and projects: Family Issues Leadership Network; creation of Northeast Network of Progressive Elected Officials; building coalitions on progressive issues; regional health care, campaign finance reform; jobs and economic concession

Major publications: Newsletter: *Northeast Leadership*

Budget: $300,000

Funding: Foundations (90%), individual contributions (10%)

Staff: 6

Staff openings/year: 1

Work Week: 50 hours

Salary/year: $18,000 (Recent College Graduate); $30,000 (Graduate with advanced degree)

Benefits: Health insurance, paid vacation, pregnancy leave

Part-Time Employees: 2

Volunteers: Yes; many

Interns: None currently, but willing to accept applications

Jobs advertised: Mailing of job description; *Community Jobs*; word-of-mouth through networks

To apply: Contact Marc Caplan, Director

NORTHERN ALASKA ENVIRONMENTAL CENTER

218 Driveway
Fairbanks, AK 99701
(907) 452-5021

Director: Rex Blazer

Purpose: The preservation of wilderness and wildlands habitat in Interior and Arctic Alaska.

Methods of operation: Public education (40%), research (10%), lobbying (10%), litigation (10%), publications (10%), community organizing (10%)

Recent issues and projects: Wilderness designation for entire Arctic National Wildlife Refuge. Reclamation, water quality and Placer mining on Alaskan rivers. Hazards associated with offshore oil and gas exploration and development in Alaska.

Major publications: Quarterly magazine: *The Northern Line*

Budget: $95,000

Funding: Individual contributions (60%), foundations (30%), direct mail (10%)

Staff: 3
1 Campaign Manager
1 Campaign Logistics Coordinator
1 Issues Specialist (half-time)
1 Office Manager (half-time)

Staff openings/year: 1

Work Week: 55 hours

Benefits: Health insurance, paid vacation

Part-Time Employees: 4

Volunteers: 5

Interns: Yes
Remuneration: Unpaid

Jobs advertised: Alaska environmental publications; national environmental newsletters

To apply: Contact Mary Zalar

NORTHERN PLAINS RESOURCE COUNCIL

419 Stapleton Building
Billings, MT 59101
(406) 248-1154

Other Offices: Helena, MT; Miles City, MT

Director: Teresa Erickson

Purpose: To empower local citizens to participate in decisions by corporations and government agencies which affect them.

Methods of operation: Community organizing (34%), research (25%), direct action (10%), public education (10%), training and technical assistance (10%), lobbying (5%), publications (5%), litigation (1%)

Recent issues and projects: Hard Rock Mining Action and Policy Project: to develop policy recommendations to address current boom in hard rock mining in Montana. Livestock petition calling for Congressional action to reverse trend towards increasing monopolization of the meat packing industry. Family Farm Crisis Project; energy; coal; air quality; rural economic development.

Major publications: Newsletter: *Plains Truth*; *For Current and Future Generations* (the Western Organization of Resource Councils' review of natural resource taxation in Montana, North Dakota, Wyoming and Colorado); *Hard Rock Minerals Policy*; citizen handbooks

Budget: $250,000

Funding: Foundations (55%), individual contributions (25%), direct mail (10%), internal fundraising (5%)

Staff: 16
5 Issue Experts
4 Organizers
2 Lobbyists
1 1/2 Foundation Fundraisers
1 Office Manager
1 Researcher
1/2 Bookkeeper/Accountant
1/3 Press Aide
1/3 Writer/Editor

Staff openings/year: 1-2

Work Week: 50 hours

Salary/year: $10,200 (Recent College Graduate);

$10,800 (Graduate with advanced degree)

Benefits: Health insurance, pregnancy leave, paid vacation

Part-Time Employees: 4

Summer Employees: 1-2

Volunteers: 10-15

Interns: 1-2
Length: 3 months
Duties: Special projects, research, assist staff and members with issue campaigns
Remuneration: $1,000 stipend for 3 months

Jobs advertised: *Community Jobs*; Peace Corps newsletter; newspapers; internships

To apply: Contact Teresa Erickson, Staff Director

NORTHWEST COALITION FOR ALTERNATIVES TO PESTICIDES (NCAP)

1249 Willamette, P.O. Box 1393
Eugene, OR 97440
(503) 344-5044

Director: Norma Grier

Purpose: To expose problems with pesticide use and to solve pest problems with good management practices and non-chemical alternatives to pesticides.

Methods of operation: Community organizing (45%), public education (30%), publications (20%), litigation (5%), lobbying (1%)

Constituency: Individuals and some groups, two-thirds of which are in the Northwest, who want a reduction in pesticide use and sustainable natural resource management

Recent issues and projects: Develop comprehensive management program for forest vegetation that has historically been sprayed; implement a model groundwater protection program for Oregon; organize in Northwest communities around incidents of pesticide exposure to leverage adequate agency response to poisonings and prevent future incidents

Major publications: Quarterly: *Journal of Pesticide Reform*; *On the Trail of a Pesticide: A Citizen's Guide to the Chemistry, Effects, and Testing of Pesticides*; factsheets and information packets on individual pesticides

Budget: $200,000

Funding: Foundations (50%), individual contributions (35%), literature sales (8%), direct mail (7%)

Staff: 6
1 Executive Director
2 Program Associates
1 Editor
1/2 Fundraiser
1/2 Office Manager
1/2 Information Services Coordinator

Staff openings/year: 0-1

Work Week: 40 hours

Salary/year: $18,200

Benefits: Health insurance, paid vacation

Part-Time Employees: 3

Volunteers: 30

Interns: Yes
Length: Varies
Duties: Various
Remuneration: None; most work for academic credit through the University of Oregon

Jobs advertised: Announcements are widely distributed within the pesticide network; local newspaper; sometimes listed nationally, as in *Community Jobs*

To apply: Contact Norma Grier, Executive Director

NORTHWEST IMMIGRANT RIGHTS PROJECT

909 Eighth Avenue
Seattle, WA 98104
(206) 587-4009

Director: Vicky Stifter

Purpose: To defend and advance the rights of immigrants and refugees through community education, advocacy and immigration legal services.

Methods of operation: Primarily legal services, community education and advocacy

Constituency: Immigrants and refugees with low-incomes

Recent issues and projects: Current projects include: political asylum representation; legal advice in-person and via regional hotline; representation of immigrant women and children; extensive regional community education effort.

Major publications: Asylum manual

Budget: $350,000

Funding: Foundations (60%), individual contributions (10%), other (30%)

Staff: 12
7 Paralegals
3 Attorneys
1 Director
1 Receptionist

Staff openings/year: 2

Work Week: 35 hours

Salary/year: $20-30,000 (Graduate with advanced degree)

Benefits: Health insurance, maternity/paternity leave, paid vacation, dental insurance

Part-Time Employees: 1

Summer Employees: 1

Volunteers: Hundreds

Interns: 2
Length: 3-6 months
Duties: Various, depending on ability and interests
Remuneration: $2,000/summer (funded by National Lawyers Guild)

To apply: Contact Sarah Ignatius, Executive Director

NORTHWEST REGIONAL FACILITATORS

East 525 Mission Avenue
Spokane, WA 99202-1824
(509) 484-6733

Director: Robert Stilger, Susan Virnig, Jayne Auld

Purpose: To help people and communities visualize the features they desire and to achieve those visions. Works to enable people to define their visions, identify their problems and act to improve the quality of their lives.

Methods of operation: Training and technical assistance (25%), direct action (25%), community organizing (25%), human services (25%)

Recent issues and projects: Community Development Program; Housing Rehabilitation Program; Nonprofit Center; Committee for a Hunger Free Washington; Children's Resource and Referral Center

Budget: $1,200,000

Funding: Contracts for services and grants (100%)

Staff: 31
6 Administrators
6 Housing Rehab Specialists and Coordinators
4 Housing Program Specialists
4 Administrative Specialists
3 Bookkeepers
2 Community Development Specialists
1 Executive Director
1 Director
1 Assistant Director
1 Loan Processor
1 Special Projects/Policy Manager
1 Loan Servicing Specialist
1 Maintenance Specialist
1 Hunger Specialist
1 Child Care Services Manager
1 Nonprofit Specialist

Staff openings/year: 4

Work Week: 40 hours

Salary/year: $16,800

Benefits: Health insurance, life insurance, pregnancy leave, pension, child care referral, paid vacation, sick leave, tuition reimbursement ($200)

Part-Time Employees: 4

Volunteers: 1

Interns: Yes
Length: Summer or 1 semester
Duties: Participates under various programs

Jobs advertised: Local newspapers; employment agencies; Employment Security Office

To apply: Contact Brenda Miller, Administrator

NORTHWEST WOMEN'S LAW CENTER

119 South Main Street, Suite 330
Seattle, WA 98104
(206) 682-9552(206) 621-7691

Director: Kimberly M. Reason

Purpose: The Law Center works to advance and protect the legal rights of women through impact litigation, state legislation, educational programs, and a free telephone information and referral service.

Methods of operation: Litigation (30%), information and referral (20%), public education (35%), legislative work (15%)

Recent issues and projects: Reproductive rights, domestic violence, sexual harassment, regional litigation project, etc.

Major publications: *Sexual Harassment in Employment and Education* (manual and video); *Family Law in Washington State* (book, Eng. and Span.); *Breaking the Cycle: Domestic Violence and the Law* (video); *Justifiable Homicide: Battered Women, Self-Defense, and the Law* (book)

Budget: $425,000

Staff: 10
1 Executive Director
1 Office Administrator
1 Lead Paralegal
1 Legal Rights Educ. Coordinator (part-time)
1 Program Assistant
1 Development Coordinator
1 Staff Litigator
1 Public Policy Counsel (part-time)
1 Litigation Coordinator (part-time)
1 Legal Secretary

Staff openings/year: 0-1

Work Week: 40 hours

Salary/year: $Varies (Recent College Graduate); $Varies (Graduate with advanced degree)

Benefits: Health insurance, family leave, paid vacation

Part-Time Employees: 4

Volunteers: 100+

Interns: Yes
Length: 3-6 months
Duties: Legal/paralegal interns
Remuneration: Volunteer or for academic credit.

To apply: Contact the Executive Director

NOW LEGAL DEFENSE AND EDUCATION FUND

99 Hudson Street, 12th Floor
New York, NY 10013
(212) 925-6635

Director: Helen Neuborne, Executive Director

Purpose: NOW LDEF is the nation's foremost legal advocacy organization for women and girls.

Methods of operation: Litigation (55%), public education (25%), research (10%), technical assistance (10%)

Constituency: NOW LDEF has close ties to the National Organization for Women (NOW) - a "sister organization" - which has members nationwide.

Recent issues and projects: NOW Legal Defense and Education Fund is a civil rights organization dedicated to fostering equality for women and girls. Established over twenty years ago, the organization handles precedent-setting cases, legal strategies, and legislative issues related to reproductive rights; reproductive health care clinic access; sexual harassment in employment; sexual harassment in schools; welfare rights; incest survivor rights; violence against U.S. and immigrant women; judicial education to eradicate gender bias in court; lesbian rights; and key issues on gender equity.

Budget: $2,200,000

Funding: Individual contributions, direct mail, corporations, foundations

Staff: 20
4 Administrative Assistants
6 Attorneys
3 Fundraisers
1 Executive Director
1 Receptionist
1 Director of Finance
1 Paralegal/Intake Coordinator
1 Communications Director
1 Bookkeeper
1 Law Fellow

Staff openings/year: Varies

Work Week: 40 hours

Salary/year: $Varies (Recent College Graduate); $Varies (Graduate with advanced degree)

Benefits: Health insurance, paid vacation, life insurance, family leave

Part-Time Employees: 1

Summer Employees: 8 interns

Volunteers: 1 volunteer attorney

Interns: Yes
Length: Month, semester, summer, year
Duties: Duties vary widely. Our Legal Intern Program is the most extensive.
Remuneration: We can pay a small number of interns; many receive full or supplemental grants from their schools.

Jobs advertised: Announcement is posted, sent to other similar organizations and advertised in some national organizational newsletters and newspapers, particularly in the greater New York area.

To apply: Contact the Executive Director

NUCLEAR AGE PEACE FOUNDATION

1187 Coast Village Road, Suite 123
Santa Barbara, CA 93108
(805) 965-3443

President: David Krieger

Purpose: The Nuclear Age Peace Foundation, a non-partisan, nonprofit, international education organization, promotes peaceful solutions to international conflicts, educates the public through programs and publications, and provides leadership toward weapons free world under international law. Founded in 1982, the Foundation is recognized by the United Nations as a Peace Messenger organization and an accredited Non-Governmental Organization at the United Nations

Methods of operation: Public education (40%), publications (40%), research (20%)

Constituency: Concerned citizens in the U.S. and abroad

Recent issues and projects: The Hague Peace Initiative, a Magna Carta for the Nuclear Age, a summit meeting for humanity, Distinguished Peace Leadership Award, the Swackhamer Peace Prizes and the International Week of Science and Peace

Major publications: *Waging Peace* booklet series; *Global Security Studies*; *Waging Peace Bulletin* newsletter

Budget: $250,000

Funding: Events (25%), endowment (25%), foundations (25%), individual contributions (25%)

Staff: 4
1 Executive Director
1 Publications Director
1 Office Manager
1 Assistant

Work Week: 40 hours

Salary/year: $Varies (Recent College Graduate); $Varies (Graduate with advanced degree)

Benefits: Paid vacation

Part-Time Employees: 3

Summer Employees: 2-3

Volunteers: 25-30

Interns: 4-6
Length: 3-6 months
Duties: Research; help with office work; community outreach
Remuneration: Hourly rate, during summer

Jobs advertised: Through local media; word of mouth

To apply: Contact Ruth Floyd, Office Manager

NUCLEAR ENERGY ACCOUNTABILITY PROJECT

1202 Sioux Street
Jupiter, FL 33458
(407) 743-0770

Director: Thomas J. Saporito, Jr.

Purpose: To protect the environment and public from the adverse effects of nuclear power generation.

Methods of operation: Research (60%), litigation (20%), public education (10%), publications (5%), community organizing (5%)

Membership: Membership consists of people in South Florida from all age groups.

Recent issues and projects: Petitioned for intervention in 2 Atomic Safety License Board Hearings relevant to the Turkey Point Nuclear Plant. Filed petitions pursuant to 100 FR 2.206 for the shutdown of Turkey Point.

Major publications: Monthly newsletter

Funding: Individual contributions (80%), direct mail (20%)

Staff:
1 Writer/Editor
1 Paralegal
1 Researcher
1 Typist
1 Issue Expert

Work Week: 30 hours

NUCLEAR FREE AMERICA

325 East 25th Street
Baltimore, MD 21218
(410) 235-3575

Director: Chuck Johnson

Purpose: NFA is an international clearinghouse and resource center for Nuclear Free Zones. They provide organizing materials, legal assistance and educational information on Nuclear Free Zones and U.S. nuclear weapons contractors and publishes a quarterly newsletter, *The New Abolitionist.*

Methods of operation: Research (25%), public education (25%), publications (25%), community organizing (25%)

Constituency: Geographically diverse (some concentration in New England and West Coast); varied from individuals to religious/other organizations; an increasing number of declared Nuclear Free Zone local governments

Recent issues and projects: A boycott of Morton salt (concluded in July, 1989 with the break off of Thiokol, the weapons manufacturer, from Morton-Thiokol Inc.); defense of Oakland, California's Nuclear Free Zone legislation (under attack by individuals and the federal government); resistance to the Federal Emergency Management Agency's (FEMA) continual planning for nuclear war/civil defense

Major publications: Quarterly newsletter: *The New Abolitionist*; *The Top 50 Nuclear Weapons Contractors* (in postcard and wallet format); customized reports on nuclear weapons and defense contractors

Budget: $55,000

Funding: Individual contributions (55%), program/merchandise (36%), foundations (9%)

Staff: 2
1 Executive Director
1 Office Manager

Staff openings/year: 0-1

Work Week: 40 hours

Salary/year: $14,000 (Recent College Graduate); $16,000 (Graduate with advanced degree)

Benefits: Health insurance, paid vacation

Part-Time Employees: 1-2

Volunteers: 10

Interns: 2
Length: 1 semester
Duties: Assist with office management and carry on special/independent projects
Remuneration: $25/week stipend, bus pass, and housing/board

Jobs advertised: *Community Jobs*; local paper; PeaceNet; and through fliers distributed to other organizations

To apply: Contact Charlene Knott, Office Manager

NUCLEAR INFORMATION AND RESOURCE SERVICE (NIRS)

1424 16th Street, NW, Suite 601
Washington, DC 20036
(202) 328-0002

Director: Michael Mariotte

Purpose: To work for a phase-out of existing nuclear reactors and their replacement with environmentally sound renewable energy sources and energy efficiency, and for the safe, scientifically defensible treatment of radioactive waste and an end to its generation.

Methods of operation: Public education (45%), publications (20%), research (20%), lobbying (5%), direct action (5%), litigation (5%)

Constituency: Local environmental groups and concerned citizens

Recent issues and projects: Nuclear Waste Project: to block deregulation of nuclear waste; Reactor Safety Project: to promote shutdown of aging, particularly dangerous reactors; Alternatives Project: to promote alternative energy sources and combat nuclear resurgence; lawsuit to overturn Nuclear Regulatory Commission (NRC) licensing rule

Major publications: Biweekly: *The Nuclear Monitor*; various reports, etc.

Budget: $275,000

Funding: Foundations (50%), individual contributions (50%)

Staff: 5
3 Issue Experts
1 Executive Director
1 Office Manager

Staff openings/year: 1

Work Week: 40 hours

Salary/year: $20,500

Benefits: Health insurance, pregnancy leave, paid vacation, good working atmosphere

Part-Time Employees: 1

Interns: 1-2
Length: 2-3 months
Duties: Varies
Remuneration: $100/week when possible

Jobs advertised: *Washington Post*; *City Paper*;

other groups; sometimes *Community Jobs*

To apply: Contact Michael Mariotte, Executive Director

NUCLEAR SAFETY CAMPAIGN

1914 North 34th Street, Suite 407
Seattle, WA 98103
(206) 547-3175

Director: Bill Mitchell

Purpose: To build and sustain a network of local, regional and national organizations for the purpose of addressing issues of public health and safety, environmental protection and government accountability as they pertain to the Department of Energy nuclear weapons complex.

Methods of operation: Public education, training and technical assistance, publications, meeting planning, organizing organizations to work together

Constituency: Organizations working on DOE issues

Recent issues and projects: Convener for the "Military Production Network," organizations work together to develop local and national strategies to reform policy regarding U.S. nuclear weapons production

Budget: $327,000

Funding: Foundations (65%), individual contributions (35%)

Staff: 3
1 Director
1 Program Associate
1 DC Representative for the Military Prod. Network
1/2 Clerical

Staff openings/year: 0-1

Work Week: 40 hours

Salary/year: $Varies (Recent College Graduate); $Varies (Graduate with advanced degree)

Benefits: Health insurance, life insurance

Part-Time Employees: 1

Summer Employees: No

OEF INTERNATIONAL

1815 H Street, NW, 11th Floor
Washington, DC 20006
(202) 466-3430

Other Offices: Tequcigalpa, HONDURAS; San Jose, COSTA RICA; Mogadishu, SOMALIA; Harare, ZIMBABWE; Dakar, SENEGAL; Guatemala City, GUATEMALA; San Salvador, EL SALVADOR

Director: Cynthia Metzler

Purpose: To increase the participation of Third World women in the process of development. OEF does this through community development, legal education and activism and small enterprise development programs.

Methods of operation: Training and technical assistance (65%), publications (15%), community organizing (15%), public education (5%)

Constituency: Development community; other private voluntary organizations (PVOs)

Recent issues and projects: Programs include: the Women, Law and Development Program; the Education for Participation Program; Development Education; Customized Trainers' Training and Consulting Services; Somali Women's Small Agricultural Enterprise Development; Mali Institutional Development, Enterprise and Nutrition Program; Community and Enterprise Development; Women, Water and Development; Support for Self-Employed Women; Women in Business; Training of Local Development Agents; Displaced Women's Enterprise Development Project; Small Scale Swine Project; Factory Women's Center

Major publications: *Learning to Teach*; *Women Working Together for Personal, Economic and Community Development*; *Navamaga: Training for Group Building, Health and Income Generation*; *Doing a Feasibility Study: Training Activities for Starting or Reviewing a Small Business*; *Empowerment and the Law: Strategies of Third World Women*

Budget: $5,000,000

Funding: U.S. government (50%), foundations (35%), individual contributions (15%)

Staff: 32
12 Program Managers
6 Assistant Directors

5 Bookkeeper/Accountants
4 Program Associates
4 Foundation Fundraisers
1 Office Manager

Staff openings/year: 3

Work Week: 45 hours

Salary/year: $17,000 (Recent College Graduate); $75,000 (Graduate with advanced degree)

Benefits: Health insurance, life insurance, pregnancy leave, pension, paid vacation

Interns: 1-6
Length: 1 semester
Duties: Clerical, research, translating, logistics
Remuneration: No stipend

Jobs advertised: Newspaper; other private voluntary organizations' (PVO) job boards

To apply: Contact Kate Tshander, Director of Personnel

OFFICE OF COMMUNICATION OF THE UNITED CHURCH OF CHRIST

700 Prospect Avenue
Cleveland, OH 44115-1100
(216) 736-2222

Other Offices: Washington, DC; New York, NY

Director: Beverly J. Chain

Purpose: To educate persons on telecommunications issues and legislation; to carry out the public relations and educational projects for the United Church of Christ.

Methods of operation: Research, litigation, publications, organizing, training and technical assistance

Constituency: Telecommunications consumers; nationwide

Recent issues and projects: Cable television education and social policy issues including access and rate regulation; opposing deregulation of radio and television; furthering equal employment opportunity in all media; active at the Federal Communications Commission (FCC), in court; conduct workshops nationwide

Major publications: News Releases and pamphlets

Budget: $500,000

Funding: Church contributions

Staff: 14
6 Writers/Editors
3 Secretaries
1 Attorney/Associate for Policy
1 Administrative Assistant
1 Office Manager/Bookkeeper
1 Education/Marketing Specialist
1 Television Production/Placement

Staff openings/year: 2

Work Week: 40 hours

Salary/year: $Varies (Recent College Graduate); $Varies (Graduate with advanced degree)

Benefits: Health insurance, pension, life insurance, pregnancy leave

Part-Time Employees: 1/2

Interns: Yes
Length: 3-6 months
Duties: Research, writing
Remuneration: Salary

Jobs advertised: Internally; relevant publications; newspapers

To apply: Contact Beverly J. Chain, Director

OFFICE OF THE CONSUMERS' COUNSEL

77 South High Street, 15th Floor
Columbus, OH 43266-0550
(614) 466-8574

Director: Vacant

Purpose: To represent Ohio's residential public utility consumers before appropriate state and federal courts, legislative and regulatory bodies. To serve Ohio's residential utility consumers by providing professional, innovative and accountable advocacy.

Methods of operation: Litigation and negotiation (50%), research (15%), lobbying (5%), publications (10%), public education (10%), training and technical assistance (10%)

Constituency: Residential utility consumers

Recent issues and projects: Utility regulatory cases at state and federal level; acid rain; least cost planning; telephone deregulation; lifeline rates; periodic review of electric, gas, telephone and water utilities

Major publications: Annual report; monthly newsletter; various consumer education and technical reports

Budget: $4,800,000

Funding: Utility company assessments (100%)

Staff: 64
15 Attorneys
12 Secretaries
6 Administrators
14 Issue Experts
3 Investigators
2 Researchers
2 Lobbyists
2 Public Information Specialists
2 Bookkeepers/Accountants
1 Computer Specialist
5 Administrative/Legal Support

Staff openings/year: 2

Work Week: 40 hours

Salary/year: $25,000 (Recent College Graduate); $30,000 (Graduate with advanced degree)

Benefits: Health insurance, life insurance, family leave, pension, credit union, paid vacation, disability leave, tuition reimbursement

Part-Time Employees: 0

Interns: None currently, but willing to accept applications

Jobs advertised: In-house postings; state employment system

To apply: Contact E. Louise Dupree, Personnel Office

OHIO ALLIANCE FOR THE ENVIRONMENT

445 King Avenue
Columbus, OH 43201
(614) 421-7819

Director: Irene Probasco

Purpose: Alliance programs facilitate the development and exchange of the most current information on environmental issues of major significance in Ohio and nationally. All programs are developed to reach key decision makers throughout Ohio and provide participants with the most current information on the issues.

Methods of operation: Publications, community organizing, public education

Membership: Membership is both individual and organizational. Members are from the citizen, business, agriculture, education, legal, government, industry and religious groups in Ohio.

Recent issues and projects: A series of programs on the use of comparative risk analysis to identify an environmental agenda for the state of Ohio. An annual broadly based environmental conference to provide information and networking potential to the various groups interested in environmental issues. The agenda is designed to appeal to representatives of the agriculture, education, business, legal, industry, citizen, religious and government groups in Ohio.

Major publications: *FOCUS* publications are written as summaries of seminars and conferences offered by the Alliance. Recent *FOCUS* publications are: *The State of Ohio's Environment* and *Guidelines for the Environmentally Conscious Consumer*

Budget: $55,000

Funding: Foundations (66%), individual contributions (33%), other (1%)

Staff:
All employees are part-time
1 Director
2 Membership Development

Work Week: 20 hours

Part-Time Employees: 3

Summer Employees: None

Volunteers: 25+

Interns: None

Jobs advertised: Usually through personal contact of Board members

To apply: Contact Irene Probasco

OHIO CITIZEN ACTION

402 Terminal Tower, 50 Public Square
Cleveland, OH 44113
(216) 861-5200

Other Offices: Akron, OH; Cincinnati, OH; Toledo, OH; Columbus, OH; Dayton, OH

Director: Sandy Buchanan

Purpose: To promote and assist citizen action as the basis for democratic change.

Methods of operation: Research, lobbying,

publications, community organizing, direct action, public education, training and technical assistance, elections, litigation

Membership: 425,000 members recruited by door-to-door canvass on the basis of environmental and consumer issue campaigns

Recent issues and projects: Toxic hazards; Support for Great Lakes Water Quality Initiative and Federal Pollution Prevention Bill; Insurance Reform: "Single-Payer" National Health Insurance; Energy and utility policy

Major publications: Newsletters: *Citizen Action* (180,000 circulation) and *Toxic Watch* (180,000 circulation); research/policy papers on consumer and environmental issues

Budget: $4,000,000

Funding: Individual contributions, foundations, canvassing, telephone solicitation

Staff: 172
150 Canvassers
5 Organizers
6 Office Managers
3 Issue Experts
4 Bookkeepers/Accountants
1 Writer/Editor
1 Lobbyist
1 Press Aide
1 Foundation Fundraiser

Staff openings/year: 2-3

Work Week: 50-60 hours

Salary/year: $18,000 (Recent College Graduate); $20,000 (Graduate with advanced degree)

Benefits: Health insurance, life insurance, pregnancy leave, paid vacation, dental insurance

Part-Time Employees: Yes

Summer Employees: Yes

Volunteers: Yes

Interns: Yes
Length: 3-6 months
Duties: Varied

Jobs advertised: Newspapers; magazines; related organizations

To apply: Contact Bill Callahan, Associate Director

OHIO ENVIRONMENTAL COUNCIL

400 Dublin Avenue, Suite 120
Columbus, OH 43215-2333
(614) 224-4900

Director: Richard Sahli

Purpose: Protection of the environment in Ohio through policy research, public education and legislative liaisons

Methods of operation: Research (25%), public education (25%), lobbying (15%), publications (10%), community organizing (10%), training and technical assistance (10%), litigation (5%)

Membership: 1,000 members statewide; 165 group members

Recent issues and projects: They are currently working on pollution prevention; toxics; energy; and groundwater

Major publications: Newsletter: *Ohio Environmental Report*

Budget: $300,000

Funding: Foundations (60%), individual contributions (30%), other (10%)

Staff: 3
1 Lobbyist
1 Office Manager
1 Researcher

Staff openings/year: 1

Work Week: 40 hours

Salary/year: $Varies (Recent College Graduate); $Varies (Graduate with advanced degree)

Benefits: Health insurance, life insurance, paid vacation

Part-Time Employees: 2

Volunteers: 22

Interns: 10
Length: 1 month
Duties: Depends on interest and our needs at the time
Remuneration: Pay for on-the-job travel

Jobs advertised: Other environmentalists and organizations are told about the positions; newspaper ads

To apply: Contact Stephen H. Sedam, Executive Director

OHIO PUBLIC INTEREST RESEARCH GROUP (OHIO PIRG)

2084 1/2 North High Street
Columbus, OH 43201
(614) 299-7474

Other Offices: Oberlin, OH

Director: John Rumpler, Campaign Director

Purpose: Ohio PIRG is a student- and citizen-based organization which works primarily on environmental issues, consumer and government reform issues. Ohio PIRG is working to expand its organizational base in the community.

Methods of operation: Research, public education, lobbying, litigation, publications

Constituency: Concerned citizens identified through the canvass and Oberlin College Students

Recent issues and projects: Currently campaigning to pass Clean Water Act and the Clean Water Litigation Project; working with the PIRG national lobbying office on pesticide and clean air issues. At Oberlin College, we have also developed a recycling proposal/plan, conducted streamwalks and provided tenants rights information.

Major publications: Newsletter: *PIRG Citizen Advocate*

Budget: $35,000

Funding: Individual contributions, canvassing, telephone solicitation

Staff: 4
1 Executive Director
1 Organizer
2 Canvass Directors
100 Canvassers (varies seasonally)

Staff openings/year: 2-5

Work Week: 60 hours

Salary/year: $14,000-18,000

Benefits: Health insurance, paid vacation, student loan repayment program

Part-Time Employees: Yes; canvass program

Summer Employees: Yes

Interns: Yes

Jobs advertised: PIRG network; mailings; postings; *Community Jobs*

To apply: Contact the Executive Director

Remarks: We have an internship program for Oberlin College students and could arrange for other interns.

OIL SAVERS GROUP

134 Mathewson Street
Providence, RI 02903
(401) 467-7694

Director: Betty Kahl, Coordinator

Purpose: Oil Savers Group runs a nonprofit heating oil buying group and which gives the profits to other Rhode Island nonprofit groups.

Methods of operation: Day-to-day running of the group (68%), public education (25%), human services (5%), training and technical assistance (2%)

Membership: Mostly young to middle-aged people; middle-class

Recent issues and projects: Grants went to a wide variety of organizations. They try to focus on those small groups most in need, ranging from housing for homeless, to scholarships, to preserving open space in Rhode Island.

Major publications: Newsletter

Budget: $10,000

Funding: Oil cooperative fees (50%), individual contributions (50%)

Part-Time Employees: 1

Volunteers: 3

Interns: None currently, but willing to accept applications
Duties: Recruiting new members
Remuneration: One-half of membership fee

To apply: Contact Betty Kahl, Coordinator

OKLAHOMA ASSOCIATION OF COMMUNITY ACTION AGENCIES, INC.

2915 Classen, Suite 520
Oklahoma City, OK 73106
(405) 524-4124

Director: Janelle Stafford

Purpose: To aid in the provision of anti-poverty programs by facilitating the operation of each community action agency.

Methods of operation: Training and technical assistance (100%)

Constituency: 21 Community Action agencies throughout the state

Recent issues and projects: Addsition of state Headstart program and housing directors to staff. Increase of funds to Headstart program.

Budget: $300,000

Staff: 4
1 Office Manager
1 State Headstart Director
1 State Housing Director
1 Executive Director

Staff openings/year: 1

Work Week: 40 hours

Salary/year: $24,000 (Recent College Graduate); $28-40,000 (Graduate with advanced degree)

Benefits: Health insurance, paid vacation, life insurance, family leave

Part-Time Employees: None

Summer Employees: None

Volunteers: Varies

Interns: None

Jobs advertised: Local newspapers

To apply: Contact Janelle Stafford, Executive Director

OKLAHOMA HEALTH CARE PROJECT

431 SW 11th
Oklahoma City, OK 73109
(405) 236-1911

Director: Angela Monson

Purpose: The ultimate goal of the Project is to ensure universal access to health care for all Oklahomans. Additionally, the Project is working toward the establishment of a statewide vehicle which allows low-income and disenfranchised people to influence public policymaking decisions.

Methods of operation: Community organizing (35%), direct action (25%), public education (20%), lobbying (10%), research (5%), training and technical assistance (5%)

Constituency: Approximately 50 percent consumer (primarily low-income) and 50 percent organizational/ agency affiliations

Recent issues and projects: Medicare assignment; long-term care; health insurance for the working uninsured and the poor uninsured; and utility issues (limited to one specific Oklahoma Community)

Budget: $75,000

Funding: Foundations (80%), individual contributions (20%)

Staff: 3
3 Organizers

Staff openings/year: 1

Work Week: 40 hours

Salary/year: $14,000 (Recent College Graduate); $18,000 (Graduate with advanced degree)

Benefits: Health insurance, life insurance, pregnancy leave, paid vacation, sick leave, dental insurance

Part-Time Employees: 1

Volunteers: 25+

Interns: Yes
Length: 12-16 weeks
Duties: Varied - research, organizing, campaign coordination, etc.
Remuneration: If budget allows, paid internships

Jobs advertised: Local papers

To apply: Contact Angela Monson, Executive Director

OLDER PERSONS ACTION GROUP, INC.

325 E. Third Avenue, Suite 300
Anchorage, AK 99501
(907) 276-1059

Other Offices: Wasilla, AK

Director: Vera Gazaway

Purpose: Older Persons Action Group, Inc. (OPAG) is a nonprofit membership organization dedicated to improving services, developing programs, educating, promoting and implementing changes to foster self-determination of older Alaskan citizens.

Methods of operation: Training and technical assistance (40%), publications (30%), research

(10%), direct action (10%), public education (10%)

Recent issues and projects: Recent projects include: Advocacy for health care reform in Alaska; expansion of community-based and in-home health support; operates job referral of caregivers; lobbies the Alaska legislators and Alaska congressional delegates

Major publications: *Senior Voice*, monthly publication with subscribers in every zip code of Alaska; *Directory of Services for Older Alaskans*

Budget: $800,000

Funding: State/local grants (98%), individual contributions (2%)

Staff: 24
4 Writers/Editors
5 Office Managers
3 Researchers
4 Administrative Assistants
2 Bookkeepers/Accountants
2 Caseworkers
3 Program Coordinators
7 Instructors
1 School Administrator
3 Employment Counselors
(21 jobs are part-time)

Staff openings/year: 4

Work Week: 40 hours

Salary/year: $19,200 (Recent College Graduate); $24,000 (Graduate with advanced degree)

Benefits: Health insurance, family leave

Part-Time Employees: 21

Summer Employees: None

Volunteers: 15

Interns: None, but willing to accept applications

Jobs advertised: Newspaper advertisements, weekly Job Support Club

---

OLDER WOMEN'S LEAGUE (OWL)
666 11th Street, NW, Suite 700
Washington, DC 20001
(202) 783-6686

Director: Joan Kuriansky

Purpose: Grassroots advocacy organization concerned with issues of importance to midlife and older women.

Methods of operation: Research, lobbying, publications, community organizing, direct action, public education

Constituency: Persons interested in issues of concern to midlife and older women

Recent issues and projects: Health care, employment, care giving, pensions, guardianship, violence against women, social security housing

Major publications: Newspaper: *OWL Observer*; *OWL Gray Papers*, with in-depth analysis of key issues; *Failing America's Caregivers: A Status Report on Women Who Care*; videotape: *A Matter of Life and Death*, to educate lay persons in the use of living wills and other legal instruments; model state legislation on such issues as osteoporosis, respite care and nursing home reform; testimony; contact office for full publications list

Budget: $1,200,000

Funding: Individual contributions, foundations, direct mail

Staff: 10
1 1/2 Organizers
2 1/2 Typists
1 Office Manager
1 Foundation Fundraiser
1 Issue Expert
1 Bookkeeper/Accountant
1 Campaign Manager

Staff openings/year: 1

Work Week: 40 hours

Salary/year: $25,000

Benefits: Health insurance, pregnancy leave, pension, paid vacation

Part-Time Employees: 6

Volunteers: 5

Interns: 1
Length: 3 months
Duties: Assist in public policy development and chapter organizing
Remuneration: Unpaid

Jobs advertised: In *Washington Post* and through some universities

To apply: Contact Jincy Boerner

Remarks: OWL has 122 chapters in 35 states.

OMB WATCH

1742 Connecticut Avenue, NW, 4th Floor
Washington, DC 20009
(202) 234-8494

Director: Gary D. Bass

Purpose: OMB Watch is a nonprofit, research, educational and advocacy organization that monitors Executive Branch activities affecting nonprofit, public interest and community groups.

Methods of operation: Research (40%), publications (30%), lobbying (5%), training and technical assistance (25%)

Constituency: Community Action Agencies, human service organizations, libraries and other related community-based organizations

Recent issues and projects: RTK NET (on-line computer database providing government information on toxics), nonprofit lobbying, federal budget fax action alerts, paperwork reduction act, regulations, advocacy for dissemination of government information

Major publications: Bimonthly: *OMB Watcher*; *Government Information Insider*; *Online*; *So You Want to Make A Difference: A Key to Advocacy*; *Using Community Right-To-Know*; *Through the Corridors of Power*; and *Budget Fax Action Alerts*

Budget: $550,000

Funding: Foundations (80%), membership (20%)

Staff: 7
1 Executive Director
1 Technical Consultant
2 Writers/Editors
1 Assistant to the Director
1 Office Manager
1 Researcher

Work Week: 40 hours

Salary/year: $20,000 (Recent College Graduate); $Varies (Graduate with advanced degree)

Benefits: Health insurance, paid vacation

Part-Time Employees: Yes

Interns: Yes
Length: 3 months
Duties: Research and writing on policy issues involving OMB and the executive branch
Remuneration: None

Jobs advertised: *Washington Post*, and *City Paper*

To apply: Contact Dan Cook, Office Manager

OPERATION CONCERN

1853 Market Street
San Francisco, CA 94103
(415) 626-7000

Director: Judith E. Stevenson

Purpose: To provide mental health and social services to the lesbian and gay community in a multicultural environment, with attention to youth, elders, the disabled, couples and families and substance abusers.

Methods of operation: Human services (80%), training, technical assistance, public education (15%), community organizing (5%)

Constituency: The lesbian/gay community

Recent issues and projects: AIDS Family Project for loved ones of PWA's (People with AIDS); Committee for a Lesbian/Gay/Bisexual Youth Center

Budget: $900,000

Funding: Government grants, United Way (60%), individual contributions (20%), foundations (20%), direct mail (5%)

Staff: 26
12 Clinicians
8 Program Coordinators/Clinicians
2 Receptionists
1 Executive Director
1 Office Manager
1 Administrative Assistant
1 Bookkeeper/Accountant

Staff openings/year: 3

Work Week: 20-40 hours

Salary/year: $24,000 (Recent College Graduate); $25-30,000 (Graduate with advanced degree)

Benefits: Health insurance, life insurance, pension, credit union, 4 week paid vacation, generous flex-time, consultation, supervision

Part-Time Employees: 16

Volunteers: 35

Interns: 13; graduate level and/or licensing practicum
Length: 1 year
Duties: Clinical practice
Remuneration: Minority student stipend available

Jobs advertised: Gay and straight media; local nonprofit corp. newsletter; county provider mailings; networking lists

To apply: Contact Executive Director or Administrative Assistant

OREGON COALITION AGAINST DOMESTIC AND SEXUAL VIOLENCE

2336 SE Belmont Street
Portland, OR 97214
(503) 239-4486

Director: Holly Pruett

Purpose: The Coalition is the statewide network of 31 grassroots programs that work with victims of rape, incest and battering.

Methods of operation: Training and technical assistance (50%), community organizing (25%), public education (5%), direct action (5%), lobbying (5%), research (5%), publications (5%)

Membership: Nonprofit grassroots programs which work to end violence against women and children

Recent issues and projects: Guided by the Five Year Plan, the Coalition will assist member programs in meeting increasing demands for services with a major resource development campaign; a statewide advocacy project focusing on children of domestic violence and child sexual abuse victims; and ongoing training, technical assistance, networking, and legislative advocacy.

Major publications: Quarterly newsletter: *Network News*

Budget: $310,000

Funding: Foundations (50%), fees for service (15%), corporations (10%), government (10%), individual contributions (10%), direct mail (5%)

Staff: 4
2 Program Coordinators
1 Attorney
1 Executive Director

Staff openings/year: 1-2

Work Week: 40 hours

Salary/year: $24,000

Benefits: Health insurance or child care, life insurance, pregnancy leave, paid vacation, mental health/sick leave

Volunteers: 5

Interns: 1-3
Length: At least 3 months
Duties: Negotiable
Remuneration: Stipend possible, job-related expenses paid

Jobs advertised: Newspapers, newsletters, mailing list

To apply: Contact Holly Pruett, Executive Director

OREGON CONSUMER LEAGUE

P.O. Box 8934
Portland, OR 97207
(503) 227-3882

Director: Patricia Ferrell-French

Purpose: To protect consumers in the marketplace through education, legislation, and research

Methods of operation: Research, lobbying, litigation, publications, clearinghouse for consumer complaints

Constituency: Persons interested in consumer advocacy mainly in the Portland metropolitan area with some out-of-state members

Recent issues and projects: Improve influence of consumers in insurance regulation; enacting legislation protecting used car buyers; legislating for licensing auto repair facilities; support for progressive taxation, that is, no sales tax and halt the epidemic of user fees and "sin" taxes, but support property tax relief for owner occupied houses; join in coalition to gain affordable health care for all

Major publications: Bi-monthly newsletter; *Consumer Resources in Oregon* pamphlet

Budget: $5,500

Funding: Membership dues and donations

Staff:
All volunteer

Interns: Yes
Remuneration: Outside funding

To apply: Contact Patricia Ferrell-French, Executive Director

OREGON ENVIRONMENTAL COUNCIL

2637 SW Water Avenue
Portland, OR 97201
(503) 222-1963

Director: John Charles

Purpose: To protect the quality and diversity of Oregon's environmental resources through organized political action, public education and agency monitoring and to cooperate with similar efforts on a national basis.

Methods of operation: Research, lobbying, litigation, publications, organizing, public education

Constituency: Concerned citizens in Oregon; about 2,200 members

Recent issues and projects: Major effort to clean up air in southern Oregon non-attainment areas; led effort to get the city of Portland's Park Bureau to use Integrated Pest Management (IPM); leading effort to pass Oregon comprehensive Clean Air Act; spearheading coalition looking into gold mining; beginning major effort to protect groundwater

Major publications: *Earthwatch Oregon* statewide environmental magazine; *Legislative Bulletins*; reports

Budget: $300,000

Funding: Membership dues, contributions, foundation grants

Staff: 6
1 Executive Director
1 Associate Director
1 Transportation Director
1 Air and Water Program Director
1 Bookkeeper
1 Administrative Assistant

Staff openings/year: 1

Work Week: 40 hours

Salary/year: $18,000 (Recent College Graduate); $30,000 (Graduate with advanced degree)

Benefits: Medical and dental insurance, tuition reimbursement, 4 weeks paid vacation, pension plan

Part-Time Employees: 3 contractors

Volunteers: 40+

Interns: None currently, but willing to accept applications
Remuneration: Outside funding or unpaid

Jobs advertised: *Earthwatch Oregon*; local newspapers; regional network; word of mouth

To apply: Contact John Charles, Executive Director

OREGON FAIR SHARE

306 SE Ash
Portland, OR 97214
(503) 239-7611

Other Offices: Medford, OR; Independence, OR; Eugene, OR; Salem, OR

Director: Katheryn Donaldson

Purpose: The purpose of Oregon Fair Share is to secure greater economic and social justice for the people of Oregon through nonviolent, grassroots-based citizen action programs. Our goals include combatting neighborhood deterioration; opposing discrimination on the basis of income, sex, race, age, religion, or origin; advocating for greater consumer rights and other forms of economic democracy; and increasing citizen control over the public decisions which affect their lives.

Methods of operation: Community organizing (45%), public education (15%), direct action (15%), lobbying (15%), research (5%), publications (5%)

Constituency: Low and middle income people

Recent issues and projects: (1) Campaign to provide access to affordable health care for all Oregonians. Actively lobbied for changes in the 1988 legislative session and currently organizing for secure single payer health care plan for Oregon. (2) Campaign for an equitable tax structure, including property tax relief and progressive (graduated) income tax; continued opposition to a sales tax; local groups involved in economic development and education issues

Major publications: Newsletter: *The Oregonizer*; *Ad Book*

Budget: $1,000,000

Funding: Canvassing (80%), foundations (15%), grassroots fundraising (5%)

Staff: 23
15 Canvassers
5 Organizers
1 Executive Director
1 Office Manager/Bookkeeper
1 Organizing Director

Staff openings/year: 12

Work Week: 40-60 hours

Salary/year: $Varies (Recent College Graduate); $Varies (Graduate with advanced degree)

Benefits: Health insurance, paid vacation, sick leave

Part-Time Employees: 2

Summer Employees: None

Volunteers: Hundreds

Interns: 2
Length: 6 months-1 year
Duties: Research, assistant to organizers
Remuneration: Fundraise own salary half-time; intern half-time

Jobs advertised: *Community Jobs*; local newspapers; mailings to similar organizations nationwide

To apply: Contact Katheryn Donaldson, Executive Director

OREGON STATE PUBLIC INTEREST RESEARCH GROUP (OSPIRG)

1536 SE 11th Street
Portland, OR 97214
(503) 231-4181

Other Offices: Eugene, OR

Director: Joel Ario

Purpose: Statewide research and advocacy organization. Conducts independent research, monitors government and corporate actions, and advocates reforms to benefit the public, primarily in the areas of environmental protection, consumer rights, and government reform.

Methods of operation: Community organizing, including student organizing (25%), research (25%), public education (25%), lobbying (10%), publications (10%), direct action (5%)

Membership: 30,000 citizen members and 30,000 student members in campus PIRG chapters

Recent issues and projects: Toxics: passed first pollution prevention law in nation in 1989; also passed state Superfund (1987) and state Right-To-Know law (1985). Toy safety: do annual survey of dangerous toys leading to numerous federal recalls. Solid waste: passed comprehensive recycling law in 1991. Other issues include pesticides and organic farming, energy conservation, banking reform and voter registration.

Major publications: *OSPIRG Agenda*, a quarterly publication for 30,000 citizen members; *OSPIRG Impact*, 3 times/year for 30,000 student members; *Renters Handbook*; *Water Quality Guide*; and other consumer guides and regular research reports on toxics

Budget: $500,000

Funding: Individual contributions, foundations, direct mail, canvassing, telephone solicitation

Staff: 18
6 Organizers
4 Citizen Outreach Directors
2 Issue Expert/Researcher/Lobbyists
1 Writer/Editor
1 Attorney/Lobbyist
1 Administrative Director
1 Bookkeeper/Accountant/Receptionist
1 Development Director
1 Campaign Manager

Staff openings/year: 3-5

Work Week: 50-60 hours

Salary/year: $14,000 (Recent College Graduate); $18,000 (Graduate with advanced degree)

Benefits: Health insurance, paid vacation, assistance with student loan repayment

Summer Employees: 50+ canvassers

Volunteers: Yes; number varies

Interns: Yes
Length: Flexible
Duties: Flexible
Remuneration: Usually need work-study or similar support

Jobs advertised: Newspapers; flyers; etc.

To apply: Contact Dianne Topp, Administrative Director

ORGANIZE TRAINING CENTER

442-A Vicksburg
San Francisco, CA 94104
(415) 821-6180

Director: Mike Miller

Purpose: To build effective, democratic, self-funding people's organizations and assist others who are leaders in, or organizers of, such organizations. To increase the understanding of the theory and practice of community organizations among organizers and the broader public.

Methods of operation: Community organizing (60%), training and technical assistance (20%), publications (10%), public education (10%)

Constituency: Clients include leaders of grassroots organizations, religious denominations, labor unions and full-time community and labor organizers

Recent issues and projects: Recent issues include: crime; drugs; public education; public transportation; environment; public housing tenant organizing; and other issues coming from the organizations with which we work

Major publications: *The People Fight Back*, describes the step-by-step process in a successful tenant organizing drive; articles on organizing movements, issue campaigns, labor, electoral politics, classics in organizing, and values, religion and organizing; *The Organizer Mailing*, a quarterly publication available to subscribers

Budget: $130,000

Funding: Fees (50%), foundations (30%), individual contributions (15%), direct mail (5%)

Staff: 2
1 Organizer
1 Office Manager/Bookkeeper

Staff openings/year: 0-1

Work Week: 40 hours

Salary/year: $25,000 (Recent College Graduate); $40,000 (Graduate with advanced degree)

Benefits: Health insurance, pension, paid vacation, paid study time

Part-Time Employees: 1

Volunteers: Occasionally

Interns: Yes
Length: 3-6 months
Duties: Training program
Remuneration: No funds

Jobs advertised: Word of mouth

To apply: Address communications to OTC

OTHER SIDE

300 West Apsley Street
Philadelphia, PA 19144
(215) 849-2178

Other Offices: Sioux, SD; Fredericksburg, VA

Director: Mark Olson

Purpose: The Other Side's purpose is to continually call Christians to the implications of their faith and to provide a forum for discussion of social problems from a Christian faith perspective. Their magazine focuses on justice and peace issues.

Methods of operation: Publications (100%)

Membership: Primarily North American Christians concerned about matters of justice, peace, and faith

Recent issues and projects: Recent issues contained articles on Haiti, capitol punishment, the abolition of prisons, liberation theology, inclusive Christianity, African American biblical hermeneutics, and gay and lesbian theology.

Major publications: *The Other Side* magazine

Budget: $360,000

Funding: Subscriptions (75%), individual contributions (25%)

Staff: 8
1 Subscription Management
2 Writers/Editors
1 Director
1 Art Director
1 Marketing Director
1 Sales Director
1 Director of Reader Support

Staff openings/year: 1

Work Week: 40-50 hours

Salary/year: $3,000-23,000

Benefits: Health insurance (100% coverage), 21 days paid vacation, pension

Volunteers: 2

Interns: Yes
Length: 3 months to 1 year
Duties: Editorial or business/subscription management, or a combination
Remuneration: Unpaid

Jobs advertised: Announcements in major publications, including *Community Jobs*; they mail out announcements, and print it in their magazine

To apply: Contact Mark Olson

OVERSEAS DEVELOPMENT NETWORK

333 Valencia Street, Suite 330
San Francisco, CA 94103
(415) 431-4204

Director: Stefano DeZerega

Purpose: To inspire and educate students to address international issues. To be a vehicle for involvement in international development.

Methods of operation: Public education (75%), research (5%), lobbying (5%), publications (5%), direct action (5%), training and technical assistance (5%)

Constituency: College age students

Recent issues and projects: Recent issues include: grassroots leaders speaking tours of Northwest and New England; regional seminars in Washington, D.C., Boston, Santa Cruz; Bike-Aid, cross country cycling trip to raise money for international development

Major publications: *Globe Links*, tri-annual newsletter;

Budget: $200,000

Funding: Individual contributions (50%), foundations (40%), direct mail (10%)

Staff: 4
2 Organizers
1 Researcher
1 Foundation Fundraiser

Staff openings/year: 1

Work Week: 60 hours

Salary/year: $18,000

Benefits: Health insurance, paid vacation

Part-Time Employees: None

Summer Employees: None

Volunteers: 2

Interns: 10
Length: 3 months
Duties: Researching, organizing, writing
Remuneration: Travel expenses

Jobs advertised: Nonprofit publications

To apply: Contact Marc Levine

OXFAM AMERICA

26 West Street
Boston, MA 02111
(617) 482-1211

Other Offices: Oakland, CA

Director: John Hammock

Purpose: Oxfam funds locally-generated grassroots development work primarily with peasants in 32 countries. They also prepare and distribute educational materials in this country on the issues of development and hunger.

Constituency: Cross section of liberal and progressive public

Major publications: Newsletter; *Legislative Alert*; various project, country and issue updates

Budget: $13,000,000

Funding: Individual contributions (87%), foundations (8%), other (5%)

Staff: 60
Includes:
7 Development Project Workers
5 Grassroots Fundraisers
2 Press Aides
3 Bookkeepers/Accountants
2 Organizers
2 Writers/Editors
2 Campaign Managers
2 Foundation Fundraisers
3 Lobbyists

Staff openings/year: 5

Work Week: 35 hours

Salary/year: $25,000 (Recent College Graduate); $30,000 (Graduate with advanced degree)

Benefits: Health insurance, life insurance, family leave, paid vacation, tuition reimbursement, pension

Part-Time Employees: 5

Volunteers: 10-15

Interns: 5
Length: Variable

Jobs advertised: Newspapers, newsletters, bulletins

To apply: Contact Debbie Colson

PACIFIC STUDIES CENTER

222 B View Street
Mountain View, CA 94041
(415) 969-1545

Director: Lenny Siegel

Purpose: (1) Document and analyze current developments in high-technology electronics, military technology, and U.S. relations with Asia and the Pacific; (2) Maintain a research library for social change.

Methods of operation: Library (40%), research (25%), publications (25%), public education (10%)

Major publications: Newsletters: *Global Electronics* monthly; *High Cost of High Tech: The Dark Side of the Chip*, by Lenny Siegel and John Markoff

Budget: $60,000

Funding: Individual contributions (25%), research (50%), other (25%)

Staff: 1
1 Director

Work Week: 40-50 hours

Salary/year: $Varies (Recent College Graduate); $Varies (Graduate with advanced degree)

Part-Time Employees: 1

Volunteers: 3

Interns: None at the moment; willing to accept applications

Jobs advertised: Informal

To apply: Contact Lenny Siegel, Director

PALOUSE-CLEARWATER ENVIRONMENTAL INSTITUTE

112 West Fourth, Suite 1, P.O. Box 8596
Moscow, ID 83843
(208) 882-1444

Director: Tom Lamar

Purpose: To increase citizen involvement in decisions that affect the region's environment. Through community organizing and education, we strive to enable residents of the inland Northwest to find effective and sustainable solutions to local environmental problems.

Methods of operation: Community organizing (50%), public education (25%), publications (10%), training and technical assistance (10%), lobbying (5%)

Membership: Varied membership from general population, 600 members

Recent issues and projects: Recent projects include: Western Sustainable Agriculture Working Group; Bike-Ped Idaho; Eastern Columbia Plateau Sole Source Aquifer; Ag Options Network; Paradise Creek Adoption; Palouse Carpool Network; Pullman-Moscow Wellhead protection

Major publications: *Environmental News*, quarterly; *Spoke and Sole*, quarterly

Budget: $150,000

Funding: Foundations (40%), contracts (30%), individual contributions (30%)

Staff: 5
3 Organizers
1 Grassroots Fundraiser
1 Executive Director

Staff openings/year: 1

Work Week: 40 hours

Salary/year: $16,000 (Recent College Graduate); $16,000 (Graduate with advanced degree)

Benefits: Health insurance, paid vacation, pregnancy leave

Part-Time Employees: 1

Summer Employees: 1

Volunteers: 100

Interns: 1
Length: 3 months
Duties: Varied and numerous
Remuneration: Yes

Jobs advertised: Local papers; *Community Jobs*

To apply: Please contact Tom Lamar

PARENTS, FAMILIES & FRIENDS OF LESBIANS AND GAYS

1101 14th Street, NW, 10th Floor
Washington, DC 20005
(202) 638-4200

Director: Sandra Gillis

Purpose: To provide support for gays, lesbians and

bisexuals, their families and friends; to educate an ill-informed public; and to advocate for equal civil rights.

Methods of operation: Community organizing (30%), training and technical assistance (30%), publications (20%), public education (20%)

Membership: 30,000 members nationwide

Recent issues and projects: Our major project is Project Open which is designed to educate mainstream America and dispel the myths about homosexuality. We also focus on the Equal Opportunity Act and other gay and lesbian positive legislation as well as opposing the radical right.

Major publications: The *PFLAGpole* newsletter published quarterly; informational booklets to educate people about gay, lesbian and bisexual issues.

Budget: $800,000

Funding: Direct mail (44%), individual contributions (35%), publications (10%), telephone solicitation (6%), foundations (5%)

Staff: 7
1 Organizer
1 Writer/Editor
1 Office Manager
1 Press Aide
1 Typist
1 Bookkeeper/Accountant
1 Director

Staff openings/year: 1-2

Work Week: 40 hours

Salary/year: $20,000 (Recent College Graduate); $30,000 (Graduate with advanced degree)

Benefits: Health insurance, child care, paid vacation, family leave

Part-Time Employees: None

Summer Employees: None

Volunteers: Yes

Interns: Yes
Length: One semester or summer
Duties: Varies upon our needs and skill/interests of applicants
Remuneration: Varies, can provide housing and sometimes a small stipend

Jobs advertised: In *Washington Blade*, *Washington Post* and other organizations

To apply: Contact Laura Bodenschatz

Remarks: PFLAG also has a very active volunteer program. About half of current staff began as volunteers/interns. Please contact volunteer coordinator if interested in getting involved.

PARTNERS FOR LIVABLE COMMUNITIES

1429 21st Street, NW
Washington, DC 20036
(202) 887-5990

President: Robert H. McNulty

Purpose: An international coalition of more than 1,200 organizations and individuals committed to improving communities, their economic health and quality of life, through collaborative resource management. With a diverse constituency ranging from local community housing coalitions and local arts agencies to national environmental groups and municipal planning offices, Partners functions both as a resource center and as a generator of civic improvements through public activity and awareness, research and technical assistance.

Methods of operation: Publications, public education, training and technical assistance, research

Constituency: Municipal governments; local, regional and national nonprofit organizations; individuals in 40 states and 13 countries

Recent issues and projects: In 1993, Partners completed the Shaping Growth in American Communities Program, in which over 50 cities, states and counties signed up to work over a four-year period on three major themes: Economics of Amenity, Managing Community Assets and Social Equity. We have since incorporated two additional themes: the New Civics and Community Leadership and the State of the Region to this initiative. Other programs include the Community Assistance Program, the Executive Consulting Service and the National Center for Community Action

Major publications: Newsletter, *Livability*; *The State of the American Community: A Community Action Agenda*; *The Entrepreneurial American City*; *Family Investment Strategies*; *The Economies of Amenity*; *The Return of the Livable City*

Budget: $1,400,000

Funding: Foundation grants, corporate contributions, government grants and contracts

Staff: 15

4 Support Staff
3 Program Associates
2 Vice-Presidents
2 Information Specialists
1 President
1 Community Development Director
1 Conference Coordinator
1 Editor

Staff openings/year: 2

Work Week: 40 hours

Salary/year: $20,000 (Recent College Graduate); $25,000 (Graduate with advanced degree)

Benefits: Health insurance (50% until 3-year employment, then 100%), life insurance, pregnancy/parental leave, paid vacation (14 days until 3-year employment, then 23 days), IRA account after 3-year employment

Part-Time Employees: 4

Volunteers: Yes

Interns: Yes
Length: 3 - 4 months
Duties: Program associates
Remuneration: Negotiable

Jobs advertised: *Washington Post*, word-of-mouth, career guides, university placement offices

To apply: Send letter to Robert H. McNulty, President

PARTNERSHIP FOR PREVENTION
1220 19th Street, NW, Suite 405
Washington, DC 20036
(202) 833-0009

Director: Karen A. Bodenhorn

Purpose: Partnership for Prevention is a national nonprofit organization founded to increase visibility and priority for prevention in health policy and practice.

Methods of operation: Education of policy-makers (40%), community organizing (15%), research (10%), publications (10%), public education (10%), training and technical assistance (10%)

Membership: Corporations, national associations, policy-makers, state health departments

Recent issues and projects: Recent projects include: California journalists education seminar on minority prevention issues; development and consensus-building among over 140 national prevention-oriented organizations; development of an employer-based immunization status survey

Major publications: *Prevention is Basic to Health Reform: Model Legislative Language*; *How to Fund Public Health Activities*; *Prevention: Benefits, Costs and Savings*

Budget: $500,000

Funding: Foundations (50%), organization membership (50%)

Staff: 4
1 Organizer
1 Writer/Editor
1 Office Manager
1 Issue Expert

Staff openings/year: 1

Work Week: 45-55 hours

Salary/year: $20,000 (Recent College Graduate); $28,000 (Graduate with advanced degree)

Benefits: Health insurance, paid vacation, life insurance, family leave

Part-Time Employees: 1

Summer Employees: None

Volunteers: 1

Interns: 1
Length: 3 months
Duties: Writing, office help, issue analysis, member management
Remuneration: Volunteer basis

Jobs advertised: Notices in newsletter, word-of-mouth

To apply: Contact Karen A. Bodenhorn, Executive Director

PARTNERSHIP FOR THE SOUNDS
P.O. Box 55
Columbia, NC 27925
(919) 796-1000

Other Offices: Washington, NC

Director: D. Rick Van Schoik

Purpose: The Partnership for the Sounds is a nonprofit organization committed to environmental education and sustainable economic development through cultural, historical and nature-based tourism in North Carolina's Albemarle-Pamlico Sounds region. The Partnership accomplishes its mission through partnerships with regional, state and national public and private partners.

Methods of operation: Public education (40%), training and technical assistance (35%), community organizing (20%), lobbying (5%)

Constituency: Remote, rural, agrarian

Recent issues and projects: Building a series of nature centers, attractions and activities

Major publications: Quarterly newsletter

Budget: $3,000,000

Funding: Government (70%), foundations (30%)

Staff: 2
1 Office Manager
1 Foundation Fundraiser

Work Week: 50 hours

Salary/year: $25,000 (Recent College Graduate); $30,000 (Graduate with advanced degree)

Benefits: Health insurance, pension, paid vacation

Part-Time Employees: 3

Summer Employees: 1

Volunteers: None

Interns: 1
Length: Semester
Duties: Special projects
Remuneration: Expenses reimbursed

Jobs advertised: Newspapers, trade, journals

To apply: Contact D. Rick Van Schoik, Executive Director

PEACE ACTION

1819 H Street, NW #640
Washington, DC 20006
(202) 862-9740

Other Offices: New York, NY

Director: Monica Green

Purpose: A grassroots-based national organization whose purpose is to educate the American people in order to recruit members and organize them into a citizen's movement with the sustained political power to abolish nuclear weapons, end the international arms trade and redirect federal spending from the Pentagon to meet human needs.

Methods of operation: Research (25%); lobbying (20%); publications (5%); community organizing (25%); direct action (5%); public education (30%); training and technical assistance (10%)

Membership: Predominantly urban, middle class, all ages, some racial diversity but more white than other ethnicity

Recent issues and projects: Achieving passage of a Congressional moratorium on U.S. nuclear testing in 1992 and extension of the moratorium by President Clinton in 1993; support for the annual Congressional Black Caucus alternative budget; end the international arms trade

Major publications: *Peace Action*, quarterly newsletter; monthly *Grassroots Organizer* packets, periodic fact sheets and briefing papers

Budget: $1,200,000

Funding: Individual contributions (12%); foundations (10%); direct mail (15%); canvassing (13%); telephone solicitation (31%); bequests (6%)

Staff: 15
5 Program Managers
5 Membership Services
3 Administrative/Finance
1 Fundraiser
1 Executive Director

Staff openings/year: 3-4

Work Week: 40 hours

Salary/year: $20,000 (Recent College Graduate); $22,000 (Graduate with advanced degree)

Benefits: Health insurance, pension (employee contribution only at this time), paid vacation, life insurance, parental leave, sick leave, sabbatical after 5, 10, 15 years

Part-Time Employees: 2

Summer Employees: None

Volunteers: Varies

Interns: 1-3
Length: Approx. 3 months in length
Duties: Research, writing, phone calls to activists, attend meetings
Remuneration: $50.00 a week

Jobs advertised: Through *Washington Post*, *Community Jobs*, and other national and D.C. area publications; to our own grassroots network

To apply: Write to Executive Director, Monica Green, who will direct resume to person hiring for opening, if any.

PEACE BRIGADES INTERNATIONAL

347 Dolores Street, #228
San Francisco, CA 94110
(415) 773-9738

Other Offices: London, ENGLAND; Bergen, NETHERLANDS; San Francisco, CA; Toronto, CANADA; Philadelphia, PA; Bangkok, THAILAND; Trier, WEST GERMANY

Director: Tim Wallis, International Secretary

Purpose: PBI seeks to establish international and nonpartisan approaches to peacemaking and to the support of basic human rights. We challenge the belief that violent institutions and warfare inevitably must dominate human affairs. We seek to demonstrate that as international volunteers, citizens can act boldly as peacemakers when their governments cannot.

Methods of operation: Direct action (90%), public education (10%)

Constituency: Interested individuals worldwide

Recent issues and projects: PBI sends peace teams invited into areas of violent repression or conflict. Their work is to reduce the violence and support local social justice initiatives through (a) protective accompaniment of those whose lives are threatened; (b) fostering reconciliation and peace dialogue among conflicting parties; and (c) educating and training in nonviolence and human rights. PBI established international Peace Teams in Guatemala (1983) and El Salvador (1987) and Sri Lanka (1989).

Major publications: *North America* and *Columbia* (1994); *USA Report*, quarterly; *PBI Project Bulletin*, monthly

Budget: $300,000

Funding: Individual contributions, foundations. Budget figure includes all offices and countries.

Staff: 2
1 Major Donor Fundraiser
1 Grants Administrator
1/4 Data Manager

Work Week: 40 hours

Salary/year: $18,000

Benefits: Health insurance, paid vacation

Part-Time Employees: 3

Volunteers: Yes; worldwide

Interns: Yes
Length: Negotiable according to needs
Duties: As negotiated, depending on talents and interest
Remuneration: Usually unpaid; housing possible

Jobs advertised: Local newspapers

To apply: Contact Tim Wallis, International Secretary

PEACE DEVELOPMENT FUND

P.O. Box 1280, 44 N Prospect Street
Amherst, MA 01004
(413) 256-8306

Other Offices: Seattle, WA

Director: Ravi P. Khanna

Purpose: Through grants, training and technical assistance, the Peace Development Fund works in partnership with funders and community-based groups to achieve peaceful, just and interdependent relationships among people and nations.

Methods of operation: Grantmaking and training and technical assistance

Major publications: *Peace Developments* (PDF's newsletter), annual report and funding guidelines

Budget: $2,000,000

Funding: Individual contributions, foundations and fees

Staff: 13
1 Development Director
1 Development Administrator
1 Bookkeeper/Accountant
1 Administrative Assistant
1 Foundation Fundraiser
3 Program Directors
2 Program Administrators
1 Trainer
1 Assistant to Executive Director
1 Office Manager

Staff openings/year: 1-2

Work Week: 40 hours

Salary/year: $20,000 (Recent College Graduate); $Varies (Graduate with advanced degree)

Benefits: Health insurance, paid vacation, life insurance and family leave

Part-Time Employees: 2

Summer Employees: None

Volunteers: Yes

Interns: No, but willing to accept applications

Jobs advertised: Newspapers, outreach mailings, word of mouth

To apply: Contact the office

PEACE FOR GUATEMALA

3700 Chestnut Street
Philadelphia, PA 19104
(215) 386-9710

Director: Barbara Gottlieb

Purpose: Created in 1983 by 41 human rights and church organizations as a unified response to the unprecedented human suffering in Guatemala. PEACE delivers $100,000 annually for small, grassroots community development projects inside Guatemala. PEACE stands for the Program for Emergency Assistance, Cooperation and Education.

Methods of operation: Fundraising organization that uses various forms of education to raise awareness and funds for Guatemalan projects

Constituency: Human rights and Central American activists, and peace education/religious activists

Recent issues and projects: Categories include: (1) rural agriculture, production and training; (2) leadership development, emphasizing indigenous communities and women; (3) emergency and medium-term support for displaced victims of violence

Major publications: Annual report

Budget: $80,000

Funding: Foundations (26%), religious, Central American support organizations, miscellaneous (26%), individual contributions (24%), direct mail (24%)

Staff: 2
1 Executive Director
1 Program Director

Staff openings/year: 1

Work Week: 40 hours

Salary/year: $16,000 (Recent College Graduate); $22,000 (Graduate with advanced degree)

Benefits: Health insurance, life insurance, paid vacation

Volunteers: 5

Interns: Yes
Length: 1 semester; we are flexible
Duties: Outreach, fundraising, and office support
Remuneration: No stipend, unfortunately

Jobs advertised: Regionally in social change channels

To apply: Contact Barbara Gottlieb

PEACEMAKING ASSOCIATES AND MILWAUKEE PEACE EDUCATION RESOURCE CTR.

2437 N. Grant Blvd.
Milwaukee, WI 53210
(414) 445-9736

Director: Jacqueline Haessly

Purpose: The Center celebrates its 20th year providing education programs on peace, justice and global awareness to adults through education, reflection and non-violent social action.

Methods of operation: Research (25%), publications (25%), public education (25%), training and technical assistance (25%)

Constituency: We train educators, social service staff, members of religious congregations

Recent issues and projects: Recent projects include: peacemaking for families workshops; peace education training and consultation; State Coordinator - 1994 International Year of the Family.

Major publications: *Peacemaking: Family Activities for Justice and Peace*; *Learning to Live Together*; *What Shall We Teach Our Children*

Funding: Fees for services (90%), individual contributions (10%)

Staff: 2
1 Writer/Editor
1 Peace Education Consultant/Trainer

Staff openings/year: 1

Work Week: 40 hours

Salary/year: $Varies (Recent College Graduate); $Varies (Graduate with advanced degree)

Benefits: None at this time

Part-Time Employees: None

Summer Employees: None

Volunteers: Yes

Interns: Yes
Length: Anywhere from 3-24 months
Duties: Office management, training in peace education, maintenance of resource library, fundraisers, accounting
Remuneration: Free room and board on-site/full privileges

To apply: Please contact Jacqueline Haessly, Director

PEDIATRIC PROJECTS, INC.
P.O. Box 571555
Tarzana, CA 91357
(818) 705-3660

Director: Ms. Pat Azarnoff

Purpose: Develops medical toys and books for children and families to help them understand children's health care. Offers support by telephone and in groups for parents so they understand the health care system, how to talk with doctors and nurses, and how to psychologically support their children. Offers professionals seminars and publications to advocate for quality mental health programs for children, including therapeutic play programs, psychological preparation for hospitalization and parent support and education.

Methods of operation: Research, publications, human services, community organizing, direct action, public education, training and technical assistance, distribution of mental health material and medically-oriented toys and books

Constituency: Parents of disabled children and professionals in health care, education, special education, researchers and others

Recent issues and projects: Publish a newsletters, *Pediatric Mental Health*, monographs, children's stories and bibliographies. Have a free telephone support program for parents, free parent support groups. Develop medically-oriented playthings and stories so children can see what their treatment means. Frequent source for mass media, on television and radio call-in shows, in the press, to advocate for children and families.

Major publications: Newsletter: *Pediatric Mental Health*; *A Buyer's Guide to Medical Toys and Books*; monograph series: *Issues in Pediatric Mental Health*; professional articles

Funding: Individual contributions, foundations

Staff:
Staff number varies by projects, from 3-18.
Many volunteers, including:
Teachers/Educators
Writers/Editors
Attorneys
Office Managers
Researchers
Press Aides
Foundation Fundraisers
Administrative Assistants
Bookkeepers/Accountants
Caseworkers

Work Week: 40-60 hours

Part-Time Employees: 2

Summer Employees: Yes

Volunteers: 45

Interns: 4
Length: 15 weeks
Duties: Varies from project to project

Remarks: Many professionals volunteer with us and then go on to paid positions in other agencies, based in part on their work here.

PENNSYLVANIA CITIZEN ACTION
1207 Chestnut Street, Fourth Floor
Philadelphia, PA 19107
(215) 568-8145

Other Offices: Pittsburgh, PA; Erie, PA; Harrisburg, PA; Allentown, PA; Wilkes-Barre, PA

Director: Jeffrey Blum

Purpose: Statewide citizen activist organization involved in lobbying and electoral campaigns

Methods of operation: Community organizing (30%), lobbying (20%), public education (20%), publications (5%), research (5%), litigation (1-2%)

Constituency: Middle and working class

Recent issues and projects: Insurance reform; toxic chemical controls and reduction; mass transit improvement

Major publications: *Citizen Action News*, quarterly; *Briefing*, periodically

Budget: $2,500,000

Funding: Individual contributions, canvassing, telephone solicitation (80%), foundations (5%), other (15%)

Staff: 40
30 Canvassers
6 Office Managers
2 Organizers
1 Writer/Editor
1 Bookkeeper/Accountant

Work Week: 45 hours

Part-Time Employees: 25

Summer Employees: Yes

Volunteers: Yes, but rarely

Interns: Yes
Length: 2-3 months
Duties: Research is best
Remuneration: Generally unpaid

Jobs advertised: Newspaper; mailings; *Community Jobs*

To apply: Contact Jeff Blum, Executive Director

PENNSYLVANIA COALITION AGAINST RAPE

910 North Second Street
Harrisburg, PA 17102
(717) 232-6745

Director: Susan J. Cameron

Purpose: To administer state and federal monies to sexual assault programs; technical assistance, advocacy, public education, legislative issues, public information, clearinghouse of materials/information on sexual violence; trainings/conferences.

Methods of operation: Contract management (50%), public education (15%), training and technical assistance (15%), publications (10%), legislative information (10%)

Membership: 6 rape crisis centers serving 9 counties, private individual and association members

Recent issues and projects: Volunteer training upgraded statewide; major training materials/videos on substance abuse and sexual assault, campus assault; Serbia/Bosnia sexual assault work; victims rights; confidentiality, sexual violence and disabled population; sex offender programs and funding for programs

Major publications: Quarterly newsletter: *Spokeswoman*; clearinghouse of articles, books, pamphlets, audiovisual materials and resources; policy papers; manuals; information packets and videos

Budget: $4,501,000

Staff: 11
1 Issue Expert
1 Executive Director
1 Contract Monitor
1 Contract Manager
1 Secretary
2 Bookkeepers/Accountants
1 Financial Manager
1 Writer/Editor/Press Aide
1 Public Policy Analyst

Staff openings/year: 1

Work Week: 35 hours

Salary/year: $23,000 (Recent College Graduate); $Varies (Graduate with advanced degree)

Benefits: Health insurance, pregnancy leave, pension, paid vacation, paid sick leave, disability insurance

Summer Employees: 0

Volunteers: 0

Interns: Yes
Length: A semester or longer
Duties: Legislation; public relations; fundraising; office managerial duties; computer programming

Jobs advertised: Newspaper; job service employment offices

To apply: Contact Susan J. Cameron, Executive Director

PENNSYLVANIA ENVIRONMENTAL COUNCIL

1211 Chestnut Street, Suite 900
Philadelphia, PA 19130
(215) 563-0275

President: Joanne R. Denworth

Purpose: The Council advocates for environmental legislation and regulation and educates citizens of PA about the importance of these measures. The council works to bring together representatives from community organizations, nonprofits, government, academia and business industry to work toward consensus on environmental issues affecting PA and its communities.

Methods of operation: Research, lobbying, publications, community organizing, direct action, public education, and training and technical assistance

Membership: Professionals in environmental fields, those in corporations and business sectors, and concerned individuals

Recent issues and projects: In 1993 the Council took an active role in the Clean Air Act and ISTEA implementation, continued to press for improved land use and growth management legislation and policies, worked for open space protection, negotiated rulemaking, reuse of old industrial sites and other initiatives

Major publications: *Guiding Growth: Building Better Communities*, 3rd edition; *Planning for the Promise of PA* video; *EAC Handbook*; *Forum Newsletter*; *Legislative Update*

Budget: $900,000

Funding: Individual contributions, foundations, corporate and governmental agencies

Staff: 12
1 President/Attorney
2 Office Directors
1 Director of Policy
2 Program Directors
2 Program Support
1 Director of Research and Education
1 Attorney Staff
1 Administrative Assistant
1 Research Associate

Staff openings/year: 1

Work Week: 35-40 hours

Salary/year: $20,000 (Recent College Graduate); $24,000 (Graduate with advanced degree)

Benefits: Health insurance, paid vacation

Part-Time Employees: 5

Summer Employees: No

Volunteers: Yes

Interns: Yes
Length: 4-6 months
Duties: Research, writing, office work
Remuneration: Depends on situation

Jobs advertised: Circulated among related organizations and interested individuals

To apply: Contact Joanne R. Denworth, President

PENNSYLVANIA PUBLIC INTEREST RESEARCH GROUP

1109 Walnut Street, 3rd Floor
Philadelphia, PA 19107
(215) 829-1926

Other Offices: Pittsburgh, PA

Director: Sheila Ballen

Purpose: PennPIRG is a statewide non-partisan, nonprofit, environmental and consumer advocacy organization. PennPIRG, a watchdog for government and corporate actions, conducts independent research, exposes problems through the media, sues polluters, lobbies decisionmakers and organizes citizen campaigns to win reforms.

Methods of operation: Citizen outreach (25%), public education (25%), lobbying, research (20%), litigation (10%), publications (10%), community organizing (10%)

Membership: 30,000 grassroots members from a wide variety of social, economic and racial backgrounds

Recent issues and projects: PennPIRG was instrumental in getting the Motor Voter Bill passed and signed into law. Additionally, PennPIRG is working for strong campaign finance reform legislation, a national bottle bill and the reauthorization of the federal Clean Water Act

Major publications: Quarterly membership newsletter; *Citizen Advocate*

Funding: Canvassing (50%), telephone solicitation (25%), individual contributions (20%), direct mail (5%)

Staff: 9
6 Grassroots Fundraisers
1 Organizer
1 Executive Director
1 Fuel Co-op Director
Phone and Field Canvassers

Work Week: 60 hours

Salary/year: $14,500 - 18,000 (Recent College Graduate); $Varies (Graduate with advanced degree)

Benefits: Health insurance, paid vacation, loan assistance

Part-Time Employees: Yes

Summer Employees: Yes

Volunteers: Yes

Interns: Yes
Length: Semester
Duties: Media coordination, organizing, coalition building
Remuneration: None

Jobs advertised: In major newspapers in the Philadelphia area; recruitment is done at colleges and universities through career placement offices around the country

To apply: Contact Sheila Ballen, Executive Director

PENSION RIGHTS CENTER

918 16th Street, NW, Suite 704
Washington, DC 20006
(202) 296-3776

Director: Karen W. Ferguson

Purpose: The Pension Rights Center is a nonprofit public interest group organized in 1976 to educate the public about pension issues, protect and promote the pension interests of workers and retirees, and develop solutions to the nation's pension problems. The Center's goal is a retirement income system that is fair, adequate and responsive to the needs of individuals and the economy.

Methods of operation: Public education (50%), training and technical assistance (20%), publications (15%), research (5%), lobbying (5%), litigation (5%)

Constituency: Workers, retirees, friends, professional colleagues

Recent issues and projects: The Women's Pension Project activities currently include the Women's Pension Advocacy Council, the Clearinghouse on Pensions and Divorce and the Women's Pension Policy Consortium. The National Pension Assistance Project is committed to increasing the availability of legal assistance to individuals with pension problems. It conducts seminars, publishes a newsletter and fact sheets and operates an information and referral service.

Major publications: *Where To Look For Help With A Pension Problem*; *Protecting Your Pension Money*; *The Pension Plan Almost Nobody Knows About*; *Can You Count On Getting A Pension*; *Your Pension Rights At Divorce: What Women Need To Know*; *NPAP Network Newsletter*

Budget: $350,000

Funding: Foundations (45%), contracts (40%), publications, interest, seminars, etc. (8%), individual contributions (7%)

Staff: 7
4 Attorneys
1 Publications Manager
1 Receptionist
1 Administrator

Staff openings/year: 1

Work Week: 40 hours

Salary/year: $22,000 (Recent College Graduate); $26,000 (Graduate with advanced degree)

Benefits: Health insurance, pension, child care, paid vacation

Part-Time Employees: 2

Summer Employees: Yes

Volunteers: 1

Interns: 2
Length: 3 months-1 year
Duties: Special projects
Remuneration: Cooperation with university program, small stipend, etc.

Jobs advertised: Law schools, law journals, newspapers ads, notices to public interest groups

To apply: Contact Ellen C. Matthews, Administrator

PEOPLE FOR PROGRESS, INC.

301 W. Arkansas Street
Sweetwater, TX 79556
(915) 235-8455

Director: Executive Director

Purpose: To research, develop and operate community service programs that resolve poverty conditions and enable low-income people to become self-sufficient.

Methods of operation: Human services (50%), research (15%), community organizing (10%), direct action (10%), public education (5%), training and technical assistance (5%)

Constituency: Clients, contributors and partners

Recent issues and projects: PPI recently developed its affordable housing program, its Child Care Management Service, Headstart and Adult Day Care Program. Current issues of interest are thee growing need for parenting programs, affordable housing, supportive housing and health care issues.

Major publications: *Community Voice*, newsletter; *CCMS News*; *The Rural Entrepreneur Newsletter*; *PPI's Best of Texas Brochure*

Budget: $5,000,000

Funding: State and federal grants (85%), foundations (10%), individual contributions (5%)

Staff: 85
3 Organizers
4 Writers/Editors
1 Attorneys
1 Paralegals
7 Teachers/Trainers
3 Researchers
1 Lobbyist
1 Press Aide
3 Canvassers 1 Campaign Manager
7 Foundation/Grassroots Fundraisers
1 Issue Expert 2 Planners
12 Administrative Assistants/Office Mgrs.
3 Bookkeepers/Accountants
4 Caseworkers
5 Food Service Workers
3 Nurses/Health Care

Staff openings/year: 7-10

Work Week: 40 hours

Salary/year: $18,500 (Recent College Graduate); $21,500 (Graduate with advanced degree)

Benefits: Health insurance, paid vacation

Part-Time Employees: Yes

Summer Employees: None

Volunteers: 5

Interns: 2

Jobs advertised: Through newsletters, bulletin board and local news

To apply: Jackie Hughes and Olga Balderas

Remarks: PFP was established in 1967 by Ms. Gladys Gerst, Executive Director who has faithfully managed the agency for 27 years.

PEOPLE FOR THE AMERICAN WAY

2000 M Street, NW, Suite 400
Washington, DC 20036
(202) 467-4999

Other Offices: Los Angeles, CA; New York, NY

President: Arthur J. Kropp

Purpose: PFAW is a 280,000 member, nonpartisan constitutional liberties organization. Through education, advocacy and litigation, People For promotes and protects individual liberties including First Amendment rights and the right to privacy. People For is active on behalf of civil rights and encourages greater citizen participation in our democracy.

Methods of operation: Research, lobbying, litigation, publications, community organizing, public education

Membership: Well-educated, older, affluent, urban, progressive

Recent issues and projects: People For is active on the following legislative issues: voter registration reform, civil rights restoration, hate crimes statistics, national service, among others. PFAW is also engaged in monitoring national and state activities of religious right, in support of reproductive freedom and in monitoring federal judicial nominations.

Major publications: Quarterly membership newsletter; quarterly activities alert; annual censorship report; various issue papers and backgrounders; textbook review series; annual report

Budget: $7,600,000

Funding: Individual contributions, foundations, direct mail, telephone solicitation

Staff: 49
6 Researchers
6 Foundation Fundraisers
6 Issue Experts
6 Typists
6 Bookkeepers/Accountants
5 Attorneys
4 Organizers
3 Lobbyists
3 Press Aides
3 Writers/Editors
2 Receptionists
1 Office Manager
1 Personnel Director
1 Mail Clerk
1 Supply Manager

Staff openings/year: 3

Work Week: 45 hours

Salary/year: $18,000 (Recent College Graduate); $18-20,000 (Graduate with advanced degree)

Benefits: Health insurance, life insurance, pension, pregnancy leave, paid vacation, dental insurance, Dependent Care Assistance Program

Part-Time Employees: 3

Summer Employees: 10-15

Volunteers: 20-25

Interns: 10-15
Length: 3 months
Duties: Research, writing, monitoring legislative programs, small amount of support work
Remuneration: Hourly rate of $5.50-$8.00 per hour, depending on education level

Jobs advertised: Newspapers; job boards; mailings to other organizations; mailings to campuses; word of mouth

To apply: Contact Judy Green, Director of Personnel

PEOPLE FOR THE ETHICAL TREATMENT OF ANIMALS (PETA)

P.O. Box 42516
Washington, DC 20015
(301) 770-7444

Other Offices: San Francisco, CA

Director: Ms. Jeanne Roush

Purpose: To advocate for the rights of nonhuman animals through education and direct action; to promote a cruelty-free, vegan lifestyle; to end human exploitation of other species.

Methods of operation: Direct action (30%), public education (30%), research (25%), publications (15%)

Membership: Over 400,000 individual members from all walks of life

Recent issues and projects: Persuaded major cosmetics and toy companies to stop testing products on animals. Encouraging people to stop wearing fur, to stop purchasing products containing animals ingredients and to stop supporting organizations that experiment on animals.

Major publications: Newsletter: *PETA News*; leaflets; fact sheets

Budget: $10,000,000

Funding: Individual contributions (61%), direct mail (27%), merchandise, sales (11%), foundations (1%)

Staff: 75
10 Writers/Editors
9 Issue Experts
7 Administrative Assistants
6 Investigators
6 Organizers
5 Typists
4 Researchers
4 Bookkeepers/Accountants
4 Caseworkers
5 Campaign Managers
4 Membership Staff
3 Foundation Fundraisers
4 Press Aides
3 Librarians
1 Office Manager

Staff openings/year: 15

Work Week: 40 hours

Salary/year: $17,500 (Recent College Graduate); $20-25,000 (Graduate with advanced degree)

Benefits: Health insurance, life insurance, pregnancy leave, paid vacation, lunch 3 times/week, dental insurance, sick leave

Part-Time Employees: 2

Summer Employees: 15

Volunteers: 25

Interns: 10
Length: 2-4 weeks
Duties: Vary depending on skills and interests of interns
Remuneration: Small stipend available

Jobs advertised: In the *Washington Post.* Also in-house on bulletin board. Occasionally in *Non-Profit Times.*

To apply: Contact Mike Rodman, Director of Personnel

PEOPLE OF COLOR AGAINST AIDS NETWORK

1200 S Jackson, Suite 25
Seattle, WA 98144
(206) 322-7061

Other Offices: Seattle, WA; Bremerton, WA; Spokane, WA; Yakima, WA

Director: Lupe Lopez

Purpose: The People of Color Against AIDS Network was founded in 1987 for the express purpose of responding to an epidemic that was having, and continues to have a devastating impact on communities of color in the United States and throughout the world. Our mission is a simple one, to create a comprehensive, multicultural AIDS prevention model that is effective and responsive to communities of color.

Methods of operation: Public education (60%), publications (10%), human services (10%), community organizing (10%), training and technical assistance (10%)

Constituency: Communities of color in Washington State

Recent issues and projects: Our recent projects include: community organizing, a focus on institutional and attitudinal change through education and persuasion; community based education and outreach, a focus on reaching high risk individuals in community settings; peer education, a focus on enlisting members of the target populations to act as educators and to provide support for behavioral change amongst their peers; community based services liaison, a focus on creating linkages between at-risk individuals and community services and providing advocacy within systems to ensure access

Major publications: *Girlfriends Talking*, numerous brochures

Budget: $1,500,000

Funding: Government grants (70%), foundations (20%), individual contributions (10%)

Staff: 32
4 Organizers
2 Office Managers
1 Foundation Fundraiser
4 Issue Experts
1 Typist
1 Bookkeeper/Accountant
8 Caseworkers

Staff openings/year: 4

Work Week: 40 hours

Salary/year: $23,000 (Recent College Graduate); $Varies (Graduate with advanced degree)

Benefits: Health insurance, paid vacation, life insurance

Part-Time Employees: 10

Summer Employees: 10

Volunteers: 100

Interns: 2
Length: 1 year
Duties: Assisting program coordinators
Remuneration: Usually through a college or high school program

Jobs advertised: Available through local press, minority press, gay/bi publications and circulated among other AIDS organizations.

To apply: Contact Carol Hasegawa, South Office Manager

PEOPLE WITH AIDS COALITION - HOUSTON

1475 West Gray, sutie 163
Houston, TX 77019
(713) 522-5428

Director: Lynn Pannill

Purpose: The People With AIDS Coalition is a unique organization of by and for people with AIDS that promotes independence and self reliance so that people with HIV/AIDS may live with dignity, self-esteem and acceptance.

Methods of operation: Human Service (100%)

Constituency: People living with AIDS

Recent issues and projects: Recent projects include: operating a housing restart program for indigent people with AIDS; give furniture and household items to people in need; operate the volunteer program at the main county clinic for indigents with AIDS

Major publications: *Among Friends*, newsletter 6 times a year

Budget: $205,000

Funding: Federal/State grants (45%), foundations (30%), individual contributions (20%), direct mail (5%)

Staff: 6
2 Administrative Assistants
1 Caseworker
2 Volunteer Coordinators
1 Executive Director

Staff openings/year: 3

Work Week: 40 hours

Salary/year: $20,000 (Recent College Graduate); $28,000 (Graduate with advanced degree)

Benefits: Health insurance, paid vacation, family leave

Part-Time Employees: 1

Volunteers: 200

Interns: No, but willing to accept applications

Jobs advertised: Newspapers, community bulletin boards

To apply: Contact Lynn Pannill, Executive Director

PEOPLE'S COMMUNITY HEALTH CENTER

3028 Greenmount Avenue
Baltimore, MD 21218
(301) 467-6040

Director: Pat Cassatt

Purpose: To provide quality health care to everyone regardless of ability to pay for that care. The ultimate goal is to allow everyone to have access to quality health care. We also work to influence state and local government regarding issues that affect our clients.

Methods of operation: Human services (100%), which encompasses community organizing, direct action, public education and training

Constituency: Basically low-income patients from the area surrounding the health center. A majority of our patients are on Medicaid or have no health insurance.

Recent issues and projects: These always include the plight of the medically uninsured and underinsured citizens. One major project that we are currently working on is furthering the "Single Payer" style of reform.

Budget: $400,000

Funding: Service revenue (80%), individual contributions (17%)

Staff: 26
7 Physicians/Physicians' Assistants
5 Medical Clerks
4 Patient Advocates
4 Financial/Computer Staff
3 Office Managers
2 Public Relations/Outreach
1 Director

Staff openings/year: 2-3

Work Week: 46 hours

Salary/year: $Varies (Recent College Graduate); $Varies (Graduate with advanced degree)

Benefits: Health insurance, paid vacation

Part-Time Employees: 16

Volunteers: 12

Interns: None currently, but willing to accept applications

Jobs advertised: Newspaper; word of mouth; staff bulletin board

To apply: Contact Pat Cassatt, Executive Director; Anita Banks, HMO Program Manager; or Bernadette Williams, Clinical Administrator

Remarks: People's is a grassroots organization started in 1970 by a group of political activists who believed that health care is a right, not a privilege. The clinic was staffed solely by volunteers and medical care was free. Today we still depend on volunteers, and modest fees are charged based upon a person's ability to pay.

PEOPLE'S MEDICAL SOCIETY

462 Walnut Street
Allentown, PA 18102
(215) 770-1670

President: Charles B. Inlander

Purpose: Bring concept of "consumerism" to the medical care delivery system. Teach consumers what they need to know when dealing with medical providers. Teach consumer advocacy and empower consumers.

Methods of operation: Publications (40%), research (30%), public education (20%), direct action (5%), community organizing (5%)

Constituency: Medical consumers aged 35+; Medicare beneficiaries; women of childbearing age

Recent issues and projects: Medical malpractice/tort reform; access to medical records; public disclosure of hospital outcome data; consumer involvement on medical licensing boards

Major publications: *PMS Newsletter*; *Take This Book to The Hospital With You*; *How to Evaluate and Select a Nursing Home*; *Medicare Made Easy*; *How to Choose A: Doctor, Dentist, Nutritionist* series; *Medicine on Trial*; *Options in Health Care*

Staff: 10
2 Writers/Editors
2 Issue Experts
2 Bookkeepers/Accountants
1 Office Manager

1 Membership Services/Fulfillment
1 Typist
1 Sales Manager

Work Week: 40+ hours

Benefits: Health insurance, life insurance, pension, paid vacation

Part-Time Employees: 2

Jobs advertised: Local and regional newspapers

To apply: Contact Charles B. Inlander, President

PESTICIDE ACTION NETWORK NORTH AMERICA REGIONAL CENTER (PAN)

116 New Montgomery, #810
San Francisco, CA 94105
(415) 541-9140

Other Offices: Quito, ECUADOR; Dakar, SENEGAL; Nairobi, KENYA; Amsterdam, NETHERLANDS; Penang, MALAYSIA

Director: Monica Moore, Program Director

Purpose: PAN is a nonprofit, tax exempt organization dedicated to eliminating the damage caused by pesticides to people and the environment around the world. PAN advocates adoption of sustainable non-chemical pest control methods in place of pesticides. Our primary approach to achieving these goals is to link the collective strengths and expertise of the North American pesticide reform movement, and individuals within it, with counterpart citizen movements in other countries. PAN is one of six regional coordinating points around the world that link and support activities of the Network.

Methods of operation: Public education (20%), publications (20%), training and technical assistance (15%), direct action (15%), research (10%), community organizing (10%), lobbying (5%)

Constituency: Organizations and individuals either directly working with, affected by or concerned about pesticides, in a global context.

Recent issues and projects: PAN serves as the coordinator for PAN International's Dirty Dozen Campaign, a long-term international public education vehicle targeting selected "Dirty Dozen" pesticides. Elimination of each of the "Dirty Dozen" will represent both significant reductions in hazard and a powerful demonstration of the power of collective citizen actions, carried out by people around the world. PAN is also deeply involved in efforts to stop the production and export of banned, unregistered and severely restricted pesticides from the U.S. (and other countries).

Major publications: Quarterly *Global Pesticide Campaigner*, contact us for a current publications list.

Budget: $300,000

Funding: Foundations (75%), individual contributions (15%), publications sales, affiliation fees, honoraria, fee for service (10%)

Staff: 5
2 Issue Experts
1 Fundraiser
1 Campaign Manager
1 Writer/Editor
1 Office Manager (half-time)
1 Bookkeeper/Accountant (half-time)

Staff openings/year: 1-2

Work Week: 40-45 hours

Salary/year: $20,000 (Recent College Graduate); $22,000 (Graduate with advanced degree)

Benefits: Health insurance, pregnancy leave, paid vacation

Part-Time Employees: 2

Volunteers: 1-4

Interns: 1-2
Length: Semester
Duties: Varies depending on what program they are hooked up with
Remuneration: Volunteer; we pay transportation stipend to and from office

Jobs advertised: Opportunity NOCs and other nonprofit job listings; sometimes through California/Bay Area press; our own job announcements mailing list, which has several hundred entries and includes many national organizations, regional and local groups

To apply: Contact Brenda Willoughby

PHILADELPHIA AREA PROJECT ON OCCUPATIONAL SAFETY AND HEALTH

3001 Walnut Street, 5th Floor
Philadelphia, PA 19104
(215) 386-7000

Director: Jim Moran

Purpose: Worker education and training; coalition building; political action on the issue of job safety and health.

Methods of operation: Training and technical assistance (35%), phone work, planning, labor organizing, meetings (31%), public education (6%), research (5%), lobbying (5%), publications (5%), human services (5%), community organizing (5%), direct action (2%), litigation (1%)

Constituency: Mostly unions, many workers, health and legal professionals

Recent issues and projects: Workers Memorial Day event; Workers Compensation Workshop; AIDS in the Workplace Project; Education and Counseling Project for Asbestos Victims; work on the issue of criminal prosecution for bosses who kill workers on the job.

Major publications: Newsletter: *Safer Times*; *Injured on the Job*; *Getting Job Hazards Out of the Bedroom* (a reproductive hazards book); factsheets; etc.

Budget: $200,000

Funding: Individual contributions (33%), foundations (18%), telephone solicitation (8%), direct mail (5%), other (36%)

Staff: 5

Work Week: 48 hours

Salary/year: $18,000 (Recent College Graduate); $30,000 (Graduate with advanced degree)

Benefits: Health insurance, life insurance, pregnancy leave, paid vacation, 15 sick days

Part-Time Employees: 2

Volunteers: 50

Interns: 2
Length: 1 year
Duties: Assist staff with projects
Remuneration: Usually credit, occasionally stipends

Jobs advertised: Area press, organizations and contacts

To apply: Contact Jim Moran, Director

Remarks: Philaposh is 18 years old, and is sponsored (financially supported) by 200 unions in the Tri-state Delaware Valley Area.

PHILADELPHIA LESBIAN AND GAY TASK FORCE

1616 Walnut Street, Suite 1005
Philadelphia, PA 19103
(215) 772-2000

Director: Rita Addessa

Purpose: To advance the civil, human and constitutional rights of lesbian women and gay men. Since 1978, the Task Force has led the struggle for the right to live and to love free from oppression and from bigotry.

Methods of operation: Public policy advocacy (20%), research (20%), community organizing (20%), public education (20%), litigation (10%), publications (5%), direct action (5%)

Recent issues and projects: Recent projects include: passage of the Philadelphia Fair Practices Act; the issuance of a Commonwealth Executive Order in 1988 to ban discrimination in state employment; conducted and published a study called Study of Discrimination and Violence Against Lesbian and Gay People in the City of Philadelphia; established the Anti-violence and Discrimination Hotline; organized the Liberty Bell protest to challenge the U.S. Supreme Court's infamous Hardwick v. Bowers decision; organized the Lesbian and Gay Bill of Rights which was presented to members of the U.S. Congress

Major publications: Send for publication lists

Budget: $200,000

Funding: Foundations (50%), individual contributions (50%)

Staff: 2
1 Organizer
1 Office Manager

Staff openings/year: 1-2

Work Week: 40-60 hours

Salary/year: $22,000 (Recent College Graduate); $25,000 (Graduate with advanced degree)

Benefits: Health insurance, paid vacation

Part-Time Employees: 1

Volunteers: 10

Interns: Yes
Length: 3 months
Duties: Varies
Remuneration: Varies

To apply: Contact Rita Addessa

PHILADELPHIA UNEMPLOYMENT PROJECT

116 South 7th Street, Suite 610
Philadelphia, PA 19106
(215) 592-0933

Director: John Dodds

Purpose: Organize low-income and working people around issues of economic justice

Methods of operation: Human services (25%), community organizing (25%), direct action (20%), public education (10%), research (10%), lobbying (5%), publications (5%)

Constituency: Low-income, multiracial

Recent issues and projects: Campaign which resulted in increase of the state minimum wage. Campaign to guarantee access to hospital care for the uninsured. Campaign to raise wages in the fast food industry. Campaign to extend unemployment compensation and prevent mortgage foreclosure. Campaign to protect city health centers.

Major publications: *PUP Newsletter*; *Wage Abuse in the Fast Food Industry*; *Survival Guide for the Unemployed*

Budget: $240,000

Funding: Foundations

Staff: 6
2 1/2 Organizers
1 1/2 Caseworkers
1 Office Manager
1 Jobs Developer

Staff openings/year: 1

Work Week: 45 hours

Salary/year: $18,000 (Recent College Graduate); $22,000 (Graduate with advanced degree)

Benefits: Health insurance, pension, paid vacation

Volunteers: 40

Jobs advertised: Newspapers; mail to organizations and universities in the city; sometimes in *Community Jobs*

To apply: Contact John Dodds, Director

PHYSICIANS FOR A NATIONAL HEALTH PROGRAM

332 S. Michigan, Suite 500
Chicago, IL 60604
(312) 554-0382

Director: Mary Ruth Herbers

Purpose: Physicians for a National Health Program works to educate the public on the need for universal health care through a publicly financed single-payer system.

Methods of operation: Public education (80%), lobbying (10%), research (10%)

Constituency: Physicians and other persons interested in single-payer health care reform

Recent issues and projects: Recent projects include: developed legislation at state and federal levels; and educate public, professionals and public officials on health care reform issues

Major publications: Quarterly newsletter; articles in medical journals

Budget: $350,000

Funding: Individual contributions (90%), foundations (10%)

Staff: 4
1 Organizer
1 Writer/Editor
1 Office Manager
1 Issue Expert

Staff openings/year: 1

Work Week: 40 hours

Salary/year: $22,000 (Recent College Graduate); $26,000 (Graduate with advanced degree)

Benefits: Health insurance, paid vacation

Part-Time Employees: None

Summer Employees: None

Volunteers: 1-2

Interns: 1-2
Length: 1 year

Jobs advertised: Local publications

To apply: Contact Mary Ruth Herbers, Executive Director

PHYSICIANS FOR HUMAN RIGHTS

100 Boylston Street, Suite 702
Boston, MA 02144
(617) 695-0041

Director: Eric Stover

Purpose: PHR is a national organization of health professionals whose goal is to bring the skills of the medical profession to the protection of international human rights. PHR works to prevent the participation of doctors in torture, to defend imprisoned health professionals, to stop physical and psychological abuse of citizens by governments and to provide medical and humanitarian aid to victims of repression.

Methods of operation: Research (25%), direct action (25%), publications (20%), public education (20%), training and technical assistance (10%)

Constituency: Physicians; other health professionals; general public

Recent issues and projects: War crimes in the former Yugoslavia; medical and social consequences of land mines; torture in Kashmir and Punjab; effect on health care delivery to Palestinians during the Intifadeh.

Major publications: Quarterly newsletter; monthly actions alerts (letterwriting campaigns); Asylum manual; country reports on medical missions (Haiti, Israel, Kashmir, Northern Somalia, Somalia, Liberia, Syracuse, New York)

Budget: $1,400,000

Funding: Foundations (50%), individual contributions (50%)

Staff: 8
1 Senior Program Associate
1 Receptionist
1 Development Director
1 Executive Director
1 Deputy Director
1 Office Manager
1 Program Assistant
1 Membership and Education Coordinator

Staff openings/year: 2-3

Work Week: 40 hours

Salary/year: $22,000 (Recent College Graduate); $Varies (Graduate with advanced degree)

Benefits: Health insurance, pregnancy leave, paid vacation, and pension

Part-Time Employees: 2

Summer Employees: 0

Volunteers: 4-5

Interns: 5
Length: Varies
Duties: Varies with interests and background
Remuneration: Outside funding

Jobs advertised: Varies by job

To apply: Contact Claire Frances, Office Manager

PHYSICIANS FOR SOCIAL RESPONSIBILITY

1101 14th Street NW, Suite 700
Washington, DC 20005
(202) 898-0150

Director: Julia A. Moore

Purpose: Founded in 1961, Physicians for Social Responsibility is a leading national organization of over 20,000 health professionals and supporters working in 100 chapters to promote arms control and international cooperation, to protect the environment, and to reduce societal violence and its causes. The PSR is the U.S. affiliate of the International Physicians for the Prevention of Nuclear War, recipient of the 1985 Nobel Peace Prize.

Methods of operation: Research, lobbying, publications, community organizing, direct action, and public education.

Membership: Medical doctors, holders of other doctoral degrees, and health professionals

Recent issues and projects: Project for treatment and prevention of lead poisoning in children of Katowice, Poland; lobbying of DOE to clean up various toxic waste sites; Great Lakes pollution seminars; initiated Project Manhattan II, an international program designed to support major reductions in nuclear weapons;played role in closing of Rocky Flats (CO) uranium enriching production site

Major publications: *PSR Reports*; *PSR Monitor*; *Dead Reckoning*; *Medicine and Global Survival*

Budget: $2,000,000

Funding: Individual contributions (42%), membership dues (29%), foundations (22%), other (7%)

Staff: 18

2 Organizers
2 Writers/Editors
1 Office Manager
2 Lobbyists
1 Foundation Fundraiser
6 Issue Experts
2 Grassroots Fundraisers
2 Administrators

Staff openings/year: 3 to 4

Work Week: 35 hours

Salary/year: $25,000 to 30,000

Benefits: Health insurance, paid vacation, life insurance

Part-Time Employees: 2

Summer Employees: 0

Volunteers: 0

Interns: 2 to 3
Length: 3 to 6 months
Duties: Varies

Jobs advertised: Newspapers, community announcements

To apply: Contact Robert Musil, Director of Policy and Programs

---

PIKE PLACE MARKET FOUNDATION

85 Pike Street, #500
Seattle, WA 98101
(206) 682-7453

Director: Marlys Erickson

Purpose: To preserve the spirit and diversity of the Pike Place Market Community by raising funds to purchase services for downtown Seattle's senior and low-income residents. Support for Pike Market clinic, senior center, child care center, food bank and housing.

Methods of operation: Fundraising (80%), community organizing (10%), public education (10%)

Membership: 5,000 donor/members making $45 average gifts as well as business and foundation support.

Recent issues and projects: We have raised $2.1 million in grants for the first 10 years of operation. Recently added $3 million campaign to "Care for the Market" and expand human services and housing plus repair markets historic buildings.

Major publications: Newsletter and book, *Sustaining a Vital Downtown Community*, funded by FOA Foundation

Budget: $500,000

Funding: Individual contributions (85%), foundations (15%)

Staff: 4
3 Foundation Fundraisers
1 Campaign Manager

Staff openings/year: 0-1

Work Week: 40-45 hours

Salary/year: $20-22,000 (Graduate with advanced degree)

Benefits: Health insurance, pension, paid vacation, life insurance, pregnancy leave

Part-Time Employees: Yes

Volunteers: Yes

Interns: None at this time, willing to accept applications.

Jobs advertised: Local newspaper and word of mouth

To apply: Please contact Marlys Erickson, Director

PLANNED PARENTHOOD FEDERATION OF AMERICA, INC.

810 Seventh Avenue
New York, NY 10019
(212) 541-7800

Director: Larry F. Beers, Acting Director

Purpose: As the nation's oldest and largest family planning agency, PPFA is dedicated to the principle that every individual has the right to make independent decisions about having children, about becoming a parent by choice, not chance.

Methods of operation: Human services (50%), lobbying (10%), litigation (10%), public education (10%), community organizing (10%), research (5%), training and technical assistance (5%)

Recent issues and projects: "Webster" Decision and other Supreme Court actions; state organization; continued advocacy for reproductive health services and education

Major publications: Annual report and service reports

Budget: $40,000,000

Funding: Government grants (35%), clinic income (34%), individual contributions, foundations, direct mail, canvassing (31%)

Staff: 235
Including:
35 Typists
10 Bookkeeper/Accountants
10 Office Managers
8 Campaign Managers
5 Attorneys
4 Writers/Editors
4 Lobbyists
4 Organizers
3 Foundation Fundraisers
3 Press Aides
3 Researchers
1 Paralegal

Staff openings/year: 15

Work Week: 35 hours

Salary/year: $22,000 (Recent College Graduate); $Varies (Graduate with advanced degree)

Benefits: Health insurance, life insurance, pension, paid vacation, tuition reimbursement

Part-Time Employees: 2

Interns: 1 legal intern
Length: 1 term
Duties: Legal research
Remuneration: $12/hour

Jobs advertised: Job bulletins and support staff listings

To apply: Contact Judy L. Williams, Personnel Recruiter

PLANNING AND CONSERVATION LEAGUE AND FOUNDATION

926 J Street, Suite 612
Sacramento, CA 95814
(916) 444-8726

Director: Gerald H. Meral

Purpose: To protect and restore the natural resources of California through the political process. We lobby in the State legislature; we run initiative campaigns.

Methods of operation: Lobbying (65%), research (15%), publications (10%), public education (10%)

Constituency: Average donation of about $100; highly educated; committed to participating in the political process to achieve results

Recent issues and projects: (1) Proposition 70: organized the effort for the California Wildlife, Coastal and Parkland Conservation Bond Act Initiative. Prop 70 was the largest state park and wildlife bond act in history ($776,000,000); (2) Proposition 99: to qualify and pass an initiative to raise the tax on tobacco. Prop 99 allocates $30 million a year for parks and wildlife throughout California; (3) Wildlife Protection Act: would prohibit the sport hunting of mountain lions; (4) Rail Transportation Bond Act: (5) Alcohol Taxation Initiative: $16 million/year for programs to reduce the impact of alcohol use in local parks; (6) 21st Century Study: a fund of about $400,000,000 a year for wildlife habitat, coast and parkland

Major publications: Bimonthly newsletter: *California Today*; *How to Design, Implement and Run a Campaign for a Land Conservation Initiative*; *Citizen's Guide to the California Environmental Quality Act*; *Governor's Environmental Report Card*; *Questions to Ask About Water Projects*; *State of the California Environment*; *The State of the State's Rivers and Bays*

Budget: $400,000

Funding: Individual contributions (60%), foundations (20%), direct mail (20%)

Staff: 8
4 Lobbyists
1 Bookkeeper/Accountant
1 Office Manager
1 Campaign Manager

Staff openings/year: 1

Work Week: 40-60 hours

Salary/year: $20,000 (Recent College Graduate); $30,000 (Graduate with advanced degree)

Benefits: Health insurance, pension, paid vacation

Part-Time Employees: 1

Summer Employees: 2-3

Volunteers: 5-10

Interns: 6
Length: 1 school year or 1 semester
Duties: Research, organizing, staff support
Remuneration: Paid if money available for a specific campaign

Jobs advertised: Through the grapevine; law schools in Sacramento and Davis

To apply: Contact Rachel Mirenberg

POPULATION ACTION INTERNATIONAL

1120 19th Street, NW, Suite 550
Washington, DC 20036-3605
(202) 659-1833

President: J. Joseph Spiedel, M.D., M.P.H.

Purpose: Population Action International is a private nonprofit research and advocacy organization which, through public education, works for universal access to good quality voluntary family planning and health services, empowerment of individuals, especially women, to make their own reproductive choices, and early stabilization of world population size. Population Action International's goal is a better quality of life for present and future generations. (Established as the Population Crisis Committee in 1965, the organization changed its name in 1993.)

Methods of operation: Research (25%), publications (25%), human services (25%), public education (25%)

Recent issues and projects: A major study of the progress made toward achieving population stabilization is forthcoming.

Major publications: Periodic briefing papers and accompanying wall charts

Budget: $3,000,000

Funding: Foundations (65%), individual contributions (25%), corporate (10%)

Staff: 29
7 Researchers
6 Typists
5 Issue Experts
3 Bookkeepers/Accountants
2 Press Aides
2 Lobbyists
1 Writer/Editor
1 Office Manager
1 Foundation Fundraiser

Staff openings/year: 2

Work Week: 40 hours

Salary/year: $18,000 (Recent College Graduate); $28,000 (Graduate with advanced degree)

Benefits: Health insurance, family leave, life insurance, pension, paid vacation

Part-Time Employees: 2

Volunteers: 6

Interns: None currently

Jobs advertised: Notices to colleagues; for support staff, newspaper ads and employment agency listings

To apply: Contact Sherry Pursch, Administrator

POPULATION INSTITUTE

107 Second Street, NE
Washington, DC 20002
(202) 544-3300

Other Offices: Colombo, SRI LANKA; Brussels, BELGIUM; Bogota, COLOMBIA

President: Werner Fornos

Purpose: To increase public awareness of the world's constantly increasing population and to foster leadership for solutions to the overpopulation problem. This is a prerequisite for bringing population into balance with the earth's resources, and thus protecting the life-sustaining ability of a finite planet and enhancing the quality of life.

Recent issues and projects: Community Leaders Division; Public Policy Division; Public Information Division; International Programs. Future Leaders of America program recruits university students and recent graduates to work for intensive 6-month stints learning about population issues and helping with Institute outreach. Third Annual World Population Awareness Week, the Institute sponsored events in all 50 states to build support for world population stabilization. The Institute's International Advisory Council develops workable policy recommendations for developing world governments and foreign aid strategies for the U.S. and other industrialized donor nations.

Major publications: Bi-monthly newspaper: *Popline*; *Toward the 21st Century* series of papers on the issues and challenges that will shape the next century, including urbanization and international security implications of population growth; *World Population News Service* provides important news stories to the nation's print media

Budget: $1,350,000

Funding: Corporation, institution, foundation grants and contributions; individual contributions; interest and dividend income; other

Staff: 10
4 Organizers
2 Office Managers
1 Writer/Editor

1 Researcher
1 Press Aide
1 Grassroots Fundraiser

Work Week: 40 hours

Salary/year: $18,000 (Recent College Graduate); $20,000 (Graduate with advanced degree)

Benefits: Health insurance, life insurance

Volunteers: 1

Interns: 6
Length: 6 months
Duties: Future Leaders: 5 will implement advance planning for World Population events, i.e. identify and contact influential community leaders
Remuneration: $200 per week and insurance; academic credit can be arranged

---

POWDER RIVER BASIN RESOURCE COUNCIL

P.O. Box 1178
Douglas, WY 82633
(307) 358-5002

Other Offices: Sheridan, WY

Director: Vickie Goodwin, Acting Co-Director

Purpose: An agriculture/conservation organization working for responsible development of Wyoming's natural resources and the maintenance of a viable agricultural base in the state. PRBRC is a grassroots organization dedicated to the goal of letting the people have a say in major development issues that have a direct bearing on their lives.

Methods of operation: Community organizing (50%), public education (15%), lobbying (10%), direct action (10%), publications (5%), research (5%), training and technical assistance (5%)

Constituency: Ranchers; farmers; citizens from all walks of life

Recent issues and projects: Water development and water conservation projects; mining and energy development-related issues; waste management problems; family farm preservation; and other conservation works at the grassroots level

Major publications: *The Powder River Breaks*

Budget: $187,000

Funding: Foundations (65%), individual contributions (30%), direct mail (3%), fundraising events (2%)

Staff: 7
4 Organizers
1 Staff Director
1 Office Manager
1 Administrative Assistant

Work Week: 20-40 hours

Salary/year: $14,000 (Recent College Graduate); $Varies (Graduate with advanced degree)

Benefits: Health insurance, paid vacation, IRA after two years

Part-Time Employees: 1

Volunteers: Yes

Interns: Yes
Length: 3 months
Duties: Varied
Remuneration: Room and board

Jobs advertised: Local and national publications

To apply: Contact Vickie Goodwin, Acting Co-Director

PRAIRIEFIRE RURAL ACTION, INC.

550 11th Street
Des Moines, IO 50309
(515) 244-5671

Director: Kathleen Duffy

Purpose: PrairieFire is an independent, nonprofit, 501(c)(3) rural organizing, education and training organization based in Des Moines, Iowa. PrairieFire's mission is to revitalize family farm agriculture and rural communities and cultivate a new generation of rural leaders.

Methods of operation: Research, lobbying, publications, human services, community organizing, direct action, public education, training and technical assistance

Constituency: Farm and rural people

Recent issues and projects: The organization's projects include: Corporate Agriculture Organizing and Training Initiative which looks at the environmental impacts of corp. livestock production, immigrant workers rights and agribusiness research; Rural Recovery Program working with farmers and rural citizens recovering from the effects of floods/weather and long-term economic displacement of farmers and Renewing Rural IA, a faith-based community organizing project.

Major publications: *Prairie Journal*; *The*

Agribusiness Examiner; *Corporate Hog Update*; *Hog Tied*

Budget: $350,000

Funding: Individual contributions, foundations

Staff: 6
1 3/4 Organizers
1 Writer/Editor
1/2 Office Manager
1 Researcher
1/4 Lobbyist
1 Foundation Fundraiser
1/2 Bookkeeper/Accountant

Work Week: 50 hours

Benefits: Health insurance

Part-Time Employees: 3

Summer Employees: Depends on funding

Volunteers: 1

Interns: Sometimes
Length: Summer or 9 months
Duties: Varies
Remuneration: Usually no financial arrangements are made

Jobs advertised: Through like-minded organizations, newspapers or Community Jobs

To apply: Please contact Kathleen Duffy

PRIMARY SOURCE

P.O. Box 381711
Cambridge, MA 02238
(617) 661-8832

Director: Anna Roelofs

Purpose: Primary Source is a nonprofit center for multicultural and global education which offers professional development and curriculum resources to teachers and school communities.

Methods of operation: Training and technical assistance (75%), research (25%)

Constituency: Teachers, administrators, educators

Recent issues and projects: Provides consultations to school districts throughout New England promoting education in the humanities that is historically accurate, culturally inclusive and explicitly concerned with ethical issues such as racism and discrimination.

Major publications: *Re:Source*, newsletter

Budget: $100,000

Funding: Contracts (70%), foundations (20%), individual contributions (10%)

Staff: 3
1 Office Manager
1/2 Administrative Assistant
1 Executive Director
1 Program Director

Staff openings/year: 1

Work Week: 60 hours

Salary/year: $20,000

Benefits: Paid vacation

Part-Time Employees: 1

Volunteers: 6-8

Interns: 3-5
Length: 1 year
Duties: Varies according to needs

Jobs advertised: Local newspapers, *Community Jobs*

To apply: Contact Lee Mason

PRO BONO ADVOCATES

165 North Canal Street, Suite 1020
Chicago, IL 60606
(312) 906-8010

Director: Barbara K. Finesmith

Purpose: We recruit and train volunteer attorneys to donate their services to the indigent of Cook County. Our practice focus is Family Law, specifically domestic violence.

Methods of operation: Direct legal services (80%), training and technical assistance (5%), advocacy (15%)

Constituency: Our volunteers come to us from every type of law practice: large firms, solo practitioners. We serve Cook County residents who earn up to 125% of the federal poverty guidelines.

Budget: $280,000

Funding: Foundations (31%), state agencies (21%), legal associations (32%), direct mail (15%)

Staff: 5
2 Attorneys (1 part-time)
2 Paralegal
1 Executive Secretary

Work Week: 40 hours

Salary/year: $Varies (Recent College Graduate); $Varies (Graduate with advanced degree)

Benefits: Health insurance, life insurance, paid vacation, pregnancy leave

Part-Time Employees: 1

Volunteers: 310

Interns: 10
Remuneration: We accept independently funded interns on their terms.

Jobs advertised: Local media and cooperating social service agencies

To apply: Contact Barbara K. Finesmith, Executive Director

PRO BONO PROJECT OF SANTA CLARA COUNTY

480 North First Street, P.O. Box 103
San Jose, CA 95103-0103
(408) 998-5298

Director: John D. Hodges

Purpose: The Pro Bono Project of Santa Clara County provides free high quality legal services to low-income residents of Santa Clara County through volunteers.

Methods of operation: Litigation (100%)

Constituency: Low-income people

Recent issues and projects: Recent projects include: homeless advocacy project; family law project; bankruptcy project; workers comp project

Budget: $250,000

Funding: Individual contributions, foundations

Staff: 2
1 Attorney
1 Administrative Assistant

Work Week: 35 hours

Salary/year: $19,000 (Recent College Graduate); $30,000 (Graduate with advanced degree)

Benefits: Health insurance, pension, paid vacation, life insurance, disability, family leave

Part-Time Employees: 2

Summer Employees: 1

Volunteers: 350

Interns: 1
Length: 6-12 weeks
Duties: Paralegal work
Remuneration: Volunteer or work study

Jobs advertised: Local newspapers and national for law students and attorneys

To apply: Contact John D. Hedges

Remarks: We always need good volunteers who want to make a difference.

PROFESSIONALS' COALITION FOR NUCLEAR ARMS CONTROL

1616 P Street, NW, Suite 320
Washington, DC 20817
(202) 332-4823

Director: Dr. Robert K. Musil

Purpose: A nationwide citizen's lobby composed of doctors, scientists and other professionals committed to reducing nuclear arms and excessive military spending.

Methods of operation: Lobbying (90%), public education (5%), training and technical assistance (5%)

Membership: 11,000 individual activist donors drawn from larger 501(c)(3) groups (Physicians for Social Responsibility, Union of Concerned Scientists, etc) and some citizen activists from the Freeze Voter network

Recent issues and projects: Campaigns to cut defense budget and to stop Star Wars, the B-2 Bomber, the MX Missile and other systems.

Major publications: Newsletter: *The Professional*

Budget: $300,000

Funding: Individual contributions (63%), foundations (30%), coalition groups (7%)

Staff: 5
1 Executive Director
1 President/Lobbyist
1 Field Director
1 Field Organizer
1 Staff Assistant

Staff openings/year: 0-1

Work Week: 40 hours

Salary/year: $21,000

Benefits: Health insurance, paid vacation, pregnancy leave

Interns: 1
Length: 1 semester
Duties: Research, writing, lobbying, clerical
Remuneration: $200/month and travel expenses

To apply: Contact Dr. Robert K. Musil, Executive Director

PROGRESSIVE
409 East Main Street
Madison, WI 53703
(608) 257-4626

Director: Matthew Rothschild, Publisher

Purpose: To bring about a more peaceful and just society; to promote pacifism, nonintervention, ecological sanctity; to fight against war, nuclear weapons, nuclear energy, corporate crime, oppressive attitudes such as racism, sexism, anti-Semitism, homophobia; and to promote citizen control.

Methods of operation: Public education through publications, research, and training and technical assistance

Recent issues and projects: (1) Publishing *The Progressive*; (2) syndicating "Second Opinion," a radio show by *The Progressive*'s editor, Erwin Knoll, to radio stations around the country; (3) writing op-eds and helping social justice organizations and activists to write and place their own op-eds in major newspapers

Major publications: *The Progressive*

Budget: $1,000,000

Funding: Direct mail, circulation (50%), individual contributions (25%), foundations (5%), list rental (5%), advertising (5%), other (10%)

Staff: 10
2 Assistant Art Directors (part-time)
1 Editor
1 Managing Editor
1 Editorial Intern
1 Circulation Director
1 Assistant Circulation Director
1 Typist
1 Art Director
1 Bookkeeper/Accountant
1 Grassroots Fundraiser
1 Foundation Fundraiser

Staff openings/year: 1

Work Week: 37.5 hours

Salary/year: $18,000

Benefits: Health insurance, pregnancy leave, pension, paid vacation

Part-Time Employees: 3

Interns: 1
Length: 3-6 months
Duties: Editorial: participate in editorial decision-making; edit copy; write editorials
Remuneration: No payment, except for published material

Jobs advertised: Internships not advertised. Job openings, depending on need, are either advertised nationally, locally, or not at all.

To apply: Contact Matthew Rothschild, Publisher or Erwin Knoll, Editor

PROGRESSO LATINO, INC.
626 Broad Street
Central Falls, RI 02863
(401) 728-5920

Director: Patricia Martinez

Purpose: Progreso latino is a non-profit, bilingual, bicultural agency committed to making social services accessible to the Rhode Island Hispanic community. Our goal is to help Hispanics achieve greater self-sufficiency and self-determination.

Methods of operation: Human services (50%), community organizing (20%), direct action (10%), public education (10%), training and technical assistance (10%)

Recent issues and projects: Recent projects include: Latino workers organizing project, a major issue is discrimination and unfair labor practices against Latino workers; and civil rights complaints

Major publications: Newsletter for Latino parents and a newsletter for ESL teachers and students

Budget: $600,000

Funding: United Way, state and federal contracts (70%), foundations (20%), individual contributions (10%)

Staff: 20
2 Organizers
2 Office Managers
1 Administrative Assistant
1 Bookkeeper/Accountant
8 Caseworkers
6 Day Care Teachers

Staff openings/year: 1-2

Work Week: 40 hours

Salary/year: $18,000 (Recent College Graduate); $22,000 (Graduate with advanced degree)

Benefits: Health insurance, paid vacation, family leave, tuition reimbursement

Part-Time Employees: 15

Summer Employees: 2-4

Volunteers: 10

Interns: 2
Length: 3-6 months
Duties: Case workers, social workers
Remuneration: Work study arrangements are possible

Jobs advertised: Internal and local newspapers

To apply: Contact Patricia Martinez, Executive Director

PROJECT NISHMA

1225 15th Street, NW
Washington, DC 20005
(202) 462-4268

Director: Thomas R. Smerling

Purpose: Project Nishma is an educational project on Israeli security in the context of the peace process. Nishma: 1) arranges briefings for Jewish leaders by senior Israeli defense analysts; 2) analyzes American Jewish opinion and articulates a security focused, pragmatic position on the peace process.

Methods of operation: Public education (40%), research (20%), publications (20%), community organizing (20%)

Constituency: Over 100 nationally recognized Jewish leaders across the U.S. as well as other supporters of peace process

Recent issues and projects: Joint Arab and Jewish-American briefings by Israeli cabinet ministers; workshops on pro-peace Israel advocacy; leadership education on support for Middle East peace process; press notification of pro-peace trends in Jewish-American attitudes.

Major publications: Monthly mailings

Budget: $310,000

Funding: Foundations (80%), individual contributions (20%)

Staff: 5
1 Office Manager
1 Press Aide
1 Issue Expert
1 Grassroots Fundraiser
1 Policy Consultant

Staff openings/year: 0-1

Work Week: 40 hours

Salary/year: $18-20,000 (Recent College Graduate); $Varies (Graduate with advanced degree)

Benefits: Health insurance, paid vacation

Part-Time Employees: None

Summer Employees: None

Volunteers: None

Interns: 1-2
Length: 3 months
Duties: Research, administrative tasks
Remuneration: $300 per month for 3 month internship

Jobs advertised: *Community Jobs, ACCESS*

To apply: Contact Jennifer Gruen, Program Coordinator

PROJECT NOW COMMUNITY ACTION AGENCY

418 19th Street, P.O. Box 3970
Rock Island, IL 61201
(309) 793-6391

Other Offices: Moline, IL; Kewanee, IL; Aledo, IL; East Moline, IL

Director: Vincent G. Thomas

Purpose: To develop, mobilize, and utilize to the maximum extent possible all available human and material resources, on the local, state and national levels, for the purpose of eliminating poverty and combating existing poverty.

Methods of operation: Human services (70%), training and technical assistance (15%), public education (10%), community organizing (5%)

Constituency: Head Start parents, senior citizens, disabled citizens, low-income, minorities

Recent issues and projects: Housing for homeless: lack of affordable and decent housing. Entrepreneurship for low-income: inability to secure small loans from local banks. Rehabilitating vacant housing: lack of funding from local cities.

Major publications: Quarterly newsletter: *Dateline NOW*

Budget: $4,800,000

Funding: Government (75%), foundations (15%), individual contributions (5%), fundraising (5%)

Staff: 150
Including:
15 Caseworkers
8 Coordinators/Program Directors
3 Bookkeeper/Accountants
1 Writer/Editor
Administrative Assistants

Staff openings/year: 3

Work Week: 40 hours

Salary/year: $13,000 (Recent College Graduate); $20,000 (Graduate with advanced degree)

Benefits: Health insurance, life insurance, pregnancy leave, paid vacation, tuition reimbursement

Part-Time Employees: 55

Summer Employees: 15

Volunteers: 100

Interns: 10
Length: 3 months
Duties: Assisting with special projects, housing, community organizing
Remuneration: Stipend may be available (depending on funding); mileage

Jobs advertised: Newspapers; agency post boards; minority organizations

To apply: Contact Vincent G. Thomas, Executive Director

PROJECT ON GOVERNMENT PROCUREMENT

613 Pennsylvania Avenue, SE, Second Floor
Washington, DC 20003
(202) 543-0883

Director: Liz Galtney

Purpose: Nonprofit, nonpartisan organization working to expose waste, fraud and mismanagement in government spending.

Methods of operation: Investigations (60%), public education (30%), publications (10%)

Constituency: General public

Recent issues and projects: Investigate whistleblower cases, and those that have merit we help to publicize; concentrate on government accountability projects in defense and other areas of government.

Major publications: *Courage Without Martyrdom: A Survival Guide for Whistleblowers* (1989); *Defense Procurement Papers* (1988); *The Pentagon Underground* (1985); *More Bucks Less Bang: How the Pentagon Buys Ineffective Weapons* (1983)

Budget: $230,000

Funding: Foundations (95%), individual contributions (3%), publications (2%)

Staff: 3
2 1/2 Investigators
1 Administrator

Work Week: 50 hours

Salary/year: $18,000 (Recent College Graduate); $20,000 (Graduate with advanced degree)

Benefits: Staff is made up of self-employed consultants

Part-Time Employees: 2

Interns: 1
Length: 3 months
Duties: Investigations, research, some clerical
Remuneration: Arranged on a case-by-case basis

Jobs advertised: Local job announcement notebook

To apply: Contact Keith Rutter, Project Administrator

PROJECT SHARE

311 South Juniper Street, Room 902
Philadelphia, PA 19107
(215) 735-6367

Other Offices: Darby, PA; Bridgeport, PA

Director: Paolo del Vecchio

Purpose: A self-help and advocacy organization run by and for people who have/had mental health problems (mental health consumers); organizing around housing, employment, and other needs and against the stigma of mental illness and its accompanying discrimination.

Methods of operation: Training and technical assistance (20%), community organizing (20%), human services (20%), publications (10%), lobbying (10%), direct action (10%), public education (10%)

Constituency: Mental health consumers

Recent issues and projects: Organizing national conference for mental health consumers in July, 1990; providing outreach, advocacy and housing for homeless consumers; developing alternatives to traditional mental health services (i.e. drop-in centers)

Major publications: Newsletter: *Brainstorm*

Budget: $1,000,000

Funding: Government grants (80%), foundations (15%), individual contributions (5%)

Staff: 40
10 Caseworkers
10 Organizers
8 Issue Experts
5 Typists
3 Office Managers
2 Writer/Editors
1 Press Aide
1 Foundation Fundraiser

Staff openings/year: 10

Work Week: 40 hours

Salary/year: $16,000 (Recent College Graduate); $18,000 (Graduate with advanced degree)

Benefits: Health insurance, pregnancy leave, paid vacation

Part-Time Employees: 10

Volunteers: 30

Interns: None currently, but willing to accept applications

Jobs advertised: Newspaper; mailings; flyers; word of mouth

To apply: Contact Paolo del Vecchio

PROJECT VOTE!
1511 K Street, NW, Suite 326
Washington, DC 20005
(202) 638-9016

Director: Sanford Newman

Purpose: We seek to empower low-income and minority individuals by involving them in the democratic process. Nonpartisan issue education and voter registration are the two main methods the nonprofit Project VOTE! uses to bring about greater civic participation.

Methods of operation: Community organizing (35%), direct action (25%), research (10%), public education (7%), training and technical assistance (7%), lobbying (5%), litigation (5%), human services (5%), publications (1%)

Constituency: Low-income and minority citizens

Recent issues and projects: In 1992, Project VOTE! registered 560,000 new low-income and minority voters, bringing its total to two million new voters registered in its history. In 1993, it successfully lobbied, along with other groups, to preserve the Motor Voter Act, when it was threatened with weakening amendments. Project VOTE! Philadelphia, a local coalition of Project VOTE! since 1991, is assisting the state of Pennsylvania in registering voters in welfare and unemployment offices and conducts an innovative, hands-on civic education program in inner city Philadelphia public schools.

Budget: $2,000,000

Funding: Individual contributions (34%), labor unions (21%), foundations (19%), other nonprofits (15%), corporate (9%) and religious (2%)

Staff: 1
1 Executive Director
(up to 14 staff in a Presidential election year)

Staff openings/year: 0-1

Work Week: 40-50 hours

Salary/year: $18,000 (Recent College Graduate); $19,000 (Graduate with advanced degree)

Benefits: Paid vacation, holidays and sick leave, access to health insurance group rates (health insurance not paid)

Part-Time Employees: 2

Volunteers: Yes

Interns: 1-6, depending on election cycle and staffing
Length: Flexible
Duties: Field, fundraising or accounting
Remuneration: $125/wk for full time

Jobs advertised: *Washington Post*; college career offices; *Roll Call*; announcement sent to other nonprofit organizations

To apply: Call or write to the Washington office

Remarks: The Project VOTE! staff is a committed, intelligent and positively-oriented group. The hours can be demanding, but the teamwork involved in the process and the goals of the organization make for a worthwhile career experience.

PUBLIC ADVOCATES, INC.

1535 Mission Street
San Francisco, CA 94103
(415) 431-7430

Director: Judy Tam, Administrative Director

Purpose: To represent low-income persons in class action impact litigation as well as advocacy and policy efforts in the areas of health, education, homelessness and corporate responsibility.

Methods of operation: Advocacy (25%), research (25%), litigation (25%), policy (10%), community organizing (5%), publications (5%), training and technical assistance (5%)

Recent issues and projects: Homeless project; bilingual education; health access for California; corporate responsiveness to low-income persons and minorities

Major publications: Newsletter; infant mortality and infant formula administrative petitions

Budget: $1,000,000

Funding: Attorneys' fees (29%), legal services (25%), interest (25%), foundations (20%), individual contributions (1%)

Staff: 13
6 Attorneys
2 Secretaries
2 Project Coordinators
1 Controller
1 Receptionist
1 Office Manager

Work Week: 37.5 hours

Salary/year: $Varies (Recent College Graduate); $34,000/law (Graduate with advanced degree)

Benefits: Health insurance, life insurance, pregnancy leave, pension, paid vacation

Part-Time Employees: 4

Summer Employees: 12

Volunteers: 3

Interns: 1
Length: Semester or quarter
Duties: Research and writing; casework
Remuneration: Work-study; clinical credit

Jobs advertised: Placement offices of law schools

To apply: Contact Judy Tam, Administrative Director

PUBLIC CITIZEN BUYERS UP

P.O. Box 18795
Washington, DC 20036
(202) 659-2500

Other Offices: Baltimore, MD; Philadelphia, PA

Director: Paul O'Connel, Regional Director

Purpose: Buyers Up is one of five divisions of Public Citizen, a national consumer advocacy organization. Founded in 1983 by Ralph Nader and Public Citizen, Buyers Up is a group-purchasing program which negotiates discount prices on home heating oil for its members.

Methods of operation: Research, publications, community organizing, direct action, public education, training and technical assistance

Membership: Over 9,000 users of home heating oil residing in Maryland, Virginia, and the District of Columbia

Recent issues and projects: Advocating for government oversight of the radon industry; Cooperative Agreement with Maryland Energy Assistance Program to serve the needs of low-income households which use oil to heat their homes; Cooperative Agreement with Community Energy Consumers of Philadelphia to assist their members in obtaining home heating oil at the discounted price offered through Buyers Up.

Major publications: *Buyers Up News* (quarterly)

Budget: $521,000

Funding: Membership and commissions

Staff: 4
1 Regional Director
1 National Director
2 Member Services Assistants

Staff openings/year: 4

Work Week: 40-60 hours

Salary/year: $14,500

Benefits: Health insurance, pension, credit union, paid vacation, dependent care assistance plan, parental leave, sick leave, 10 paid holidays

Part-Time Employees: None

Summer Employees: None

Volunteers: 20

Interns: None at this time

Jobs advertised: Posted internally for one week; advertised in local papers; disseminated to colleges and universities and a variety of organizations

To apply: Contact Paul O'Connell

PUBLIC CITIZEN LITIGATION GROUP

2000 P Street, NW, Suite 700
Washington, DC 20036
(202) 833-3000

Director: David C. Vladelr

Purpose: PCLG is principally engaged in the federal courts involving a wide variety of public interest issues. It also engages in writing and research, provides testimony and expertise to Congress and does some lobbying.

Methods of operation: Litigation (90%), public education (5%), lobbying (5%)

Membership: Those concerned about government and corporate accountability and health and safety issues

Recent issues and projects: Current legal activities include separation of powers, health and safety, First Amendment and government and corporate accountability.

Budget: $700,000

Staff: 12
10 Attorneys
1 Typist
1 Office Manager

Staff openings/year: 1-2

Work Week: 50 hours

Salary/year: $Varies (Recent College Graduate); $26,000 (Graduate with advanced degree)

Benefits: Health insurance, paid vacation, credit union

Part-Time Employees: 2

Summer Employees: Yes

Volunteers: Yes

Interns: Yes
Length: 3 months
Duties: Legal research and writing
Remuneration: Some stipends are available

Jobs advertised: Legal periodicals

To apply: Contact Brian Wolfman, Staff Attorney

PUBLIC CITIZEN'S CRITICAL MASS ENERGY PROJECT

215 Pennsylvania Ave. SE
Washington, DC 20003
(202) 546-4996

Director: Bill Magavern

Purpose: We advocate building a sustainable energy future by decreasing reliance on nuclear and fossil fuels and increasing the efficiency of energy use and the development of cleaner, safer renewable technologies like solar and wind power

Constituency: Citizens, safe-energy activitists

Recent issues and projects: Released internal nuclear industry critiques of reactor safety; campaigned to terminate the Dept. of Energy's liquid metal reactor; advocated 60% increase in fuel efficiency standard for new cars and light trucks

Major publications: *Nuclear Lemons*; *Twenty Years After the Embargo*; *Hear No Evil, See No Evil, Speak No Evil: What the NRC Won't Tell You About America's Nuclear Reactors*

Budget: $200,000

Funding: Individual contributions (67%), foundations (33%)

Staff: 5
1 Researcher
1 Lobbyist
3 Issue Experts

Staff openings/year: 1

Work Week: 50 hours

Salary/year: $17,000 (Recent College Graduate); $24,000 (Graduate with advanced degree)

Benefits: Health insurance, pension, child care, paid vacation, family leave

Part-Time Employees: None

Summer Employees: None

Volunteers: 2

Interns: 2

Length: 10-15 weeks
Duties: Research; organizing; administrative
Remuneration: Reimbursement for travel and other expenses

Jobs advertised: Public interest listings

To apply: Contact Bill Magavern, Director

PUBLIC CITIZEN'S HEALTH RESEARCH GROUP

2000 P Street, NW, Suite 700
Washington, DC 20036
(202) 833-3000

Director: Dr. Sidney M. Wolfe

Purpose: To fight for the public's health by monitoring the work of the medical establishment, the drug industry and the health related regulatory agencies. Writes and distributes publications that help give consumers more control over their own health decisions.

Methods of operation: Research, lobbying, publications, direct action, public education

Constituency: Individual contributors to public citizen and concerned consumers nationwide

Recent issues and projects: Published report on mentally ill individuals held in jails; published a best-selling update to publication on dangers of prescription drugs; published book on over 1,000 doctors sanctioned by state medical boards; petitioned FDA to ban Halcion.

Major publications: Monthly newsletter

Budget: $600,000

Funding: Individual contributions, publications

Staff: 8
1 Office Managers
6 Researchers
1 Director

Staff openings/year: 2

Work Week: 55 hours

Salary/year: $15,000 (Recent College Graduate); $22,000 (Graduate with advanced degree)

Benefits: Health insurance, pension (after 2 years), paid vacation, pregnancy leave

Part-Time Employees: Yes

Summer Employees: Yes

Volunteers: Yes

Jobs advertised: Paper; medical journals

To apply: Please contact Phyllis McCarthy

PUBLIC COUNSEL

3535 West Sixth Street, Suite 100
Los Angeles, CA 90020
(213) 385-2977

Director: Steven A. Nissen

Purpose: Public Counsel is a public interest law office which works with private bar and legal services organizations to provide free representation to poverty and public interest clients.

Methods of operation: Litigation (35%), nonlitigation representation of community-based organizations and affordable housing groups (15%), training and technical assistance (15%), research (10%), community organizing (10%), public education (5%), publications (5%), human services (3%), lobbying (2%)

Constituency: General community and legal community

Recent issues and projects: Consumer fraud, housing discrimination, children's rights, child care, immigration (political asylum and amnesty), affordable housing, homelessness, disaster relief

Major publications: Newsletters; annual reports; pamphlets available for all projects

Budget: $1,950,000

Funding: Individual contributions (40%), local and state bar associations (35%), foundations (20%), direct mail (5%)

Staff: 26
9 Attorneys
7 Paralegals
2 Typists
2 Administrative Assistants
1 Foundation Fundraiser
1 Grassroots Fundraiser
1 Bookkeeper/Accountant
1 Office Manager
2 Social Workers

Staff openings/year: 1-2

Work Week: 40 hours

Salary/year: $21,000 (Recent College Graduate); $25,000 (Graduate with advanced degree)

Benefits: Health insurance, life insurance, pension, paid vacation, pregnancy leave

Part-Time Employees: 3

Summer Employees: 6-8

Volunteers: Many

Interns: 2
Length: Flexible
Duties: Client interviews, research, administrative assistance
Remuneration: Flexible; work study preferred

To apply: Contact Steven A. Nissen, Executive Director, or Carol Leemon, Administrator

PUBLIC INTEREST CLEARINGHOUSE

200 McAllister Street
San Francisco, CA 94102-4978
(415) 255-1714

Director: Nancy Strohl

Purpose: The Public Interest Clearinghouse provides a central source of information and support to the public interest community. Its services, publications and resources are used by legal services programs, public interest law firms, pro bono attorneys, community activists, law students and others engaged in representing the underrepresented in our legal system.

Methods of operation: Training and technical assistance (80%), publications (10%), research (5%), public education (5%)

Constituency: Consumers, workers, citizens, students

Recent issues and projects: Established a telecommunications network, "LegalAid/Net," which allows participating legal services programs to be linked electronically 24-hours-a-day. Cosponsored a Public Interest Job Fair. Published a compliance manual of government regulations relevant to legal services programs. Conducts research on alternative methods of funding legal services.

Major publications: *Public Interest Employment Report*; *Directory of Public Interest Law Firms in Northern California*; *Guide to 600 Bay Area Public Interest Organizations*; *Client Education Video Directory*; *Legal Services Bulletin*, a bi-monthly newsletter; bi-monthly *Computer Newsletter*; *The Advocate*, a monthly newsletter posting jobs and internships open to law students

Budget: $300,000

Funding: State Bar of California Legal Services Trust Fund (50%), Federal Legal Services Corporation (17%), foundations (13%), individual contributions (10%), contracts and fees for services (10%)

Staff: 8
1 Organizer
1 Writer/Editor
1 Administrator
1 Office Manager
3 Attorneys
1 Director

Staff openings/year: 0-1

Work Week: 35 hours

Salary/year: $18,500 (Recent College Graduate); $25,000 (Graduate with advanced degree)

Benefits: Health insurance, pregnancy leave, paid vacation

Part-Time Employees: 1

Summer Employees: 1

Volunteers: 2

Interns: 2
Length: Varies
Duties: Research, writing, editing, etc.

Jobs advertised: Universities and job listings

To apply: Contact Nancy Strohl

PUBLIC INTEREST LAW CENTER OF PHILADELPHIA (PILCOP)

125 South 9th Street, Suite 700
Philadelphia, PA 19107
(215) 627-7100

Director: Michael Churchill

Purpose: Social change through legal services on behalf of minorities, disabled, poor and community groups. Legal services include negotiation, training and cooperation with other social services as well as litigation.

Methods of operation: Litigation (70%), training and technical assistance (10%), research (10%), public education (10%)

Constituency: Community groups and national organizations

Recent issues and projects: Development of community services and closing institutions for mentally disabled; employment discrimination suits against major employers; fostering community monitoring and control over environmental polluters

Major publications: Newsletter twice a year; *Report on Housing in Philadelphia* (1988)

Budget: $850,000

Funding: Attorneys fees (50%), legal community (20%), foundations (15%), individual contributions (15%)

Staff: 15
7 Attorneys
5 Administrative Assistants
1 Receptionist
1 Foundation Fundraiser
1 Bookkeeper/Accountant

Staff openings/year: 1

Work Week: 40-50 hours

Salary/year: $16,000 (Recent College Graduate); $19,000 (Graduate with advanced degree)

Benefits: Health insurance, life insurance, pregnancy leave, paid vacation

Part-Time Employees: 1-2

Summer Employees: 5

Volunteers: 2-3

Interns: Yes; on an ad hoc basis

Jobs advertised: Depends on job. Local newspapers; national recruiting services for legal services attorneys; Pennsylvania Higher Education Authority

To apply: Contact Michael Churchill, Chief Counsel

PUBLIC INTEREST RESEARCH GROUP FUEL BUYERS

1109 Walnut Street, 3rd Floor
Philadelphia, PA 19107
(215) 829-0808

Director: Sheila Ballen

Purpose: PIRG Fuel Buyers is the largest home heating oil buying group in the Delaware Valley. Our more than 2,000 members give us the negotiating power to negotiate for lower prices on home heating oil. Our average price for oil is 8-14 cents lower than the average retail price. Consumers can save up to $200 on their oil bills each year

Methods of operation: Public education (50%), community organizing (25%), consumer service (25%)

Membership: Home heating oil consumers

Budget: $60,000

Funding: Individual contributions (100%)

Staff: 2
1 Director of Operations
1 Organizer

Staff openings/year: 1

Work Week: 60 hours

Salary/year: $14,500 (Recent College Graduate); $Varies (Graduate with advanced degree)

Benefits: Health insurance, paid vacation, student loan payback

Part-Time Employees: 1

Volunteers: Yes

Interns: Yes
Length: 1 semester
Duties: Marketing and press relations
Remuneration: Course credit

Jobs advertised: Newspaper, word-of-mouth

To apply: Contact Shela Ballen

PUBLIC INTEREST RESEARCH GROUP IN MICHIGAN (PIRGIM)

338 1/2 South State Street
Ann Arbor, MI 48104
(313) 662-6597

Other Offices: Royal Oak, MI; Kalamazoo, MI

Director: Tom Geiger

Purpose: PIRGIM conducts independent research on environmental and consumer problems, develops innovative solutions, educates the public, lobbies for legislation to benefit the general public and files lawsuits against violators of environmental laws.

Methods of operation: Research (25%), public education (25%), lobbying (15%), litigation (12%), community organizing (12%), publications (11%)

Constituency: Residents of Michigan

Recent issues and projects: Clean Water Act Campaign: campaigned in all but one MI congressional district building support for pollution prevention and strict enforcement of renewed Clean Water Act; State Toxics Use Reduction/Worker

Right to Act Campaign: Campaign to require TUR planning and increase worker's rights to take action to reduce workplace exposure; State Toxics in Art Supply legislation: bills would mandate they only use non-toxic art supplies in the day-care and K-12 schools in the state; National Reduce Reuse Recycle Campaign: campaign to pass recycled content legislation, ban the construction of new incinerators and pass a national Bottle Bill; Campaign for a Clean Congress, pass national campaign finance reform including strong public financing

Major publications: Newsletter: *Citizen Connection*; *Cost Characterizations of Michigan Bell*; *A Will But Not A Way*, comparative study of Michigan's toxic waste cleanup laws; *Toxic Waste and Cancer Mortality in Michigan: An Exploratory Analysis*; *Out of Control: Air Pollution Controls and Toxic Air Emissions in Michigan*; *One Year Later ... The Crisis Continues*, anniversary assessment of the Environmental Cleanup Bond

Funding: Canvassing (50%), telephone solicitation (50%)

Staff: 30
Including:
6 Canvassers
5 Telephone Outreach Fundraisers
5 Grassroots Fundraisers
1 Lobbyist
1 Researcher
1/2 Attorney
1/2 Organizer

Staff openings/year: 6

Work Week: 45 hours

Salary/year: $11,500 (Recent College Graduate); $16,000 (Graduate with advanced degree)

Benefits: Health insurance, life insurance, paid vacation, student loan repayment program

Part-Time Employees: 11

Summer Employees: 80

Volunteers: 120

Interns: 3
Length: 15 weeks
Duties: Research, organizing, political activity, canvassing
Remuneration: Unpaid

Jobs advertised: Career placement offices; newspapers; posters

To apply: Contact Mary Faber, Project Director

PUBLIC MEDIA CENTER

466 Green Street, Suite 300
San Francisco, CA 94133
(415) 434-1403

Director: Herbert Chao Gunther

Purpose: Public Media Center is a nonprofit public interest ad agency and public relations group that specializes in developing media campaigns on social issues. PMC produces TV and radio spots, print ads, marketing and media strategies, direct mail and provides technical assistance to other nonprofit groups.

Methods of operation: Research, publications, public education, training and technical assistance, media production and strategy, press, publicity

Recent issues and projects: PMC has produced media campaigns on saving the rainforests, saving dolphins, oil spills, reproductive rights, hunger, crime, toxic waste, Central America, apartheid and the environment.

Major publications: *Talking Back: A Guide to the Fairness Doctrine*; *Strategies for Access*; *Stand Up: A Guide to Worker's Rights*; *Asbestos Alert*; *Index of Progressive Funders*

Budget: $800,000

Funding: Foundations, individual contributions and grants

Staff: 20
6 Account Executives
2 Support Staff
1 Executive Director
1 Creative Director
1 Art Director
1 Business Manager
1 Office Manager
1 Direct Mail Buyer
1 Bookkeeper/Accountant
1 Media Buyer
3 Graphic Designers
1 Health Educator

Staff openings/year: 0-1

Work Week: 40-50+ hours

Salary/year: $26,000 (Recent College Graduate); $Varies (Graduate with advanced degree)

Benefits: Health insurance, life insurance, dental/optical insurance, pregnancy leave, pension, savings plan, paid vacation

Part-Time Employees: 5

Interns: Rarely
Length: Varies
Duties: Vary
Remuneration: Varies

Jobs advertised: Word of mouth; postings in different community employment centers; notices circulated to community networks

To apply: Contact Glenn Hirsch

PUBLIC VOICE FOR FOOD AND HEALTH POLICY

1001 Connecticut Avenue, NW, Suite 522
Washington, DC 20036
(202) 659-5930

Director: Carol Marek and Allen Rosenfeld, Acting Co-directors

Purpose: To bring the citizen's interest into public and private decision-making on food and health issues.

Methods of operation: Research (30%), public education (25%), advocacy with Congress and federal agencies (20%), publications (10%), lobbying (10%), training and technical assistance (5%)

Constituency: Individuals concerned about food safety, nutrition and women's health issues

Recent issues and projects: Working with Congress to establish a comprehensive, mandatory federal fish inspection program; working for stronger federal pesticide regulations; researching the nutritional status of the rural poor and making policy recommendations to improve access to a safe and affordable food supply; educating consumers on new food labels and promoting safe/healthy eating for children.

Major publications: Monthly newsletter for consumer leaders: *Advocacy Update*; monthly news resource for food and health writers: *Nutrition Media Sheet*

Budget: $900,000

Funding: Individual contributions, foundations, direct mail, corporations

Staff: 15
2 Administrative Assistants
2 Researchers
2 Press Aides
2 Lobbyists/Advocates
1 Organizer
1 Finance Administrator
1 Administrator
1 Receptionist
1 Research Associate
2 Fundraisers

Work Week: 40 hours

Salary/year: $Varies (Recent College Graduate); $Varies (Graduate with advanced degree)

Benefits: Health insurance, pension, paid vacation

Part-Time Employees: 2

Summer Employees: Yes; usually interns

Volunteers: 1

Interns: 2-3
Length: 1 semester or longer

Jobs advertised: Through universities; other public interest groups; *Washington Post*

To apply: Contact Carol Marek, Administrative Director

PUERTO RICAN LEGAL DEFENSE AND EDUCATION FUND

99 Hudson Street, 14th Floor
New York, NY 10013
(212) 219-3360

President: Juan A. Figueroa

Purpose: PRLDEF was founded in 1972 to protect the civil rights of Puerto Ricans and other Latinos and to ensure their equal protection under the law. PRLDEF carries out its mission through a combination of litigation and advocacy and through the management of a unique legal education program geared toward increasing the number of people of color entering the legal profession.

Methods of operation: Litigation (70%), legal education training (20%), community education (5%), advocacy (5%)

Recent issues and projects: PRLDEF's work is carried out in the areas of education, employment discrimination, access to housing, language rights, voting rights and women's and community empowerment.

Major publications: Annual report and quarterly newsletter

Budget: $1,400,000

Funding: Foundations (53%), Corporations (10%),

Individuals (9%), Special Events (7%), Other (21%)

Staff: 19
1 Administrative Assistant
6 Attorneys
1 Education Coordinator
1 Education Director
1 Fiscal Director
3 Fundraisers
2 Legal Secretaries
1 Office Clerk
1 Paralegal
2 Receptionists

Staff openings/year: Varies

Work Week: 35 hours

Salary/year: $Varies (Recent College Graduate); $Varies (Graduate with advanced degree)

Benefits: Health insurance, life insurance, dental insurance, pregnancy leave, paid vacation

Summer Employees: Yes

Volunteers: Yes

Interns: Yes
Length: 8 weeks(FT) or 4 months (PT)
Remuneration: Stipend for summer interns, academic credit for school year interns

Jobs advertised: Major newspapers; mailings to colleges and universities

To apply: Contact Juan A. Figueroa, President and General Counsel

---

QUEENSBORO COUNCIL FOR SOCIAL WELFARE, INC.

221-10 Jamaica Avenue
Queens Village, NY 11428
(718) 468-8025

Director: Joan Serrano Laufer

Purpose: To provide a means for individuals and representatives from organizations and agencies, both public and private, to plan for and to promote the general welfare of the Borough of Queens, City of New York.

Methods of operation: Training and technical assistance (60%), public education (10%), community organizing (10%), human services (10%), publications (10%)

Recent issues and projects: The Council provides technical assistance to professionals and human service agencies in Queens County in the areas of housing, social services, fundraising, etc. We work closely with other organizations to coordinate meetings around major issues, such as AIDS, domestic violence and day care.

Major publications: *The Human Services Newsletter of Queens* is published 5 times/year.

Budget: $200,000

Funding: Government (60%), foundations (25%), individual contributions (15%)

Staff: 6
2 Issue Experts
1 Organizer
1 Caseworker
1 Office Manager
1 Bookkeeper/Accountant

Staff openings/year: 2

Work Week: 35 hours

Salary/year: $26,000 (Graduate with advanced degree)

Benefits: Health insurance, paid vacation, pregnancy leave

Part-Time Employees: 2

Volunteers: 3

Interns: 1
Length: 10 months
Duties: Varies
Remuneration: Varies

Jobs advertised: Newspapers; mailings to other organizations

To apply: Contact Joan Serrano Laufer, Executive Director

RACHEL CARSON COUNCIL, INC.

8940 Jones Mill Road
Chevy Chase, MD 20815
(301) 652-5622

Director: Dr. Diana Post

Purpose: International clearinghouse for information on pesticides and other toxic chemical contaminants of the environment, for both scientists and laymen, through direct response to inquiries, publications, and symposia. This entails continual research to keep library and files current with the latest scientific research, keeping track of the actions of such agencies as EPA and other regulatory bodies, and cooperation with organizations in related fields. Library and files available for public use.

Methods of operation: Research (50%), publications (30%), response to information requests (20%)

Recent issues and projects: Production of our long-term project, the *Basic Guide to Pesticides*, giving essential current information on the 600 or so most-used pesticide ingredients; related booklets; our symposium on Ethics of Pesticides and preparation of a publication of the proceedings.

Major publications: *If Rachel Carson Were Writing Today: Silent Spring in Retrospect*; *Losing the War Against Cancer: Who's to Blame and What to do About It*; *Beware the Zest of the Lemon*; pamphlets on lawn care and pesticides

Budget: $70,000

Funding: Foundations (70%), individual contributions (30%)

Staff: 4
1 Writer/Editor
1 Researcher
1 Volunteer Foundation Fundraiser
1/2 Office Manager
1/4 Bookkeeper/Accountant
1/5 Typist

Staff openings/year: 1

Work Week: 40 hours

Salary/year: $15,000 (Recent College Graduate); $18-20,000 (Graduate with advanced degree)

Benefits: Health insurance (1/2), paid vacation

Part-Time Employees: 3

Summer Employees: 1

Volunteers: 4

Interns: Yes; 1 occasionally
Length: 1 year
Duties: Research assistant
Remuneration: Minimum wage to $7 or $8/hour

Jobs advertised: University job centers; environmental publications

To apply: Contact Dr. Diana Post, Executive Director

Remarks: We are not a major employer, but specialized people with chemistry background desirable.

RAINFOREST ACTION NETWORK
450 Sansome, Suite 700
San Francisco, CA 94111
(415) 398-4404

Director: Randy Hayes

Purpose: RAN is a nonprofit activist organization working to save the world's rainforests. Begun in 1985, RAN works internationally in cooperation with other environmental and human rights organizations on major campaigns to protect rainforests.

Methods of operation: Direct action, public education, community organizing, publications

Constituency: Grassroots activists that span the spectrum

Recent issues and projects: Tropical timber consumer boycott; campaign to pressure Mitsubishi Corporations to stop destroying the rainforests

Major publications: Monthly *Action Alert*; quarterly *World Rainforest Report*; fact sheets; *Tropical Timber* book; *Amazon Resource Guide*; *Southeast Asia Resource Guide*

Budget: $500,000

Funding: Individual contributions (70%), foundations (20%), special events (10%)

Staff: 11
2 Organizers
2 Campaign Managers
2 Bookkeeper/Accountants
2 Grassroots Fundraisers
1 Issue Expert
1 Writer/Editor
1 Office Manager

Staff openings/year: 0-1

Work Week: 35 hours

Salary/year: $Varies (Recent College Graduate); $Varies (Graduate with advanced degree)

Benefits: Paid vacation

Part-Time Employees: 5

Volunteers: 10

Interns: 3-5
Length: 3-6 months
Duties: Assist program staff

Jobs advertised: Word of mouth; through rainforest network

To apply: Contact Volunteer/Intern Coordinator

Remarks: We are only interested in applicants for internships at present, not for full-time staff positions.

RAINFOREST ALLIANCE

65 Bleecker Street
New York, NY 10012
(212) 677-1900

Director: Daniel R. Katz

Purpose: The Rainforest Alliance is an international nonprofit organization dedicated to the conservation of the world's endangered tropical forests. Our mission is to develop and promote economically viable and socially desirable alternatives to tropical deforestation. We pursue this mission through education, resource management, research in the social and natural sciences, and the establishment of cooperative partnerships with businesses, governments, and local peoples.

Methods of operation: Research Projects (55%), Education (35%), Publications (10%)

Membership: International, but primarily North American, mostly college-educated

Recent issues and projects: Current projects include: Timber Program; Natural Resources and Rights Program; Conservation Media Center; Banana Program; The Amazon Rivers Program; The Catalyst Grants Program; Kleinhans Fellowship

Major publications: Newsletter: *The Canopy*

Budget: $2,000,000

Funding: Foundations (50%), individual contributions and membership (40%), corporations, events and misc. (10%)

Staff: 25
1 Executive Director/President
1 Director of Finance and Administration
12 Project Directors and Associates
5 Development (full-time and part-time)
6 Administrative (includes part-time)

Staff openings/year: 2-3

Work Week: 40 hours

Salary/year: $20,000 (Recent College Graduate); $30,000 (Graduate with advanced degree)

Benefits: Health insurance, paid vacation

Part-Time Employees: 9

Volunteers: 20

Interns: 3-5
Length: Semester or summer
Duties: Varies; usually working on projects or public information
Remuneration: Unpaid

Jobs advertised: Newspapers, job newsletters

To apply: Contact Karin Kreider, Director of Finance and Administration

RAINFOREST RELIEF

P.O. Box 281
Red Bank, NJ 07701-0281
(908) 842-6030

Director: Tim Keating

Purpose: To educate the public about the causes and consequences of the loss of rainforests through programs which highlight local impacts and participation in this global issue.

Methods of operation: Public education (50%), merchandising (15%), lobbying (10%), publications (10%), research (5%), community organizing (5%), direct action (5%)

Membership: Environmentally concerned individuals, mostly in New Jersey

Recent issues and projects: *Ecoteria* store and environmental center opened September 1, 1993 (green retailing, environmental marketing, etc.); *Rainforest Friendly*, a certification program to certify businesses or institutions reducing their impact on rainforests; Ongoing education of thousands of students in New Jersey; Introduction of tropical timber purchasing legislation into State Legislature

Major publications: *Roots*, a quarterly newsletter; *Raindrops*, a monthly update; *Rainforest Relief Reports*, estimation of carbon released from the production of a sheet of tropical plywood

Budget: $20,000

Funding: Individual contributions (65%), merchandise sales (35%)

Staff: 1
1 Organizer

Staff openings/year: 1

Work Week: 75 hours

Salary/year: $5,000

Volunteers: 8-20

Interns: 2
Length: 3 months
Duties: Legislative, administrative, education and marketing

Jobs advertised: Through college co-op and intern programs

To apply: Contact Tim Keating, Director

RAPE CRISIS CENTER
1025 Hermosa, S.E.
Albuquerque, NM 87108
(505) 266-7711

Director: Lillian Biffle, M.A.

Purpose: The Albuquerque Rape Crisis Center (ARCC) provides emotional support and advocacy for people who have been raped or sexually assaulted in any way. Services are also available for family and friends.

Methods of operation: Human services, direct action, public education, training and technical assistance

Constituency: Low and low/moderate income clients

Recent issues and projects: In December 1993, we celebrated our 20th Anniversary with a party for the community, honoring founding mothers. Prevention and awareness in elementary schools this Spring.

Major publications: Newsletter every month to volunteers, staff and friends of the Center

Budget: $350,000

Funding: Individual contributions, telephone solicitation

Staff:
1 Office Manager
8 Issue Experts
2 Administrative Assistants
1 Director
3 1/2 Counselors
1 Crisis Services Coordinator
1 Crisis Services Specialist
1 1/2 Community Education Coordinator

Staff openings/year: 1

Work Week: 40 hours

Salary/year: $17,000 (Recent College Graduate); $20,000 (Graduate with advanced degree)

Benefits: Health insurance, paid vacation, life insurance, credit union, tuition reimbursement

Part-Time Employees: 3

Volunteers: 75

Interns: 1
Length: 4 - 9 months
Duties: Counselor positions
Remuneration: None

Jobs advertised: Through UNM Personnel Department and local newspapers

To apply: Contact Carolyn Ford, Crisis Services Coordinator or Lillian Biffle, M.A., Acting Director

RAPTOR CENTER OF THE VERMONT INSTITUTE OF NATURAL SCIENCE
Church Hill Road, RR 2, Box 532
Woodstock, VT 05091
(802) 457-2779

Director: Julie A. Tracy

Purpose: Provide top quality medical care and rehabilitation for injured birds, particularly birds of prey, with the goal of releasing them into the wild. Permanently disabled birds, displayed in spacious flight habitats, are part of the educational outreach programs which broaden public awareness and appreciation for Vermont raptors and their vital role in nature.

Methods of operation: Research, public education, training and technical assistance, and medical treatment and rehabilitation of birds

Recent issues and projects: 634 birds were rehabilitated in 1993

Staff: 2
1 Director
1 Coordinator
1 Part-time Administrator

Work Week: 40 hours

Interns: Varies
Length: 3 months
Duties: Training in basic care, treatment, and handling of injured birds; assisting in monitoring about 80 nonreleasable raptors; other various jobs
Remuneration: $250 a month, plus housing

To apply: Contact Julie Tracy, Raptor Center Director

RECYCLE! NASHVILLE

P.O. Box 24934
Nashville, TN 37202
(615) 726-1424

President: Chip Forrester

Purpose: Recycle! Nashville's main purpose is to ensure the success of recycling through education and promotion.

Methods of operation: Public education (55%), research (15%), community organizing (15%), publications (10%), lobbying (5%)

Constituency: Individuals, businesses, some industry

Recent issues and projects: Recycle! Fest is an annual event, held in May, in which Recycle! Nashville and other organizations involved in recycling have the opportunity to set up booths and distribute information on recycling issues.

Major publications: Monthly newsletter; other educational literature on waste reduction, recycling and composting

Funding: Individual contributions (100%)

Work Week: 40 hours

Salary/year: $Varies (Recent College Graduate); $Varies (Graduate with advanced degree)

Volunteers: 20

Interns: None currently, but willing to accept applications

Jobs advertised: Newsletter and word of mouth

To apply: Contact Chip Forrester, President

REDWOOD ALLIANCE

P.O. Box 293
Arcata, CA 95521
(707) 822-7884

Director: Michael Welch, Office Coordinator

Purpose: Environmental organization working on energy issues.

Methods of operation: Public education (50%), litigation (10%), community organizing (20%), lobbying (10%), direct action (10%)

Constituency: Folks concerned about environment and energy

Recent issues and projects: Humboldt Bay Nuclear Power Plant watchdog; Public Utility Commission intervention; photovoltaic demonstration center; Home Power computer bulletin board system; Ward Valley Radioactive Waste Dump

Budget: $25,000

Funding: Direct mail (60%), benefits (30%), individual contributions (10%), foundation grants (10%)

Part-Time Employees: 2

Volunteers: 1-5

Interns: None currently, but willing to accept applications

To apply: Contact Michael Welch, Office Coordinator

REFUGEES INTERNATIONAL

21 Dupont Circle, NW
Washington, DC 20036
(202) 547-3785

Director: Lionel A. Rosenblatt

Purpose: Refugees International is a nonprofit refugee advocacy organization which seeks to educate the public and policymakers about threats to refugees' rights around the world and encourages compassionate national and international refugee policies.

Methods of operation: Lobbying (40%), research (20%), public education (20%), publications (20%)

Constituency: Primarily concerned individuals, some church groups and non-governmental organizations

Recent issues and projects: Annual awards dinner/global briefing brings together refugee experts, advocates and concerned individuals from around the world, and honors refugees and refugee advocates who have made outstanding contributions on behalf of refugee rights.

Major publications: Quarterly: *RI Newsletter*; topical *Issue Briefs*, *RI Bulletins* and *Action Alerts* are published throughout the year to coincide with refugee-related events around the world

Budget: $500,000

Funding: Individual contributions (60%), foundations (40%)

Staff: 6
1 Foundation Fundraiser
1 Deputy Director
1 Outreach Director
1 Advocacy Associate
1 Advocacy Assistant
1 Administrative Assistant

Staff openings/year: 1

Work Week: 45 hours

Salary/year: $18,000 (Recent College Graduate); $30,000 (Graduate with advanced degree)

Benefits: Health insurance, paid vacation

Part-Time Employees: 0

Volunteers: Yes; usually 1

Interns: 1-2
Length: 10 weeks
Duties: Assist in production/distribution of RI publications, including writing and research; attend relevant hearings; pitch in wherever necessary
Remuneration: Usually none; occasionally a small stipend

Jobs advertised: Paid positions are advertised through newspapers and nonprofit newsletters; internships are advertised through college career planning departments.

To apply: Contact Lynn Heichel Kneedler, Deputy Director

Remarks: Because RI's office is so small, it is desirable that potential employees and interns have a broad range of skills, and that they be extremely adaptable, innovative and self-motivated, in addition to having a refugee policy and/or foreign affairs background or interest.

RELIGIOUS COALITION FOR REPRODUCTIVE CHOICE

1025 Vermont Avenue, Suite 1130
Washington, DC 20005
(202) 628-7700

Director: Ann Thompson Cook

Purpose: Coalition of 34 national religious agencies representing Presbyterian (USA), United Methodist, Episcopal, United Church of Christ, Major Reform, Reconstructionists and Conservative Judaism and other major denominations. With over 40 state and local affiliates, the Coalition engages in public outreach, education and advocacy for family planning, sexuality education and legal abortion.

Methods of operation: Public education (55%), publications (25%), community organizing (15%), training and technical assistance (5%)

Constituency: National religious denominations and agencies that support a woman's right to choose

Recent issues and projects: Reproductive services in health care reform; opposition for "family caps" in welfare reform; Medicaid funding for abortion; opposition to anti-abortion violence; supporting women who choose abortion

Major publications: *Religious Coalition Newsletter*; Pro-choice religious educational series; voter's guide; women of color publications; annual report

Budget: $1,200,000

Funding: Direct mail (60%), foundations (25%), individual contributions (15%)

Staff: 6
2 Organizers
1 Writer/Editor
1 Office Manager
1 Press Aide
1 Foundation Fundraiser
1 Bookkeeper/Accountant

Staff openings/year: 2

Work Week: 35 hours

Salary/year: $22,000

Benefits: Health insurance, paid vacation, life insurance, family leave

Part-Time Employees: 4

Summer Employees: None

Volunteers: 3

Interns: 3
Length: 3 months
Duties: Vary
Remuneration: Vary

Jobs advertised: Major periodicals and pro-choice/progressive organizations

To apply: Contact Jay Heavner

RENEW AMERICA

1400 16th Street, NW, Suite 710
Washington, DC 20036
(202) 232-2252

Director: Dale Didion

Purpose: Renew America is the nation's only organization specializing in broad-based environmental program identification, verification and promotion of positive models for change. They advance solutions to environmental problems by encouraging the replication of successful community-based initiatives. By seeking out, promoting and awarding exemplary programs among all sectors, they offer innovative, constructive models to inspire communities and businesses to meet environmental challenges.

Methods of operation: Research (30%), public education (30%), publications (30%), community organizing (10%)

Membership: 7,500 members; $25/year

Recent issues and projects: The "Environmental Success Index" program, a national effort to local, successful environmental programs/projects in 20 different categories, which concludes with an awards ceremony.

Major publications: *State of the States Report*; The *Environmental success Index* (1987-89); Renew America *Topic Reports* (water resource protection, renewable energy, energy efficiency, transportation efficiency, hazardous waste reduction and more); *Sustainable Energy*

Budget: $800,000

Funding: Foundations (50%), individual contributions (30%), corporate donations (20%)

Staff: 8
2 Researchers
1 Organizer
1 Receptionist
1 Writer/Editor
1 Office Manager
1 Press Aide
1 Fundraiser

Staff openings/year: 4

Work Week: 45 hours

Salary/year: $15,000 (Recent College Graduate); $25,000 (Graduate with advanced degree)

Benefits: Health insurance, paid vacation

Part-Time Employees: 3

Volunteers: Yes

Interns: 6
Length: 3-6 months
Duties: Researching, writing
Remuneration: Stipend available

Jobs advertised: Word-of-mouth

To apply: Contact Terri Mead

REPORTERS COMMITTEE FOR FREEDOM OF THE PRESS

1735 Eye Street, NW, Suite 504
Washington, DC 20006
(202) 466-6313

Director: Jane E. Kirtley

Purpose: The Reporters Committee is a voluntary, unincorporated association of reporters and editors dedicated to protecting the First Amendment interests of the news media.

Methods of operation: Research, litigation, publications, public education, provide free legal assistance to working journalists

Recent issues and projects: Continuing activities include monitoring developments in libel, invasion of privacy, reporters privilege, and government access. Recently published *Tapping Officials' Secrets*, a comprehensive guide to state open records and open meetings laws.

Major publications: Quarterly magazine: *The NEWS Media and The LAW*; *First Amendment Handbook* (Second Edition); *How to Use the Federal FOI Act* (Sixth Edition); *Tapping Officials' Secrets*

Budget: $450,000

Funding: Individual contributions, foundations, direct mail

Staff: 15
5 Attorneys/Writers/Editors
3 Issue Experts
2 Foundation Fundraisers
2 Researchers
1 Bookkeeper/Accountant
1 Paralegal
1 Office Manager

Work Week: 45-50 hours

Salary/year: $Varies (Recent College Graduate); $Varies (Graduate with advanced degree)

Benefits: Health insurance, paid vacation

Part-Time Employees: 1

Summer Employees: 2

Volunteers: 1-3

Interns: 6 per year
Length: 1 semester or 10 summer weeks

Duties: Monitoring developments in press and access issues; writing for publications
Remuneration: $750 per semester; pro rate part-time/volunteer

Jobs advertised: Notices are sent to law and journalism schools.

To apply: For fellowships, contact Jane E. Kirtley, Executive Director. For internships, contact Rebecca Daugherty, Director, FOI Service Center

Remarks: The Committee offers 2 legal fellowships each year; fellows earn $16,000/year.

RESOURCE CENTER FOR NONVIOLENCE

515 Broadway
Santa Cruz, CA 95060
(408) 423-1626

Purpose: To educate the public on current issues locally, nationally and internationally. An advocate of nonviolence as a means of social change on personal and societal issues.

Methods of operation: Public education (80%), community organizing (20%)

Constituency: The public; 50% local, 50% outside our area

Recent issues and projects: Ongoing workshops, trainings and programs on Central America and the Middle East. Operate a bookstore, a library and a facility for other local organizations.

Major publications: Periodic newsletters and "Updates." Monthly announcements of program events. Occasionally co-publish books and articles.

Budget: $100,000

Funding: Events, bookstore

Staff: 7
7 half-time staff

Benefits: Health insurance

Part-Time Employees: 7

Summer Employees: Sometimes

Volunteers: Yes; many

Interns: Yes
Length: Varies depending on applicant
Duties: All organizational and special projects
Remuneration: No money available from us; needs to be self-supporting intern

To apply: Contact Anita Hechman or Rosalie Pizzo-Strain

RESOURCE CENTER OF THE AMERICAS

317 - 17th Avenue, SE
Minneapolis, MN 55414
(612) 627-9445

Director: Pam Costain

Purpose: Education and information center on issues related to Latin America, the Carribbean and U.S. foreign policy toward the region.

Methods of operation: Public education (50%), publications (25%), community organizing (15%), research (10%)

Constituency: Teachers, students, professors, members of religious communities and labor community

Recent issues and projects: (1) Largest public library on Latin America in Upper Midwest; (2) Speakers Bureau and national curriculum project on Latin America and diversity issues; (3) public education; (4) publications; (5) media work

Major publications: Monthlies: *Minnesota Central America Connection* and *Executive News Summary*; quarterly: *Religion Report*; background: *Nicaragua*; *Annotated Bibliography of Central America Resources*; *Central America Classroom Resources K-12*

Budget: $205,000

Funding: Individual contributions (40%), events (15%), foundations (10%), earned income (35%)

Staff: 9
1 Director
2 Education Coordinator
1 Writer/Editor
1 Grassroots Fundraiser
1 Bookkeeper/Accountant
1 1/2 Labor Project Coordinator
1 1/2 Receptionist

Staff openings/year: 1

Work Week: 40-45 hours

Salary/year: $13,200

Benefits: Health insurance, pregnancy leave, paid vacation

Part-Time Employees: 3

Volunteers: Yes

Interns: Yes
Length: 2-6 months
Duties: Varies
Remuneration: No pay, college credit often available

Jobs advertised: Nonprofit sector, newspaper, peace and justice newsletters

To apply: Contact Pam Costain

RESOURCES FOR THE FUTURE
1616 P Street, NW
Washington, DC 20036
(202) 328-5000

Director: Robert W. Fri

Purpose: Resources for the Future (REF) is an independent nonprofit organization engaged in research and public education on natural resources and environmental issues. Its mission is to create and disseminate knowledge that helps people make better decisions about the conservation and use of their natural resources and the environment.

Methods of operation: Research (70%), publications (20%), public education (10%)

Constituency: Government and industry officials, public interest advocacy groups, nonprofit organizations academic researchers and the press

Recent issues and projects: Analysis of key issues in the Superfund reauthorization debate; the distributional and environmental consequences of energy taxes; the use of risk assessment in setting national environmental priorities; analysis of the cost effectiveness of various policies designed to reduce emissions from cars and other mobile sources of pollution.

Major publications: *Resources*, a quarterly periodical; *Making National Energy Policy*, edited by Hans Landsberg; *Current Issues in U.S. Environmental Policy*, edited by Paul R. Portney

Budget: $7,000,000

Funding: Endowment (40%), government (33%), corporate (18%), foundations (7%), individual contributions (2%)

Staff: 80
3 Organizers
5 Writers/Editors
3 Office Managers
50 Researchers
2 Foundation Fundraisers
10 Administrative Assistants
3 Bookkeepers/Accounts
1 Librarian
3 Computer Services

Staff openings/year: 1-2

Work Week: 40 hours

Salary/year: $23,000 (Recent College Graduate); $25,000 (Graduate with advanced degree)

Benefits: Health insurance, long-term disability,

Part-Time Employees: 5

Summer Employees: 10-15

Volunteers: None

Interns: 10-15
Length: 2-3 months
Duties: Assist Senior Fellows and Fellows with research
Remuneration: $375 per week with M.A.; $350 per week with B.A.

Jobs advertised: Professional organizations, newspapers, universities

To apply: Please contact Debbie Groberg, Personnel Manager

RESULTS
236 Massachusetts Avenue, NE, Suite 110
Washington, DC 20002
(202) 543-9340

Other Offices: Seattle, WA; Bloomington, IN

Director: Sam Harris

Purpose: International citizens' lobby working to create the political will to end hunger.

Methods of operation: Support of grassroots volunteers (55%), publications (20%), lobbying (15%), research (10%)

Constituency: Citizen volunteers in six countries: the U.S., the U.K., Japan, Germany, Canada, Australia, Britain

Recent issues and projects: Microenterprise credit for the poor; Global Poverty Reduction Act; homelessness in the U.S.; UNICEF's *State of the World's Children* report press conferences; WIC; Head Start; World Summit for Children

Major publications: Quarterly newsletter: *Entry*

Point

Budget: $650,000

Funding: Individual contributions (99%), other nonprofits (1%)

Staff: 9
2 Organizers
1 Executive Director
1 Executive Assistant
1 Issue Expert
1 Office Manager
1 Staff Assistant

Staff openings/year: 1

Work Week: 60 hours

Salary/year: $18,000 (Recent College Graduate); $23,000 (Graduate with advanced degree)

Benefits: Health insurance, life insurance, pregnancy leave, paid vacation

Part-Time Employees: 3

Summer Employees: 1

Volunteers: 5

Interns: 1-2
Length: 2-3 months/summer
Duties: Staff support, typing, data entry, messenger, calling Capitol Hill staff
Remuneration: Paid $100 every two weeks

Jobs advertised: Mailings; announcements in publications of various organizations

To apply: Contact David Schnetzer, Executive Assistant

Remarks: RESULTS has over 105 groups in the U.S. and more than 45 groups in 5 other countries (listed above). Each group consists of 4 key volunteers called "partners." The majority of the work in the Washington, DC office consists of supporting them and supplying them with materials.

ROCKY MOUNTAIN INSTITUTE

1739 Snowmass Creek Road
Old Snowmass, CO 81654
(303) 927-3851

Purpose: RMI is a nonprofit research and educational foundation with a vision across boundaries. Our goal is to foster the efficient and sustainable use of resources as a path to global security. Program areas include: Energy, Water, Agriculture, Economic Renewal, and Energy Security, transportation and Green Development Services.

Methods of operation: Research, technical assistance, public education, publication of research findings, direct action, community organizing

Constituency: People around the world who care about the issues we work on; particular service to electric utility industry, its major customers, and approx. 15,000 newsletter subscribers and small rural communities

Recent issues and projects: Efficient use of resources in areas of energy, water, agriculture, economic renewal, security, transportation and green development services.

Major publications: RMI Newsletter; *Least-Cost Energy: Solving the CO2 Problem*; numerous articles and testimony; *Practical Home Energy Saving Efficient House Sourcebook*

Budget: $1,929,853

Funding: Foundations (54%), enterprise income (44%), individual and corporate contributions (12%)

Staff: 32
14 Researchers/Writers
8 Contract Researchers
3 Typist/Secretaries
2 Cleaning/Maintenance (hourly)
2 Writer/Editor/Contractors
1 Foundation Fundraiser
1 Office Manager
1 Bookkeeper/Accountant

Work Week: 40 hours

Salary/year: $15,000 (Recent College Graduate); $20-25,000 (Graduate with advanced degree)

Benefits: Health insurance, paid vacation, housing for some staff, ski pass, lunch, sickness/wellness days, food allowance for interns

Part-Time Employees: 10 hourly and contract

Volunteers: Yes

Interns: Yes
Length: 1 year
Duties: Research and writing in one of our program areas
Remuneration: Small stipend, housing, food allowance, ski pass, health insurance

Jobs advertised: Through colleges and universities; colleagues. We tend to have more qualified applicants than we can hire.

To apply: For internships, contact James Dyer, Intern Program Director and Ag/Water Program

Director. For all other positions, contact Farley Sheldon, Personnel Director.

Remarks: RMI is located 16 miles from Aspen, CO in a rural setting. We have severe space limitations. Applicants must have at least an undergraduate degree (BA,BS) and exceptional technical writing ability, plus training/ experience. No summer internships at present; will consider if we get more space.

ROCKY MOUNTAIN PEACE CENTER

P.O. Box 1156
Boulder, CO 80306
(303) 444-6981

Purpose: Created in a spirit of unconditional nonviolence, Rocky Mountain Peace Center is dedicated to research, education and action in nonviolence as a way of life and a means of change. Build a just and peaceful society, challenge systemic oppression through grassroots organizing and encourage nonviolence as a way of life.

Methods of operation: Public education (20%), training and technical assistance (20%), direct action (15%), publications (15%), community organizing (15%), research (15%)

Recent issues and projects: Current projects include: The Allies Program; The Disarmament Program; The Education Program; The International Relations Program.

Major publications: *Citizen's Guide to Rocky Flats* 1992 expanded update; *Communities of Conversation and Action* (on creating base communities in North America)

Budget: $60,000

Funding: Individual contributions (75%), direct mail (15%), foundations (5%), telephone solicitation (5%)

Staff: 6
4 Organizers (part-time)
2 Administrative and Fundraisers

Staff openings/year: 1-2

Work Week: 20-40 hours

Salary/year: $Varies (Recent College Graduate); $Varies (Graduate with advanced degree)

Part-Time Employees: 6

Summer Employees: Occasionally

Volunteers: Yes

Interns: 12
Length: 3-12 months
Duties: Educational series; organizing with base communities
Remuneration: No stipend; may get academic credit

Jobs advertised: Mail and/or newsletter

To apply: Contact Edelle Corrine

RURAL ADVANCEMENT FUND OF THE NATIONAL SHARECROPPERS FUND

2128 Commonwealth Avenue
Charlotte, NC 28205
(704) 334-3051

Other Offices: Pittsboro, NC; Lumberton, NC

Director: Ronald K. Charity

Purpose: Works for the preservation of the family farm, a balanced agriculture, conservation of our natural resources, rural justice and equal rights and opportunities for all rural people.

Recent issues and projects: (1) Farm Survival Project: placing the tools of advocacy, empowerment and mutual assistance in farmers' hands to sustain America's family farm system. Formed the United Farmers Organization for this purpose; (2) Community Empowerment Project: targets the chronically poor counties of North Carolina to increase minority and low-income participation at various levels of the democratic process; (3) RAF Justice Project: organizing minority and low-income citizens of Robeson County, NC, to enable the community to hold accountable officials in the criminal justice system; (4) Rural Advancement Fund International: to preserve the diversity of agricultural genetic resources and to orient emerging biotechnologies to meet real and basic needs of society.

Major publications: Quarterly *Rural Justice Report*; quarterly newsletter: *Rural Advance*; monthly *RAFI Communique*

Funding: Individual contributions, foundations, direct mail

Staff: 21
13 Organizers
1 Director of Administration
1 Direct Mail Coordinator
1 Office Manager
1 Researcher

1 Writer/Editor
1 Office Assistant
1 Secretary
1 Bookkeeper/Accountant

Work Week: 40 hours

Benefits: Health insurance, life insurance, pregnancy leave, pension, paid vacation, tuition reimbursement

Volunteers: Occasionally

Interns: Not accepting applications at present time

Jobs advertised: Newspaper, circulation among staff and nonprofit organizations

To apply: Lois Brock, Director of Administration

RURAL ALLIANCE FOR MILITARY ACCOUNTABILITY

6205 Franktown Road
Carson City, NV 89704
(702) 885-0166

Other Offices: Wishaam, WA; Questa, NM

Director: Marla Painter

Purpose: Support rural communities struggling to protect their communities from the abuses of the U.S. military, and support for communities with economies controlled or dominated by the military.

Methods of operation: Community organizing (30%), research (20%), public education (20%), training and technical assistance (30%)

Constituency: Rural grassroots groups organizing around military issues

Recent issues and projects: Military airspace project, SKYGUARD; assistance to the National Campaign to Stop MX; economic education workshops

Major publications: *SKYGUARD* newsletter and fact sheets

Budget: $200,000

Funding: Foundations (60%), individual contributions (25%), contract (15%)

Staff: 5
1 Executive Director

Staff openings/year: 1

Work Week: 40+ hours

Salary/year: $20,000 (Recent College Graduate); $Varies (Graduate with advanced degree)

Benefits: Health insurance, paid vacation

Part-Time Employees: Yes

Interns: No but willing to accept applications

To apply: Contact Marla Painter

RURAL COALITION

2001 S Street, NW, Suite 500
Washington, DC 20009
(202) 483-1500

Director: Judith D. Coats

Purpose: A national alliance of over 100 organizations, mostly from the grassroots, dedicated to the development and implementation of public policies that will benefit rural Americans, especially those who are poor or otherwise disadvantaged and their communities. The Coalition serves as a source of support for member organizations and their constituencies in coordinating the pursuit of common goals.

Methods of operation: Research (30%), conducting programs that cross lines of race, culture and issue for developing joint policy strategies (30%), public education (20%), publications (10%), training and technical assistance (10%)

Constituency: 110 nonprofit member organizations; people concerned about rural issues and poverty

Recent issues and projects: Minority Farmers Rights Act; North Carolina land grant university study; Farmer/Farm Worker Leadership Exchange; American Indian groundwater studies

Major publications: Newsletter: *Update*; *Rural Poverty in Perspective* (1988); *Saturn: Tomorrow's Jobs, Yesterday's Wages and Myths* (1988)

Budget: $320,000

Funding: Foundations (90%), individual contributions (7%), membership dues (3%)

Staff: 5
2 Researchers
1 Executive Director (fundraising/management)
1 Network Coordinator
1 Office Manager

Staff openings/year: 1

Work Week: 40+ hours

Salary/year: $Varies (Recent College Graduate); $Varies (Graduate with advanced degree)

Benefits: Health insurance, pregnancy leave, paid vacation

Part-Time Employees: 2-3 consultants

Volunteers: 2

Jobs advertised: In local newspaper and through local nonprofit network and membership

To apply: Contact Judith D. Coats, Executive Director

S.I. NEWHOUSE CENTER FOR LAW AND JUSTICE, RUTGERS UNIVERSITY

15 Washington Street
Newark, NJ 07102
(201) 648-5209

Other Offices: New Brunswick, NJ

Director: Carol Shapiro

Purpose: To facilitate a bridge between academia, applied research and field work in the area of criminal justice reform. The Center's focus is on developing alternatives to incarceration and developing collaboration between victim advocates and community corrections staff.

Methods of operation: Training and technical assistance (60%), research (25%), public education (10%), community organizing (5%)

Recent issues and projects: Work with Alabama Board of Pardons and Parole in enhancing probation and parole capabilities; developing comprehensive strategy to alleviate prison crowding in Oregon; identify common areas of interest between victims and community corrections staff

Major publications: *The Probation Development Project: Successes, Failures, and Question Marks*; *Classification for Custody and the Assessment of Risk in the Colorado Department of Corrections*; *Making It Work: Addressing Victim Concerns through Community Corrections Programs*; *Is Legislation the Chameleon of the Victims Movement? A Look at Restitution and Community Service*

Budget: $250,000

Funding: Foundations (80%), federal, local governments (20%)

Staff: 7
4 Researchers (mostly grad students)
2 Issue Experts
1 Typist

Staff openings/year: 2

Work Week: 35 hours

Salary/year: $20,000 (Recent College Graduate); $30,000 (Graduate with advanced degree)

Benefits: Health insurance, life insurance, paid vacation, pregnancy leave, pension, tuition reimbursement

Part-Time Employees: Yes; consultants

Summer Employees: Yes

Interns: None currently, but willing to accept applications

To apply: Contact Carol Shapiro, Director

SAFE ENERGY COMMUNICATION COUNCIL (SECC)

1717 Massachusetts Avenue, NW, Suite 805
Washington, DC 20036
(202) 483-8491

Director: Scott Denman

Purpose: SECC is a nonprofit, national coalition of environmental, energy and public interest media organizations working to increase public awareness of the ability of energy efficiency and renewable energy to meet an increasing share of our nation's energy needs, and of the serious economic and environmental liabilities of nuclear power. We train and assist hundreds of local groups in media skills and strategy. We publish well-documented and hard-hitting information about safe energy.

Methods of operation: Research, publications, community organizing, public education, training and technical assistance, safe energy, TV and radio spots

Constituency: The vast array of citizen organizations that work to promote safe energy, a clean and sustainable environment and consumer protection

Recent issues and projects: They are currently working on shifting the federal energy budget away from nuclear programs and into renewables and energy efficiency; fighting to terminate taxpayer support for the breeder and other "advanced reactors; working with local activists and state officials to promote sustainable energy at the local level; fighting the deregulation of nuclear waste;

and a host of related issues. They played a major role in the defeat of and termination of the Rancho Seco nuclear plant in 1989 and others since then. During the 1980's, SECC-assisted local groups have gained more than $8 million through appropriate use of the Fairness Doctrine. SECC is one of the organizations leading the effort to codify the Fairness Doctrine.

Major publications: The *MYTHBusters* series of reports on key energy topics, particularly the debunking of the nuclear industry's many myths; *Viewpoint*, a bi-monthly op-ed service on safe energy topics sent to every U.S. daily newspaper; *ENFacts*, a timely, graphic energy facts piece also sent bi-monthly to every U.S. daily paper. Independent op-eds are also frequently published by SECC in many papers. They have a radio PSA program and an energy polling program.

Budget: $300,000

Funding: Foundations (67%), individual contributions (33%)

Staff: 4
1 Executive Director
1 Communications Director
1 Administrative Director
1 Research Director

Staff openings/year: 1

Work Week: 45 hours

Salary/year: $18-22,000

Benefits: Health insurance, paid vacation, pregnancy leave, partial dental insurance

Part-Time Employees: 2-3

Summer Employees: 1-2

Volunteers: 1-2

Interns: 1-2
Length: 3-6 months
Duties: Varied depending upon the intern's interest and capabilities; normally, research and writing, grassroots networking organizing, etc.
Remuneration: $50.00/week

Jobs advertised: Job notices are sent to a broad cross-section of national, local and statewide public interest groups. We advertise in *Community Jobs*, *JOB SCAN*, *Environmental Opportunities*, *Advocate's Advocate*, and *Washington Post*.

To apply: Contact Amy Steinberg, Administrative Director

Remarks: SECC was established in 1979 to respond to the establishment of annual, multi-million dollar public relations campaigns by the nuclear and utility industries. In 1983, SECC spurred Congressional hearings into the nuclear industry's PR efforts and their relationship with the Department of Energy. SECC publicly debates industry representatives at every opportunity and constantly challenges the myths presented as fact in the industry's advertising. SECC conducts state-by-state energy outreach tours with safe energy experts to promote renewables and energy efficiency.

SAMARITAN INNS INC.
2712 Ontario Road, NW
Washington, DC 20009
(202) 667-8831

Director: David Erickson

Purpose: To help homeless people overcome the causes of their homelessness and return to healthy, productive, self-sufficient lives.

Methods of operation: Human services (80%), program expansion (15%), research (5%)

Constituency: Homeless people and those interested in homeless issues

Recent issues and projects: Currently operate two transitional houses for homeless men and one for homeless pregnant women; an 85-unit single room housing community for formerly homeless men and women; currently developing a second 49-unit single room housing community.

Budget: $750,000

Funding: Foundations and corporations (30%), individual contributions (22%), rents (48%)

Staff: 20
5 Innkeepers
3 Social Workers
1 Social Work Associate
2 Addictions Counselors
3 Resident Managers (85-unit housing commun.)
6 Management, Administrative and Development

Staff openings/year: 6

Work Week: 40 hours

Salary/year: $6-18,000 (Recent College Graduate); $24,000 (Graduate with advanced degree)

Benefits: Health insurance, housing, paid vacation, tuition reimbursement

Part-Time Employees: 1

Summer Employees: 1

Volunteers: 5

Interns: 1
Length: 3-12 months
Duties: Resident manager at transitional houses
Remuneration: By arrangement; based on needs

Jobs advertised: Newspapers; local job boards; churches

To apply: Contact David Erickson

SAN FERNANDO VALLEY NEIGHBORHOOD LEGAL SERVICES, INC.

13327 Van Nuys Blvd.
Pacoima, CA 91331
(818) 896-5211

Director: Neal Dudovitz

Purpose: The San Fernando Valley Neighborhood Legal Services, Inc. provides low-income persons access to the government and public infrastructures, to help them obtain power over their lives and futures and to provide representation where able and appropriate before administrative, legislative and judicial bodies.

Methods of operation: Direct action (35%), litigation (30%), research (10%), public education (10%), training and technical assistance (10%), community organizing (5%), publications (2%)

Constituency: Low-income persons of the San Fernando, Santa Clarita and Antelope Valleys

Recent issues and projects: Recent projects include: resource for low-income schools; earthquake relief; community participation in empowerment zone; fight health care and welfare cuts; affordable housing preservation and development; ensuring community participation in redevelorness in immigration appeals process

Major publications: Domestic Violence book will be published in the near future

Budget: $2,700,000

Funding: Public monies and grants

Staff: 34
14 Attorneys
10 Paralegals
1 Office Manager
6 Administrative Assistants
2 Bookkeepers
3 Receptionists

Staff openings/year: 2

Work Week: 14 hours

Salary/year: $25,000 (Recent College Graduate); $35,000 (Graduate with advanced degree)

Benefits: Health insurance, paid vacation, life insurance, retirement, family leave

Part-Time Employees: 2

Summer Employees: 8-12

Volunteers: 3

Interns: None; but willing to accept applications

Jobs advertised: Newspapers, public interest publications, word-of-mouth, community meetings/publications

To apply: Contact R. Mona Tawatao, Directing Attorney

SAN FRANCISCO AIDS FOUNDATION

25 Van Ness Avenue, 6th Floor
San Francisco, CA 94102
(415) 864-5855

Director: Patricia Christen

Purpose: The AIDS Foundation provides direct services to people with AIDS and HIV disease; they help educate the public to prevent transmission of HIV; help individuals make informed choices about treatment options and other AIDS-related concerns; protect the dignity and human rights of those affected by HIV; initiate and support public policies that further these goals.

Methods of operation: Lobbying, publications, human services, community organizing, direct action, public education, training and technical assistance

Constituency: People living with or affected by HIV disease/AIDS

Recent issues and projects: Recent projects include: Trilingual Hotline (English/Spanish/Filipino); "Breathe Freely" ad campaign informing HIV+ people that they can receive free or low cost medication for pneumocystis pneumonia; emergency housing vouchers for people living with HIV disease; and advocating for the health care reform plan to reflect the needs of people with HIV disease/AIDS

Major publications: *BETA* (Bulletin of Experimental Treatments of AIDS); *Positive News*, newsletter in English, Spanish, Filipino and Chines

Budget: $10,000,000

Funding: Events (32%), government grants (30%), individual contributions (12%), direct mail (10%), canvassing (8%), foundations (5%), telephone solicitation (3%)

Staff: 100
2 Organizers
3 Writers/Editors
1 Office Manager
2 Lobbyists
2 Press Aides
10 Foundation Fundraisers
10 Issue Experts
17 Administrative Assistants
7 Bookkeepers/Accountants
22 Caseworkers
5 Campaign Managers

Staff openings/year: 20

Work Week: 40 hours

Salary/year: $27,960

Benefits: Health insurance, pension, paid vacation, life insurance, credit union, family leave, tuition reimbursement

Part-Time Employees: 2

Summer Employees: 4

Volunteers: 500

Interns: Yes
Length: 3 months
Duties: Social work, office support, volunteer services, client services, education, publications, hotline, communications
Remuneration: Varies

Jobs advertised: *San Francisco Chronicle/Examiner*, *Opportunity NOCS*

To apply: Contact Norma Stocker, Director of Personnel

SAN FRANCISCO LEAGUE OF URBAN GARDENERS

2540 Newhall Street
San Francisco, CA 94124
(415) 468-0110

Director: Mohammed Nuru

Purpose: To foster the development of community and school gardens; to promote environmental education and awareness; to employ and train inner city people.

Methods of operation: Community organizing (20%), direct action (20%), human services (20%), public education (15%), publications (5%), research (5%), training and technical assistance (20%)

Constituency: Multi-ethnic; diverse incomes

Recent issues and projects: Implement Environmental Education Center in San Francisco; establish horticultural therapy programs; promote sustainable urban planning

Major publications: Quarterly newsletter: *The SLUG Update*; factsheets on everything from organic pest control to home composting

Budget: $1,000,000

Funding: Local government (80%), individual contributions (20%)

Staff: 6
1 Executive Director
1 Administrator
1 Education Director
1 Administrative Assistant
1 Compost Educator
1 Construction Educator/Community Garden Coordinator

Staff openings/year: 1-2

Work Week: 40 hours

Salary/year: $18,000 (Recent College Graduate); $22,000 (Graduate with advanced degree)

Benefits: Health insurance, life insurance, paid vacation

Part-Time Employees: 2

Volunteers: 1-10 VISTA Vols.

Interns: 1-10
Length: 3-6 months
Duties: Community, school gardening, office work, press, and fundraising
Remuneration: Mileage

Jobs advertised: Newspapers; bulletins for nonprofit employment

To apply: Contact Susan M. O'Keefe, Administrator

SAN FRANCISCO TENANTS UNION

558 Capp Street
San Francisco, CA 94110
(415) 282-5525

Purpose: Tenants rights counseling, information, advocacy, research. The TU is a nonprofit membership organization committed to preserving affordable and decent rental housing in San Francisco. As tenant advocates we oppose evictions and rent increases, support rent controls, and defend the right of tenants to organize and negotiate collectively with landlords.

Methods of operation: Research, lobbying, publications, public education, counseling, direct action

Constituency: Low/moderate income renters in the city of San Francisco

Recent issues and projects: Homes not jails, squatting movement for homeless people.

Major publications: *Tenant Rights Handbook*; *Tenant Times* newspaper; occasional research reports

Budget: $50,000

Funding: Individual contributions

Part-Time Employees: 1

Volunteers: 20

Interns: None currently, but willing to accept applications

Jobs advertised: Community newspapers, word-of-mouth

To apply: Contact Office Manager

Remarks: The SF Tenants Union is now celebrating its 20th anniversary, as one of the oldest citywide tenants unions in California.

SAN JOSE HOUSING SERVICE CENTER

110 East Gish Road
San Jose, CA 95112
(408) 453-3464

Other Offices: Milpitas, CA

Director: Lori Klein

Purpose: Counseling and legal representation for low and moderate income tenants; some telephone counseling for landlords; public education.

Methods of operation: Human services (80%), litigation (20%)

Constituency: Primarily low-income tenants in San Jose

Recent issues and projects: Individual representation for tenants in cases of eviction; recovery of illegal sidepayments and security deposits; housing discrimination; counseling of low-income homeowners to prevent foreclosure

Budget: $325,000

Funding: Government grants, California State Bar (97%), individual contributions (3%)

Staff: 11
5 Paralegals
2 Attorneys
2 Typists
1 Executive Director
1 Administrative Analyst

Staff openings/year: 3

Work Week: 40 hours

Salary/year: $17,000 (Recent College Graduate); $26,000 law (Graduate with advanced degree)

Benefits: Health insurance, life insurance, paid vacation, dental and disability insurance, bar dues paid for staff attorneys

Volunteers: Yes

Interns: Yes
Length: Generally a semester/3 months
Duties: Telephone counseling, legal research and writing
Remuneration: Will pay mileage for local travel

Jobs advertised: Job announcements are mailed to local schools, community organizations and the Public Interest Clearinghouse

To apply: Contact Lori Klein, Executive Director

SAVE AMERICA'S FORESTS

4 Library Ct., SE
Washington, DC 20003
(202) 544-9219

Director: Carl Ross and Mark Winstein

Purpose: Save America's Forests is the nationwide campaign to protect and restore America's wild and natural forests. Save America's Forests is dedicated to improving the political strength of citizens groups, responsible businesses, and concerned individuals in all parts of the U.S. who share the common goals of the Save America's platform, and to representing their interests in the U.S. Congress.

Methods of operation: Lobbying (50%), organizing (40%), publications (10%)

Membership: Concerned citizens, responsible businesses and local forest, water, or general environmental groups

Recent issues and projects: HR 1164, The Forest Biodiversity and Clearcutting Prohibition Act, is the leading nationwide forest protection bill in Congress because of the strength of the Save America's Forests coalition. This redirection for public forest policy would ban clearcutting and all even-age management, stop roadbuilding in sixty million acres of Roadless Areas thereby saving the U.S. taxpayer upwards of $200 million per year, and provide strong citizen enforcement provisions to safeguard its provisions.

Major publications: *DC Update*, newsletter; *Fax Action Network*

Funding: Individuals and foundations

Staff: 5
1 Administrative/Fundraising
2 Co-Directors
2 Organizing/writing/editing/researching

Staff openings/year: 0-1

Work Week: 45 + hours

Salary/year: $17,000 (Recent College Graduate); $17,000 (Graduate with advanced degree)

Benefits: Health insurance

Part-Time Employees: None

Volunteers: 2

Interns: 3
Length: Semester
Duties: Varied
Remuneration: $1,000 per semester

Jobs advertised: Environmental job listings, word-of-mouth

To apply: Send resumes to Carl Ross, Co-Director

SAVE OUR CUMBERLAND MOUNTAINS (SOCM)

P.O. Box 457
Jacksboro, TN 37757
(615) 562-6247

Purpose: SOCM is a membership-based and membership-run organization that has been doing community organizing in East Tennessee and the Cumberland Plateau since 1972. Our members work to improve the quality of life in their communities by trying to find solutions to specific local and statewide problems and by focusing on leadership development to create a stronger organization.

Methods of operation: Community organizing (100%); within our organization we have publications, do training, lobbying, research

Constituency: Mostly rural residents of East Tennessee and the Tennessee Cumberland Plateau area

Recent issues and projects: Stripmining; working on garbage and toxics issues; local control over siting of commercial hazardous waste facilities; strengthening the laws protecting full-time and temporary workers; mineral taxation; strengthening surface rights law

Major publications: *SOCM Sentinel*

Budget: $170,000

Funding: Individual contributions, direct mail, events (60%), foundations (40%)

Staff: 8
6 Organizers
1 Office Manager
1 Foundation and Grassroots Fundraiser

Work Week: 40 hours

Salary/year: $16,000 (Recent College Graduate); $18,500 (Graduate with advanced degree)

Benefits: Health insurance, life insurance, pension, paid vacation

Part-Time Employees: 0

Volunteers: Yes

Interns: None at present, willing to accept applications.

Jobs advertised: Local newsletters; *Community Jobs*

To apply: Contact Buck Gorrell

SAVE THE CHILDREN FEDERATION, INC.

54 Wilton Road
Westport, CT 06880
(203) 221-4000

President: Charles F. MacCormack

Purpose: Save The Children makes lasting, positive differences in the lives of disadvantaged children.

Methods of operation: Direct action, public education, training and technical assistance

Constituency: Individuals concerned about the plight of children

Recent issues and projects: Community development programs focussing on health/nutrition; economic opportunity development and early childhood development; and emergency humanitarian relief/rehabilitation

Major publications: Annual Report; *Impact*, quarterly magazine

Budget: $84,947,000

Funding: Individual contributions, foundations, direct mail, U.S. Government AID

Staff: 175
175 at Main Office
3000 in Field Offices

Staff openings/year: Varies

Work Week: Varies hours

Salary/year: $Varies (Recent College Graduate); $Varies (Graduate with advanced degree)

Benefits: Health insurance, pension, paid vacation, life insurance, pregnancy leave

Part-Time Employees: Yes

Volunteers: Yes

Interns: Yes
Length: Varies
Duties: Varies

Jobs advertised: Trade newsletters, newspapers

To apply: Contact Patrick Shields, Recruitment Specialist

SAVE-THE-REDWOODS LEAGUE

114 Sansome Street, Room 605
San Francisco, CA 94104
(415) 362-2352

Director: John B. Dewitt

Purpose: (1) To rescue from destruction representative areas of our primeval forests; (2) To cooperate with the California State Park Commission, the National Park Service, and other agencies, in establishing Redwood parks and other parks and reservations; (3) To purchase Redwood groves by private subscription; (4) To foster and encourage a better and more general understanding of the value of the primeval Redwood or Sequoia and other forests of America as natural objects of extraordinary interest to present and future generations; (5) To support reforestation and conservation of our forest areas.

Methods of operation: Publications (20%), direct action (70%), research (5%), lobbying (5%)

Membership: 50% are Californians; 50% are out-of-state

Recent issues and projects: Acquisition of 2,000 acres of redwoods for addition to Redwood State Park

Major publications: Biannual newsletter; *Guide to Redwood Parks*; *Redwoods of the Past*; *Story Told by a Fallen Redwood*; *Trees, Shrubs and Flowers of the Redwood Region*

Budget: $950,000

Funding: Individual contributions (70%), foundations (15%), direct mail (15%)

Staff: 10
2 Typists
2 Clerks
1 Executive Assistant
1 Writer/Editor
1 Attorney
1 Office Manager
1 Bookkeeper/Accountant
1 Assistant Secretary

Staff openings/year: 0-1

Work Week: 35 hours

Salary/year: $18,500

Benefits: Health insurance, life insurance, pregnancy leave, pension, paid vacation, dental insurance, sick leave

Summer Employees: 1

Interns: No; do not have space or time to train

Jobs advertised: Job openings are filled when vacant from list of candidates who submit resumes to this office.

To apply: Contact John B. Dewitt, Executive Director or Mary Angle-Franzini, Assistant Secretary

Remarks: Since 1918, the Save-the-Redwoods League has helped purchase over 260,000 acres of redwood parklands and donated $75 million for this purpose. This land now forms the core of California's 36 Redwood State Parks and Redwood National Park.

SEARCH FOR COMMON GROUND

1601 Connecticut Ave., NW, Suite 200
Washington, DC 20009
(202) 265-4300

Director: John Marks

Purpose: SCG is an independent, non-profit organization dedicated to finding workable solutions to divisive national and international problems. Our programs aim to channel conflict toward constructive outcomes by employing a common ground approach for discovering possibilities of mutual gain.

Methods of operation: Public education (35%), public education (35%), direct action (15%), publications (15%)

Constituency: Private citizens (in the U.S. and abroad) and NGO's interested in conflict resolution and citizen diplomacy

Recent issues and projects: Recent projects include: The Initiative for Peace and Cooperation in the Middle East; the Initiative for Conflict Management in Russia; search for common ground in South Africa; search for common ground in Macedonia; and the Network for Life and Choice

Major publications: *The Bulletin of Regional Cooperation in the Middle East*, a quarterly publication

Budget: $1,200,000

Funding: Foundations (65%), government (30%), individual contributions (5%)

Staff: 11
1 Writer/Editor
9 Issue Experts
1 Bookkeeper/Accountant

Staff openings/year: 2

Work Week: 40 hours

Salary/year: $17,000 (Recent College Graduate); $24 - 48,000 (Graduate with advanced degree)

Benefits: Health insurance, paid vacation

Part-Time Employees: No

Summer Employees: No

Volunteers: No

Interns: Yes
Length: 6 months to 1 year
Duties: Assist in all aspects of project advancement
Remuneration: Stipend

Jobs advertised: Through related listings, publications, universities and other like organizations

To apply: Please contact Cynthia Wolfe

Remarks: At Search for Common Ground, we are convinced that adversarial ways of dealing with conflict are inadequate and that alternatives exist which maximize the gain of the involved parties. We believe that once adversaries recognize that they share interests, they can often work together and become partners in satisfying mutual needs. To promote the "common ground approach," we conduct workshops and conferences which bring people together for dialogue and collaborative problem solving. All of our programs seek to employ the most advanced methodologies and techniques of conflict resolution. We function as facilitators for the process of working together and working through conflict.

SEATTLE YOUNG PEOPLE'S PROJECT

2366 Eastlake Ave., East, Suite 330
Seattle, WA 98102
(206) 860-9606

Director: Flip Rosenberry

Purpose: The Seattle Young People's Project is a nonprofit, youth action organization dedicated to unconditionally supporting young people in the efforts that they undertake to participate in the social change process.

Methods of operation: Community organizing (45%), direct action (30%), public education (25%)

Constituency: We serve young people, our donors consist of adults within the community

Recent issues and projects: Recent projects include: Project Street Life (homeless youth educating the community); Puget Sound Student Alliance (education reform from the student's perspectives); *Urban Agenda* (newspaper by and for youth of color); sexual harassment in schools (educating students about the issue using forums set up in schools)

Major publications: *Urban Agenda*, newspaper by and for youth of color

Budget: $100,000

Funding: Individual contributions (70%), foundations (25%), direct mail (5%)

Staff: 2
1 Organizer
1 Grassroots fundraiser

Staff openings/year: 1

Work Week: 40 hours

Salary/year: $24,960 (Recent College Graduate); $24,960 (Graduate with advanced degree)

Benefits: Health insurance, paid vacation, pregnancy leave

Part-Time Employees: 4

Summer Employees: 4

Volunteers: 1-5

Interns: Varies
Length: 3-7 months
Duties: Providing support for youth initiated efforts
Remuneration: Varies

Jobs advertised: Through local newspapers and non profit newsletters

To apply: Contact Flip Rosenberry, Executive Director

SERVICE TRAINING FOR ENVIRONMENTAL PROGRESS

202 Architecture Annex, VPI & SU
Blacksburg, VA 24061
(703) 231-6953

Purpose: STEP is a technical assistance program of the Center for Environmental and Hazardous Materials Studies of Virginia Polytechnic Institute and State University (VPI and SU). The program's objectives are to (1) provide resources to communities that lead to the study and resolution of environmental problems; (2) train students in conducting research; and (3) assist and encourage local, community leadership.

Methods of operation: Training and technical assistance (85%), research (10%), public education (5%)

Constituency: We work with community organizations throughout Virginia and West Virginia.

Recent issues and projects: A case study of PCB contamination of the old National Carbide Plant in Ivanhoe, VA; developing a monitoring network on the Rappahannock River; a water quality survey of the North Fork of the Shenandoah River; community health and PCB exposure in Minden, West Virginia.

Budget: $142,000

Funding: Foundations (59%), VA-Tech (31%), community organizations (10%)

Staff: 3
2 STEP Co-Directors
1 Laboratory Technician

Staff openings/year: 1

Work Week: 40 hours

Salary/year: $14,000

Benefits: Health insurance, life insurance, pension, credit union, paid vacation, tuition reimbursement

Interns: 6
Length: 10 weeks
Duties: Work with community organizations by providing technical assistance
Remuneration: $165/week, room and board, travel expenses paid

Jobs advertised: Information is sent to all Virginia and West Virginia four year colleges' and universities' career planning and placement offices and to professors of these institutions who are known to be interested in environmental health problems.

To apply: Contact David Conn at 703-231-7508

SHARE OUR STRENGTH (SOS)

1511 K Street, NW, Suite 623
Washington, DC 20005
(202) 393-2925

Director: Bill Shore

Purpose: SOS works primarily through the restaurant industry to raise funds and awareness for the relief of hunger, homelessness and illiteracy in the U.S. and overseas.

Methods of operation: Grants program, through which SOS distributes nearly $1 million annually (50%), public education (30%), community organizing (10%), publications (7%), research (3%)

Constituency: Restaurant and food service industry

Recent issues and projects: SOS raises most of their funds through the Taste of the Nation event, in which restaurants and wineries donate their products and talents for a nationwide taste festival.

Major publications: Quarterly newsletter: *News From SOS...*; national survey on Good Samaritan Laws in each state

Budget: $1,085,000

Funding: Events (75%), corporate donors (15%), foundations (6%), individual contributions (4%)

Staff: 6
2 Grassroots Fundraisers
1 Organizer
1 Campaign Manager
1 Press Aide
1 Office Manager

Staff openings/year: 2

Work Week: 40+ hours

Salary/year: $16,000 (Recent College Graduate); $Varies (Graduate with advanced degree)

Benefits: Health insurance, paid vacation

Volunteers: 6

Interns: None currently, but willing to accept applications

Jobs advertised: Local newspapers

To apply: Contact Bill Shore, Executive Director

SIERRA CLUB

730 Polk Street
San Francisco, CA 94109
(415) 776-2211

Other Offices: Washington, DC; Saratoga Springs, NY; Annapolis, MD; Birmingham, AL; Madison, WI; Sheridan, WY; Dallas, TX; Boulder, CO; Phoenix, AZ; Salt Lake City, UT; Los Angeles, CA; Oakland, CA; Seattle, WA; Anchorage, AK; North Palm Beach, FL

Director: Carl Pope

Purpose: The Sierra Club is a nonprofit, member-supported, public interest organization that promotes conservation of the natural environment by influencing public policy decisions, legislative, administrative, legal and electoral. Our purpose is to explore, enjoy and protect the wild places of the earth; to practice and promote the responsible use of the earth's ecosystems and resources; to educate and enlist humanity to protect and restore the quality of the natural and human environment; and to use all lawful means to carry out these objectives.

Methods of operation: Research, lobbying, publications, community organizing, public education

Recent issues and projects: Current projects include: Permanent Protection of Public Lands; ancient forests; public lands management reform; Endangered Species Act; Population Stabilization; North American Free Trade Agreement; International Lending Reform; Tropical Hardwoods; Energy; Clean Water/Wetlands; Resource Conservation and Recovery Act (RCRA) and the Centennial Campaign

Major publications: *Sierra* magazine; *National News Report*, 26/year; *Earth Day Source Book*; newsletters

Budget: $35,000,000

Staff: 375
Includes:
Organizers
Writers/Editors
Office Managers
Lobbyists
Media Reps
Foundation Fundraisers
Bookkeepers/Accountants

Chapter Employees
Field Organizers
Financial Analysts

Staff openings/year: 60-80

Work Week: 37.5 hours

Salary/year: $21,000 (Recent College Graduate); $28,000 (Graduate with advanced degree)

Benefits: Health insurance, life insurance, family leave, pension, credit union, paid vacation, trip and merchandise discounts

Part-Time Employees: Yes

Volunteers: Yes

Interns: Yes
Length: Semester
Remuneration: Sometimes stipends

Jobs advertised: Local and national newspapers; employment agencies; specialized periodicals

To apply: Contact Lynn Hawley

SIERRA CLUB - ATLANTIC CHAPTER

353 Hamilton Street
Albany, NY 12210
(518) 426-9144

Other Offices: New York, NY

Director: John Stouffer

Purpose: To ensure the enactment of sound environmental legislation through public education and lobbying the New York State legislature.

Methods of operation: Lobbying (50%), community organizing (20%), publications (10%), community organizing (20%), public education (10%)

Recent issues and projects: Recent projects include: enactment (in 1993) of the NYS Environmental Protection Act; NYS Clean Air Compliance Act (conforming with 1990 Federal Mandate); Cancellation of energy purchase contracts between NYS and Hydro-Quebec, the developer of James any.

Major publications: *Sierra Atlantic*, a state-wide newsletter

Staff: 1
1 Organizer/Writer/Lobbyist/Press

Staff openings/year: .5

Benefits: Health insurance, dental insurance, life insurance, family leave

Part-Time Employees: 3

Summer Employees: None

Volunteers: Varies

Interns: 4
Length: One semester
Duties: Track legislation through committee process; draft letters, factsheets and articles for distribution and possible publication.
Remuneration: None

Jobs advertised: Internal newsletters, newspapers, word-of-mouth

To apply: Please contact Bob Kerr, Staff and Personnel Committee Chair

SIERRA CLUB - NEW JERSEY CHAPTER

57 Mountain Avenue
Princeton, NJ 08540
(609) 924-3141

Other Offices: San Francisco, CA; Washington, DC

Director: Tim Dillingham

Purpose: To preserve, protect and enjoy our natural resources, through citizen based action in legislative issues involving clean air, land use, urban revitalization, clean water and solid waste management.

Methods of operation: Community organizing (40%), lobbying (35%), public education (15%), research (5%), training and technical assistance (5%)

Membership: 16,000 members statewide; 600,000 nationwide and in Canada

Recent issues and projects: We are sponsoring a series of hikes into the NY/NJ Highlands, a region of Northern New Jersey and Southern New York experiencing unmanaged growth and poor land use patterns.

Major publications: *The Jersey Sierran* quarterly, statewide newsletter to members and subscribers

Budget: $125,000

Funding: Individual contributions (80%), foundations (10%), direct mail (10%)

Staff: 1
1 Director
2 Part-time Workers

Work Week: 40-50 hours

Salary/year: $30,000 (Recent College Graduate); $35,000 (Graduate with advanced degree)

Benefits: Health insurance, paid vacation

Part-Time Employees: 2

Summer Employees: None

Volunteers: 75

Interns: 5
Length: One semester
Duties: Research, environmental legislation in NJ legislature and in U.S. Congress; grassroots organizing basics
Remuneration: Based on ability to secure grant or project specific

Jobs advertised: Newspapers and other environmental organizations

To apply: Interested applicants should inquire to NJ Chapter Sierra Club, 57 Mountain Ave., Princeton, NJ 08540

SIERRA CLUB LEGAL DEFENSE FUND

180 Montgomery Street, Suite 1400
San Francisco, CA 94104
(415) 627-6700

Other Offices: Denver, CO; Juneau, AK; Washington, DC; Seattle, WA; Honolulu, HI; Tallahassee, FL; New Orleans, LA; Bozeman, MT

Director: Vanter Parker

Purpose: Providing legal representation to the environmental movement

Methods of operation: Litigation (96%), publications (2%), public education (2%)

Constituency: 120,000 individual supporters nationwide

Recent issues and projects: Litigation to preserve forests, parks, endangered species and to abate air pollution, toxic contamination, water pollution, etc.

Major publications: Quarterly newsletter: *In Brief*; *The Poisoned Well: New Strategies for Groundwater Protection* (Island Press, 1989); *Wild By Law*

Budget: $9,500,000

Funding: Individual contributions (75%), foundations (15%), court-awarded fees and expenses (10%)

Staff: 100
33 Attorneys
25 Secretaries
8 Office Managers
3 Management
7 Researchers
5 Fundraisers
2 Bookkeepers/Accountants
2 Writers/Editors
15 Other

Staff openings/year: 15

Work Week: 35 hours

Salary/year: $20,000 (Recent College Graduate); $28,000 law (Graduate with advanced degree)

Benefits: Health insurance, life insurance, pregnancy leave, pension, paid vacation

Part-Time Employees: 3

Summer Employees: Yes; law clerks

Interns: Law clerks/legal interns
Length: 3 months
Duties: Legal research, writing
Remuneration: Modest stipend

Jobs advertised: Local newspapers, word-of-mouth

To apply: For non-legal positions, contact Nanci Peterson legal positions, contact Vawter Parker

SILICON VALLEY TOXICS COALITION

760 North First Street
San Jose, CA 95112
(408) 287-6707

Director: Ted Smith

Purpose: Our purpose is to protect people from the hazards of the high-tech electronics industry, to seek new methods of technological production that are occupationally and environmentally benign and to push for the cleanup of the degradation of the workplace and environment that has already taken place.

Methods of operation: Public education (20%), community organizing (20%), training and technical assistance (20%), research (10%), lobbying (10%), publications (10%), direct action (10%)

Constituency: Neighborhood residents affected by toxics; unions and their members; environmentalists; public health workers; etc.

Recent issues and projects: Superfund cleanup (29 sites, the most in the nation); efforts to promote the phaseout of CFCs and other chemicals that are destroying the ozone layer; organizing efforts to reduce reproductive hazards on the job; development of a new Toxic Gas Model ordinance; use of SARA Title III data to pressure the electronics industry to use fewer and less toxic chemicals; promoting the clean-up and conversion of military bases and defense contractors

Major publications: Quarterly newsletter: *Silicon Valley Toxics Action*; *The Legacy of High-Tech Development*; *From Day Care to DARPA: Bargaining for a New Industrial Policy*

Budget: $240,000

Funding: Foundations (60%), individual contributions (30%), events, government (10%)

Staff: 4
1 Executive Director
1 Program Director
1 Administrative Director
1 Administrative Assistant

Staff openings/year: 1-2

Work Week: 50-60 hours

Salary/year: $25,000 (Recent College Graduate); $28,000 (Graduate with advanced degree)

Benefits: Health insurance, tuition reimbursement, paid vacation

Summer Employees: 1-3

Volunteers: 25

Interns: 3-44
Length: 1 semester
Duties: Research and organizing
Remuneration: School credit; sometimes work-study

Jobs advertised: Through our newsletter and other newsletters

To apply: Contact Ted Smith, Executive Director

Remarks: The SVTC was formed in response to the January 20, 1982 discovery that deadly chemicals used and stored at the Fairchild Semiconductor plant in South San Jose had poisoned the drinking water supplies of an entire neighborhood.

SLEEPY CREEK FARM

Route 2, Box 211
Berkeley Springs, WV 25411
(304) 258-4018

Other Offices: Washington, DC

Director: Norman Hunter

Purpose: To provide food free from pesticides and herbicides, organically grown, at a price people can afford.

Methods of operation: Farming, marketing

Recent issues and projects: Upgrading farm housing

Funding: Marketing (100%)

Staff: 8
4-6 Farmhands
2 Owners

Staff openings/year: 4

Work Week: 50 hours

Benefits: Housing, board, all necessities, Social Security, workers' compensation

Part-Time Employees: 4

Summer Employees: 4

Volunteers: Yes

Interns: Yes
Length: 12 months
Duties: Learning basic farming and homesteading skills
Remuneration: Depends on length of time committed

Jobs advertised: *Community Jobs*; *Peace Corps Hotline*; various magazines and newspapers

To apply: Contact Norman Hunter

Remarks: We seek people who are committed to learning alternative agriculture. Experience is not necessary.

SNAKE RIVER ALLIANCE

P.O. Box 1731
Boise, ID 83701
(208) 344-9161

Other Offices: Boise, ID; Pocatello, ID

Director: Beatrice Braitsford

Purpose: Disarmament and environmental protection focusing on Department of Energy nuclear facility in Idaho. National work on peace and nuclear waste issues.

Methods of operation: Public education (45%), community organizing (27%), lobbying (10%), direct action (5%), research (10%), litigation (3%)

Constituency: Diverse cross section of southern Idaho with scattering from northern Idaho, Wyoming and the nation

Recent issues and projects: Campaign to stop special isotope separation plutonium plant; campaign to stop new tritium production reactors; campaign to clean up nuclear and hazardous wastes at Idaho National Engineering Lab

Major publications: Monthly newsletter; monthly issue *Bulletin*

Budget: $175,000

Funding: Individual contributions (50%), foundations (50%)

Staff: 4

Work Week: 40 hours

Salary/year: $Varies (Recent College Graduate); $Varies (Graduate with advanced degree)

Benefits: Health insurance, paid vacation

Part-Time Employees: 0

Volunteers: 10

Interns: None currently, but willing to accept applications

Jobs advertised: Local newspapers and organization newsletter

To apply: Contact Nicole LeFavour, Boise Area Coordinator

SOCIETY OF ENVIRONMENTAL JOURNALISTS

9425 Stenton Ave., Suite 209
Philadelphia, PA 19118
(215) 247-9710

Director: Beth Parke

Purpose: To enhance the quality and accuracy of environmental reporting.

Methods of operation: Publications, training and technical assistance

Constituency: Journalists, journalism students and educators

Recent issues and projects: National Conference in 1993

Major publications: *SE Journal*, quarterly

Funding: Foundations, dues

Staff: 2
1 Office Manager
1 Foundation Fundraiser

Staff openings/year: 0-1

Work Week: 40 hours

Benefits: Health insurance, paid vacation, pregnancy leave

Part-Time Employees: 1

Summer Employees: Sometimes

Volunteers: 2-3

Interns: None

Jobs advertised: Newspapers, *SE Journal*

To apply: Please contact Christine Rigel, Systems Manager and Program Assistant

---

SOJOURNERS

2401 15th Street, NW
Washington, DC 20009
(202) 328-8842

Director: Jim Wallis

Purpose: *Sojourners* seeks to be a voice of renewal within the churches and a prophetic voice of social change within society. *Sojourners* is a meeting place for people from diverse backgrounds who are turning their lives toward a gospel vision of justice and peace.

Methods of operation: Publications (75%), direct action (10%), research (4%), community organizing (10%), public education (1%)

Constituency: Dominantly people from the Christian faith who are committed to peace and justice

Recent issues and projects: Recent issues of *Sojourners* focused on issues ranging from the environmental crisis to El Salvador, to women and poverty, to the blossoming of democracy around the world.

Major publications: *Sojourners* magazine

Budget: $1,200,000

Funding: Membership (85%), other (15%)

Staff: 25
9 Writer/Editors
5 Typists
3 Researchers
2 Organizers
2 Issue Experts
2 Office Managers
1 Bookkeeper/Typist
1 Press Aide

Staff openings/year: 4

Work Week: 37 hours

Salary/year: $18,000

Benefits: Health insurance, pregnancy leave, paid vacation

Part-Time Employees: 4

Volunteers: 1

Interns: 5
Length: 1 year
Duties: Various staff support responsibilities
Remuneration: Room, board, health benefits, subsistency stipend

Jobs advertised: Usually through our magazine; occasionally through job services

To apply: Contact Joe Roos, Publisher

SOUTH DAKOTA PEACE AND JUSTICE CENTER

123 1/2 E. Kerrys, P.O. Box 405
Watertown, SD 57201
(605) 882-2822

Director: Legia L. Spicer

Purpose: The South Dakota Peace and Justice center is a statewide, interfaith, grassroots organization whose members work on social issues from a spiritual foundation. The Center, founded in 1979, has over 700 members, including individuals, congregations, organizations and institutions. Our goal is to change social structures toward a more just application to the entire population through education and action in 6 major areas.

Methods of operation: Public education (45%), community organizing (20%), research (10%), direct action (10%), publications (5%), training and technical assistance (5%), lobbying (3%)

Membership: Over 700 members including: 4 races; all classes; all ages; interfaith (including Native American traditional)

Recent issues and projects: Current Center priority issues include: Native American/reconciliation; economic development that is environmentally/socially sound and that prioritizes family agriculture; disarmament/peace conversion; poverty/hunger; Central America; revocation of death penalty

Major publications: *South Dakota Sun*, newsletter published 6 times a year

Budget: $67,500

Funding: Individual contributions (70%), foundations (30%)

Staff: 1
1 Director and Advocate

Staff openings/year: 0

Work Week: 40 hours

Salary/year: $18,000 (Recent College Graduate); $20,000 (Graduate with advanced degree)

Benefits: Health insurance, pension (small), paid vacation (4 weeks)

Part-Time Employees: 1

Summer Employees: None

Volunteers: Varies

Interns: 2 in past 2 years
Length: 3 weeks to 3 months
Duties: Administrative functions, computer assistance, field work
Remuneration: Interns must pay own living expenses

Jobs advertised: *Community Jobs*

To apply: Contact Legia L. Spicer, Director

SOUTH END PRESS

116 Saint Botolph Street
Boston, MA 02115
(617) 266-0629

Purpose: South End Press is a nonprofit, collectively run book publisher for progressive movement activists and academics.

Methods of operation: Publications (100%)

Constituency: Activists and academics

Major publications: New titles include: *Sisters of the Yam*; *Rethinking Camelot*; *Global Visions*; *The New Resource Wars*; *Private Interests, Public Spending*

Budget: $1,500,000

Funding: Sales (100%)

Staff: 6
6 Writer/Editors

Staff openings/year: 1

Work Week: 40-45 hours

Salary/year: $27,500 (Recent College Graduate); $Varies (Graduate with advanced degree)

Benefits: Health insurance, dependent allowance, family leave, paid vacation, sabbatical

Part-Time Employees: 0

Interns: 3
Length: 3-6 months
Duties: Combination of editorial and publishing
Remuneration: No stipend available; sorry

Jobs advertised: Ads, flyers

To apply: Contact Personnel Coordinator

Remarks: Applicants for full-time positions must be familiar with political theory from the left, feminist or anti-racist perspectives. Activist experience is important as well. Must be committed to radical social change.

SOUTH PROVIDENCE TUTORIAL, INC.

1 Louisa Street
Providence, RI 02905
(401) 785-2126

Director: Malvene J. Brice

Purpose: Specifically, but not exclusively, the mission of the organization is to conduct an after-school/summer tutorial program, staffed by volunteers and paid employees, for the children in the South Providence neighborhood. The purpose of this program is to supplement and broaden the education of school-aged children, to enhance the students' abilities to grow academically and to enable them to perform better within the normal school system.

Methods of operation: Human services, training and technical assistance

Constituency: Low-income minority groups with very low literacy rates.

Recent issues and projects: Monitoring the Providence School Department Desegregation Plan at a high-school level.

Budget: $150,000

Funding: Individual contributions (10%), foundations (40%), direct mail (5%), grant writing (45%)

Staff: 3
1 Program Director
1 Executive Director
1 Executive Secretary

Staff openings/year: 3

Work Week: 35 hours

Salary/year: $22,000 (Recent College Graduate); $36,000 (Graduate with advanced degree)

Benefits: Health insurance, paid vacation

Part-Time Employees: 3

Summer Employees: 2-4

Volunteers: 25-50

Interns: Varies
Length: 1 semester
Duties: Case work, resource instructor, master tutoring
Remuneration: 100% by resource agency

Jobs advertised: Postings at related organizations

To apply: Contact Malvene J. Brice, Executive Director

SOUTHEAST ALASKA CONSERVATION COUNCIL (SEACC)

419 6th Street, #328
Juneau, AK 99801
(907) 586-6942

Other Offices: Washington, DC

Director: Kate Crockett

Purpose: SEACC is a grassroots conservation coalition for Southeast Alaska. Comprised of 15 member groups plus over 1,000 individuals, SEACC is dedicated to preserving the integrity of Southeast Alaska's magnificent environment. The protection of the renewable resource values found in our region's old growth forests is essential for perpetuating the unique way of life in our region.

Methods of operation: Community organizing

(50%), publications (10%), public education (10%), litigation (10%), lobbying (10%), research (10%)

Constituency: Southeast Alaskan residents, fishermen, hunters, small loggers, government employees, out-of-state individuals.

Recent issues and projects: National and regional campaign to reform management of the Tongass National Forest. The Tongass is our nation's largest National Forest and contains the last large uncut tracts of North America's coastal, temperate rain forest.

Major publications: Quarterly newsletter: *The Ravencall*

Funding: Individual contributions (60%), foundations (40%)

Staff: 7
1 Executive Director
2 Organizers
1 Attorney
1 Issues Expert
1 Office Manager
2 Part-Time Administrators/Bookkeepers

Staff openings/year: 0-1

Work Week: 40 hours

Salary/year: $Varies (Recent College Graduate); $Varies (Graduate with advanced degree)

Benefits: Health and dental insurance, paid vacation and sick leave

Part-Time Employees: 2

Volunteers: Yes

Interns: None currently, but willing to accept applications

Jobs advertised: Local media

To apply: Contact Linda Murray, Executive Director.

SOUTHERN CENTER FOR HUMAN RIGHTS

83 Poplar Street, NW
Atlanta, GA 30303
(404) 688-1202

Director: Stephen B. Bright

Purpose: To enforce the prohibition against cruel and unusual punishment and to eliminate discrimination and other human rights abuses against racial minorities, the poor and the disadvantaged in the criminal justice systems and correctional facilities.

Methods of operation: Litigation (60%), public education (15%), training and technical assistance (15%), community organizing (10%)

Constituency: Prisoners in prisons and jails in eleven Southern states; those condemned to die in those same states

Recent issues and projects: Challenges to exclusion of minorities from the criminal justice system; efforts to bring about systemic improvement of the quality of legal representation to persons facing the death penalty; challenges to cruel and inhumane conditions in prisons and jails, including discrimination against women prisoners; community education programs on alternatives to incarceration for many crimes and discriminatory use of the death penalty; training programs on providing representation to those facing the death penalty and prisoners.

Major publications: Two reports each quarter: *Discrimination and Death* on the death penalty work, and *Prison and Jails Report*, on prison and jail litigation

Budget: $600,000

Funding: Foundations (85%), individual contributions (15%)

Staff: 15
9 Attorneys
1 Organizer
1 Paralegal
1 Office Manager
1 Administrative Assistant
1 Investigator
1 Secretary

Staff openings/year: 1

Work Week: 60 hours

Salary/year: $20,000

Benefits: Health insurance, life insurance, paid vacation

Part-Time Employees: 1

Volunteers: 1

Interns: 6
Length: Flexible
Duties: Investigation, legal research, client contact and community education. We accept students for any type of internships or externships.
Remuneration: Depends upon the need of the student

Jobs advertised: Mailings to law schools, notices in various publications

To apply: Contact Stephen B. Bright, Director

Remarks: The Center spreads its resources as far as possible to do as much as possible with limited funds. Those interested in applying for positions should be committed to work on behalf of the imprisoned and condemned, willing to work long hours, and willing to work for salaries far below what is generally expected in the legal profession.

SOUTHERN CHRISTIAN LEADERSHIP CONFERENCE

334 Auburn Avenue, NE
Atlanta, GA 30312
(404) 522-1420

President: Dr. Joseph E. Lowery

Purpose: To provide moral and spiritual leadership, and stimulate mass involvement of people in the struggle against racial oppression.

Methods of operation: Research, lobbying, litigation, publications, human services, organizing, public education, nonviolent protest

Recent issues and projects: National AIDS Program; Women's Health Program: "Wings of Hope" anti-drug program; SCLC Women's Learning Center - to help people get their G.E.D.; Anti-Ku Klux Klan network; study on the crisis in health care for blacks and poor whites; waged successful campaign to make Dr. Martin Luther King Jr.'s birthday a national holiday

Major publications: *SCLC Magazine*, four to six times a year

Funding: Membership, contributions

Staff: 35
Includes:
President
Office Administrators
Crisis Intervention Committee
Receptionists
Administrative Assistants
National AIDS Program Coordinators
Women's Health Program Coordinators
Director of Fundraising
Membership Director
Chapters and Affiliates Director
Printer
Wings of Hope Program Director
Student Affairs Director
Communications Director

Staff openings/year: 1

Work Week: 60 hours

Benefits: Health insurance, life insurance, pregnancy leave, paid vacation, dental insurance

Part-Time Employees: 6

Volunteers: Yes

Interns: Yes
Length: 3 months
Duties: Depends on department
Remuneration: Varies: stipend, work-study, volunteer

Jobs advertised: *SCLC Magazine*; newspaper

To apply: Contact Reverend Osburn

Remarks: SCLC has 300 chapters nationwide.

SOUTHERN COMMUNITY PARTNERS

PO Box 19745, 100 William Jones Bldg./NCCU
Durham, NC 27707
(919) 683-1840

Director: Julia Scatliff

Purpose: The Southern Community Partners Program seeks young people who propose projects which inspire other young people to meet the pressing community needs in the south. Each year, we award up to seven two-year individual grants of $54,000.

Methods of operation: Public education (20%), training and technical assistance (80%)

Recent issues and projects: Projects and issues range from building partnerships with public schools to developing community service programs at historically black colleges and universities to connecting the arts with community organizing and more.

Budget: $500,000

Funding: Foundations (100%)

Staff: 9
7 Organizers
2 Office Managers

Staff openings/year: 7

Work Week: 40 hours

Salary/year: $16,500

Benefits: Health insurance, life insurance, and paid vacation

Part-Time Employees: 0

Summer Employees: 0

Volunteers: 0

Interns: Varies
Length: Varies

Jobs advertised: Direct mailing

To apply: Contact Antonia Smith, Program Associate (919) 683-1840

SOUTHERN EMPOWERMENT PROJECT

323 Ellis Avenue
Maryville, TN 37801
(615) 984-6500

Director: June Rostan

Purpose: SEP was created to recruit and train new community organizers for Southern member-based organizations and to develop training and skills workshops to improve the quality of Southern organizing. Much of SEP's training centers on building strong, member-run organizations that use direct action organizing as their primary approach to winning an issue.

Methods of operation: Training and technical assistance, planning and development (90%)

Membership: Eight member-based organizations

Recent issues and projects: Fall workshop: "Using Training in Organizing" workshop on coalition building for Grassroots Assembly Day in Nashville; 109 trainees have participated in the SEP organizers school in its first seven years.

Major publications: *Southern Empowerment Project News* (free on request); *Current Jobs* information for graduates and other interested parties

Budget: $100,000

Staff: 3
1 Coordinator
1 Recruiter
1 Trainer

Work Week: 40 hours

Salary/year: $20,000

Benefits: Health insurance, life insurance, pension coming

Interns: 15-20
Length: 6 weeks f-t; 1-4 weeks p-t
Duties: Six weeks of training in three states at four sites plus field placements
Remuneration: Write for fee, stipend and scholarship information since details change each year.

Jobs advertised: Through organizations, mailings, news releases, campus visits, public service announcements

To apply: Contact Walter Davis or Rosemary Derrick

Remarks: SEP's 9 member organizations are: Community Farm Alliance, Kentuckians for the Commonwealth, Just Organized Neighborhoods Area Headquarters (JONAH), Solutions to Issues of Concern to Knoxvillians, Save Our Cumberland Mountains, Charlotte Organizing Project, the North Carolina A. Philip Randolph Institute, Citizens Organized to End Poverty in the Commonwealth and Western North Carolina Alliance.

SOUTHERN FINANCE PROJECT

329 Rensselder Ave.
Charlotte, NC 28203
(704) 338-7754

Other Offices: Durham, NC

Director: Tom Schlesinger

Purpose: SFP monitors financial markets and policy issues. The center provides research, analysis and policy development services to citizen groups, policymakers and journalists.

Methods of operation: Research, public education, training and technical assistance, policy development, publications

Constituency: Grassroots organizations, unions, journalists, public agencies and officials

Recent issues and projects: Research on insurance industry and retirement income security; helped spearhead Financial Democracy Campaign.

Budget: $125,000

Funding: Individual contributions, foundations

Staff: 2
2 Researchers

Staff openings/year: 1

Work Week: 40-60 hours

Salary/year: $22,000

Benefits: Health insurance, pregnancy leave, paid vacation

Part-Time Employees: Yes

Summer Employees: Yes

Volunteers: Yes

Interns: Yes
Length: 3 months
Duties: Research and analysis, publications production, etc.

Jobs advertised: Classifieds; electronic billboards; university placement services

To apply: Contact Tom Schlesinger, Director

SOUTHERN POVERTY LAW CENTER, INC.

400 Washington Avenue
Montgomery, AL 36195-5101
(205) 264-0286

Director: Edward Ashworth

Purpose: To advance the legal rights of impoverished victims of injustice through public education and litigation.

Methods of operation: Public education (50%), litigation (30%), publications (10%), research (10%)

Constituency: Individuals nationwide through direct mail

Recent issues and projects: Voting rights; litigation against the Ku Klux Klan, Skinheads and other white supremacist organizations; discrimination; class action suits; hate crimes

Major publications: *SPLC Report*, quarterly; *Seeking Justice*, a brief history and objectives of the Center; *The Klan: A History of Racism and Violence*; *Free at Last*; *Intelligence Report*, a publication of Klanwatch; Teaching Tolerance Kits and Magazines, publications of Teaching Tolerance Department

Budget: $5,537,000

Funding: Individual contributions (94%), bequests and grants (6%)

Staff: 48
19 Typists, Clerical Assistants
4 Attorneys
8 Office Managers
4 Researchers
4 Writer/Editors
3 Foundation Fundraisers
3 Paralegal
2 Organizer
1 Bookkeeper/Accountant

Staff openings/year: 2

Work Week: 35 hours

Salary/year: $25,000 (Recent College Graduate); $35,000 (Graduate with advanced degree)

Benefits: Health insurance, life insurance, paid vacation, 403(b), (7) retirement plan

Part-Time Employees: 4

Summer Employees: 1

Volunteers: 0

Interns: Yes
Length: 3 months
Duties: Paralegal, research
Remuneration: Usually receive college credits

Jobs advertised: Through colleges, newspapers, agencies

To apply: Contact JoAnn Chancellor, Administrator, Secretary-Treasurer

---

SOUTHERNERS FOR ECONOMIC JUSTICE

P.O. Box 240
Durham, NC 27702-0240
(919) 683-1361

Director: Cynthia Brown

Purpose: Comprised of workers, civil rights and religious leaders and activists. Southerners for Economic Justice is a multi-racial, inter-faith, nonprofit organization committed to enabling workers to direct the institutions and policies affecting them. Since 1976 SET has championed the economic and political advancements of the South's unorganized working poor through documentation and publications, worker organization, leadership development and education, public policy advocacy, church partnerships and coalition building.

Methods of operation: Community organizing (60%), publications (10%), public education (10%), training and technical assistance (10%), research (5%), lobbying (5%)

Constituency: Low-income and marginalized

workers in primarily in the triangle area

Recent issues and projects: Recent projects include: Work Youth Project which develops leadership and advocacy skills to enable them to address immediate concerns in home, school and work; The Working Women's Organizing Project helps women workers eradicate the root causes of their poverty; and the Public Policy Education Project documents trends in the Southern economy, compiles alternative economic strategies and proposals and provides technical assistance.

Major publications: *Common Good*, quarterly newsletter; *Betrayal of Trust*; *Everybody's Business: A People's Guide to Survival*; *Building Just Relationships for the Next 500 Years*

Budget: $230,000

Funding: Foundations (91%), other (8%), individual contributions (1%)

Staff: 4
2 Organizers
1 Foundation Fundraiser
1 Training and Technical Assistant
1/4 Writer/Editor
1/4 Bookkeeper/Accountant
1/4 Grassroots Fundraiser

Staff openings/year: 1

Work Week: 40 hours

Salary/year: $18,000 (Recent College Graduate); $23,000 (Graduate with advanced degree)

Benefits: Health insurance, paid vacation, life insurance, family leave

Part-Time Employees: Varies

Summer Employees: None

Volunteers: Varies

Interns: Varies
Length: 1 semester to 1 year
Duties: Assist organizers
Remuneration: School credit

Jobs advertised: Local newspapers, announcements to organizations in network

To apply: Please contact Colleen Lanigan, Fiscal Development Director

SOUTHFACE ENERGY INSTITUTE

P.O. Box 5506
Atlanta, GA 30307
(404) 525-7657

Director: Dennis Creech

Purpose: A private, nonprofit energy education and research organization with concentrations in energy efficient construction, passive solar design, water conservation, and southeastern U.S. energy issues

Methods of operation: Training and technical assistance (35%), public education (35%), research (20%), publications (10%)

Constituency: Mostly southeastern; consumers interested in energy conservation/environmental issues; conscientious building and energy professionals

Recent issues and projects: Solar demonstration projects; research on indoor air quality and healthy homes; installation of xeriscape and graywater irrigation system at our office; ongoing sessions of the Homebuilding School courses

Major publications: Quarterly: *The Southface Journal of Energy and Building Technology*

Budget: $450,000

Funding: Contract projects (90%), individual contributions (5%), direct mail (5%)

Staff: 8
2 Issue Experts
2 Researchers
1 Office Manager
1 Press Aide
1 Typist
1 Graphic Artist

Staff openings/year: 1

Work Week: 40 hours

Salary/year: $13,000 (Recent College Graduate); $20,000 (Graduate with advanced degree)

Benefits: Health insurance, pregnancy leave, paid vacation

Volunteers: Yes

Interns: 4 per year
Length: 3 months
Duties: Assist with Southface projects
Remuneration: $320/month stipend plus $200/month for housing

Jobs advertised: *Southface Journal*; local papers

and journals of environmental organizations

To apply: Contact June Gartrell, Internship Coordinator

Remarks: Southface is headquartered in a renovated Victorian house which serves as an Alternative Energy Demonstration Center, open to the public. We have a library and are available to answer technical questions. Southface runs a Homebuilding School which focuses on energy efficient construction. The Savannah, GA office is the Coastal Energy Institute.

SOUTHWEST ORGANIZING PROJECT (SWOP)

211 10th Street, SW
Albuquerque, NM 87102
(505) 247-8832

Director: Jeanne Gauna

Purpose: To empower the disenfranchised in the southwest to realize racial and gender equality, and social and economic justice.

Methods of operation: Community organizing (50%), research (10%), publications (10%), direct action (10%), public education (10%), training and technical assistance (10%)

Constituency: Primarily low-income, working class people of color, mostly Chicano-Latino

Recent issues and projects: Recent projects include: work on environmental and economic justice; campaigns on worker/community impacts of micro-electronics industry; opposition to education on NAFTA; border justice; electoral participation; sustainable development

Major publications: *Voces Unidas*, quarterly newsletter; *500 Years of Chicano History in Pictures*; *Intel Inside New Mexico*

Budget: $175,000

Funding: Foundations (60%), material sales (20%), individual contributions (10%), direct mail (10%)

Staff: 4
2 Organizers
1/2 Writer/Editor
1/2 Researcher
1/2 Foundation Fundraiser
1/2 Grassroots Fundraiser

Staff openings/year: 1

Work Week: 50 hours

Salary/year: $16,000

Benefits: Health insurance, paid vacation

Part-Time Employees: 1

Summer Employees: 1

Volunteers: 30

Interns: 1
Length: 1 year
Duties: Varies
Remuneration: Usually outside funding (churches and universities)

Jobs advertised: Local newspapers

To apply: Contact Jeanne Gauna, Director

SOUTHWEST RESEARCH AND INFORMATION CENTER

P.O. Box 4524
Albuquerque, NM 87106
(505) 262-1862

Other Offices: Washington, DC; Espanola, NM

Director: Don Hancock, Administrator

Purpose: SRIC's purpose is to provide high quality information to the public and technical assistance to citizen groups on natural resources, energy, and environmental issues to promote more involvement of affected citizens.

Methods of operation: Public education (35%), training and technical assistance (35%), research (20%), publications (10%)

Constituency: Primarily community groups

Recent issues and projects: Nuclear waste safety, opposing the WIPP project, a nuclear waste disposal site; developing a national citizens' network on oil and gas wastes; assisting low-income communities affected by contaminated water supplies; helping develop a statewide solid waste program, including waste minimization and recycling

Major publications: Quarterly magazine: *The Workbook*

Budget: $275,000

Funding: Foundations (65%), individual contributions (20%), sales, consulting (15%)

Staff: 8
7 Issue Experts
1 Writer/Editor

ings/year:** 1

eek: 50 hours

Sa... ear: $16,000 (Recent College Graduate); $20,000 (Graduate with advanced degree)

Benefits: Health insurance, life insurance, pension/profit sharing, tuition reimbursement, paid vacation

Part-Time Employees: 3

Volunteers: 1-3

Interns: 1-2
Length: 1-4 months
Duties: Research and writing; depends in part on issue focus
Remuneration: Usually interns get college credit or have some financial assistance from college or other source.

Jobs advertised: Local newspapers, notices to community groups

To apply: Contact Don Hancock, Administrator

ST. ELIZABETH SHELTER
804 Alarid St.
Santa Fe, NM 87501
(505) 982-6611

Director: Hank Hughes

Purpose: Providing shelter and related services to the homeless individuals and families of today. Working toward the end of homelessness in the future.

Methods of operation: Human services (100%)

Constituency: Homeless individuals and families; those concerned with the problem of homelessness

Recent issues and projects: Continued projects to provide transitional housing for the homeless; working toward obtaining permanent housing as well

Major publications: *Home at St. E's*

Budget: $500,000

Funding: Individual contributions (30%), foundations (20%), direct mail (30%), government grants (20%)

Staff: 4
2 Caseworkers
2 Shelter Directors

Staff openings/year: 6

Work Week: 35-40 hours

Salary/year: $17,000 (Recent College Graduate); $20,000 (Graduate with advanced degree)

Benefits: Health insurance, paid vacation, housing, board

Part-Time Employees: 5

Summer Employees: 0

Volunteers: 100

Interns: 5
Length: 6 months to 1 year
Duties: Varies
Remuneration: Room and Board, Health insurance and stipend

Jobs advertised: Local newspapers and community internship offers

To apply: Contact Hank Hughes, Executive Director

STUDENT COALITION FOR ACTION IN LITERACY EDUCATION
Unv. of North Carolina, CB #3500
Chapel Hill, NC 27599
(919) 962-1542

Director: Lisa Madry

Purpose: To mobilize college student involvement with literacy education. We assist college students with starting and strengthening their campus-based literacy program.

Methods of operation: Community organizing (30%), public education (30%), training and technical assistance (30%), publications (10%)

Constituency: College students, literacy practitioners (these are folks we mobilize). They in turn provide literacy education in their communities. These populations vary tremendously in terms of age, income, etc.

Recent issues and projects: Recent projects include: Literacy Impact Campaign, a program for any college student who wants to start a campus-based literacy program. We provide support such as training resources, community relations and program management.

Major publications: *Foresight* a bi-monthly newsletter; *Approaches to Literacy*, a campus tutors guide; *Literacy Impact Organizing Handbook*; *Literacy Resource Guide*; *The Politics of Literacy Programs*; *Mobilizing Student Leaders in Literacy*

Budget: $350,000

Funding: Foundations (80%), individual contributions (20%)

Staff: 18
7 Organizers
1 Writer/Editor
2 Office Managers
1 Foundation Fundraiser
2 Issue Experts
1 Bookkeepers/Accountant
1 Executive Director
1 Managing Director
1 Program Director
1 Fund Development Coordinator

Staff openings/year: 8

Work Week: 40 hours

Salary/year: $20,000 (Recent College Graduate); $22,000 (Graduate with advanced degree)

Benefits: Health insurance, paid vacation, life insurance, credit union, family leave, board, tuition reimbursement

Part-Time Employees: 8

Summer Employees: 1-2

Volunteers: 1-5 (varies)

Interns: 1-2
Length: 3 months (summer)
Duties: Coordinate National Literacy Action Week and our national conferences
Remuneration: Paid hourly for 40 hours a week with no benefits

Jobs advertised: On internet, national newspapers, newsletters, direct mail from database

To apply: Please contact Kim Gordon, Managing Director

STUDENT CONSERVATION ASSOCIATION

P.O. Box 550
Charlestown, NH 03603
(603) 826-5206

Other Offices: Washington, DC; Seattle, WA; Boulder, CO; Newark, NJ; Los Angeles, CA; Oakland, CA

President: Scott Izzo

Purpose: SCA offers students and adults the opportunity to assist in conservation work in the National Park Service, U.S. Forest Service and other federal and state agencies nationwide.

Methods of operation: Direct action (75%), public education (15%)

Constituency: Past participants, people interested in conservation work

Recent issues and projects: Greater Yellowstone Recovery Corps; Earthwork

Major publications: *JobScan*; *Resource Assistant Listing of Opportunities*; *High School Work Group Listing of Opportunities*; biannual member newsletter; *Conservation Career Development Program Opportunities*

Budget: $6,300,000

Funding: Federal agreements (45%), individual contributions (25%), foundations (15%), direct mail (15%)

Staff: 60
Including:
4 Directors
8 Program Managers
3 Typists
3 Bookkeeper/Accountants
10 Program Directors
2 Office Managers
1 Canvasser
1 Foundation Fundraiser
1 Grassroots Fundraiser

Staff openings/year: 3-5

Work Week: 45+ hours

Salary/year: $25,000 (Recent College Graduate); $Varies (Graduate with advanced degree)

Benefits: Health insurance, pregnancy leave, paid vacation, credit union, tuition reimbursement

Part-Time Employees: 10+

Summer Employees: 100+

Volunteers: 1,000+

Interns: 1,000+
Length: 12 weeks
Duties: Varies, depending on area (over 400 nationally)
Remuneration: Travel, subsistence stipend, housing provided

Jobs advertised: National magazines; newspapers; our magazine *Earthwork*; word of mouth

To apply: Contact Valerie Shand, Business/Administration

STUDENT ENVIRONMENTAL ACTION COALITION

PO Box 1168
Chapel Hill, NC 2751-1168
(919) 967-4600

Director: Miya Yoshitani

Purpose: SEAC is a grassroots, youth run coalition of 2,000 high school and college groups (in all fifty states) working for environmental protection and social justice.

Methods of operation: Lobbying, publications, community organizing, direct action, public education, and training and technical assistance

Constituency: Mostly high school and college students interested in environmental and social justice.

Recent issues and projects: Working on recycling programs at high schools and college campuses around the country; stopped construction of a dam in Canada which would have destroyed the homeland of the indigenous Cree nation; co-founded an international network of 47 countries to articulate the voice of youth and the message of social justice at the 1992 Earth Summit.

Major publications: *Threshold*; also numerous organizing manuals and fact sheets

Funding: Individual contributions, foundations

Staff: 6
3 Organizers
1 Writer/Editor
1 Foundation Fundraiser
1 Executive Director

Staff openings/year: 3

Work Week: 40 hours

Salary/year: $13,200

Benefits: Health insurance, paid vacation, life insurance

Part-Time Employees: 0

Summer Employees: 0

Volunteers: 10

Interns: 10
Length: 3 months
Duties: Varies
Remuneration: Unpaid

Jobs advertised: In magazines and through organization newsletter

To apply: Contact Miya Yoshitani, Executive Director

STUDENT HEALTH COALITION

Center for Health Services, P.O. Box 567, Station 17
Nashville, TN 37232
(615) 322-4179

Director: Lizette Tucker

Purpose: The Coalition is a community health outreach project based at the Center for Health Services at Vanderbilt University. Since 1969, the coalition has been led by the vision and energy of students from every discipline, including the liberal arts, medicine and nursing, to improve the health and quality of life throughout Tennessee and Central Appalachia. SHC internships place students with community groups and rural, primary health care facilities that are addressing health problems.

Methods of operation: Human services (50%), medical student education (40%), training and technical assistance (10%)

Constituency: Persons we serve are largely from the rural South.

Recent issues and projects: Students participate either as members of a mobile health fair team, providing health education, screenings and physical exams, and in-home visits in several communities, or as community workers, working in pairs to provide organizing and research assistance to a single sponsoring community group for the entire summer. Recent projects have included work with the Child Care Project, Clarkville Hunger Coalition, in which 2 ASHC interns helped to design a plan to meet child care needs; and aid to the Health Providers Project, The Shelter, in which 3 ASHC interns worked extensively with local health care providers to start an advocacy and referral program for the victims of domestic violence.

Major publications: Fall and spring newsletter

Budget: $103,000

Funding: Foundations (90%), direct mail (10%)

Staff: 6
2 Organizers
2 Office Managers
2 Grassroots Fundraisers

Staff openings/year: 1

Salary/year: $22,000

Benefits: Health insurance, paid vacation

Interns: 20-25
Length: During summer, 6 or 10 weeks
Duties: Members of a mobile health care team or community workers
Remuneration: Paid stipends of $170-200 per week; room and board provided

Jobs advertised: Campus career placement offices; in the Tennessee area through campus visits

To apply: Contact Lizette Tucker

STUDENT PRESS LAW CENTER

1735 Eye Street, NW, Suite 504
Washington, DC 20006
(202) 466-5242

Director: Mark Goodman

Purpose: To provide free legal assistance to high school and college student journalists about their First Amendment rights and to serve as an information source and educational center about the importance of press freedom for young people.

Methods of operation: Legal advice (40%), research (25%), publications (20%), public education (15%)

Constituency: High school and college student journalists and their advisors

Recent issues and projects: Supreme Court case Hazelwood School District v. Kuhlmeier, involving censorship of high school student newspaper; battles by college media (and others) to get access to information about crime occurring on campus

Major publications: *Student Press Law Center Report*, a periodical published 3 times/year; *Law of the Student Press*

Budget: $150,000

Funding: Foundations (60%), individual contributions (40%)

Staff: 3
2 Attorneys
1 Office Manager

Staff openings/year: 0-1

Work Week: 40 hours

Benefits: Health insurance, paid vacation

Interns: 2-4
Length: 12 weeks
Duties: Undergraduates: reporters and editors for magazine; law students: legal research and counseling
Remuneration: $750 stipend per internship

Jobs advertised: Position announcement sent to schools; ads in local newspapers

To apply: Contact Mark Goodman, Executive Director

STUDENT PUGWASH USA

1638 R Street, NW, Suite 32
Washington, DC 20009
(202) 328-6555

Director: Betsy Fader

Purpose: Educational organization concerned with the ethical implications of science and technology; for students of high school, undergraduate or graduate level, and professionals.

Methods of operation: Student and public education (80%), publications (20%)

Constituency: Varied: students, educators and concerned citizens

Recent issues and projects: Biennial International Conference; ongoing chapter program with regional conferences; New Careers Program; Professional Pugwash Program for non-students

Major publications: *New Careers: A Directory of Jobs and Internships in Technology and Society*; quarterly newsletter: *Tough Questions*; *The Mentorship Guide*

Budget: $400,000

Funding: Foundations (100%)

Staff: 5
3 Program Coordinators
1 Office Manager
1 Foundation Fundraiser

Staff openings/year: 1-3

Work Week: 40 hours

Salary/year: $18,000 (Recent College Graduate); $22,000 (Graduate with advanced degree)

Benefits: Health insurance, paid vacation

Interns: Yes
Length: 1 semester or summer
Duties: Varies
Remuneration: Stipend available

Jobs advertised: *Washington Post*, *Community Jobs*, *City Paper*, and posted at Common Cause, *Opportunities in Public Affairs*

To apply: Contact Betsy Fader

STUDY CIRCLES RESOURCE CENTER

P.O. Box 203, 697 A Pomfret Street
Pomfret, CT 06258
(203) 928-2616

Director: Phyllis Emigh

Purpose: SCRC promotes small-group democratic discussions on social and political issues.

Methods of operation: Publications (50%), training and technical assistance (50%)

Constituency: People using small-group discussion as a means for informal adult education on social and political issues

Recent issues and projects: Special projects include promoting newspaper-sponsored discussion programs and community-wide programs based on *Can't We All Just Get Along?*, a manual for discussion programs on racism and race relations

Major publications: Topical discussion programs on a variety of issues, quarterly newsletter (focus on study circles)

Budget: $330,000

Funding: Foundations (100%)

Staff: 4
1 Writer/Editor
1 Office Manager
1 Issue Expert
1 Networker

Staff openings/year: 0-1

Work Week: 40 hours

Salary/year: $20,000 (Recent College Graduate); $25,000 (Graduate with advanced degree)

Benefits: Pension, paid vacation, pregnancy leave (unpaid)

Part-Time Employees: 1

Summer Employees: None

Volunteers: None

Interns: 1
Length: 1 year
Duties: Research, writing, general support
Remuneration: 18,000 a year

To apply: Contact Phyllis Emigh

SUN

107 North Robertson Street
Chapel Hill, NC 27516
(919) 942-5282

Editor: Sy Safransky

Purpose: *The Sun* is a monthly magazine of ideas, which publishes a wide range of essays, interviews, fiction and poetry.

Methods of operation: Publications (100%)

Budget: $600,000

Funding: Subscriptions (95%), individual contributions (5%)

Staff: 5
3 Editors
1 Business Manager
1 Office Manager

Staff openings/year: 2

Work Week: 40 hours

Salary/year: $16,000

Benefits: Health insurance, paid vacation

Part-Time Employees: 1

Interns: Yes
Length: Negotiable; 3 months-1 year
Duties: Editorial/clerical
Remuneration: Volunteer

Jobs advertised: Local newspapers and in *The Sun* magazine

To apply: Contact Sy Safransky, Editor

SUNSHINE NEWS/SUNSHINE PRESS

325 Pennsylvania Avenue, SE
Washington, DC 20003
(202) 544-3647

Director: Edward Roeder

Purpose: Research and reporting on undemocratic influences on the U.S. government, especially campaign finance.

Methods of operation: Research (80%), publications (14%), training and technical assistance (5%), litigation (1%)

Constituency: For all services, major newspapers; for books and reports, libraries and political community

Recent issues and projects: Newswork reporting on political action committee (PAC) funding by Savings and Loans, by chemical manufacturers, by the securities industry, by pro-Israel PACs, by ideological PACs, and by the weapons industry.

Major publications: Directory: *PACs Americana*; *Profiles in Cash* report; *Congress on Disk* database; *Quarterly Campaign Finance Summary* report; *PAC-TRACK* diskette program

Budget: $60,000

Funding: Sales (100%)

Staff: 2
1 Writer/Editor
1 Researcher

Staff openings/year: 1

Work Week: 45-55 hours

Benefits: Free coffee!

Volunteers: 2

Interns: 1-4
Length: 500 hours
Duties: Research, editing
Remuneration: Unpaid

Jobs advertised: Directories such as *Good Works*

To apply: Contact Edward Roeder

SUPPORT CENTER OF WASHINGTON

2001 O Street, NW
Washington, DC 20036
(202) 835-0300

Director: Sherborne Laughlin

Purpose: To increase the effectiveness of nonprofit management. We train and consult hundreds of non-profit organizations each year.

Methods of operation: Training and technical assistance (100%)

Constituency: 501(c)3 organizations

Budget: $350,000

Staff: 5
1 Office Manager
1 Foundation Fundraiser
1 Typist
1/2 Bookkeeper/Accountant
1 Training Director
1 Consulting Director

Staff openings/year: 0-1

Work Week: 40 hours

Salary/year: $23,000 (Recent College Graduate); $33,000 (Graduate with advanced degree)

Benefits: Health insurance, paid vacation, flex time

Part-Time Employees: 2

Summer Employees: 1

Volunteers: 2

Interns: 1
Length: 3 months
Duties: Depends on program, work in training or consulting
Remuneration: Stipend/small

Jobs advertised: Word-of-mouth

To apply: Please contact Sherborne Laughlin

SURVIVAL INTERNATIONAL USA

2121 Decatur Place, NW
Washington, DC 20008
(202) 265-1077

Other Offices: London, ENGLAND; Milan, ITALY; Madrid, SPAIN; Paris, FRANCE

Director: Mary George Hardman

Purpose: Survival International is a worldwide movement to support tribal peoples. It stands for their right to decide their own future and helps them to protect their lands, environment and way of life.

Methods of operation: U.S. office: public education (60%), direct action (40%)

Recent issues and projects: Campaign and medical relief fund for Yanomami Indians in Brazil; work with a federation of Amazonian Indians; Southeast Asia Campaign

Major publications: Distribute *Survival International News*; *Urgent Action Bulletins* on particular cases to letter writing network

Budget: $120,000

Funding: Individual contributions (60%), foundations (30%), sales (10%)

Staff: 3
1 Executive Director

1 Administrative Director
1 Membership Coordinator

Staff openings/year: 1

Work Week: 45 hours

Salary/year: $20,000

Benefits: Health insurance, paid vacation

Part-Time Employees: 1

Volunteers: 5

Interns: 2 per semester
Length: Semester/summer
Duties: 60% project work (public advocacy and outreach); 40% administrative
Remuneration: Non-salaried

Jobs advertised: Newspapers; journals

To apply: Contact Sonya Horowitz, Administrative Director

SUSTAINABLE AGRICULTURE PROJECT, CENTER FOR RURAL AFFAIRS

Box 736, 104 East Main
Hartington, NE 68739
(402) 254-6893

Other Offices: Walthill, NE

Director: Ron Krupicka

Purpose: Stimulate public dialogue about the sustainability of agriculture to include family farmers, rural communities and natural resources. Develop an alternative vision and approach for the future.

Methods of operation: Research (25%), publications (25%), public education (25%), training and technical assistance (25%)

Constituency: Serve small to mid-size farmers

Recent issues and projects: On-farm research; farmer workshops on agricultural alternatives; developing a beginning farmer curriculum in sustainable agriculture

Major publications: *Resource Farming Primer, Small Farm Energy Primer, Resource Audit and Planning Guide, Beneath the Wheels of Fortune*

Budget: $125,000

Funding: Individual contributions, foundations

Staff: 3
1 Office Manager
1 Researcher
1 Issue Expert

Staff openings/year: 1

Work Week: 50 hours

Salary/year: $15,000

Benefits: Health insurance, life insurance, pension, paid vacation

Summer Employees: 1

Interns: Yes
Length: 3 months-1 year
Duties: On-farm research, writing, issue research
Remuneration: Paid

Jobs advertised: Newsletter; *Community Jobs*; direct mailing

To apply: Contact Larry Krcil

SYRACUSE PEACE COUNCIL

924 Burnet Avenue
Syracuse, NY 13203
(315) 472-5478

Purpose: SPC, founded in 1936, is a community-based, autonomous, antiwar/social justice organization. SPC educates, agitates and organizes for a world where war, violence and exploitation in any form will no longer exist. It challenges the existing unjust power relationships among nations, among people and between ourselves and the environment. As members, we work to replace inequality, hierarchy, domination and powerlessness with mutual respect, cooperation, and a sense of community.

Methods of operation: Community organizing (50%), direct action (25%), public education (25%)

Constituency: Local progressive multi-issue people

Recent issues and projects: Central America; nuclear/low level waste siting; local issues; U.S. foreign policy; tax resistance; justice/prisons; SPC-TV (public access)

Major publications: *Peace Newsletter*

Budget: $26,000

Funding: Individual contributions (100%)

Staff: 1
1 Organizer
1/4 Bookkeeper/Accountant

Staff openings/year: 1-2

Work Week: 40 hours

Salary/year: $8,320 (Recent College Graduate); $Varies (Graduate with advanced degree)

Benefits: Health insurance

Volunteers: 10

Interns: 1-3
Length: Semester
Duties: Projects based on interest
Remuneration: Not available; possibly board

Jobs advertised: *Community Jobs*; locally; through newsletter

To apply: Contact Bill Mazza

TEAMSTERS FOR A DEMOCRATIC UNION

P.O. Box 10128
Detroit, MI 48210
(313) 842-2600

Director: Kenneth Paff

Purpose: Teamsters for a Democratic Union was founded in 1976 as a rank and file caucus supporting reform of the Teamsters Union. TDU has provided an organized center for efforts to democratize the union, end mob control and promote rank and file mobilization. TDU works with the Teamster's education, legal and defense foundation in support of these goals.

Methods of operation: Public education (40%), publications (30%), training and technical assistance (20%), research (5%), direct action (5%)

Membership: Members of the Teamsters Union who support a reform agenda

Recent issues and projects: TDU was and continues to be a key element of the reform coalition that won top office in the Teamster Union. TDU was instrumental in winning timely notification of contract language prior to ratification votes as well as other procedural changes to promote democracy in the union.

Major publications: *Convoy Dispatch*, newspaper

Staff: 8
5 Organizers
1 Writer/Editor
1 Bookkeeper/Accountant
1 Grassroots Fundraisers

Staff openings/year: 0-2

Work Week: 40 hours

Salary/year: $20,000 (Recent College Graduate); $20,000 (Graduate with advanced degree)

Benefits: Health insurance, paid vacation, life insurance

Part-Time Employees: No

Summer Employees: No

Volunteers: No

Interns: 1
Length: 3-6 months
Duties: Office work
Remuneration: $100 a month

Jobs advertised: Word of mouth, progressive publications

To apply: Please contact Marilyn Penttinen

TELECOMMUNICATIONS COOPERATIVE NETWORK (TCN)

505 8th Avenue, Suite 2000
New York, NY 10018
(212) 967-2180

Other Offices: Washington, DC; Boston, MA

President: Robert Loeb

Purpose: TCN is a not-for-profit buying cooperative designed to help organizations minimize communications costs and maximize their use of new technologies. TCN members receive discounts on commercial communications services, as well as help evaluating their technology needs.

Methods of operation: Research, publications, public education, training and technical assistance, cooperative purchasing, consulting

Constituency: Nonprofit organizations

Recent issues and projects: TCN offers access to a variety of products and services, including: a long distance savings program, 800/900 numbers, conference calling, auditorium teleconferencing, audiotext, fax broadcasting, fax-on-demand, electronic data communications, LAN links, telephone/voice mail consulting, data consulting, and strategic communications planning.

Major publications: Quarterly newsletter: *Connections*; *Technology is Not the Answer*

pamphlet for non-technology managers

Budget: $1,000,000

Funding: Foundations, self-sustaining

Staff: 17
1 President
1 Vice President, Finance and Administration
1 Director of Operations
1 Director of Voice Services
1 Director of Data Services
1 Director of Membership Services
1 Membership Representative
1 Manager of Information Systems
1 Membership - Support
2 Voice Services - Support
2 Data Services - Support
2 Finance - Support
2 Administrative Assistants

Staff openings/year: 1-2

Work Week: 40 hours

Salary/year: $20,000+ (Recent College Graduate); $50,000 (Graduate with advanced degree)

Benefits: Health insurance, life insurance, paid vacation

Part-Time Employees: 1-2

Interns: None; but willing to accept applications

Jobs advertised: Newspapers

To apply: Contact Karl Peterson, Vice President of Finance and Administration

Remarks: TCN is also considering adding video services to augment our current voice and data communications capabilities.

TELECOMMUNICATIONS RESEARCH & ACTION CENTER (TRAC)

P.O. Box 12038
Washington, DC 20005
(202) 462-2520

Director: David Wagenhauser

Purpose: Ensure viewer/consumer access to media; represent consumer interests in telecommunications - broadcast, cable, telephone; media reform.

Methods of operation: Public education and research (30%), publications (25%), litigation (20%), direct action (15%), community organizing (5%), lobbying (5%)

Constituency: Residential consumers and small businesses

Recent issues and projects: Telephone regulatory reform; Fairness Doctrine; Cable reform; telephone educational publications

Major publications: *Tele-Tips Comparison Charts for Residential and Business Consumers*; *Tele-Tips Away-From-Home Chart; Phonewriting: A Consumers Guide to New Information Services*

Funding: Individual contributions, direct mail

Staff: 2
1 Attorney
1 Office Manager

Staff openings/year: 0-1

Work Week: 50 hours

Salary/year: $15,000

Part-Time Employees: 1

Volunteers: 1

Interns: 1
Length: 2-4 months
Duties: Research, writing, administrative

To apply: Contact David Wagenhauser

TENANT RESOURCE CENTER, INC.

122 State Street, Suite 507A
Madison, WI 53703-2500
(608) 257-0143

Director: Michelle Olson

Purpose: To provide housing, counseling, education, publications and advocacy.

Methods of operation: Counseling (50%), public education (15%), publications (15%), training and technical assistance to volunteers (10%), community organizing (5%), consultation with government officials (5%)

Constituency: Renters, area landlords

Major publications: *Tenants Rights in Wisconsin*; *Tenants Times*, a quarterly newsletter; *Apartment Management in Wisconsin* (second edition, 1993)

Budget: $66,000

Funding: Individual contributions, publication sales, landlord seminars

Staff: 3
1 Executive Director

1/2 Volunteer Coordinator
1/8 Financial Manager

Staff openings/year: 1

Work Week: 40 hours

Salary/year: $18,000 (Recent College Graduate); $Varies (Graduate with advanced degree)

Benefits: Health insurance, paid vacation

Part-Time Employees: 2

Volunteers: 25

Interns: Publications and community organizing interns
Length: Varies
Duties: Varies

Jobs advertised: Local newspapers and mailings

To apply: Contact Michelle Okin, Executive Director

TENANTS UNION

3902 South Ferdinand Street
Seattle, WA 98118
(206) 722-6848

Director: Irene Woo

Purpose: The purpose of Tenants Union is to educate tenants of their rights under the law. Their goal is to "level the playing field" that landlords and tenants meet on.

Methods of operation: Training and technical assistance (55%), community organizing (20%), direct action (20%), lobbying (5%)

Constituency: Primarily low to moderate income and multi-racial

Recent issues and projects: Recently we passed the "Rental Agreement Regulation Ordinance" which require landlords to provide landlord tenant information to tenants at the time of the rental.

Budget: $137,000

Funding: Community development block grant (70%), foundations (20%), individual contributions (10%)

Staff: 6
4 Organizers
1 Paralegal
1 Office Manager/Fundraiser/Campaign Manager

Staff openings/year: 1-2

Work Week: 40+ hours

Salary/year: $15,000

Benefits: Health insurance, pregnancy leave, child care, paid vacation

Volunteers: Yes

Interns: Yes

Jobs advertised: *Community Jobs*; local progressive recruitment flyer; local papers

To apply: Contact Irene Woo, Executive Director

Remarks: We are always recruiting minority applicants even though positions do not currently exist.

TENANTS' ACTION GROUP OF PHILADELPHIA (TAG)

311 South Juniper Street, Room 1000
Philadelphia, PA 19107
(215) 735-8261

Director: Eva Gladstein

Purpose: TAG is a tenant organizing group with the expressed purpose of empowerment and the betterment of tenants in Philadelphia. The goal of this organization is to equalize the relationship between landlords and tenants.

Methods of operation: Human services (40%), community organizing (20%), training and technical assistance (20%), direct action (10%), public education (10%)

Constituency: TAG is largely made up of minority female-headed households who are tenants.

Recent issues and projects: TAG provides instruction in tenants' rights, eviction defense and related tenant issues. In addition, TAG operates several cash assistance programs aimed at assisting tenants in maintaining their homes.

Major publications: *Tenant Survival Book*; various tenant pamphlets and booklets, including: *A Guide to Tenants Rights*, *Eviction Defense*, *How to Find Public and Subsidized Housing*, and *How to Negotiate a Lease*

Budget: $300,000

Funding: Foundations (25%), individual contributions (5%), direct mail (1%), other (69%)

Staff: 30
10 Caseworkers
5 Administrators

3 Typists
3 Bookkeepers/Accountants
3 Office Managers
2 Organizers
1 Writer/Editor
1 Foundation Fundraiser
1 Grassroots Fundraiser
1 Housing Counselor

Staff openings/year: 7

Work Week: 40+ hours

Salary/year: $20,000 (Recent College Graduate); $Varies (Graduate with advanced degree)

Benefits: Health insurance, life insurance, disability insurance, pregnancy leave, credit union, child care allowance, tuition reimbursement, paid vacation, dental, personal leave, sick leave

Part-Time Employees: 2

Summer Employees: 1-2

Volunteers: 10

Interns: Yes
Length: 1 semester or 4 months
Duties: Usually involves tenant organizing and/or counseling
Remuneration: Based on individual situation

Jobs advertised: Local newspapers, community papers, and electronic media

To apply: Contact Victoria Mapp, Administrative Assistant to the Director

Remarks: TAG is always looking for individuals interested in community empowerment. Our human services are delivered in a manner which empowers our clients to speak and act for themselves. TAG has been around for approximately 17 years as Philadelphia's only citywide tenant organization. We would be very interested in hearing from organizers and those wishing to be organizers from around the country.

TENNESSEE ENVIRONMENTAL COUNCIL
1700 Hayes Street, South 101
Nashville, TN 37203
(615) 321-5075

Director: John Noel, Acting Director

Purpose: Environmental advocacy coalition and individual membership association formed for the purposes of public and legislative education and information.

Methods of operation: Research, publications, community organizing, public education, training and technical assistance, attending regulatory board meetings

Constituency: Environmentally-concerned citizens and organizations

Recent issues and projects: Ground water protection program, toxics prevention program

Major publications: Newsletter: *Protect*

Budget: $250,000

Funding: Individual contributions, foundations, direct mail

Staff: 5
1 Issue Expert
1 Executive Director
1 Development Director
1 Membership Services Coordinator
1 Office Manager

Staff openings/year: 1

Work Week: 40 hours

Salary/year: $18,000

Benefits: Health insurance

Part-Time Employees: 1

Volunteers: Yes

Interns: None currently, but willing to accept applications

Jobs advertised: Classifieds in newspaper, word of mouth

To apply: Contact Jennifer Walker, Membership Services

TENNESSEE HUNGER COALITION
P.O. Box 120961
Nashville, TN 37212-0961
(615) 298-3888

Other Offices: Jackson, TN; Kingsport, TN

President: Jean Stone

Purpose: THC's organizational goals are to eliminate and alleviate conditions of poverty in Tennessee; to enable people to understand and use power to gain control over their lives; to change systems to be responsive to real needs in ways that enhance the quality of life for individuals and communities and promote dignity and self-respect; to bring people together to take action and to recognize and eliminate barriers which interfere with being organized; and to build and maintain an organization which can achieve these goals.

Methods of operation: Advocacy (30%), community organizing (10%), public education (30%), training and technical assistance (10%), research (15%), publications (5%)

Constituency: Statewide; multi-racial; all classes and income levels, but mainly low-income

Recent issues and projects: Tennessee Grassroots Assembly Day held on February 13, 1994: over 200 participants from grassroots organizations across the state participated in workshops and seminars centering around coalition building and meeting legislators. Community Childhood Hunger Identification Project (CCHIP) is a door-to-door survey to document the incidence of hunger among families with children ages 12 and under.

Major publications: Quarterly newsletters; *A Tennessean's Guide to Grassroots Advocacy*

Budget: $179,000

Funding: Individual contributions (60%), foundations (30%), direct mail (10%)

Staff: 4
3 Regional Coordinators
1 Issue Expert

Work Week: 50 hours

Salary/year: $17,000 (Recent College Graduate); $18,000 (Graduate with advanced degree)

Benefits: Health insurance, pregnancy leave, paid vacation

Part-Time Employees: 1

Volunteers: 1

Interns: 4
Length: 1 semester
Duties: Varied: e.g., compiling a food program booklet for Tennessee; research; clerical
Remuneration: None

Jobs advertised: Statewide newspapers; job announcement sent to organizations, churches; word of mouth

To apply: Contact Jean Stone, President

TEXAS ALLIANCE FOR HUMAN NEEDS

2520 Longview, Suite 311
Austin, TX 78705
(512) 474-5019

Director: Jude Filler

Purpose: To affect progressive policies for Texas' low and moderate income population; provide technical assistance for grassroots organizations.

Methods of operation: Lobbying (20%), publications (20%), community organizing (20%), public education (20%), research (10%), training and technical assistance (10%)

Constituency: Consumer, labor, religious, disabled, elderly and low-income organizations

Recent issues and projects: Welfare reform; creation of affordable, accessible housing; access to food programs; affordable, accessible health care; tax equity and state fiscal policy to supply revenue for needed social welfare programs

Major publications: Regular newsletter; social issue factsheets; occasional special publications, such as directories

Budget: $120,000

Funding: Foundations (50%), individual contributions (20%), direct mail (20%), events (10%)

Staff: 4
2 Organizers
1 Executive Director
1 Office Manager

Staff openings/year: 2

Work Week: 50 hours

Salary/year: $15,600 (Recent College Graduate); $20,000 (Graduate with advanced degree)

Benefits: Health insurance, paid vacation

Volunteers: 5-10

Interns: 3-6
Length: Open
Duties: From clerical to research and organizing
Remuneration: Free housing; no salary

Jobs advertised: Free press

To apply: Contact Jude Filler, Executive Director

TEXAS CENTER FOR POLICY STUDIES

P.O. Box 2618
Austin, TX 78768
(512) 474-0811

Director: Mary Kelly

Purpose: The Texas Center for Policy Studies is a Sec. 501(c) (3) nonprofit research and advocacy organization formed in 1983 and located in Austin, TX. TCPS has substantial on-going work dealing with environmental issues in the Texas/Mexico border region, including: 1) providing policy and technical assistance services to a bi-national network of environmental and community organizations in Texas and Northeastern Mexico and 2) policy analysis of transboundary pollution issues in the context of increasing economic integration between the U.S. and Mexico. The Texas Center for Policy Studies also has several other projects dealing with the intersection of environmental and economic development policies.

Methods of operation: Research, policy analysis, training and technical assistance

Constituency: Citizen groups, workers, farmers, chemically-sensitive individuals

Recent issues and projects: Several projects on pesticides and toxics; project on environmental opportunities in the Savings and Loan bailout; they are beginning to move into U.S.-Mexico border environmental issues.

Major publications: *NAFTA Environmental Analyses* (1993); *S & L Bailout and Environment* (1992); *Rural Economic Development Policy* (1992)

Budget: $300,000

Funding: Foundations (100%)

Staff: 6
2 Attorneys
3 Issue Experts
1 Office Manager

Staff openings/year: 0-1

Work Week: 40 hours

Salary/year: $Varies (Recent College Graduate); $Varies (Graduate with advanced degree)

Benefits: Paid vacation

Part-Time Employees: 2

Summer Employees: Not generally

Interns: Under fellowship programs

Jobs advertised: Newsletters; word of mouth

To apply: Contact Mary Kelly

TEXAS CITIZEN ACTION

3625 Manchaca Road, Suite 202
Austin, TX 78704
(512) 444-8588

Other Offices: Fort Worth, TX

Purpose: Consumer and environmental protection organization with a membership through canvassing

Methods of operation: Community organizing (60%), research (10%), lobbying (10%), public education (10%), training and technical assistance (10%)

Membership: Middle-class and lower-middle class consumers

Recent issues and projects: Insurance reform; utility regulation; products liability; environment

Major publications: Quarterly membership newsletter

Funding: Individual contributions, foundations, canvassing, telephone solicitation

Staff:
50 Canvassers
2 Organizers
1 Executive Director

Work Week: 40+ hours

Salary/year: $16,224

Benefits: Health insurance, paid vacation

Part-Time Employees: 1

Summer Employees: Yes

Volunteers: Yes

Interns: None currently, but willing to accept applications

Jobs advertised: Local papers

TEXAS RURAL LEGAL AID, INC.

259 S. Texas
Weslaco, TX 78596
(210) 968-6574

Director: David G. Hall

Purpose: Texas Rural Legal Aid (TRLA) is a large legal services program with a strong reputation for providing aggressive, high quality legal representation to low-income clients in South and West Texas. The program serves some of the poorest areas in the nation, where racial discrimination and exploitation of low wage laborers are still very common. TRLA's energetic civil rights, labor and poverty law practice has made it one of the leading public interest law firms in the Southwest.

Methods of operation: Litigation (90%), training and technical assistance (5%), public education (3%), lobbying (2%)

Constituency: Our clients are low-income, mostly Hispanic, residents of south and west Texas. Many are migrant farm workers whose home-base is in our service area

Recent issues and projects: Within its Basic Field and Farm Worker Divisions, TRLA has the following special projects: Colonias; farm worker health and safety; health law; civil rights and H-2

Budget: $7,000,000

Funding: Federal and State (100%)

Staff: 130
47 Attorneys
37 Paralegal
14 Office Managers
24 Typists
4 Bookkeepers/Accountants
2 Computer Coordinators
2 Private Attorneys/Pro bono Coordinators

Staff openings/year: 5-10

Work Week: 40 hours

Salary/year: $16,000 (Recent College Graduate); $24,600 (Graduate with advanced degree)

Benefits: Health insurance, pension, paid vacation, life insurance, credit union, tuition reimbursement

Part-Time Employees: 4

Summer Employees: 20

Volunteers: 2

Interns: 4
Length: Semester
Duties: Research, investigation, interviews, community education
Remuneration: Interns are reimbursed for travel or out-of-pocket expenses

Jobs advertised: Local newspapers, bar journals, legal services publications, local bar associations

To apply: Please contact David G. Hall, Executive Director

Remarks: The program seeks attorneys with a strong commitment to spirited and effective advocacy on behalf of low-income clients. Ability to speak Spanish is preferred but not essential. TRLA maintains a strong affirmative action, equal opportunity employment policy.

THE NATION

72 Fifth Avenue
New York, NY 10011
(212) 242-8400

Other Offices: Washington, DC

Editor: Katrina Vanden Heuvel

Purpose: Throughout its 128-year history, *The Nation* has maintained its tradition of independence, buttressed by an overriding commitment to civil liberties, human rights, social justice and the quest for peace. A journal of opinions, *The Nation* analyses, muckrakes, reports news ignored by the mainstream press, provides alternative perspectives and puts new issues on the national agenda.

Methods of operation: Publications (100%)

Constituency: 90,000 subscribers

Budget: $4,000,000

Funding: Individual contributions, direct mail, subscriptions

Staff: 34
7 Writers/Editors
4 Typesetters
3 Copy Editors
3 Bookkeepers/Accountants
3 Circulation/Subscriptions
2 Production
2 Receptionists
2 Management
2 Nation Associates-direct mail/contributions
2 Advertising
1 Assistant to the Editor
1 Mail Clerk
1 Press Aide/Publicity
1 Office Manager

Staff openings/year: 3-4

Work Week: 40 hours

Salary/year: $18-20,000 (Recent College Graduate); $30,000 (Graduate with advanced degree)

Benefits: Health insurance, life insurance, pregnancy/ parental leave, paid vacation, 1 personal day per year

Interns: 8
Length: 3-4 months
Duties: Fact checking, research, some clerical, general magazine work
Remuneration: $75/week

Jobs advertised: Internships advertised in *Community Jobs* and *The Nation*; jobs listed in *The Nation* and other publications depending on position

To apply: For internships, contact Peter Meyer or Micah Sifry. For other positions, contact Neil Black.

THIRD WORLD RESOURCES

c/o DataCenter, 464 19th Street
Oakland, CA 94612-9761
(510) 835-4692

Director: Thomas P. Fenton and Mary J. Heffron

Purpose: To gather, evaluate, organize and publicize education/action resources on Third World regions and issues. Resources include organizations, books, periodicals, pamphlets and audiovisuals.

Methods of operation: Networking and publications (75%), responding to information requests (15%), training and technical assistance (10%),

Constituency: Educators and activists concerned about Third World struggles for justice and peace

Recent issues and projects: Production of 160-page paperback directories on Third World regions and issues; publication of quarterly review; maintenance of documentation center; electronic networking via PeaceNet and Interdoc.

Major publications: Quarterly review: *Third World Resources*, 24 pages; Resource Directories for the Third World, Asia and Pacific, Africa, Latin America and Caribbean, Middle East, Women in the Third World, Food, Hunger and Agribusiness, Human Rights, Transnational Corporational Corporations, Labor and Peace

Budget: $50,000

Funding: Foundations (50%), sales (30%), individual contributions (20%)

Staff: 2
2 Writers/Editors

Work Week: 40 hours

Benefits: Health insurance, pregnancy leave, paid vacation

Volunteers: 4

Interns: Yes
Length: Varies
Duties: Documentation and publishing; networking
Remuneration: Open to discussion

Jobs advertised: *Community Jobs*; Opportunity NOCs; mailings to colleagues

To apply: Contact Directors

Remarks: Volunteers and interns who work or have worked with TWR become familiar with a wide range of international and national organizations and the print and audiovisual resources they produce on human rights, labor, development, women, peace, and numerous other Third World-related issues. TWR works in a systematic manner to cover all Third World regions and all Third World-related issues. We promote the use of print and audiovisual resources that reflect the perspective of those who are struggling to build just and equitable societies in the Third World.

THREE MILE ISLAND ALERT

315 Peffer Street
Harrisburg, PA 17102
(717) 233-3072

Director: Kay Pickering, Coordinator; Deborah Baker, Chairperson

Purpose: TMIA is a nonprofit citizens group formed in 1977 after the construction of TMI Unit I and Unit II. Over the past decade, they have been an active intervenor in hearings before the Nuclear Regulatory Commission (NRC) on safety, managerial and technical issues. In addition, they have served the community as a resource center providing information, educational materials and speakers.

Methods of operation: Research (25%), litigation (20%), public education (15%), training and technical assistance (15%), publications (10%), lobbying (10%), direct action (5%)

Constituency: Mostly residents of Central Pennsylvania

Recent issues and projects: TMIA continues to monitor the cleanup of Unit II and the restart of Unit I.

Major publications: *Alert* membership newsletter; *A Decade of Delay, Deceit and Danger: Three Mile Island 1979-1989*

Budget: $5,000

Funding: Individual memberships (75%), foundations (15%), sales (10%)

Volunteers: 10

Interns: Yes
Remuneration: Volunteer only

To apply: Contact Kay Pickering, Office Coordinator

TIKKUN/COMMITTEE FOR JUDAISM AND SOCIAL JUSTICE (CJSJ)

5100 Leona Street
Oakland, CA 94619
(415) 482-0805

Editor: Michael Lerner

Purpose: *TIKKUN* is a bi-monthly Jewish critique of politics, culture and society. CJSJ is the Committee for Judaism and Social Justice, TIKKUN's education arm, organizing 1) against Israeli occupation of the West Bank; and 2) to make the Democratic Party sensitive to psychological and ethical issues.

Methods of operation: Publications (85%), public education (15%)

Constituency: 80% liberal Jews; 20% media; policy world

Recent issues and projects: Recent projects include: conferences of progressive Jewish intellectuals in New York, San Francisco, and Los Angeles; ads and public statements against Shamir's policy towards Palestinians; gatherings of progressive Democrats to change the Democratic Party

Major publications: *TIKKUN* bi-monthly magazine

Budget: $1,000,000

Funding: Individual contributions (70%), direct mail (20%), telephone solicitation (10%)

Staff: 6
3 Writer/Editors
1 Organizer
1 Office Manager
1 Typist

Staff openings/year: 1

Work Week: 50 hours

Salary/year: $14,000 (Recent College Graduate); $22,000 (Graduate with advanced degree)

Benefits: Health insurance, paid vacation

Volunteers: 3

Interns: 4
Length: 1 year
Duties: Editing, selecting manuscripts for publication, soliciting donations, organizing conferences, office help, rejecting manuscripts
Remuneration: Unpaid

Jobs advertised: In the magazine. We take applicants each January-April for summer internships and internships beginning September 1.

To apply: Write a long self-revealing letter about yourself and your ideas about *TIKKUN*, suggestions for what should be different, criticisms, what you like about the magazine and why you should work at it, to Michael Lerner, Editor.

Remarks: TIKKUN is the voice of the "silenced Jewish majority" - American Jews who have liberal and progressive politics which are not adequately articulated by the conservative leaning voices of the organized Jewish community.

TOBACCO CONTROL RESOURCE CENTER/ TOBACCO PRODUCTS LIABILITY PROJECT

400 Huntington Avenue
Boston, MA 02115
(617) 373-2026

Director: Professor Richard Daynard, Esq.

Purpose: To provide information and support to 17 state, local and federal government agencies pursuing tobacco control; and individuals and attorneys suing tobacco companies. Write amicus briefs and legal policy papers.

Methods of operation: Research (30%), litigation (20%), publications (20%), lobbying (6%), community organizing (6%), direct action (6%), public education (6%), training and technical assistance (6%)

Recent issues and projects: Production of legal policy papers for Massachusetts Tobacco Control Program; litigation support to Castano Class Action in New Orleans; annual CDC-sponsored conference on tobacco litigation; demonstration project on tobacco and the Americans with Disabilities Act

Major publications: *Tobacco on Trial*, newsletter; *Tobacco Products Liability Reporter*

Budget: $250,000

Funding: Government funding (60%), foundations (35%), individual contributions (5%)

Staff: 6
1 Writer/Editor
4 Attorneys
1 Issue Expert

Staff openings/year: 1

Work Week: 35 hours

Salary/year: $25,000 (Recent College Graduate); $35,000 (Graduate with advanced degree)

Benefits: Health insurance, paid vacation

Part-Time Employees: 2

Summer Employees: 3

Interns: 2-3
Length: Academic semester or summer
Duties: Undergraduate: administrative, research and writing; Law School Students: legal research and writing
Remuneration: Some Everrett Foundation funds available for summer interns

To apply: Please contact Graham E. Kelder, Jr., Managing Attorney

TOBACCO PRODUCTS LIABILITY PROJECT (TPLP)

Northeastern School of Law, 400 Huntington Avenue
Boston, MA 02115
(617) 373-2026

Director: Managing Attorney

Purpose: TPLP is dedicated to helping plantiffs' attorneys sue tobacco companies as a public health strategy.

Methods of operation: Litigation (50%), publications (20%), research (15%), public education (15%)

Constituency: Tobacco litigators, public health activists

Recent issues and projects: We assist plantiffs' attorneys in all the major tobacco cases. The most recent cases in which we have been involved include Cipollone v. Liggett Group in New Jersey, and Horton v. American Tobacco in Mississippi. We also publish a newsletter to keep attorneys and other interested parties abreast of developments in the field.

Major publications: Newsletter: *Tobacco on Trial*, 10 times/year. Our sister organization, TPLR, publishes a quarterly reporter, *The Tobacco Products Litigation Reporter*

Budget: $50,000

Funding: Foundations (90%), individual contributions (10%)

Staff: 3
2 Attorneys
1 Office Manager

Staff openings/year: 1-2

Work Week: 40 hours

Salary/year: $18,000 (Recent College Graduate); $25,000 (Graduate with advanced degree)

Benefits: Health insurance, paid vacation

Summer Employees: 1

Volunteers: Several

Interns: Yes
Length: 1 semester
Duties: Research and writing
Remuneration: Work-study funding available

Jobs advertised: Local newspapers and direct mail to law schools

To apply: Contact Richard A. Daynard, J.D., Ph.D., Chairman

TOXICS COORDINATING PROJECT

942 Market Street, Suite 502
San Francisco, CA 94102
(415) 781-2745

Director: Debbi Lerman

Purpose: TCP is a coalition of environmental, labor, public health and community organizations and individuals working to prevent the adverse impact of toxics on California's health, economy and environment.

Methods of operation: Research, publications, direct action, public education, coalition building, convene meetings and conferences, joint actions and strategies

Constituency: Local, regional and statewide toxics-related organizations and activists, and other lay contacts

Recent issues and projects: Toxics Use Reduction Campaign to prevent pollution by decreasing the use of hazardous chemicals in the home, workplace and environment; California Toxics Coalition Support Program to provide support for policy development and direct action for toxics use reduction and strict toxics control

Major publications: Newsletter: *Toxics Watchdog*, 6 times/year; *Citizen's Guide to the New Federal Right-to-Know Law*; *Toxics, Jobs and the Environment: A Workbook on California's Toxic Economy*

Budget: $150,000

Funding: Individual contributions, foundations

Staff: 1
1 Executive Director

Work Week: 50 hours

Benefits: Health insurance, pregnancy leave, paid vacation

Part-Time Employees: 1

Interns: Yes
Length: Flexible
Duties: Flexible; depends on student's qualifications
Remuneration: For school credit only

Jobs advertised: Through environmental and toxics community; our mailing list; a few key public interest job placement agencies such as Opportunity NOCs at the Management Center in San Francisco

To apply: Contact Debbi Lerman, Executive Director

TRANET

P.O. Box 567
Rangeley, ME 04970
(207) 864-2252

Director: William N. Ellis

Purpose: TRANET is a transnational network of, by and for organizations and individuals in all parts of the world who are working toward local self-reliance. The Rangeley office is merely a switchboard which helps members find others with common interests with which they can develop mutual aid programs. A second project is the TRANET/UNESCO A.T. Library. This is a 100-book library for which TRANET raises funds and ships to Third World villages. The books are do-it-yourself manuals covering all aspects of appropriate technology, from how to grow your own food to how to build a house, maintain family health and otherwise be self-reliant.

Methods of operation: Publications (80%), research (10%), direct action (10%)

Membership: TRANET members are 25% organizations and 75% individuals who are concerned with social issues and the future

Recent issues and projects: TRANET's primary tool for helping members link up with one another is a bimonthly newsletter-directory. Each issue provides names, addresses and brief descriptions of 150 to 200 organizations participating in cultural transformation. Many issues have a special topic directory section developed by volunteers outside of Rangeley.

Major publications: Bimonthly newsletter-directory

Funding: Individual contributions (80%), direct mail (20%)

Staff:
Volunteer including:
2 Writer/Editors
1 Bookkeeper/Accountant
1 Grassroots Fundraiser

Volunteers: Yes

Interns: Yes
Remuneration: Unpaid

Remarks: TRANET is currently a 100% volunteer organization. We do often have college students, retirees and others come to spend a few months with us. Interns have included members from Zimbabwe, England and India as well as the United States. These volunteers have come under grants or other support not supplied by TRANET. We welcome such assistance but do not provide financial support.

TRIAL LAWYERS FOR PUBLIC JUSTICE (TLPJ)

1625 Massachusetts Avenue, NW, Suite 100
Washington, DC 20036
(202) 797-8600

Director: Arthur Bryant

Purpose: Precedent-setting litigation protecting the

rights of citizens through tort and trial law.

Methods of operation: Litigation (75%), public education (20%), publications (5%)

Constituency: Mainly plaintiff trial lawyers; some non-lawyers interested in our work

Recent issues and projects: Consumer rights, Environmental Enforcement Project, Exxon Valdez lawsuit, civil liberties, toxic torts, employment rights protection, preserving the civil justice system.

Major publications: Quarterly newsletter; *Trial Lawyers Doing Public Justice*; *In the News*

Funding: Individual contributions (95%), foundations (5%)

Staff: 12
4 Attorneys
2 Administrative Assistants
1 Writer/Editor
1 Organizer
2 Foundation Fundraisers
1 Office Administrator
1 Receptionist

Staff openings/year: 1

Work Week: 45-55 hours

Salary/year: $Varies (Recent College Graduate); $Varies (Graduate with advanced degree)

Benefits: Health insurance, life insurance, paid vacation

Interns: 2-3
Length: Semester
Duties: Help prepare cases, legal research, help prepare briefs
Remuneration: Stipend

Jobs advertised: *Washington Post*; public interest network; *City Paper*; *Legal Times*

To apply: Contact Priscilla Budeiri

TRUST FOR PUBLIC LAND (TPL)

116 New Montgomery, 4th Floor
San Francisco, CA 94105
(415) 495-4014

Other Offices: Washington, DC; Norwich, VT; Sacramento, CA; Austin, TX; Costa Mesa, CA; Los Angeles, CA; New York, NY; Morristown, NJ; Minneapolis, MN; Boston, MA; Tallahasssee, FL; Atlanta, GA; South Miami, FL; Santa Fe, NM; Seattle, WA; Portland, OR

President: Martin J. Rosen

Purpose: The Trust for Public Land (TPL) is a nonprofit land conservation organization that works nationwide to conserve land for people to enjoy. Founded in 1972, the Trust for Public Land specializes in conservation real estate, applying its expertise in negotiation, public finance and law to protect land for public use. Working with private landowners, communities and government agencies, TPL has helped protect more than 1,000 special places nationwide for people to enjoy as parks playgrounds, community gardens, recreation areas, historic landmarks and wilderness lands.

Methods of operation: Research, lobbying, litigation, publications, public education, training and technical assistance, land acquisition and Open space financing

Constituency: Communities which want to protect a landscape feature through land acquisition

Recent issues and projects: Recent issues include: Monroe School: Preservation of the side of the Brown v. Board of Education decision which ruled segregation in American schools unconstituional; Walden Woods: Preservation of the property and a part of the surrounding open space where Henry David Thoreau lived two years in solitude. Will be both a nonprofit education center for the study of Thoreau and his writings as well as a beautiful open space near Boston; Green Cities Initiative: dedicates 50% of TPL's efforts to urban open space issues with the hope of broadening the environmental movement while improving metropolitan areas.

Major publications: *Land and People*, bi-annual magazine; *Regional Newsletters*

Budget: $18,000,000

Funding: Land Sales (70%), foundations (20%), individual contributions (10%)

Staff: 180
2 Writers/Editors
12 Attorneys
4 Paralegals
8 Office Managers
10 Researchers
6 Lobbyists
8-10 Foundation Fundraisers
35-40 Administrative Assistants
10 Bookkeepers/Accountants
2 Campaign Managers
60 Project Managers
5 Information Services

Staff openings/year: 15-20

Work Week: 40 hours

Salary/year: $Low 20's (Recent College Graduate); $Varies (Graduate with advanced degree)

Benefits: Health insurance, pension, paid vacation, life insurance, credit union, family leave

Part-Time Employees: Varies

Interns: Varies
Length: Varies
Duties: Varies with each internship, may include research, writing, administrative duties
Remuneration: All are paid, but usually no benefits

Jobs advertised: Newspapers, nonprofit periodicals, mailing lists, colleges

To apply: Nancy Van Vleet, Human Resources Assistant

Remarks: The Trust for Public Land is interested in encouraging ethnic diversity within the environmental movement and applies this interest towards our hiring practices.

TRUSTEES FOR ALASKA

725 Christensen Drive, Suite 4
Anchorage, AK 99501-2101
(907) 276-4244

Director: Ann L. Rothe

Purpose: TFA is a nonprofit public interest environmental law group working for the preservation and wise development of Alaska's resources. Areas of focus include oil and gas drilling, hazardous waste and placer mining.

Methods of operation: Litigation (60%), research (20%), public education (20%)

Membership: 1,100 members both within and outside of Alaska

Recent issues and projects: Cases involve water and air pollution, logging, public lands, wetland issues and habitat preservation.

Major publications: Quarterly newsletter; *A Guide to Wetlands Protection in Alaska*

Budget: $344,000

Funding: Foundations (50%), attorney fees (25%), individual contributions (20%), direct mail (5%)

Staff: 4
3 Attorneys
1 Office Manager

Staff openings/year: 1

Work Week: 50 hours

Salary/year: $Varies (Recent College Graduate); $Varies (Graduate with advanced degree)

Benefits: Health insurance, paid vacation

Volunteers: Yes

Interns: 3-4
Length: 10 weeks
Duties: Summer law clerks and externships for credit/pay
Remuneration: $500/month in addition to work-study and school grants, if available

Jobs advertised: Job newsletters and periodicals relating to the conservation community; notices to law schools and other environmental groups

To apply: Contact Ann Rothe

UNION OF CONCERNED SCIENTISTS

26 Church Street
Cambridge, MA 02238
(617) 547-5552

Other Offices: Washington, DC; Berkeley, CA

Director: Howard Ris

Purpose: UCS is dedicated to advancing responsible public policies in areas where technology plays a critical role. Established in 1969, UCS has created a unique alliance between many of the nation's leading scientists and thousands of committed citizens. This partnership addresses the most serious environmental and security threats facing humanity. UCS is currently working to:

encourage responsible stewardship of the global environment and life-sustaining resources; promote energy technologies that are renewable, safe, and cost-effective; reform transportation policy and curtail weapons proliferation.

Methods of operation: Public education (50%), research (30%), publications (10%), lobbying (6%), training and technical assistance (4%)

Constituency: Scientists and other concerned citizens

Recent issues and projects: Midwest renewable electricity project; Renewables Are Ready, a national campaign; Action for Global Sustainability, a scientists campaign; and lobbying on energy and arms control issues

Major publications: *Nucleus*, a quarterly magazine; *The Gene Exchange*, a newsletter on biotechnology; *Cool Energy: Renewable Solutions to Environmental Problems*; *Steering a New Course: Transportation, Energy, and the Environment*; *The Scientists Warning Briefing Book*; *Nonproliferation and the National Interest*

Budget: $4,100,000

Funding: Individual contributions/direct mail (63%), foundations (27%), other (10%)

Staff: 32
Including:
6 Organizers
6 Researchers
6 Issue Experts
3 Lobbyists
2 Press Aides
2 Office Managers
2 Bookkeepers/Accountants
1 Foundation Fundraiser
1 Writer/Editor
2 Direct Mail Specialists

Staff openings/year: 1-4

Work Week: 40 hours

Salary/year: $Varies (Recent College Graduate); $Varies (Graduate with advanced degree)

Benefits: Health insurance, life insurance, pregnancy leave, pension, paid vacation

Part-Time Employees: 2

Volunteers: 6

Interns: Yes; number varies
Length: 3-6 months
Duties: Varies
Remuneration: Paid a monthly stipend; no health benefits

Jobs advertised: Newspapers; journals; organizational networks; college placement offices

To apply: Contact Howard Ris, Executive Director

UNITARIAN UNIVERSALIST SERVICE COMMITTEE

130 Prospect Street
Cambridge, MA 02139
(617) 868-6600

Other Offices: Washington, DC

Director: Richard S. Scobie, Executive Director

Purpose: Grounded in Unitarian Universalist principles that affirm the worth, dignity and human rights of every person and the interdependence of all life, the Unitarian Universalist Service Committee is a voluntary nonsectarian membership organization working to advance justice throughout the world.

Methods of operation: Public education (40%), publications (25%), community organizing (15%), training and technical assistance (15%), lobbying (5%)

Membership: Members of Unitarian Universalist congregations and other concerned U.S. citizens; membership dues are $25/year

Recent issues and projects: Grassroots-based international development projects in India, East and West Africa, the Caribbean and Central America; human rights work in Central America and the Philippines; and education/ mobilization around U.S. children's issues at both the national and community levels

Major publications: Quarterly newsletter: *Service Committee News*; special reports on human rights issues in Central America and the Phillipines, children's rights and international development

Staff: 40
Including:
6 Issue Experts
4 Organizers
2 Writers/Editors
1 Lobbyist
1 Press Aide
1 Foundation Fundraiser
1 Bookkeeper/Accountant
9 Administrative Assistants

Staff openings/year: 4-6

Work Week: 35+ hours

Salary/year: $20,000 (Recent College Graduate); $25,000+ (Graduate with advanced degree)

Benefits: Health/dental insurance, life insurance, parental leave, pension, paid vacation, sabbaticals, flexible spending accounts

Part-Time Employees: 3

Jobs advertised: Job announcements sent to Boston area schools, advocacy and community nonprofits. Advertisements in the *Boston Globe*, *Bay State Banner* and specialized publications.

To apply: Contact Gordon Gottlieb, Associate for Human Resource Management

UNITED ACTIVITIES UNLIMITED, INC.

485 Clawson Street
Staten Island, NY 10306
(718) 987-8111

Director: Louis DeLuca

Purpose: To provide, for the youth of Staten Island, recreation, education, and counseling as positive alternatives to "hanging out" or having artificial highs.

Methods of operation: Youth services (85%), public education (5%), training and technical assistance (5%), community organizing (5%)

Constituency: Youth from the communities where we have afternoon, evening and summer centers, most held in NYC public school buildings

Recent issues and projects: The Beacon Center is open 365 days a year and provides a safe haven for the community. The center offers a number of activities including GED preparation, recreation, sports, arts and crafts, day care.

Budget: $350,000

Funding: Government grants (95%), foundations (5%)

Staff: 8
1 Executive Director
1 Associate Executive Director
2 Assistant Executive Directors
1 Center Director
1 Assistant Center Director
1 Fiscal Officer
1 Office Manager

Staff openings/year: 1

Work Week: 35 hours

Salary/year: $18,000 (Recent College Graduate); $23,000 (Graduate with advanced degree)

Benefits: Health insurance, paid vacation

Part-Time Employees: 120

Summer Employees: 80

Volunteers: Yes; number varies

Interns: None currently, but willing to accept applications

Jobs advertised: Newspaper

To apply: Contact Lois DeLuca, Executive Director

UNITED CHURCH OF CHRIST COMMISSION FOR RACIAL JUSTICE

700 Prospect Avenue East
Cleveland, OH 44115-1100
(216) 736-2167

Other Offices: Rocky Mount, NC; Washington, DC; New York, NY

Director: Bernice Powell Jackson

Purpose: To increase the involvement of the United Church of Christ in the continuing struggle for racial justice and to assist the Church in making this involvement relevant. To provide a national denomination liaison with ecumenical, interfaith, secular and other concerned efforts seeking to effect social change wherein racial justice becomes a reality.

Methods of operation: Research, publications, human services, community organizing, direct action, public education, training and technical assistance, overseas work, national forums

Recent issues and projects: (1) Information and Resource Development Program: responsible for information on the programs and work of the Commission; responsible for weekly tapes and distribution of Civil Rights Journal commentaries mailed to thousands of newspapers weekly. (2) Leadership Development and Training Programs: Black and minority constituencies of the UCC encouraged to take part in racial and social justice forums via the Ministers for Racial and Social Justice (MRSJ) and United Black Christians (UBC).

Major publications: *Toxic Waste and Race in the United States*, a major report on the problem of toxic waste in minority communities in the U.S.; *Rites of Passages* booklet, a teenage pregnancy prevention resource; *The Black Family*, an Afro-Centric perspective

To apply: Contact Reverend Benjamin F. Chavis, Jr., Executive Director

Remarks: In May 1988, CRJ was invited by the People's Republic of Angola to organize a fact-finding mission to travel to Angola, August 7-24, 1988, for the purpose of conducting an independent investigation of the impact of the current war situation within that country. CRJ was interested in paying particular attention to the effects of South Africa's invasion of the sovereign territory of Angola and the nature and extent of human rights violations against the Angolan people by paramilitary or other groups financed and supported by South Africa and the U.S. Since that year, CRJ has made one other trip to that country for further fact-finding, out of which came the formation of the Angola Foundation and a young people's group, Free Africa Youth:USA.

UNITED COMMUNITIES AGAINST POVERTY, INC. (UCAP)

1400 Doewood Lane
Capitol Heights, MD 20743
(301) 322-5700

Purpose: Dedicated to improving the health, education training, housing and general welfare of Prince Georges County's low and moderate income residents. Also seeks to improve community relations, promote peace, good will, and respect for human rights and dignity.

Methods of operation: Human services (55%), training and technical assistance (30%), community organizing (10%), publications (5%)

Constituency: Low-income residents of Prince George's County

Recent issues and projects: Displaced homemakers; homeless and housing issues; information and referral; senior opportunities and services; health education; and outreach

Major publications: Quarterly newsletters; brochures on projects

Budget: $650,000

Funding: Foundations (99.5%), individual contributions (.5%)

Staff: 14
2 Housing Counselors
2 Secretaries
1 Fiscal Manager
1 Executive Director
1 Fiscal Manager
1 Administrative Assistant
1 Social Service Supervisor
1 Driver
1 Administrator/Coordinator
1 Receptionist
2 Employment Counselors

Staff openings/year: 3

Work Week: 40 hours

Salary/year: $17,500 (Recent College Graduate); $23,500 (Graduate with advanced degree)

Benefits: Health insurance, life insurance, paid vacation

Volunteers: 2-20

Interns: Yes
Length: 3 months
Duties: Displaced Homemakers Program, assignments related to their field of expertise

Jobs advertised: Newspapers, community agencies, colleges, employment services

To apply: Contact Sophia Evans, Administrative Assistant

UNITED CONNECTICUT ACTION FOR NEIGHBORHOODS, INC. (UCAN)

P.O. Box 6422
Hartford, CT 06106
(203) 522-9946

Director: Alta Lash

Purpose: To provide technical assistance to organizing groups in Connecticut and to assist them in developing coalitions on issues of mutual interest.

Methods of operation: Community organizing (90%), research (10%)

Constituency: The organizing groups UCAN serves are predominantly located in urban areas

Recent issues and projects: Provided staff assistance to United Seniors in Action in their fight to rollback rate increases in Medicaid policies. Established a consortium of organizing groups to deal with problems created by substance abuse.

Budget: $100,000

Funding: Foundations (50%), contracts (45%), individual contributions (5%)

Staff: 2
2 Organizers

Work Week: 45 hours

Salary/year: $18,000

Benefits: Health insurance

Part-Time Employees: 1

Jobs advertised: Mailings, newspapers and national publications

To apply: Contact Alta Lash, Director

Remarks: UCAN serves as a clearinghouse for recruitment and organizing for all organizing groups in Connecticut. They have 10-15 openings per year.

UNITED FARM WORKERS OF AMERICA, AFL-CIO

P.O. Box 62
Keene, CA 93531
(805) 822-5571

Other Offices: Los Angeles, CA; San Francisco, CA; Austin, TX; Fort Lauderdale, FL; Detroit, MI; New York, NY; Cranford, NY

President: Arturo Rodriquez

Purpose: To concentrate on ending the exploitation of farm workers. To provide consumers with quality and affordable food. To ban the use of cancer-causing chemicals in agriculture. To prevent the misuse of taxpayers' money in subsidizing the agricultural land barons.

Methods of operation: Direct action, public education, community organizing, human services, training and technical assistance, litigation, publications, research, fundraising, advertising, specialty sales, social marketing

Constituency: Farm workers and people interested in human dignity and social justice

Recent issues and projects: Currently engaged in the boycott of California table grapes. The goal focuses on reestablishing free and fair elections for the 60,000 California table grape workers, and good faith bargaining with their employers. It calls for the ban of cancer-causing chemicals used on grapes.

Major publications: *No Grapes* documentary film (multilingual); *Food and Justice* magazine (English); *El Malcriado* magazine (bilingual)

Funding: Dues (75%), direct mail (15%), individual contributions (10%)

Staff:
60 Organizers
20 Data Entry
18 Printshop Staff
15 Caseworkers
10 Paralegals
10 Ad Specialty Account Executives
10 Radio Managers and Announcers
10 Bookkeepers/Accountants
6 Attorneys
5 Office Managers
5 Mechanics
5 Campaign Managers
2 Writers/Editors
1 Press Aide
20 Negotiators

Work Week: 50 hours

Salary/year: $Varies (Recent College Graduate); $Varies (Graduate with advanced degree)

Benefits: Family leave, credit union, board, housing, child care, paid vacation, transportation

Volunteers: 90% of staff

Interns: Yes
Length: 6 months-1 year

Jobs advertised: Newspaper, radio, magazine, direct mail, speaking tours

To apply: Contact Human Resource Department

UNITED SENIORS HEALTH COOPERATIVE

1334 G Street, NW, Suite 500
Washington, DC 20005
(202) 393-6222

Director: James P. Firman

Purpose: To help older persons remain healthy, independent and financially secure.

Methods of operation: Human services (40%), research (20%), publications (10%), lobbying (10%), public education (10%), community organizing (10%)

Membership: 12,000 older persons in the greater Washington, DC area

Recent issues and projects: Health Care Help Line for seniors; consumer research on health insurance; computer software to help people get public benefits

Major publications: *United Seniors Health Report*; *LTC: A Dollar and Sense Guide*; *Finance After Fifty*; *Managing Your Health Care Finance*

Budget: $850,000

Funding: Foundations (40%), sales (35%), individual contributions (25%)

Staff: 13
4 Issue Experts
2 Computer Programmers
1 Organizer
1 Caseworker
1 Writer/Editor
1 Administrative Assistant
1 Foundation Fundraiser
1 Researcher
1 Office Manager

Staff openings/year: 3

Work Week: 40 hours

Salary/year: $20,000

Benefits: Health insurance, paid vacation, life insurance

Part-Time Employees: 1

Summer Employees: 2

Volunteers: 10

Interns: Yes
Length: 3 months
Duties: Consumer research
Remuneration: Expenses only

Jobs advertised: Newspaper

To apply: Contact Chris Timmons

UNITED STATES PUBLIC INTEREST RESEARCH GROUP (USPIRG)

215 Pennsylvania Avenue, SE
Washington, DC 20003
(202) 546-9707

Director: Gene Karpinski

Purpose: US PIRG is the national lobbying office for state PIRGs around the country. PIRGs are nonprofit, non-partisan advocacy groups that focus on the following issue areas: environmental protection, consumer protection, energy and government reform.

Methods of operation: Lobbying (45%), community organizing (20%), public education (20%), research (10%), publications (5%)

Membership: 25,000 citizen members; state PIRGs have 500,000 student members and 500,00 citizen members

Recent issues and projects: They are now involved in federal legislative campaigns in the following issue areas: clean air, energy, food safety, ozone protection, global warming, good government, toxics and consumer protection.

Major publications: Quarterly newsletter: *Citizen Agenda*; frequently publish investigative reports, including *As the World Burns: Documenting America's Failure to Address the Ozone Crisis* (April 1989); *Exhausting Our Future: An Eighty-Two City Study of Smog in the 80's* (March 1989); *Widespread Confusion: Why Congress Must Codify the Fairness Doctrine*; and studies on the political action committees (PACs) for nuclear energy, pesticides, banks, grocery manufacturers and other industries

Budget: $380,000

Funding: Individual contributions from canvass (50%), state PIRGs (50%)

Staff: 36
5 Lobbyists
3 Canvass Directors
2 Administrative Assistants
1 Organizer
1 Executive Director
1 Administrative Director
1 Field Director
3 Phone Canvass Directors
1 Assistant Field Director
1 Field Associate
17 Canvassers

Staff openings/year: 4

Work Week: 50 hours

Salary/year: $14,000 (Recent College Graduate); $20,000 (Graduate with advanced degree)

Benefits: Health insurance, pregnancy leave, paid vacation, college loan assistance program

Part-Time Employees: 16

Summer Employees: 60-80

Interns: 10
Length: 3 months
Duties: Assist lobbying/legal staff in their research and advocacy
Remuneration: Work-study or volunteer

Jobs advertised: College-based career placement offices, career/job fairs, career/job bulletins and catalogues, through public interest group network, newspapers, posters

To apply: Contact Liz Hitchcock, Administrative Director

UNITED STATES STUDENT ASSOCIATION (USSA)

815 15th Street, NW, Suite 838
Washington, DC 20005
(202) 347-8772 Memory device: (202) 347-USSA

President: Tchiyuka Cornelius

Purpose: USSA, through a grassroots network of student activists, lobbies for student interests on Capitol Hill and trains students on campuses nationwide in the techniques of direct action organizing. USSA's overriding goal in all its work is student empowerment and increasing access to higher education.

Methods of operation: Training and technical assistance (25%), lobbying (20%), membership services (credit card, health insurance, etc.) (15%), community organizing (10%), publications (10%), direct action (10%), public education (10%)

Membership: Campus student unions and state student associations

Recent issues and projects: USSA has two conferences annually: a legislative conference in March and a membership meeting in August. Other campaigns focus on the federal education budget, tuition, civil rights, and reproductive rights. USSA also works on issues like on-campus child care and eliminating standardized tests and other issues of expansion of access to higher education.

Major publications: Bi-weekly editions of the *Legislative Update* are published during the Congressional session. The *Update* comes out less frequently when Congress is not in session.

Budget: $300,000

Funding: Membership dues (50%), conferences (50%)

Staff: 10
2 Officers
4 Organizers
2 Field Organizers
1 Member Services Coordinator
1 Lobbyist

Staff openings/year: 2

Work Week: 50 hours

Salary/year: $16,500

Benefits: Health insurance

Volunteers: 4

Interns: 5
Length: 3 months
Duties: Vary widely
Remuneration: Unfortunately, USSA cannot offer compensation. We will, however, help interns find housing.

Jobs advertised: *Community Jobs*, *Common Cause*, various job boards, mailings to membership, and to organizations USSA works with

To apply: Contact the Vice President

UNITED TENANTS OF ALBANY, INC.

33 Clinton Avenue
Albany, NY 12207
(518) 436-8997

Director: Roger and Maria Markovics

Purpose: (1) To promote and maintain tenants' rights in all housing situations; (2) to stop the displacement of tenants from sound housing; (3) to upgrade and improve inadequate or deteriorated housing conditions; (4) to stimulate the development of more low and moderate income housing; (5) to increase opportunities for tenants to have ownership or control of their housing; and (6) to preserve the long-term affordability of housing.

Methods of operation: Human services, community organizing, public education, training and technical assistance

Constituency: Low and moderate income tenants

Recent issues and projects: Development of a Land Trust; reinvestment organizing resulting in mortgage pool for low-income housing; extensive counseling on eviction prevention

Major publications: Newsletter: *United Tenants of Albany News*

Budget: $150,000

Funding: State government grants (70%), foundations (20%), individual contributions (10%)

Staff: 5
2 Housing Counselors
1 Organizer

1 Office Manager
1 Issue Expert

Staff openings/year: 1

Work Week: 40+ hours

Salary/year: $15,000 (Recent College Graduate); $Varies (Graduate with advanced degree)

Benefits: Health insurance, paid vacation, dental insurance

Volunteers: Yes

Interns: 2
Length: 9 months
Duties: Counseling, special projects (e.g. Land Trust)
Remuneration: None

Jobs advertised: Local newspapers

To apply: Contact Roger and Maria Markovics, Directors

UNIVERSITY CONVERSION PROJECT

P.O. Box 748
Cambridge, MA 02142
(617) 354-9363

Director: Rich Cowan

Purpose: The University Conversion Project is a national clearinghouse founded during the Gulf War to promote peace activism and investigative journalism on campus. UCP encourages campus communities to envision and prepare for a non-violent future. We question widespread military and right-wing funding on campus and advocate peaceful alternatives: full funding for scholarships, environmental research, and innovative programs in conflict resolution and human services. UCP now helps students and faculty work for peace on more than 100 campuses in the U.S. and Canada.

Methods of operation: Publications (30%), research (25%), community organizing (25%), public education (10%), training and technical assistance (10%)

Constituency: Students (undergraduate/graduate); alumni; faculty; others interested in peace and justice issues

Recent issues and projects: Current projects include: promoting conversion to a nonviolent society; challenging idealogical extremism on campus (*Guide to Uncovering the Right on Campus*); advocating a socially responsible curriculum.

Major publications: *Study War No More*, quarterly bulletin; *Guidebook for Young Campus Peace Groups*; *Directory of Campus Peace Groups*; *Guide to Creating Peace and Justice Studies*; *Justice Studies Career Guide for Young Scientists*

Budget: $25,000

Funding: Individual contributions (50%), foundations (50%)

Staff:
Only part-time, volunteers, and interns:
Organizers
Writers/Editors
Researchers
Foundation Fundraisers
Administrative
Grassroots Fundraisers

Staff openings/year: 1

Work Week: 15-30 hours

Salary/year: $13,000 (Recent College Graduate); $13,000 (Graduate with advanced degree)

Benefits: None

Part-Time Employees: 1

Summer Employees: 1-2

Volunteers: 5-10

Interns: 2-4 a year
Length: 3-6 months (negotiable)
Duties: Publishing, development, organizing, fundraising, administrative
Remuneration: $400/month for 6-month commitment

Jobs advertised: Internship offices, listings, word of mouth, through professors

To apply: Send a resume with a cover letter describing your relevant activist, fundraising, or research experience to our office specifying how many hours you are willing to work.

URBAN COALITION WEST

845 N 2nd Ave., Suite 1E
Phoenix, AZ 85003
(602) 263-5600

Director: Al Preciado

Purpose: To revitalize communities and produce affordable housing. To stimulate job creation activities for the urban disadvantaged through economic development. To provide specialized housing for persons with special needs and others at risk of displacement. To generate funding for neighborhood improvement projects to upgrade and improve the quality of life in urban neighborhoods.

Methods of operation: Direct action (70%), training and technical assistance (20%), community organizing (10%)

Constituency: Inner city poor

Recent issues and projects: Developed 50 units of affordable housing; funded $2 million loan pool for small business lending and technical assistance program; work with citizens in designing and planning revitalization strategies.

Budget: $200,000

Funding: Foundations (60%), fee for services (40%)

Staff: 4
1 Attorney
1/2 Organizer
1/2 Writer/Editor
1/2 Office Manager
1/2 Foundation Fundraiser
1/2 Typist
1/2 Bookkeeper/Accountant
1/4 Issue Expert

Staff openings/year: 1

Work Week: 45 hours

Salary/year: $18,000 (Recent College Graduate); $28-32,000 (Graduate with advanced degree)

Benefits: Health insurance, credit union, paid vacation

Part-Time Employees: 3

Summer Employees: 1

Volunteers: 25

Interns: 1
Length: 3 months
Duties: Issue research, feasibility studies
Remuneration: Paid hourly

Jobs advertised: Job description flyer distributed through network

To apply: Contact Gertrude Hodges-Randall or Al Preciado

URBAN HOMESTEADING ASSISTANCE, INC. (UHAB)

40 Prince Street, 2nd Floor
New York, NY 10012
(212) 226-4119

Director: Andrew Reicher

Purpose: UHAB has been providing technical assistance to low-income tenants associations and cooperatives in New York City and nationally for 20 years. UHAB fosters the development of self-help cooperative housing and assists these groups in the operation of their housing.

Methods of operation: Training and technical Assistance (70%), publications (10%), community organizing (10%), research (5%), public education (5%)

Constituency: Tenant and cooperative groups located in low-income neighborhoods throughout New York City. Technical assistance also provided on a national level.

Recent issues and projects: UHAB works with over 1,000 homesteading and cooperative groups through training and technical assistance in bookkeeping, rehab financing, board of director training, architectural and construction assistance, etc. We have recently started organizing local networks of cooperative buildings and local mutual housing associations.

Major publications: *Self Help: In Our Own Words*; *UHAB Tenth Year Report*; *Becoming a Cooperative: A Guide for Tenants Who Manage Their Own Buildings*; *A Guide to Cooperative Ownership*

Budget: $1,000,000

Funding: Government contracts (70%), foundations (28%), individual contributions (2%)

Staff: 31
11 Organizers/Field Workers
5 Architects/Construction Technical Assts
4 Administrators/Program Directors
3 Trainers
2 Writer/Editors
2 Bookkeeper/Accountants
2 Typists
1 Office Manager
1 Foundation Fundraiser

Staff openings/year: 2

Work Week: 40 hours

Salary/year: $22,000 (Recent College Graduate); $32,000 (Graduate with advanced degree)

Benefits: Health insurance, life insurance, pregnancy leave, pension, paid vacation

Part-Time Employees: 3

Summer Employees: Yes

Volunteers: Yes

Interns: Yes
Length: 3 months (summer)
Duties: Depends upon interns' experience and interests
Remuneration: Generally supported through special programs

Jobs advertised: Newspapers, journals, community publications

To apply: Contact Susan Wefald, Assistant Director

Remarks: UHAB is operated by a staff of 31 and has developed procedures that facilitate a high degree of democratic participation by the staff at all levels.

URBAN INSTITUTE
2100 M Street, NW
Washington, DC 20037
(202) 833-7200

President: William Gorham

Purpose: The Urban Institute is a nonprofit, nonpartisan policy and research organization established at the request of Congress and with the support of the White House in Washington, D.C., in 1968. Our purpose is to conduct research, evaluations, and policy analysis related to the social and economic issues facing the U.S. (or related to the same issues in developing nations); to improve government decisions and their implementation; and to facilitate informed debate and decision making by policy makers

Methods of operation: Research (90%), publications (5%), training and technical assistance (5%)

Constituency: Policy-level staff and officials in the federal executive branch and the Congress and other counterparts in state and local governments

Recent issues and projects: Establishment of Urban Networking Project to assist communities in defining their needs and evaluating the outcomes of programs designed to meet those needs. Series of reports on reforming the nation's health care system, focusing on issues of access, spending, and financing. Creation of Program for Research on Immigrant Policy to promote the economic and social integration of immigrants into the U.S.

Major publications: *Medicare Now and in the Future* (1993); *State-Level Data Book on Health Care Access and Financing* (1993); *Drugs, Crime, and Social Isolation: Barriers to Urban Opportunity* (1992); *Clear and Convincing Evidence: Measurement of Discrimination in America* (1992); *Urban Labor Markets and Job Opportunity* (1992); *Annual Report*; *Research Report*; *Policy Bites*; *Sourcebook for Reporters*

Budget: $21,000,000

Funding: Government grants and contracts (65%), foundations (35%)

Staff: 220
125 Research Staff
95 Administrative Staff

Staff openings/year: 35

Work Week: 45 hours

Salary/year: $23-28,000 (Recent College Graduate); $30,000 (Graduate with advanced degree)

Benefits: Health insurance, life insurance, pension, tuition reimbursement, paid vacation

Part-Time Employees: 10

Summer Employees: 10

Volunteers: Yes

Interns: 10 a year
Duties: Varies
Remuneration: Varies

Jobs advertised: Most jobs are advertised in the *Washington Post*; job announcements for research positions are sent to many colleges and universities; and there is an Institute Jobline (202)857-8604

To apply: Send resume, transcript, and references to Personnel Recruitment, The Urban Institute, 2100 M St., N.W., Washington, D.C. 20037

URBAN LEAGUE OF ARKANSAS, INC.
2200 South Main Street, P.O. Box 164039
Little Rock, AR 72216
(501) 372-3037

Director: Mr. Virgil F. Gettis

Purpose: To eliminate negative influences and policies in education, employment, economic development, housing, health, consumer education and social services while providing research and clearinghouse services in Arkansas.

Methods of operation: Human services (40%), community organizing (20%), public education (20%), training and technical assistance (20%)

Membership: From all sectors of the state, public and private

Major publications: Newsletter; annual reports; *State of Black Arkansas*; and monthly status reports

Budget: $21,500,000

Funding: Corporate (60%), foundations (15%), canvassing (10%), direct mail (10%), individual contributions (5%)

Staff: 20
5 Organizers
2 Writer/Editor
1 Office Manager
4 Researchers
2 Typists
1 Bookkeeper/Accountant
5 Grassroots Fundraiser

Staff openings/year: 3

Work Week: 40-45 hours

Salary/year: $13,000 (Recent College Graduate); $16,500 (Graduate with advanced degree)

Benefits: Health insurance, pension, paid vacation, life insurance, family leave

Part-Time Employees: 1

Summer Employees: None

Volunteers: 47

Interns: None, but willing to accept applications

Jobs advertised: Local newspapers, Arkansas Employment Security Divisions, board and staff referrals

To apply: Please contact J. Sandra Key, Assistant to the President/Personnel Officer

---

USSA FOUNDATION

815 15th Street, Suite 838
Washington, DC 20005
(202) 347-4768

Director: Deepak Pateriya

Purpose: To provide educational materials about the United States Student Association's (USSA) student issue campaigns; to provide technical assistance to campus organizers; to train student activists in Direct Action Organizing.

Methods of operation: Training and technical assistance (50%), public education (20%), community organizing (20%), publications (10%)

Constituency: Students at U.S. universities, colleges and community colleges

Recent issues and projects: GROW (GrassRoots Organizing Weekends training project) has trained over 5000 students across the country in the past 7 years in the skills of grassroots organizing and building strong student organizations.

Major publications: Various organizing manuals including electoral work, letter-writing campaigns, coalition building. *Students Respond*, a collection of student essays on multiculturalism in higher education and students efforts to increase access to higher education.

Budget: $200,000

Funding: Foundations (60%), program fees (35%), individual donors (5%)

Staff: 5
1 Executive Director
4 Program Coordinators
10 Part-time Trainers/Consultants

Staff openings/year: 2-3

Work Week: 55 hours

Salary/year: $16,500

Benefits: Health insurance, 2 weeks paid vacation, paid holidays

Part-Time Employees: 10

Volunteers: 5

Interns: 5
Length: Semester or summer
Duties: Defined by intern interest; organizing, writing, etc.
Remuneration: Usually no stipend

Jobs advertised: Mailings to members and friendly organizations; classified ads; *Community Jobs*

To apply: Contact Mary Beth Maxwell

UTILITY CONSUMERS' ACTION NETWORK

1717 Kettner Blvd., Suite 105
San Diego, CA 92101
(619) 696-6966

Director: Michael Shames, Esq.

Purpose: UCAN was created in 1983 to protect San Diego consumers from SDG&E's escalating gas and electric rates. Today, UCAN has expanded its advocacy efforts to include other regulated industries including auto and health insurance, Cable TV, and cellular companies. UCAN is a non-profit consumer advocacy group supported by the tax deductible donations of its members.

Methods of operation: Litigation (50%), research (25%), public education (15%), publications (5%), lobbying (5%)

Membership: 57,000 San Diego residential and small business customers of SDG&E

Recent issues and projects: Annual rate cases; promoting conversation; insurance sales practices, insurance rate increases, Cable TV rate rollbacks.

Major publications: Quarterly newsletter

Budget: $300,000

Funding: Direct mail, membership

Staff: 5
1 Executive Director
1 Office Manager
2 Attorney's
1 Public Outreach

Staff openings/year: 0-1

Work Week: 50 hours

Salary/year: $Varies (Recent College Graduate); $Varies (Graduate with advanced degree)

Benefits: Health insurance, paid vacation and sick leave

Part-Time Employees: 4

Summer Employees: Sometimes

Volunteers: Yes

Interns: None; but willing to accept applications

Jobs advertised: Usually word of mouth

To apply: Contact Michael Shames, Executive Director

VALLEY PROGRAMS, INC.

129 King Street
Northampton, MA 01060
(413) 584-7329

Other Offices: Greenfield, MA; Sunderland, MA; Amherst, MA; S. Deerfield, MA; Orange, MA

Director: Susan L. Stubbs

Purpose: To provide alternative psychiatric services, residential alternatives and supportive services to adults with mental illness; and to provide sheltering services to homeless families and individuals. Housing, case management, counseling, daily living skills training, psychotherapy, substance abuse counseling, day treatment and medication services are offered.

Methods of operation: Human services

Recent issues and projects: Working on more scattered site housing; moving people into more normalized settings; more integrated housing; more flexible user-friendly alternatives to psychiatric hospitalization

Budget: $5,000,000

Funding: State Department of Mental Health, State Department of Public Welfare, U.S. HUD, State Department of Social Services, State Department of Mental Retardation, grants and individual contributions

Staff: 175
100 Counselors
32 Program Directors, Assistant Directors and other Managers
6 Bookkeeper/Accountants
4 Secretaries
33 Clinicians

Work Week: 40 hours

Salary/year: $15,000 (Recent College Graduate); $Varies (Graduate with advanced degree)

Benefits: Health insurance, life insurance, good vacation/ holidays, pregnancy leave

Part-Time Employees: Yes

Volunteers: Yes

Interns: Yes
Length: Varies
Duties: Counseling case management
Remuneration: Small stipend may be available

Jobs advertised: Local newspapers; affirmative action agencies; internally posted

To apply: Contact Medora Paquette, Director of Personnel

VEGETARIAN RESOURCE GROUP

P.O. Box 1463
Baltimore, MD 21203
(410) 366-8343

Purpose: Educate the public about vegetarianism and the inter-related topics of health, environment and ethics. All nutrition information is reviewed by registered dietitians.

Methods of operation: Research, publications, community organizing, public education, training and technical assistance

Constituency: People interested in vegetarianism and healthy diets

Recent issues and projects: Recent projects include: school lunch program; publication of Vegetarian Journal; outreach to dietitians and physicians through presentations and booths at professional conferences; outreach to educators and students; annual essay contest; publication of *I Love Animals and Broccoli Coloring Book and Lesson Plan*; *Vegetarian Nutrition for Teenagers*

Major publications: *Vegetarian Journal*, bimonthly magazine; *Vegetarian Journal's Food Service Update* newsletter; *Simply Vegan*; *Meatless Meals for Working People*; *Simple, Lowfat and Vegetarian*; *Vegetarian Journal's Guide to Natural Foods Restaurants in the U.S. and Canada*; *I Love Animals and Broccoli Activity Book*; *No-Cholesterol Passover Recipes*; *The Lowfat Jewish Vegetarian Cookbook*

Funding: Publications (100%)

Staff: 6
Staff includes:
Organizers
Writers/Editors
Researchers
Press Aides
Foundation Fundraisers
Issue Experts
Typists
Bookkeepers/Accounts
Campaign Managers
Registered Dietitians

Staff openings/year: 1-2

Work Week: 40 hours

Salary/year: $20,000

Benefits: Health insurance, pension, paid vacation, life insurance

Part-Time Employees: 1-4

Summer Employees: None

Volunteers: Yes

Interns: 1-3 at a time
Length: Semester
Duties: Depends on interests and skills of interns. Usually related to journalism, nutrition or business.
Remuneration: Generally interns are not paid, but may receive college credit

Jobs advertised: *Vegetarian Journal*; *Community Jobs*

Remarks: To apply for a job, send a resume with letter detailing: 1) position you are applying for 2) Why you want to work for The Vegetarian Resource Group 3) What type of work would most interest you and 4) What skills and experiences you bring which would be of help to VRG. Please also include a writing sample.

VERMONT INSTITUTE OF NATURAL SCIENCE (VINS)

Church Hill Road, RR 2, Box 532
Woodstock, VT 05091
(802) 457-2779

Director: Christine A. Jauhola

Purpose: VINS is a nonprofit organization dedicated to environmental education, natural history research and bird rehabilitation since 1972.

Methods of operation: Public education (50%), research (20%), avian rehabilitation (20%), publications (5%), training and technical assistance (5%)

Membership: 5,000 members

Recent issues and projects: Reaching 10,000 Vermont school children each month through 1,000 volunteers teaching Environmental Learning for the Future, a hands-one educational program. Avian research projects include peregrine falcon monitoring, studies of state endangered common loons and common terns, and a forest bird monitoring program. Over 550 injured and orphaned songbirds are treated each year at the Vermont Raptor Center, a living museum with 25 species of hawks, owls and eagles on permanent display.

Major publications: Quarterly newsletter; *Records of Vermont Birds* (published quarterly); *A Guide to Bird Finding in Vermont*, 1981; *The Atlas of Breeding Birds in Vermont*, 1985, *Hands on Nature*, 1987; *Waste Away*, 1989

Budget: $750,000

Funding: Programs/contracts (47%), individual contributions (29%), foundations (14%)

Staff: 13
1 Office Manager
1 Foundation Fundraiser
1 Typist
1 Bookkeeper/Accountant
6 Educators
1 Research Biologist
2 Rehabilitators
1 Executive Director

Staff openings/year: 2-4

Work Week: 40 hours

Salary/year: $18,000 (Recent College Graduate); $24,000 (Graduate with advanced degree)

Benefits: Health insurance, paid vacation, pregnancy leave

Part-Time Employees: 14

Summer Employees: 10

Volunteers: 1500

Interns: 9
Length: 4 months
Duties: Care, handling and treatment of injured and resident birds
Remuneration: $250 per month plus housing provided

Jobs advertised: Environmental job opportunity newsletters, regional newspapers

To apply: Contact Christine Jauhola, Executive Director

VERMONT NATURAL RESOURCES COUNCIL

9 Bailey Avenue
Montpelier, VT 05602
(802) 223-2328

Other Offices: Manchester, VT

Director: Ned Farquhar, Associate Director

Purpose: Private nonprofit membership-based environmental organization founded in 1963 to promote the wise use of Vermont's natural resources through lobbying, advocacy, research and education.

Methods of operation: Research, lobbying, litigation, publications, community organizing, public education

Constituency: Vermont conservationists

Recent issues and projects: Lobbying for protection of laws on land use planning, forest and agricultural land protection and water quality.

Major publications: Bi-annual magazine: *Vermont Environmental Report*; *Vermont Environmental Directory* - guide to environmental groups, government and more; *Citizen Involvement Kit*; *So Goes Vermont*, video

Budget: $300,000

Funding: Unrestricted contributions (37%), membership dues and renewals (28%), restricted grants and projects (23%), interest and dividends (10%), other (2%)

Staff: 7
1 Deputy Director for Policy
1 Operations Manager
3 Program Directors
1 Membership Director
1 Development Associate
1/2 Grassroots Coordinator

Work Week: 50 hours

Salary/year: $15-20,000 (Recent College Graduate); $25,000 (Graduate with advanced degree)

Benefits: Health insurance, pregnancy leave, paid vacation

Part-Time Employees: 2

Volunteers: 3-10

Interns: Yes
Length: 3 months
Duties: Research
Remuneration: One internship with small stipend; all others volunteer

VERMONT PUBLIC INTEREST RESEARCH GROUP (VPIRG)

43 State Street
Montpelier, VT 05602
(802) 223-5221

Other Offices: Burlington, VT

Director: Katherine Vose, Interim Director

Purpose: Represent consumer and environmental interests in legislature, administrative agencies and other public policy forums. Research and education on issues of importance to constituents.

Methods of operation: Lobbying (30%), research (20%), community organizing (20%), publications (12%), public education (12%), direct action (5%), litigation (1%)

Constituency: 25,000 Vermont citizens

Recent issues and projects: Recent projects include: solid waste organizing; health care reform; toxics; indoor air pollution; least cost energy planning; toy safety

Major publications: Quarterly newsletter. Reports: *Economics Of Early Retirement Of Vermont Yankee Nuclear Power Plant* (1989); *Toxics Released* (1989); *A Call to Action: Global Warming Strategies for Vermont* (1990); *Citizen Guide to Mandatory Recycling* (1990)

Budget: $400,000

Funding: Individual contributions, foundations

Staff: 8
2 Lobbyists
2 Organizer
1 Office Manager
1 Grassroots Fundraiser
1 Development Director
1 Executive Director

Staff openings/year: 1-2

Work Week: 50-55 hours

Salary/year: $20,000 (Recent College Graduate); $Varies (Graduate with advanced degree)

Benefits: Health insurance, paid vacation

Part-Time Employees: 5

Summer Employees: 20-40

Volunteers: 5-10

Interns: 3
Length: Semester
Duties: Research, administrative support, organizing
Remuneration: Work-study; match stipends when resources available

Jobs advertised: *Community Jobs*; local papers; circulated notices

To apply: Contact Rob Stuart, Executive Director

VETERANS FOR PEACE (VFP)

P.O. Box 3881
Portland, ME 04104
(207) 773-1431

Director: Jerry Genesio

Purpose: To educate the general public concerning the dangers inherent in global arms trading, overt and covert intervention in the internal affairs of other nations, the human costs of war, and the exigency of abolishing war as an instrument of state policy.

Methods of operation: Public education (75%), direct action (25%)

Constituency: U.S. military veterans of all eras

Recent issues and projects: Recent projects include: Children of War Rescue Project evacuating and providing probono medical care for child war victims of the ongoing conflicts in the former Yugoslav republics; The Central America War Relief Project delivering medical and humanitarian aid to Nicaragua, Guatemala and El Salvador and assisting former FMLN and El Salvadoran military veterans establish a prosthetics center

Major publications: *VFP Quarterly Journal*; special issues on the Abolish War Campaign and Central American; also special issue on Operation Angel Ambulance Rescue Convoy to Mostar Bosnia-Herzegovina

Budget: $85,000

Funding: Individual contributions (90%), foundations (10%)

Staff: 1
1 Office Manager

Staff openings/year: 40-60

Work Week: 40-60 hours

Benefits: Health insurance, paid vacation

Part-Time Employees: 2

Summer Employees: None

Volunteers: 15-20

Interns: None, but willing to accept applications

To apply: Please contact Jerry Genesio, Executive Director

VIRGINIA CITIZENS CONSUMER COUNCIL (VCCC)

7115 Leesburg Pike #215
Falls Church, VA 22043
(703) 536-8642

Other Offices: Yorktown, VA

President: Jean Ann Fox

Purpose: A grassroots consumer organization formed and directed by volunteers to represent consumers before the General Assembly, state regulatory agencies, and businesses. VCCC sponsors seminars, publishes consumer information, and conducts market studies.

Methods of operation: Lobbying (33%), publications (16%), research (16%), direct action (16%), public education (10%), training and technical assistance (9%)

Constituency: Virginia consumers statewide

Recent issues and projects: Legislation to repeal the Rule of 78 on long-term credit contracts; auto insurance reform; basic banking; health spa regulation; safety labeling of light trucks; ATV age restrictions; insurance antitrust exemption modification; credit insurance rates and protections; electric rate increases; telephone deregulation; caller-ID blocking

Major publications: Bimonthly newsletter: *VCCC Voice*; *VCCC Basic Banking Consumer Survey*; *Annual VCCC Legislative Agenda*; "Lemon Aid For New Car Buyers;" *Consumer's Guide to Credit Card Rates*

Budget: $8,000

Funding: Individual contributions (50%), grants (30%), conference registration (20%)

Volunteers: 1

Interns: Yes
Duties: Research, investigation
Remuneration: Expenses reimbursed

To apply: Contact Jean Ann Fox, President, (804) 867-8544

VOICES FOR ILLINOIS CHILDREN

53 West Jackson, Suite 515
Chicago, IL 60604
(312) 427-4080

President: Jerome Stermer

Purpose: VIC champions the full development of every child in Illinois. It seeks to guide the efforts of individuals and public and private institutions to assure that all our children are born healthy, remain healthy, and are nurtured to become educated, productive and responsible citizens.

Methods of operation: Research (40%), public education (40%), publications (15%), lobbying (5%)

Constituency: Civic, community and business leaders, social service providers, parents, persons interested in children's issues

Recent issues and projects: Promoting a state earned income tax credit; family preservation; welfare reform; and working on issues related to juvenile justice, mental health and early intervention

Major publications: Newsletter: *Voices*; *A Children's Agenda: Into the '90s*

Budget: $700,000

Funding: Individual contributions, foundations

Staff: 12
3 Administrative Assistants
2 Researchers
1 President
1 Vice-President/Early Intervention Issues
1 Research and Policy Vice-President
1 Writer/Editor
1 Foundation Fundraiser
1 Bookkeeper/Accountant
1 Issue Expert

Staff openings/year: 0-2

Work Week: 40 hours

Salary/year: $Varies (Recent College Graduate); $Varies (Graduate with advanced degree)

Benefits: Health insurance, life insurance, pregnancy leave, pension, paid vacation, dental insurance

Part-Time Employees: 1

Summer Employees: 1

Interns: 1
Length: 1 year
Duties: Assist in research

Remuneration: Stipend

Jobs advertised: Newspapers and mailings

To apply: Contact Jerome Stermer, President

VOLUNTEER - THE NATIONAL CENTER

1111 North 19th Street, Suite 500
Arlington, VA 22209
(703) 276-0542

Director: Frank H. Bailey

Purpose: VOLUNTEER works to support and stimulate more effective volunteering to help solve local problems.

Methods of operation: Public education, training and technical assistance, publications

Constituency: Volunteer centers, state volunteer agencies, corporations, nonprofits

Recent issues and projects: "Volunteer Connection" - a national media campaign to promote volunteerism; President's Volunteer Action Awards - President Bush recognizes outstanding volunteer efforts

Major publications: Magazine: *Voluntary Action Leadership*; newsletters; distributes publications through "Volunteer Readership" catalog service

Staff: 17
6 Organizers
3 Typists
2 Issue Experts
1 1/2 Foundation Fundraisers
1 1/2 Writer/Editors
1 Office Manager
1 Press Aide
1 Bookkeeper/Accountant

Staff openings/year: 1/2

Work Week: 40 hours

Benefits: Health insurance, pregnancy leave, pension, paid vacation

Volunteers: 10-15 per year

Interns: None currently, but willing to accept applications

VOLUNTEER LAWYERS FOR T... ARTS (VLA)

1 East 53rd Street, 6th Floor
New York, NY 10022
(212) 319-2787

Director: Sharon Gersten Luckman

Purpose: VLA provides arts-related legal assistance to artists and arts organizations in all creative fields who cannot afford private counsel. VLA also works to prevent legal entanglements through education programs, including seminars, publications, and the maintenance of an Art Law Library.

Methods of operation: Legal services to indigent artists and emerging or small arts organizations (90%), research (3%), publications (3%), public education (3%), lobbying (1%)

Membership: VLA's membership is made up of approximately 200 lawyers, 800 volunteer lawyers and thousands of artists and arts organizations.

Major publications: *To Be or Not To Be: An Artist's Guide to Not-for-Profit Incorporation*; *This Way Up: Legal and Business Essentials for Nonprofits*; *The Art of Filing: A Tax Workbook for Visual, Performing, and Literary Artists*; *Artists' Housing Manual: A Guide to Living in New York City*; *Legal Guide for the Visual Artist*; etc.

Budget: $500,000

Funding: Foundations, corporations (53%), benefits, government (39%), individual contributions (8%)

Staff: 7
2 Administrators
2 Attorneys
1 Paralegal
1 Typist
1 Foundation Fundraiser

Staff openings/year: 1-2

Work Week: 45-50 hours

Benefits: Health insurance, life insurance, paid vacation

Part-Time Employees: 2-3

Volunteers: 5, plus 800 lawyers

Interns: 35
Length: 1 semester or 2 summer months
Duties: Screening clients, research and answering questions on the telephone hotline
Remuneration: None

Jobs advertised: *New York Times*; *ArtSearch*

To apply: Contact Daniel Mayer, Executive Director

Remarks: There are other independent VLAs in 42 cities nationwide. VLA provides $2 million in pro bono legal services annually.

VOLUNTEERS FOR PEACE

43 Tiffany Road
Belmont, VT 05730
(802) 259-2759

Director: Peter Coldwell

Purpose: We are one planet. With today's technology and communication we can overcome the need, violence and environmental decay witnessed today. We need to put down our ideological baggage and work together to improve life for everyone.

Methods of operation: Direct action (50%), human services (20%), community organizing (10%), publications (5%), training and technical assistance (5%), research (2%)

Constituency: The average age of our workcamper is 22. The majority are from colleges, are high school graduates or are those who love to travel.

Recent issues and projects: Sent 450 North Americans to 600 camps including 220 people to Eastern Europe and the CIS; hosted 500 Europeans in 45 domestic camps.

Major publications: Annual newsletter: *The International Workcamper*, published in January, free; Annual *International Workcamp Directory*, published in early April, $10 postage paid

Budget: $300,000

Funding: Individual contributions (100%)

Staff: 3
3 Co-Directors

Staff openings/year: 1-2

Work Week: 30-80 hours

Salary/year: $Varies (Recent College Graduate); $Varies (Graduate with advanced degree)

Volunteers: Sometimes

Interns: The program itself consists of internships

Jobs advertised: Through references

To apply: Contact VFP

Remarks: We operate with minimal staff and expenses to place as many volunteers as we can in our workcamps.

WAR RESISTERS LEAGUE

339 Lafayette Street
New York, NY 10012
(212) 228-0450

Other Offices: Norwich, CT

Purpose: WRL opposes war and the causes of war (racism, sexism, economic exploitation) through education and nonviolent action.

Methods of operation: Public education (40%), publications (20%), training and technical assistance (10%), direct action (10%), community organizing (10%), research (5%)

Recent issues and projects: Current projects address disarmament, military service, war taxes, intervention, high school activism and nonviolence.

Major publications: *The Nonviolent Activist*; *Organizers Manual*; *Guide to War Tax Resistance*; Peace Calendar

Budget: $400,000

Staff: 6
3 Organizers
1 Writer/Editor
1 Bookkeeper/Accountant
1 Grassroots Fundraiser

Staff openings/year: 1

Work Week: 40 hours

Salary/year: $20,000

Benefits: Health insurance, pregnancy leave, pension, paid vacation

Part-Time Employees: 1

Volunteers: Yes; many

Interns: 4
Length: Range: 2 months-1 year
Duties: Program and/or fundraising work
Remuneration: Possible housing

Jobs advertised: *Community Jobs*; our publications; movement publications

To apply: Contact Ralph DiGia

WASHINGTON CITIZEN ACTION

100 S. King Street, Suite 240
Seattle, WA 98104
(206) 389-0050

Other Offices: Tacoma, WA

Director: David West

Purpose: Consumer advocacy, lobbying, community organizing on health care, economic justice, and poverty issues

Methods of operation: Lobbying (40%), community organizing (20%), research (10%), publications (10%), public education (10%), training and technical assistance (10%)

Membership: 40,000 members, plus coalition of senior, labor, church and community

Recent issues and projects: Passing health care access bill in State legislature

Major publications: Organizational newsletter; occasional reports

Budget: $150,000

Funding: Canvassing (50%), foundations (30%), institutional contributions (20%)

Staff: 26
20 Canvassers
2 Organizers
1 Lobbyist
1 Foundation Fundraiser
1 Bookkeeper/Accountant
1 Office Manager

Staff openings/year: 1-2

Work Week: 40-60 hours

Salary/year: $15-25,000

Benefits: Health insurance, pregnancy leave

Part-Time Employees: 5-10

Summer Employees: Yes; canvass

Volunteers: 5

Interns: 2-4
Length: 6 months
Duties: Research, organizing, media
Remuneration: Canvassing

Jobs advertised: Internally with posting; externally in newspaper

To apply: Contact David West, Executive Director

WASHINGTON CITIZENS FOR RECYCLING

157 Yesler Way, Suite 309
Seattle, WA 98104
(206) 343-6171

Director: Jan Glick

Purpose: WCFR is dedicated to saving natural resources through waste reduction, recycling and market development.

Methods of operation: Public education (80%), training and technical assistance (4%), publications (4%), community organizing (4%), research (4%), lobbying (4%)

Membership: We have a membership base of 2,700 persons, the majority live throughout Washington State

Recent issues and projects: WCFR is working towards increasing markets for recycled content products as well as educating consumers on this issue.

Major publications: Quarterly newsletter, guides and directories which support our campaign work (Reach for Unbleached, Buy Recycled, Waste Reduction, Used Motor Oil Collect, etc.)

Budget: $195,000

Funding: Individual contributions (32%), foundations (26%), government (23%), direct mail (9.5%), telephone solicitation (9.5%)

Staff: 6
Some positions overlap:
1 Office Manager
1 Lobbyist
2 Foundation Fundraisers
2 Issue Experts
2 Bookkeepers/Accountants
1 Grassroots Fundraiser
3 Campaign Managers
1 Executive Director
2 Volunteer Coordinators
4 Organizers

Staff openings/year: 1

Work Week: 45 hours

Salary/year: $Varies (Recent College Graduate); $Varies (Graduate with advanced degree)

Benefits: Health insurance, paid vacation

Part-Time Employees: None

Summer Employees: None

Volunteers: 55

Interns: 12
Length: 3-9 months
Duties: Varied, depends on program assignment
Remuneration: Internships are unpaid, possible to earn college credits

Jobs advertised: Local newsletters and newspapers, environmental job listings, word of mouth, posting notices at Universities and community centers

To apply: Please contact Marie Pearl, Office Manager/Volunteer Coordinator

Remarks: Interested applicants should contact the office before sending resumes or applying for internships.

WASHINGTON COUNCIL OF AGENCIES

1001 Connecticut Avenue, NW, Suite 925
Washington, DC 20036
(202) 457-0540

Director: Betsy Johnson

Purpose: WCA is an association of Washington area nonprofits working together to provide technical services, collective buying power and influence that members might not otherwise obtain operating on their own.

Methods of operation: Administration (10%), publications (25%), public education (55%), training and technical assistance (10%)

Membership: 501(c)3's in DC area

Recent issues and projects: Passage by D.C. Council of Volunteer Protection Law; Postal rates NPO status; Provide health insurance, retirement, office supply discount, oil heat discount, general liability and Directors and Officers Liability Insurance; mailing and list maintenance service; accounting, computer equipment discount

Major publications: *WCA Nonprofit Agenda*; *Catalog of Services*; *Hiring, Firing and Supervising Legally*; *125 Places to Meet*

Budget: $460,000

Funding: Fees (50%), membership (30%), foundations (20%)

Staff: 7
3 Project Managers
2 Administrators
1 Receptionist
1 Bookkeeper/Accountant/Office Manager

Staff openings/year: 1/2

Work Week: 35 hours

Salary/year: $18,000 (Recent College Graduate); $25,000 (Graduate with advanced degree)

Benefits: Health insurance, life insurance, pregnancy leave, paid vacation, retirement benefits

Interns: None currently, but willing to accept applications
Remuneration: Unpaid

Jobs advertised: *Washington Post*; *WCA Nonprofit Agenda*; word of mouth

To apply: Contact Betsy Johnson

Remarks: We have a job board where job openings at member organizations are posted. Job seekers are welcome to look.

WASHINGTON HEIGHTS-INWOOD COALITION

652 West 187th Street
New York, NY 10033
(212) 781-6722

Director: John Swauger

Purpose: Organize tenants and block associations; resolve disputes that might otherwise go to court; offer youth positive alternatives to crime and drug use; prevent child abuse and neglect

Methods of operation: Human services (60%), community organizing (30%), public education (10%)

Recent issues and projects: Launched a reading enrichment program and child abuse prevention program for immigrants

Budget: $630,000

Funding: Government contracts (67%), foundations (33%)

Staff: 16
11 Caseworkers
3 Organizers
1 Bookkeeper/Accountant
1 Office Manager

Staff openings/year: 2

Work Week: 35 hours

Salary/year: $22,250 (Recent College Graduate);

$26,250 (Graduate with advanced degree)

Benefits: Health insurance, life insurance, pregnancy leave, paid vacation

Part-Time Employees: 1

Summer Employees: 1

Volunteers: 15

Interns: None currently, but willing to accept applications

Jobs advertised: Local newspaper; notices to community organizations

To apply: Contact John Swauger, Executive Director

Remarks: Service staff must all be bilingual in Spanish and English.

WASHINGTON LEGAL CLINIC FOR THE HOMELESS

1800 Massachusetts Ave., NW, 6th Floor
Washington, DC 20036
(202) 872-1494

Director: Patricia Mullaby Fugere

Purpose: The Washington Legal Clinic for the Homeless is committed to making justice a reality for all people. Since our founding in 1986, the Legal Clinic has endeavored to meet the legal needs of children, women and men who are homeless or at-risk of becoming so, assuring access to a system too often inaccessible to those without ability to pay. Our mission may be summed up in two words: Service and Solutions. We dedicate ourselves to providing quality, free legal services to clients who are homeless, most often through volunteers whom we are committed to support. In addition, we seek permanent solutions to the challenges which our clients face, by working through systemic advocacy and law reform to improve the programs and benefits.

Methods of operation: Research, lobbying, litigation, publications, human services, public education, training and technical assistance, administrative representation of clients

Constituency: WLCH represents homeless clients primarily through volunteer network of the DC Legal Community

Recent issues and projects: The Washington Legal Clinic for the Homeless provides pro-bono legal services to clients who are homeless in the District of Columbia. Much of this work is carried out by a team of more than 250 volunteer attorneys, paralegals and law students, who visit ten area shelters, soup kitchens and day centers to see clients at the Legal Clinic's intake sites. The Legal Clinic staff recruits, trains and counsels the volunteers in their efforts. The Legal Clinic also is dedicated to accomplishing systemic reforms to improve programs and services for our clients, which we pursue through class action litigation, legislative and administrative advocacy, and community education.

Budget: $310,000

Funding: Special events (50%), foundations (30%), individual contributions (20%)

Staff: 6
2 Attorneys
1 Administrator
1 Staff Assistant
1 Volunteer Coordinator
1 Executive Director

Staff openings/year: 0-1

Work Week: 37.5 hours

Salary/year: $21,000 (Recent College Graduate); $26,000 (Graduate with advanced degree)

Benefits: Health insurance, paid vacation, life insurance

Part-Time Employees: None

Summer Employees: None

Volunteers: 250

Interns: 1
Length: Summer or semester
Duties: Client representation and other duties as assigned
Remuneration: Interns arrange for own funding

Jobs advertised: Local newspapers, law school placement offices, legal service offices and other community groups.

To apply: Please contact Patty Mullahey Fugere, Executive Director

---

WASHINGTON MONTHLY COMPANY

1611 Connecticut Avenue, NW, Suite 7
Washington, DC 20009
(202) 462-0218

Director: Charles Peters

Purpose: We publish the *Washington Monthly*, a national magazine about politics and government.

Methods of operation: Publications (100%)

Constituency: Subscribers include key White House, Congressional and other government officials, as well as journalists, business executives and educators.

Major publications: *The Washington Monthly*

Budget: $700,000

Funding: Subscriptions (80%), advertising (20%)

Staff: 6
3 Writer/Editors
1 Circulation Director
1 Business Manager
1 Advertising Director

Staff openings/year: 2

Work Week: 50 hours

Salary/year: $10,000

Benefits: Health insurance, paid vacation

Part-Time Employees: 2

Interns: 4-6
Length: Flexible; 3 months average
Duties: Assist in all aspects of publication

Jobs advertised: See *The Washington Monthly*; also newspaper classifieds

To apply: Contact Charles Peters, Editor

WASHINGTON OFFICE ON AFRICA

110 Maryland Ave. #112
Washington, DC 20002
(202) 546-7961

Director: Imani Countess

Purpose: The mission of the Washington Office on Africa (WOA) is to coordinate, link, and promote American and African grassroots agendas that affect policies in the United States which support peace and political and economic justice in Africa.

Methods of operation: Research, lobbying, public education

Constituency: Individuals and organizations across the U.S. and abroad who are interested in African issues

Recent issues and projects: WOA primary focus is to: support the movement for freedom from white-minority rule in southern Africa; and to serve as a resource for the broader anti-apartheid movements and a variety of other non-governmental organizations.

Major publications: *Washington Notes on Africa*, newsletter 3 times a year; *Zaire: A Nation Held Hostage*

Budget: $150,000

Funding: Churches (100%)

Staff: 2
1 Office Manager
1 Lobbyist

Work Week: 50 hours

Salary/year: $21,000

Benefits: Health insurance, paid vacation, family leave

Part-Time Employees: 1

Summer Employees: None

Volunteers: 3

Interns: 3
Length: 3 to 4 months
Duties: Tracking Africa related legislation; working with coalition partners on Africa issues
Remuneration: Unpaid

Jobs advertised: Electronic networks; mailings to African advocacy community

To apply: Contact Kristen Lee, Executive Assistant

WASHINGTON OFFICE ON LATIN AMERICA (WOLA)

110 Maryland Avenue, NE, Suite 404
Washington, DC 20002
(202) 544-8045

Director: George R. Vickers

Purpose: WOLA aims to shape a foreign policy that advances human rights, democracy and peace in the hemisphere. WOLA monitors human rights practices, political developments and U.S. policies in Latin America and the Caribbean; provides U.S. policymakers and the public with information and analysis about the region; and fosters thoughtful interchange among people with diverse perspectives who share our goals.

Methods of operation: Public education (60%), research (20%), publications (18%), lobbying (2%)

Constituency: We work on behalf of the people of Latin America, with NGOs (Non-Governmental Organizations), policymakers and the media.

Recent issues and projects: Weekly seminars are held all year round, two to three conferences are held yearly, and up-to-date, objective documentation and analysis is provided to Congress and the media. Our work is structured around three themes relating democracy to human rights: military accountability, democratic governance and social dimensions of democratization.

Major publications: Bimonthly newsletter: *Enlace* (in Spanish); 10-12 publications produced yearly

Budget: $500,000

Funding: Individual contributions, foundations, direct mail, religious organizations

Staff: 12
6 Writer/Editors
2 Organizers
2 Researchers
1 Office Manager
1 Foundation Fundraiser

Staff openings/year: 2

Work Week: 40 hours

Salary/year: $14,000 (Recent College Graduate); $19,000 (Graduate with advanced degree)

Benefits: Health insurance, life insurance, pregnancy leave, paid vacation

Volunteers: Varies

Interns: 4 per semester
Length: 3 months
Duties: Primarily administrative; some research involved. Work involves organizing seminars and helping with mailings and other communications.
Remuneration: Unpaid; course credit may be available

Jobs advertised: Through mailings to colleague organizations and other constituents

To apply: Contact the Deputy Director

WASHINGTON PEACE CENTER

2111 Florida Avenue, NW
Washington, DC 20008
(202) 234-2000

Director: Lisa Fithian

Purpose: We are a 26 year old multi-issue, anti-racist peace and justice organization committed to nonviolent social change.

Methods of operation: Training and technical assistance (20%), direct action (20%), publications (20%), community organizing (15%), public education (25%)

Recent issues and projects: Current projects include Anti-racism Workshops and Film series, Stopping Cooke Stadium, and Indigenous Peoples Rights.

Major publications: *Peace Letter*, 11 times/year, carrying a comprehensive calendar and informative articles on issues and actions

Budget: $75,000

Funding: Direct mail (50%), individual contributions (20%), foundations (10%), other (20%)

Staff: 2

Staff openings/year: 1

Work Week: 50 hours

Salary/year: $18,000

Benefits: Health insurance, paid vacation

Volunteers: 30

Interns: Yes
Length: A semester
Duties: Mutually decided upon
Remuneration: None

Jobs advertised: Variety of publications: left journals and *Community Jobs*

To apply: Contact Lisa Fithian

WASHINGTON PUBLIC INTEREST RESEARCH GROUP (WASHPIRG)

340 15th Avenue East, Suite 350
Seattle, WA 98112
(206) 322-9064

Other Offices: Olympia, WA; Seattle, WA

Director: Rebecca Levison

Purpose: Nonprofit, nonpartisan consumer and environmental issues advocacy organization. Represent about 30,000 members statewide and two campus chapters. Main strategies are grassroots organizing, legislative advocacy and initiatives/referenda.

Methods of operation: Lobbying (20%), public

education (20%), community organizing (20%), research (20%), litigation (10%), publications (10%)

Membership: About 5,000 student members on two campuses; about 30,000 non-voting citizen members in cities throughout the state

Recent issues and projects: 1985-86: led campaign to block siting of high-level nuclear waste dump at Hanford; 1987-88 campaign to pass statewide ballot initiative to clean up hazardous waste dumps; 1989-present: Pesticide Use Reduction Campaign to protect groundwater, ensure food safety and reduce household exposure

Major publications: Newsletter: *WashPIRG Reports*, published 3 times yearly for members; periodic research reports to support campaigns

Budget: $150,000

Funding: Telephone solicitation (40%), individual contributions (25%), canvassing (20%), foundations (10%), direct mail (5%)

Staff: 20
10 Canvassers
2 Organizers
3 Phone Canvass Staff
2 Canvass Directors
1 Field Organizer
1/2 Bookkeeper/Accountant

Staff openings/year: 4

Work Week: 60 hours

Salary/year: $12,500 (Recent College Graduate); $Varies (Graduate with advanced degree)

Benefits: Health insurance, paid vacation, student loan repayment assistance

Part-Time Employees: 15

Summer Employees: 40-60

Volunteers: 2

Interns: 1
Length: 1 academic quarter
Duties: Vary widely from legislative internships to research and publication of reports to campaign work, media work, citizen organizing
Remuneration: None; students receive academic credit

Jobs advertised: Through college placement offices (CPO recruitment is done cooperatively with other PIRGs); announcements in newspapers and other publications

To apply: Contact Rick Bunch, Executive Director

Remarks: PIRGs nationwide cooperate extensively, broadening the number of job opportunities beyond the 20 staff positions available in Washington state. Staff frequently move from state to state to gain experience, skills, knowledge and advancement.

WASHINGTON TOXICS COALITION

4516 University Way, NE
Seattle, WA 98105
(206) 632-1545

Purpose: Our mission is to reduce society's use of toxic chemicals through advocacy, education and information.

Methods of operation: Fundraising, research, lobbying, publications, public education

Membership: 1500 members statewide

Recent issues and projects: Green gardening project; advocating phase-out of chlorine use at pulp mills; halting development of hazardous waste incinerators; state groundwater contamination map

Major publications: *Alternatives*, quarterly; *Home Safe Home* (fact sheets); *Consumer Guide*; *At the Source* (fact sheets); *Smoke Screen: The Myth of Incinerator Need*

Budget: $300,000

Funding: Foundations (61%), individual contributions (12%), contracts (12%)

Staff: 8
1 Grassroots Fundraiser
4 Project Directors
1 Administrative Director
1 Outreach Specialist
1 Project Assistant

Staff openings/year: 1-2

Work Week: 40 hours

Salary/year: $24,000 (Recent College Graduate); $24,000 (Graduate with advanced degree)

Benefits: Health insurance, paid vacation, life insurance, family leave

Part-Time Employees: 1

Summer Employees: 1

Volunteers: 15

Interns: Yes
Length: 3-9 months
Duties: Project assistant
Remuneration: Usually unpaid

Jobs advertised: Sound opportunities, *Seattle Times*, local non-profits

To apply: Please contact Jeff Cohn, Director of Administration

Remarks: We are a non-hierarchical-consensus based organization with the bulk of our work divided among four projects which are Home Safe Home, Industrial Toxics, Pesticide Reform and Groundwater Protection and information and Education services.

WASHINGTON WILDERNESS COALITION

4649 Sunnyside Avenue, N, Apt. 209
Seattle, WA 98103
(206) 633-1992

Director: Cathie Currie

Purpose: The Washington Wilderness Coalition (WWC) was founded in 1979 to foster and organize grassroots efforts within the wilderness movement in Washington state. Composed of over 40 organizations and 1,000 individuals, WWC provides a support network for front-line groups fighting to protect our public lands from irresponsible logging, poor management, mining and other threats.

Methods of operation: Public education (25%), research (20%), community organizing (18%), publications (10%), lobbying (10%), litigation (2%)

Constituency: Washington State citizens concerned about the protection and preservation of our wildlands

Recent issues and projects: WWC's major programs for 1994 include: protecting Washington's wild lands by providing support to grassroots Forest Watch groups in their efforts to monitor and halt potentially destructive forest management decisions; laying the groundwork for permanent protection of our remaining roadless areas through the development of a new Wilderness campaign; and protecting public lands from the environmental threat of large-scale chemical leach mining by watch-dogging the mining industry and lobbying for strong state and Federal regulations.

Major publications: *Washington Wildfire*, bi-monthly magazine

Budget: $100,000

Funding: Individual contributions, foundations, direct mail, workplace giving

Staff: 2
1 Organizer
3/4 Researcher
1/4 Lobbyist
1/2 Foundation Fundraiser

Staff openings/year: 1

Work Week: 50 hours

Salary/year: $18-21,000 (Recent College Graduate); $21-28,000 (Graduate with advanced degree)

Benefits: Health insurance, paid vacation, family leave

Part-Time Employees: 1

Volunteers: 15

Interns: 5
Length: 3-4 months
Duties: Research the impacts of mining and timber industry activities on public lands. Organize citizen support for public lands protection.

Jobs advertised: *Seattle Times*, *Community Jobs*, *Sound Opportunities*, local and national public interest organizations

To apply: Contact Cathie Currie, Executive Director

Remarks: Send for description of internship and volunteer opportunities.

WEST MICHIGAN ENVIRONMENTAL ACTION COUNCIL

1432 Wealthy St. SE
Grand Rapids, MI 49506
(616) 451-3051

Director: Andrew Davis

Purpose: To protect and enhance the environment of West Michigan through education and advocacy.

Methods of operation: Public education (75%), training and technical assistance (10%), publications (10%), community organizing (5%)

Constituency: People, organizations and businesses who live or work in West Michigan

Recent issues and projects: Recent projects include: Adopt-A-Stream; YIKES!, a youth environmental group; and Project Greenspace, to inventory, identify and protect greenspaces. Issues include: Regional land use and transportation planning; sand dune protection; air and water quality issues.

Major publications: Monthly newsletter, *Action Issue*; occasional reports, booklets and fact sheets

Budget: $200,000

Funding: Individual contributions (50%), foundations (25%), endowment (25%)

Staff: 4
2 Issue Experts
1/4 Writer/Editor
1/4 Office Manager
1/4 Bookkeeper/Accountant
1 Development/Fundraiser
1/4 Volunteer Coordinator/Youth Advisor

Staff openings/year: 0-1

Work Week: 40 hours

Salary/year: $20,000 (Recent College Graduate); $25,000 (Graduate with advanced degree)

Benefits: Health insurance, pension, paid vacation, pregnancy leave

Part-Time Employees: None

Summer Employees: None

Volunteers: 10-30

Interns: 1-4
Length: One semester
Duties: Work on a specific project with one staff person
Remuneration: None

Jobs advertised: Environmental and job listing newsletters, local and state papers, through environmental organization networks

To apply: Please contact Andrew D. Davis, Executive Director

WEST VIRGINIA SCHOLARS ACADEMY

Main & Dogwood Streets
Franklin, WV 26807
(304) 358-2401

Director: Belle Zars

Purpose: West Virginia has one of the nation's lowest college attendance rates. The WVSA works to raise the state's college attendance rate by working with motivated disadvantaged students across the state to encourage college attendance and to help them formulate strategies for attending college. The WVSA helps these students get adequate financial aid and to gain admissions to an appropriate college.

Methods of operation: Direct action (50%), public education (20%), publications (20%), research (10%)

Constituency: West Virginia high school and college students

Recent issues and projects: The core of the program is counseling the West Virginia Honor Roll, a group of 100 students selected each year from across the state during junior year of high school. These students receive WVSA counseling services throughout their high school and college years. Recent expansions include: (1) a college peer counseling program where Honor Roll members attending college receive a stipend for returning to their high schools to do college counseling; (2) a summer writing project staffed by Honor Roll members who are in college, giving high school students a chance to develop writing skills; (3) a summer internship program for Honor Roll members run with the cooperation of the state of West Virginia.

Major publications: *WVSA Guide to Financial Aid*; *Take a Seat-A Guide to Colleges That Meet 100% of Financial Need; Apple Seed-A Newsletter to Support Peer Counseling*; *College Section Aid*; *A Guide to the College Admissions Process*; *Transition Skills Booklet-Surviving the Jump From High School to College*; *Alumni Newsletter*

Budget: $318,000

Funding: Foundations (80%), individual contributions (10%), in-kind (10%)

Staff: 4
1 College Counselor
1 Public Relations
1 Student Recruitment
1 Program Development

Staff openings/year: 2

Work Week: 40 hours

Salary/year: $17,500 (Recent College Graduate); $25,000 (Graduate with advanced degree)

Benefits: Health insurance, pregnancy leave, paid vacation, flexible hours/work schedule

Part-Time Employees: 3

Summer Employees: 3-4

Volunteers: Yes; part-time

Interns: None currently, but willing to accept

applications
Remuneration: Unpaid

Jobs advertised: Local newspapers; *Chronicle of Higher Education*; *Community Jobs* and various newsletters

To apply: Contact Belle Zars, Director

WESTERN CAROLINA COALITION FOR SOCIAL CONCERNS

2 Wall Street, Suite 115, Miles Building
Asheville, NC 28801
(704) 274-2088

Director: Eleanor H. Lloyd, Chair

Purpose: To provide support services for nonprofit organizations that carry on educational efforts for social issues, including peace, the environment and social and economic justice.

Methods of operation: Training and technical assistance (30%), human services (20%), public education (20%), community organizing (10%), research (10%), publications (10%)

Recent issues and projects: Money-raising for a replacement computer; working on April 22, 1990 Earth Day; providing technical assistance for people to improve their economic conditions by better employment or small business endeavors

Budget: $1,500

Funding: Nonprofit organizations (60%), individual contributions (40%)

Volunteers: 10

Interns: None currently, but willing to accept applications

To apply: Contact Eleanor H. Lloyd, Chair

WESTERN COLORADO CONGRESS

P.O. Box 472, 7 North Cascade
Montrose, CO 81402
(303) 249-1978

Other Offices: Durango, CO

Director: Kevin L. Williams

Purpose: WCC is an organization of citizens and a coalition of community groups united for citizen empowerment on issues that affect the quality of life on the western slope of Colorado. We organize citizens on the issues of utility, water, waste, etc.

Methods of operation: Community organizing (63%), research (10%), public education (10%), lobbying (5%), direct action (5%), publications (5%), litigation (2%)

Membership: Primarily residents of western Colorado; a wide variety of ages, income levels, etc.

Recent issues and projects: Stopped a radioactive waste dump proposal; fighting electric utility rate hike proposals; fighting huge proposed increases in timber harvesting in the National Forests

Major publications: Newsletter: *The Clarion*, published 10 times/year

Budget: $165,000

Funding: Foundations (66%), individual contributions (20%), internal income (10%), direct mail (4%)

Staff: 4
3 Organizers
1 Staff Director

Staff openings/year: 1

Work Week: 55 hours

Salary/year: $9,600

Benefits: Health insurance, paid vacation

Part-Time Employees: 4

Volunteers: 75-100

Interns: None currently, but willing to accept applications

Jobs advertised: *Community Jobs*; *Environmental Opportunities*; *Peace Corps Job Hotline*; *Job-Scan*; *Western Environmental Jobletter*

To apply: Contact Kevin L. Williams, Staff Director

Remarks: WCC is part of the Western Organization of Resource Councils.

WESTERN NORTH CAROLINA ALLIANCE

70 Woodfin Street, P.O. Box 18087
Asheville, NC 28814
(704) 258-8737

Director: Melissa Lane, Coordinator

Purpose: To promote public education and

participation in decisions affecting environmental quality in the mountain region of western North Carolina. Environmental protection through citizen empowerment.

Methods of operation: Training and technical assistance (20%), research (10%), publications (10%), direct action (20%), public education (15%), community organizing (20%), lobbying (5%)

Constituency: All types, especially focused towards building constituency in rural areas

Recent issues and projects: Reduction of clearcutting and better balanced management of Nantahala-Pisgah National Forests; investigations and citizen efforts to protect water quality; establishment of solid waste/recycling programs in rural counties; reforming N.C. transportation policies

Major publications: Quarterly newsletter: *Accent*; Papers - monthly forest management essays and bulletin

Budget: $200,000

Funding: Foundations (70%), individual contributions (30%)

Staff: 5
1 Coordinator
1 Administrator
2 Organizers
1 Staff Ecologist

Staff openings/year: 1-2

Work Week: 40 hours

Salary/year: $16,000 (Recent College Graduate); $Varies (Graduate with advanced degree)

Benefits: Paid vacation, health insurance, camaraderie

Part-Time Employees: 2-3 consultants

Volunteers: Yes; many

Interns: No

Jobs advertised: Local and regional papers; grassroots monthly newspapers (*Appalachia Reader*, etc.)

To apply: Contact Melissa Lane, Coordinator

Remarks: We have a 2nd office in Macon County and chapters throughout WNC.

WESTERN STATES CENTER

522 SW 5th, Suite 1390
Portland, OR 97204
(503) 228-8866

Other Offices: Seattle, WA

Director: Jeff Malachowsky

Purpose: Western States Center is a regional resource center committed to building a movement for social and economic justice. We work in Oregon, Washington, Idaho, Utah, Wyoming, Nevada, Montana and Alaska.

Methods of operation: Organizing, training, research and technical assistance to support community organizing, coalition building, and efforts to encourage citizen participation in the political process

Constituency: Social change activists, leaders and organizations, and progressive elected officials, in 8 western states

Recent issues and projects: Regional network of progressives in public office; community leadership training program; advanced leadership and mentorship program; Wise Use Movement public exposure project; "Money in Western Politics" project

Major publications: Newsletter, 3-4 times/year; *God, Land and Politics: The Wise Use and Christian Right Connection in 1992 Oregon Politics*; *The Covert Crusade: The Christian Right and Politics in the West*; *The Price of Democracy: The High and Hidden Costs of Politics in the West*; *Money and Politics: A Regional Study on Campaign Finance Laws in the West*

Budget: $700,000

Funding: Individual contributions, foundations and events

Staff: 10
3 Project Directors
2 Researchers/Organizers
1 Development Director
1 Finance and Administration Director
1 Executive Director
2 Admin/Support Staff

Staff openings/year: 1

Work Week: 40-50 hours

Salary/year: $20-33,000 (Recent College Graduate); $Varies (Graduate with advanced degree)

Benefits: Health insurance, pregnancy leave, paid vacation, training

Part-Time Employees: Yes

Summer Employees: Occasionally

Volunteers: Yes

Interns: Occasionally
Duties: Varies

Jobs advertised: Mail and newspapers

To apply: Contact Nicitha You

WETLANDS PRESERVE
161 Hudson Street
New York, NY 10013
(212) 966-5244

Director: James Hansen

Purpose: Wetlands is a grassroots environmental center working with environmental and social justice groups/issues

Methods of operation: Research, lobbying, community organizing, direct action, public education

Membership: 200+ environmental activists

Recent issues and projects: We are the information action center for N.Y.C. for Earth First!, Earth Institute, Rainforest Action Network and Save America's Forests

Funding: Individual contributions

Staff: 2
2 Organizers

Staff openings/year: 0-1

Work Week: 50 hours

Salary/year: $Varies (Recent College Graduate); $Varies (Graduate with advanced degree)

Benefits: Paid vacation

Part-Time Employees: 2

Summer Employees: None

Volunteers: 200+

Interns: 6-12
Length: 1 Semester
Duties: Organizing, lobbying, research
Remuneration: unpaid internships only

Jobs advertised: Local mailings, flyers, ads

To apply: James Hansen, Environmental Director

Remarks: We strive to provide a unique and alternative educational experience for our interns and volunteers. All are welcome to our weekly environmental program each Tuesday at 6:30 p.m. We host the Wetlands Rainforest Action Group each first Tuesday and the Federal Land Action Group each fourth Tuesday.

WIDER OPPORTUNITIES FOR WOMEN (WOW)
1325 G Street, NW, Lower Level
Washington, DC 20005-3104
(202) 638-3143

Director: Cynthia Marano

Purpose: To promote economic independence and equality of opportunity for women and girls.

Methods of operation: Training and technical assistance (30%), public education (20%), publications (20%), research (20%), community organizing (10%)

Constituency: Economically disadvantaged women. WOW's membership consists of women's employment organizations.

Recent issues and projects: Career Development Services; Nontraditional Work Programs; Women's Work Force - a national network of women's employment organizations that conducts research and advocacy; Intergenerational Literacy Research Action Project

Major publications: Newsletter: *Women At Work*; send for publications list

Budget: $1,500,000

Funding: Foundations (45%), public funds (30%), events (10%), individual contributions (10%), publications (5%)

Staff: 18
3 Project Managers
3 Administrative Assistants
2 Teachers
2 Writer/Editors
2 Researchers
2 Issue Experts
2 Bookkeeper/Accountants
1 Employment Specialist
1 Caseworker

Staff openings/year: 2-3

Work Week: 40 hours

Salary/year: $23,000 (Recent College Graduate); $28,000 (Graduate with advanced degree)

Benefits: Health insurance, life insurance, pregnancy leave, paid vacation

Part-Time Employees: Yes

Summer Employees: 2

Volunteers: 0-5

Interns: 4-6 per year
Length: 2-3 months
Duties: Research/logistics, writing
Remuneration: $35 per week, transportation and lunch

Jobs advertised: *Washington Post*

To apply: Contact Cynthia Marano

WISCONSIN CITIZEN ACTION

152 West Wisconsin Avenue, Suite 308
Milwaukee, WI 53203
(414) 272-2562

Other Offices: Madison, WI; Racine/Kenosha, WI; Eau Claire, WI; Green Bay, WI

Director: Jeff Eagan

Purpose: Fight for social and economic justice at local, state, and federal levels through issue organizing, grassroots lobbying, and electoral action

Methods of operation: Lobbying (40%), public education (30%), community organizing (25%), research (10%), direct action (5%)

Membership: 190 affiliated labor, senior, community and consumer organizations, and 85,000 family members

Recent issues and projects: Won first ban on Bovine Growth Hormone in the country; fighting for insurance reform, health care for all; an end to toxic pollution; electing community leaders to public office; and other issues effecting medium and low-income families

Major publications: Quarterly newsletter; issue frequent studies and reports

Budget: $1,500,000

Funding: Individual contributions (85%), dues, grassroots fundraising (10%), foundations (5%)

Staff:
40 Canvassers (field and phone)
3 Organizers
1 Office Manager
1 Executive Director
1 Legislative and Campaign Director
1 Bookkeeper/Accountant

Staff openings/year: 3-4

Work Week: 45-50 hours

Salary/year: $22-25,000 (Recent College Graduate); $25-30,000 (Graduate with advanced degree)

Benefits: Health insurance, life insurance, pregnancy leave, training reimbursement, paid vacation, disability insurance, dental insurance

Part-Time Employees: 2-3

Summer Employees: 2-3

Volunteers: 4-5

Interns: 5-10 annually
Length: Summer or a semester
Duties: Research; lobbying; organizing
Remuneration: Some stipends; work-study approved

Jobs advertised: Local papers; *Community Jobs*

To apply: Contact Jeff Eagan, Executive Director

WISCONSIN STUDENT PUBLIC INTEREST RESEARCH GROUP (WISPIRG)

306 North Brooks Street
Madison, WI 53715
(608) 251-1918

Director: Benson Chiles

Purpose: WISPIRG is designed to educate students about being active citizens through research, organizing and advocacy. Students work with professional staff to promote responsible solutions to societal problems.

Methods of operation: Research (30%), public education (30%), publications (15%), community organizing (15%), lobbying (5%), direct action (5%)

Constituency: WISPIRG is made up of students at the University of Wisconsin-Madison and concerned citizens interested in seeking responsible solutions to societal problems.

Recent issues and projects: WISPIRG's current focus is on environmental protection, waste reduction, endangered species, ancient forests, hunger/homelessness, and consumer protection.

Major publications: WISPIRG frequently produces reports or guides on the issues it works on.

Budget: $45,000

Funding: Student fees, individual contributions

Staff: 3
1 Organizer
2 Canvass Directors
30 Canvassers (part-time)

Staff openings/year: 1-2

Work Week: 50 hours

Salary/year: $14,500 (Recent College Graduate); $17,000 (Graduate with advanced degree)

Benefits: Health insurance, paid vacation, student loan assistance

Summer Employees: Yes

Volunteers: 70+

Interns: 20+
Length: 1 semester
Duties: Open to intern's field of interest; publications, media relations, research
Remuneration: Stipends may be offered

Jobs advertised: Newspapers; announcements to other interested organizations

To apply: Contact Benson Chilas, Project Coordinator

WISCONSIN'S ENVIRONMENTAL DECADE & INSTITUTE

122 State Street, Suite 200
Madison, WI 53703
(608) 251-7020

Other Offices: Milwaukee, WI; Eau Claire, WI

Purpose: A citizen's organization working to improve and protect the quality of Wisconsin's environment. The Decade monitors the performance of Wisconsin's legislature and state agencies in protecting our land, providing consumers with safe, affordable energy and preventing water and air pollution.

Methods of operation: Lobbying, litigation, publications, community organizing, public education

Membership: We have 18,000 active members. Wisconsin citizens make up our constituency.

Recent issues and projects: Projects include: state recycling bill; land use; transportation; air toxics; water toxics; energy conservation; source reduction; and agricultural pollution

Major publications: *The Second Decade*; *Wisconsin's Environmental Update*

Budget: $500,000

Funding: Foundations, canvassing

Staff: 18
18 Canvassers
3 Lobbyists
1 Writer/Editor
1 Attorney
1 Office Manager
1 Bookkeeper/Accountant

Work Week: 40-45 hours

Salary/year: $18,000 (Recent College Graduate); $22,000 (Graduate with advanced degree)

Benefits: Health insurance, life insurance, paid vacation

Part-Time Employees: Yes

Summer Employees: Yes; work-study

Volunteers: Yes

Jobs advertised: Newspapers; word of mouth

To apply: Contact the Director, Wisconsin's Environmental Decade

WITNESS FOR PEACE

P.O. Box 567
Durham, NC 27701
(919) 688-5049

Other Offices: Washington, DC; Syracuse, NY; Berkeley, CA; Managua, NICARAGUA

Director: Alma Blount

Purpose: The purpose of Witness for Peace is to develop an everbroadening, prayerful, biblically-based community of U.S. citizens who stand with the Nicaraguan and other Central American people by acting in continuous nonviolent resistance to U.S. covert and overt intervention in their countries, to mobilize public opinion and help change U.S. foreign policy to one which fosters justice, peace and friendship with our Central American neighbors, and to welcome others to this endeavor who vary in spiritual approach, but are one with us in purpose.

Methods of operation: Documentation, media and permanent presence work (50%), community organizing (15%), public education (15%), lobbying (10%), direct action (5%), publications (5%)

Constituency: Grassroots organization of faith-based people across the United States committed to change U.S. foreign policy toward Central America

Recent issues and projects: (1) A citizens' campaign for free and fair elections so that American citizens may know the truth about Nicaraguan elections; (2) sending seven delegations of U.S. citizens to monitor the Nicaraguan elections as official monitors; (3) launching in 1990 a campaign to normalize relations with Nicaragua, end the embargo and repair the damage of past U.S. foreign policy; (4) educate the grassroots with ongoing trainings in the action-reflection method of forming Christian-based communities; and (5) continue our program of sponsoring long-term volunteers and short-term delegations in Nicaragua

Major publications: Quarterly newsletter: *Witness for Peace*; Witness for Peace weekly hotline of Contra attacks documented by our volunteers in Nicaragua; annual *What We Have Seen and Heard* reports; and the video *Slender Wooden Crosses*, about how Contra attacks have disrupted the election process

Budget: $1,100,000

Funding: Direct mail (57%), individual contributions (20%), churches, religious organizations, publications and resources (16%), foundations (7%)

Staff: 15
8 Program Coordinators
3 Grassroots Fundraisers
2 Bookkeeper/Accountants
1 Executive Director
1 Office Manager

Staff openings/year: 2-3

Work Week: 45 hours

Salary/year: $16,500 (Recent College Graduate); $16,500-18,500 (Graduate with advanced degree)

Benefits: Health insurance, life insurance, pregnancy leave, paid vacation, moving benefits

Part-Time Employees: 2

Volunteers: 150 delegates/year

Interns: 15-20
Length: 2 weeks in Nicaragua
Remuneration: Volunteers receive housing and board in Nicaragua

Jobs advertised: Mainstream national liberal press (e.g. *Sojourners, Community Jobs*); *Witness for Peace* newsletter; alumni network; regional coordinators

To apply: Volunteers contact the long-term/short-term program coordinator in Durham. Contact the executive director in Durham for all other staff positions.

Remarks: We have staff and volunteer positions both in the United States and in Nicaragua. Witness for Peace strives to be an inclusive organization. Women and people of color are encouraged to apply.

WOMANKIND, INC.

P.O. Box 493
Machias, ME 04654
(207) 255-4785

Other Offices: Calais, ME

Director: Collective

Purpose: Prevention of, and education about, domestic violence. Direct assistance to women and children who are victims of domestic abuse in Washington County. Services include 24 hour crisis line, emergency shelter, counseling and advocacy, legal assistance and community education.

Methods of operation: Human services (40%), public education (30%), training and technical assistance (20%), publications (4%), research (2%), direct action (2%), community organizing (2%)

Recent issues and projects: Expansion of emergency shelter services, including purchase and renovation of a building. Extensive prevention and education project in local schools. Work on both state and local levels with police departments, court systems and other professionals. Business venture program provided carpentry training for local women, with the end goal of establishing a business which would help support WomanKind.

Major publications: Monthly newsletter

Budget: $140,000

Funding: State and federal funds (96%), direct mail (2%), individual contributions (2%)

Staff: 6
1 Financial Coordinator

1 Community Response Coordinator
1 Volunteer Coordinator
1 Childrens Program Coordinator
1 Shelter Coordinator
1 Office Coordinator

Staff openings/year: 1

Work Week: 40+ hours

Salary/year: $17,700

Benefits: Health insurance, pregnancy leave, paid vacation

Part-Time Employees: 3

Volunteers: 10-15

Interns: 2
Duties: Internships are very flexible and depend on agency needs, student training and requests.
Remuneration: None

Jobs advertised: Newspaper

To apply: Contact office

Remarks: WomanKind is part of the Maine Coalition for Family Crisis Services, which is made up of 9 domestic violence projects located throughout Maine, and which serve all counties in Maine.

WOMEN EMPLOYED

22 West Monroe Street, Suite 1400
Chicago, IL 60603
(312) 782-3902

Director: Anne Ladky

Purpose: Promotes economic equity for women through advocacy, direct service and public education.

Methods of operation: Research, publications, public education, training and technical assistance

Constituency: Working women in all professions, at all levels of employment

Recent issues and projects: Ongoing activities include research in occupational segregation and work and family, program development of seminars for members, individual career counseling, advocacy presentations to community groups, and service delivery to displaced homemakers and disadvantaged teenage girls.

Major publications: Newsletter: *Women Employed News*; *Workers and Families: A Policy Guide for Employers*; *Occupational Segregation*

Funding: Individual contributions, foundations, dues, services

Staff: 9
4 Issue Experts
2 Bookkeeper/Accountants
2 Direct Service Providers
1 Office Manager
1 Grassroots Fundraiser
1 Foundation Fundraiser

Work Week: 42 hours

Salary/year: $17,000 (Recent College Graduate); $23,000 (Graduate with advanced degree)

Benefits: Health insurance, life insurance, pregnancy leave, paid vacation

Part-Time Employees: 2

Summer Employees: Yes

Volunteers: Yes

Interns: Yes
Length: 4 months
Duties: Vary
Remuneration: Varies; chiefly unpaid

Jobs advertised: Our own job bank; direct mailing of announcements; newspaper advertisements

To apply: Contact Joan Smith

WOMEN FOR:

8913 West Olympic Boulevard
Beverly Hills, CA 90211
(213) 657-7411

Director: Lucie Bava, Coordinator

Purpose: To support local, national and world issues of our choice through political action. This gives us strength and independence and enables us to direct our energies toward our common causes and goals: the advancement of human and civil rights; the improvement of the quality of public education; the advancement of peace and the preservation of natural resources.

Methods of operation: Public education (80%), lobbying (10%), research (5%), community organizing (3%), publications (2%)

Membership: We have 2,000 members, mostly women, although about 1% are men. We have a chapter in Orange County that numbers 200 and which began 5 years ago. We would be considered a liberal organization.

Recent issues and projects: Central America; Choice and public funding for poor women's abortions; economic conversion; national health insurance; ERA; family equity; insurance reform; limiting terms of office for elected officials

Major publications: Newsletter. We send out a ballot card before each primary and general election with our recommendations on candidates and issues of our choice. We hold monthly Politics meetings with speakers on subjects of political interest and send notices of same to the entire membership.

Budget: $150,000

Funding: Individual contributions, membership dues, Women of Achievement luncheon event

Staff: 2
1 Coordinator
1 Office Manager

Work Week: 25-30 hours

Salary/year: $12,000

Benefits: Paid vacation

Part-Time Employees: 1

Volunteers: 35

Interns: Yes
Duties: General

Jobs advertised: Networking and word of mouth

To apply: Contact Mollie Pepper, Administrative Assistant

Remarks: The office manager/administrative assistant is paid $640 for a 4-day week of 25-30 hours.

WOMEN IN COMMUNITY SERVICE, INC.

1900 N. Beauregard Street, Suite 103
Alexandria, VA 22311
(203) 671-0500

Other Offices: Boston, MA; New York, NY; Philadelphia, PA; Atlanta, GA; Chicago, IL; Dallas, TX; Denver, CO; Kansas City, MO; San Francisco, CA; Seattle, WA

Director: Ruth Herman

Purpose: Women in Community Service, Inc. is a national nonprofit organization dedicated to helping at-risk women and youth overcome multiple barriers, enter the workforce and achieve economic independence. It provides disadvantaged and low-income women with practical ancillary services that enhance the outcome of training and education for the job market.

Methods of operation: Direct action (20%), public education (20%), training and technical assistance (20%), human services (15%), community organizing (15%), publications (10%)

Recent issues and projects: The organization actively addresses issues surrounding unemployment, job training, welfare reform, pay equity, cultural diversity, poverty, hunger and malnutrition. Recent major projects include mentoring programs and lifeskills.

Major publications: Quarterly newsletter

Funding: Individual contributions, foundations, federal contracts

Staff: 150
20 Organizers
5 Writers/Editors
11 Office Managers
5 Press Aides
11 Foundation Fundraisers
15 Issue Experts
70 Caseworkers

Staff openings/year: 10

Work Week: 40 hours

Salary/year: $19,000 (Recent College Graduate); $40,000 (Graduate with advanced degree)

Benefits: Health insurance, pension, paid vacation

Part-Time Employees: Yes

Summer Employees: Yes

Volunteers: Yes

Interns: Yes
Length: 3 months
Duties: Support Service, counseling, communications, project implementation
Remuneration: Usually volunteer, often for college credit

Jobs advertised: Nonprofit newspapers, local papers, mailings, internet

To apply: Contact Ruth Herman

WOMEN MAKE MOVIES

462 Broadway, Suite 500
New York, NY 10013
(212) 925-0606

Director: Debra Zimmerman

Purpose: WMM is a nonprofit, feminist media center founded in 1972 to facilitate production, promotion and distribution of women's films and videotapes. We also provide support services to emerging and established women film and video artists.

Methods of operation: Training and technical assistance (30%), publications (30%), community organizing (30%), lobbying (10%)

Constituency: Independent women film/video artists and community groups, universities, women's groups

Recent issues and projects: Through our distribution efforts we are able to increase the visibility of media with a feminist perspective while expanding the public's awareness of women's accomplishments in the media arts.

Major publications: We publish an annual catalogue of our collection, and a newsletter 3 times per year.

Budget: $1,125,000

Funding: Earned income (70%), foundations (25%), individual contributions (5%)

Staff: 9
1 Executive Director
1 Director, Development and Production
1 Director, Membership and Production Service
1 Director of Marketing
1 Distribution Manager
1 Distribution Coordinator
1 Administrative Manager
1/2 Administrative Aide
1/2 Bookkeeper

Staff openings/year: 1

Work Week: 35 hours

Salary/year: $20,000 (Recent College Graduate); $30,000 (Graduate with advanced degree)

Benefits: Health insurance, life insurance, paid vacation

Part-Time Employees: 2

Volunteers: 3-4

Interns: 3-4
Length: Per semester or longer
Duties: Assisting in all phases of day to day operations of distribution/nonprofit media arts center
Remuneration: Nonpaid position

Jobs advertised: Through industry newsletters; word of mouth; announcements sent to other similar organizations

To apply: Contact Claudette Furloje, Administrative Manager

WOMEN VENTURE

2324 University Avenue
St. Paul, MN 55114
(612) 646-3808

Director: Kay Gudmestad

Purpose: To secure a stronger economic future for women through career development, business development, and employment programs. The organization operates a variety of programs for women seeking economic self-sufficiency.

Methods of operation: Training and technical assistance

Constituency: Women

Recent issues and projects: Capital Access Program for women; Self-Employment Programs for women on public assistance and residence in public housing; non-traditional occupation training programs

Major publications: 3 workbooks on how to start a business

Budget: $1,100,000

Funding: Government grants, program service fees (50%), foundations (45%), individual contributions (5%)

Staff: 18
4 Program Managers
1 Executive Director
2 Support Staff
1 Foundation Fundraiser
1 Office Manager
1 Bookkeeper/Accountant
1 Receptionist
1 Data Manager
1 Volunteer Program Manager
5 Direct Service Providers

Staff openings/year: 5

Work Week: 45 hours

Salary/year: $Varies (Recent College Graduate); $25-40,000 (Graduate with advanced degree)

Benefits: Flexplan, health insurance

Part-Time Employees: Yes

Volunteers: 20

Interns: 2-4
Length: 6 weeks-6 months
Duties: Depends on program; available in career development, business, and research
Remuneration: Depends on funding availability

Jobs advertised: Newspapers; letter to other agencies; word of mouth

To apply: Contact Kay Gudmestad, Executive Director

WOMEN WORK! THE NATIONAL NETWORK FOR WOMEN'S EMPLOYMENT

1625 K Street, NW, Suite 300
Washington, DC 20006
(202) 467-6346

Director: Jill Miller

Purpose: Women Work! is a grassroots organization of displaced homemaker and single parent program staff, the women they serve and their advocates. We work to increase women's opportunities for economic self-sufficiency through legislative advocacy, public education and by providing technical assistance to displaced homemaker programs.

Methods of operation: Training and technical assistance (50%), public education (15%), research (10%), publications (10%), community organizing (10%), lobbying (5%)

Constituency: Displaced Homemaker and Single Parent Program operators and participants; other women's advocates

Recent issues and projects: STATE (State Technical Assistance and Training Effort) - indepth training and technical assistance with ten states per year); Model Demonstration Projects on serving older women and women of color. Primary legislative issues: vocational education, JobTraining Partnership Act, welfare reform, minimum wage, housing, health insurance, pay equity

Major publications: Newsletters: *Network News* and *Women Work!*; *A Status Report on Displaced Homemakers, Single Parents and Teen Parents in the U.S.* (reports on 30 states also); *Update on State Displaced Homemaker Legislation*; *Network Know How*

Budget: $650,000

Funding: Individual contributions, foundations, technical assistance and training contracts

Staff: 10
3 Trainers/Field Staff
2 Typists
1 Writer/Editor
1 Office Manager
1 Lobbyist
1 Fundraiser
1 Executive Director

Staff openings/year: 1

Work Week: 40-50 hours

Salary/year: $20,000 (Recent College Graduate); $25,000 (Graduate with advanced degree)

Benefits: Health insurance, life insurance, pregnancy leave, pension, paid vacation, disability insurance

Interns: 1-2
Length: Negotiable; 3 months-1 year
Duties: Assist with legislative activities; research and/or draft reports and other publications
Remuneration: Negotiable

Jobs advertised: Job announcements published in newsletter, sent to women's organizations in Washington, DC and published in *Washington Post*

To apply: Contact Jill Miller, Executive Director, for full-time positions. Contact Rubie Coles, Deputy Director, for internships.

WOMEN'S ACTION ALLIANCE

370 Lexington Ave., Suite 603
New York, NY 10017
(212) 532-8330

Director: Karel R. Amaranth

Purpose: Dedicated to vision of self determination for all women. Mission is to create, test and implement innovative program models through community-based organizations to effect positive image for women and girls.

Methods of operation: Training and technical assistance (60%), public education (30%), human services (5%), publications (5%)

Constituency: Predominately women's service providers from community based organizations and clients of those organizations (low-income, minority)

Recent issues and projects: Recent projects include: Women's Alcohol and Drug Education Project (substance abuse prevention); Bosom Buddies (breast cancer - early detection); Resource Mothers (prenatal care training to prevent infant mortality and birth defects); Project Tell (domestic violence and sexual harassment awareness and prevention)

Major publications: *WADEP NEWS*; *Aliance News*; many periodicals in child development, nonprofit management, substance abuse and AIDS

Budget: $200,000

Funding: Foundations (54%), government (45%), individual contributions (1%)

Staff: 11
1 Organizer
1 Bookkeeper/Accountant
6 Caseworkers
1 Project Assistant
1 Executive Assistant

Staff openings/year: 1-2

Work Week: 35 hours

Salary/year: $25,000

Benefits: Health insurance, paid vacation, family leave, dental insurance

Part-Time Employees: 1

Summer Employees: None

Volunteers: 2

Interns: 2
Length: Semester
Duties: Public outreach; research
Remuneration: Unpaid

Jobs advertised: Ethnic media; organizations with whom we have an affiliation

To apply: Please contact Tanya Nieri, Executive Assistant

WOMEN'S ACTION FOR NEW DIRECTIONS (WAND)

P.O. Box B
Arlington, MA 02174
(617) 643-6740

Other Offices: Washington, DC

Purpose: To empower women to act politically to reduce violence and militarism and redirect military resources toward human and environmental needs.

Methods of operation: Community organizing, lobbying, research, training and technical assistance, public education, publications

Constituency: Women (about 75%) and men; middle-class; educated; 10,000 members

Recent issues and projects: (1) WAND Action - grassroots network lobbying members of Congress; (2) The Women Legislators' Lobby (WILL) - a network of 800 women legislators working to redirect military resources; (3) WAND PAC - financially supporting women peace candidates; (4) Women's call to action

Major publications: *WAND Bulletin*; *WAND Activists* - organizing information to grassroots; fact sheets on military spending and weapons programs

Budget: $300,000

Funding: Individual contributions (60%), direct mail (20%), foundations (20%)

Staff: 7
2 WILL: Director and Political Director
1 Lobbyist
1 Office Manager/Bookkeeper
1 Development and Publications
1 Women's Call to Action
1 Executive Director

Staff openings/year: 0-1

Work Week: 40 hours

Salary/year: $Varies (Recent College Graduate); $Varies (Graduate with advanced degree)

Benefits: Health insurance, pregnancy leave, paid vacation

Volunteers: Yes

Interns: Yes
Length: 1 semester
Duties: Field organizing, research, lobbying, fundraising
Remuneration: Volunteer

Jobs advertised: Through peace community newsletters; newspapers; word of mouth

To apply: Contact Executive Director

Remarks: WAND is a grassroots organization working in cooperation with our direct lobbyist (the only woman working full-time on these issues) in Washington, DC. We work at the local level, state (women state legislators), and federal level (women candidates for Congress), creating a united approach for increasing women's political and lobbying presence for peace.

WOMEN'S CAMPAIGN FUND

120 Maryland Avenue, NE
Washington, DC 20009
(202) 234-3700

Director: Amy S. Conroy

Purpose: The Women's Campaign Fund is the only bipartisan political action committee devoted solely to recruiting, funding, and helping elect viable women candidates who support equal rights and freedom of choice for all women.

Methods of operation: Political action (100%)

Recent issues and projects: The Women's Campaign Fund is involved each year in women's campaigns across the country.

Budget: $1,000,000

Funding: Individual contributions, direct mail, corporations

Staff: 6
1 Fundraiser
1 Executive Director
1 Political Director
1 Administrative Assistant
1 Deputy Director
1 Political Assistant

Staff openings/year: 2

Work Week: 50 hours

Salary/year: $17,000 (Recent College Graduate); $25,000 (Graduate with advanced degree)

Benefits: Health insurance, pregnancy leave, paid vacation

Volunteers: Yes

Interns: Yes
Length: 3 months
Duties: Tracking women candidates' political progress
Remuneration: $800 per month

Jobs advertised: Newspaper advertisements; job announcements sent to other public interest groups

To apply: Contact Barbara A. Hanson, Deputy Director

WOMEN'S INSTITUTE FOR FREEDOM OF THE PRESS

3306 Ross Place, NW
Washington, DC 20008
(202) 966-7783

Director: Dr. Martha Leslie Allen

Purpose: Research and publishing to increase communication among women and to move toward re-structuring the communications systems in the world based on people speaking for themselves

Methods of operation: Research, publications

Constituency: Women in and concerned about media

Recent issues and projects: First women's international teleconference by satellite from Copenhagen and Nairobi; have published annual *Directory of Women's Media* for 15 years; also monthly *Media Report to Women* and 2 books on women and media; now publishing a booklet series on communications improvements worldwide and of special concern to women

Major publications: *Media without Democracy And What To Do About It, What's Wrong with Mass Media for Women*

Funding: Sales of our publications (80%), individual contributions (20%)

Work Week: 30-40 hours

Volunteers: 2-3

Interns: 2-3
Length: 2-3 months
Duties: Research, writing, office work related to publishing (which we all do)
Remuneration: None except reimbursement for direct costs, phone calls and the like

To apply: Contact Dr. Martha Leslie Allen, Director

WOMEN'S INSTITUTE FOR HOUSING AND ECONOMIC DEVELOPMENT

179 South Street
Boston, MA 02111
(617) 423-2296

Director: Marcie Laden

Purpose: Provides technical assistance to women's groups and community organizations interested in housing and business development for low-income women and their children

Methods of operation: Technical assistance (75%), publications (25%)

Constituency: Low-income women and their children; social service and other community nonprofits

Recent issues and projects: Transitional and permanent housing for formerly homeless families, women with AIDS, battered women and pregnant teens.

Major publications: Newsletter: *Bricks and Roses*; *Making it Ourselves*: A primer on women's housing and business development; *More Than Shelter*: A Manual on Transitional Housing

Budget: $300,000

Funding: Foundations (65%), fees (35%)

Staff: 8
General Staff

Staff openings/year: 1

Work Week: 35 hours

Salary/year: $Varies (Recent College Graduate); $Varies (Graduate with advanced degree)

Benefits: Health insurance

Part-Time Employees: 4

Summer Employees: Yes

Volunteers: Yes

Interns: Yes
Length: 3-6 months
Duties: Varies

Jobs advertised: Newspapers; schools; mailings to other nonprofit organizations

To apply: Contact Sonia Young

WOMEN'S INTERNATIONAL LEAGUE FOR PEACE AND FREEDOM

1213 Race Street
Philadelphia, PA 19107-1691
(215) 563-7110

Other Offices: Washington, DC

Manager: Pamela Jones-Burnley, Susan Jenkins, Carol V. Moore

Purpose: To achieve those social, political, economic, and psychological conditions that can ensure peace and freedom throughout the world

Constituency: Women, some men, and a growing minority membership in over 100 U.S. communities

Recent issues and projects: WILPF's Plan of Action includes the Campaign for Racial Justice (training for members to organize against racism), Campaign for Disarmament 2000 (Tax Day actions, support for a Comprehensive Test Ban Treaty, and promotion of our third edition of the Women's Budget), Campaign Against U.S. Global Intervention, and an international Women vs. Violence Campaign.

Major publications: *Peace and Freedom*, 6 times/year; *Program and Legislative Action*, 6 times/year

Funding: Primarily membership

Staff: 11

Work Week: 40 hours

Salary/year: $Varies (Recent College Graduate); $Varies (Graduate with advanced degree)

Benefits: Health insurance, disability, 4 weeks paid vacation, some travel

Part-Time Employees: Yes

Volunteers: Yes

Interns: Yes
Length: 10 weeks to 1 year
Duties: Varies
Remuneration: Varies

Jobs advertised: Newspapers; bulletin boards; *Community Jobs*

To apply: Contact Pamela Jones-Burnlee, Administrative Director

Remarks: The International Internship in Geneva offers 3 possible positions with the UN, in disarmament, human rights, or development. A living allowance is provided.

WOMEN'S INTERNATIONAL NETWORK (WIN)

187 Grant Street
Lexington, MA 02173
(617) 862-9431

Editor: Fran P. Hosken

Purpose: WIN is a nonprofit, worldwide, open participatory communication system by, for and about women of all backgrounds, beliefs, nationalities and age groups. *WIN News* serves the general public, institutions and organizations by transmitting internationally information about women and women's groups. WIN Service is a technical assistance and consulting service for women's development.

Recent issues and projects: In *WIN News*, news from the United Nations of concern to women is regularly reported; *Women and Health* is a special column that reports on family planning, nutrition, abortion, childbirth, fertility and more; a worldwide investigation on female circumcision/genital mutilation has been carried on since 1975 with new information in every issue; *Women and Development* is one of the largest columns; *Women and Environment* and *Women and Violence* are regular features; *Women and Media* reports on women's publications and films; *Women and International Affairs: Clearinghouse* surveys career opportunities for women working in the international field.

Major publications: *WIN News*, published 4 times/year, 80 pages; *The Universal Childbirth Picture Book*; *The Hosken Report: Genital and Sexual Mutilation of Females*; *Universal Childbirth Picture Book*

WOMEN'S INTERNATIONAL RESOURCE EXCHANGE (WIRE)

122 W. 27th , Floor 10
New York, NY 10001
(212) 741-2955

Director: Sybil Wong

Purpose: Publisher of articles/pamphlets on and about Third World women. WIRE is a small, nonprofit feminist collective.

Methods of operation: Publications (90%), community organizing (5%), research (3%), public education (2%)

Constituency: Individuals, women's organizations, Women's Studies departments, libraries, bookstores, Latin American Studies departments

Major publications: Spring/summer 1992 publications include: *Beyond Labour Issues: Women Workers in Asia*; *Some Thoughts on the Left and the "Woman Question" in South Asia*; *Reproductive Choice in Cuba and El Salvador*; *On the Question of Women in South Africa*; *Japan's Economic Success Founded on the Sacrifice of Women*; *Third World Lesbians Organizing*

Budget: $20,000

Funding: Individual contributions (40%), direct mail (40%), foundations (20%)

Staff:
1/2 Staff

Work Week: 7 hours

Part-Time Employees: 1

Interns: Yes
Length: 1 semester
Duties: Research, evaluating articles for reprint
Remuneration: Intern's own school

Jobs advertised: Contact Women's Studies departments

To apply: Contact Sybil Wong, or other members of the collective who answer the phone at WIRE

WOMEN'S LEGAL DEFENSE FUND

1875 Connecticut Ave., NW, Suite 710
Washington, DC 20009
(202) 986-2600

President: Judith L. Lichtman

Purpose: Since 1971 WLDF has been a leading force in the drive to achieve equality for women throughout the United States. To help women become full and equal participants in their public and private lives, WLDF advocates public policies that focus on work and family concerns. We provide technical assistance to activists and policymakers. We participate in targeted litigation to challenge gender bias. We reach out to communities to develop leadership and strengthen grassroots constituencies. And we educate the public about the human and social costs of gender discrimination.

Methods of operation: Lobbying, litigation, publications, community organizing, public education, training and technical assistance

Constituency: National constituency of women and men concerned about issues of gender discrimination

Recent issues and projects: The WLDF agenda includes such critical issues as family and medical leave, affirmative action, sexual harassment, wage discrimination, reproductive freedom, child support, and domestic violence. Underlying all of WLDF's work is a commitment to seek remedies for the problems experienced by poor women and women of color.

Major publications: *WLDF News*; annual report; policy-oriented reports and guides

Budget: $1,800,000

Funding: Individual contributions, foundations, unions, corporations

Staff: 24
7 Attorneys
4 Administrative Assistants
2 Development Staff
1 Receptionist
1 Paralegal
1 Office Manager
2 Communications Staff
1 Bookkeeper/Accountant
1 Comptroller

Staff openings/year: 3-4

Work Week: 37 hours

Salary/year: $Varies (Recent College Graduate); $Varies (Graduate with advanced degree)

Benefits: Health insurance, life insurance, family and medical leave, pension, paid vacation

Part-Time Employees: Yes

Volunteers: Yes

Interns: Yes
Length: Varies
Duties: Vary
Remuneration: Usually unpaid; some paid internships for law students

Jobs advertised: Classified ads; public interest network postings

WOMEN'S STATE WIDE LEGISLATIVE NETWORK OF MASSACHUSETTS

37 Temple Place, 3rd Floor
Boston, MA 02111
(617) 426-1878

Director: Diane Balser

Purpose: The Network seeks to increase the effective participation of women in the legislative and budgetary processes, as well as influence the process of public policy decision-making on women's and family issues.

Methods of operation: Public education (60%), training and technical assistance (40%)

Membership: Approximately 100 organizations statewide and approximately 600 public officials, legislators and individuals

Recent issues and projects: We recently held 4 public policy hearings and conferences across the state to examine 8 public policy issues on a grassroots and statewide level. We are developing a "Women's Agenda for the 1990's" to be released in May 1990 and to be used in the gubernatorial and statewide elections.

Budget: $130,000

Funding: Foundations (50%), individual contributions (25%), membership (25%)

Staff: 3
3 Organizers
3 Typists
1 Legislative Monitoring
1 Office Manager
1 Foundation Fundraiser
1 Bookkeeper/Accountant

Staff openings/year: 1

Work Week: 40 hours

Salary/year: $22,500 (Recent College Graduate); $Varies (Graduate with advanced degree)

Benefits: Health insurance, dental insurance, paid vacation, pension in the planning stages

Volunteers: 3-5

Interns: 4-6
Length: 6 months
Duties: Administrative support, conference coordinators, membership outreach, legislative updates
Remuneration: College work-study; some stipends;

transportation

Jobs advertised: *Boston Globe*; locally-based minority publications; women's papers; college internship/career development offices

To apply: Contact Michelle Weiner, Director of Legislative and Educational Services

WOMENS WAY

1233 Locust Street, Suite 300
Philadelphia, PA 19107
(215) 985-3322

President: Constance G. Beresin

Purpose: We are a fundraising coalition for women's services working on behalf of equal rights for women and children.

Methods of operation: Fundraising

Constituency: Feminists; individuals; corporate

Recent issues and projects: Major issues are those that concern women and children: domestic violence and sexual assault, job and wage inequity, reproductive rights, career and education opportunities, the growing population of elderly women, etc.

Major publications: Semiannual newsletter for 20,000 supporters

Budget: $1,200,000

Funding: Individual contributions, workplace (40.3%), foundations (25.2%), special events (20%), corporate contributions (14.5%)

Staff: 35
2 Writer/Editors/Special Events
2 Support Staff
2 Grassroots Fundraisers
1 Office Manager
1 Bookkeeper/Accountant

Staff openings/year: 2

Work Week: 40 hours

Salary/year: $20,000 (Recent College Graduate); $25,000 (Graduate with advanced degree)

Benefits: Health insurance, paid vacation

Part-Time Employees: 1

Summer Employees: 1

Volunteers: 200

Interns: None currently, but willing to accept applications

Jobs advertised: Local newspapers; flyers to social service agencies

WOODLANDS MOUNTAIN INSTITUTE

Main & Dogwood Streets
Franklin, WV 26807
(304) 358-2401

Other Offices: Kathmandu, NEPAL; Shigalee, TIBET

President: Jane Pratt

Purpose: To advance mountain cultures and preserve mountain environments worldwide. Based in Appalachian Mountains with international programs in the Himalayas and the Andes.

Methods of operation: Direct action (50%), human services (20%), research (10%), training and technical assistance (10%), membership development (10%)

Constituency: Wide

Recent issues and projects: Helping 20,000 high school students in West Virginia go to college each year; promoting environmentally sustainable and equitable development through conservation activities in Nepal and Tibet; alternative solutions for mountain communities in education, economic development and cultural preservation

Major publications: Variety of publications on college-going for West Virginians, on ecology of Mount Everest area and Andean culture.

Budget: $1,500,000

Funding: Government Grants (U.S., Canada, Netherlands) and Individual contributions (50%), foundations (50%)

Staff: 50
20 Researchers
10 Issue Experts
3 Office Managers
3 Typists
2 Writer/Editors
2 Bookkeeper/Accountants
2 Foundation Fundraisers

Staff openings/year: 5

Work Week: 40-50 hours

Salary/year: $17,000 (Recent College Graduate);

$35,000 (Graduate with advanced degree)

Benefits: Health insurance, pregnancy leave, housing, paid vacation

Part-Time Employees: 3

Summer Employees: 3

Jobs advertised: Contacts lead to candidates and/or positions described in mailings

To apply: Contact Jane Pratt

Remarks: Looking for people excited about the relationship between people and the land for mountains; looking for people who accept the premise that to work on these issues one must live with them; looking for people who believe in pursuing a common vision through partnerships with local people.

WOODSTOCK INSTITUTE

407 South Dearborn
Chicago, IL 60605
(312) 427-8070

President: Malcolm Bush

Purpose: To promote forms of investment in disadvantaged communities that contribute to economic opportunity, community capacity, equity formation and the creation of economically and racially diverse communities.

Methods of operation: Technical assistance (30%), research (25%), program design (25%), publications (20%)

Recent issues and projects: Recent projects include: Technical assistance and policy development on community development; financial institutions; reinvestment by insurance companies and mortgage bankers; and the Community Reinvestment Act

Major publications: *Credit and the War on Poverty: An Analysis of the Credit Union Programs of the Office of Economic Opportunity*; *The Unknown Lenders: Part Two*; *Banking on Communities*; *The Unknown Lenders*; *Making CRA Work for You*; *Lenders of First Resort: Community Development Loan Fund*; *The Business of Self-Sufficiency*; *Banking in the Public's Interest*; *Banking Services for the Poor*

Budget: $617,000

Funding: Foundations and Banks

Staff: 7
3 Issue Experts
1 Project Manager for National Project
1 Staff Associate
1 Development Assistant
1 Office Manager
1 Foundation Fundraiser
1 Receptionist

Work Week: 40 hours

Salary/year: $20-25,000 (Recent College Graduate); $30-35,000 (Graduate with advanced degree)

Benefits: Health insurance, paid vacation, credit union, pregnancy leave after 2 years

Part-Time Employees: None

Summer Employees: Yes; as needed

Interns: Yes; as needed
Length: We prefer 3-12 months
Duties: Research assistance, writing, some clerical
Remuneration: Varies

Jobs advertised: In local papers and to our mailing list

To apply: Contact Malcolm Bush, President

WORK ON WASTE - USA

82 Judson Street
Canton, NY 13167
(315) 379-9200

Director: Paul Connett

Purpose: Rational Waste/Resource Management. Researching and reporting on currently operating incinerators and the environmental and economic impacts on the community. Reports on the health impacts of incineration. Documenting proposals and community responses. Mainly network with environmental, grassroots groups. Major goal: sharing information on how to UNMAKE WASTE.

Methods of operation: Public education (100%), including research, publications and videos on waste/resource issue

Constituency: Citizens, grassroots groups, environmental activist groups

Recent issues and projects: Major issue is incineration of solid waste - reports on currently operating incinerators and their environmental and economic impacts. Also alternatives to solid waste incineration - reports on successful programs. Publish *Waste Not* newsletter.

ns: Weekly newsletter: *Waste Not*, s/year

...ual contributions (70%), foundations (30%)

Staff: 1
1 Director
1 Filing, Mailings (part-time)
1 Bookkeeper (volunteer)
1 Attorney (volunteer)
22 Helpful Advisory Board Members

Staff openings/year: N/A

Work Week: 72 hours

Part-Time Employees: 1

Volunteers: Yes

Interns: None currently, but willing to accept applications

To apply: Contact Ellen Connett, Co-Editor of *Waste Not*

Remarks: Whether paid or not, every one of us has to utilize our skills and talents in efforts to reverse what seems like almost total irreparable damage. Working with citizen's groups in small/large communities is basically essential environmental work. No one has the luxury of sitting back to 'watch' what goes on. Political controversy is inevitable, because pollution is political. Working with victims keeps one on the straight path. Once groups remove themselves from 'ordinary' people, they should beware. So please, involve yourself as much as you can in the 'little fights,' the fights to rescue our environment from county, state and federal nightmarish plans, which are devastating our planet.

WORK, ACHIEVEMENT, VALUES AND EDUCATION

501 School Street, SW, Suite 600
Washington, DC 20024-2754
(202) 484-0103

President: Lawrence C. Brown, Jr.

Purpose: WAVE, Inc. provides education, job skills training and motivation to economically and educationally disadvantaged youth, usually between the ages of 16 and 21.

Methods of operation: Human services (40%), training and technical assistance (40%), research (5%), lobbying (5%), publications (5%), direct action (5%)

Constituency: Teachers, principals, administrators, private industry councils, community-based organizations

Recent issues and projects: Breaking Down the Boundaries is a new program that brings volunteers from the business world into the classroom to open up the world of work to at-risk youth. WAVE in Middle Schools expands WAVE's dropout prevention program to at-risk youth in 7th and 8th graders.

Major publications: Quarterly youth newspaper, *The Rising Tide*; corporate report, annually; feature articles

Budget: $3,200,000

Funding: U.S. Department of Labor (43.8%); local contracts (34.6%); foundations (17.1%); individual contributions (4.5%)

Staff: 28
10 Organizers
6 Administrative Assistants
3 Bookkeepers/Accountants
1 Writer/Editor
2 Foundation Fundraisers
1 Office Manager
5 Trainers

Staff openings/year: 1-4

Work Week: 40 hours

Salary/year: $Varies (Recent College Graduate); $Varies (Graduate with advanced degree)

Benefits: Health insurance, life insurance, pregnancy leave, pension, tuition reimbursement, paid vacation

Volunteers: 500

Interns: 2 per semester in Washington, D.C.
Length: 1 semester
Duties: Editorial, legislative and fundraising support
Remuneration: Depends on program

Jobs advertised: Internally and through classified advertising

To apply: Contact Christy Taylor Mumford

WORKPLACE HEALTH FUND, INDUSTRIAL UNION DEPARTMENT, AFL-CIO

815 16th Street, NW
Washington, DC 20006
(202) 842-7830

Director: Sheldon W. Samuels

Purpose: Work environment research and education

Methods of operation: Training and technical assistance (40%), research (20%), public education (20%), publications (10%), human services (10%)

Constituency: Workers and their unions

Recent issues and projects: Nuclear workers education and risk management. Chemical release prevention (No More Bhopals). Hazardous child labor research and education.

Major publications: Pamphlets, newsletters, videos, reports

Budget: $750,000

Funding: Government, corporations (60%), individual contributions (30%), foundations (10%)

Staff:
3 Researchers
2 Issue Experts
2 Typists
1 Writer/Editor
1 Foundation Fundraiser
1 Bookkeeper/Accountant

Work Week: 32.5 hours

Salary/year: $24,000 (Recent College Graduate); $28,000 (Graduate with advanced degree)

Benefits: Health insurance, life insurance, pension, paid vacation, tuition reimbursement, personal leave, flex time for students, union contract

Part-Time Employees: Yes

Summer Employees: 1

Volunteers: Yes

Interns: 1
Length: 6 months
Duties: Depends on background; provides professional training
Remuneration: $20,000 annually

Jobs advertised: Jobs not usually advertised, except vacancies within bargaining unit

To apply: Contact S.W. Samuels, Executive Vice President

Remarks: We have a long reputation for advancing the careers of undergraduates, graduates and post-graduates. We require: achievers, social conscience/commitment, team players, liberally educated, hard workers, open minds and a moral sense. Applicants must have at least a strong minor in a Natural Science or Mathematics.

WORLD FEDERALIST ASSOCIATION

418 7th Street, SE
Washington, DC 20003
(202) 546-3950

Other Offices: New York, NY; Boston, MA; San Francisco, CA; Los Angeles, CA; Pittsburgh, PA; Chicago, IL

Director: Tim Barner

Purpose: Nonprofit, public education organization seeking the abolition of war and the preservation of a livable world through just and enforceable World Law.

Methods of operation: Publications (25%), community organizing (20%), public education (20%), direct action (20%), research (10%), lobbying (5%)

Membership: Nationwide membership

Recent issues and projects: Managing sponsor of convocations on global governance structures through the U.N. Charter review process in 1995. Alliance for Our Common Future Coalition.

Major publications: Newsletter, monographs, books, posters and pamphlets

Budget: $500,000

Funding: Individual contributions, foundations, direct mail

Staff: 10
2 Organizers
2 Writers/Editors
2 Typists
1 Lobbyist
1 Press Aide
1 Foundation Fundraiser
1 Bookkeeper/Accountant

Work Week: 40 hours

Salary/year: $15,000 (Recent College Graduate); $19,000 (Graduate with advanced degree)

Benefits: Health insurance, pension, paid vacation

Part-Time Employees: 2

Volunteers: 20

Interns: 2
Length: 3 months
Duties: Research, correspondence, support work
Remuneration: $100/month stipend

Jobs advertised: Newspaper; college employment placement offices; membership

To apply: Contact Aaron Knight, Student Program Director

WORLD INSTITUTE ON DISABILITY

510 16th Street
Oakland, CA 94612
(415) 763-4100

Director: Joan Leon

Purpose: The World Institute on Disability is a policy center run by persons with disabilities. Our goal is to use research, public education, training and model program development as a means to create a more accessible and supportive society for all people - disabled and nondisabled alike.

Methods of operation: Public education (35%), research (25%), training and technical assistance (20%), publications (10%), direct action (5%), community organizing (5%)

Constituency: People of all ages with disabilities, policymakers, service providers, government analysts, researchers, advocates, families

Recent issues and projects: Policy Research and Analysis (personal assistance services, access to health care); Training and Public Education (making public transit more accessible, developing employment opportunities, partners in policymaking, quality-of-life issues, the future of independent living centers, telecommunications and disability); Aging and Disability; International Affairs

Major publications: *Attending to America*; *Personal Assistance for Independent Living*; *Ideas Newsletter*; *Just Like Everyone Else*; Impact Semi-Annual Report; and other project reports

Budget: $2,500,000

Funding: Government grants and contracts (70%), foundations (15%), corporations (5%), fees and publications (5%), individual contributions (5%)

Staff: 30
14 Issue Experts
5 Researchers
3 Typists
2 Foundation Fundraisers
2 Bookkeepers/Accountants
1 President
1 Director of Administration
1 Personnel Director
1 Receptionist

Staff openings/year: 5-6

Work Week: 37.5 hours

Salary/year: $22,000 (Recent College Graduate); $varies (Graduate with advanced degree)

Benefits: Health insurance, life insurance, pension, paid vacation, trying to set up a durable medical equipment fund as part of benefits

Part-Time Employees: 3

Summer Employees: 1-2

Volunteers: 3-5

Interns: 2-4
Length: 2-6 months
Duties: Research, organizing, information/referral, library work, evaluation
Remuneration: Small stipend

Jobs advertised: Newspaper; mailing list to private nonprofit organizations

To apply: Contact Caesar Perrotti, Director of Administration

WORLD PEACE NEWS - A WORLD GOVERNMENT REPORT

777 UN Plaza, 11th Floor
New York, NY 10017-3521
(212) 686-1069

Editor: Thomas Liggett, Editor and Publisher

Purpose: Publishes an 8-page tabloid newspaper on issues and projects in world government, 6 times a year, with emphasis on recreation of the UN.

Methods of operation: Publication, public education

Recent issues and projects: 23rd Annual World Government Seminar

Budget: $15,000

Funding: Subscriptions, donations

Work Week: 45 hours

Volunteers: Yes

To apply: Write or call *World Peace News.*

WORLD POLICY INSTITUTE AT THE NEW SCHOOL FOR SOCIAL RESEARCH

65 Fifth Ave., Suite 413
New York, NY 10003
(212) 229-5808

Director: Sherle Schwenninger

Purpose: Analyze United States foreign policy and international developments and propose alternative strategies for international security, economic cooperation and political development

Methods of operation: Publications (60%), public education (20%), research (20%)

Constituency: Educators and scholars, public officials and policymakers, national leaders and opinion makers, political activists and concerned citizens

Recent issues and projects: Recent projects include the North America Project, the Arms Trade Project and the Collective Security Project

Major publications: *World Policy Journal* and associated reprints

Budget: $900,000

Funding: Individual contributions (50%), earned income (25%), foundations (25%)

Staff: 10
4 Writers/Editors
2 Executive Assistants
1 Bookkeeper/Accountant
1 Foundation Fundraiser
1 Advertising/Circulation
1 Fulfillment/Circulation

Staff openings/year: 1/3-1/2

Work Week: 40 hours

Salary/year: $15,000 (Recent College Graduate); $20,000 (Graduate with advanced degree)

Benefits: Health insurance, life insurance, pension, paid vacation

Interns: Yes
Length: Occasional need for interns
Duties: Vary; administrative/clerical; editorial/research; rarely, marketing
Remuneration: No set policy/program

Jobs advertised: First in-house; then via bulletin boards of other organizations, word of mouth, and sometimes newspapers

To apply: Contact Personnel

WORLD RESOURCES INSTITUTE

1709 New York Avenue, NW, 7th Floor
Washington, DC 20006
(202) 638-6300

President: James Gustave Speth

Purpose: To provide accurate information about global resources and environmental conditions, analyze emerging issues, and develop creative yet workable policy responses

Methods of operation: Research (47.5%), publications (30%), outreach on research and publications (10%), training and technical assistance (7.5%), public education (5%)

Recent issues and projects: Global strategy for conserving biological diversity; the economics of sustainable agriculture; environmental indicators, providing policy-relevant measures of key environmental trends; natural resources accounting natural resources in income accounts; national and international responses to global warming

Major publications: *World Resources 1990-91*; *Solar Hydrogen: Moving Beyond Fossil Fuels*; *The Greenhouse Trap: What We're Doing to the Atmosphere and How We Can Slow Global Warming*; *Taking Stock: The Tropical Forestry Action Plan*

Budget: $8,500,000

Funding: Foundations, corporations (52.8%), institutions, government (36.2%), individual contributions (.6%)

Staff: 85
30 Researchers/Issue Experts
22 Administrative Assistants
9 Program Directors
5 Officers
4 Bookkeepers/Accountants
4 Foundation Fundraisers
4 Writers/Editors
1 Office Manager
1 Press Aide

Staff openings/year: 5-7

Work Week: 37.5 hours

Salary/year: $22-25,000 (Recent College

Graduate); $30-45,000 (Graduate with advanced degree)

Benefits: Health insurance, life insurance, pregnancy leave, pension, paid vacation, sabbatical

Interns: 5-7
Length: 3 months
Duties: Research assistance
Remuneration: Interns are paid an hourly stipend ranging from $7.50 to $10 an hour

Jobs advertised: Job notices are circulated to associates at other organizations. WRI also uses a personnel agency to fill some positions.

To apply: Contact Barbara Christophe, Administrative Assistant

WORLD SERVICE AUTHORITY

1012 14th Street, NW, Suite 1106
Washington, DC 20005
(202) 638-2662

Other Offices: Tokyo, JAPAN

President: Ingrid Dennison

Purpose: The World Service Authority serves the world public in implementing fundamental human rights as defined by the Universal Declaration of Human Rights, various international treaties, and world customary law. WSA registers world citizens and issues global identity documents, such as the WSA Passport. WSA is effecting peace, justice, ecological and human security by promoting and enforcing world law and grassroots constitutional processes at the global level.

Methods of operation: Public education (50%), human services (25%), publications (10%), community organizing (10%), direct action (5%)

Constituency: Registered and self-declared world citizens and WSA document holders

Recent issues and projects: The World Syntegrity Project is sponsoring "syntegrations" or 30-person meetings occurring periodically in cities throughout the world in order to answer the question, "How can we, sovereign world citizens, govern our world?" in order to evolve a flexible world constitution.

Major publications: *World Citizen News*, bi-monthly newsletter covering world citizen activities including commentary on world events, human rights news, passport news, world law, women's issues and other topics that expand and document global interdependency; *Passport To Freedom*, by Garry Davis; *Government Validation of the WSA Passport*

Budget: $750,000

Funding: Document issuance fees (95%), individual contributions (5%)

Staff: 23
2 Writers/Editors
1 Attorney
1 Paralegal
1 Office Manager
6 Issue Experts
3 Typists
1 Bookkeepers/Accountants
6 Caseworkers
1 Legal Consultant
1 Foreign Language Consultant

Staff openings/year: 0-1

Work Week: 40 hours

Salary/year: $23,000 (Recent College Graduate); $25,000 (Graduate with advanced degree)

Benefits: Health insurance, pension, paid vacation, tuition reimbursement

Part-Time Employees: 2

Summer Employees: None

Volunteers: None

Interns: 1-2
Length: 3 months
Duties: Assisting other staff members with letter-writing, answering phone queries, etc.
Remuneration: None or small stipend

Jobs advertised: Local college placement offices

To apply: Contact Erin McEnany, Internship Coordinator or David Gallup, General Counsel

WORLD WILDLIFE FUND/THE CONSERVATION FOUNDATION

1250 24th Street, NW
Washington, DC 20037
(202) 293-4800

Other Offices: Gland, SWITZERLAND

President: Kathryn S. Fuller

Purpose: World Wildlife Fund is a leading private U.S. organization working worldwide to protect endangered wildlife and wildlands. Its top priority is conservation of tropical forests of Latin America,

Asia and Africa - places characterized by high biological diversity. Sustainable use of natural and biological resources as well as the fostering of general conservation awareness are of particular interest to WWF in its more than 25 years of international work. In 1985, WWF formally affiliated with The Conservation Foundation. While programs of the two remain distinct, finance, administration, communications and development services are combined. CF is committed to improving the quality of the environment and securing wise use of the earth's resources.

Methods of operation: Training and technical assistance (35%), direct action (25%), research (15%), community organizing (10%), publications (5%), human services (5%), public education (5%)

Membership: WWF has a broad-based membership - no particular groups are represented - contributions range from $15 to $1000 plus.

Recent issues and projects: Recent major projects include the conclusion of significant studies on America's wetlands and a 2-year study with a Canadian institute on the Great Lakes; the operation of model use land planning and community development programs throughout the U.S.; and a policy paper on the role of the World Bank in promoting energy conservation in the Third World. Major projects outside of the regional and multiregional efforts include campaigning to save the African elephant and several debt-for-nature swaps including Madagascar and Ecuador. Current programs include Land, Heritage, and Wildlife; Environmental Dispute Resolution; Environmental Quality; International Environment; and the Osborn Center for Economic Development.

Major publications: Bimonthly newsletter: *WWF FOCUS*; *WWF Letter*; *CF Letter*; *Great Lakes, Great Legacy?* (CF); *State of the Environment: A View Toward the Nineties* (CF); *International Wildlife Trade: Whose Business is It?* (WWF); *Voices From Africa* (WWF); *Choosing A Sustainable Future* (WWF); *A Gardner's Guide to Plant Conservation* (WWF)

Budget: $50,000,000

Funding: WWF: individuals (60-65%), royalties/other (20%), investments (10%), foundations (7%), government (5%), corporations (3%). CF: foundations (49%), government (23%), corporations (8%), investments (7%), publications, films (7%), individual donors (6%)

Staff openings/year: 50

Work Week: 35 hours

Benefits: Health insurance, pension, child care, paid vacation, life insurance, gym facilities, dental, MERP, long and short term disability, sick and paid holidays, supplemental life insurance

Part-Time Employees: Yes

Summer Employees: Yes

Interns: Yes
Length: 6 months
Duties: Some research, general clerical, writing, etc.
Remuneration: Monthly stipend may be available

Jobs advertised: Mailings lists; paid advertisements

To apply: Contact the Personnel Department

Remarks: WWF's annual budget is $45,000,000. CF's annual budget is $4-5,000,000.

WORLDTEACH

Harvard Inst. for Intl. Dev., 1 Eliot Street
Cambridge, MA 02138
(617) 495-5527

Other Offices: Ecuador; Poland; Russia; South Africa; Thailand; China; Namibia

---

Director: Steve Kirk

Purpose: WorldTeach was founded to assist in education and promote cultural exchange, both overseas and in the United States. WorldTeach places university graduates as teachers in developing countries. Currently WorldTeach sends volunteers to Poland, Russia, Namibia, South Africa, Costa Rica, Ecuador, Thailand and China.

Methods of operation: Public education (80%), publications (10%), research (5%), training and technical assistance (5%)

Recent issues and projects: WorldTeach seeks to provide teachers in countries where there are shortages. We work in local schools and universities, either directly or through local organizations or local government organizations. Future projects include expansion to more countries especially in Africa, and attracting more mid-career and retired applicants.

Major publications: Quarterly newsletter: *The WorldTeach Dispatch*. WorldTeach produces preparatory literature for each program and health guides. In addition, volunteers in the field receive monthly newsletters from field offices and from the central office. Publications are for internal use.

Budget: $514,425

Funding: Fees (65%), schools overseas (28%), individual contributions, foundations (12%)

Staff: 14
13 Administrators (8 overseas)
1 Office Manager

Staff openings/year: 2-3

Work Week: 40 hours

Salary/year: $18 - 30,000

Benefits: Health insurance, paid vacation

Part-Time Employees: 30

Summer Employees: 5

Volunteers: 300 teachers

Interns: Yes
Length: See remarks
Duties: See remarks
Remuneration: Varies

Jobs advertised: College career offices; career books; other organizations' referrals; occasional newspaper/radio/magazine/public service announcements and/or ads.

To apply: Contact Kym McCarty, Director of Recruiting

Remarks: Our U.S. staff consists of 5 full-time employees, and about 30 work-study students. Full-time staff spend their time writing, editing, networking, meeting, strategizing, fundraising, and doing at least 20 other things. Work-study students average 8 hours/week in the office. During the summer, we have 5-6 interns. These interns stay longer and work full-time, so they are given more responsibility than the work-study students, although they still do some routine office work. Teachers are paid employees of schools overseas.

WORLDWATCH INSTITUTE

1776 Massachusetts Avenue, NW
Washington, DC 20036
(202) 452-1999

Director: Lester R. Brown

Purpose: A nonprofit research institute established to alert policymakers and the general public to emerging global trends in the availability and management of resources, both human and natural.

Methods of operation: Research, publications

Constituency: Global policymakers, academics, national and international development agencies and concerned citizens

Recent issues and projects: Results of the Institute's research and projects are published in a series of Worldwatch papers and books and in scholarly and popular periodicals. Its *State of the World* report is an annual series of guides to the world's resources and how they are being managed.

Major publications: *Worldwatch Papers* series - comprehensive and authoritative treatments of individual topics of global concern; *State of the World* series, annually; *World Watch* bimonthly magazine; *Vital Signs: The Trends That Are Shaping Our Future*, a new annual of data and analysis on some 40 major trends; *The Environmental Alert Series*

Budget: $2,500,000

Funding: Foundations, publication sales, honoraria, United Nations organizations

Staff: 30
17 Researchers
8 Administrative Staff
5 Communications Staff

Staff openings/year: 1-2

Work Week: 40+ hours

Salary/year: $Varies (Recent College Graduate); $Varies (Graduate with advanced degree)

Benefits: Health insurance, life insurance, pregnancy leave, pension, paid vacation, dental insurance, disability

Part-Time Employees: 1

To apply: Contact Receptionist

Remarks: The typical Worldwatch researcher is a generalist with a bachelor's or master's degree, with a demonstrated writing and research ability and preferably some background in environmental science.

YOUTH ACTION

1830 Connecticut Ave., NW
Washington, DC 20009
(202) 483-1432

Director: Karen Stults

Purpose: Youth Action provides young people (ages 15-25) with resources and opportunities to participate effectively in creating change in their communities.

Methods of operation: Public education (46%), training and technical assistance (46%), publications (8%)

Constituency: Young people ages 15-25 from low to moderate income communities and communities of color

Recent issues and projects: Ongoing projects place young organizers in community-based organizations to develop lasting youth leadership programs and provide young leaders with tools and information to help them participate in the creation of a more genuine democracy

Major publications: *Democracy Papers* (periodically: approximately every 2-6 months)

Budget: $350,000

Funding: Foundations (84%), churches (15%), individual contributions (1%)

Staff: 6
4 Organizers
1 1/2 Foundation Fundraisers
1/2 Writer/Editor

Staff openings/year: 2 1/2

Work Week: 50 hours

Salary/year: $18,000 (Recent College Graduate); $21,000 (Graduate with advanced degree)

Benefits: Health insurance, paid vacation, life insurance

Part-Time Employees: 2

Summer Employees: 1 or 2

Volunteers: none

Interns: 2 or 3
Length: 3 months
Duties: Short-term projects; assisting the Director; assisting the organizers
Remuneration: $500 - $1000 a month

Jobs advertised: National and youth organization networks; *ACCESS/Community Jobs*; local job boards

To apply: Contact Karen Stults, Executive Director

Remarks: YouthAction was founded in 1987 to provide resources and opportunity to a new generation of young people concerned about social justice. Based in WDC, YouthAction operated as a special project of the Partnership for Democracy for its first five years. Upon the closing of PFD in 1992, YouthAction became a project of the Tides Foundation and has operated as such since that time. YouthAction believes there is a need for young people of diverse backgrounds and from low-to-moderate-income communities, to participate in building a more genuine democracy through citizen participation and organizing.

YOUTH BUILD USA

58 Day Street, P.O. Box 440322
Somerville, MA 02144
(617) 623-9900

Director: Dorothy Stoneman

Purpose: Mission: To create and sustain a broad-based national movement in support of policies and programs which enable young people to assume leadership in order to rebuild their communities and lead responsibilities.

Methods of operation: Training and technical assistance (70%), publications (15%), lobbying (5%), fundraising (10%)

Constituency: Youth serving community organizations

Recent issues and projects: Youth Build model replication and programs established in Boston, Cleveland, Talla

Major publications: *Youth Build Manual*; *Youth Build Leadership Development Manual*; *Youth Build Newsletter*

Budget: $3,000,000

Funding: Foundations (99%), individual contributions (1%)

Staff: 28
1 Organizer
1 Office Manager
9 Administrative Assistants
2 Bookkeepers/Accountants
5 Leadership Development Advisors
5 Technical Assistants
1 President
1 Director of Administration
1 Publications Manager
1 Assistant to President

Staff openings/year: 3-6

Work Week: 40 hours

Salary/year: $28,000 (Recent College Graduate); $40,000 (Graduate with advanced degree)

Benefits: Health insurance, paid vacation, life insurance, family leave, dependent care and non-insured health cost reimbursement

Part-Time Employees: 1

Summer Employees: None

Interns: Not at the time

Jobs advertised: National and local newspapers, mailings to similar organizations, word-of-mouth

To apply: Address inquiries to: Personnel Department, Attention Colette Feracho

YOUTH LAW CENTER

114 Sansome Street, Suite 950
San Francisco, CA 94104
(415) 543-3379

Other Offices: Washington, DC

Director: Carole B. Shauffer

Purpose: Youth Law Center focuses on reform of the law in juvenile justice, foster care and health issues. The overall purpose is to protect children from abuse (focusing upon those in out-of-home placement), and to ensure that they receive the treatment and services to which they are legally entitled.

Methods of operation: Litigation (40%), research (25%), training and technical assistance (25%), publications (10%)

Constituency: Children, the majority of whom are in the juvenile justice or child welfare systems

Recent issues and projects: Recent projects include: confidentiality between agenices; special education/juvenile justice; neighborhood community service centers. Recent litigation includes: Kentucky juveniles/jail; Los Angeles child welfare; San Francisco child welfare; Louisiana detention.

Major publications: *Glass Walls*; *Representing the Child Client*

Budget: $1,400,000

Funding: Foundations (58%), attorney fees/government/law firms/publications (32%), individual contributions (5%), direct mail (5%)

Staff: 14
8 Attorneys
1 Paralegal
1 Foundation Fundraiser
3 Typists
1 Bookkeeper/Accountant

Work Week: 40 hours

Benefits: Health insurance, pension, paid vacation, credit union, family leave

Part-Time Employees: 1

Summer Employees: 5

Volunteers: 3

Interns: 2-3
Length: Semester or summer
Duties: Law clerks: legal research and writing. Undergraduate volunteers: office work and some research
Remuneration: Work study or recipient of a public interest grant

Jobs advertised: Law clerk positions listed at law schools

To apply: Contact Mamie Yee, Recruitment Coordinator/Paralegal

Remarks: The YLC is a nonprofit public interest law program that works in the Bay Area, statewide and nationally to protect the rights, health and lives of disadvantaged children and families. The work of the Youth Law Center focuses on reform of the law in juvenile justice, child welfare, and health. Staff attorneys work through consultation, technical assistance, training, writing and dissemination of written materials on children's issues, and litigation when necessary. Staff attorneys work with other legal service organizations, social service personnel, law enforcement personnel, judges and private attorneys representing youth and children.

YOUTH POLICY INSTITUTE

1221 Massachusetts Avenue, NW, Suite B
Washington, DC 20005
(202) 638-2144

Director: David L. Hackett

Purpose: Youth Policy Institute is a nonprofit, nonpartisan research organization that is interested in America's children, youth and families. YPI conducts unbiased research on policy options with a staff composed principally of young people.

Methods of operation: Research (50%), training young people during the research process, publications (50%)

Major publications: *Future Choices: Toward a National Youth Policy*; *Youth Policy*; *Youth Record*; *American Family*; *Student Press Service*

Budget: $300,000

Funding: Foundations (50%), individual

contributions (25%), subscriptions (25%)

Staff: 11
9 Writers/Editors/Researchers
1 Foundation Fundraiser
1 Bookkeeper/Accountant

Staff openings/year: 5

Work Week: 45 hours

Salary/year: $14,000 (Recent College Graduate); $30,000 (Graduate with advanced degree)

Benefits: Health insurance

Part-Time Employees: 5

Volunteers: 1

Interns: Several
Length: 2 1/2-3 months
Duties: Major research project leading to a published article
Remuneration: Unsalaried positions usually

Jobs advertised: Announcements on university bulletin boards and in local newspapers; posted with career service offices

To apply: Contact David L. Hackett, Executive Director

YOUTH VOLUNTEER CORPS OF AMERICA
6310 Lamar Ave. #145
Overland Park, KS 66202
(913) 432-9822

President: David Battey

Purpose: The Youth Volunteer Corps of America's mission is to create and increase volunteer opportunities to enrich America's youth, address community needs and develop a lifetime commitment to service.

Methods of operation: Training and technical assistance (75%), community organizing (25%)

Constituency: Local nonprofit direct service organizations that sponsor local YVC programs

Recent issues and projects: Recent projects include: youth volunteerism; service-learning; and intergenerational programming

Major publications: *Reflections*, bi-annual, national newsletter

Budget: $250,000

Funding: Foundations (90%), individual contributions (10%)

Staff: 4
1 Organizer
1 Writer/Editor
1 Office Manager
1 President

Staff openings/year: 1

Work Week: 40 hours

Salary/year: $Varies (Recent College Graduate); $Varies (Graduate with advanced degree)

Benefits: Health insurance, paid vacation, life insurance

Part-Time Employees: None

Summer Employees: 100

Volunteers: Yes

Interns: Yes
Length: Summer or semester
Duties: Work in Communications Department
Remuneration: Credit

To apply: Contact David Battey, President

YWCA OF THE USA
726 Broadway, 5th Floor
New York, NY 10003
(212) 614-2700

Director: Dr. Prema Mathai-Davis

Purpose: The YWCA of the U.S. works to empower women and eliminate racism.

Methods of operation: Research, publications, human services, community organizing, direct action, public education, training and technical assistance

Recent issues and projects: Recent issues include the National Day of Commitments to Eliminate Racism.

Major publications: *Interchange*, newsletter; annual report

Funding: Individual contributions, foundations, direct mail, membership

Staff: 75
Writers/Editors
Researchers
Organizers
Foundation Fundraisers
Issue Experts

Bookkeepers/Accountants
Grassroots Fundraisers
Administrative Assistants

Work Week: 40 hours

Benefits: Health insurance, pension, paid vacation, life insurance, family leave

Part-Time Employees: 5

Summer Employees: None

Volunteers: Yes

Interns: None at this time, willing to accept applications

Jobs advertised: Internally, *New York Times*, *Nonprofit Times*

To apply: Contact Louise R. Fawcett

ZERO POPULATION GROWTH

1400 16th Street, NW, Suite 320
Washington, DC 20036
(202) 332-2200

Other Offices: Los Angeles, CA

Director: Susan Weber

Purpose: Zero Population Growth is a national nonprofit membership organization working to achieve a sustainable balance of population, resources, and the environment - both in the United States and worldwide. ZPG supports voluntary efforts to stabilize population through its education and advocacy programs.

Methods of operation: Research, lobbying, publications, community organizing, public education, training and technical assistance

Recent issues and projects: Work to establish U.S. population policy, make family planning services universally available, uphold reproductive rights, expand contraceptive research, expand environmental education and other related matters

Major publications: Bimonthly:*The ZPG Reporter*; *USA By Numbers*; *Urban Stress Test*; *Planning the Ideal Family: The Small Family Option*; assorted materials for educators including a teaching kit: *For Earth's Sake: Lessons in Population and the Environment*; *The Children's Stress Index*

Budget: $2,500,000

Funding: Individual contributions (77%), foundations (17%), other (6%)

Staff: 25
16 Program
3 Membership
4 Administration
2 Fundraising

Staff openings/year: 3

Work Week: 40 hours

Salary/year: $21,500

Benefits: Health insurance, life insurance, pregnancy leave, paid vacation, pension

Part-Time Employees: 3

Volunteers: 3

Interns: Up to 5
Length: 6 months
Duties: Assist in research, program activities
Remuneration: Minimum of $1000 a month

Jobs advertised: Newspaper; notice to other organizations

To apply: For internships, contact Jay Keller; for general, contact Susan Weber

RESOURCES

Part One: Publications

GENERAL READING

BOOKS: Following are books that many people have found helpful in explaining the nature and scope of some of the issues this country confronts today and has confronted in the past. This list is but a starting point; it should not be considered all-encompassing.

Abbots, John and Ralph Nader. *The Menace of Atomic Energy.* New York: W.W. Norton Co., Inc., 1977.

Adams, Walter and James W. Brock. *The Bigness Complex: Industry, Labor and Government in the American Economy.* New York: Pantheon Books, 1986.

Albert, Michael. *Stop the Killing Train: Radical Visions for Radical Change.* Boston: South End Press.

Alinsky, Saul D. *Reveille for Radicals.* New York: Vintage Books, 1969.

________. *Rules for Radicals.* New York: Vintage Books, 1971.

American Civil Liberties Union. *The Rights of Aliens and Refugees.* Carbondale, IL: Southern Illinois University Press, 1990.

________. *The Rights of Authors and Artists.* Carbondale, IL: Southern Illinois University Press, 1992.

________. *The Rights of Crime Victims.* Carbondale, IL: Southern Illinois University Press, 1985.

________. *The Rights of Employees.* Carbondale, IL: Southern Illinois University Press, 1994.

________. *The Rights of Gay People.* Carbondale, IL: Southern Illinois University Press, 1994.

________. *The Rights of Older Persons.* Carbondale, IL: Southern Illinois University Press, 1988.

________. *The Rights of Patients.* Carbondale, IL: Southern Illinois University Press, 1989.

________. *The Rights of Prisoners.* Carbondale, IL: Southern Illinois University Press, 1988.

________. *The Rights of Single People.* Carbondale, IL: Southern Illinois University Press, 1985.

________. *The Rights of Students.* Carbondale, IL: Southern Illinois University Press, 1988.

________. *The Rights of Teachers.* Carbondale, IL: Southern Illinois University Press, 1984.

________. *The Rights of Women.* Carbondale, IL: Southern Illinois University Press, 1993.

________. *The Rights of Young People.* Carbondale, IL: Southern Illinois University Press, 1985.

________. *Your Right to Government Information.* Carbondale, IL: Southern Illinois University Press, 1985.

________. *Your Right to Privacy.* Carbondale, IL: Southern Illinois University Press, 1990.

Anderson, Joanne. *For the People.* Boston: Addison-Wesley, 1977.

Arendt, Hannah. *The Human Condition.* Chicago: University of Chicago Press, 1970.

Aron, Nan. *Liberty and Justice for All: Public Interest Law in the 1980s and Beyond.* Boulder, CO: Westview Press, Inc., 1989.

Bagdikian, Ben. *The Media Monopoly.* Boston: Beacon Press, 1990.

Balis, Lawrence. *Passion for Equality: George Wiley and the Movement.* New York: W.W. Norton Co., Inc., 1972.

Baran, Paul and Paul Sweezy. *Monopoly Capital: An Essay on the American Economy and Social Order.* New York: Monthly Review Press, 1966.

Barber, Benjamin. *Strong Democracy: Participatory Politics for a New Age.* Berkeley: University of California Press, 1984.

Barnet, Richard J. and Ronald E. Muller. *Global Reach: The Power of the Multinational Corporations.* New York: Touchstone Books, 1976.

Barth, Allen. *Prophets with Honor.* New York: Alfred J. Knopf, Inc., 1979.

Bellah, Robert, et al. *Habits of the Heart: Individualism and Commitment in American Life.* New York: Harper Collins, 1986.

________. *The Good Society.* New York: Alfred A. Knopf, 1991

Berle, Peter. *Does the Citizen Stand a Chance?* New

York: Barron's Educational Series, 1974.

Biko, Steve. *I Write What I Like.* Borgo Press, 1991.

Birnbaum, Jeffrey H. *The Lobbyists: How Influence Peddlers Get Their Way in Washington.* New York: Times Books, 1992.

Birnbaum, Norman. *The Radical Renewal: The Politics of Ideas in Modern America.* New York: Pantheon Books, 1988.

Black, George. *The Good Neighbor: How the U.S. Wrote the History of Central America and the Caribbean.* New York: Pantheon, 1988.

Block, Fred. *Origins of International Economic Disorder.* Berkeley: University of California Press, 1977.

Bluestone, Barry and Bennet Harrison. *The Deindustrialization of America.* New York: Basic Books, 1984.

Blumenthal, Sidney. *The Rise of the Counter-Establishment: From Conservative Ideology to Political Power.* New York: Harper and Row, 1988.

Bobo, Kim, Jackie Kendall and Steve Max. *Organizing for Social Change: A Manual for Activists in the 1990s.* Washington, DC: Seven Locks Press, 1991.

Bok, Derek and John Dunlap. *Labor and the American Community.* New York: Simon and Schuster, 1970.

Bonner, Raymond. *Weakness and Deceit: U.S. Policy and El Salvador.* New York: Random House, 1988.

________. *Waltzing With A Dictator: The Marcoses.* New York: Random House, 1988.

Bookchin, Murray. *Remaking Society: Pathways to a Green Future.* Boston: South End Press, 1990.

Bowles, Samuel, David M. Bordon and Thomas E. Weisskopf. *After the Waste Land: A Democratic Alternative to Economic Decline.* Armonk, NY: M.E. Sharpe, 1990.

Boyarsky, Nancy and William Boyarsky. *Backroom Politics.* New York: Hawthorne Books, 1973.

Boyer, Richard and Herbert Morais. *Labor's Untold Story.* New York: United Electrical Radio and Machine Workers of America, 1986.

Boyte, Harry C. *The Backyard Revolution: Understanding the New Citizen Movement.* Philadelphia: Temple University Press, 1980.

________. *Citizen Action and the New American Populism.* Philadelphia: Temple University Press, 1986.

________. *Commonwealth: A Return to Citizen Politics.* New York: The Free Press, 1989.

________. *Community Is Possible: Repairing America's Roots.* New York: Harper & Row, 1984.

Boyte, Harry C. and Frank Reissman, eds. *The New Populism: The Politics of Empowerment.* Philadelphia: Temple University Press, 1986.

Braverman, Harry. *Labor and Money Capital: The Degradation of Work in the Twentieth Century.* New York: Monthly Review Press, 1976.

Brodeur, Paul. *Outrageous Misconduct: The Asbestos Industry on Trial.* New York: Pantheon Books, 1985.

Brown, Dee Alexander. *Bury My Heart at Wounded Knee.* Austin, TX: Holt, Rinehart & Winston, 1971.

Brown, Lester. *State of the World, 1994.* New York: W.W. Norton & Co., 1994.

Brown, Michael. *Laying Waste: The Poisoning of America by Toxic Chemicals.* New York: Pantheon Books, 1981.

Brownmiller, Susan. *Against Our Will: Men, Women and Rape.* New York: Fawcett, 1993.

Brownstein, Ronald, et al. *Who's Poisoning America?* San Francisco: Sierra Club Books, 1981.

Bullard, Robert D. ed. *Unequal Protection: Environmental Justice & Communities of Color.* San Francisco: Sierra Club Books, 1994.

Calhoun, Craig, ed. *Habermas and the Public Sphere.* Boston: MIT Press, 1993.

Cantarow, Ellen. *Moving the Mountain: Women Working for Social Change.* New York: The Feminist Press, 1980.

Caplan, Marc. *A Citizen's Guide to Lobbying.* New York: Dembner Books, 1983.

Caplan, Rocihard and John Feffer, eds. *State of the Union, 1994.* Boulder, CO: Westview Press, 1994.

Cardoso, Fernando Henrique and Enzo Faletto. *Dependency and Development in Latin America.* Berkeley: University of California Press, 1979.

Carmichael, Stokely and Charles Hamilton. *Black Power: The Politics of Liberation in America.* New York: Vintage, 1967.

Carnoy, Martin and Derek Shearer. *Economic Democracy: The Challenge of the 1980s.*

New York: M.E. Sharpe, Inc., 1980.

Caro, Robert A. *The Power Broker: Robert Moses and the Fall of New York*. New York: Alfred A. Knopf, Inc., 1974.

Carson, Clayborne. *In Struggle: SNCC and the Black Awakening of the 1960s*. Cambridge: Harvard University Press, 1981.

Cevitan, Sar A. *Still a Dream*. Cambridge: Harvard University Press, 1975.

Chen, Edwin. *PPB: An American Tragedy*. Englewood Cliffs, NJ: Prentice-Hall, Inc., 1979.

Chomsky, Noam. *Necessary Illusions: Thought Control in Democratic Societies*. Boston: Southend Press, 1989.

________. *On Power and Ideology: The Managua Lectures*. Boston: South End Press, 1987.

________. *Turning the Tide: U.S. Intervention in Central America and the Struggle for Peace*. Boston: South End Press, 1985.

Chomsky, Noam and Edward Herman. *Manufacturing Consent*. New York: Pantheon, 1988.

Clairmonte, Frederick and John Canavagh. *Merchants of Drink: Transnational Control of World Beverages*. Third World Network, 1988.

Clark, Wilson. *Energy for Survival*. Garden City: Anchor Books, 1974.

Claybrook, Joan. *Retreat from Safety: Reagan's Attack on America's Health*. New York: Pantheon Books, 1984.

Clinard, Marshall B. *The Abuse of Corporate Power*. Greenwood, 1990.

Clinard, Marshall B. and Peter C. Yeager. *Corporate Crime*. New York: Free Press, 1983.

Cobb, Jonathan and Richard Sennett. *The Hidden Injuries of Class*. New York: Random House, 1973.

Cobble, Dorothy Sue. *Women and Unions: Forging a Partnership*. Ithaca: ILR Press, 1993.

Cohen, Gary and John O'Connor. *Fighting Toxics: A Manual for Protecting Your Family, Community, and Workplace*. Washington, DC: Island Press, 1990.

Cohen, Marcia. *The History of Feminism*. New York: Simon and Schuster, 1988.

Collins, Joseph. *Nicaragua: What Difference Could a Revolution Make?* Grove-Atlantic Press, 1986.

Commoner, Barry. *Making Peace with the Planet*. New York: Pantheon Books, 1990.

Commoner, Barry. *The Closing Circle*. New York: Alfred J. Knopf, Inc., 1971.

Costikyan, Edward. *How to Win Votes: The Politics of 1980*. New York: Harcourt, 1980.

Crick, Bernard. *In Defense of Politics*. Chicago: University of Chicago Press, 1973.

Cullen, Frank, et al. *Corporate Crime Under Attack: The Ford Pinto Case and Beyond*. Cincinnati: Anderson Publishing Company, 1987.

Danneker, Gail and Richard Grossman. *Energy, Jobs and the Economy*. Boston: Carrier Pidgeon, 1979.

Davis, Angela. *Women, Race and Class*. New York: Random House, 1983.

Davis, James W. *National Conventions*. Greenwood, 1983.

De Beauvoir, Simone. *The Second Sex*. New York: Random House, 1989.

Delgado, Gary. *Organizing the Movement: The Roots and Growth of ACORN*. Philadelphia: Temple University Press, 1986.

DeLorean, John. *On a Clear Day You Can See General Motors*. New York: W.W. Norton, Inc., 1979.

Dengler, Carl. *Out of Our Past: The Forces That Shaped Modern America*. New York: Harper and Row, 1970.

De Tocqueville, Alexis. *Democracy in America*. New York: Amereon Ltd., 1966.

Dionne, E.J. *Why Americans Hate Politics*. New York: Simon & Schuster, 1991.

Dixon, Marlene, ed. *Nicaragua Under Siege*. San Francisco: Synthesis Publications, 1985.

Domhoff, William. *The Higher Circles*. New York: Random House, 1970.

________. *Who Rules America Now? A View for the 80s*. New York: Simon & Schuster, Inc., 1983.

Dubofsky, Melvyn. *The State and Labor in Modern America*. NC: The University of North Carolina Press, 1994.

Echols, Alice. *Daring to Be Bad: Radical Feminism in America*. Minneapolis: University of Minnesota Press, 1989.

Edsall, Thomas Byrne and Mary D. Edsall. *Chain Reaction: The Impact of Race, Rights, and Taxes on American Politics*. New York: W.W. Norton & Company, 1991.

Edsall, Thomas Byrne. *The New Politics of Inequality*. New York: W.W. Norton, 1985.

Eisenstein, Hester. *Contemporary Feminist Thought*.

New York: MacMillan, 1983.

Ellis, Robert L., ed. *Taking Ideals Seriously: The Case for a Lawyers' Public Interest Movement.* Washington, DC: Equal Justice Foundation, 1981.

Ellison, Ralph. *The Invisible Man.* New York: Random House, 1992.

Elrich, Paul. *The Expendable Americans.* New York: Viking, 1979.

Epstein, Edward. *News From Nowhere.* New York: Random House, 1973.

Epstein, Samuel. *The Politics of Cancer.* San Francisco: Sierra Club Books, 1978.

Epstein, Samuel, Lester O. Brown and Carl Pope. *Hazardous Waste in America.* San Francisco: Sierra Club, 1983.

Erikson, Kai. *The Wretched of the Earth.* New York: Black Cat Books, 1965.

Evans, Sara. *Personal Politics: The Roots of Women's Liberation in the Civil Rights Movement and the New Left.* New York: Random House, 1979.

________. *Born for Liberty: A History of Women in America.* New York: Free Press, 1989.

Evans, Sara M. and Harry C. Boyte. *Free Spaces: The Sources of Democratic Change in America.* New York: Harper & Row, 1986.

Ferguson, Thomas and Joel Rogers, eds. *The Hidden Election: Politics and Economics in the 1980 Presidential Campaign.* New York: Pantheon, 1982.

________. *Right Turn: The Decline of the Democrats and the Future of American Politics.* New York: Hill and Wang, 1986.

Ferree, Myra Marx and Beth B. Hiss. *Controversy and Coalition.* New York: MacMillan and Co., 1985.

Fine, Sidney. *Sit-Down: The General Motors Strike of 1936-1937.* Ann Arbor, MI: University of Michigan Press, 1969.

Finks, David P. *The Radical Vision of Saul Alinsky.* New York: Paulist Press, 1984.

Fisher, Robert. *Let the People Decide: Neighborhood Organizing in America.* Boston: G.K. Hall, 1984.

Fitzgerald, Frances. *America Revised.* New York: Random House, 1980.

Flacks, Richard. *Making History: The American Left and the American Mind.* New York: Columbia University Press, 1989.

Flexner, Eleanor. *Century of Struggle: The Woman's Rights Movement in the United States.* Cambridge, MA: Belknap Press, Harvard University Press, 1975 [1959].

Ford Foundation. *A Time to Choose.* Cambridge: Ballinger Books, 1974.

Forman, James. *The Making of Black Revolutionaries: A Memoir.* Washington, DC: Open Hand Press, 1985.

Friedan, Betty. *The Feminine Mystique.* New York: Dell Publishing, 1963.

Friere, Paulo. *Pedagogy of the Oppressed.* New York: Free Press of Glenco, 1963.

Fulbright, J. William. *Arrogance of Power.* New York: Random House, 1966.

Fulbright, J. William and Seth Tillman, *The Price of Empire.* New York: Pantheon, 1989.

Fuller, John. *Poison That Fell From the Sky.* New York: Random House, 1977.

Galbraith, John Kenneth. *The Culture of Contentment.* Boston: Houghton Mifflin Co., 1992.

Gallagher, Carole. *American Ground Zero.* NY: Random House, 1993.

Gamson, William A. *Talking Politics.* Boston: Cambridge, 1992.

Gardner, John. *Strategies for Community Organizing.* New York: New York Public Interest Research Group, 1975.

Garland, Anne Witte. *Women Activists: Challenging the Abuse of Power.* New York: The Feminist Press, 1988.

Gaventa, John. *Power and Powerlessness: Quiescence and Rebellion in an Appalachian Valley.* Urbana: University of Illinois Press, 1980.

Gilligan, Carol. *In a Different Voice.* Cambridge: Harvard University Press, 1982.

Gilman, Charlotte Perkins. *Herland.* New York: Peter Smith, 1992.

________. *Women and Economics.* New York: Harper Collins, 1966 [1898].

Ginzberg, Eli and Robert M. Solow. *The Great Society.* New York: Basic Books, Inc., 1974.

Gitlin, Todd. *Campfires of the Resistance.* New York: Macmillan, 1970.

________. *The Sixties.* New York: Bantam Books, 1989.

________. *Uptown: Poor Whites in Chicago.* New York: Harper & Row, [1970].

________. *The Whole World is Watching: Mass Media in the Making and Unmaking of the*

New Left. Berkeley: University of California Press, 1980.

Geoghegan, Thomas. *Which Side Are You On?* New York: Farrar, Straus & Giroux, 1991.

Goodwyn, Lawrence. *The Populist Moment: A Short History of Agrarian Revolt in America*. New York: Oxford University Press, 1978.

Gornick, Vivian. *Women in Sexist Society: Studies in Power and Powerlessness*. New York: Basic Books, 1971.

Green, Mark J. ed. *Changing America: Blueprints for the New Administration*. New York: Newmarket Press, 1992.

________. *Ideas That Work: 60 Solutions for America's 3rd Century*. New York: The Democracy Project, 1988.

________. *Who Runs Congress?* New York: Bantam Books, 1979.

________. *Winning Back America*. New York: Bantam Books, 1982

Green, Mark and Robert Massie, Jr. eds. *The Big Business Reader: Essays on Corporate America*. New York: Pilgrim Press, 1983.

Green, Mark and Norman Waitzman. *Business War on the Law*. Washington, DC: Corporate Accountability Research Group, 1981.

Griffin, Kelly. *More Action for a Change*. New York: Dembner Books, 1987.

Gutman, Herbert G. *Power & Culture: Essays on the American Working Class*. New York: Peter Smith, 1987.

Gyorgy, Anna & Friends. *No Nukes: Everyone's Guide to Nuclear Power*. Boston: South End Press, 1979.

Habermas, Jurgen. *The Structural Transformation of the Public Sphere*. Boston: MIT Press, 1991.

Hacker, George A., Ronald Collins and Michael Jacobson. *Marketing Booze to Blacks*. Washington, DC: Center for Science in the Public Interest, 1987.

Hahn, Steven. *Roots of Southern Populism*. New York: Oxford Press, 1983.

Halberstam, David. *The Powers That Be*. New York: Random House, 1975.

Hampton, Harry and Steve Fayer. *Voices of Freedom: An Oral History of the Civil Rights Movement from the 1950s*. New York: Bantam Books, 1990.

Harrington, Michael. *The Long-Distance Runner*. New York: Paragon House, 1991.

________. *The New American Poverty*. New York: Holt, Rinehart and Winston, 1985.

________. *The Next America*. New York: Holt, Rinehart and Winston, 1981.

________. *The Other America*. New York: Macmillan and Co., 1994.

________. *Socialism, Past and Future*. New York: Saturday Review Press, [1972].

________. *Toward a Democratic Left*. New York: MacMillan & Co., 1968.

________. *The Twilight of Capitalism*. New York: Simon and Schuster, 1976.

________. *The Vast Majority*. New York: Simon & Schuster, 1977.

Hawken, Paul. *The Ecology of Commerce: A Declaration of Sustainability*. New York: Harper Business, 1993.

Hecht, Susanna and Alexander Cockburn. *The Fate of the Forest: Developers, Destroyers and Defenders of the Amazon*. New York: Verso, 1989.

Heilbroner, Robert L. *In the Name of Profit*. Garden City: Doubleday, 1972.

Hellman, Lillian. *Scoundrel Time*. Boston: Little, Brown and Co., 1979.

Herman, Edward. *Corporate Control, Corporate Power*. New York: Cambridge University Press, 1981.

Hersh, Seymour. *Chemical and Biological Warfare*. Indianapolis: Bobbs-Merrill, 1968.

________. *Cover-up*. New York: Random House, 1972.

________. *My Lai.*. New York: Random House, 1970.

________. *The Price of Power*. New York: Summit Books, 1983.

Hertsgaard, Mark. *On Bended Knee: The Press and the Reagan Presidency*. New York: Shocken Books, 1989.

Hirsch, Alan. *Talking Heads*. New York: St. Martin's Press, 1991.

Hitchens, Christopher. *Blood, Class, and Nostalgia*. New York: Farrar, Straus & Giroux, 1990.

________. *Imperial Spoils*. New York: Hill and Wang, 1988.

Horwitt, Sanford. *Let Them Call Me Rebel: Saul Alinsky — His Life and Legacy*. New York: Knopf, 1989.

Howe, Irving. *The World of the Blue Collar Worker*. New York: Quadrangle Books, 1972.

Howe, Irving and B.J. Widick. *The UAW and Walter Reuther*. Albany, NY: State University of New York Press, 1988.

Huberman, Leo. *Man's Worldly Goods: The Story of the Wealth of Nations.* New York: Monthly Review Press: 1936.

Huberman, Leo and Paul M. Sweezy. *Introduction to Socialism.* New York: Monthly Review, 1968.

Huenfeld, Joh. *The Community Activist's Handbook.* Boston: Beacon Press, 1970.

Hunter, Beatrice. *Consumer Beware.* New York: Simon and Schuster, 1979.

Hutchinson, John. *The Imperfect Union.* New York: Dutton, 1970.

Ibsen, Henrik. *Enemy of the People.* New York: Oxford University Press, 1989.

Isaac, Katherine. *Civics for Democracy.* Washington, DC: Essential Books, 1992.

Jackson, George. *Blood in my Eye.* New York: Black Classic, 1990.

________. *Soledad Brother: The Prison Letters of George Jackson.* New York: Bantam Books, 1970.

Jacobson, Michael. *Nutrition Scoreboard: Your Guide to Better Eating.* New York: Avon Books, 1975.

Jacobson, Michael, Robert Atkins and George Hacker. *The Booze Merchants: The Inebriating of America.* Washington, DC: Center for Science in the Public Interest.

Jezer, Marty. *The Dark Ages: Life in the United States, 1945-1960.* Boston: South End Press, 1982.

Jones, Jaqueline. *Labor of Love, Labor of Sorrow: Black Women, Work and the Family, From Slavery to the Present.* New York: Random House, 1986.

Kahn, Si. *How People Get Power.* New York: McGraw Hill, 1991.

________. *Organizing: A Guide for Grassroots Leaders.* New York: McGraw Hill, 1991.

Katznelson, Ira. *City Trenches: Urban Politics and the Patterning of Class in the US.* New York: UCHP, 1982.

Kedgogar, Robert J. *Hungry for Profits: U.S. Food and Drug Multinationals in Latin America.* New York: IDOC/North America, 1976.

Kelly, Petra. *Thinking Green!.* Berkeley: Parallax Press, 1994.

King, Martin Luther, Jr. *Where Do We Go From Here? Chaos or Community.* Boston: Beacon Press, 1967.

________. *Why We Can't Wait.* New York: Harper & Row, 1963.

Kinoy, Arthur. *Rights on Trial.* Cambridge, Mass: Harvard University Press, 1983.

Kittner, Robert. *The Life of the Party.* New York: Viking, 1987.

Kluger, Richard. *Simple Justice: The History of Brown v. Board of Education and Black America's Struggle for Equality.* New York: Vintage Books, 1975.

Kolko, Gabriel. *Triumph of Conservatism.* New York: Free Press of Glenco, 1977.

Kolko, Joyce. *Restructuring the World Economy.* New York: Pantheon, 1977.

Kotz, Mary L. and Nick Koltz. *A Passion for Equality.* New York: W.W. Norton, 1977.

Kozol, Jonathan. *The Night is Dark and I am Far From Home: Savage Inequality.* Boston: Houghton Mifflin Co., 1975.

Kramer, Nancy and Steven Newman. *Getting What You Deserve.* New York: Doubleday, 1979.

Kwitny, Jonathan. *The Crimes of Patriots.* New York: Simon & Schuster, Inc. 1988.

________. *Endless Enemies: The Making of an Unfriendly World.* New York: Viking Penguin, Inc., 1986.

La Botz, Dan. *Mask of Democracy: Labor Suppression in Mexico Today.* Boston: South End Press, 1992.

LaFeber, Walter. *Inevitable Revolutions.* New York: W.W. Norton, 1984.

Lappe, Frances Moore and Joseph Collins. *Food First: Beyond the Myth of Scarcity.* New York: Ballantine Books, 1978.

________. *Rediscovering America's Values.* New York: Ballantine Books, 1989.

________. *Taking Population Seriously.* San Francisco: Institute for Food and Development Policy, 1990.

________. *World Hunger: Twelve Myths.* New York: Grove Atlantic, 1986.

Lekachman, Robert. *Greed Is Not Enough.* New York: Pantheon, 1982.

Lens, Sidney. *The Promise and Pitfalls of Revolution.* New York: Pilgrim Press, 1974.

Leonard, H. Jeffrey, et al. *Environment and the Poor: Development Strategies for a Common Agenda.* New Brunswick, NJ: Transaction, 1989.

Levy, Jacques E. *Cesar Chavez: Autobiography of La Causa.* New York: W.W. Norton, 1975.

Lewis, Anthony. *Gideon's Trumpet.* New York:

Random House, 1989.

Lindblom, Charles. *Politics and Markets: The World's Political-Economic Systems.* New York: Basic Books, 1980.

Lofgren, Don. *Dangerous Premises: An Insider's View of OSHA Enforcement.* Ithaca, NY: Cornell University ILR Press, 1989.

Lovins, Amory. *Energy Unbound: A Fable for America's Future.* New York: Sierra, 1986.

Lyman, Francesca, et al. *The Greenhouse Trap: What We're Doing to the Atmosphere and How We Can Slow Global Warming.* Boston: Beacon Press, 1990.

Lynd, Alice and Staughton Lynd, eds. *Rank and File: Personal Histories by Working-Class Organizers.* New York: Monthly Review Press, 1988.

MacKinnon, Catharine A. *Toward A Feminist Theory of the State.* Cambridge: Harvard University Press, 1989.

Magdoff, Harry and Paul Sweezy. *The Deepening Crisis of American Capitalism.* New York: Monthly Review Press, 1981.

Malcolm X. *The Autobiography of Malcolm X.* New York: Ballantine Books, 1976.

Marcuse, Herbert. *Counterrevolution and Revolt.* Boston: Beacon Press, 1972.

McKibben, Bill. *The End of Nature.* New York: Random House, 1989.

Melman, Seymour. *Profits Without Production.* Pennsylvania: University of Pennsylvania Press, 1987.

Memmi, Albert. *The Colonizer and the Colonized.* Boston: Beacon Press, 1991.

Meyer, Jane ed. *We Are All Part of One Another: A Barbara Deming Reader.* Philadelphia: New Society Publishers, 1984.

Miliband, Ralph. *The State in Capitalist Society: An Analysis of the Western System of Power.* New York: Basic Books, 1978.

Miller, John C. *Sam Adams: Pioneer in Propaganda.* California: Stanford University Press, 1986.

Millett, Kate. *Sexual Politics.* New York: S & S Trade, 1990.

Mills, C. Wright. *The Causes of World War II.* New York: Greenwood, 1976.

________. *The Power Elite.* Oxford: Oxford University Press, 1956.

Mintz, Morton. *At Any Cost: Corporate Greed, Women and the Dalkon Shield.* New York: Pantheon, 1985.

Mintz, Morton and Jerry S. Cohen. *Power, Inc.* New York: Bantam Books, 1976.

Mokhiber, Russell. *Corporate Crime and Violence: Big Business Power and the Abuse of the Public Trust.* San Francisco: Sierra Club Books, 1988.

Moody, Kim. *An Injury to All: The Decline of American Unionism.* New York: Verso, 1988.

Morgan, Robin. *Sisterhood Is Powerful: An Anthology of Writings from the Women's Liberation Movement.* New York: Random House, 1970.

Moskowitz, Milton, ed. *Everybody's Business: An Almanac.* New York: Doubleday, 1990.

Moyers, Bill D. *Global Dumping Ground.* Washington, DC: Seven Locks Press, 1990.

Nader, Ralph. *Unsafe At Any Speed: The Designed-In Dangers of the American Automobile.* New York: Grossman Publishers, 1973.

Nader, Ralph, ed. *The Consumer and Corporate Accountability.* New York: Harcourt Brace Jovanovice, Inc., 1973.

Nader, Ralph and Donald Ross. *Action for a Change: A Student's Manual for Public Interest Organizing.* New York: Grossman Publishers, 1972.

Nader, Ralph and William Taylor. *The Big Boys.* New York: Pantheon Books, 1986.

Newfield, Jack. *A Populist Manifesto.* New York: Praeger, 1972.

Newfield, Jack and Paul A. DeBrul. *The Abuse of Power.* New York: Penguin Books, 1978.

Noble, David F. *America by Design: Science, Technology and the Rise of Corporate Capitalism.* New York, Oxford University Press, 1977.

Norris, Ruth, ed. *Pills, Pesticides & Profits.* Croton-on-Hudson, NY: North River Press, Inc., 1982.

O'Connor, James. *The Fiscal Crises of the State.* New York: St. Martin's Press, 1973.

Olsen, Mancur, Jr. *The Logic of Collective Action: Public Good and the Theory of Groups.* Cambridge: Harvard University Press, 1971.

Paehlke, Robert C. *Environmentalism and the Future of Progressive Politics.* New Haven: Yale University Press, 1989.

Pertschuk, Michael. *Revolt Against Regulation: The Rise and Pause of the Consumer Movement.* Berkeley: University of California Press,

1982.

________. *Giant Killers*. New York: Norton, 1986.

Petchesky, Rosalind Pollack. *Abortion and Women's Choice*. Boston: Northeastern University Press, 1984.

Phillips, Kevin. *The Politics of Rich and Poor: Wealth and the American Electorate in the Reagan Administration*. New York: Random House, 1990.

Pilisuk, Marc and Phyllis Pilisuk. *How We Lost the War on Poverty*. New York: Transaction Books, 1973.

Pitkin, Hannah. *Fortune is a Woman*. Berkeley: University of California Press, 1984.

Piven, Frances Fox and Richard A. Cloward. *The New Class War: Reagan's Attack on the Welfare State and Its Consequences*. New York: Pantheon, 1982.

________. *Poor People's Movements: Why They Succeed, How They Fail*. New York: Random House, Inc., 1977.

________. *Regulating the Poor*. New York: Random House, Inc., 1972.

________. *Why Americans Don't Vote*. New York: Pantheon, 1989.

________. *The Politics of Turmoil: Poverty, Race, and the Urban Crisis*. New York: Vioks, 1965.

Poulantzes, Nicos. *Political Power and Social Classes*. New York: Routledge, Chapman and Hill, 1987.

Powers, Ron. *The Newscasters*. New York: St. Martins Press, 1977.

Preis, Art. *Labor's Giant Step: Twenty Years of the CIO*. New York: Path Press, 1972 [c1964].

Raskin, Marcus. *Common Good*. London: Routledge & Kegan Paul, 1986.

Raskin, Marcus and Chester Hartman, eds. *Winning America: Ideas & Leadership for the 1990s*. Boston: South End Press, 1988.

Rawls, John. *Theory of Justice*. Cambridge: Harvard University Press, 1971.

Reece, Ray. *The Sun Betrayed: A Study of the Corporate Seizure of U.S. Solar Energy Development*. Boston: South End Press, 1979.

Reuther, Victor. *The Brothers Reuther and the Story of the UAW: A Memoir*. Boston: Houghton Mifflin, 1976.

Ridgeway, James. *Blood in the Face*. New York: Thunder's Mouth Press, 1990.

________. *The Closed Corporation*. New York: Random House, 1968.

________. *The Haiti Files*. Washington, DC: Essential Books, 1994.

________. *New Energy*. Boston: Beacon Press, 1975.

________. *The Politics of Ecology*. New York: Dutton, 1970.

________. *Who Owns the Earth*. New York: MacMillan, c1980.

Rifkin, Jeremy, ed. *The Green Lifestyle Handbook: 1001 Ways You Can Heal the Earth*. New York: Henry Holt & Co., 1990.

Robinson, William and Kent Norsworthy. *David & Goliath: The U.S. War Against Nicaragua*. New York: Monthly Review Press, 1987.

Rosen, Wumner M. *Economic Power Failure: The Current American Crisis*. New York: McGraw Hill, 1975.

Ross, Donald K. *A Public Citizen Action Manual*. New York: Grossman Publishers, 1973.

Ryan, William. *Blaming the Victim*. New York: Random House, 1976.

Said, Edward. *Orientalism*. New York: Random House, 1979.

Said, Edward and Christopher Hitchens. *Blaming the Victims: Spurious Scholarship and the Palestinian Question*. New York: Verso, 1988.

Sale, Kirkpatrick. *The Conquest of Paradise*. New York: Knopf, 1990.

________. Dwellers in the Land. San Francisco: New Society Publications, 1991.

________. *Human Scale*. New York: Coward, McCann & Geoghegan, 1980.

________. *SDS: Ten Years Toward a Revolution*. New York: Vintage Books, 1974.

Saul, John and Stephen Gelb. *The Crisis in South Africa*. New York: Monthly Review Press, 1986.

Schechter, Susan. *Women and Male Violence*. Boston: South End Press, 1982.

Scheingold, Stuart A. *The Politics of Rights: Lawyers, Public Policy, and Political Change*. New Haven: Yale University Press, 1974.

Schiller, Herbert. *Culture, Inc*. New York: Oxford University Press, 1991.

Schlesinger, Arthur M. *The Disuniting of America: Reflections on a Multicultural Society*. New York: W.W. Norton & Company, 1991.

Schlesinger, Stephen and Stephen Kinzer. *Bitter*

Fruit: The Untold Story of the American Coup in Guatemala. Garden City, NY: Anchor Books, 1982.

Schmidt, David D. *Citizen Lawmakers: The Ballot Initiative Revolution*. Philadelphia: Temple University Press, 1989.

Schumacher, E.F. *Small is Beautiful: Economics As If People Mattered*. New York: Harper & Collins, 1991.

Scott, James. *Weapons of the Weak*. New Haven: Yale University Press, 1987.

Seldes, George. *Freedom of the Press*. New York: Da Capo Press, 1971 [c1938].

________. *Never Tire of Protesting*. New York: L. Stuart, 1968.

________. *You Can't Do That*. New York: Da Capo Press, 1972 [c1938].

________. *You Can't Print That!* Crosse Pointe Woods, MI: Scholarly Press, 1968.

________. *Witness to a Century*. New York: Ballantine Books, 1988.

Sennett, William. *The Fall of Public Man*. New York: Alfred A. Knopf, 1977.

Serrin, William. *Homestead: The Glory and Tragedy of an American Steel Town*. Times Books, 1992.

Shabecoff, Philip. *A Fierce Green Fire: The American Movement*. New York: Hill and Wang, 1993.

Shaiken, Harley. *Work Transformed: Automation & Labor in the Computer Age*. New York: Holt, Rinehart and Winston, 1986.

Sinclair, Upton. *The Jungle*. New York: Doubleday, Page & Co., 1906.

Sklar, Holly, ed. *Trilateralism: The Trilateral Commission and Elite Planning for Wilderness Management*. Boston: South End Press, 1980.

Slayton, Robert. *Back of the Yards: The Making of a Local Democracy*. Chicago: University of Chicago Press, 1988.

Sleeper, Jim. *The Closest of Strangers*. New York: W.W. Norton, 1990.

Steele, Shelby. *Content of Our Character: A New Vision of Race in America*. New York: St. Martin's Press, 1990.

Steinfels, Peter. *The Neo-Conservatives*. New York: Simon and Schuster, 1980.

Stern, Philip. *The Best Congress Money Can Buy*. New York: Pantheon Books, 1988.

Stone, Christopher. *Where the Law Ends: The Social Control of Corporate Behavior*. New York: Waveland, 1991.

Stone, I.F. *The I.F. Stone's Weekly Reader*. New York: Random House, 1973.

________. *The Best of I.F. Stone's Weekly*. Harmondsworth: Penguin, 1973.

Sullivan, William. *Reconstructing Public Philosophy*. Berkeley: University of California Press, 1982.

Sutherland, Edwin H. *White Collar Crime*. New York: Yale University Press, 1983.

Taylor, Peter. *The Smoke Ring: Tobacco, Money and Multinational Politics*. New York: Pantheon, 1984.

Terkel, Studs. *Hard Times*. New York: Pantheon, 1970.

________. *Working*. New York: Pantheon Books, 1974.

Thoreau, Henry David. *Walden, and Civil Disobedience*. New York: W.W. Norton, 1966.

________. *Walden, and Other Writings*. New York: Modern Library, 1950.

Thurow, Lester. *Zero Sum Society*. New York: Viking Penguin, 1980.

Todd, Alden. *Finding Facts Fast*. New York: Ten Speed Press, 1992.

Tolchin, Susan J. and Martin Tolchin. *Dismantling America: The Rush to Deregulate*. Boston: Houghton Mifflin Company, 1983.

Tribe, Laurence H. *Abortion: The Clash of Absolutes*. New York: Norton, 1991.

Van Den Bosch, Robert. *The Pesticide Conspiracy*. California: University of California Press, 1989.

Vanden Heuvel, Katrina, ed. *The Nation, 1865-1990*. New York: Thunder's Mouth Press, 1990.

Wasserman, Harvey. *Harvey Wasserman's History of the United States*. New York: Four Walls Eight Windows, 1988.

Weir, David and Mark Shapiro. *Circles of Poison: Pesticides and People in a Hungry World*. San Francisco: Institute for Food and Development Policy, 1981.

West, Cornel. *Race Matters*. New York: Vintage Books, 1993.

Whiteside, Thomas. *The Pendulum and the Toxic Cloud*. New Haven: Yale University Press, 1979.

Williams, Gary. *Nixon Agonistes: The Crisis of the Self-Made Man*. Boston: Houghton Mifflin

Co., 1969.

Williams, Juan. *Eyes on the Prize: America's Civil Rights Years, 1954-1965*. New York: Viking, 1988.

Williams, T. Harry. *Huey Long*. New York: Alfred J. Knopf, Inc., 1969.

Woodward, Bob and Carl Bernstein. *All the President's Men*. New York: Warner Books, 1987.

Woolf, Virginia. *A Room of One's Own*. New York: Harcourt, Brace and Jovanovich, Inc., 1989.

Wylie, Jeanie. *Poletown: Community Betrayed*. Urbana: University of Illinois Press, 1989.

Zinn, Howard. *A People's History of the United States*. New York: Harper Collins, 1985.

PERIODICALS

The following are national news periodicals to which most college libraries subscribe. They cover some of the issues of concern to the groups we list in the Directory section.

Common Cause, 2030 M Street, NW, Washington, DC 20036, (202) 833-1200. Bimonthly.

Extra!, 130 West 25th Street, New York, NY 10001, (212) 633-6700. Bimonthly with special issues in the summer and winter.

Greenpeace, 1436 U Street, NW, Washington, DC 20009, (202) 462-1177. Quarterly newsletter.

In These Times, 2040 North Milwaukee Avenue, Chicago, IL 60647, (312) 772-0100. Bi-monthly.

Mother Jones, 1663 Mission Street, San Francisco, CA 94103, (415) 558-8881. Monthly, except combined issues in February/March and July/August.

Multinational Monitor, P.O. Box 19405, Washington, DC 20036, (202) 387-8030. Monthly, except combined issues in January/February and July/August.

Not Man Apart, 218 D Street, SE, Washington, DC 20003, (202) 783-7400. Quarterly.

The Nation, 72 Fifth Avenue, New York, NY 10011, (212) 242-8400. Weekly (except for the first week in January and biweekly in July and August).

Nutrition Action Healthletter, Center for Science in the Public Interest, 1875 Connecticut Avenue, NW, Suite 300, Washington, DC 20009, (202) 332-9110. Monthly except combined issues in July/August and January/February.

The Progressive, 409 East Main Street, Madison, WI 53703, (608) 257-4626. Monthly.

Public Citizen, 2000 P Street, NW, Suite 610, Washington, DC 20036, (202) 293-9142. Bimonthly.

Student Lawyer, 750 North Lake Shore Drive, Chicago, IL 60611, (312) 988-6048/49. Monthly, September through May.

Utne Reader, 1624 Harmon Place, Minneapolis, MN 55403, (612) 338-5040. Six bimonthly issues per year.

The Workbook, P.O. Box 4524, Albuquerque, NM 87106, (505) 262- 1862. Quarterly.

Z Magazine, 150 West Canton Street, Boston, MA 02118, (508) 548-9063. Monthly except one issue for July/ August.

FINDING SOCIAL CHANGE WORK

Various tabloids, bulletins and placement services:

ACCESS: Networking in the Public Interest, 50 Beacon Street, Boston, MA 02108, (617) 720-JOBS. Performs nonprofit organization searches for those seeking employment within 100 nonprofit field categories (e.g. environmental, health, arts). A $25 processing fee gives you a personal directory of organizations fitting your specific criteria. Organizational descriptions are included.

The Environmental Careers Organization (ECO), 286 Congress Street, 3rd Floor, Boston, MA 02110, (617) 426-4375. Nonprofit placement service offering paid, short-term environmental positions for senior undergraduates, graduate and doctoral students, those recently graduated and other entry-level environmental job-seekers. ECO provides jobs and internships with nonprofits, local, state and federal government agencies, corporations and consulting firms.

The Clearinghouse Review, published by the National Clearinghouse for Legal Services, Inc., 205 West Monroe, 2nd Floor, Chicago, IL 60606; (312) 263-3830. A periodical containing a job market section listing positions available in Legal Service Corporation-funded programs at public interest law centers. Back issues $15; individuals $95; organizations

$125; and $145 for subscriptions outside the United States.

Community Jobs, published by ACCESS: Networking in the Public Interest, 50 Beacon Street, Boston, MA 02108, (617) 720-JOBS. A national nonprofit employment newspaper listing 250-300 nonprofit jobs each month, including articles and information on the nonprofit sector. Subscription rates are: $25 for three months; $39 for six months; $69 for one year.

Earth Work, published by the Student Conservation Association, P.O. Box 550, Charlestown, NH 03603, (603) 543-1700. This monthly magazine "for and about people who work to protect the land and environment" contains a *JobScan* listing of full-time and seasonal jobs and internships in conservation and natural resources. Subscription rates are $29.95 a year; 19.95 for six months; or $6 per single copy.

Environmental Opportunities, Sanford Berry, ed., Box 788, Walpole, NH 03608, (603) 756-4553. Monthly bulletin which lists more than 100 environmentally-oriented jobs throughout the country in each issue, including seasonal work and internships. $24/six months; $44/year; $4.50/single copy.

The Job Seeker, Becky Potter, ed., Route 2, Box 16, Warrens, WI 54666, (608) 378-4290. Environmental job listings in the areas of forestry, biology, fisheries, environmental sciences, conservation, environmental action/policy, administration, environmental education, soil and water conservation, parks/recreation and internships. Two issues per month. Individual rates: $19.50/6 issues, $36/12 issues, $60/24 issues. Organizations: $22.50/6 issues, $44/12 issues. Summer Jobs Special of 9 issues, from December 6-April 6, is $10.

Opportunities in Public Interest Law, ACCESS: Networking in the Public Interest, 50 Beacon Street, Boston, MA 02108, (617) 720- JOBS. Listing of current jobs and internships in nonprofit and government public interest law organizations. Published 2 times a year; $175/year for institutions, individual rate is $42.90 for single issue. Many law school career placement offices subscribe to this resource.

Opportunity NOCs (Nonprofit Classifieds), Sharon Johnson, ed. once a week by The Management Center, 870 Market Street, Suite 800, San Francisco, CA 94102, (415) 362-9735. Each issue lists 80-100 San Francisco Bay Area nonprofit sector job opportunities and includes information about workshops, training, and services for nonprofit agencies. Full and part-time openings in human services, the arts, environmental and educational organizations. $10/three months; $46/year.

Public Interest Employment Report, Jessica Manly Bucciarelli, ed. Published by the Public Interest Clearinghouse, 200 McAllister Street, San Francisco, CA 94102-4978, (415) 255-1714. A twice-monthly newsletter listing approximately 75 social change jobs in each issue, primarily in California and the West, for attorneys and others. $30/3 months if employed; $15/3 months if unemployed, a student, or a Clearinghouse member.

On internship opportunities:

Beresovski, Catherine. *NAPIL Directory of Public Interest Legal Internships*, 1993-94. Published by the National Association for Public Interest Law, 1666 Connecticut Avenue, NW, Suite 424, Washington, DC 20009, (202) 462-0120. Contains employer listings for over 150 organizations, $25 individuals and $20 for students.

Butterworth, Amy S. and Sally A. Migliore, eds. *The National Directory of Internships, 1994-95*. Published by the National Society for Experiential Education, 3509 Haworth Drive, Suite 207, Raleigh, NC 27609, (919) 787-3263. Lists opportunities in 61 fields for college, graduate and high school students and for adults and youth. $24, or $20 for NSEE members.

Jobst, Katherine. *1989 Internships: 38,000 On-The-Job Training Opportunities for College Students and Adults*. Published by Pedersons, (513) 531-2222, Cincinnati. Includes listings of public service/public interest internships.

Peace and International Security Internships in the Washington, DC Area, 1994. Published by ACCESS, 1511 K Street, Suite 643, Washington, DC 20005, (202)783-6050.

On volunteer opportunities:

Alternatives to the Peace Corps: A Directory of Third World and U.S. Volunteer Opportunities. Sixth edition, 1994. Published by the Institute for Food and Development Policy, 398 60th Street, Oakland, CA 94103, (510) 864-4400. Listings for international and U.S. voluntary service organizations, study tours and alternative travel groups. $6.95.

Angus, Susan G., ed. *Invest Yourself: The Catalogue of Volunteer Opportunities,* 1986. Published by The Commission on Voluntary Service and Action, Inc., P.O. Box 117-02, New York, NY 10009, (212)788-4636. Lists 180 non-government volunteer organizations with international and intercultural, workcamp, and other opportunities for full-time volunteers. $7.50 postpaid.

Cohen, Marjorie Adoff. *Volunteer! The Comprehensive Guide to Voluntary Service in the U.S. and Abroad, 1988-89.* Published by the Council on International Educational Exchange (CIEE) and The Council of Religious Volunteer Agencies. Contact CIEE, 205 East 42nd Street, New York, NY 10017, (212) 661-1414. Lists short and long-term service opportunities with 200 voluntary service organizations, including workcamps, VISTA and the Peace Corps. $8.95.

Kipps, Harriet Clyde, ed. *Volunteerism: The Directory of Organizations, Training, Programs and Publications, 1990-91.* Published by R.R. Bowker, 245 West 17th Street, New York, NY 10011, (800) 521-8110. Lists over 5,300 national, regional and local associations.

1991 International Workcamp Directory. Published by Volunteers for Peace, 43 Tiffany Road, Belmont, VT 05730, (802) 259-2759. Over 700 opportunities in 34 countries listed for volunteers. Updated annually. $10 included postage.

Volunteer-The National Center, 1111 North 19th Street, Suite 500, Arlington, VA 22209, (703) 276-0542. Provides referrals to over 100 volunteer clearinghouses across the country.

On international jobs:

Beckman, David M., Timothy J. Mitchell and Linda L. Powers. *The Overseas List: Opportunities for Living and Working in Developing Countries.* Augsburg Publishing House, 426 South Fifth Street, Box 1209, Minneapolis, MN 55440; 1985. Lists opportunities for living and working in Africa, Asia and Latin America; chapters describe working in private development assistance, church missions, study and tourism, teaching and journalism, international organizations, U.S. government and business.

Kocher, Eric. *International Jobs: Where They Are And How to Get Them.* Reading, MA: Addison-Wesley, 1989.

Descriptions of social change work:

Beitz, Charles and Michael Washburn. *Creating the Future: A Guide to Living and Working for Social Change.* New York: Bantam Books, Inc., 1974. Out of print.

Boyte, Harry C. *Backyard Revolution.* Philadelphia: Temple University Press, 1980.

Boyte, Harry C., Heather Booth and Steve Max. *Citizen Action and the New American Populism.* Philadelphia: Temple University Press, 1986.

Garland, Anne Witte. *Women Activists: Challenging the Abuse of Power.* New York: The Feminist Press, 1988.

Griffin, Kelly. *More Action for a Change.* New York: Dembner Books, 1987.

Jobs in Social Change. Philadelphia: Social and Educational Research Foundation (SERF), 1975. Out of print.

There are many current books and workbooks on job-seeking skills and life planning. Here are four of the better ones:

Bolles, Richard Nelson. *What Color Is Your Parachute? A Practical Manual for Job-Hunters & Career-Changers.* Berkeley: Ten Speed Press, 1990. Updated annually. Considered the "bible" of career/life planning; includes useful exercises to help you determine career field interests. $11.95

Figler, Howard. *The Complete Job-Search Handbook.* New York: Henry Holt and Company Inc., 1988. Includes exercises that emphasize development of job-hunting skills. $11.95.

Jackson, Tom. *Guerilla Tactics in the Job Market: A*

Practical Manual. New York: Bantam Books, 1989. $4.95.

Miller, Saul. *After Law School? Finding a Job in a Tight Market.* Boston: Little, Brown and Co., 1978. Out of print.

Invaluable resource books on networking:

Lipnack, Jessica and Jeffrey Stamps. *Networking: The First Report and Directory.* New York: Doubleday, 1982. Examines what a network is, why it works and how to use it, and includes a comprehensive directory of over 1,500 key social change networks.

Lipnack, Jessica and Jeffrey Stamps. *The Networking Book: People Connecting With People.* New York: Routledge & Kegan Paul, 1986. This revised edition includes discussions of networking with computers, global networks, and an abbreviated directory of 86 networking organizations.

BIBLIOGRAPHIES AND DIRECTORIES

The following resources provide listings of groups with common interests, funding sources, alternative degrees, referrals, or readings to help you find out more about specific issues.

ACCESS Resource Guide: An International Directory of Information on War, Peace, and Security. Edited by William H. Kincade and Priscilla B. Hayner. Published by Ballinger Publishing Company, Cambridge, MA, 1988. $14.95 plus $2.50 shipping and handling. Order c/o ACCESS, 1511 K Street, NW, Suite 643, Washington, DC 20036, (202) 783-6050.

Africa: Human Rights Directory & Bibliography. Edited by Laurie S. Wiseberg and Laura Reiner. Published by Human Rights Internet, 57 Louis Pasteur, 5th Floor, Ottowa, ONTARIO KIN6N5. $35.

Alternative Press Index. Published by Alternative Press Center, Inc., P.O. Box 33109, Baltimore, MD 21218, (410) 243-2471. A quarterly subject index to articles in 200 alternative and underground magazines and newspapers. Aims to increase access to alternative periodicals.

Bear's Guide to Earning Non-Traditional College Degrees. 11th edition. By John Bear, PhD. Published by Ten Speed Press, Box 7123, Berkeley, CA 94707, (510) 559-1600. The most up-to-date, accurate and extensive catalog on nontraditional degree programs, including graduate, specialized and professional degrees. $11.95.

The Best Political Action Newsletters from Around the Country. Excerpts, circulation and order information from 53 newsletters in the areas of the workplace, civil rights, environment, policy, health and peace. Published by Social Policy, 25 West 43rd Street, Room 620, New York, NY 10036. $5 per copy (212)354-8525.

Black Americans Information Directory Third edition, 1992-93. Edited by Van de Sade. Detroit: Gale Research Inc., 1993. Includes national, regional, state and local associations, cultural and religious organizations, research centers and studies programs ($85).

Building a New South: A Guide to Southern Justice Organizations. March 1994. Contact New South Directory, 701 Camino Drive, Lexington, KY 40502, (606) 266-7455. Descriptive listings for several hundred social justice and grassroots citizen groups working in Appalachia and the South. $20.

The Complete Guide to Environmental Careers. CEIP Fund, 1994. Published by Island Press, P.O. Box 7, Covelo, CA 95428, 1-800-828-1302. Job outlook, salary level, volunteer, internship, and entry requirement information in the fields of environmental protection, natural resource management, planning, and environmental education and communications. $15.95.

Consumer Sourcebook. Eighth edition, 1994-95. Edited by Robert Wilson. Published by Gale Research Inc., Book Tower, Detroit, MI 48226, (313) 961-2242. A subject guide to approximately 7,000 federal, state and local government agencies; national, regional and grassroots associations and organizations; information centers, clearinghouses, and related consumer resources. $210.

Directory of Bay Area Public Interest Organizations. Fourth edition, 1991. Published by the Public Interest Clearinghouse, 200 McAllister Street, San Francisco, CA 94102-4978, (415) 565-4695. Lists over 600 groups. $27.

Directory of Puerto Rican Organizations. Third edition, 1993. Published by the National

› Rican Coalition, 1700 K Street, NW, ...ite 500, Washington, DC 20006, (202) 223-3915. Describes national, state and local organizations identified as Puerto Rican or as serving the Puerto Rican community throughout the U.S. $10.

A Directory of Public Interest Law Centers. Published in June 1990 by the Alliance for Justice, 1601 Connecticut Avenue, NW, Suite 600, Washington, DC 20009, (202) 332-3224. Listings for 185 public interest law centers. $4.

Education for Action: Graduate Studies with a Focus on Social Change. 1991, by Andrea Freedman with Kim Berry and Mary Crain. Published by the Institute for Food and Development Policy, 398 60th Street, Oakland, CA 94618, (510) 654-4400. 98 program descriptions and faculty contacts in such areas as anthropology, development studies, ethnic studies, law, social economy, and women's studies. $6.95 plus $2.00 postage.

Encyclopedia of Associations and National Organizations. 29th edition. Edited by Deborah M. Burek, Karin E. Koek and Annette Novallo. Updated each year. Detroit: Gale Research Inc. $415, 3 volume set.

Finding Co-ops: A Resource Guide and Directory. Available from the National Cooperative Business Association, 1401 New York Avenue, NW, Suite 1100, Washington, DC 20005-2160, (202) 638-6222. (1984) $4.95. Listings divided by type, sector, and state.

The Foundation Directory. Updated annually. Published by the Foundation Center of New York, 79 5th Avenue, New York, NY 10003-3076, 16th edition. $170 soft cover/$195 hard cover plus $4.50 shipping.

The Grant Seeker's Guide. Third edition, 1989. Edited by Jill R. Shellow and Nancy C. Stella for the National Network of Grantmakers. Published by Moyer Bell Limited, Colonial Hill/RFD 1, Mount Kisco, NY 10549. Describes hundreds of national, regional and local grantmaking organizations. $24.95.

Great Careers: The Fourth of July Guide to Careers, Internships, and Volunteer Opportunities in the Nonprofit Sector. 1990. Edited by Devon Smith. Published by Garrett Park Press, P.O. Box 190, Garrett Park, MD 20896. Thoroughly reviews opportunities, organizations and resources in such areas as the environment and renewable energy, animal rights, homelessness, social action and people with disabilities. $35.

Guide to Multicultural Resources. Edited by Alex Boyd. Published by Highsmith Inc. W5527 Highway 106, P.O. Box 800, Fort Atkinson, WI 53538-0800. (414) 563-9671. Indexes minority and multicultural organizations and associations involved with the African American, Hispanic American, Asian American, Native American and other multicultural communities. $49.

Healthy Harvest IV: A Directory of Sustainable Agriculture and Horticulture Organizations, 1989-90. Published by Potomac Valley Press, 1424 16th Street, NW, #105, Washington, DC 20036. 1,000 entries, with geographic and subject indexes and organizational contacts.

Human Rights Directory: Latin America and the Caribbean. Edited by Laurie S. Wiseberg, Guadalupe Lopez and Sarah Meselson. Published by Human Rights Internet, 1990. $50.

The Independent Study Catalog: The NUCEA Guide to Independent Study Through Correspondence Instruction. 5th edition. 1992. P.O. Box 2123, Princeton, NJ 08543-2123, (800) 338-3282.

The International Directory of Little Magazines and Small Presses. 25th edition, 1989-90. Len Fulton, Editor. Published by Dustbooks, P.O. Box 100, Paradise, CA 95967. (1989) $23.95.

Minority Organizations: A National Directory. Fourth edition, 1992. Published by Garrett Park Press, P.O. Box 190C, Garrett Park, MD 20896-0190, (301) 946-2553.

Guide to Black, Hispanic, Asian and Native American Organizations, listing over 9,700 professional and trade groups, and historical/cultural organizations. $50 ($45 prepaid).

NAAO Directory. Third edition, 1992. Published by the National Association of Artists' Organizations, 918 F Street, NW Suite 611, Washington, DC 20004, (202) 347-6350. Lists member and service organizations, members of the National Alliance of Media Arts Centers, literary arts centers, the Volunteer Lawyers for the Arts network, state and regional arts agencies and selected foundations. $25 including postage.

The NAPIL Fellowships Guide 1994-95. Published by the National Association for Public Interest Law, 1666 Connecticut Avenue, NW, Suite 424, Washington, DC 20009, (202) 462-0120. Lists approximately 100 fellowship openings with public interest organizations for graduating law students. $20 for students, $25 for others.

NASCO Guide to Cooperative Careers. Sharon Pedersen, Editor. Published by North American Students of Cooperation, P.O. Box 7715, Ann Arbor, MI 48107, (313) 663-0889. $3. A brief look at jobs within individual cooperative sectors, with resource organizations and associations providing career training and education.

National Directory of Safe Energy Organizations. Compiled by Ken Bossong. Published March 1989 by Public Citizen Critical Mass Energy Project, 215 Pennsylvania Avenue, SE, Washington, DC 20003, (202) 546-4996. $5.

National Issues Forums, 100 Commons Road, Dayton, OH 45459, (513)434-7300. *Forums* now includes about 1,500 discussion groups, ranging from community colleges and labor unions to civic associations and prisoner discussion circles. *Forums* renews the old American traditions like Lyceum and Chataqua, aimed at increasing citizen discussion and cultivating the arts of public debate about the issues of the day.

New Careers: Internships and Professional Opportunities in Technology and Social Change. Fourth edition, 1993. Edited by Barry Lasky. Student Pugwash USA, 1638 R Street, NW, Suite 32, Washington, DC 20009, (202) 328-6555. $10 for students; $18 all others, plus $3 postage and handling.

The New Complete Guide to Environmental Careers, Second edition, 1993. Edited by John Cook, Kevin Doyle, and Bill Sharp. Published by Island Press, Washington, DC.

1992 Directory of State and Local Consumer Organizations. Published by Consumer Federation of America, 1424 16th Street, NW, Suite 604, Washington, DC 20036 (202)387-6121. $5.

1991 Conservation Directory. Published by the National Wildlife Federation, 1400 16th Street, NW, Washington, DC 20036-2266, (703) 790-4000. Updated annually. Lists organizations, agencies and officials concerned with natural resources. $20 per copy, plus $4.85 shipping charge.

The Public Interest Handbook: A Guide to Legal Careers in Public Interest Organizations. Geoffrey Kaiser and Barbara Mule. Published by Locust Hill Press, P.O. Box 260, West Cornwall, CT 06796, (215) 672-0060. 1987 $29.95.

Public Interest Profiles 1988-1989. The Foundation for Public Affairs, 1992. Dept. R71, P.O. Box 7816, 300 Raritan Center Parkway, Edison, NJ 08818, (908) 225-1900. Published by Congressional Quarterly Books. Files on over 2,500 public interest groups, including statement of purpose, funding information, and effectiveness and political orientation according to press clips. $169.

Reading Lists in Radical Social Science. Edited by Mark Maier and Dan Gilroy. Published by the Monthly Review Press/Union for Radical Political Economics, 62 West 14th Street, New York, NY 10011, (212) 691-2555. (1982), $10. Over 50 syllabi from university courses across the U.S. in such areas as political economy, women's studies, racism, health and labor.

Research Centers Directory 1990. Edited by Thomas Cichonskci. Detroit: Gale Research Inc. 835 Penobscot Bldg., Detroit, MI 48226 (800) 877-4253. Covers research units in Life Sciences, Physical Sciences and Engineering, Private and Public Policy, Social and Cultural Studies, and Multidisciplinary and Coordinating Centers.

Service Learning: An Annotated Bibliography. Janet Luce, editor. Published by the National Society for Experiential Education, Suite 207, 3509 Haworth Drive, Raleigh, NC 27609, (919) 787-3263. 1988 $15.

T*hird World Resources Directories.* April 1994. Edited by Thomas P. Fenton and Mary J. Heffron. Published by Orbis Books. To order contact DataCenter, 464 19th Street, Oakland, CA 94612, (510) 835-4692 59.95 plus postage.

Who's Involved With Hunger: An Organization Guide for Education and Advocacy. Fifth edition, 1992. Edited by Patricia L. Kutzner. Published by World Hunger Education Service, P.O. Box 29056, Washington, DC 20017, (202)298-9803. Lists 400 organizations in the U.S. and Canada working on hunger issues. $10.50.

World Directory of Environmental Organizations. Third edition, September 1989. Edited by Thaddeus C. Trzyna. Published by the California Institute for Public Affairs, P.O. Box 189040, Sacramento, CA 95818, (916) 442-2472. Over 2,600 national and international organizations in over 200 countries concerned with protecting the earth's resources. $45 plus $2 handling.

Part Two: Networks

"The growth of an array of support networks for grassroots organizations is both an indicator of the new level of sophistication and professionalism and a contributing factor to it. The umbrella organizations, clearinghouses, action-research projects, resources, and training schools help to develop issues, devise strategies, train organizers and leaders, devise policy, promote fundraising, recruit staff and facilitate communications between the groups and their constituencies and among the groups themselves."

Janice Perlman, "Grassroots Empowerment and Government." Social Policy, Vol. 10, No. 2, September/October, 1979, p. 17. The following networks have indicated a willingness to refer job-seekers to social change groups falling within their arenas.

AMERICAN YOUTH WORK CENTER, 1751 N Street, NW, Suite 302, Washington, DC 20036, (202) 785-0764. Assists the management and staff of human service organizations for the improvement of service to youth and children through domestic and international conferences and training events, American and foreign youth service publications, and technical assistance to the youth work community. Referrals to coalitions of young workers, city youth worker coalitions, and Washington, DC organizations serving youth. Contact William Treanor, Executive Director.

ASSOCIATION FOR COMMUNITY BASED EDUCATION, 1805 Florida Avenue, NW, Washington, DC 20009, (202) 462-6333. A national membership organization for alternative educational institutions, the Association has a directory of community-based groups involved in adult and community education. Involved in setting up programs and developing training that may be utilized by community groups. Contact office.

ASSOCIATION OF COMMUNITY ORGANIZATIONS FOR REFORM NOW (ACORN), 300 Flatbush Avenue, Brooklyn, NY 11217, (718) 789-5600. An organization of low to moderate income families working in 19 states for political and economic justice. Referrals to local ACORN chapters and other local community organizations. Contact John Kest.

CAMPUS OUTREACH OPPORTUNITY LEAGUE (COOL), 386 McNeal Hall, University of Minnesota, St. Paul, MN 55108. COOL is a youth-initiated network of more than 600 campus service projects that facilitate student involvement in community problem-solving efforts. Provides organizing resources and training. Referrals to League members and projects. Contact Kristin Parrish, Director.

CENTER FOR COMMUNITY CHANGE, 1000 Wisconsin Avenue, NW, Washington, DC 20007, (202) 342-0519. Provides technical assistance tailored to meet the programmatic and administrative needs of community-based organizations. Referrals to community- based social service groups and national and regional technical assistance agencies. Contact Pablo Eisenberg, Vice-President.

CENTER FOR POLICY ALTERNATIVES, 1875 Connecticut Avenue, NW, Suite 710, Washington, DC 20009, (202)387-6030. One of the major centers of information exchange among progressives. The Center's issues include family and work issues, women's economic justice and reproductive rights, election law reform, sustainable growth, public capital and economic reform. Referrals to other public interest groups working in these areas. Contact Linda Tarr-Whelan, Director.

CITIZEN ACTION, National Office: 1120 19th Street, NW, Washington, DC 20036, (202) 775-1580. A consortium of 13 statewide citizen organizations, including the Connecticut Citizen Action Group (CCAG), Illinois Public Action Council (IPAC), Massachusetts Fair Share, Ohio Public

Interest Campaign (OPIC), Minnesota COACT, Pennsylvania Public Interest Coalition, Citizen Action of Indiana, and other organizing projects in five additional states. Referrals to member organizations. Contact Ira Arlook.

CITIZENS CLEARINGHOUSE FOR HAZARDOUS WASTES (CCHW), 119 Rowell Court, P.O. Box 6806, Falls Church, Virginia 22040 (703) 237-2249. A clearinghouse offering training and technical assistance to grassroots groups fighting toxic polluters. Referrals to community and national advocacy groups working on toxics issues. Contact the office.

CITIZENS FOR TAX JUSTICE, 1311 L Street, NW, 4th Floor, Washington, DC 20005, (202) 626-3780. A national citizen/labor coalition that seeks tax justice for working people, the elderly, and those on fixed incomes; and opposes measures to shift the tax burden onto these groups. Referrals to national citizen groups and labor unions. Contact Robert S. McIntyre, Director.

CLEAN WATER ACTION PROJECT, 1320 18th Street, NW, Washington, DC 20036, (202) 547-1286. Works with national and local citizen groups and leaders to eliminate water pollution. Referrals to environmental groups and other public interest groups, especially those with canvass staffs. Contact Personnel Director.

COMMUNITY INFORMATION EXCHANGE, 1029 Vermont Avenue, NW, Suite 710, Washington, DC 20005, (202) 628-2981. A national interactive network that meets the need of urban and rural community-based groups for reliable, in-depth information on strategies and resources for community development. Referrals to grassroots community development organizations. Contact Kathy Desmond, President.

CONSTITUTIONAL RIGHTS FOUNDATION, 601 South Kingsley Drive, Los Angeles, CA 90805, (213) 487-5590. Publishes *School Youth Service Network*, a quarterly newsletter that reports on youth service projects around the country and the progress of state-wide community service programs.

COUNCIL FOR THE ADVANCEMENT OF CITIZENSHIP, 44 Canal Center Plaza, Alexandria, VA 22314. Works to promote informed, responsible citizenship education through clearinghouse services, publications and reports. Publishes *Citizenship Education News*, quarterly.

HOMELESSNESSINFORMATIONEXCHANGE, 1612 K Street, NW, Suite 1004, Washington, DC 20006, (202) 775-1322. Gathers and distributes information about model homeless programs, funding sources, and experts in the field. Referrals to organizations and individuals working to combat homelessness nationwide. Contact Dana Harris-Trovato.

INDEPENDENT COMMUNITY CONSULTANTS, INC., Box 141, Hampton, AR 71744, (501) 798-4510. Provides planning research, training and evaluation services to nonprofit minority, social change community development and anti-poverty groups as well as government agencies. ICC's clients are primarily umbrella groups, and willing to make referrals to those interested job-seekers.

NATIONAL ASSOCIATION FOR PUBLIC INTEREST LAW (NAPIL), 1118 22nd Street, NW, Third Floor, Washington, DC 20037, (202)466-3686 A national coalition of law student organizations that offer grants and other forms of assistance to students and recent graduates engaged in public interest employment. Publishes the *NAPIL Directory of Public Interest Legal Internships* and the *NAPIL Fellowships Guide*. Referrals to law student organizations and public interest law centers. Contact Kathleen Welch.

NATIONAL ASSOCIATION OF NEIGHBORHOODS, 1651 Fuller Street, NW, Washington, DC 20009, (202) 332-7766. An association of neighborhood groups, citywide federations, and other coalitions and organizations concerned with neighborhood problems. Referrals to neighborhood associations, city-wide coalitions and community development corporations (CDC's). Contact Deborah Crain.

NATIONAL COALITION AGAINST DOMESTIC VIOLENCE, 10121 4th Street, NW, Suite 807, Washington, DC 20005, (202) 638-6388. NCADV is a membership organization providing national systems advocacy and technical assistance for its constituents. Referrals to grassroots shelter and service programs for battered women. Contact Nancy Turner.

NATIONAL CONGRESS OF NEIGHBORHOOD WOMEN, 249 Manhattan Avenue, Brooklyn, NY 11211, (718) 388-6666. A women's organizing and technical assistance group whose goal is the empowerment of women as community leaders. Conducts workshops; provides training in job development and fundraising. Referrals to women's organizations. Contact Lisa Cooper.

NATIONAL COUNCIL OF LA RAZA, 810 First Street, NE, Suite 300, Washington, DC 20002, (202) 289-1380. A resource and information clearinghouse, coordination body and funding source for Hispanic organizations. Has 125 affiliates in 21 states. Does research and advocacy in support of all Hispanic minorities and provides technical assistance and programmatic support to Hispanic community-based organizations. Referrals to Hispanic organizations. Contact Michelle Waldron.

NATIONAL ORGANIZATION FOR WOMEN (NOW), 1000 16th Street, NW, Suite 700, Washington, DC 20036, (202) 331-0066. The largest women's rights organization, NOW works on the local, state and federal level to bring women into the mainstream of American society and into fair and equal partnership with men. Referrals to NOW's 700 offices and chapters, and other women's groups nationwide. Contact Kim Gandy in Personnel.

NORTH AMERICAN STUDENTS OF COOPERATION (NASCO), Box 7715, Ann Arbor, MI 48107, (313) 663-0889. A consortium of North American student cooperatives. Issues publications, including the *NASCO Guide to Campus Cooperatives in North America*, holds conferences, does consulting and conducts cooperative board training for members and the general public. Referrals to cooperatives and co-op resource organizations; offers development assistance to newly created student cooperatives. Contact Margaret Martin for referrals and student housing cooperative assistance; Renee Ordeneaux for cooperative development assistance.

NUCLEAR INFORMATION AND RESOURCE SERVICE (NIRS), 1424 16th Street, NW, Suite 601, Washington, DC 20036 (202) 328-0002. Provides energy activists with information and resources to end nuclear power development. Referrals to national anti-nuclear power organizations. Contact Michael Mariotte.

PEACE ACTION, 1819 H Street, NW, Suite 1000, Washington, DC 20006, (202) 862-9740. A national group organizing at the grassroots level to reverse the arms race, abolish nuclear weapons, lower the military budget, promote economic conversion and construct a world of peace and justice. Referrals to over 150 chapters and affiliate groups nationwide with a membership of 50,000. Contact Monica Green.

PUBLIC MEDIA CENTER, 466 Green Street, Suite 300, San Francisco, CA 94133, (415) 434-1403. A nonprofit public interest advertising and media resource agency, also involved in media advocacy. Referrals to environmental groups, energy organizations, media fairness and media access groups, and San Francisco-based community action organizations. Contact Herb Gunther.

UNITED STATES PUBLIC INTEREST RESEARCH GROUP (USPIRG), 215 Pennsylvania Avenue, SE, Washington, DC 20003, (202) 546-9707. National, nonpartisan consumer and environmental organization conducting independent research on consumer and environmental issues, monitoring corporate and governmental actions affecting the average citizen, and lobbying in the public interest. Serves as a national office for a number of the state Public Interest Research Groups that have been formed throughout the country since 1971.

UNITED STATES STUDENT ASSOCIATION (USSA), 815 15th Street NW, Suite 838, Washington, DC 20005, (202) 347-8772. A research, information and training organization that promotes students' rights to a post-secondary education. Provides technical information and publishes student organizing manuals. Contact President.

PIRG DIRECTORY

Public Interest Research Groups (PIRGs) are nonprofit, nonpartisan organizations directed by students. College students vote democratically to form a PIRG on campus and then assess themselves a fee to support it. Student directors employ staffs of attorneys, scientists, writers and others to help them with their projects. The common principle underlying all PIRGs is that students are citizens and that therefore their education should include experience in recognizing and solving society's problems. PIRGs work on a wide range of issues, such as consumer and environmental protection, human rights, corporate accountability, energy and government responsiveness. They produce research reports, lobby, litigate, and organize for social change at the campus, community and state levels. Listed below are the PIRG state headquarters in the United States and Canada. Call or write to them for issue information and for the addresses of other PIRG offices.

Alaska PIRG (AKPIRG), P.O. Box 101093, Anchorage, AK 99510, (907) 278-3661.

Arizona PIRG (AZPIRG), P.O. Box 32479, Tucson, AZ 85751-2474, (602)326-2732.

British Columbia PIRG (BCPIRG), Simon Fraser University, Room TC- 304-305, Burnaby, BC V5A-1S6, (604) 291-4360.

California PIRG (CalPIRG), 1147 South Robertson Boulevard, Suite 203, Los Angeles, CA 90035, (213) 278-9244.

Colorado PIRG (CoPIRG), 1724 Gilpin Street, Denver, CO 80218, (303) 355-1861.

Connecticut PIRG (ConnPIRG), 300 Summit Street, P.O. Box 6000, Hartford, CT 06106, (203) 233-7554.

Florida PIRG (FPIRG), 420 East Call Street, Tallahassee, FL 32301, (904) 224-5304.

Illinois PIRG, 209 West Lake 3-F, Chicago, IL 60606, (312) 845- 9768.

Iowa PIRG, Iowa State University, Memorial Union, Room 306, Ames, IA 50011, (515) 294-8094.

Maine PIRG, University of Southern Maine, 96 Falmouth, Portland, ME 04103, (207) 874-6597.

Maryland PIRG (MaryPIRG), 3121 Saint Paul Street, Suite 26, Baltimore, MD 21218, (410) 467-0439.

Massachusetts PIRG (MassPIRG), 29 Temple Place, Boston, MA 02111, (617) 292-4800.

PIRG in Michigan (PIRGIM), 338 1/2 South State Street, Ann Arbor, MI 48104, (313) 662-6597.

Minnesota PIRG (MPIRG), 2512 Delaware Street, SE, Minneapolis, MN 55414, (612) 627-4035.

Missouri PIRG (MoPIRG), 4069 1/2 Shenandoah Avenue, St. Louis, MO 63110, (314) 772-7710.

Montana PIRG (MontPIRG), 363 Corbin Hall, Missoula, MT 59812, (406) 243-2907.

New Jersey PIRG (NJPIRG), 103 Bayard Street, New Brunswick, NJ 08901, (201) 247-4606

New Mexico PIRG (NMPIRG), Box 66 SUB, University of New Mexico, Albuquerque, NM 87131, (505) 277-2757.

New York PIRG (NYPIRG), 9 Murray Street, New York, NY 10007, (212) 349-6460.

Ohio PIRG (OPIRG), 2084 1/2 North High Street, Columbus, OH 43201, (614) 299-7474.

Ontario PIRG (OPIRG), 455 Spadina Avenue, Toronto, Ontario, M5S 2G8, (416) 598-1576.

Oregon PIRG (OSPIRG), 027 SW Arthur, Portland, OR 97201, (503) 222-9641.

Pennsylvania PIRG (PennPIRG),1109 Walnut Street, Philadelphia, PA 19107, (215) 829-1926.

Rhode Island PIRG (RIPIRG), 221 Waterman Street, Providence, RI 02906, (401) 331-7474.

U.S. PIRG, 215 Pennsylvania Avenue, SE, Washington, DC 20003, (202) 546-9707.

Vermont PIRG (VPIRG), 43 State Street, Montpelier, VT 05602, (802) 223-5221.

Washington PIRG (WashPIRG), 340 15th Avenue, East, Seattle, WA 98112, (206) 322-9064.

Wisconsin PIRG (WISPIRG), 306 North Brooks, Madison, WI 53715, (608) 251-1918.

Part Three: Training Schools

Commitment goes a long way, but activists agree that effective social change advocacy requires hands-on experience and a variety of skills. The organizations listed below provide training for citizen activists and community groups.

THE ADVOCACY INSTITUTE, 1730 Rhode Island Avenue, NW, Suite 600, Washington, DC 20036, (202) 659-8475. Training in public interest advocacy skills through seminars organized by the Institute, or through staff participation in programs organized by various groups in the advocacy community. Counseling to groups primarily in the areas of pressuring legislative bodies, media advocacy techniques and building a broad coalition.

AFL-CIO ORGANIZING INSTITUTE, 1444 Eye Street, NW, #701, Washington, DC 20005, (202) 408-0700. RTP Program is designed to Recruit, Train and Place people in jobs as union organizers. Four to six month field training program. Training exposes interns/apprentices to all aspects of job of lead organizer on a union representation campaign. Graduates are offered placement services for jobs with AFL-CIO affiliated unions.

CENTER FOR ORGANIZATIONAL AND COMMUNITY DEVELOPMENT, Room 377 Hills South, University of Massachusetts, Amherst, MA 01003, (413) 545-2038/2231. Provides workshops, training, technical assistance and consultation to citizen/community groups and nonprofit organizations. Also publishes a series of training manuals.

CENTER FOR TEACHING PEACE, 4501 Van Ness Street, NW, Washington, DC (202) 537-1372. Gives students an intellectual grounding in the methods, history and practice of peacemaking. Offers campus visits by *Washington Post* columnist Colman McCarthy, home-study courses and high school and college course curricula. Also provides a placement service and stipend for peace teachers.

CENTER FOR THIRD WORLD ORGANIZING, 1218 East 21st Street, Oakland, CA 94606, (510) 533-7583. Offers comprehensive training sessions bringing together experienced organizers from across the U.S. and activists from community, labor, church and women's organizations, two to three times a year. Conducts summer-long Minority Activist Apprenticeship Program (MAPP) for young people of color. Also provides on-site consultation services.

COMMUNITY ORGANIZING AND TRAINING DEPARTMENT OF THE CATHOLIC YOUTH ORGANIZATION, 305 Michigan Avenue, Detroit, MI 48226, (313) 963-7172. Offers community dispute resolution training as needed to volunteers in the Detroit area. Target Area Grassroots Organizing Project to develop and strengthen groups for community revitalization. Customized training to area citizen groups.

COMMUNITY TRAINING AND ASSISTANCE CENTER, 30 Winter Street, 7th Floor, Boston, MA 02108, (617) 423-1444. Offers training and technical assistance to community groups and nonprofits in such areas as funding, organizational development, community organizing and advocacy, research, publicity and the media, and networking.

COMMUNITY TRAINING AND RESOURCE CENTER, 47 Ann Street, New York, NY 10038-2515, (212) 964-7200. CTRC helps to improve conditions for low income tenants & neighborhoods by providing training and technical assistance to neighborhoods, housing groups and building leaders. Advocates in favor of equitable housing policies and resources for low income New Yorkers.

DEVELOPMENT TRAINING INSTITUTE, 2500 Maryland Avenue, Baltimore, MD 21218, (410) 338-2512. Training programs and technical assistance for community-based economic development organizations. Programs include the Leadership and Management Program; the Project Development Program; Specialized Training Design; and consulting.

DIRECT ACTION AND RESEARCH TRAINING CENTER, INC. (DART), 137 NE 19th Street, Miami, FL 33132, (305) 576-8020/22. DART's 3-month Internship Program trains people - especially minorities and women - to become professional community organizers. Also offers periodic 3-5 day workshops on community organizing principles and techniques.

FEDERATION OF SOUTHERN COOPERATIVES, Rural Training and Research Center, P.O. Box 95, Epes, AL 35460, (205) 652-9676. Provides training to credit unions, cooperatives and other community-based organizations in 14 Southern states.

FUNDS FOR THE COMMUNITY'S FUTURE, 1050 Connecticut Avenue, Washington, DC 20036, (202) 775-5760. To empower and motivate both students and residents in targeted communities, with skills that will enhance the futures of their communities. Identifying one neighborhood at a time, FCF creates within each core group of "Community Coordinators". These coordinators create a neighborhood investment fund and facilitate community service projects, organize social events, grant scholarships from the fund, and assist in the creation of new businesses within the community.

GRASSROOTS LEADERSHIP, P.O. Box 36006, Charlotte, NC 28236, (704) 332- 3090. Provides organizing assistance to grassroots organizations throughout the South in membership recruitment, issue strategies, long- term planning, fundraising, board development, financial management and leadership development.

HIGHLANDER RESEARCH AND ACTION CENTER, 1959 Highlander Way, New Market, TN 37820, (615) 933-3443. Provides educational programs aimed at sustaining and aiding emergent leadership in Appalachia and the South. Workshops cover such topics as environmental issues, economic development and youth leadership. Aim is to provide a concrete example of how groups and individuals can work together democratically to solve common problems.

INDUSTRIAL AREAS FOUNDATION, 36 New Hyde Park Road, Franklin Square, NY 11010, (516) 354-1076. Started by Saul Alinsky, the Foundation provides training for local community groups and individuals. IAF emphasizes an on-site program in which trainees are placed with organizations for 1-5 years of training.

INSTITUTE FOR CULTURAL AFFAIRS, 4220 North 25th Street, Phoenix, AZ 85016, (602) 955-4811. Provides training designed for specific group needs and a series of facilitations methods courses, covering such skills as working with groups, short-term and long range planning, and holding effective meetings. Three regional centers in New York, Chicago, and Phoenix focus on different issues, e.g. the concerns of the multicultural population (innercity boroughs, Native American tribes) in the West and Southwest, and school reform in Chicago.

INSTITUTE FOR SOCIAL JUSTICE, 523 West 15th, Little Rock, AR 72202, (501)376-2528. Working closely with ACORN, the Institute provides training, referrals to local groups and publications. Contact Elana Hanggi for more information.

THE LEARNING ALLIANCE, 494 Broadway, New York, NY 10012, (212) 226-7171. More education than training-oriented, the Learning Alliance works with the staff and individuals as well as community and social change organizations to provide the public with workshops, conferences, travel, and action/study groups. Programs in a wide range of social concerns, including environmental justice, organizing skills, multiculturalism, alternative careers, and housing and the homelessness.

MIDWEST ACADEMY, 255 West Ohio Street, Suite 250, Chicago, IL 60610, (312) 645-6010. Conducts week-long training sessions, Organizing for Social Change, six to eight times a year. Also develops specialized organizing training sessions for specific organizations.

MISSISSIPPI ACTION FOR COMMUNITY EDUCATION, 119 South Theobold Street,

Greenville, MS 38701, (601) 335-3523. Ongoing training for community-based groups in the Mississippi Delta area, and technical and financial assistance to groups in the Arkansas Delta region. Runs the Rula Economic Development Training Institute to give rural community organizations organizing experience and aid them in self-help initiatives.

NATIONAL COUNCIL OF LA RAZA, 810 First Street, NE, Suite 300, Washington, DC 20002, (202) 289-1380. Offers training and on-site assistance to Hispanic organizations and those groups serving the Hispanic community. Topics include board training, writing proposals, fundraising, advocacy training, coalition building, and how to proceed on issues such as AIDS prevention and education, housing design and development for low- income communities, and employment and training.

NATIONAL TRAINING AND INFORMATION CENTER, 810 North Milwaukee Avenue, Chicago, IL 60622-4103, (312) 243-3035. Offers 3-day core courses for beginning organizers three times a year, and core training on how to Take Back Your Community, on the drug issue. Published the manual, *Taking Back Your Community*. Also provides on-site training tailored to local situations.

ORGANIZER TRAINING CENTER, 442A Vicksberg Street, San Francisco, CA 94114, (415) 821-6180. Offers workshops, tutorials & internships in community organizing. Also provides consulting services, a publication list of organizing materials and publishes The Organizer Mailing (TOM), a quarterly compilation of articles and reprints of interest to organizers and grassroots leaders.

PICO - A NATIONAL INSTITUTE FOR COMMUNITY ORGANIZATIONS, 171 Santa Rosa Avenue, Oakland, CA 94610, (510) 655-2801. Provides innerrcity leadership workshops, organizer and staff training, and on-site training. Holds week-long workshops twice each year, in summer and winter.

PUBLIC ALLIES, 1511 K Street, NW, Suite 330, Washington, DC 20005, (202) 638-3300. Inspires and develops new community leaders through a ten-month apprenticeship program. It is a multicultural organization designed and run by young people for young people.

SOUTHERN EMPOWERMENT PROJECT, 323 Ellis Avenue, Maryville, TN 37801, (615) 984-6500. SEP offers a 5-week summer training program for community organizers in the Southeast. Three weeks are residential and cover the basics of organizing, as well as overcoming classism, homophobia, racism, sexism, and giving a background of organizing in the South. Two weeks of the five are field placements with community organizations.

UNITED STATES STUDENT ASSOCIATION (USSA), 815 15th Street, NW, Suite 838, Washington, DC 20005, (202) 347-USSA. Sponsors GrassRoots Organizing Weekends (GROW) to provide student activists with the skills to "fight apathy, win issue campaigns, and strengthen student organizations." GROW sessions are held on selected weekends.

WESTERN ORGANIZATION OF RESOURCE COUNCILS, 2401 Montana Avenue, Suite 301, Billings, MT 59101, (406) 252-9672. Offers a 4-day Principles of Community Organizing Training Session, covering such topics as membership recruitment, developing an issue campaign, how to do action-oriented research, grassroots fundraising and working with the media.

WESTERN STATES CENTER, 522 SW 5th Avenue, Suite 1390, Portland, OR 97204, (503) 228-8866. Trainings and workshops to support and address the specific needs of activists and community groups in the region. Also the "Leadership in the 90's" program for individual organizers.

The following are accredited programs that offer degrees in social change-related fields:

ANTIOCH UNIVERSITY, The McGregor School of Antioch University, 800 Livermore Street, Yellow Springs, OH 45387, (513) 767-6322. Offers an Individualized Master of Arts (IMA) degree. Students select an area of study (e.g. social change work), recruit a degree committee, design a curriculum, select professors, and study where they live, and document their learning.

AUDREY COHEN COLLEGE, 345 Hudson Street, New York, NY 10014, (212) 989-2002. Offers short-term training programs and combined Bachelor's/ Master's degree programs to prepare men and women to become effective human service practitioners with a commitment to citizen empowerment. Evaluation is based on the demonstration of service delivery, called "constructive action."

ENVIRONMENTAL EDUCATION & ADVOCACY PROGRAMS, University of Michigan School of Natural Resources & Environment, Dana Building, 430 East University, Ann Arbor, MI 48109-1115, (313) 764- 6453. BS or MS degrees in Natural Resources. Teaches people how to build and/or maintain organizations for effective social and environmental change.

ENVIRONMENTAL CONSERVATION EDUCATION PROGRAM, Department of Culture & Communications, School of Education, New York University, 737 East Building, 239 Greene Street, New York, NY 10003, (212) 998-5637. MA program in environmental conservation education. Purpose is to initiate students into the study of philosophical historical & cultural aspects of environmental issues in internship programs with environmental organizations.

GRADUATE PROGRAM, at Vermont College of Norwich University, Montpelier, VT 05602, (802) 828-8500. Offers 18-month MA degreeprogram in Social Change Work. Independent Study Program curriculum is developed, in part, by students. Off campus program designed for working adults.

INSTITUTE FOR THE STUDY OF SOCIAL CHANGE, University of California at Berkeley, 2420 Bowditch Street, Berkeley, CA 94720, (510) 642-0813. Student training and research institute for graduate students pursuing degrees at the University of California at Berkeley. Current research programs examine minority groups in the professional and academic arena, and look at issues and strategies for solving various community problems including issues around child welfare, youth delinquency, and alcohol.

NATIONAL URBAN/RURAL FELLOWS PROGRAM, 577 7th Avenue, New York, NY 10019, (212) 921- 9400. National fellowship programs that provide intensive training in rural development or in urban settings over a 14-month period. Fellows receive a Master's degree in Public Administration from Bernard Baruch College at the City College of New York (CUNY).

NEIGHBORHOOD WOMEN OF WILLIAMSBURG-GREENPOINT, 249 Manhattan Avenue, Brooklyn, NY 11211, (718) 388-6666. A consortium of Brooklyn "neighborhood colleges," NWWG offers a Liberal Arts curriculum with a focus on Neighborhood Studies, Community Development, and Leadership Skills Development. Learning involves both theoretical study and practical application using the communities involved as learning laboratories. Students, mainly women, can earn an AA degree.

NEW SCHOOL FOR SOCIAL RESEARCH, 66 West 12th Street, New York, NY 10011, (212) 229-5400. MS in Urban Policy Analysis and Management with concentrations in Social Policy, Employment and Economic Development, Housing and Community Development, Public Management, and Nonprofit Management.

SPRINGFIELD COLLEGE SCHOOL OF HUMAN SERVICES, 263 Alden Street, Springfield, MA 01109, (413) 748-3204. Offers BS degree in Human Services with concentrations including Community-Based Development, Criminal Justice and Labor Studies; MS program in Human Services with concentrations in Human Services Administration, Community Psychology, Gerontology, and Community-Based Development; and MS in Social Work. Combines community work and classroom learning.

THE UNION INSTITUTE, The Graduate School, Office of the Dean, 440 East McMillan Street, Cincinnati, OH 45206-1947, (513) 861-6400. Offers PhD through an "interdisciplinary, individualized and socially relevant graduate program." Learners develop and pursue self-styled "learning agreements" for study and experience that promote social change. BA or BS degree programs also available through the University's College of Undergraduate Studies.

UNIVERSITY CENTER FOR COOPERATIVES, University of Wisconsin-Madison, College of Agricultural and Life Sciences, 513 Lowell Hall, 610 Langdon Street, Madison, WI 53703, (608) 262-3981. MA/MS with emphasis on cooperatives through the Agricultural Economics Department, Graduate School of Business, Continuing & Vocational Education Department, or Agricultural Journalism Department.

UNIVERSITY OF MARYLAND, Department of Family Studies, Room 1204, Marie Mount Hall, College Park, MD 20742, (301) 405-3672. Offers BS or MS in Family Studies. Optional, emphasis on marriage & family therapy. Accredited by American Association of Marriage & Family Therapy.

UNIVERSITY OF MISSOURI, College of Agriculture, 723 Clark Hall, Columbia, MO 65211, (314) 882-8393. Offers MS degrees in Community Development with such specializations as Youth Agency Administration, Urban Affairs, International Development or Community Economic Development.

UNIVERSITY OF RHODE ISLAND, Graduate School, Kingston, RI 02881, (401) 792-2262. MA in Community Planning and Area Development, or Public Administration.

UNIVERSITY WITHOUT WALLS OF THE UNIVERSITY OF MASSACHUSETTS, Montague House, Amherst, MA 01003, (413) 545-1378. Offers a BA in any human services area; students design their own degree programs and area of concentration, such as Public and Community Service, Legal Service, Housing and Community Development. The program requires 45 on-campus credits at one of the UWW learning centers in Amherst, and Springfield and offers as part of the degree process for earning credit for work and life experience.

URBAN AND REGIONAL PLANNING PROGRAM, University of Wisconsin-Madison, Madison, WI 53706, (608) 262-1004. MS or PhD with concentration in Economics, Natural Resources, Land Use Housing & Growth Management.

WESTERN INSTITUTE FOR SOCIAL RESEARCH, 3220 Sacramento Street, Berkeley, CA 94702, (510) 655-2830. Offers PhD in Higher Education and Social Change, MA in Education or Social Philosophy, and MA and BA programs in Human Services and Community Development, Psychology, Humanities/ Community Arts, and Social Science. All programs provide community-involved adults with combined academic study and full-time work on community problems. Also sponsors seminars and workshops open to the public on core themes, such as Action Research, Community Development, Human Services, and Higher Education and Social Change.

A growing number of law schools have instituted programs of training in such fields as poverty law, criminal justice, geriatric law, consumer law, landlord-tenant relations, and environmental law. The following law schools are committed specifically to training lawyers who are interested in the law as a means of achieving social change.

CITY UNIVERSITY OF NEW YORK LAW SCHOOL AT QUEENS COLLEGE, 65-21 Main Street, Flushing, NY 11367, (718) 575-4386. Three-year JD program begun in 1983 to train lawyers dedicated to working in the public interest. Approximately 70% of graduates hold legal positions in government, nonprofit and community agencies that deliver services to the poor and disadvantaged of New York City.

THE DISTRICT OF COLUMBIA SCHOOL OF LAW, 719 13th Street, NW, Washington, DC 20005, (202) 727-5225. The successor to Antioch School of Law, DCSL is a 3-year clinical program with dual missions: (1) to recruit and enroll students from racial, ethnic and other backgrounds traditionally underrepresented at the bar, and (2) to the maximum extent feasible, to represent the legal needs of low-income people through the School's legal clinics. In addition to the traditional core law school curriculum, students represent poor tenants, battered women, children with special needs, the elderly, the homeless, government whistleblowers, and those deprived of statutory entitlements such as social security.

FRANKLIN PIERCE LAW CENTER, 2 White Street, Concord, NH 03301, (603) 228-1541. A 3-year JD degree program, with a concentration in the Public Interest and Social Services available. Major clinic fields are Civil Practice, Criminal Defense and Intellectual Property. "Most of our faculty are activists - as lawyers and as teachers ... we believe the disproportionate influence of lawyers in the United States implies some responsibility to teach high standards for private conduct and to encourage both thought and action in the public interest."

THE MAX E. AND FILOMEN M. GREENBERG CENTER FOR LEGAL EDUCATION AND URBAN POLICY, Urban Legal Studies Program, City College of New York, Room 8, Shepherd Hall, 140th Street and Convent Avenue, New York, NY 10031, (212) 650-5941. A 6-year BA-JD degree program that integrates the study of the law and liberal arts. "Dedicated to training a new kind of lawyer: one who is ... highly qualified in aspects of the law most relevant to urban citizens - landlord tenant relations, civil liberties and civil rights, poverty law - sensitive to the social needs and legal problems of the urban community, and committed to serving that community."

NEW COLLEGE OF CALIFORNIA SCHOOL OF LAW, 50 Fell Street, San Francisco, CA 94102, (415) 373-2395. The New College seeks to graduate lawyers who work for social change. The School offers JD and LLB (Bachelor's of Law) in part-time and full-time programs, with a unique apprenticeship program where students work in public interest law firms.

NORTHEASTERN LAW SCHOOL, 400 Huntington Avenue, Boston, MA 02115, (617) 437-2395. Offers JD degree in the only cooperative legal education system in the country. During the second and third years of the program, students alternate full-time academic study with full-time law-related work experience, many of the employers being public interest law centers. Over 50 percent of graduates go into non-private legal positions, with 16 percent practicing public interest law.

Indexes

Geographical Index

Colorado

Connecticut

Delaware

District of Columbia

Florida

Georgia

Hawaii

Idaho

Illinois

Indiana

Iowa

Kansas

Kentucky

Louisiana

Maine

Maryland

Massachusetts

Michigan

Minnesota

Missouri

Montana

Nebraska

Nevada

New Hampshire

New Jersey

New Mexico

New York

North Carolina

North Dakota

Ohio

Oklahoma

Ontario

Oregon

Pennsylvania

Rhode Island

South Dakota

Tennessee

Texas

Utah

Vermont

Virginia

Washington

West Virginia

Wisconsin

Wyoming

Topical Index

Agriculture

Arts

Building Citizen Organizations

Civil Liberties/Civil Rights

Communications

Consumer Access

Economic Democracy/Economic Development

Education

Emotionally/Physically Disabled

Energy

Food and Nutrition

Foreign and Military Policy

Health

Housing/Landlord-Tenant/Homelessness

Human Rights

Labor Occupational Safety & Health

Legal Services

Minorities

Natural Resources/Environment

Peace/Disarmament

Political/Government Reform

Senior Citizens/Aging/NursingHomes

Taxes

Training/Technical Assistance